# CALCULUS

## Concepts and Applications

PAUL A. FOERSTER

KEY CURRICULUM PRESS
Innovators in Mathematics Education

**Editor:** Bill Medigovich
**Mathematical Reviewers:** Cavan Fang, Leslie Nielsen, Loyce Collenback
**Art Development:** Casey FitzSimons
**Editorial Assistant:** Romy Snyder
**Copyeditors:** Greer Lleuad, Luanna Richards
**Production Editors:** Deborah Cogan, Joe Todaro
**Production Service:** Greg Hubit Bookworks
**Production Manager:** Luis Shein
**Text Design:** Terry Lockman, Lumina Designworks
**Cover Design:** Maryann Ohki
**Technical Art:** Jason Luz, Ann Rothenbuhler
**Photo Research:** Ellen Hayes
**Composition:** Peter Vacek, Eigentype Compositors

**Cover Photograph:** Images ©1995 PhotoDisc, Inc.

**Publisher:** Steve Rasmussen
**Editorial Director:** John Bergez



ISBN 1-55953-117-7

Printed in the United States of America

10 9 8 7 6 5 4 3 01 00 99 98

The graphs in this text were created using PSMathGraphs II. PSMathGraphs is a trademark of MaryAnn Software.

Photo credits appear on the last page of the book.

## Consultants

Donald J. Albers, Mathematical Association of America, Washington, D.C.
Judith Broadwin, Jericho High School, Jericho, New York
Joan Ferrini-Mundy, University of New Hampshire, Durham, New Hampshire
Gregory D. Foley, Sam Houston State University, Huntsville, Texas
John Kenelly, Clemson University, Clemson, South Carolina
Dan Kennedy, Baylor School, Chattanooga, Tennessee
Deborah B. Preston, Keystone School, San Antonio, Texas

## Field Testers

Betty Baker, Bogan High School, Chicago, Illinois
Glenn C. Ballard, William Henry Harrison High School, Evansville, Indiana
Bruce Cohen, Lick-Wilmerding High School, San Francisco, California
Christine J. Comins, Pueblo County High School, Pueblo, Colorado
Deborah Davies, University School of Nashville, Nashville, Tennessee
Linda E. de Sola, Plano Senior High School, Plano, Texas
Paul A. Foerster, Alamo Heights High School, San Antonio, Texas
Joan M. Gell, Palos Verdes Peninsula High School, Rolling Hills Estates, California
Valmore E. Guernon, Lincoln Junior/Senior High School, Lincoln, Rhode Island
David S. Heckman, Monmouth Academy, Monmouth, Maine
Don W. Hight, Pittsburg State University, Pittsburg, Kansas
Edgar Hood, Dawson High School, Dawson, Texas
Ann Joyce, Issaquah High School, Issaquah, Washington
John G. Kelly, Arroyo High School, San Lorenzo, California
Linda Klett, San Domenico School, San Anselmo, California
George Lai, George Washington High School, San Francisco, California
Katherine P. Layton, Beverly Hills High School, Beverly Hills, California
Debbie Lindow, Reynolds High School, Troutdale, Oregon
Robert Maass, International Studies Academy, San Francisco, California
Guy R. Mauldin, Science Hill High School, Johnson City, Tennessee
Windle McKenzie, Brookstone School, Columbus, Georgia
Bill Medigovich, Redwood High School, Larkspur, California
Sandy Minkler, Redlands High School, Redlands, California
Deborah B. Preston, Keystone School, San Antonio, Texas
Susan M. Smith, Ysleta Independent School District, El Paso, Texas
Sanford Siegel, School of the Arts, San Francisco, California
Gary D. Starr, Girard High School, Girard, Kansas
Tom Swartz, George Washington High School, San Francisco, California
Tim Trapp, Mountain View High School, Mesa, Arizona
Dixie Trollinger, Mainland High School, Daytona Beach, Florida
David Weinreich, Queen Anne School, Upper Marlboro, Maryland
John P. Wojtowicz, Saint Joseph's High School, South Bend, Indiana
Tim Yee, Malibu High School, Malibu, California

## Author's Acknowledgments

This text was written during the period when graphing calculator technology was making radical changes in the teaching and learning of calculus. The fundamental differences embodied in the text have arisen from teaching my own students using this technology. In addition, the text has been thoroughly revised to incorporate comments and suggestions from the many consultants and field testers listed on the previous page.

Thanks in particular to the original field test people—Betty Baker, Chris Comins, Debbie Davies, Val Guernon, David Heckman, Don Hight, Kathy Layton, Guy Mauldin, Windle McKenzie, Debbie Preston, Gary Starr, and John Wojtowicz. These instructors were enterprising enough to venture into a new approach to teaching calculus and to put up with the difficulties of receiving materials at the last minute.

Special thanks to Bill Medigovich for editing the book, coordinating the field test program, and organizing the first two summer institutes for instructors. Special thanks also to Debbie Preston for drafting the major part of the Instructor's Guide and parts of the Solutions Manual, and for working with the summer institutes for instructors. By serving as both instructors and consultants, these two have given this text an added dimension of clarity and teachability.

Thanks also to my students for enduring all those handouts, and for finding things to be changed! Special thanks to my students Craig Browning, Meredith Fast, William Fisher, Brad Wier, and Matthew Willis for taking good class notes so that the text materials could include classroom-tested examples.

Finally, thanks to the late Richard V. Andree and his wife, Josephine, for allowing their children, Phoebe Small and Calvin Butterball, to make occasional appearances in my texts.

*Paul A. Foerster*

## Dedication

- *To people from the past, including James H. Marable of Oak Ridge National Laboratory, from whom I first understood the concepts of calculus; Edmund Eickenroht, my former student, whose desire it was to write his own calculus text; and my late wife, Jo Ann.*
- *To my wife Peggy, who shares my zest for life and accomplishment.*

# Foreword

**by John Kenelly,** Clemson University

In the era of calculus reform initiated in January 1986 at the Sloan Conference and fueled by the explosion of technology in mathematics instruction, we have all had to deal increasingly with the question "When machines do mathematics, then what do mathematicians do?" Many feel that our historical role has not changed, but that the emphasis is now clearly on selection and interpretation rather than manipulation and methods. As teachers, we sense the need for a major shift in the instructional means we employ to impart mathematical understanding to our students. At the same time, we recognize that behind any technology there must be human insight.

In a world of change, we must build on the past and take advantage of the future. Applications and carefully chosen examples still guide us through what works. Challenges and orderly investigations still develop mature thinking and insights. As much as the instructional environment might change, quality education remains our goal. What we need are authors and texts that bridge the transition. It is in this regard that Paul Foerster and his text provide an outstanding answer.

In *Calculus: Concepts and Applications*, Paul is at his famous best. The material is presented in an easily understood fashion, with ample technology-based examples and exercises. The wealth of applications are intimately connected with the topics and amplify the key elements in each section. The material is loaded with both fresh items and ancient insights that have stood the test of time. For example, you will find both Escalante's "cross hatch" method of repeated integration by parts right alongside Heaviside's thumb trick for solving partial fractions! The students are repeatedly sent to their "grapher." Early on, when differentiation is introduced, local linearity is discussed, and later the zoom features in calculators are exploited in the coverage of l'Hospital's rule. That's fresh. Later on, the logistic curve and slope fields in differential equations are discussed. All of these are beautiful examples of how computing technology has changed the calculus course.

Throughout the book you will see how comprehensive Paul is in his study of the historical role of calculus and yet how current he is in his understanding of the AP community and collegiate "calculus reform." Brilliant, timely, solid, and loaded with tons of novel applications—your typical Foerster!

---

*John Kenelly has been involved with the Advanced Placement Calculus program for the past 30 years. He was Chief Reader and later on Chairman of the AP Calculus Committee when Paul Foerster was grading the AP exams in the 1970s, and was instrumental in getting the reading sessions moved to Clemson University when they outgrew the prior facilities. He is a leader in development of the graphing calculator and in pioneering its use in college and school classrooms. His organization of TICAP sessions following recent AP readings has allowed calculus instructors to share ideas for implementing the changes in calculus that have been made inevitable by the advent of technology.*

# Contents

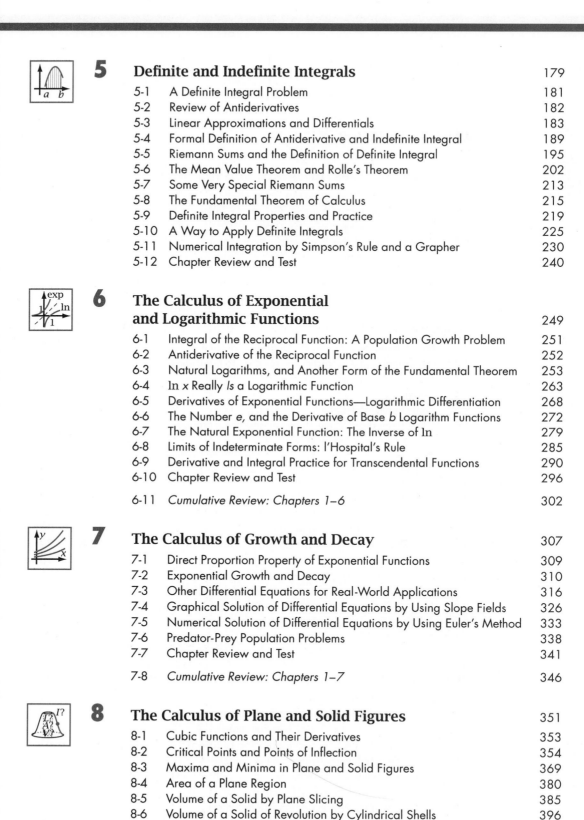

# Experiments and Projects

# A Note to the Student

Calculus, since its invention over 300 years ago, has been the culmination of elementary mathematics and the springboard from which much of higher mathematics gets its start. The factoring, algebraic fractions, equation solving, and graphing you have experienced were done at least in part because "You will need them in calculus."

The advent of the computer and hand-held graphing calculator (the "grapher") has changed much of this, both for how mathematics is learned before you reach calculus and for how it is used after calculus.

Nevertheless, in this course you will learn that the underlying concepts of calculus are still important. Calculus deals with functions that behave "continuously" or "smoothly." Digital computers and calculators work "discretely," by small steps. The discrete operations of calculators and computers can help you understand the idea of limit, on which the continuous behavior of functions in calculus is based. As you watch the calculator plot a graph you will get a feeling for what the rate of change of a function means. Perhaps the most significant thing you will find is that the calculator gives you ways to solve real-world calculus problems approximately, using graphs and tables of values, before you have developed all of the algebraic techniques needed for their exact solution.

You will, of course, learn how to do calculus on paper or in your head. If you are standing in front of the Board of Directors presenting your proposed project, you can't afford to lose their attention by saying, "Just a minute. Let me find my calculator." The ability to do things yourself will give you more confidence in answers that come from a computer. Fortunately, you will not have to make a career out of doing difficult computations on paper.

The time saved by using technology for solving problems and learning concepts can be used to develop your ability to write about mathematics. You will be asked to keep a written journal recording the concepts and techniques you have been learning, and to verbalize about things you may not yet have mastered.

At times you will feel you are becoming submerged in details. When that happens, just remember that calculus involves only four concepts:

- limits,
- derivatives,
- integrals, and
- integrals.

Ask yourself, "Which of these concepts does my present work apply to?" That way, you will better see the big picture. Best wishes as you venture into the world of higher mathematics!

*Paul A. Foerster*
*Alamo Heights High School*
*San Antonio, Texas*

CHAPTER

# 1 Limits, Derivatives, Integrals, and Integrals

In the design of a new car model, it is possible to predict its performance characteristics even before the first prototype is built. From information about the acceleration, designers can calculate the car's velocity as a function of time. From the velocity they can predict the distance it will go while it is accelerating. Calculus provides the mathematical tools to analyze quantities that change at variable rates.

# Mathematical Overview

Calculus deals with calculating things that change at variable rates. The four concepts invented to do this are

- limits
- derivatives
- integrals (one kind)
- integrals (another kind)

In Chapter 1 you will study three of these concepts in four ways.

***Graphically*** The logo atop each even-numbered page of this chapter illustrates a limit, a derivative, and one kind of integral.

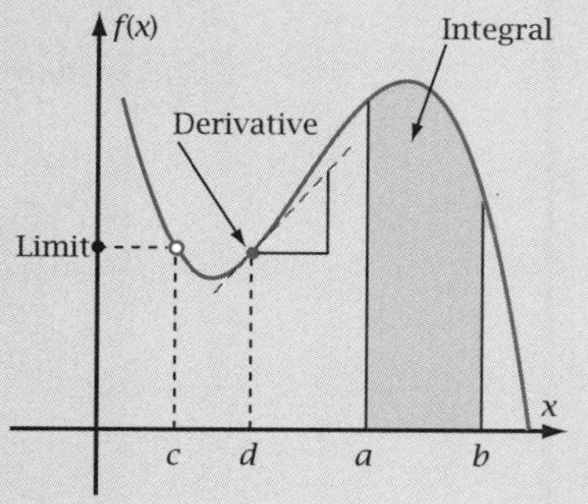


***Numerically***

| $x$ | $x - d$ | slope |
|---|---|---|
| 2.1 | 0.1 | 1.071666 ... |
| 2.01 | 0.01 | 1.007466 ... |
| 2.001 | 0.001 | 1.000749 ... |
| ... | ... | ... |

***Algebraically*** $\text{Average rate of change} = \dfrac{f(x) - f(2)}{x - 2}.$

***Verbally*** *I have learned that a definite integral is used to measure the product of x and f(x). For instance, velocity multiplied by time gives the distance traveled by an object. The definite integral is used to find this distance if the velocity varies.*

# 1-1 The Concept of Instantaneous Rate

If you push open a door that has an automatic closer, it opens fast at first, slows down, stops, starts closing, then slams shut. As the door moves, the number of degrees it is from its closed position depends on how many seconds it has been since you pushed it. Figure 1-1a shows such a door from above.

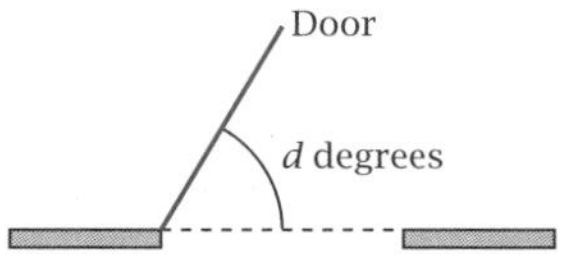


Figure 1-1a

The questions to be answered are, "At any particular instant in time, is the door opening or closing?" and "How fast is it moving?" As you progress through this course, you will learn to write equations expressing the rate of change of one variable quantity in terms of another. For the time being, you will answer such questions graphically and numerically.

***OBJECTIVE***

Given the equation for a function relating two variables, estimate the instantaneous rate of change of the dependent variable with respect to the independent variable at a given point.

Suppose that a door is pushed open at time $t = 0$ sec and slams shut again at time $t = 7$ sec. While the door is in motion, assume that the number of degrees, $d$, from its closed position is modeled by the following equation.

$$d = 200t \cdot 2^{-t} \quad \text{for} \quad 0 \le t \le 7$$

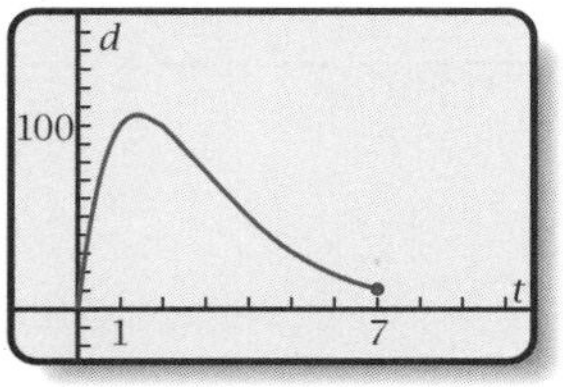


Figure 1-1b

How fast is the door moving at the instant when $t = 1$ sec? Figure 1-1b shows this equation on a grapher (graphing calculator or computer). When $t$ is 1, the graph is going *up* as $t$ increases from left to right. So the angle is increasing and the door is opening. You can estimate the rate numerically by calculating values of $d$ for values of $t$ close to 1.

$$t = 1: \quad d = 200(1) \cdot 2^{-1} = 100^\circ$$
$$t = 1.1: \quad d = 200(1.1) \cdot 2^{-1.1} = 102.633629\ldots^\circ$$

The door's angle increased by $2.633\ldots^\circ$ in 0.1 sec, meaning that it moved at a rate of about $(2.633\ldots)/0.1$, or $26.33\ldots$ deg/sec. However, this rate is an *average* rate, and the question was about an *instantaneous* rate. In an "instant" that is 0 sec long, the door moves $0^\circ$. Thus, the rate would be 0/0, which is awkward because of division by zero.

To get closer to the instantaneous rate at $t = 1$ sec, find $d$ at $t = 1.01$ sec and at $t = 1.001$ sec.

$$t = 1.01: \quad d = 200(1.01) \cdot 2^{-1.01} = 100.30234\ldots, \text{ a change of } 0.30234\ldots^\circ$$
$$t = 1.001: \quad d = 200(1.001) \cdot 2^{-1.001} = 100.03064\ldots, \text{ a change of } 0.03064\ldots^\circ$$

Here are the average rates for the time intervals 1 sec to 1.01 sec and 1 sec to 1.001 sec.

$$1\text{sec to }1.01\text{sec:} \quad \text{average rate} = \frac{0.30234\ldots}{0.01} = 30.234\ldots \text{ deg/sec}$$

$$1\text{sec to }1.001\text{sec:} \quad \text{average rate} = \frac{0.03064\ldots}{0.001} = 30.64\ldots \text{ deg/sec}$$

The important thing for you to notice is that as the time interval gets smaller and smaller, the number of degrees per second doesn't change much. Figure 1-1c shows why. As you zoom in on the point (1, 100), the graph appears to be straighter, so the change in $d$ divided by the change in $t$ becomes closer to the slope of a straight line.

If you list the average rates in a table, another interesting feature appears. The values stay the same for more and more decimal places.

| sec | average rate |
|---|---|
| 1 to 1.01 | 30.23420 ... |
| 1 to 1.001 | 30.64000 ... |
| 1 to 1.0001 | 30.68075 ... |
| 1 to 1.00001 | 30.68482 ... |
| 1 to 1.000001 | 30.68524 ... |

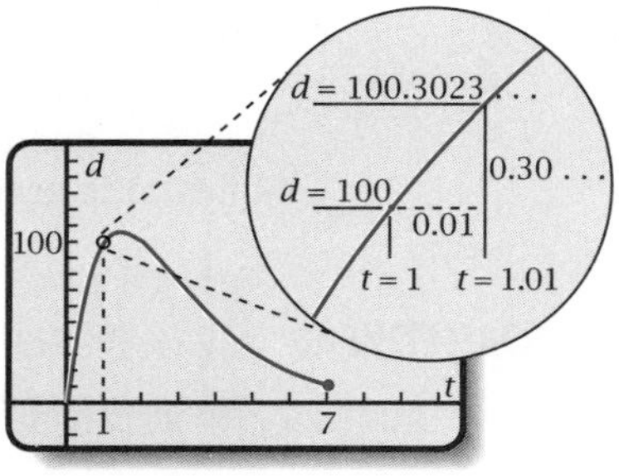


Figure 1-1c

There seems to be a *limiting* number that the values are approaching.

Estimating the instantaneous rate at $t = 3$ gives the following results.

$$
\begin{aligned}
t = 3: &\quad d = 200(3)\cdot 2^{-3} &&= 75^\circ\\
t = 3.1: &\quad d = 200(3.1)\cdot 2^{-3.1} &&= 72.310056\ldots^\circ\\
t = 3.01: &\quad d = 200(3.01)\cdot 2^{-3.01} &&= 74.730210\ldots^\circ\\
t = 3.001: &\quad d = 200(3.001)\cdot 2^{-3.001} &&= 74.973014\ldots^\circ
\end{aligned}
$$

Here are the corresponding average rates.

$$3 \text{ sec to } 3.1 \text{ sec}: \quad \text{average rate} = \frac{72.310056\ldots - 75}{3.1 - 3} = -26.899\ldots \text{deg/sec}$$

$$3 \text{ sec to } 3.01 \text{ sec}: \quad \text{average rate} = \frac{74.730210\ldots - 75}{3.01 - 3} = -26.978\ldots \text{deg/sec}$$

$$3 \text{ sec to } 3.001 \text{ sec}: \quad \text{average rate} = \frac{74.973014\ldots - 75}{3.001 - 3} = -26.985\ldots \text{deg/sec}$$

Again, the rates seem to be approaching some limiting number, this time around $-27$. So the instantaneous rate at $t = 3$sec should be somewhere close to $-27$ deg/sec. The negative sign tells you that the number of degrees, $d$, is *decreasing* as time goes on. Thus, the door is closing when $t = 3$. It is opening when $t = 1$ because the rate of change is positive.

For the door example shown above, the angle is said to be a **function** of time. Time is the **independent variable** and angle is the **dependent variable**. These names make sense, because the number of degrees the door is open *depends* on the number of seconds since it was pushed. The instantaneous rate of change of the dependent variable is said to be the **limit** of the average rates as the time interval gets closer to zero. This limiting value is called the **derivative** of the dependent variable with respect to the independent variable.

## Problem Set 1-1

1. *Pendulum Problem:* A pendulum hangs from the ceiling (Figure 1-1d). As the pendulum swings, its distance, $d$ cm, from one wall of the room depends on the number of seconds, $t$, since it was set in motion. Assume that the equation for $d$ as a function of $t$ is

$$d = 80 + 30\cos\frac{\pi}{3}t, \quad t \geq 0.$$

It is desired to find out how fast the pendulum is moving at a given instant, $t$, and whether it is approaching or going away from the wall.

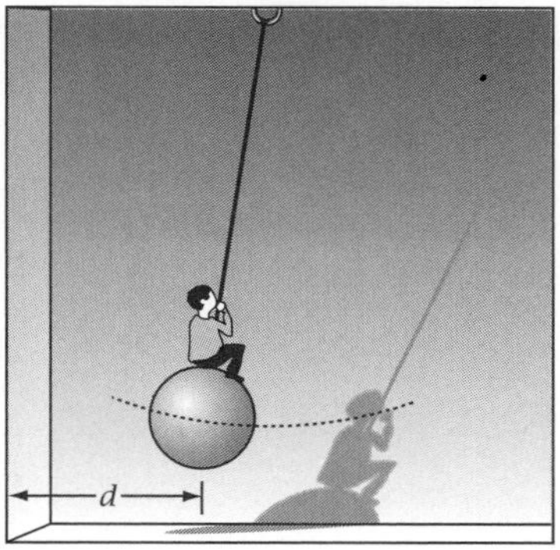

Figure 1-1d

   a. Find $d$ when $t = 5$. If you don't get 95 for the answer, make sure your calculator is in radian mode.
   b. Estimate the instantaneous rate of change of $d$ at $t = 5$ by finding the average rates for $t = 5$ to 5.1, $t = 5$ to 5.01, and $t = 5$ to 5.001.
   c. Why can't the actual instantaneous rate of change of $d$ with respect to $t$ be calculated using the method in 1b?
   d. Estimate the instantaneous rate of change of $d$ with respect to $t$ at $t = 1.5$. At that time is the pendulum approaching the wall or going away from it? Explain.
   e. How is the instantaneous rate of change related to the average rates? What name is given to the instantaneous rate?
   f. What is the reason for the domain restriction $t \geq 0$? Can you think of any reason that there would be an *upper* bound to the domain?

2. *Board Price Problem:* If you check the prices of various lengths of lumber, you will find that a board twice as long as another of the same type does not necessarily cost twice as much. Let $x$ be the number of feet long a 2″ × 6″ board is (Figure 1-1e) and let $y$ be the number of cents you pay for the board. Assume that $y$ is given by

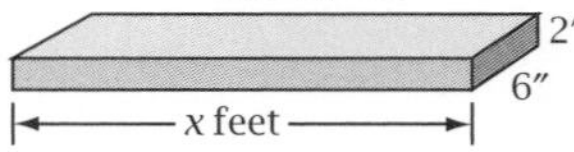

Figure 1-1e

$$y = 0.2x^3 - 4.8x^2 + 80x.$$

   a. Find the price of 2″ × 6″ boards that are 5 ft long, 10 ft long, and 20 ft long.
   b. Find the average rate of change of the price in cents per foot for 5 ft to 5.1 ft, 5 ft to 5.01 ft, and 5 ft to 5.001 ft.
   c. The average number of cents per foot in 2b is approaching an *integer* as the change in $x$ gets smaller and smaller. What integer? What is the name given to this rate of change?
   d. Estimate the instantaneous rate of change in price if $x$ is 10 ft and if $x$ is 20 ft. You should find that each of these rates is an integer.
   e. One of the principles of marketing is that when you buy in larger quantities, you usually pay less per unit. Explain how the numbers in Problem 2 show that this principle does *not* apply to buying longer boards. Think of a reason *why* it does not apply.

# 1-2 Rate of Change by Equation, Graph, or Table

In Section 1-1, you explored functions for which an equation related two variable quantities. You estimated the rate of change of one variable as the other increased. In this section you will do the same for functions specified not only by an equation but also by a graph or by a table of values.

**OBJECTIVE**

> Given a function specified by a graph, by a table of values, or by an equation, and given a value of $x$, tell whether the $y$-value is increasing or decreasing as $x$ increases through that value, and estimate how fast the $y$-value is changing.

### *Background: Function Terminology and Types of Functions*

The price you pay for a certain kind of board depends on how long it is. In mathematics the symbol $f(x)$ (pronounced "$f$ of $x$" or "$f$ at $x$") is often used for the dependent variable. The letter $f$ is the name of the function, and the number in parentheses is either a value of the independent variable or the variable itself. If $f(x) = 3x + 7$, then $f(5)$ is $3(5) + 7$, or 22.

The equation $f(x) = 3x + 7$ is the **particular equation** for a linear function. The **general equation** for a linear equation is written $y = mx + b$, or $f(x) = mx + b$, where $m$ and $b$ represent the constants. The following box shows the names of some types of functions and their general equations.

> ***Definitions: Types of Functions***
>
> **Linear:** $f(x) = mx + b$; $m$ and $b$ stand for constants, $m \neq 0$
>
> **Quadratic:** $f(x) = ax^2 + bx + c$; $a$, $b$, and $c$ stand for constants, $a \neq 0$
>
> **Polynomial:** $f(x) = a_0 + a_1x + a_2x^2 + a_3x^3 + a_4x^4 + \cdots + a_nx^n$; $a_0, a_1, \ldots$ stand for constants, $n$ is a positive integer, $a_n \neq 0$ ($n$th degree polynomial function)
>
> **Power:** $f(x) = ax^n$; $a$ and $n$ stand for constants
>
> **Exponential:** $f(x) = ab^x$; $a$ and $b$ stand for constants, $a \neq 0$, $b > 0$, $b \neq 1$
>
> **Rational Algebraic:** $f(x) =$ (polynomial)/(polynomial)
>
> **Absolute value:** $f(x)$ contains |(expression)|
>
> **Trigonometric or Circular:** $f(x)$ contains $\cos x$, $\sin x$, $\tan x$, $\cot x$, $\sec x$, or $\csc x$

**■ *Example 1*** Figure 1-2a shows the graph of a function. At $x = a$, $x = b$, and $x = c$, tell if $y$ is increasing, decreasing, or neither as $x$ increases, and tell if the rate of change is fast or slow.

***Solution*** At $x = a$, $y$ is increasing quickly as you go from left to right.

At $x = b$, $y$ is decreasing slowly because $y$ is dropping as $x$ goes from left to right, but it's not dropping very quickly.

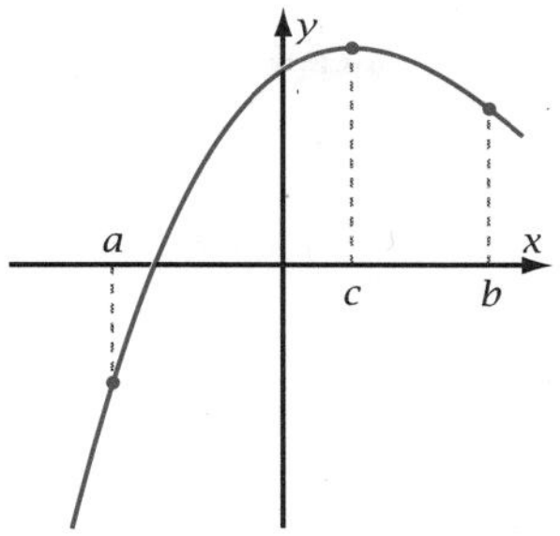


Figure 1-2a

At $x = c$, $y$ is neither increasing nor decreasing, as shown by the fact that the graph has leveled off at $x = c$. ■

■ ***Example 2*** A mass is bouncing up and down on a spring hanging from the ceiling (Figure 1-2b). Its distance, $y$ feet, from the ceiling is measured by strobe photography each 1/10 sec, giving the adjacent table of values, in which $t$ is time in seconds.

a. Tell how fast $y$ is changing at each time.

   i. $t = 0.3$

   ii. $t = 0.6$

   iii. $t = 1.0$

b. At time $t = 0.3$sec, is the mass going up or down? Justify your answer.

| $t$ | $y$ |
|---|---|
| 0.2 | 3.99 |
| 0.3 | 5.84 |
| 0.4 | 7.37 |
| 0.5 | 8.00 |
| 0.6 | 7.48 |
| 0.7 | 6.01 |
| 0.8 | 4.16 |
| 0.9 | 2.63 |
| 1.0 | 2.00 |
| 1.1 | 2.52 |

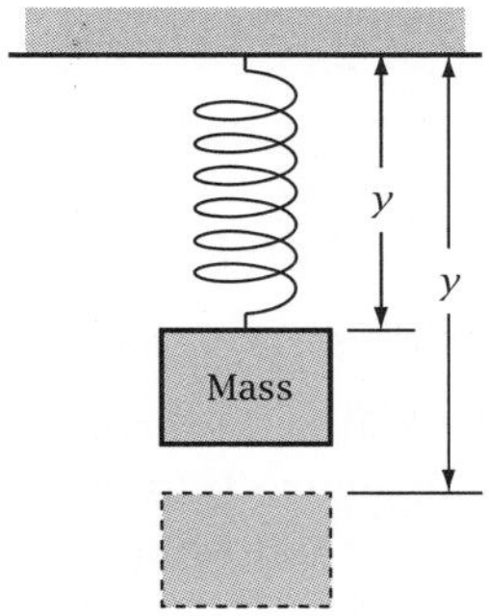


Figure 1-2b

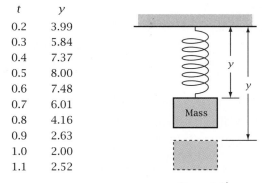

***Solution*** a. If data is given in numerical form, you cannot get better estimates of the rate by taking values of $t$ closer and closer to 0.3. However, you can get a better estimate by using the $t$-values on both sides of the given value. A time-efficient way to do the computations is shown below. If you like, do the computations mentally and write only the final answer.

| t | y | difference | rate | average rate |
|---|---|---|---|---|
| 0.2 | 3.99 | | | |
| | | 1.85 | 1.85/0.1 = 18.5 | |
| 0.3 | 5.84 | | | 16.9 |
| | | 1.53 | 1.53/0.1 = 15.3 | |
| 0.4 | 7.37 | | | |
| 0.5 | 8.00 | | | |
| | | -0.52 | -0.52/0.1 = -5.2 | |
| 0.6 | 7.48 | | | -9.95 |
| | | -1.47 | -1.47/0.1 = -14.7 | |
| 0.7 | 6.01 | | | |
| 0.8 | 4.16 | | | |
| 0.9 | 2.63 | | | |
| | | -0.63 | -0.63/0.1 = -6.3 | |
| 1.0 | 2.00 | | | -0.55 |
| | | 0.52 | 0.52/0.1 = 5.2 | |
| 1.1 | 2.52 | | | |

All you need to write on your paper are the results, as shown below.

i. $t = 0.3$ : increasing at about 16.9 ft/sec

ii. $t = 0.6$ : decreasing at about 9.95 ft/sec

iii. $t = 1.0$ : decreasing at about 0.55 ft/sec

Write real-world answers with units.

b. At $t = 0.3$, the rate is about 16.9 ft/sec, a *positive* number. This fact implies that $y$ is *increasing*. As $y$ increases, the mass goes *downward*. ■

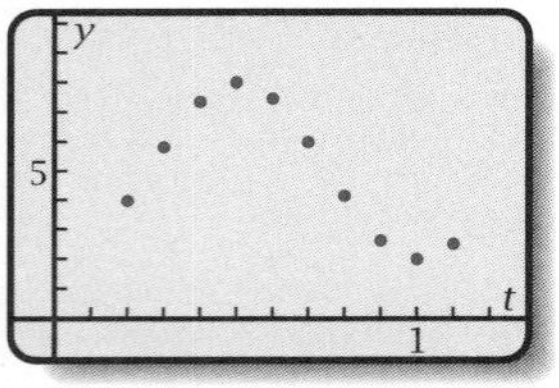


Figure 1-2c

Note that although a graph is not asked for in Example 2, plotting the data either on graph paper or by scatter plot on the grapher will help you understand what is happening. Figure 1-2c shows such a scatter plot.

The technique in Example 2 for estimating instantaneous rates by going forward and backward from the given value of $x$ can also be applied to functions specified by an equation. The result is usually more accurate than the rate estimated by going just forward as you did in the last section. Example 3 shows how this computation can be done.

### ■ *Example 3*

An inflated toy balloon is tied to a small rock, then the rock and the balloon are thrown into the air. While it's moving, the rock's height, $f(x)$ feet above the ground, is given by the quadratic function

$$f(x) = -x^2 + 8x + 2,$$

where $x$ is time in seconds since the rock was thrown. The graph of this function is shown in Figure 1-2d. At approximately what rate is $f(x)$ increasing or decreasing if $x$ equals the following times?

a. $x = 3$

b. $x = 7$

c. $x = 4$

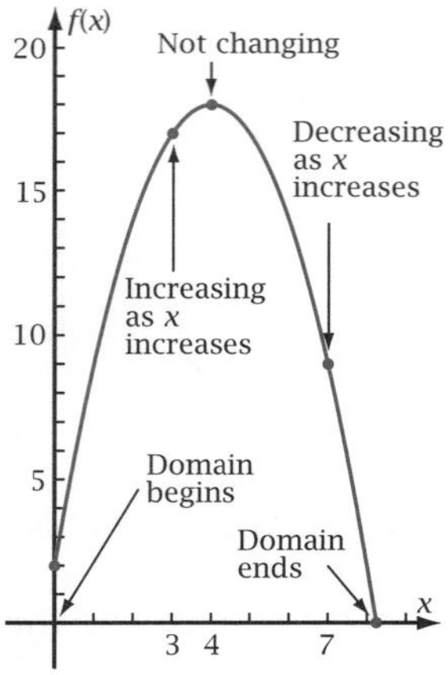


Figure 1-2d

**Solution**

a. Find out how much $f(x)$ changes from $x = 2.99$ to $x = 3$ and divide by the change in $x$. Do the same as $x$ goes from 3 to 3.01. Using the trace feature

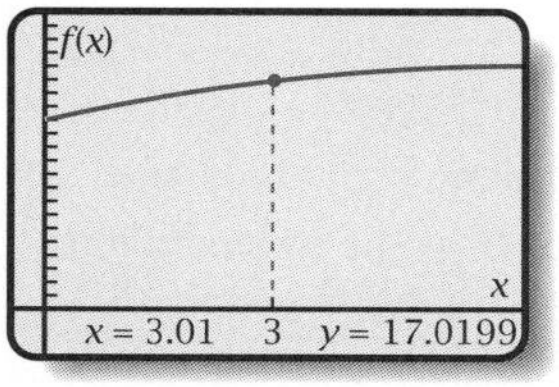


Figure 1-2e

on the grapher is a time-efficient way to do this. Figure 1-2e shows the graph drawn in a "friendly" window for which $x = 3$ is a grid point and the $x$-increment is 0.01.

$f(2.99) = 16.9799$

$f(3) = 17$     difference $= 17 - 16.9799 = 0.0201$

$f(3.01) = 17.0199$     difference $= 17.0199 - 17 = 0.0199$

From $f(2.99)$ to $f(3)$, rate $\approx \dfrac{0.0201}{0.01} = 2.01$ ft/sec.

From $f(3)$ to $f(3.01)$ rate $\approx \dfrac{0.0199}{0.01} = 1.99$ ft/sec.

Averaging these values gives 2.00.

$\therefore f(x)$ is increasing by about 2 ft/sec when $x = 3$.

b. Choose a friendly window for which $x = 7$ is a grid point and the $x$-increment is 0.01.

$f(6.99) = 9.0599$

$f(7) = 9$     difference $= 9 - 9.0599 = -0.0599$

$f(7.01) = 8.9399$     difference $= 8.9399 - 9 = -0.0601$

From $f(6.99)$ to $f(7)$, rate $\approx \dfrac{-0.0599}{0.01} = -5.99$ ft/sec.

From $f(7)$ to $f(7.01)$, rate $\approx \dfrac{-0.0601}{0.01} = -6.01$ ft/sec.

Averaging these values gives $-6.00$

$\therefore f(x)$ is decreasing by about 6 $y$-units per $x$ unit (6 ft/sec) when $x = 7$.

c. Choose a friendly window for which $x = 4$ is a grid point and the $x$-increment is 0.01.

$f(3.99) = 17.9999$

$f(4) = 18$     difference $= 18 - 17.9999 = 0.0001$

$f(4.01) = 17.9999$     difference $= 17.9999 - 18 = -0.0001$

From $f(3.99)$ to $f(4)$, rate $\approx \dfrac{0.0001}{0.01} = 0.01$ ft/sec

From $f(4)$ to $f(4.01)$, rate $\approx \dfrac{-0.0001}{0.01} = -0.01$ ft/sec

Averaging these values gives 0.

$\therefore f(x)$ is *not changing* when $x = 4$. ■

As you learned in Section 1-1, the instantaneous rate of change of a function at a given value of $x$ is called the **derivative** of the function at that point. The following describes the meaning of the word *derivative.* You will learn the precise definition when it is time to calculate derivatives exactly.

### *Meaning of Derivative*

The derivative of a function at a particular value of the independent variable is the *instantaneous rate of change* of the dependent variable with respect to the independent variable.

Note that "with respect to the independent variable" implies that you are finding how fast the dependent variable changes *as the independent variable changes.*

### *Preview: Definition of Limit*

In Section 1-1, you saw that the average rate of change of the $y$-value of a function got closer and closer to some fixed number as the change in the $x$-value got closer and closer to zero. That fixed number is called the **limit** of the average rate as the change in $x$ approaches zero. The following is a verbal definition of limit. The full meaning will become clearer to you as the course progresses.

### *Verbal Definition of Limit*

$L$ is the limit of $f(x)$ as $x$ approaches $c$
if and only if
$L$ is the *one* number you can keep $f(x)$ arbitrarily close to
just by keeping $x$ close enough to $c$, but not equal to $c$.

## Problem Set 1-2

### *Do These Quickly*

Starting here, there will be ten short problems for you to work at the beginning of most problem sets. Some of the problems are intended for review of skills from previous sections or chapters. Others are to test your general knowledge. Speed is the key here, not detailed work. You should be able to do all ten problems in less than five minutes.

***Q1.*** Name the type of function: $f(x) = x^3$.

***Q2.*** Find $f(2)$ for the function in Problem Q1.

***Q3.*** Name the type of function: $g(x) = 3^x$.

***Q4.*** Find $g(2)$ for the function in Problem Q3.

***Q5.*** Sketch the graph: $h(x) = x^2$.

***Q6.*** Find $h(5)$ for the function in Problem Q5.

***Q7.*** Write the general equation for a quadratic function.

***Q8.*** Write the particular equation for the function in Figure 1-2f.

***Q9.*** Write the particular equation for the function in Figure 1-2g.

***Q10.*** What name is given to the instantaneous rate of change of a function?

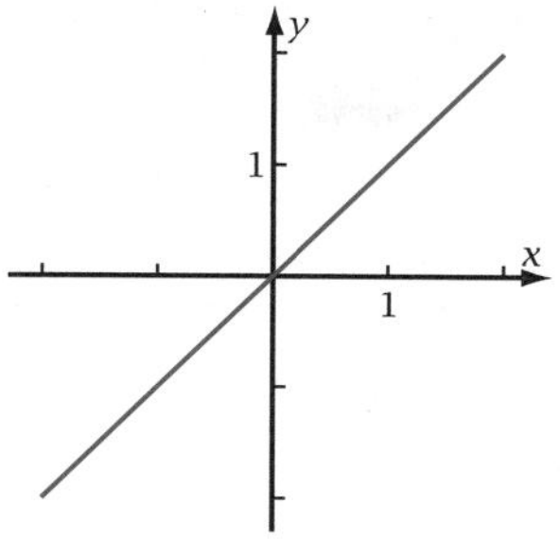


Figure 1-2f

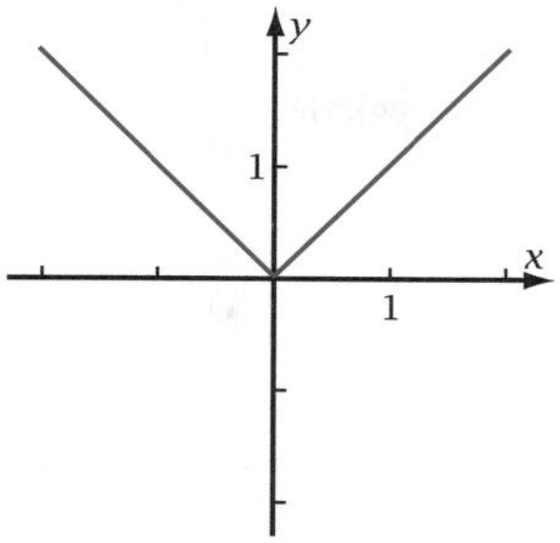


Figure 1-2g

Problems 1–10 show graphs of functions with values of $x$ marked $a$, $b$, etc. At each marked value, tell whether the function is increasing, decreasing, or neither as $x$ increases from left to right, and tell whether the rate of increase or decrease is fast or slow.

1.

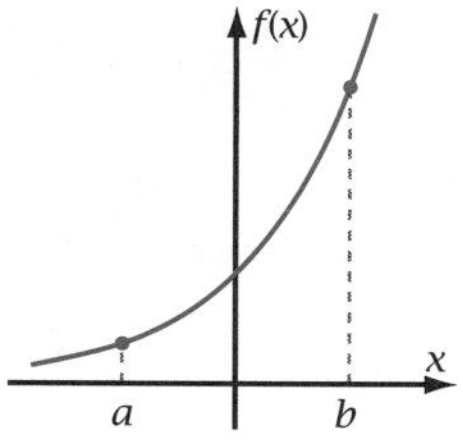


2.

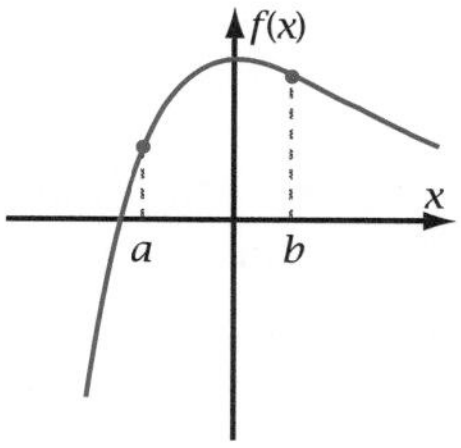


3.

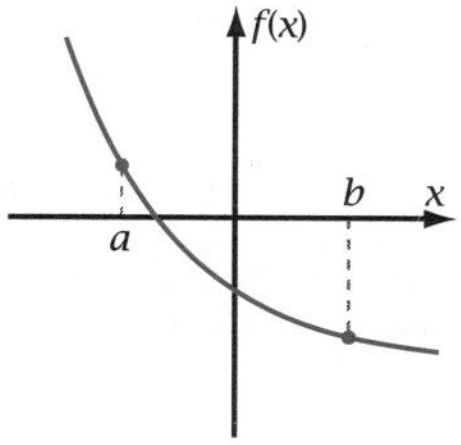


4.

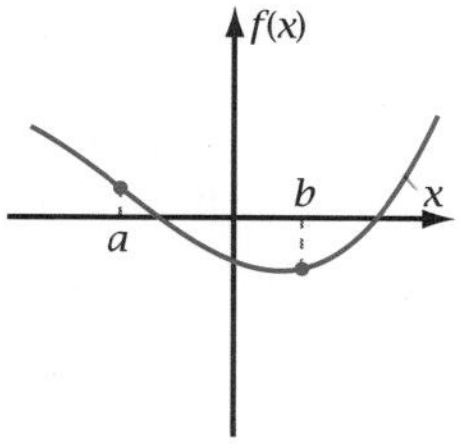


5.

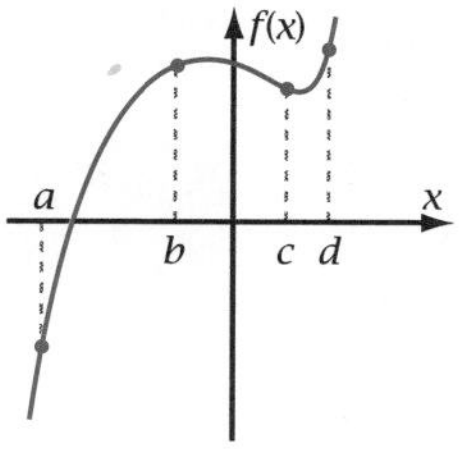


6.

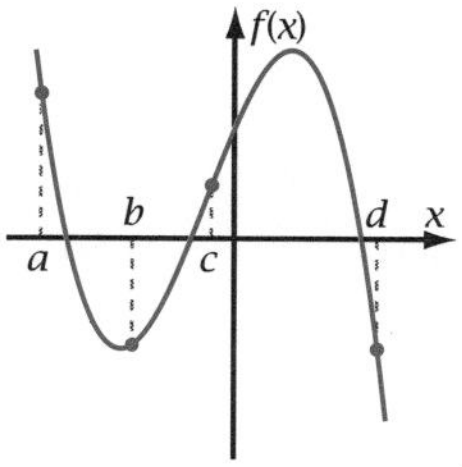


7.

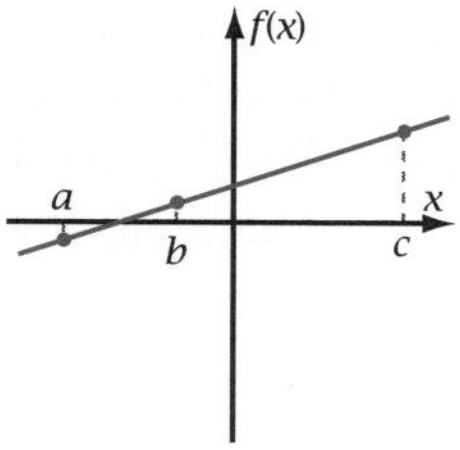


8.

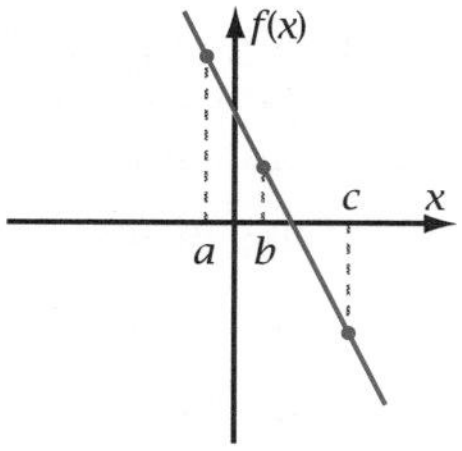


9.

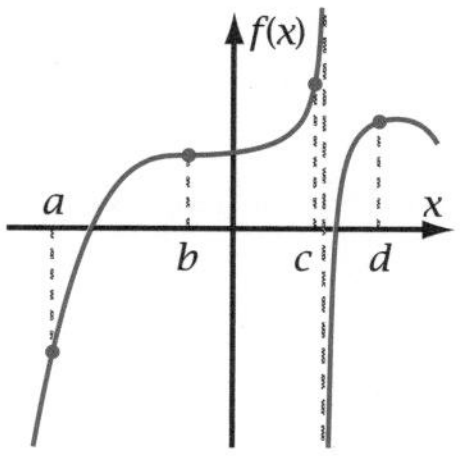


10.

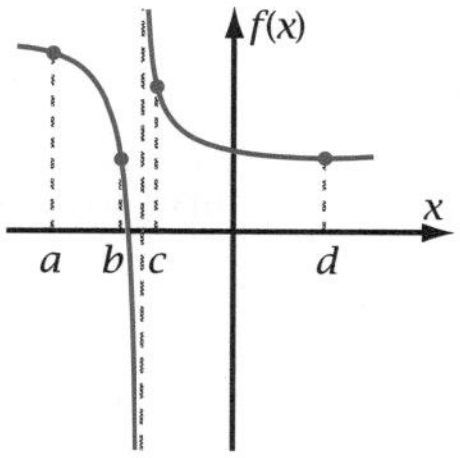

For Problems 11 and 12, $x$ is in minutes and $y$ is in centimeters. Find, approximately, the rate of change of $y$ at the given values of $x$, and tell whether $y$ is increasing or decreasing.

11. a. $x = 1.5$
    b. $x = 3.0$
    c. $x = 4.0$

| $x$ min | $y$ cm |
|---|---|
| 0.0 | 10.0 |
| 0.5 | 7.6 |
| 1.0 | 8.0 |
| 1.5 | 10.4 |
| 2.0 | 14.0 |
| 2.5 | 18.1 |
| 3.0 | 22.0 |
| 3.5 | 24.9 |
| 4.0 | 26.0 |
| 4.5 | 24.6 |

12. a. $x = 1.0$
    b. $x = 3.0$
    c. $x = 4.5$

| $x$ min | $y$ cm |
|---|---|
| 0.5 | 8.24 |
| 1.0 | 8.30 |
| 1.5 | 8.26 |
| 2.0 | 8.20 |
| 2.5 | 8.19 |
| 3.0 | 8.30 |
| 3.5 | 8.61 |
| 4.0 | 9.20 |
| 4.5 | 10.14 |
| 5.0 | 11.50 |

13. *Rolling Tire Problem:* A pebble is stuck in the tread of a car tire (Figure 1-2h). As the wheel turns, the distance, $y$ inches, between the pebble and the road at various times, $t$ seconds, is given by the adjacent chart.
    a. About how fast is $y$ changing at each time?
        i. $t = 1.4$
        ii. $t = 1.7$
        iii. $t = 1.9$
    b. At what time does the stone strike the pavement? Justify your answer.

| $t$ sec | $y$ in. |
|---|---|
| 1.2 | 0.63 |
| 1.3 | 0.54 |
| 1.4 | 0.45 |
| 1.5 | 0.34 |
| 1.6 | 0.22 |
| 1.7 | 0.00 |
| 1.8 | 0.22 |
| 1.9 | 0.34 |
| 2.0 | 0.45 |

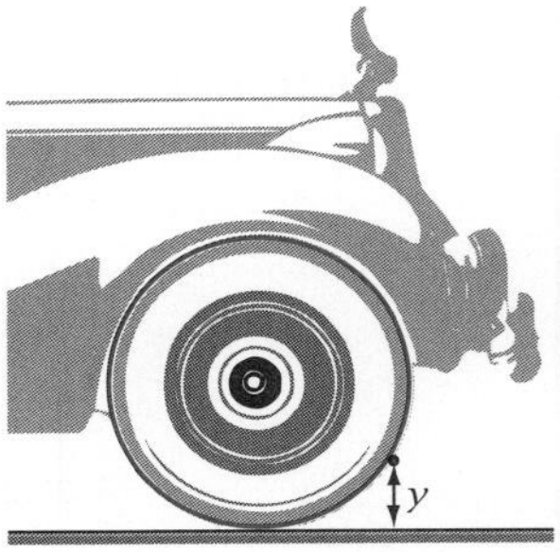

Figure 1-2h

14. *Flat Tire Problem:* A tire is punctured by a nail. As the air leaks out, the distance, $y$ inches, between the rim and the pavement (Figure 1-2i) depends on the time, $t$ minutes, since the tire was punctured. Values of $t$ and $y$ are given in the adjacent chart.
    a. About how fast is $y$ changing at each time?
        i. $t = 2$
        ii. $t = 8$
        iii. $t = 14$
    b. How do you interpret the *sign* of the rate at which $y$ is changing?

| $t$ min | $y$ in. |
|---|---|
| 0 | 6.00 |
| 2 | 4.88 |
| 4 | 4.42 |
| 6 | 4.06 |
| 8 | 3.76 |
| 10 | 3.50 |
| 12 | 3.26 |
| 14 | 3.04 |
| 16 | 2.84 |

Figure 1-2i

For Problems 15–24, do the following.
a. Tell the type of function (linear, quadratic, etc.),
b. Find $f(c)$
c. Tell whether $f(x)$ is increasing or decreasing at $x = c$, and at approximately what rate.

15. $f(x) = x^2 + 5x + 6,\ c = 3$

16. $f(x) = -x^2 + 8x + 5,\ c = 1$

17. $f(x) = 3^x,\ c = 2$

18. $f(x) = 2^x,\ c = -3$

19. $f(x) = \dfrac{1}{x-5},\ c = 4$

20. $f(x) = -\dfrac{1}{x},\ c = -2$

21. $f(x) = -3x + 7$, $c = 5$

22. $f(x) = 0.2x - 5$, $c = 8$

23. $f(x) = \sin x$, $c = 2$ (Radian mode!)

24. $f(x) = \cos x$, $c = 1$ (Radian mode!)

25. *Accurate Graph of a Cubic Function Problem:* Plot on the grapher the graph of

$$f(x) = 0.004x^3 - 0.02x^2 - 0.2x + 4$$

and sketch the result. Answer the following questions.

a. How can you tell when $f(x)$ is increasing *quickly*?

b. In what part of the domain is $f(x)$ decreasing?

c. True or false: When $f(x)$ is positive, the function is increasing.

d. At approximately what value of $x$ is $f(x)$ decreasing the most quickly?

26. *Accurate Graph of a Rational Function Problem:* Plot this function on your grapher.

$$f(x) = \frac{0.2x^2 - 1}{x - 3}$$

Pick a window for which $x = 3$ is a grid point. Sketch the result, then answer the following questions.

a. Describe how $f(x)$ is changing when $x$ is far away from 3.

b. Describe how $f(x)$ is changing when $x$ is close to 3.

c. At approximately what value of $x$ does $f(x)$ stop increasing and start decreasing?

d. At approximately what value of $x$ does $f(x)$ stop decreasing and start increasing?

e. In what domain is the value of $f(x)$ a real number?

f. Based on your work in 26a–e, what would you say the range of $f$ is?

27. *Definition of Limit Problem:* Write the verbal definition of limit. Compare it with the definition in this text. If you did not state all parts of the definition correctly, read it again. Then try writing the definition again until you get it completely correct.

28. *Discussion Problem: Meaning of Limit:* Finding a derivative involves finding a ratio: the change in $y$ divided by the change in $x$ when the change in $x$ is zero. You don't get an answer when you divide by zero. But you can keep the change in $x$ very close to zero. When you do, the value of the ratio seems to stay close to some particular number. Based on the verbal definition of limit, tell why the derivative of a function is the same as the limit of the ratio

$$\frac{\text{change in } y}{\text{change in } x}.$$

# 1-3 One Type of Integral of a Function

The title of this chapter is "Limits, Derivatives, Integrals, and Integrals." In Section 1-2 you estimated the derivative of a function, which is the instantaneous rate of change of $y$ with respect to $x$. In this section you will learn about one type of integral, the definite integral.

Suppose you start off in your car. The velocity increases for a while, then levels off. Figure 1-3a shows the velocity increasing from zero, then approaching and leveling off at 60 ft/sec.

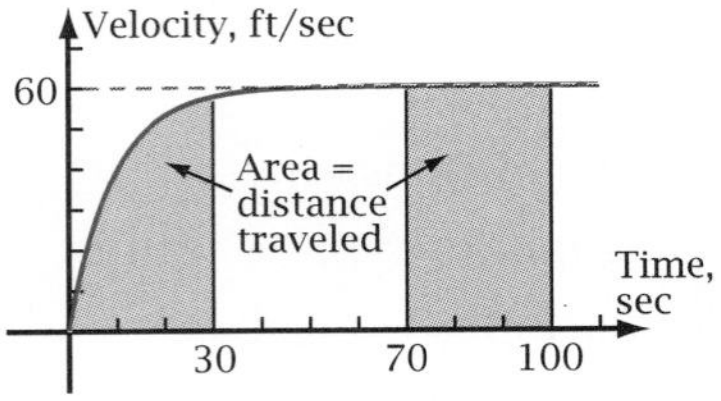


Figure 1-3a

In the 30 sec between time $t = 70$ and $t = 100$, the velocity is a constant 60 ft/sec. Because distance = rate × time, the distance you go in this time interval is

$$60 \text{ ft/sec} \times 30 \text{ sec} = 1800 \text{ ft}.$$

Geometrically, 1800 is the area of the rectangle shown in Figure 1-3a. The width is 30 and the length is 60. Between 0 sec and 30 sec, where the velocity is changing, the area of the region under the graph also equals the distance traveled. Because the length varies, the area cannot be found simply by multiplying two numbers.

The process of evaluating a product in which one factor varies is called finding a **definite integral**. Definite integrals can be evaluated by finding the corresponding area. In this section you will find the approximate area by counting squares on graph paper (by "brute force"!). Later, you will apply the concept of limit to calculate definite integrals *exactly*.

**OBJECTIVE**

Given the equation or the graph for a function, estimate on a graph the definite integral of the function between $x = a$ and $x = b$ by counting squares.

If you are given only the equation, you can plot it with your grapher's grid on feature, estimating the number of squares in this way. However, it is more accurate to use a plot on graph paper to count squares. You can get plotting data by using your grapher's trace or table feature.

**■ Example 1** Estimate the definite integral of the exponential function $f(x) = 8(0.7)^x$ from $x = 1$ to $x = 7$.

**Solution** You can get reasonable accuracy by plotting $f(x)$ at each integer value of $x$ (Figure 1-3b).

The integral equals the area under the graph from $x = 1$ to $x = 7$. "Under" the graph means "between the graph and the $x$-axis." To find the area, first count the whole squares. Put a dot in each square as you count it to keep track, then estimate the area of each partial square to the nearest 0.1 unit. For instance, less than half a square is 0.1, 0.2, 0.3, or 0.4. You be the judge. You should get

| $x$ | $f(x)$ |
|---|---|
| 0 | $f(0) = 8$ |
| 1 | $f(1) = 5.6$ |
| 2 | $f(2) \approx 3.9$ |
| 3 | $f(3) \approx 2.7$ |
| 4 | $f(4) \approx 1.9$ |
| 5 | $f(5) \approx 1.3$ |
| 6 | $f(6) \approx 0.9$ |
| 7 | $f(7) \approx 0.7$ |

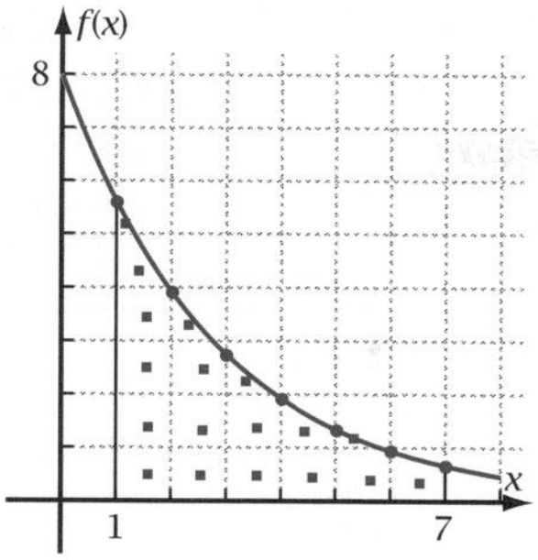


Figure 1-3b

about 13.9 square units for the area, so the definite integral is approximately 13.9. Answers anywhere from 13.5 to 14.3 are reasonable. ■

If the graph is already given, you need only count the squares. Be sure you know how much area each square represents! Example 2 shows you how to do this.

**■ Example 2** Figure 1-3c shows the graph of the velocity function $v(t) = -100t^2 + 90t + 11$, where $t$ is in seconds and $v(t)$ is in feet per second. Estimate the definite integral of $v(t)$ with respect to $t$ for the time interval from $t = 0$ sec to $t = 1$ sec.

***Solution*** Notice that each space in the $t$ direction is 0.1 sec and each space in the $v(t)$ direction is 2 ft/sec. Thus, each square represents (0.1)(2), or 0.2 ft. You should count about 113.4 squares for the area. Thus, the definite integral will be about

$$(113.4)(0.2) \approx 22.7 \text{ ft.}$$ ■

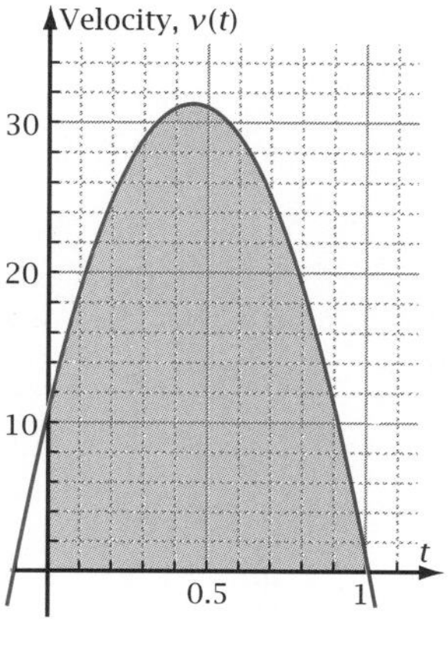


Figure 1-3c

The following is the meaning of definite integral. The precise definition is in Chapter 5, where you will learn an algebraic technique for calculating *exact* values of definite integrals.

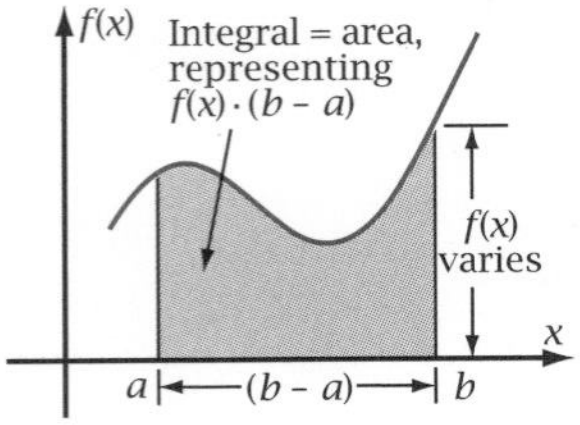


Figure 1-3d

### *Meaning of Definite Integral*

The definite integral of the function $f$ from $x = a$ to $x = b$ gives a way to find the product of $(b - a)$ and $f(x)$, even if $f(x)$ is not a constant. See Figure 1-3d.

## Problem Set 1-3

### *Do These Quickly*

The following problems are intended to refresh your skills. You should be able to do all ten problems in less than five minutes.

***Q1.*** Find $f(5)$ if $f(x) = x - 1$.

***Q2.*** Find the area of the trapezoid in Figure 1-3e.

***Q3.*** Sketch the graph of a linear function with positive $y$-intercept and negative slope.

***Q4.*** Sketch the graph of a quadratic function opening downward.

***Q5.*** Sketch the graph of an increasing exponential function.

***Q6.*** At what value(s) of $x$ is $f(x) = (x - 4)/(x - 3)$ undefined?

***Q7.*** Write the particular equation for the function graphed in Figure 1-3f.

***Q8.*** Write the particular equation for the function graphed in Figure 1-3g.

***Q9.*** Write the particular equation for the function graphed in Figure 1-3h.

***Q10.*** Write the particular equation for the function graphed in Figure 1-3i.

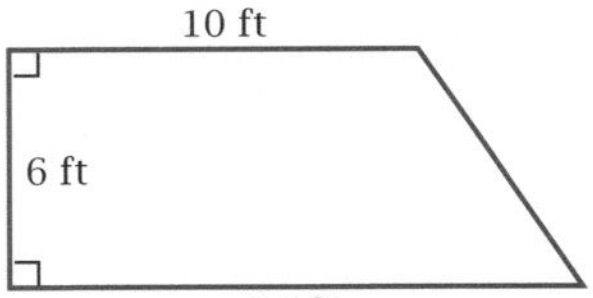


Figure 1-3e

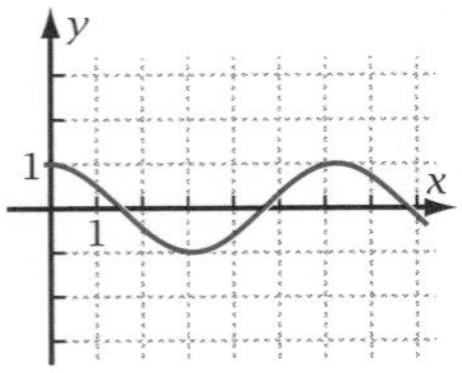


Figure 1-3f

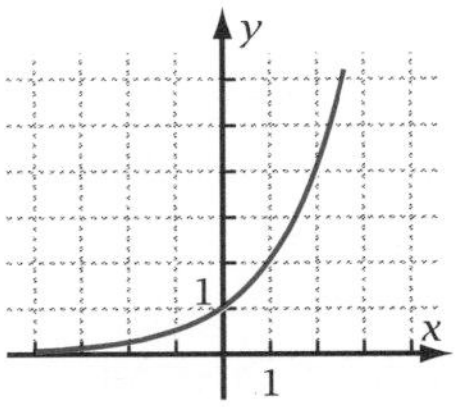


Figure 1-3g

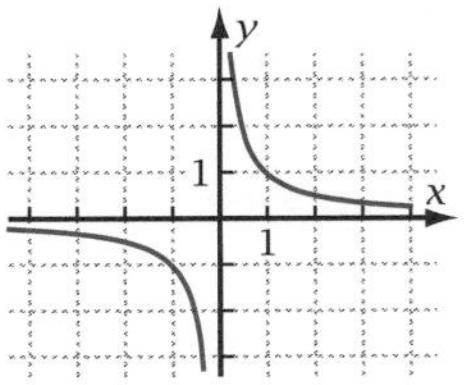


Figure 1-3h

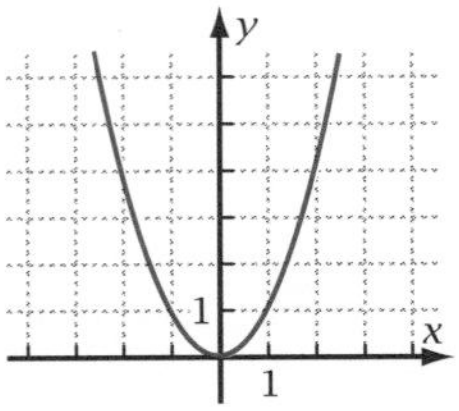


Figure 1-3i

For Problems 1–4, estimate the definite integral by counting squares on a graph.

1. $f(x) = -0.1x^2 + 7$
   a. $x = 0$ to $x = 5$
   b. $x = -1$ to $x = 6$

2. $f(x) = -0.2x^2 + 8$
   a. $x = 0$ to $x = 3$
   b. $x = -2$ to $x = 5$

3. $h(x) = \sin x$
   a. $x = 0$ to $x = \pi$
   b. $x = 0$ to $x = \pi/2$

4. $g(x) = 2^x + 5$
   a. $x = 1$ to $x = 2$
   b. $x = -1$ to $x = 1$

5. In Figure 1-3j, a car is slowing down from a speed of $v = 60$ ft/sec. Estimate the distance it goes from time $t = 5$ sec to $t = 25$ sec by finding the definite integral.

6. In Figure 1-3k, a car speeds up slowly from $v = 55$ mi/hr during a long trip. Estimate the distance it goes from time $t = 0$ hr to $t = 4$ hr by finding the definite integral.

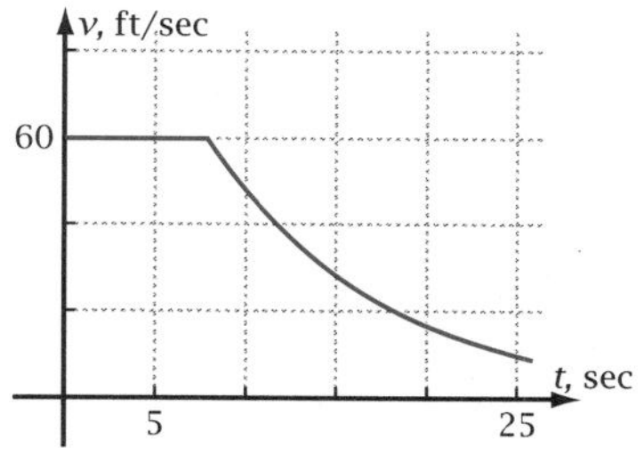

Figure 1-3j

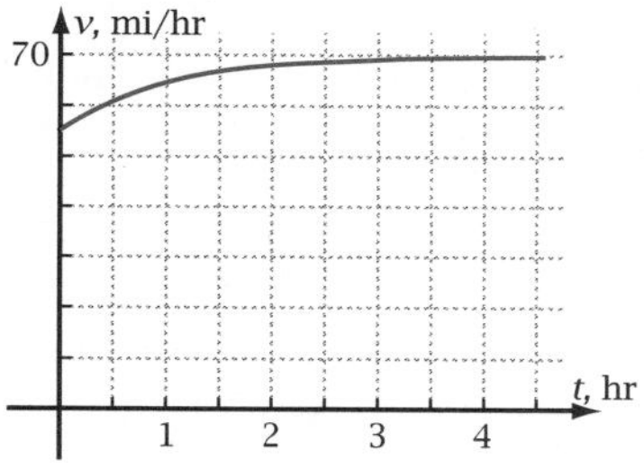

Figure 1-3k

For Problems 7 and 8, estimate the derivative of the function at the given value of $x$.

7. $f(x) = \tan x$, $x = 1$

8. $h(x) = -7x + 100$, $x = 5$

9. *Sports Car Problem:* You have been hired by an automobile manufacturer to analyze the predicted motion of a new sports car they are building. When accelerated hard from a standing start, the velocity of the car, $v(t)$ ft/sec, is expected to vary exponentially with time, $t$ seconds, according to the equation

$$v(t) = 100(1 - 0.9^t).$$

   a. Draw the graph of function $v$ in the domain [0, 10].
   b. What is the range of the velocity function?
   c. Approximately how many seconds will it take the car to reach 60 ft/sec?
   d. Approximately how far will the car have traveled when it reaches 60 ft/sec?
   e. At approximately what rate is the velocity changing when $t = 5$?
   f. What special name is given to the rate of change of velocity?

10. *Slide Problem:* Phoebe sits atop the swimming pool slide (Figure 1-3l). At time $t = 0$ sec she pushes off. Calvin ascertains that her velocity, $v(t)$, is given by

$$v(t) = 10\sin 0.3t,$$

where $v(t)$ is in feet per second. Phoebe splashes into the water at time $t = 4$ sec.

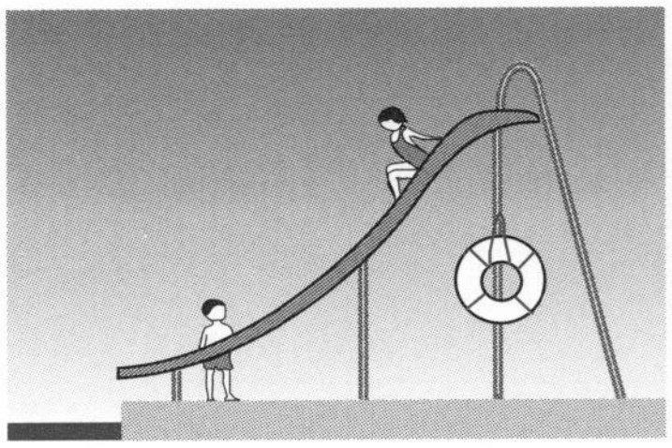

Figure 1-3l

   a. Plot the graph of function v. (Don't forget to set your calculator to radian mode!)
   b. What are the domain and range of the velocity function?
   c. How fast was she going when she hit the water?
   d. Approximately how long is the slide?
   e. At approximately what rate was her velocity changing at $t = 3$?
   f. What special name is given to the rate of change of velocity?

11. *Negative Velocity Problem:* Velocity differs from speed in that it can be *negative.* If the velocity of a moving object is negative, then its distance from its starting point is *decreasing* as time increases. The graph in Figure 1-3m shows $v(t)$centimeters per second as a function of $t$ seconds after its motion started. How far is the object from its starting point when $t = 9$ sec?

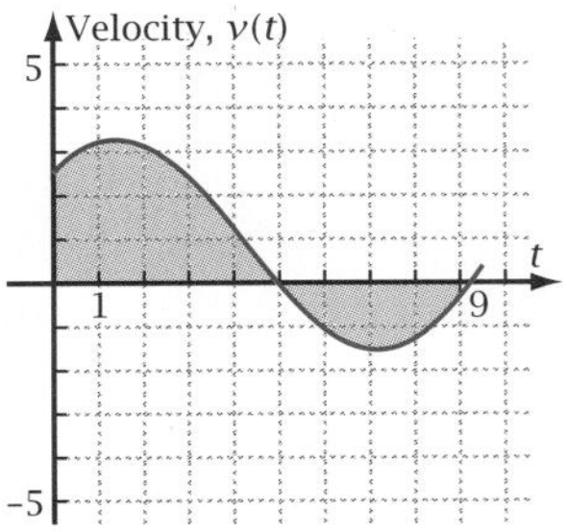


Figure 1-3m

12. Write the meaning of derivative.
13. Write the meaning of definite integral.
14. Write the verbal definition of limit.

# 1-4 Definite Integrals by Trapezoids, from Equations and Data

In Section 1-3, you learned that the definite integral of a function is the product of $x$- and $y$-values, where the $y$-values may be different for various values of $x$. Because the integral is represented by the area of a region under the graph, you were able to estimate it by counting squares. In this section you will learn a more efficient way of estimating definite integrals.

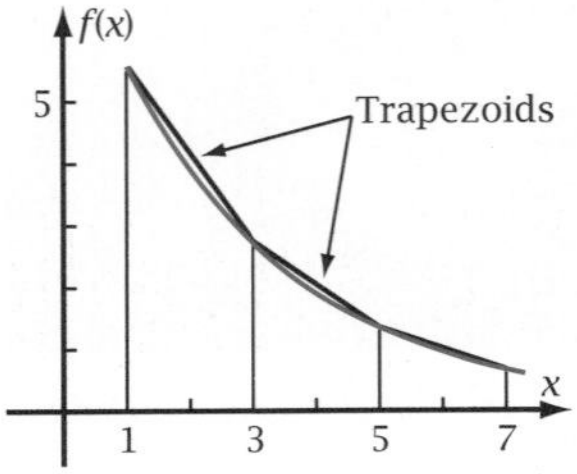


Figure 1-4a

Figure 1-4a shows the graph of

$$f(x) = 8(0.7)^x,$$

which was the function in Example 1 of Section 1-3. Instead of counting squares, divide the region into vertical strips and connect the boundaries to form trapezoids. Although the trapezoids have areas slightly different from the region under the graph, their areas are easy to calculate and add. From geometry you recall that the area of a trapezoid is the average of the parallel sides multiplied by the altitude.

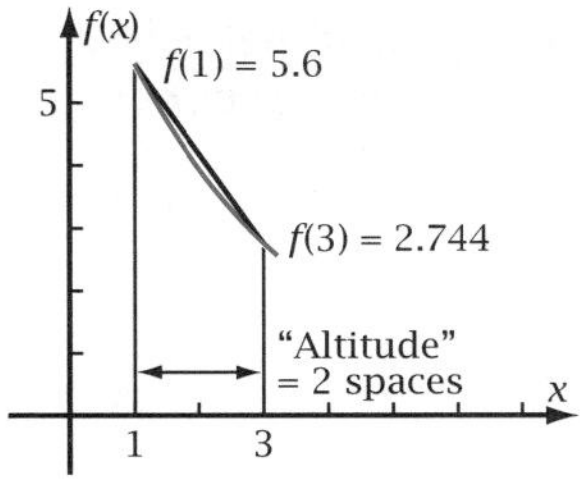


Figure 1-4b

Figure 1-4b shows the trapezoid between $x = 1$ and $x = 3$. Its parallel sides are $f(1) = 5.6$ and $f(3) = 2.744$, and its altitude is $(3 - 1) = 2$. Thus its area is

$$\tfrac{1}{2}(5.6 + 2.744)(2) = 8.344.$$

The areas of the other two trapezoids in Figure 1-4a can be found the same way.

$$\tfrac{1}{2}(2.744 + 1.34456)(2) = 4.08856$$
$$\tfrac{1}{2}(1.34456 + 0.6588344)(2) = 2.0033944$$

The total area of the trapezoids is approximately equal to the definite integral.

$$\text{Integral} \approx 8.344 + 4.08856 + 2.0033944 = 14.4359544 \approx 14.4$$

The answer is slightly larger than the 13.9 that was estimated in Example 1 of Section 1-3. This result is reasonable, because the trapezoids include slightly more area than the region under the graph.

***OBJECTIVE***

Estimate the value of a definite integral by dividing the region under the graph into trapezoids.

To accomplish the objective in a time-efficient way, observe that each $y$-value in the sum appears *twice,* except for the first and the last values.

$$\tfrac{1}{2}(5.6 + 2.744)(2) + \tfrac{1}{2}(2.744 + 1.34456)(2) + \tfrac{1}{2}(1.34456 + 0.6588344)(2)$$

The sum can be rearranged as shown.

$$\left[\tfrac{1}{2}(5.6) + 2.744 + 1.34456 + \tfrac{1}{2}(0.6588344)\right](2)$$

The four terms inside the brackets are the $y$-values at the boundaries of the four vertical strips. (There is one more boundary than there are strips.) To find the area, you simply add the $y$-values, taking half of the first one and half of the last one. The answer is this sum multiplied by the width of each strip (2, in this case). This procedure for finding an approximate value of a definite integral is called the **trapezoidal rule**.

***Example 1*** Use the trapezoidal rule to estimate the definite integral of $f(x) = 8(0.7)^x$ from $x = 1$ to $x = 7$. Use ten increments.

***Solution*** From $x = 1$ to $x = 7$ there are 6 $x$-units, so the width of each strip will be $6/10 = 0.6$ units. An efficient way to do the computation is to list the $x$-values in table form, then compute and add the corresponding $y$-values, multiplying the first and last by 1/2. Finally, multiply the sum by 0.6 to get the answer.

| $x$ | $y = f(x)$ | |
|---|---|---|
| 1 | 5.6 | ← Use *half* of this one. |
| 1.6 | 4.5211 . . . | |
| 2.2 | 3.6501 . . . | |
| 2.8 | 2.9468 . . . | |
| 3.4 | 2.3791 . . . | |
| 4 | 1.9208 | |
| 4.6 | 1.5507 . . . | |
| 5.2 | 1.2519 . . . | |
| 5.8 | 1.0107 . . . | |
| 6.4 | 0.8160 . . . | |
| 7 | 0.6588 . . . | ← Use *half* of this one. |

Sum = 23.1770 . . .    Without rounding, add the $y$-values as you calculate them.

Integral ≈ (23.1770 . . .)(0.6) = 13.9062452 . . . ■

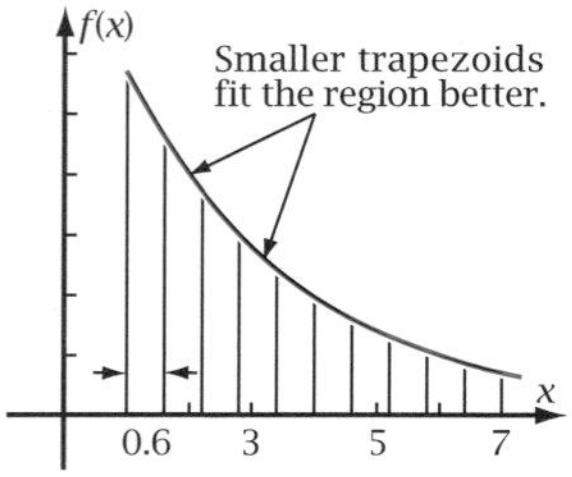

Figure 1-4c

Note that this answer is closer to 13.9, the answer to Example 1 in Section 1-3. This result is to be expected, because the smaller trapezoids fit the region under the graph better, as shown in Figure 1-4c. If you were to increase the number of strips you drew in, the value you'd get for the integral would get closer and closer to 13.8534138. . . . This number is the *limit* of the areas of the trapezoids as their widths approach zero. In Chapter 5, you will learn how to calculate exact values of integrals.

The trapezoidal rule is advantageous if you must find the definite integral of a function specified in table form, rather than by equation. Example 2 shows you how to do this.

### ■ *Example 2*

On a ship at sea, it is easier to measure how fast you are going than it is to measure how far you have gone. Suppose you are navigator aboard a supertanker. The speed of the ship is measured each 15 min and recorded in the table shown. Estimate the distance the ship has gone between 7:30 p.m. and 9:15 p.m.

| time | mi/hr | time | mi/hr |
|---|---|---|---|
| 7:30 | 28 | 8:30 | 7 |
| 7:45 | 25 | 8:45 | 10 |
| 8:00 | 20 | 9:00 | 21 |
| 8:15 | 22 | 9:15 | 26 |

### *Solution*

Figure 1-4d shows the given points. Because no information is known for times between the given ones, the simplest thing to assume is that the graph is a sequence of line segments. Because miles equals (miles/hour)(hours), the answer will equal a definite integral. The integral can be found from the area of the shaded region in Figure 1-4d, using the trapezoidal rule.

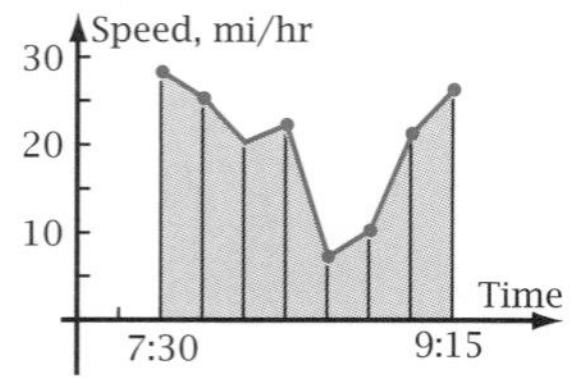

Figure 1-4d

$$\text{area} = \left(\tfrac{28}{2} + 25 + 20 + 22 + 7 + 10 + 21 + \tfrac{26}{2}\right) = 132$$

$\therefore$ integral = 0.25 × 132 = 33    Why 0.25?

$\therefore$ distance is about 33 mi. ■

## Problem Set 1-4

### *Do These Quickly*

The following problems are intended to refresh your skills. You should be able to do all ten problems in less than five minutes.

**Q1.** The value of $y$ changes by 3 units when $x$ changes by 0.1 unit. About how fast is $y$ changing?

**Q2.** The value of $y$ changes by $-5$ units when $x$ changes by 0.01 unit. Approximately what does the derivative equal?

**Q3.** Sketch the graph of the absolute value function, $y = |x|$.

**Q4.** Find $f(3)$ if $f(x) = x^2$.

**Q5.** What is 50 divided by 1/2?

**Q6.** Evaluate: $\sin(\pi/2)$

**Q7.** How many days are there in a leap year?

**Q8.** The instantaneous rate of change of a function is called the —?— of the function.

**Q9.** The product of $x$ and $y$ for a function is called the —?— of the function.

**Q10.** At what value(s) of $x$ is $f(x) = (x - 4)/(x - 3)$ equal to zero?

1. *Spaceship Problem:* A spaceship is being launched from Cape Canaveral. As the last stage of the rocket motor is firing, the velocity is given by

$$v(t) = 1600 \times 1.1^t,$$

where $v(t)$ is in feet per second and $t$ is the number of seconds since the last stage started.

a. Plot the graph of $v(t)$ versus $t$, from $t = 0$ to $t = 30$. Sketch the result.

b. Tell why the area of the region under the graph represents the distance the spaceship went in this 30-sec interval.

c. Find, approximately, the distance traveled between $t = 0$ and $t = 30$ by using trapezoids of width corresponding to 5 sec. Sketch these trapezoids on your graph.

d. What mathematical term is used for the product of velocity and time found in this way?

e. To go into orbit around the earth, the spaceship must be going at least 27,000 ft/sec. Will it be going this fast when $t = 30$? Justify your answer.

2. *Walking Problem:* Pace Walker enters a walkathon. She starts off at 4 mi/hr, speeds up as she warms up, then slows down again as she gets tired. She estimates that her speed is given by

$$v(t) = 4 + \sin 1.4t,$$

where $t$ is the number of hours since she started and $v(t)$ is in miles per hour.

a. Pace walks for 3 hr. Draw the graph of $v(t)$ as a function of $t$ for these three hours. Sketch the result on your paper. (Be sure your calculator is in radian mode!)

b. Tell why a definite integral would be used to find the distance Pace has gone in 3 hr.

c. Estimate the integral in 2b, using six trapezoids. Show these trapezoids on your graph. About how far did Pace walk in the 3 hr?

d. How fast was Pace walking at the end of the 3 hr? When did her maximum speed occur? What was her maximum speed?

3. *Aircraft Carrier Landing Problem:* In 1993, Kara Hultgreen became one of the first female pilots authorized to fly navy planes in combat. Assume that as she comes in for a landing on the carrier, her speed in feet per second takes on the values shown in the table. Find, approximately, how far her plane travels as it comes to a stop. Is her plane in danger of running off the other end of the 800-ft-long flight deck?

| sec | ft/sec |
|---|---|
| 0.0 | 300 |
| 0.6 | 230 |
| 1.2 | 150 |
| 1.8 | 90 |
| 2.4 | 40 |
| 3.0 | 0 |

4. *Water over the Dam Problem:* The amount of water that has flowed over the spillway on a dam can be estimated from the flow rate and the length of time the water has been flowing. Suppose that the flow rate has been recorded every 3 hr for a 24-hr period, as shown in the table. Estimate the number of cubic feet of water that has flowed over the dam in this period.

| time | $ft^3$/hr | time | $ft^3$/hr |
|---|---|---|---|
| 12:00 a.m. | 5,000 | 12:00 p.m. | 11,000 |
| 3:00 a.m. | 8,000 | 3:00 p.m. | 7,000 |
| 6:00 a.m. | 12,000 | 6:00 p.m. | 4,000 |
| 9:00 a.m. | 13,000 | 9:00 p.m. | 6,000 |
| | | 12:00 a.m. | 9,000 |

If a graph is already drawn accurately, it may be more efficient to estimate a definite integral by counting squares. For Problems 5 and 6, count squares to estimate the definite integral for the function shown.

5. Integral from $x = 1$ to $x = 6$

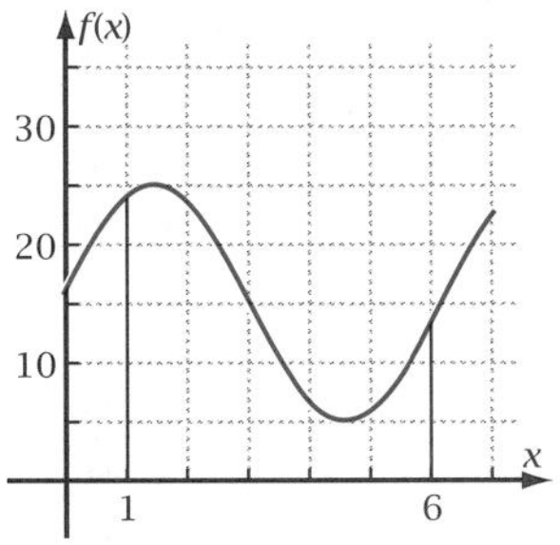


6. Integral from $x = 0.4$ to $x = 2$

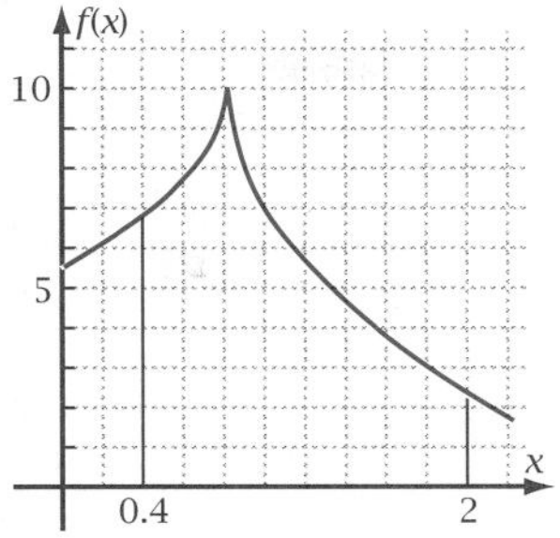


7. *Program for Trapezoidal Rule Problem:* For use now and later, it is advantageous to have a program for your grapher that will evaluate integrals by the trapezoidal rule. Write and save such a program. A clever way to write it for a grapher is to specify the function on the $y =$ menu—as $y_1$, for instance—then set up a loop that changes $x$ by the appropriate amount, evaluates $y_1$ for the current value of $x$, and adds the result to the sum of the previous $y_1$ values. The input should be the values of $a$ and $b$, the lowest and highest $x$-values for the region under the graph, and $n$, the number of increments (trapezoids) to be used. The output should be the approximate value of the integral. Be sure that the program uses only *half* of the first and last $y$-values.

8. Debug the program in Problem 7 by using it for the integral in Example 1. If the program does not give the correct answer, go back and fix it.

For Problems 9 and 10, find the definite integrals indicated. These are the same integrals you found by counting squares in Problems 1 and 4 in Problem Set 1-3.

9. Integral of $f(x) = -0.1x^2 + 7$ from:
   a. $x = 0$ to $x = 5$, 10 increments
   b. $x = -1$ to $x = 6$, 10 increments
   c. $x = -1$ to $x = 6$, 100 increments

10. Integral of $g(x) = 2^x + 5$ from:
   a. $x = 1$ to $x = 2$, 10 increments
   b. $x = -1$ to 1, 10 increments
   c. $x = -1$ to 1, 100 increments

11. *Trapezoidal Rule Error Problem:* The trapezoidal rule overestimates the integral in one of Problems 9 and 10, and underestimates it in the other. Which is which? How do you tell?

12. *Elliptical Table Problem:* Figure 1-4e shows the top of a coffee table in the shape of an ellipse. The ellipse has the equation

$$\left(\frac{x}{110}\right)^2 + \left(\frac{y}{40}\right)^2 = 1,$$

where $x$ and $y$ are in centimeters. Use the trapezoidal rule to estimate the area of the table. Will this estimate be too high or too low? Explain. What is the *exact* area of the ellipse?

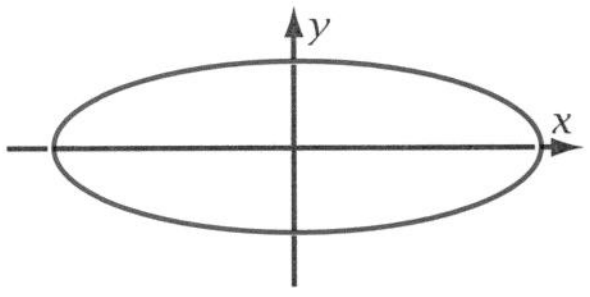


Figure 1-4e

13. *Football Problem:* The table shows the cross-sectional area, $A$, of a football at various distances, $d$, from one end. The distances are in inches and the areas are in square inches. Use the trapezoidal rule to find, approximately, the integral of area with respect to distance. What are the units of this integral? What, then, do you suppose the integral represents?

| $d$ (in.) | $A$ (in$^2$) | $d$ (in.) | $A$ (in$^2$) |
|---|---|---|---|
| 0 | 0.0 | 7 | 30.3 |
| 1 | 7.0 | 8 | 27.2 |
| 2 | 10.5 | 9 | 23.0 |
| 3 | 23.0 | 10 | 10.5 |
| 4 | 27.2 | 11 | 7.0 |
| 5 | 30.3 | 12 | 0.0 |
| 6 | 31.8 | | |

14. *Integral as a Limit Problem:* Now that you have a program to calculate definite integrals approximately, you can see what happens to the value of the integral as you use narrower trapezoids. Estimate the definite integral of $f(x) = x^2$ from $x = 1$ to $x = 4$, using 10, 100, and 1000 trapezoids. What number do the values seem to be approaching as the number of trapezoids gets larger and larger? Make a conjecture about the *exact* value of the definite integral as the width of each trapezoid approaches zero. This number is the —?— of the areas of the trapezoids as the limit of their widths approaches zero. What word goes in the blank?

15. *Derivative from Graph Problem:* You recall that the derivative of a function is the instantaneous rate of change of the $y$-value as the $x$-value increases. If the graph of a function is already drawn, you can estimate its derivative at a given point by drawing a line *tangent* to the graph at that point. If you put a ruler on the concave side of the graph (see Figure 1-4f), with a bit of the graph projecting beyond the ruler, you can draw a reasonably accurate tangent. Pick a convenient run and measure the rise to find the slope.

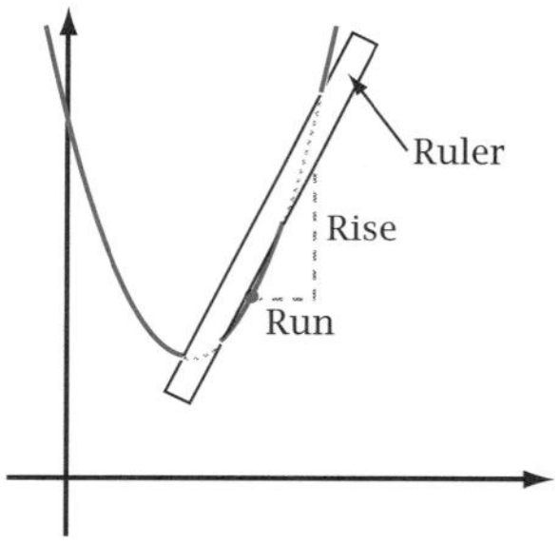

Figure 1-4f

a. Find the derivative of $f(x)$ at $x = 2$ for Problem 5 of this problem set.

b. Find the derivative of $f(x)$ at $x = 0.6$ for Problem 6 of this problem set.

16. *Exact Integral Conjecture Problem:* The *exact* definite integral of $g(x) = x^3$ from $x = 1$ to $x = 5$ is an *integer*. Make a conjecture about what this integer equals. Justify your answer.

*17. *Meaning of Limits Problem:* In this problem you will learn something about the *meaning* of the word *limit* and how this meaning relates to the *verbal* definition. Let

$$f(x) = \frac{2x^2 - 50}{x - 5}.$$

a. Explain why $f(5)$ is undefined.

*This problem prepares you for the next section.

b. Find $f(4.9)$ and $f(5.1)$. If you like, you may simplify the expression for $f(x)$ first.

c. What number are $f(4.9)$ and $f(5.1)$ both close to?

d. Find $f(4.99)$ and $f(5.01)$. Are these both close to the number you wrote in 17c?

e. Let $L$ be the number in 17c. Write the following sentence, filling the appropriate number into the blank: "If $x$ is within 0.01 units of 5 (but not equal to 5), then $f(x)$ is within -?- units of $L$."

# 1-5 Limit of a Function

Calculus involves four concepts: limits, derivatives, integrals, and integrals. You have learned that a derivative is the rate of change of a function, and that a definite integral gives a way of calculating a product—such as (rate)(time)—in which one of the factors varies.

The formal definitions of derivative and definite integral involve the concept of the limit of a function. In Section 1-2 you learned a verbal definition of limit. In this section you will learn a formal definition, and see how this relates to the meaning of limit.

***OBJECTIVE***

Given the graph or the equation of a function, tell whether or not the function has a limit as $x$ approaches the given value and tell how your answer relates to the definition of limit.

Consider the rational algebraic function

$$f(x) = \frac{0.4x^2 - 10}{x - 5}.$$

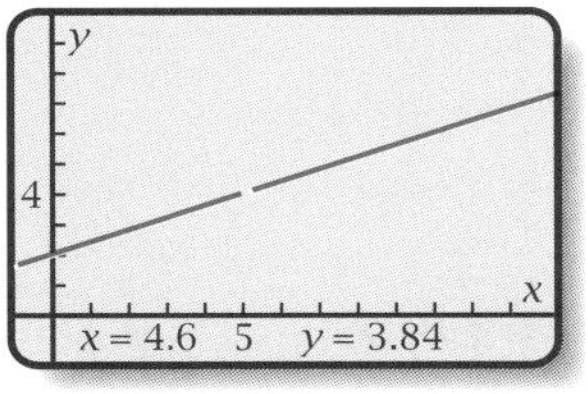

Figure 1-5a

If you plot the function on the grapher, you get a straight line with a gap in it, as shown in Figure 1-5a. The gap occurs where $x = 5$, and is due to the fact that the denominator, $x - 5$, is zero when $x$ is 5. It will show up if you use a window that includes $x = 5$ as a grid point.

An interesting thing shows up if you use the trace or the table feature of your grapher. Using a window with an $x$-increment of 0.1, you get the values shown. No $y$-value appears where $x = 5$, but following the pattern suggests that $y$ should be exactly 4 when $x = 5$.

| | |
|---|---|
| $x = 4.6$ | $y = 3.84$ |
| $x = 4.7$ | $y = 3.88$ |
| $x = 4.8$ | $y = 3.92$ |
| $x = 4.9$ | $y = 3.96$ |
| $x = 5$ | $y =$ |
| $x = 5.1$ | $y = 4.04$ |
| $x = 5.2$ | $y = 4.08$ |

Try to find $f(5)$ by direct substitution.

$$f(5) = \frac{0.4(5^2) - 10}{5 - 5} = \frac{0}{0}, \text{ which is undefined because of division by zero.}$$

The fraction 0/0 is called an **indeterminate form**. Algebra shows you what is going on.

$$f(x) = \frac{0.4(x + 5)(x - 5)}{x - 5}$$

$$f(x) = 0.4x + 2, \text{ provided that } x \neq 5.$$

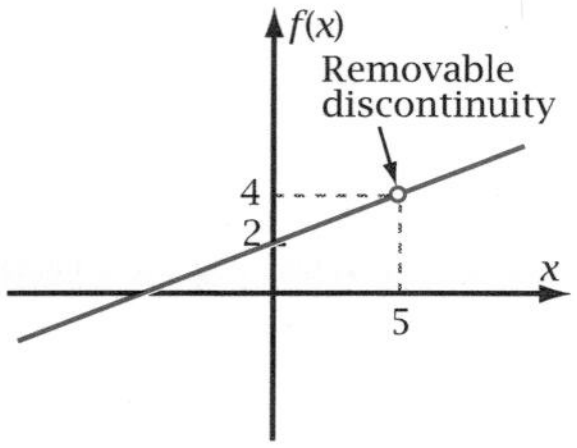

Figure 1-5b

Substituting 5 for $x$ in the simplified expression gives $0.4(5) + 2 = 4$, which is the value you would get by following the pattern in the table.

The graph in Figure 1-5b is said to have a **removable discontinuity** at $x = 5$. The function is discontinuous because of the gap, but the gap can be removed simply by defining $f(5)$ to be 4. When you draw such a graph on your paper, it is customary to show an open circle at the discontinuity, indicating that there is no value of $y$ for that one value of $x$.

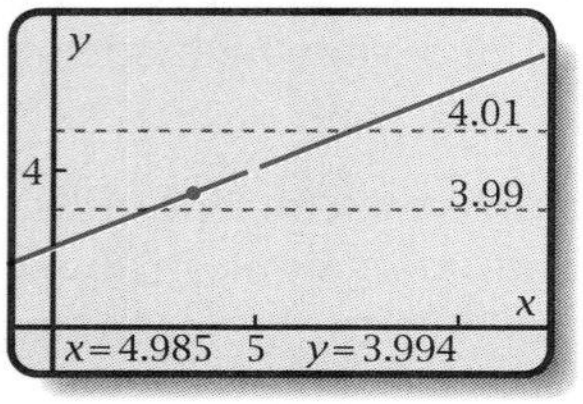

Figure 1-5c

The number 4, which $f(x)$ is close to when $x$ is close to 5, is the **limit** of $f(x)$ as $x$ approaches 5. You should begin to see how the parts of the verbal definition of limit are coming together. You can make $f(x)$ as close as you like to 4 just by keeping $x$ close enough to 5 (but not *equal* to 5). Suppose someone tells you, "Keep $f(x)$ within 0.01 unit of 4." To find approximately how close you must keep $x$ to 5, you can trace on the graph (Figure 1-5c) or make a table.

| | |
|---|---|
| $x = 4.97$ | $y = 3.988$ |
| $x = 4.975$ | $y = 3.99$ |
| $x = 4.98$ | $y = 3.992$ |
| $x = 4.985$ | $y = 3.994$ |
| $x = 4.99$ | $y = 3.996$ |
| $x = 4.995$ | $y = 3.998$ |
| $x = 5$ | $y =$ |
| $x = 5.005$ | $y = 4.002$ |
| $x = 5.01$ | $y = 4.004$ |
| $x = 5.015$ | $y = 4.006$ |
| $x = 5.02$ | $y = 4.008$ |
| $x = 5.025$ | $y = 4.01$ |
| $x = 5.03$ | $y = 4.012$ |

(Rows $x = 4.98$ through $x = 5.02$: $x$ within 0.025 unit of 5; $y$ within 0.01 unit of 4)

You can also use algebra to find out *exactly* how close to keep $x$ to 5.

$$3.99 < f(x) < 4.01$$
$$3.99 < 0.4x + 2 < 4.01$$
$$1.99 < 0.4x < 2.01$$
$$4.975 < x < 5.025 \text{ (and } x \neq 5)$$

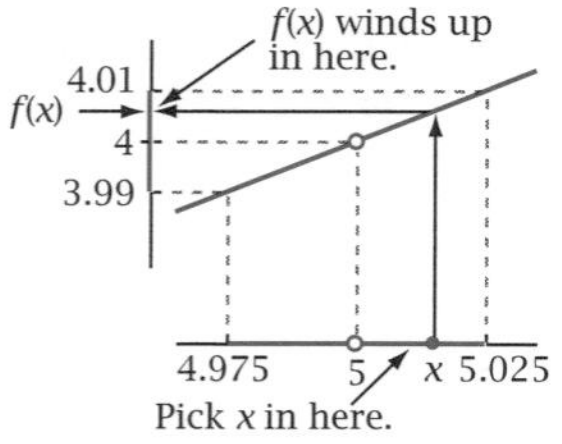

Figure 1-5d

The last inequality says that $x$ is within 0.025 unit of 5. By reversing the steps, you can see that *if* $x$ is within 0.025 unit of 5, *then* $f(x)$ is within 0.01 unit of 4 (Figure 1-5d).

The above work leads to the following formal definition of limit. You should commit this definition to memory so that you will be sure to remember its various parts.

> **Formal Definition of Limit**
>
> $L$ is the limit of $f(x)$ as $x$ approaches $c$
> if and only if
> for any positive number epsilon, no matter how small,
> there is a positive number delta such that
> if $x$ is within delta units of $c$ (but not equal to $c$),
> then $f(x)$ is within epsilon units of $L$.

You should be able to make the following connections:

- 4 is the value of $L$. It is the *one* number $f(x)$ stays arbitrarily close to if $x$ is close to 5.
- 5 is the value of $c$. It is the number you keep $x$ close to in order for $f(x)$ to stay close to 4.
- 0.01 is a value of epsilon (quite small!). It is picked "arbitrarily" to tell how close to 4 you are supposed to keep $f(x)$.
- 0.025 is the corresponding value of delta. It tells how close to 5 is "close enough" to keep $x$ in order that $f(x)$ will wind up somewhere within 0.01 unit of 4.

Note that $f(x)$ would not be within 0.01 unit of 4 if $x$ were *equal* to 5 because there is no value of $f(5)$ to begin with!

**Example 1**

Tell whether or not the function graphed in Figure 1-5e has a limit at the given $x$-value, and tell why or why not. If there is a limit, give its value.

a. $x = 1$ b. $x = 2$ c. $x = 3$

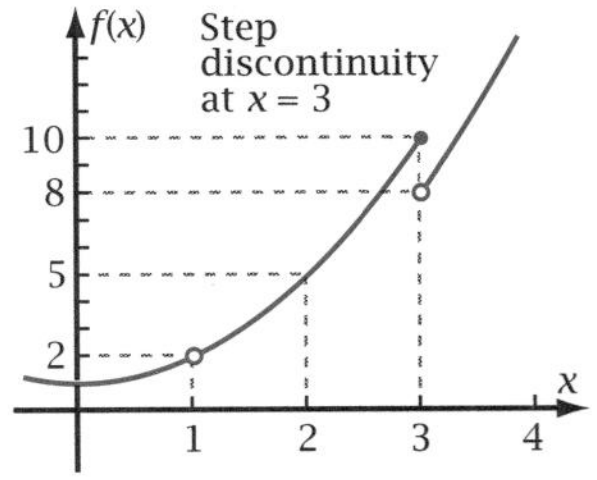


Figure 1-5e

**Solution**

a. As $x$ approaches 1, the limit is 2. If $x$ is close to 1 but not equal to 1, $f(x)$ is close to 2.

b. As $x$ approaches 2, the limit is 5. If $x$ is close to 2 but not equal to 2, $f(x)$ is close to 5. The fact that $x$ *can* equal 2 is of no consequence in this problem.

c. As $x$ approaches 3, there is no limit. If $x$ is close to 3 on the left, $f(x)$ is close to 10. If $x$ is close to 3 on the right, $f(x)$ is close to 8. So there is no *one* number $f(x)$ can be kept close to just by keeping $x$ close to 3 but not equal to 3. ■

*Note:* The discontinuity shown in Figure 1-5e is called a **step discontinuity**.

Problems 11–14 in Problem Set 1-5 will show you in a "learn as you go" manner how to find a limit if an equation is given.

# Problem Set 1-5

### *Do These Quickly*

The following problems are intended to refresh your skills. You should be able to do all ten problems in less than five minutes.

**Q1.** Sketch the graph of a function that is positive and increasing fast at $x = 2$.

**Q2.** Sketch a graph showing the meaning of definite integral.

**Q3.** Sketch the graph of $y = \sin x$.

**Q4.** Evaluate: $\tan(\pi/4)$

**Q5.** Evaluate: $3^{-2}$

**Q6.** Simplify: 24/36

**Q7.** Find 30% of 600.

**Q8.** How many weeks are there in a year?

**Q9.** What type of function has a graph like that shown in Figure 1-5f?

**Q10.** What is the name for the instantaneous rate of change of a function?

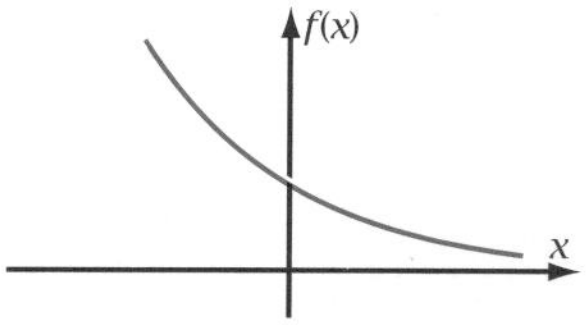

Figure 1-5f

For Problems 1–10, tell whether or not the function has a limit as $x$ approaches $c$; if so, tell what the limit equals.

1.
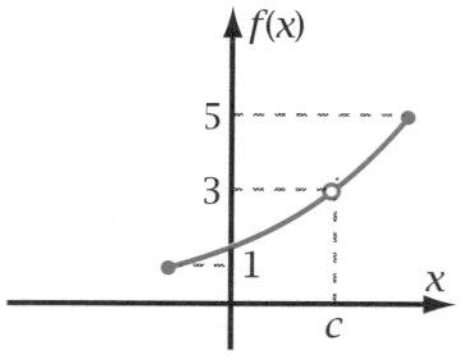


2.
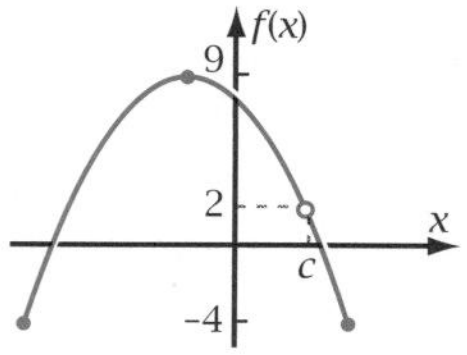


3.
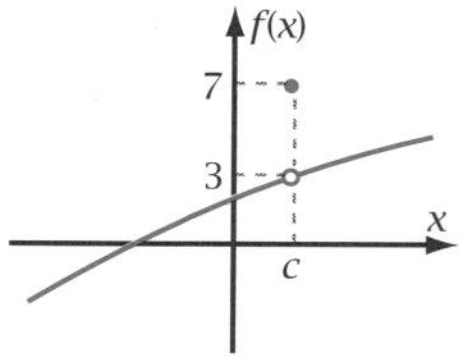


4.
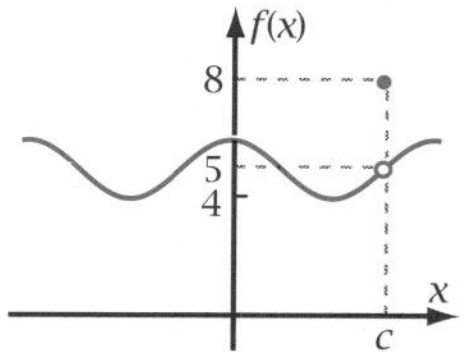


5.
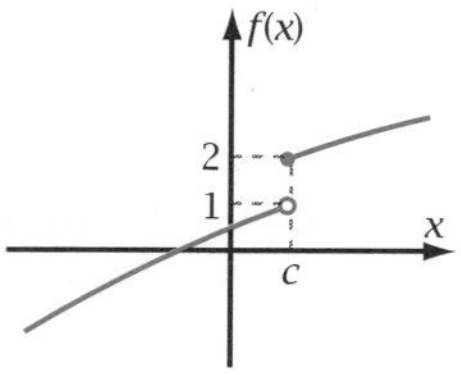


6.
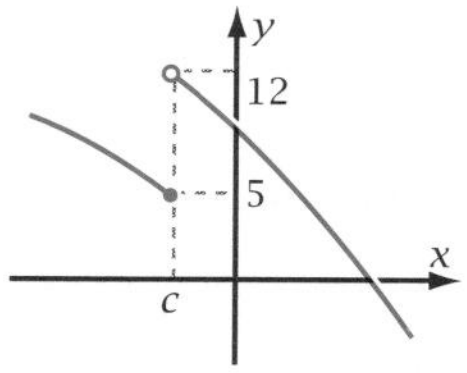


7.
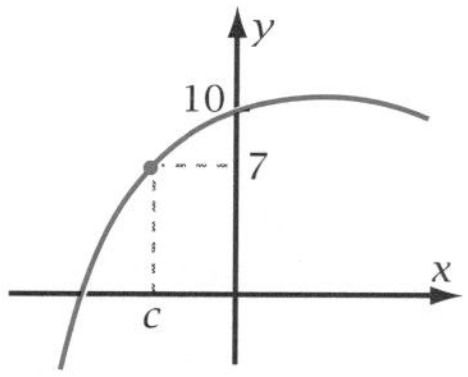


8.
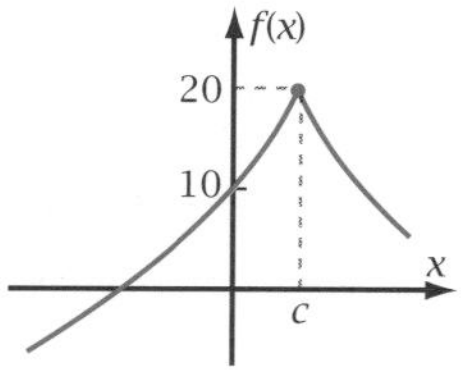


9.
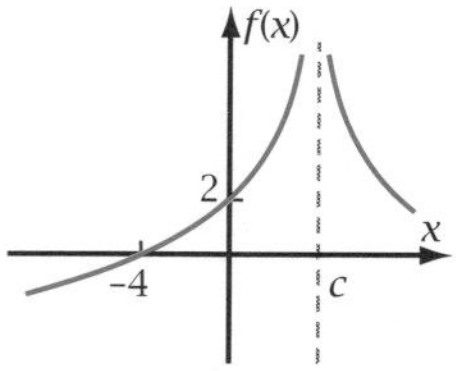


10.
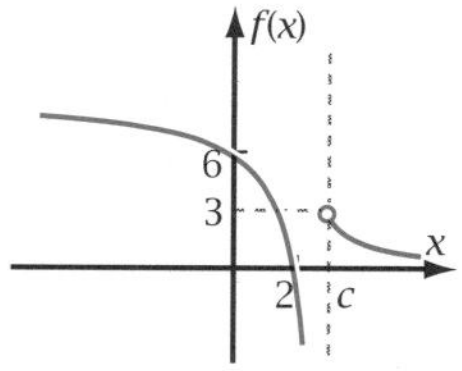

Problems 11–14 are intended for you to work in groups. The goal is to find out how various parts of the definition of limit apply when a function is specified by an equation.

11. *Definition of Limit I:*
    a. Write the formal definition of limit.
    b. The graph of $f(x) = 3x - 7$ is shown in Figure 1-5g. Show that $f(4) = 5$.
    c. You can keep $f(x)$ close to 5 just by keeping $x$ close to 4. How close to 4 must you keep $x$ in order for $f(x)$ to stay within 0.6 unit of 5?
    d. The 0.6 in 11c is a value of epsilon in the definition of limit. The answer to 11c is a value of delta. Sketch how epsilon and delta are related to the graph.

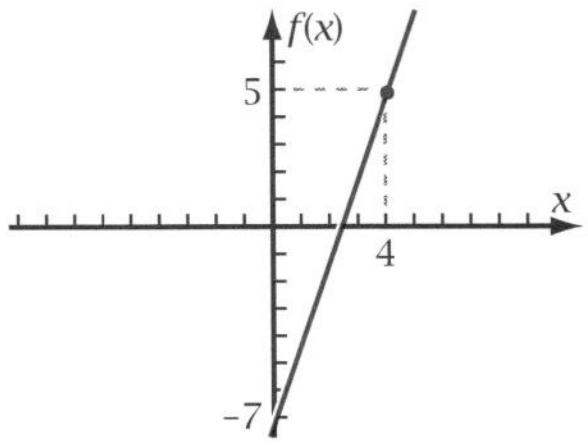

Figure 1-5g

    e. Pick a value of $x$ that is within delta units of 4 but *not* equal to 4. Show that $f(x)$ really *is* within epsilon units of 5.
    f. The number 5 fits the definition of limit because you could find a value for delta no matter how small epsilon is. Show that you understand the meaning of this statement by finding a value of delta if epsilon is 0.00012. Tell how you found this value of delta.

12. *Definition of Limit II:* The function

$$f(x) = \frac{4x^2 - 7x - 2}{x - 2}$$

is undefined when $x = 2$. In this problem you will show that $f(x)$ *does* have a limit as $x$ approaches 2.
    a. Plot the graph of $f$. Use a friendly window that includes $x = 2$ as a grid point. Sketch the graph and name the feature that seems to be present at $x = 2$.
    b. From the graph, tell what you think the limit of $f(x)$ is as $x$ approaches 2.
    c. Try to evaluate $f(2)$ by direct substitution. What form does the answer take? What name is given to a form such as this?
    d. Factor the numerator and simplify the expression by canceling the common factor. Although the simplified expression does not equal $f(2)$, you *can* substitute 2 for $x$ and get an answer. What is this answer and what does it represent?
    e. How close to 2 would you have to keep $x$ in order for $f(x)$ to be between 8.9 and 9.1?
    f. How close to 2 would you have to keep $x$ in order for $f(x)$ to be within 0.001 unit of the limit in 12b? Answer in the form " $x$ must be within -?- units of 2."
    g. Four constants appear in the definition of limit: $L$, $c$, epsilon, and delta. What are the values of these four constants in 12f?
    h. Explain how you could find a suitable value of delta no matter *how* small epsilon is.
    i. What is the reason for the restriction "...but not equal to $c$" that appears in the definition of limit?

13. *Definition of Limit III:* The function

$$f(x) = \frac{(x^2 - 6x + 13)(x - 2)}{(x - 2)}$$

is undefined when $x = 2$. However, if you cancel the $(x - 2)$ factors, the equation becomes $f(x) = x^2 - 6x + 13$ $(x \neq 2)$. So $f$ would be a quadratic function, except that there is a removable discontinuity where $x = 2$ (Figure 1-5h). The $y$-value of this missing point is the limit of $f(x)$ as $x$ approaches 2.

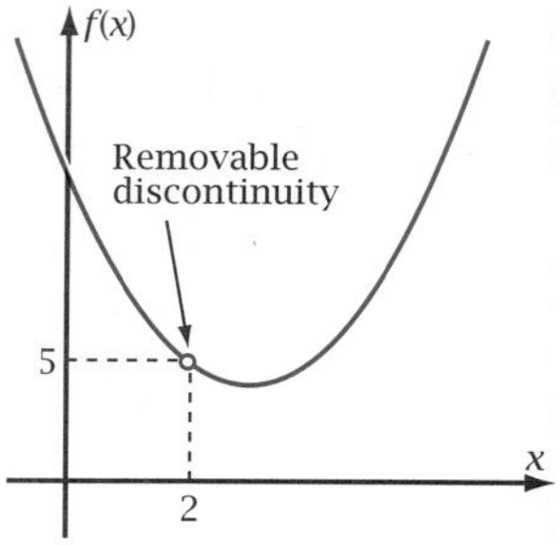


Figure 1-5h

a. Show that $f(2)$ has the indeterminate form 0/0. Do an appropriate calculation to show that 5 is the limit of $f(x)$ as $x$ approaches 2.

b. Plot the graph close to the discontinuity. Use a friendly window that includes $x = 2$ as a grid point and has an $x$-increment of 0.001. Then use your grapher's trace or table feature to make a table of values of $f(x)$ for each value of $x$ from 1.990 through 2.010. For which values of $x$ in the table is $f(x)$ within 0.01 unit of 5? Complete the statement "If $x$ is within -?- units of 2, then $f(x)$ is within 0.01 unit of 5."

c. Find the *largest* interval of values of $x$ for which $f(x)$ is within 0.01 unit of 5. You can do this by setting $f(x) = 4.99$ and solving to find the value of $x$ nearest 2. Repeat for $f(x) = 5.01$. Keep as much precision as your calculator will give you.

d. Sketch the part of the graph close to $x = 2$. Show how the numbers in 13c relate to the graph.

e. Find the *largest* number you could put in the blank of the statement in 13b. Take into account that the interval in 13c is of a different width on one side of 2 than on the other.

f. Write the values of the constants $L$, $c$, epsilon, and delta for 13a–e.

14. *Definition of Limit IV:* Answer the following questions for the function

$$f(x) = x - \frac{x - 2}{|x - 2|}.$$

a. Plot the graph of $f$. Sketch the result, showing the discontinuity at $x = 2$.

b. Find $f(1.99)$ and $f(2.01)$. Based on these numbers and the graph, explain why there is *no one* number $L$ for which $f(x)$ is very close to $L$ when $x$ is close, but not equal, to 2.

15. *One-Sided Limit Problem:* The following function has a **step discontinuity** at $x = 2$.

$$f(x) = 3 + \frac{1}{2}x + \frac{|x - 2|}{x - 2}$$

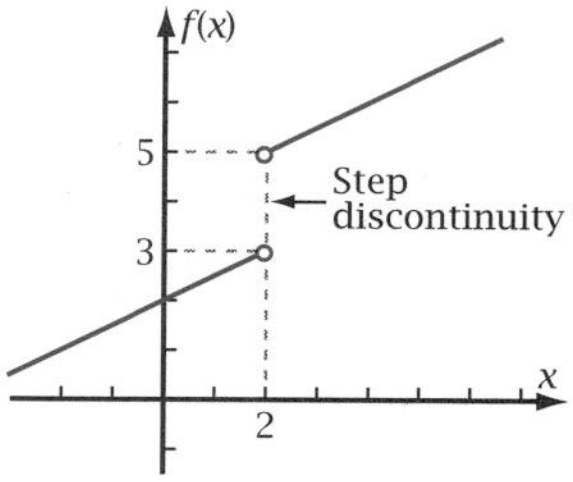


Figure 1-5i

a. Figure 1-5i shows the graph of $f$. Explain why the graph takes a jump at $x = 2$.

b. What is the limit of $f(x)$ as $x$ approaches 2 from the *left* side?

c. What is the limit of $f(x)$ as $x$ approaches 2 from the *right* side?

d. Explain why there is *no* single number that can be the limit of $f(x)$ as $x$ approaches 2.

16. *Piecewise-Defined Function Problem:* A function may be defined by different equations in different parts of its domain. If this is the case, a single brace is used to bracket together the different equations and to indicate the $x$-values for which they apply. Consider the following function.

$$f(x) = \begin{cases} x+1, & \text{if } x < 2 \quad \text{Graph is called the left branch.} \\ 1, & \text{if } x = 2 \quad \text{Graph is called the middle branch.} \\ x^2 - 6x + 11, & \text{if } x > 2 \quad \text{Graph is called the right branch.} \end{cases}$$

a. Plot the graph of $f$. Sketch the result, showing the behavior around $x = 2$.

b. Because the equation $y = x + 1$ is used only for $x < 2$ and the equation $y = x^2 - 6x + 11$ only for $x > 2$, there is a discontinuity at the end of each branch. Are these two discontinuities at the same point?

c. Does $f(x)$ have a limit as $x$ approaches 2? If so, what is that limit? If not, tell why not.

d. Is $f(2)$ equal to the limit of $f(x)$ as $x$ approaches 2? Explain.

e. The graph of $f$ is *discontinuous* at $x = 2$. What number would $f(2)$ have to equal in order for $f$ to be *continuous* at $x = 2$?

17. For $r(x) = 1/x$, estimate the derivative of $r$ at $x = -3$.

18. For $j(x) = 10 - 2^x$, estimate the definite integral for $x = 0$ to $x = 3$.

19. *Don't Believe Everything You See Problem!* Ima B. Leaver sets her grapher's window to $[-0.1, 0.1]$ for $x$ and $[-0.07, 0.07]$ for $y$. Then she plots the graphs of

$$y_1 = \sin x \quad \text{and} \quad y_2 = x.$$

Because the graphs seem to coincide (Figure 1-5j), Ima believes the two functions are identical. Explain to Ima how she reached this wrong conclusion and some ways in which she could quickly show that there are really two *different* graphs on the screen.

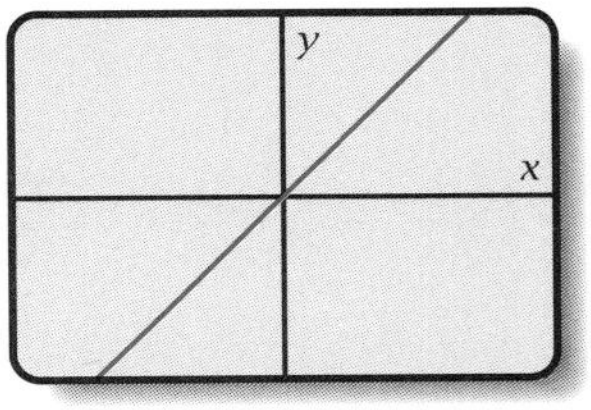


Figure 1-5j

# 1-6 Calculus Journal

You have been learning calculus by reading, by listening, by discussing, and by working problems. An important ability you should develop for any subject you study is the ability to *write* about it. To gain practice in this technique you will be asked to keep a **journal** recording what you have been learning. (*Journal* comes from the same source as the French word *jour,* meaning "day." *Journey* comes from the same source and means "a day's travel.")

**OBJECTIVE**

Start writing a journal in which you can record things you've learned about calculus and what questions you still have about certain concepts. In doing so, you'll gain practice in writing about mathematics, and you'll have a source of reference in your own words to review before tests.

Rather than buy a spiral or loose-leaf notebook, you might find it useful to invest in a bound notebook that will hold up under daily use. Bound notebooks are often used by researchers as they record their findings in the laboratory. You should record both the date on which you make a particular journal entry and the general heading under which the entry is classified. A typical entry might look something like the one shown here.

> *Topic: Limits* 9/15
>
> *We learned the definition of limit on the first day of class, but I hadn't realized until today that a limit is a number. It's the number that y stays close to when x is close to 2, for example. I also learned that a graph does not need to have a "hole" in it for there to be a limit. The members of my study group told me that since the definition of limit says ". . . but $x \neq c$," it really doesn't matter whether or not there is a value of y at $x = c$.*
>
> *I also learned that I can find limits of fractions like*
>
> $\frac{(2x+7)(x-3)}{(x-3)}$ *that go to* $\frac{0}{0}$ *as the denominator approaches*
>
> *by doing the canceling and by substituting 3 for x in what is left. I'm still not sure why I can do this, when the definition clearly says $x \neq c$. But it seems to work and produces the right answer. (0/0 is called an indeterminate form.)*
>
> *Problem 5 in the homework assignment didn't make sense to me. I can't understand why the back of the book says there was no limit when it looks to me like the limit is 2. Have to ask the instructor about this next class.*

The journal should *not* simply be a transcription of your class notes. Nor should you take notes directly in the journal. The purpose of the journal is to write things down after you've had a chance to think about them for a while.

## Problem Set 1-6

1. Start a journal in which to record your understandings about calculus. The first entry should include such things as those listed here.
   - The four concepts of calculus
   - The distinctions among derivative, definite integral, and limit
   - The fact that you still don't know what the other kind of integral is
   - The techniques you know for calculating derivatives, definite integrals, and limits
   - Any questions that still aren't clear in your mind

# 1-7 Chapter Review and Test

In this chapter you have had a brief introduction to the major concepts of calculus.

Limits
Derivatives
Definite integrals
Another type of integrals

The derivative of a function is its instantaneous rate of change. A definite integral of a function involves a product of the dependent and independent variables, such as (rate)(time). A limit is a number that $y$ can be kept close to, just by keeping $x$ suitably restricted. The other kind of integral is called an *indefinite integral,* also known as an *antiderivative.* You will see why the word integral is used twice when you learn the fundamental theorem of calculus in Chapter 5.

You have learned how to calculate approximate values of derivatives by dividing small changes in $y$ by the corresponding change in $x$. Definite integrals can be found using areas under graphs and can thus be estimated by counting squares. Limits of functions can be calculated by finding the $y$-value of a removable discontinuity in the graph. Along the way you have refreshed your memory about the shapes of certain graphs.

The Review Problems below are numbered according to the six preceding sections of this chapter. The Concepts Problems allow you to apply your knowledge to new situations. The Chapter Test is more like a typical classroom test your instructor might give you.

## Review Problems

R1. *Bungee Problem:* Lee Per attaches himself to a strong bungee cord and jumps off a bridge. At time $t = 3$ sec the cord first becomes taut. From that time on, Lee's distance, $d$ feet, from the river below the bridge is given by the following equation.

$$d = 90 - 80 \sin 1.2(t - 3)$$

a. How far is Lee from the water when $t = 4$?

b. Find the average rate of change of $d$ with respect to $t$ for the interval $t = 3.9$ to $t = 4$, and for the interval $t = 4$ to $t = 4.1$. Approximately what is the instantaneous rate of change at $t = 4$? Is Lee going up or going down at time $t = 4$? Explain.

c. Estimate the instantaneous rate of change of $d$ with respect to $t$ when $t = 5$.

d. Is Lee going up or down when $t = 5$? How fast?

e. What mathematical name is given to the instantaneous rate of change?

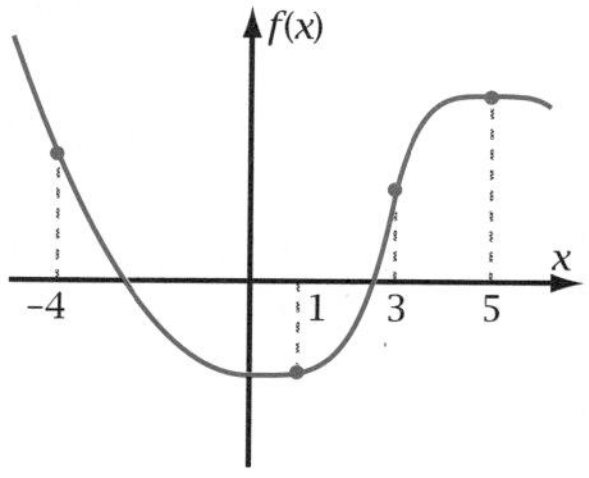

Figure 1-7a

R2. a. What is the physical meaning of the derivative of a function?

b. For the function in Figure 1-7a, tell how $f(x)$ is changing (increasing or decreasing, quickly or slowly) when $x$ equals $-4$, 1, 3, and 5.

c. If $f(x) = 5^x$, find $f(2)$ and the value of the derivative, approximately, at $x = 2$.

d. Mary Thon runs 200 m in 26 sec! Her distance from the start at various times is given in the table. Estimate her instantaneous speed in meters per second when $t = 2$, when $t = 18$, and when $t = 24$. For what interval of times did her speed stay relatively constant? Why is the speed at $t = 24$ reasonable in relation to the speeds at other times?

| $t$ sec | $m$ | $t$ sec | $m$ |
|---|---|---|---|
| 0 | 0 | 14 | 89 |
| 2 | 7 | 16 | 103 |
| 4 | 13 | 18 | 119 |
| 6 | 33 | 20 | 138 |
| 8 | 47 | 22 | 154 |
| 10 | 61 | 24 | 176 |
| 12 | 75 | 26 | 200 |

R3. a. Izzy Sinkin winds up his toy boat and lets it run on the pond. Its speed is given by

$$v(t) = (5t)(0.8)^t,$$

where $v(t)$ is in feet per second and $t$ is time in seconds since he let it go. Draw the graph of this function.

b. Find, approximately, the distance the boat travels between $t = 2$ and $t = 10$.

c. Name the concept of calculus used in finding this quantity.

R4. The graph in Figure 1-7b is for

$$f(x) = -0.5x^2 + 1.8x + 4.$$

a. Confirm on your grapher that the graph is correct. Use a friendly interval that includes values of $x$ at the grid lines.

b. Find the definite integral of $f(x)$ from $x = 1$ to $x = 4$ by counting squares.

c. Make a table of values of $f(x)$ for each 0.5 unit, from $x = 1$ to $x = 4$. Based on the results, use trapezoids to estimate the integral.

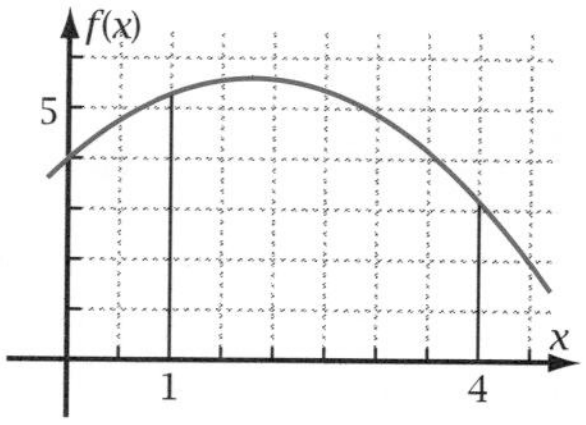

Figure 1-7b

R5. a. Write the formal definition of limit.

b. Given the function $f(x) = \dfrac{(x^2 - 8x + 5)(x - 3)}{x - 3}$, find the limit of $f(x)$ as $x$ approaches 3.

c. What *one* number tells how far $x$ can be from 3 so that $f(x)$ will be within 0.01 unit of the limit in R5b?

d. Pick a value of $x$ that is within the number of units of 3 you found in R5c, and show that $f(x)$ really *is* within 0.01 unit of the limit.

e. Sketch the graph of a function for which the limit of $f(x)$ is 5 as $x$ approaches $-1$.

R6. What is the purpose of keeping a journal in calculus? What type of information should be in the journal? Must you know the answer to everything you write in your journal? Explain.

## Concepts Problems

C1. *Exact Value of a Derivative Problem:* You have been calculating approximate values of derivatives by finding the change in $y$ for a given change in $x$, then by dividing. In this problem you will apply the concept of limit to the concept of derivative to find the *exact* value of a derivative. Let $y = f(x) = x^2 - 7x + 11$.

a. Find $f(3)$.

b. Suppose that $x$ is slightly different from 3. Find an expression in terms of $x$ for the amount by which $y$ changes, $f(x) - f(3)$.

c. Divide the answer to C1b by $x - 3$ to get an expression for the approximate rate of change of $y$. Simplify.

d. Find the limit of the fraction in C1c as $x$ approaches 3. The answer is the *exact* rate of change at $x = 3$.

C2. *Tangent to a Graph Problem:* If you worked Problem C1 correctly, you found that the instantaneous rate of change of $f(x)$ at $x = 3$ is exactly $-1$ $y$-unit per $x$-unit. Plot the graph of function $f$. On the same screen, plot a line through the point $(3, f(3))$ having slope $-1$. What do you notice about the line and the curve as you zoom in on the point $(3, f(3))$?

## Chapter Test

T1. Sketch the graph of a function that is increasing quickly at (2, 3) and decreasing slowly at (5, 6). Make the function "continuous" (no discontinuities).

T2. Sketch the graph of a function with a removable discontinuity at (4, 1).

T3. If $f(x) = 2\cos x$, find, approximately, the instantaneous rate of change of $f(x)$ with respect to $x$ when $x$ is 1. Name the concept of calculus that represents the instantaneous rate.

T4. Given $f(x) = 1.2^x$, find, approximately, the definite integral of $f$ from $x = 1$ to $x = 5$, using trapezoids of width 0.5 $x$-unit.

T5. Let $g(x) = \dfrac{5x^2 + 17x + 14}{x + 2}$.

a. Plot the graph, using a window that includes $x = -2$. Sketch the graph on your paper.

b. What is the limit of $g(x)$ as $x$ approaches $-2$? Show this feature on the graph.

c. Show on the graph the interval of $x$-values for which $g(x)$ will be within 0.4 unit of the limit in T5b.

d. For T5c, what are the values of $c$, $L$, epsilon, and delta in the definition of limit?

e. What is the reason for the restriction "...but not equal to $c$" in the definition of limit?

T6. The velocity of a moving object is given by $v(t) = 2.718^t$ in./min.

a. How fast is the object moving when $t = 1$ min?

b. At approximately what rate is the speed changing when $t = 1$ min?

c. Approximately how far does the object go between $t = 0$ min and $t = 1$ min?

T7. Cy Kling coasts down the hill on his bicycle, then up the next hill. Every 4 sec, he notes the speed the bike is going, recording the values in the table. How far did he go in the 28 sec?

| sec | ft/sec | sec | ft/sec |
|---|---|---|---|
| 0 | 16 | 16 | 37 |
| 4 | 26 | 20 | 36 |
| 8 | 30 | 24 | 32 |
| 12 | 34 | 28 | 25 |

CHAPTER

# 2 Properties of Limits

Finding the average speed of a moving vehicle requires dividing the distance it goes by the time taken to go that distance. The instantaneous velocity can be calculated by taking the limit of the average velocity as the interval of time approaches zero. Limits are also used to find exact values of definite integrals. Thus limit is the foundation for the other three concepts of calculus.

# Mathematical Overview

Informally, the limit of a function $f$ as $x$ approaches $c$ is the $y$-value $f(x)$ stays close to when $x$ is kept close enough to $c$ but not equal to $c$. In Chapter 2 you will formalize the concept of limit by studying it in four ways.

***Graphically*** The logo on each even-numbered page of this chapter shows that $f(x)$ is close to $L$ when $x$ is close enough to $c$ but not equal to $c$.

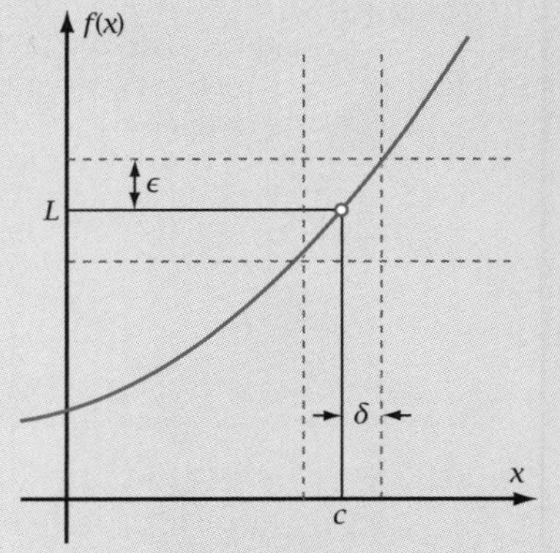


***Numerically***

| $x$ | $f(x)$ |
|---|---|
| 3.01 | 3.262015 |
| 3.001 | 3.251200 ... |
| 3.0001 | 3.250120 ... |
| 3.00001 | 3.250012 ... |
| ... | ... |

***Algebraically*** $0 < |x - c| < \delta \Rightarrow |f(x) - L| < \epsilon$, part of the limit definition.

***Verbally*** *I have learned that a limit is a y-value that f(x) can be kept arbitrarily close to just by keeping x close enough to c but not equal to c. I remember δ and ϵ go with x and y, respectively, because they come in the same alphabetical order. Limits are used to find exact values of derivatives. Limits as x approaches infinity are related to horizontal asymptotes.*

# 2-1 Numerical Approach to the Definition of Limit

In Chapter 1, you were asked to memorize the definition of limit. Then you got an intuitive idea that a limit is a number that $y$ stays close to when $x$ is close, but not equal, to $c$. In this section you will explore the function shown in Figure 2-1a not only to discover something about the meanings of the various parts of the definition of limit, but also to see how those meanings relate to the graph.

**OBJECTIVE**

For the cube root function $f(x) = (x - 2)^{1/3} + 3$, make tables of values that show how close $x$ must be kept to 2 in order for $f(x)$ to be within given ranges of $f(2)$.

The problems in this section are meant for you to do on your own or with your study group as an assignment after your test on Chapter 1.

## Exploratory Problem Set 2-1

1. Let $f(x) = (x - 2)^{1/3} + 3$, as in Figure 2-1a.
   a. Plot this graph on your grapher. Does your graph agree with Figure 2-1a?
   b. Make a table of values of $f(x)$ for each 0.0001 unit of $x$ from 1.9995 units to 2.0005 units. Use a time-efficient method.
   c. For which values of $x$ in your table ($x \neq 2$) is $f(x)$ within 0.07 unit of 3? That is, for which values of $x$ is $2.93 < f(x) < 3.07$?
   d. For which values of $x$ in your table ($x \neq 2$) is $f(x)$ within 0.05 unit of 3?
   e. Would it be possible to keep $f(x)$ within 0.01 unit of 3 without having $x$ *equal* 2? If so, find out how close. If not, tell why not.
   f. The numbers $L$, $c$, epsilon, and delta in the definition of limit all appear in 1c. Which number is which?
   g. How could you calculate a value of delta for *any* given value of epsilon, no matter how small the value of epsilon is?

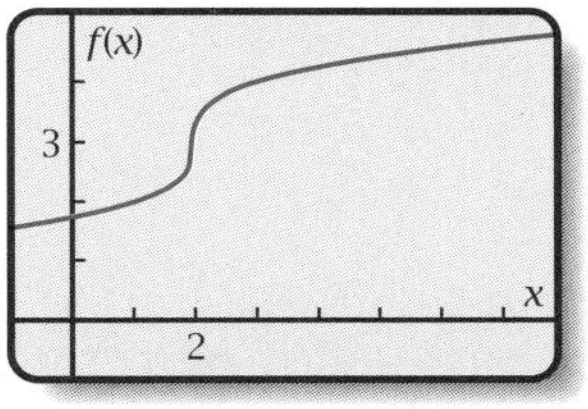

Figure 2-1a

2. Let $g(x) = (x - 3)\sin\left(\dfrac{1}{x - 3}\right) + 2$. Plot the graph of $g$ by using a window that includes $y = 2$ and for which $x = 3$ is a grid point. Then zoom in on the point (3, 2) by a factor of 10 in both the $x$- and $y$-directions. Sketch the resulting graph. Does $g(x)$ seem to be approaching a limit as $x$ approaches 3? If so, what does the limit equal? If not, tell why not.

3. Let $h(x) = \sin\left(\dfrac{1}{x - 3}\right) + 2$. Plot the graph of $h$ by using a window with a $y$-range of about 0 to 3 and for which $x = 3$ is a grid point. Then zoom in on the point (3, 2) by a factor of 10 in the $x$-direction. Leave the $y$-scale the same. Sketch the resulting graph. Does $h(x)$ seem to be approaching a limit as $x$ approaches 3? If so, what does the limit equal? If not, tell why not.

# 2-2 Graphical and Algebraic Approaches to the Definition of Limit

The definition of limit you memorized in Chapter 1 can be shortened somewhat by using $\epsilon$ for epsilon and $\delta$ for delta. (*Epsilon* and *delta* are the English words for the lowercase Greek letters $\epsilon$ and $\delta$.) The definition can be shortened more by using algebraic symbols and by leaving out words that were added for clarity. The word *limit* is abbreviated lim, and the words *x approaches c* are expressed as $x \to c$. The shortened version is shown in the box.

**Definition of Limit (shortened version)**

$L = \lim_{x\to c} f(x)$ if and only if
for any number $\epsilon > 0$,
there is a number $\delta > 0$ such that
if $x$ is within $\delta$ units of $c$ (but $x \neq c$),
then $f(x)$ is within $\epsilon$ units of $L$.

The words *no matter how small* that describe $\epsilon$ have been left out because they are unnecessary. However, you should remember that $\epsilon$ will usually be very close to zero.

**OBJECTIVE**

Given values of the three numbers $L, c$, and $\epsilon$, calculate the corresponding value of $\delta$ in the definition of limit and show by graph that you understand the significance of these numbers.

Figure 2-2a shows the graph of $f(x) = (x - 2)^{1/3} + 3$, which you worked with in Problem Set 2-1. The limit of $f(x)$ as $x$ approaches 2 is 3, the same as the value of $f(2)$. To see how the definition of limit relates to this function, let $\epsilon = 0.8$. The figure on the left shows what happens if $\delta = 0.2$. All the corresponding values of $f(x)$ (the solid part of the graph) will be between the horizontal lines at $y = 2.2$ and $y = 3.8$.

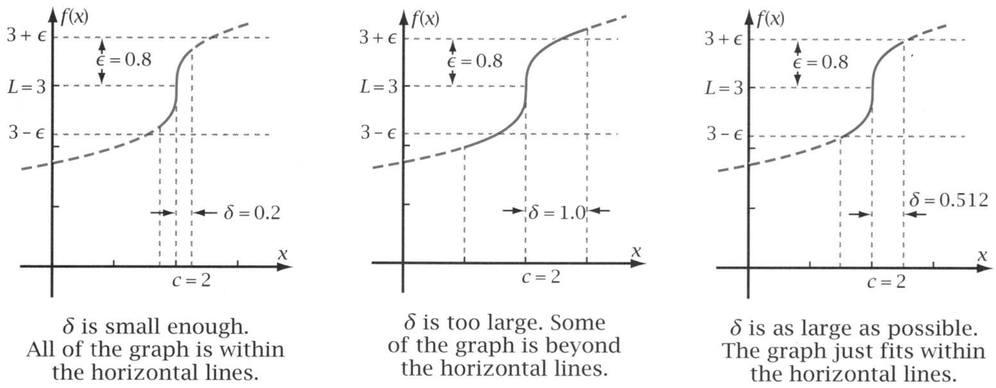

f(x)
3 + ϵ
ϵ = 0.8
L = 3
3 − ϵ
δ = 0.2
x
c = 2
δ is small enough. All of the graph is within the horizontal lines.
f(x)
3 + ϵ
ϵ = 0.8
L = 3
3 − ϵ
δ = 1.0
x
c = 2
δ is too large. Some of the graph is beyond the horizontal lines.
f(x)
3 + ϵ
ϵ = 0.8
L = 3
3 − ϵ
δ = 0.512
x
c = 2
δ is as large as possible. The graph just fits within the horizontal lines.

Figure 2-2a

If $\delta = 1.0$ as shown in the middle figure, some of the corresponding values of $f(x)$ will be above or below the horizontal lines. Thus, 1.0 is too big to be a suitable value of $\delta$ in this case. Example 1 shows you how to make the value of $\delta$ "just right," as shown in the figure on the right.

**■ Example 1**

For the point marked on the graph in Figure 2-2b, write the limit of $f(x)$ as $x$ approaches 2 using proper limit terminology. If $\epsilon = 0.6$, estimate to one decimal place the largest possible value of $\delta$ that can be used to keep $f(x)$ within $\epsilon$ units of the marked point when $x$ is within $\delta$ units of 2.

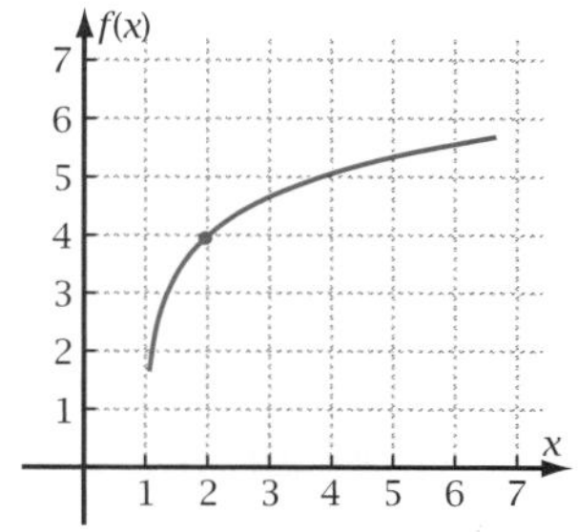


Figure 2-2b

***Solution***

$\lim_{x \to 2} f(x) = 4$, as shown on the graph.

Because $\epsilon = 0.6$, draw lines 0.6 unit above and below $y = 4$, as in Figure 2-2c. Where these lines cross the graph, go down to the $x$-axis and estimate the corresponding $x$-values to get $x \approx 1.6$ and $x \approx 2.8$.

Thus, $x$ can go as far as 0.4 unit to the left of $x = 2$ and 0.8 unit to the right. The smaller of these units, 0.4, is the value of $\delta$. ■

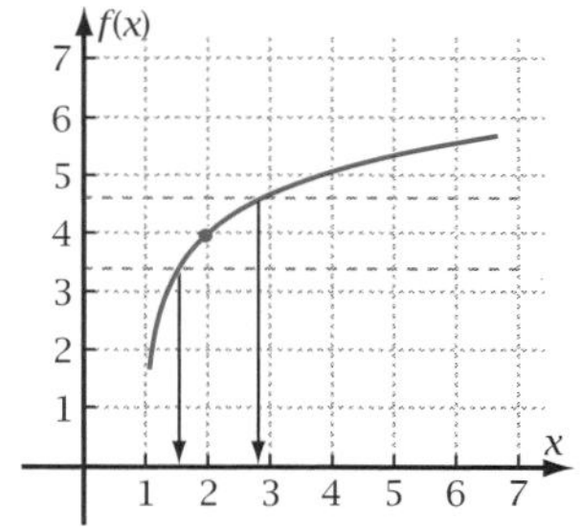


Figure 2-2c

**■ Example 2**

For the function $f(x) = (x - 2)^{1/3} + 3$, estimate the largest possible value of $\delta$ that can be used to keep $f(x)$ within $\epsilon = 0.8$ unit of 3 when $x$ is within $\delta$ units of 2.

***Solution***

Figure 2-2d shows the graph of $f$, zooming in on the point (2, 3). Because $\epsilon = 0.8$, $f(x)$ must be between 2.2 and 3.8. Tracing the graph shows that for $x = 2.51$, $f(x) \approx 3.798957$, which is okay. However, if $x = 2.52$, then $f(x) \approx 3.8041452$, which is too big. Similarly, $x$ can go as low as 1.49 and still have $f(x)$ above 2.2. Thus, the largest possible value of $\delta$ is about 0.51. ■

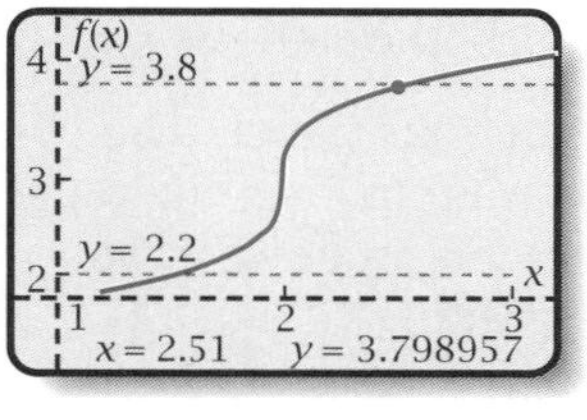


Figure 2-2d

If the value of $\epsilon$ is very small, it may be easier to find $\delta$ algebraically than it would be to find a suitable friendly window. The algebra will also let you show that there is *always* a positive value of $\delta$ that will do the job, no matter how small $\epsilon$ is. Example 3 shows how.

**■ Example 3**

For $f(x) = (x - 2)^{1/3} + 3$, calculate algebraically the largest possible value of $\delta$ that can be used for a given value of $\epsilon > 0$ to keep $f(x)$ within $\epsilon$ units of 3 when $x$ is within $\delta$ units of 2.

**Solution** The function $f(x)$ must be between $3 - \epsilon$ and $3 + \epsilon$. Write an inequality and solve it to find $x$.

$3 - \epsilon < (x - 2)^{1/3} + 3 < 3 + \epsilon$ — $f(x)$ must be between $3 - \epsilon$ and $3 + \epsilon$.

$-\epsilon < (x - 2)^{1/3} < \epsilon$ — Subtract 3 from all three members of the inequality.

$-\epsilon^3 < x - 2 < \epsilon^3$ — Cube all three members of the inequality.

$2 - \epsilon^3 < x < 2 + \epsilon^3$

$\therefore$ largest possible value of $\delta$ is $\epsilon^3$.

Because the steps are reversible, $f(x)$ will be within $\epsilon$ units of 3 whenever $x$ is within $\epsilon^3$ units of 2. ■

■ **Example 4** For the function in Example 3, show that the value of $\delta$ you get when $\epsilon = 0.007$ really does keep $f(x)$ within 0.007 unit of 3 when $x$ is within $\delta$ units of 2.

**Solution** $\delta = \epsilon^3 = 0.007^3 = 0.000000343$

Keeping $x$ within 0.000000343 unit of 2 is equivalent to making $x$ satisfy the inequality

$1.999999657 < x < 2.000000343.$

$-0.000000343 < x - 2 < 0.000000343$ — Subtract 2 from all three members.

$-0.007 < (x - 2)^{1/3} < 0.007$ — Take the cube root of all three members.

$2.993 < (x - 2)^{1/3} + 3 < 3.007$

$2.993 < f(x) < 3.007$

$\therefore$ if $x$ is within 0.000000343 unit of 2, then $f(x)$ is within 0.007 unit of 3. ■

■ **Example 5** Let $f(x) = 0.2(2^x)$.

a. Plot the graph on your grapher.

b. Find the limit of $f(x)$ as $x$ approaches 3.

c. Calculate the maximum value of $\delta$ that can be used for $\epsilon = 0.5$ at $x = 3$.

d. Show how to calculate a positive value of $\delta$ for any $\epsilon > 0$, no matter how small.

**Solution**

a. Figure 2-2e shows the graph.

b. Because the graph has no discontinuities, the limit is 1.6, the same as $f(3)$.

c. Figure 2-2f shows how you might draw the graph on your paper. The horizontal lines at $y = 1.1$ and $y = 2.1$ show that you want to keep the value of $f(x)$ within 0.5 unit of 1.6. To find the largest possible value of $\delta$, you must find out where these horizontal lines cross the graph.

$$0.2(2^x) = 1.1 \Rightarrow 2^x = 5.5 \Rightarrow$$
$$\log 2^x = \log 5.5 \Rightarrow x \log 2 = \log 5.5 \Rightarrow$$
$$x = \frac{\log 5.5}{\log 2} = 2.4594\ldots \approx 2.46$$

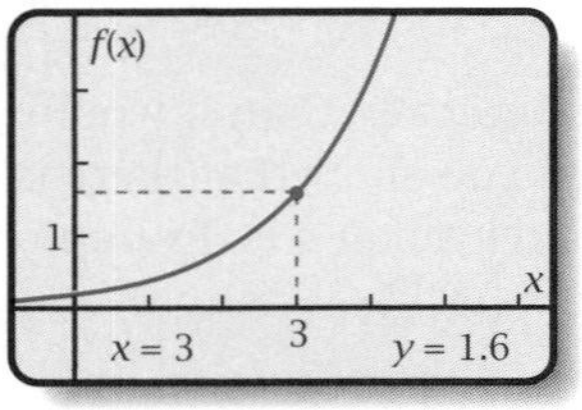


Figure 2-2e

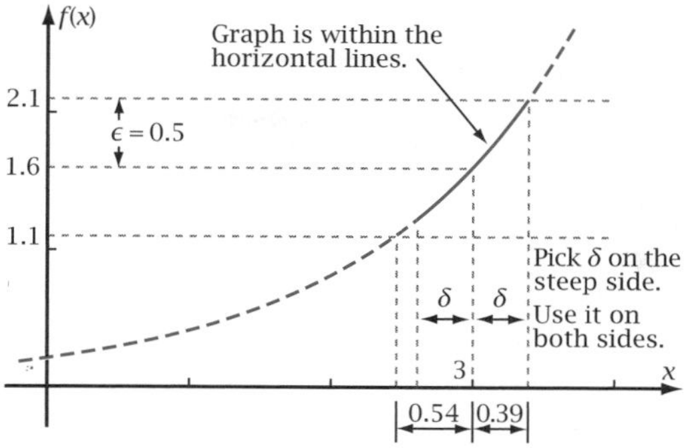


Figure 2-2f

The value is rounded up because $x$ must be closer to 3 than 2.4594 is.... Similarly, if $f(x) = 2.1$, then

$$x = \frac{\log 10.5}{\log 2} = 3.3923\ldots \approx 3.39.$$

This value is rounded down, again to make $x$ closer to 3 than 3.3923 is.... Thus, $\delta$ could be

$3 - 2.46 = 0.54$ on the left side or

$3.39 - 3 = 0.39$ on the right side.

The one value of $\delta$ in the definition of limit will be the smaller of these two, $\delta = 0.39$. Note that this value occurs on whichever side of $x = c$ the graph is steeper.

d. To show that there is a value of $\delta$ for any $\epsilon > 0$, no matter how small, repeat the calculations for step c, using $\epsilon$ instead of 0.5. Picking $\delta$ on the right (steeper) side of $x = 3$ means that $f(x)$ will equal $1.6 + \epsilon$.

$$0.2(2^x) = 1.6 + \epsilon \Rightarrow 2^x = 8 + 5\epsilon \Rightarrow$$

$$\log 2^x = \log(8 + 5\epsilon) \Rightarrow x \log 2 = \log(8 + 5\epsilon) \Rightarrow x = \frac{\log(8 + 5\epsilon)}{\log 2}$$

$$\therefore \delta = \frac{\log(8 + 5\epsilon)}{\log 2} - 3$$

You should check that $\delta > 0$. Because $(\log 8)/(\log 2) = 3$, $\log(8 + 5\epsilon)/\log 2$ will be greater than 3. Thus, $\delta$ will be positive, which was to be shown. ■

## Problem Set 2-2

### *Do These Quickly*

The following problems are intended to refresh your skills. You should be able to do all ten problems in less than five minutes.

**Q1.** Sketch an ellipse.

**Q2.** Sketch the graph of a function with a removable discontinuity at (2, 5).

**Q3.** Evaluate: $|-49|$

**Q4.** Evaluate: $\sqrt{-25}$

**Q5.** Evaluate: $|7 - 3|$

**Q6.** Fill in the blank: $\log(5 \times 3) = \log 5$ -?- $\log 3$.

**Q7.** Fill in the blank: $\log 5^3 =$ -?- $\log 5$.

**Q8.** Which axiom is illustrated by the equation $3(x + 2) = 3(2 + x)$?

**Q9.** Sixty is 30% of what number?

**Q10.** Is $f(x) = \sin x$ increasing or decreasing at $x = 2$?

For Problems 1–6, photocopy or sketch the graph. For the point marked on the graph, use proper limit terminology to write the limit of $f(x)$. For the given value of $\epsilon$, estimate to one decimal place the largest possible value of $\delta$ that can be used to keep $f(x)$ within $\epsilon$ units of the marked point when $x$ is within $\delta$ units of the value shown.

1. $x = 3$, $\epsilon = 0.5$

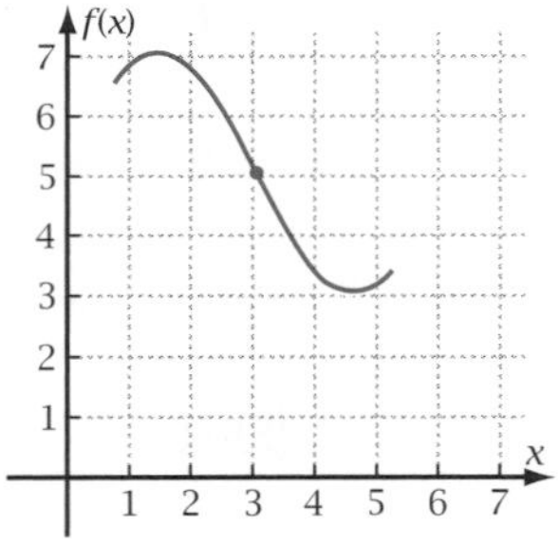


2. $x = 2$, $\epsilon = 0.5$

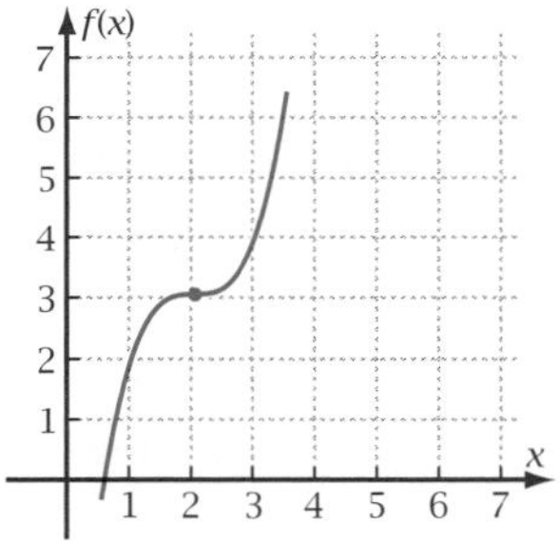


3. $x = 6$, $\epsilon = 0.7$

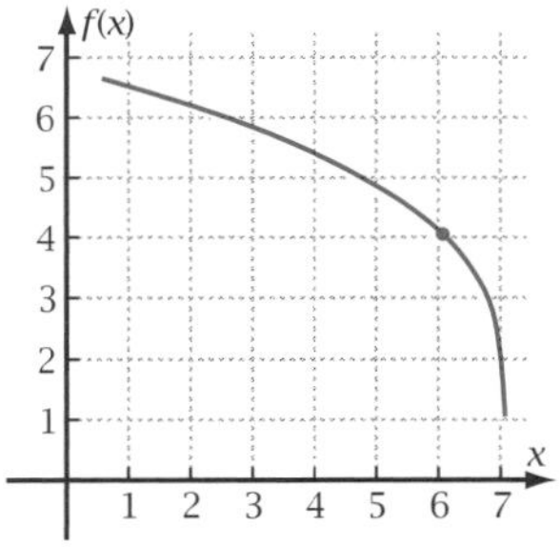


4. $x = 4$, $\epsilon = 0.8$

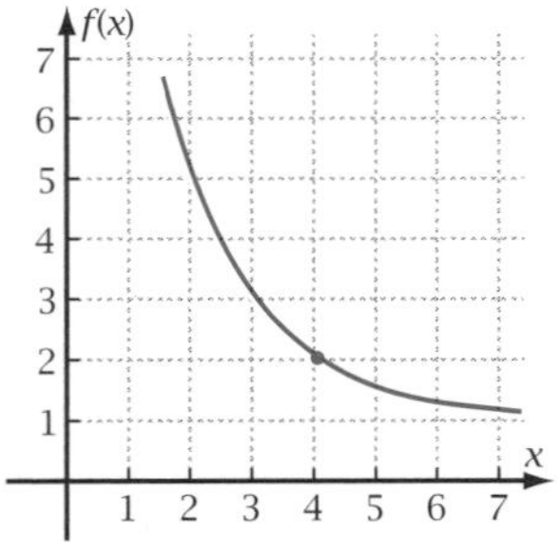


5. $x = 5$, $\epsilon = 0.3$

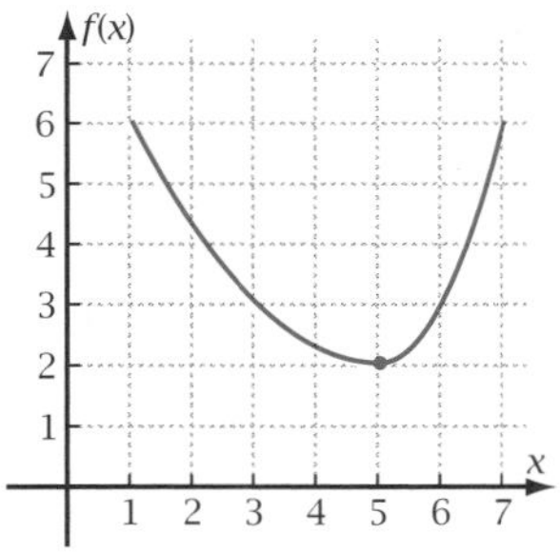


6. $x = 3$, $\epsilon = 0.4$

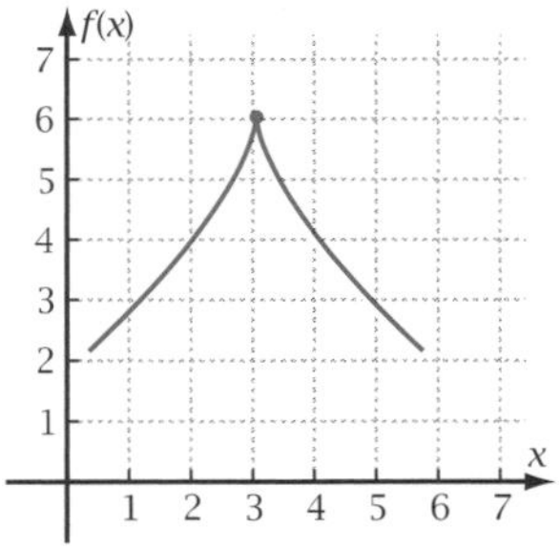

For Problems 7–12, do the following.

a. Plot the graph on your grapher (what interesting thing do you notice?)
b. Find the limit of the function as $x$ approaches the given value.
c. Calculate the maximum value of $\delta$ that can be used for the given value of $\epsilon$ at the point.
d. Calculate algebraically a positive value of $\delta$ for any $\epsilon > 0$, no matter how small.

7. $f(x) = 5 - 2\sin(x-3)$
$x = 3, \epsilon = 0.5$

8. $f(x) = (x-2)^3 + 3$
$x = 2, \epsilon = 0.5$

9. $f(x) = 1 + 3\sqrt[3]{7-x}$
$x = 6, \epsilon = 0.7$

10. $f(x) = 1 + 2^{4-x}$
$x = 4, \epsilon = 0.8$

11. $f(x) = \begin{cases} 0.25(x-5)^2 + 2, & \text{if } x < 5 \\ (x-5)^2 + 2, & \text{if } x \geq 5 \end{cases}$
$x = 5, \epsilon = 0.3$

12. $f(x) = 6 - 2(x-3)^{2/3}$
$x = 3, \epsilon = 0.4$

13. *Limits Applied to Derivatives Problem:* Suppose you start driving off from a traffic light. Your distance, $d(t)$ feet, from where you started is given by

$$d(t) = 3t^2,$$

where $t$ is time in seconds since you started.

a. Figure 2-2g shows $d(t)$ versus $t$. Write as an algebraic fraction the average speed, $m(t)$, for the time interval from 4 to $t$.
b. Plot the graph of function $m$ on your grapher. Use a friendly window that includes $t = 4$. What does this graph have at the point $t = 4$? Sketch the graph.
c. The speed you are going at the instant $t = 4$ is the limit of the average speed as $t$ approaches 4. What does this limit appear to equal? What are the units of this limit?

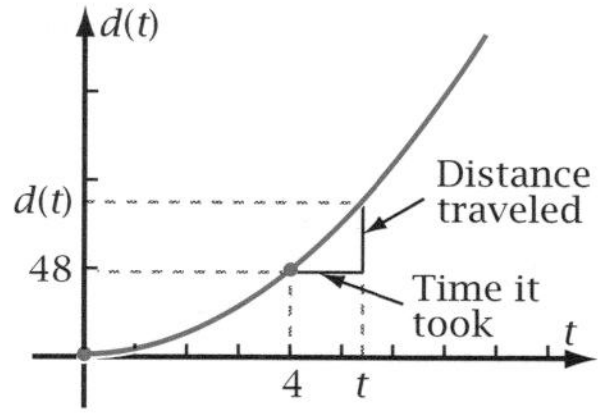


Figure 2-2g

d. How close to 4 would you have to keep $t$ for $m(t)$ to be within 0.12 unit of the limit? This is an easy problem if you simplify the algebraic fraction first.
e. Explain why the results of this problem give the *exact* value for a derivative.

# 2-3 The Limit Theorems

Suppose that $f(x)$ is given by the algebraic fraction

$$f(x) = \frac{3x^2 - 48}{x - 4}.$$

There is no value for $f(4)$ because of division by zero. Substituting 4 for $x$ gives

$$f(4) = \frac{3 \cdot 4^2 - 48}{4 - 4} = \frac{0}{0}.$$

$f(4)$ is undefined because it has an indeterminate form.

Because the numerator is also zero, there may be a limit of $f(x)$ as $x$ approaches 4. Limits such as this arise when you try to find exact values of derivatives. You may have seen this fraction already in Problem 13 of Problem Set 2-2. Simplifying the fraction before substituting 4 for $x$ gives

$$f(x) = \frac{(3x+12)(x-4)}{x-4}$$
$$= 3x + 12, \text{ provided } x \neq 4.$$

Surprisingly, the limit can be found by substituting 4 for $x$ in the *simplified* expression.

$$\lim_{x \to 4} = 3(4) + 12 = 24$$

From Section 1-5, recall that 0/0 is called an **indeterminate form**. Its limit can be different numbers depending on just what expressions went to zero in the numerator and denominator. Fortunately, there are properties (called the **limit theorems**) that allow you to find such limits by making substitutions, as shown above. In this section you will learn these properties so that you can find exact values of derivatives and integrals the way Newton and Leibniz did more than 300 years ago.

**OBJECTIVE**

For the properties listed in the table in this section, be able to *state* them, *use* them in a proof, and *explain* why they are true.

### Limit of a Product or a Sum of Two Functions

Suppose that $g(x) = 2x + 1$ and $h(x) = 5 - x$. Let $f(x)$ be the product: $f(x) = g(x) \cdot h(x)$, or

$$f(x) = (2x+1)(5-x).$$

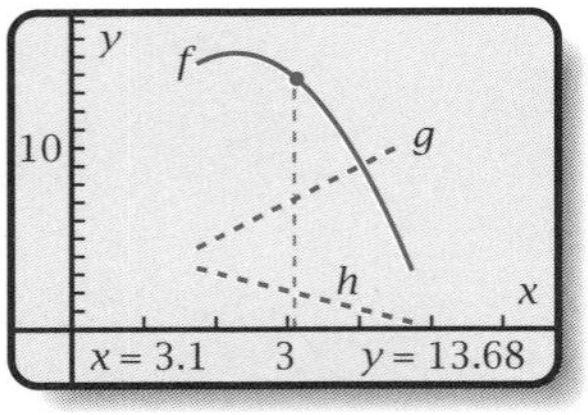

Figure 2-3a

You are to find the limit of $f(x)$ as $x$ approaches 3. Figure 2-3a shows the graphs of functions $f$, $g$, and $h$. Direct substitution gives

$$f(3) = (2 \cdot 3 + 1)(5 - 3) = (7)(2) = 14.$$

The important idea concerning limits is that $f(x)$ stays close to 14 when $x$ is kept close to 3. You can demonstrate this fact by making a table of values of $x$, $g(x)$, $h(x)$, and $f(x)$.

| $x$ | $g(x)$ | $h(x)$ | $f(x) = g(x) \cdot h(x)$ | |
|---|---|---|---|---|
| 2.95 | 6.9 | 2.05 | 14.145 | |
| 2.96 | 6.92 | 2.04 | 14.1168 | |
| 2.97 | 6.94 | 2.03 | 14.0882 | When $g(x)$ and $h(x)$ are close |
| 2.98 | 6.96 | 2.02 | 14.0592 | to 7 and 2, respectively, |
| 2.99 | 6.98 | 2.01 | 14.0298 | $f(x)$ is close to 14. |
| | | | | |
| 3.01 | 7.02 | 1.99 | 13.9698 | |
| 3.02 | 7.04 | 1.98 | 13.9392 | |
| 3.03 | 7.06 | 1.97 | 13.9082 | |
| 3.04 | 7.08 | 1.96 | 13.8768 | |

You can keep the product as close to 14 as you like by keeping $x$ close enough to 3, even if $x$ is not allowed to equal 3. From this information you should be able to see that the limit of a product of two functions is the product of the two limits. A similar property applies to sums of two functions. By adding the values of $g(x)$ and $h(x)$ in the table above, you can see that the sum $g(x) + h(x)$ is close to $7 + 2$, or 9, when $x$ is close, but not equal, to 3.

### *Limit of a Quotient of Two Functions*

The limit of a quotient of two functions is equal to the quotient of the two limits, provided that the denominator does not approach zero. Suppose that function $f$ is defined by

$$f(x) = \frac{g(x)}{h(x)} = \frac{2x+1}{5-x},$$

and you want to find the limit of $f(x)$ as $x$ approaches 3. The values of $g(3)$ and $h(3)$ are 7 and 2, respectively. By graphing or by compiling a table of values, you should be able to see that if $x$ is close to 3, then $f(x)$ is close to $7/2 = 3.5$. You can keep $f(x)$ as close as you like to 3.5 by keeping $x$ close enough to 3. (When $x$ is equal to 3, $f(x)$ happens to equal 3.5, but that fact is of no concern when you are dealing with limits.)

There is no limit of $f(x)$ as $x$ approaches 5. The denominator goes to zero, but the numerator does not. Thus, the absolute value of the quotient becomes infinitely large, as shown in the table below. Figure 2-3b shows that the graph of $f$ has a vertical asymptote at $x = 5$.

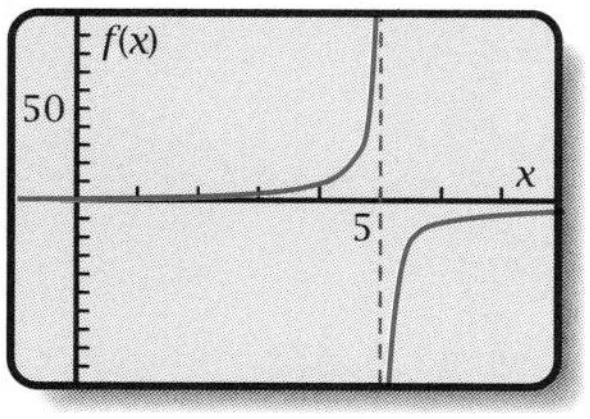

Figure 2-3b

| $x$ | $g(x)$ | $h(x)$ | $f(x) = g(x)/h(x)$ |
|---|---|---|---|
| 4.96 | 10.92 | 0.04 | 273 |
| 4.97 | 10.94 | 0.03 | 364.6 . . . |
| 4.98 | 10.96 | 0.02 | 548 |
| 4.99 | 10.98 | 0.01 | 1098 |
| 5.00 | 11.00 | 0.00 | None (infinite) |
| 5.01 | 11.02 | -0.01 | −1102 |
| 5.02 | 11.04 | -0.02 | −552 |
| 5.03 | 11.06 | -0.03 | −368.6 . . . |
| 5.04 | 11.08 | -0.04 | −277 |

The following box summarizes the important properties of limits. Proofs of these properties involve some exciting algebra! They all revolve around finding a value of $\delta$ that is small enough to make $f(x)$ stay within $\epsilon$ units of the limit whenever $x$ is within $\delta$ units of $c$.

### *Some Properties of Limits: The Limit Theorems*

**Limit of a Product of Two Functions:** If $\lim_{x \to c} g(x) = L_1$ and $\lim_{x \to c} h(x) = L_2$, then $\lim_{x \to c}[g(x) \cdot h(x)] = \lim_{x \to c} g(x) \cdot \lim_{x \to c} h(x) = L_1 \cdot L_2$.

Informal words: Limit distributes over multiplication; or, the limit of a product equals the product of the limits.

**Limit of a Sum of Two Functions:** If $\lim_{x \to c} g(x) = L_1$ and $\lim_{x \to c} h(x) = L_2$, then $\lim_{x \to c}[g(x) + h(x)] = \lim_{x \to c} g(x) + \lim_{x \to c} h(x) = L_1 + L_2$.

Informal words: Limit distributes over addition; or, the limit of a sum equals the sum of the limits.

**Limit of a Quotient of Two Functions:** If $\lim_{x \to c} g(x) = L_1$ and $\lim_{x \to c} h(x) = L_2$, where $L_2 \neq 0$, then $\lim_{x \to c} \frac{g(x)}{h(x)} = \frac{\lim_{x \to c} g(x)}{\lim_{x \to c} h(x)} = \frac{L_1}{L_2}$.

Informal words: Limit distributes over division, except for division by zero; or, the limit of a quotient equals the quotient of the limits.

**Limit of a Constant Times a Function:** If $\lim_{x \to c} g(x) = L$, then $\lim_{x \to c}[k \cdot g(x)] = k \cdot \lim_{x \to c} g(x) = kL$.

Informal words: The limit of a constant times a function equals the constant times the limit.

**Limit of the Identity Function:** $\lim_{x \to c} x = c$

Informal words: The limit of $x$ as $x$ approaches $c$ is simply $c$.

**Limit of a Constant Function:** If $f(x) = k$, where $k$ is a constant, then $\lim_{x \to c} f(x) = k$.

Informal words: The limit of a constant is that constant.

**Limit of a Composite Function:** If $x \to c \Rightarrow u \to k$, then $\lim_{x \to c} f(u) = \lim_{u \to k} f(u)$.

Informal words: If $f(u)$ is close to $L$ when $u$ is close to $k$, and if $u$ is close to $k$ when $x$ is close to $c$, then $f(u) = f(g(x))$ is close to $L$ when $x$ is close to $c$; or, you can replace $u \to k$ with $x \to c$ in a limit provided $x \to c$ implies $u \to k$.

**■ Example 1** Use the limit properties to prove that $\lim_{x\to 4} \frac{3x^2 - 48}{x - 4} = 24$. Justify each step.

**Solution**

$$\lim_{x\to 4} \frac{3x^2 - 48}{x - 4} = \lim_{x\to 4} \frac{(3x + 12)(x - 4)}{x - 4}$$ Algebra.

$$= \lim_{x\to 4}(3x + 12)$$ The canceling can be done because the definition of limit keeps $x$ from equaling 4.

$$= \lim_{x\to 4} 3x + \lim_{x\to 4} 12$$ Limit of a sum of two functions.

$$= 3\lim_{x\to 4} x + \lim_{x\to 4} 12$$ Limit of a constant times a function.

$$= 3(4) + \lim_{x\to 4} 12$$ Limit of $x$ as $x \to c$ equals $c$.

$$= 3(4) + 12$$ Limit of a constant is that constant.

$$= 24, \text{Q.E.D.}$$ The abbreviation Q.E.D. represents the Latin *quod erat demonstratum*, meaning "which was to be demonstrated." ■

# Problem Set 2-3

### *Do These Quickly*

The following problems are intended to refresh your skills. You should be able to do all ten problems in less than five minutes.

**Q1.** Find the limit of $13x/x$ as $x$ approaches zero.

**Q2.** Sketch the graph of a function if 3 is the limit as $x$ approaches 2 but $f(2)$ is undefined.

**Q3.** Sketch the graph of a function that is decreasing slowly when $x = -4$.

**Q4.** Sketch the graph of a quadratic function.

**Q5.** Sketch the graph of $y = x^3$.

**Q6.** Factor: $x^2 - 100$

**Q7.** Thirty is what percentage of 40?

**Q8.** How far do you go in 20 min at 30 mi/hr?

**Q9.** Simplify: $(12x^{30})/(3x^{10})$

**Q10.** What is meant by definite integral?

1. *Limit of a Function Plus a Function Problem:* Let $g(x) = x^2$, and let $h(x) = 12/x$. Plot the two graphs on your grapher, along with the graph of $f(x) = g(x) + h(x)$. Sketch the result, showing that the limit of $f(x)$ as $x$ approaches 2 is equal to the sum of the limits of $g(x)$ and $h(x)$ as $x$ approaches 2. Make a table of values which shows that $f(x)$ is close to the limit when $x$ is close, but not equal, to 2.
2. *Limit of a Constant Times a Function Problem:* Plot $g(x) = x^2$ and $f(x) = 0.2x^2$ on your grapher. Sketch the result. Find the limit of $f(x)$ as $x$ approaches 3 and the limit of $g(x)$ as $x$ approaches 3. Show that the limit of $f(x)$ is 0.2 multiplied by the limit of $g(x)$. Make a table which shows that $f(x)$ is close to the limit when $x$ is close, but not equal, to 3.
3. *Limit of a Constant Problem:* Let $f(x) = 7$ . Sketch the graph of $f$. (Don't waste time using your grapher!) Show on the graph that the limit of $f(x)$ as $x$ approaches 3 is equal to 7. Does it bother you that $f(x)$ equals 7, even if $x$ is not equal to 3?

4. *Limit of x Problem:* Let $f(x) = x$. Sketch the graph of $f$. (Don't waste time using your grapher!) Then explain why the limit of $f(x)$ as $x$ approaches 6 must be equal to 6.

5. *Limit of a Product Problem:* Let $f(x) = x^2 \tan x$. Write the values of $1.5^2$ and $\tan 1.5$, then multiply them to find $f(1.5)$. By experimenting on your calculator, find a value of $\delta$ that keeps $f(x)$ within 0.01 unit of $f(1.5)$ when $x$ is within $\delta$ units of 1.5. When $x = 1.5 + \delta$, how close are $x^2$ and $\tan x$ to $1.5^2$ and $\tan 1.5$, respectively?

6. *Limit of a Quotient Problem:* Let $r(x) = 2^x/\sin x$. Write the values of $2^3$ and $\sin 3$. Then divide them to find $r(3)$. By experimenting with your calculator, find a value of $\delta$ that keeps $r(x)$ within 0.1 unit of $r(3)$ when $x$ is within $\delta$ units of 3. When $x = 3 + \delta$, how close are $2^x$ and $\sin x$ to $2^3$ and $\sin 3$, respectively?

For Problems 7–17, complete the following.

a. Plot the graph on your grapher, using a friendly window that includes the given $x$-value. Sketch the result.

b. Find the limit of $f(x)$ as $x$ approaches the given value.

c. Prove that your answer is right by using the appropriate limit properties.

7. $f(x) = 3x - 7, \quad x \to 4$

8. $h(x) = -5x + 23, \quad x \to 2$

9. $f(x) = x^2 - 9x + 5, \quad x \to 3$

10. $p(x) = x^2 + 3x - 6, \quad x \to -1$

11. $r(x) = \dfrac{x^2 - 4x - 12}{x + 2}, \quad x \to -2$

12. $f(x) = \dfrac{x^2 + 3x - 40}{x - 5}, \quad x \to 5$

(For Problems 13–17, you will have to recall how to factor a higher degree polynomial or how to long divide or synthetically divide the numerator by the denominator.)

13. $f(x) = \dfrac{x^3 - 3x^2 - 4x - 30}{x - 5}, \quad x \to 5$

14. $f(x) = \dfrac{x^3 + x^2 - 5x - 21}{x - 3}, \quad x \to 3$

15. $f(x) = \dfrac{x^3 - 4x^2 - 2x + 3}{x + 1}, \quad x \to -1$

16. $f(x) = x^3 - 10x^2 + 7x - 11, \quad x \to 2$

17. $f(x) = \dfrac{x^4 - 11x^3 + 21x^2 - x - 10}{x - 2}, \quad x \to 2$

18. *Check the Answer by Table Problem:* For Problem 13, let $\epsilon = 0.1$. Calculate the corresponding value of $\delta$. (Recall the quadratic formula!) Then make a table containing six conveniently-spaced $x$-values, each within $\delta$ unit of 5, and show that $f(x)$ is really within 0.1 unit of the limit for all these values.

19. *Limit of a Composite Function Problem:* Let $g(x) = \cos x$ and let $f(u) = \tan u$. Then $f(x)$ is the composite function

$$f(g(x)) = \tan(\cos x).$$

In this problem you will show that the limit of $f(g(x))$ as $x$ approaches 0 is the same as the limit of $f(u)$ as $u$ approaches 1.

a. Sketch a graph that shows $\cos x$ is close to 1 when $x$ is close to 0.

b. Plot the graph of $y = \tan x$ on your grapher. Use a friendly window for which $x = 1$ is a grid point. Show that $y$ stays close to $\tan 1$ when $x$ is kept close to 1.

c. Plot the graph of $y = \tan(\cos x)$ on your grapher and sketch the result. What value does $y$ stay close to when $x$ is close to 0?

d. Complete the equations.

$\lim_{x \to 0} \cos x = $ -?- $\lim_{u \to 1} \tan u = $ -?- $\lim_{x \to 0} \tan(\cos x) = $ -?-

20. *Pizza Delivery Problem:* Ida Livermore starts off on her route. She records her truck's speed, $v(t)$ miles per hour, at various numbers of seconds, $t$, since she started.

a. Show Ida that these data fit the equation $v(t) = 5t^{1/2}$.

| $t$ | $v(t)$ |
|---|---|
| 0 | 0 |
| 1 | 5 |
| 4 | 10 |
| 9 | 15 |
| 16 | 20 |

b. The truck's acceleration, $a(t)$, is the instantaneous rate of change of $v(t)$. Estimate $a(9)$ by using $v(9)$ and $v(9.001)$. Make a conjecture about the exact value of $a(9)$. What are the units of $a(t)$?

c. $a(9)$ is exactly equal to the limit of $[v(t) - v(9)]/(t - 9)$ as $t$ approaches 9. Factor the denominator as a difference of two "squares." Then find the limit as $t$ approaches 9 by applying the limit properties. Does this limit agree with your conjecture in 20b?

d. Approximately how far did Ida's truck go between $t = 1$ and $t = 9$?

21. *Exact Derivative Problem:* Let $f(x) = x^3$.

a. Find, approximately, the derivative of $f$ at $x = 2$ by dividing the change in $f(x)$ from $x = 2$ to $x = 2.1$ by the corresponding change in $x$.

b. In 21a you evaluated the fraction $[f(x) - f(2)]/(x - 2)$ to get an approximate value of the derivative. The exact value is the limit of this fraction as $x$ approaches 2. Find this limit by first simplifying the fraction. Prove that your answer is right by citing limit properties.

c. Plot the graph of $f$. Through the point (2, 8), construct a line whose slope is the value of the derivative in 21b. What relationship does the line seem to have to the graph?

22. Find, approximately, the derivative of $f(x) = 0.7^x$ when $x = 5$.

23. Find, approximately, the definite integral of $f(x) = 1.4^x$ from $x = 1$ to $x = 5$.

24. *Mathematical Induction Problem—The Limit of a Power:* You recall that $x^2 = x \cdot x$, so the limit of a product property can be used to prove that

$$\lim_{x \to c} x^2 = c^2.$$

Prove by mathematical induction that

$$\lim_{x \to c} x^n = c^n$$

for any positive integer value of $n$. The recursive definition of $x^n$, which is $x^n = x \cdot x^{n-1}$, should be helpful in doing the induction part of the proof.

25. *Journal Problem:* Update your calculus journal. You should consider the following.
    - The one most important thing you have learned since your last journal entry
    - What you now understand more fully about the definition of limit
    - How the shortened definition of limit corresponds to the definition you learned in Chapter 1
    - Why the limit properties for sums, products, and quotients are so obviously true
    - The meaning of the limit of a composite function property
    - What may still bother you about the definition of limit

# 2-4 Continuity

A function such as

$$g(x) = \frac{x^2 - 9}{x - 3}$$

has a discontinuity at $x = 3$ because the denominator is zero there. It seems reasonable to say that the function is "continuous" everywhere else because the graph seems to have no other "gaps" or "jumps" (Figure 2-4a). In this section you will use limits to define precisely the property of continuity.

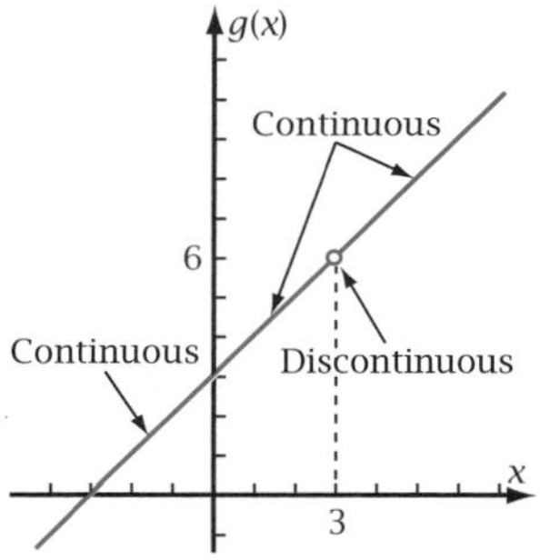

Figure 2-4a

**OBJECTIVE**

Define continuity. Learn the definition by using it in several ways.

Figures 2-4b through 2-4g show graphs of six functions, some of which are continuous at $x = c$ and some of which are not.

The first two functions have a limit as $x$ approaches $c$. In Figure 2-4b, $f$ is discontinuous at $c$ because there is no value of $f(c)$. In Figure 2-4c, $f$ is discontinuous at $c$ because $f(c) \neq L$. Both are **removable discontinuities**. The value of $f(c)$ can be defined or redefined to make $f$ continuous there.

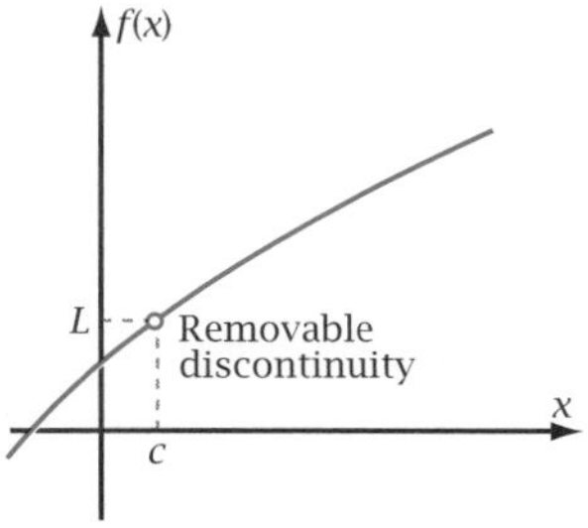


Not continuous. No $f(c)$

Figure 2-4b

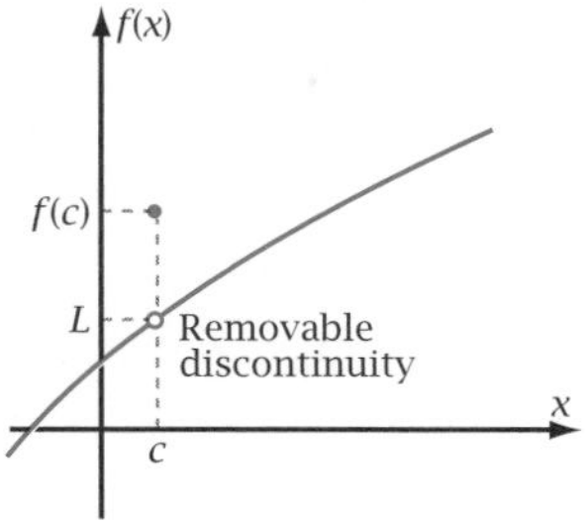


Not continuous. $f(c) \neq L$

Figure 2-4c

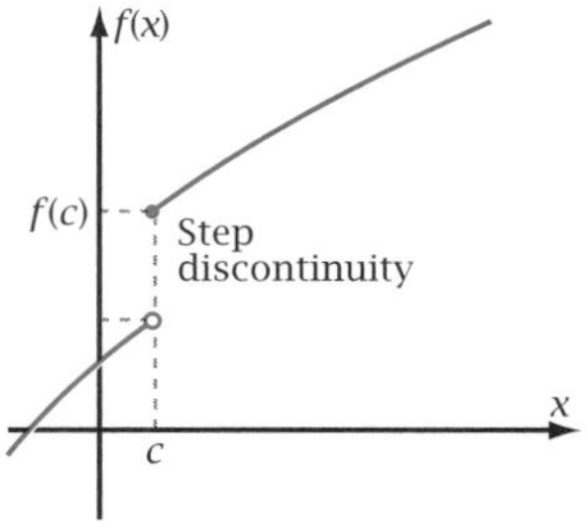


Not continuous. No $L$

Figure 2-4d

In Figure 2-4d, $f$ has a **step discontinuity** at $x = c$. Although there is a value of $f(c)$, $f(x)$ approaches different values from the left of $c$ and the right of $c$. Thus, there is no limit of $f(x)$ as $x$ approaches $c$. A step discontinuity cannot be removed simply by redefining $f(c)$.

In Figure 2-4e, $f$ is discontinuous at $x = c$ because it has a **vertical asymptote** at $c$. There is neither a value of $f(c)$ nor a finite limit of $f(x)$ as $x$ approaches $c$. Again, the discontinuity is not removable just by redefining $f(c)$. In Section 2-5, you will study such **infinite limits**.

Figures 2-4f and 2-4g show graphs of functions that are continuous at $x = c$. The value of $f(c)$ equals the limit of $f(x)$ as $x$ approaches $c$. The branches of the graph are "connected" by $f(c)$.

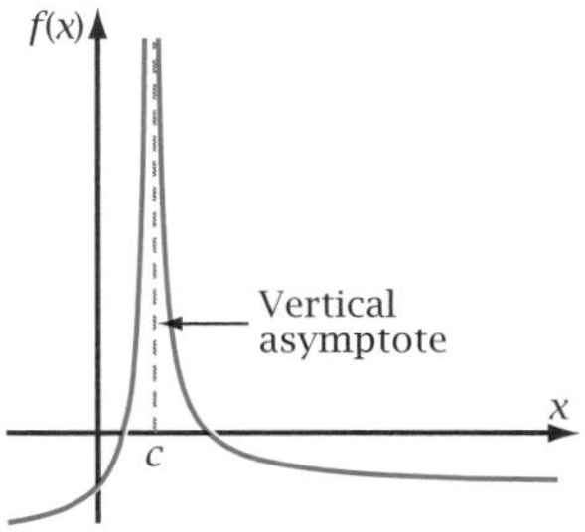


Not continuous. No $f(c)$, no $L$

Figure 2-4e

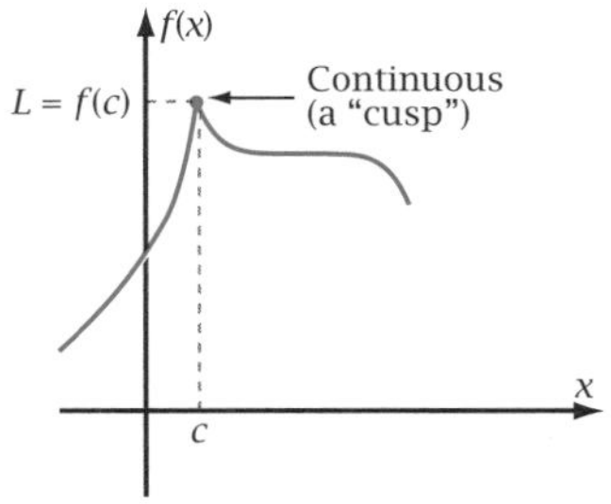


Continuous. $L = f(c)$

Figure 2-4f

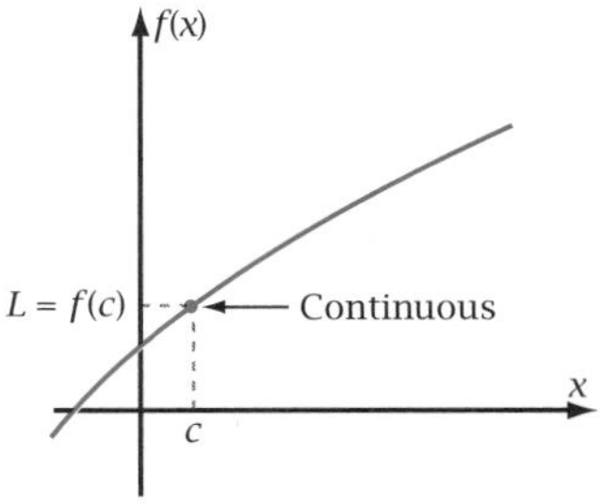


Continuous. $L = f(c)$

Figure 2-4g

The above examples lead to a formal definition of continuity.

### *Definition: Continuity*

**Continuity at a Point:** Function $f$ is continuous at $x = c$ if and only if:

1. $f(c)$ exists,
2. $\lim_{x \to c} f(x)$ exists, and
3. $\lim_{x \to c} f(x) = f(c)$.

**Continuity on an Interval:** Function $f$ is continuous on an interval of $x$-values if and only if it is continuous at each value of $x$ in that interval.

Note that the graph can have a **cusp** (an abrupt change in direction) at $x = c$ and still be continuous there (Figure 2-4f). The word *bicuspid* in relation to a tooth comes from the same root word.

### *Definition: Cusp*

A cusp is a point on the graph at which the function is continuous but the derivative is discontinuous.

Informal words: A cusp is a sharp point or an abrupt change in direction.

Figures 2-4h, 2-4i, and 2-4j illustrate why a function must satisfy all three parts of the continuity definition. The graph in Figure 2-4h has a limit as $x$ approaches $c$ but it has no function value. The graph in Figure 2-4i has a function value, $f(c)$, but no limit as $x$ approaches $c$. The graph in Figure 2-4j has both a function value and a limit, but they are not equal.

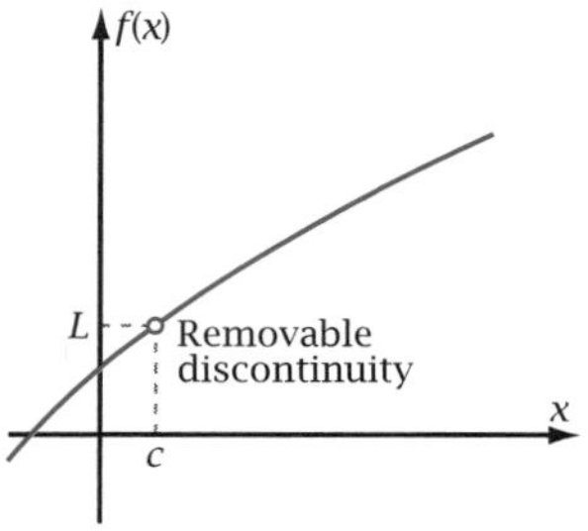

Limit but no value for $f(c)$.

Figure 2-4h

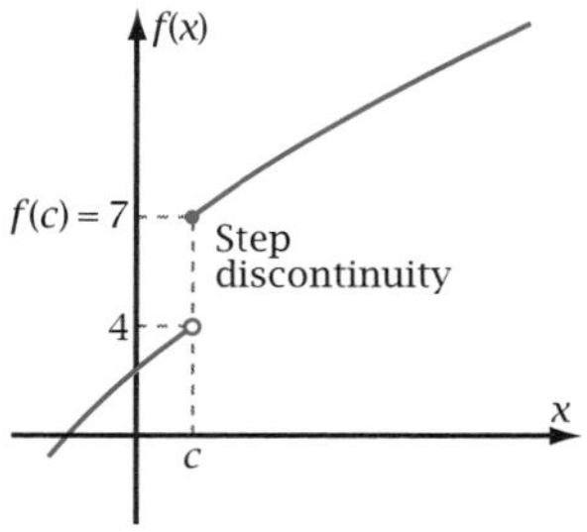

Value $f(c)$ but no value for limit.

Figure 2-4i

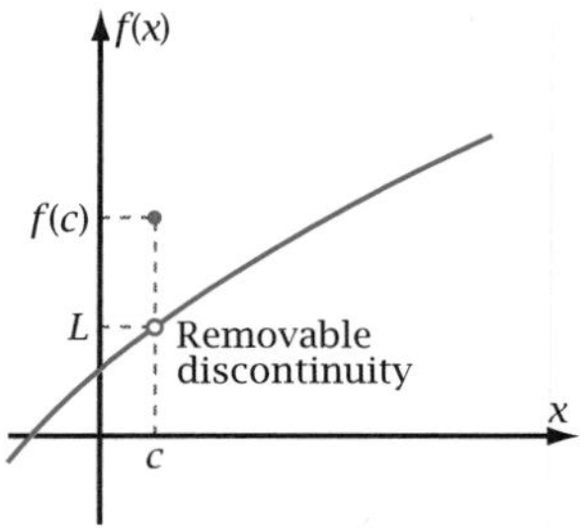

Unequal values for limit and $f(c)$.

Figure 2-4j

The graph in Figure 2-4i illustrates the concept of a **one-sided limit**. If $x$ is close to $c$ on the left side, $f(x)$ is close to 4. If $x$ is close to $c$ on the right, $f(x)$ is close to 7. The symbols shown in the following box are used for left- and right-sided limits.

### *Symbols: One-Sided Limits*

$\lim_{x \to c^-} f(x)$ $x \to c$ from the left (through values of $x$ on the negative side of $c$)

$\lim_{x \to c^+} f(x)$ $x \to c$ from the right (through values of $x$ on the positive side of $c$)

**■ Example 1** Let the function $f(x) = \begin{cases} 0.5x + 3, & \text{if } x < 2 \\ -x^2 + 6x - 2, & \text{if } x \geq 2. \end{cases}$

a. Draw the graph.

b. Find $\lim_{x \to 2^-} f(x)$ and $\lim_{x \to 2^+} f(x)$.

c. Tell whether or not $f(x)$ is continuous at $x = 2$.

***Solution***

a. Figure 2-4k shows the graph. You can probably sketch it without the grapher. There is a step discontinuity at $x = 2$ because the two branches do not connect.

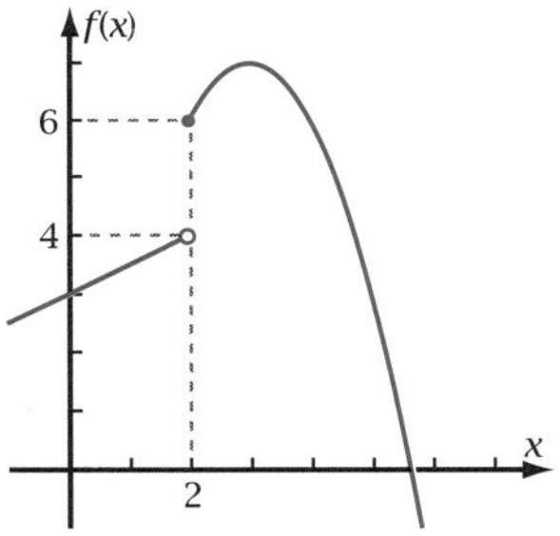

Figure 2-4k

b. $\lim_{x \to 2^-} f(x) = 4$, because $f(x)$ is close to 4 when $x$ is close to, but less than, 2.
$\lim_{x \to 2^+} f(x) = 6$, because $f(x)$ is close to 6 when $x$ is close to, but greater than, 2.

c. The function $f$ is not continuous at $x = 2$ because $f(x)$ has no limit as $x \to 2$. The value of $f(x)$ is close to no one number when $x$ is near 2 but $x \neq 2$. ■

Example 1 illustrates the relationship between limits and one-sided limits. A function has a (two-sided) limit at $x = c$ if and only if both one-sided limits are equal.

### *Property: Equal Left and Right Limits*

$L = \lim_{x \to c} f(x)$ if and only if $L = \lim_{x \to c^-} f(x)$ and $L = \lim_{x \to c^+} f(x)$.

**■ Example 2** Let the function $h(x) = \begin{cases} |x - 3| + 4, & \text{if } x \geq 2 \\ kx^2, & \text{if } x < 2. \end{cases}$

a. Find the value of $k$ that makes the function continuous at $x = 2$.

b. Plot and sketch the graph.

***Solution***

a. For $h$ to be continuous at $x = 2$, the left and right limits must be equal. Set the expressions for the left and right branches equal to each other at $x = 2$ and solve for $k$.

$$|2 - 3| + 4 = k(2^2) \Rightarrow 5 = 4k \Rightarrow k = 1.25$$

b. To make the grapher plot only in a given domain, you can use the logic test menu to get inequality signs. For instance, for the second branch of the function, enter the following equation.

$$y_2 = \frac{1.25x^2}{x < 2}$$

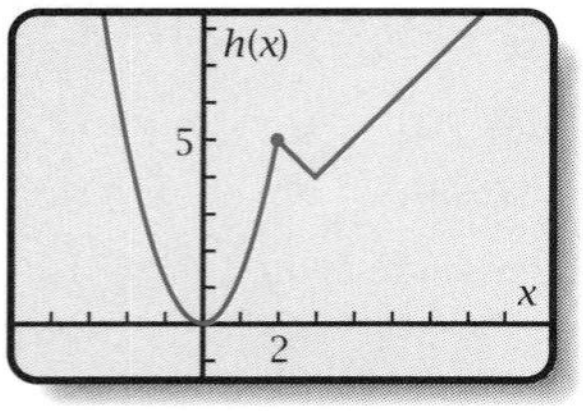


Figure 2-4l

If $x$ is *not* less than 2, the quantity $(x < 2)$ is zero. Dividing by zero makes $y_2$ undefined, and the grapher plots nothing. Figure 2-4l shows that the two branches "link up" to each other at $x = 2$. ■

## Problem Set 2-4

### *Do These Quickly*

The following problems are intended to refresh your skills. You should be able to do all ten problems in less than five minutes.

**Q1.** What is meant by the derivative of a function?

**Q2.** What is meant by the definite integral of a function?

**Q3.** If $f(x) = 200x + 17$, what is the maximum value of $\delta$ that will ensure $f(x)$ is within 0.1 unit of $f(3)$ when $x$ is within $\delta$ units of 3?

**Q4.** Draw a pair of alternate interior angles.

**Q5.** What type of function has a graph like that in Figure 2-4m?

**Q6.** Sketch the graph of $y = \cos x$.

**Q7.** Factor: $x^2 + 5x - 6$

**Q8.** Evaluate: $53^{2001}/53^{2000}$

**Q9.** Evaluate: 5!

**Q10.** Quick! Divide 50 by 1/2 and add 3.

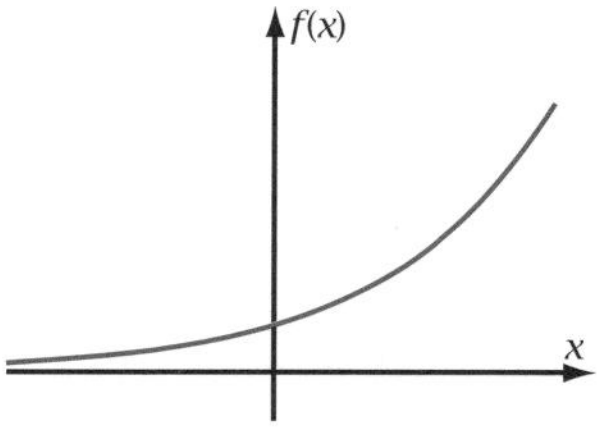


Figure 2-4m

For Problems 1–20, tell whether or not the graph illustrates a function that

a. has left and right limits at the marked value of $x$,

b. has a limit at the marked value of $x$,

c. is continuous at the marked value of $x$. If it is not continuous there, tell *why* not.

1.
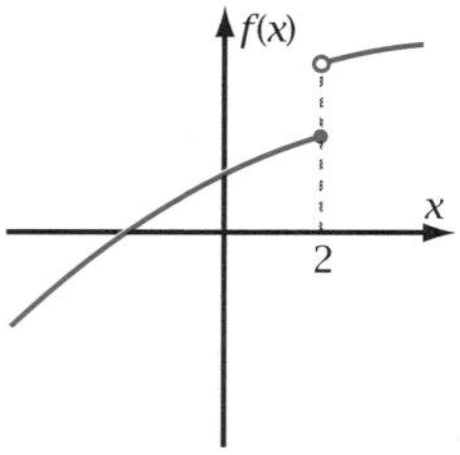


2.
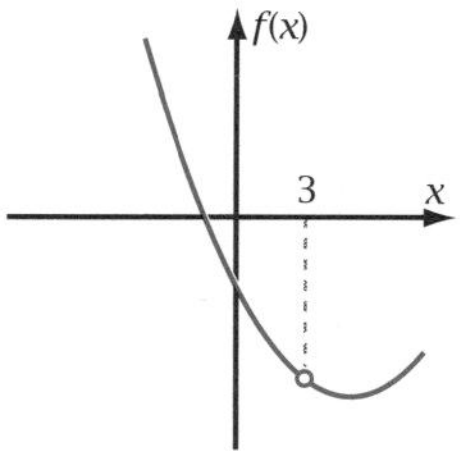


3.
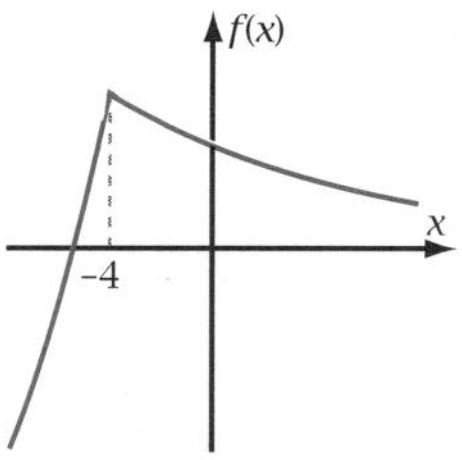


4.
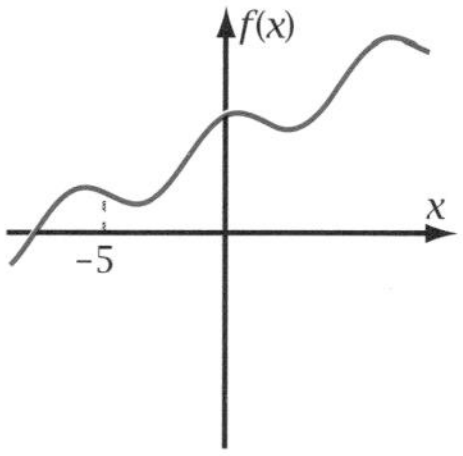

5.
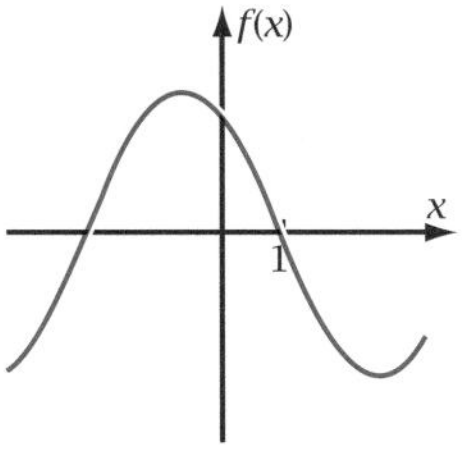


6.
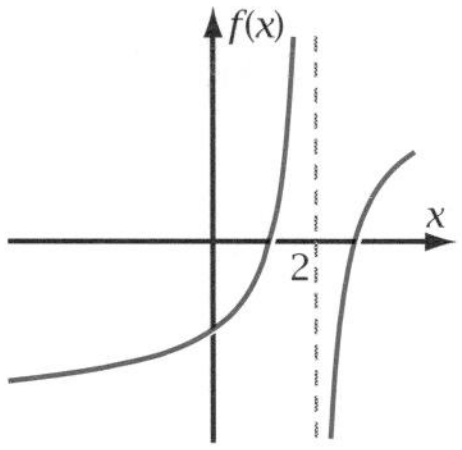


7.
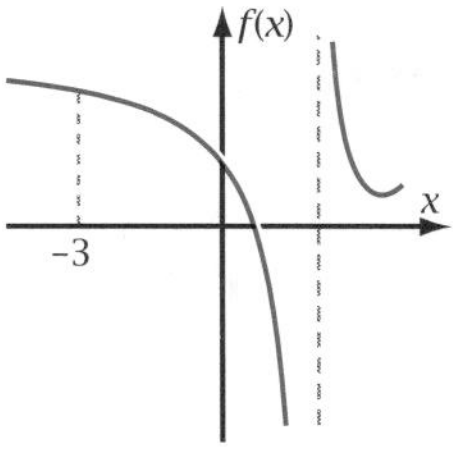


8.
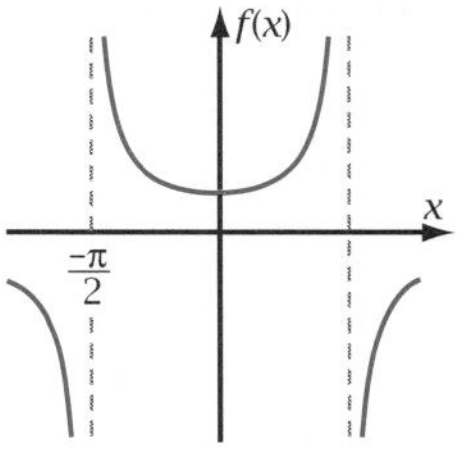


9.
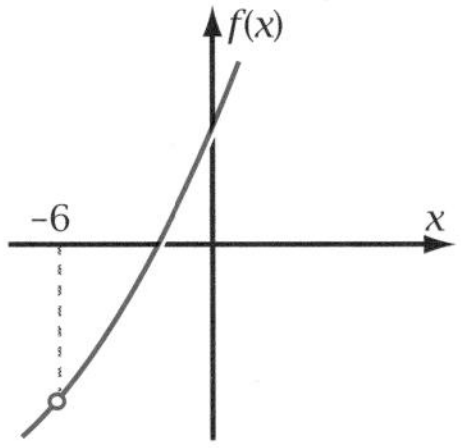


10.
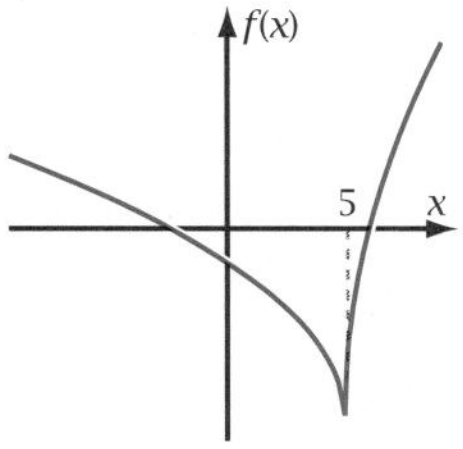


11.
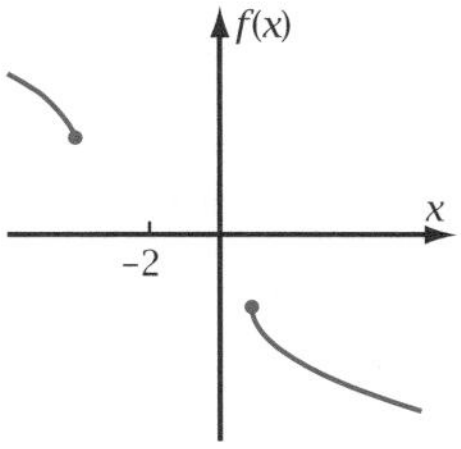


12.
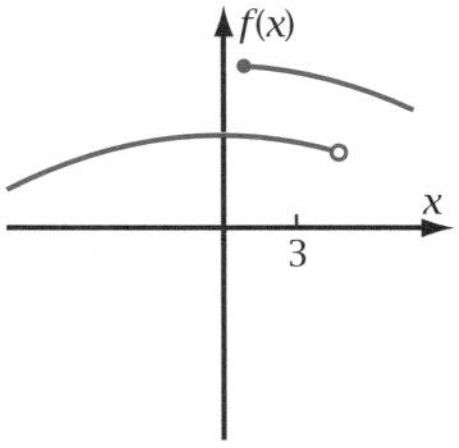


13.
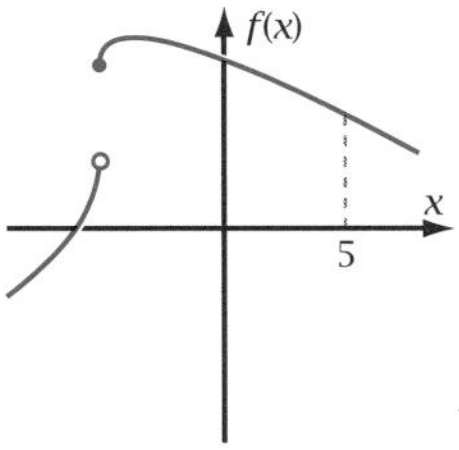


14.
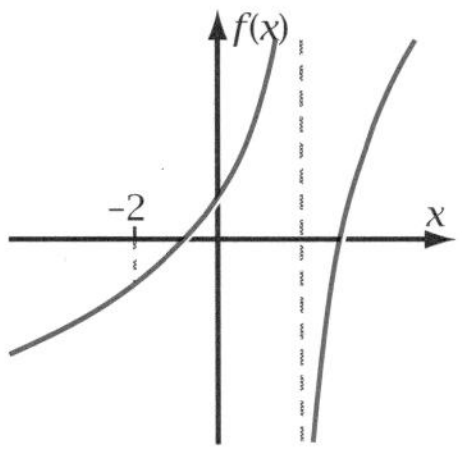


15.
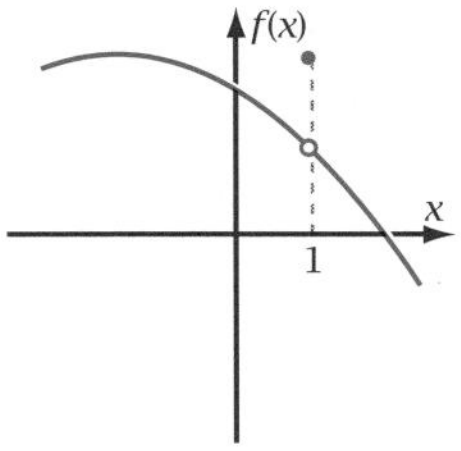


16.
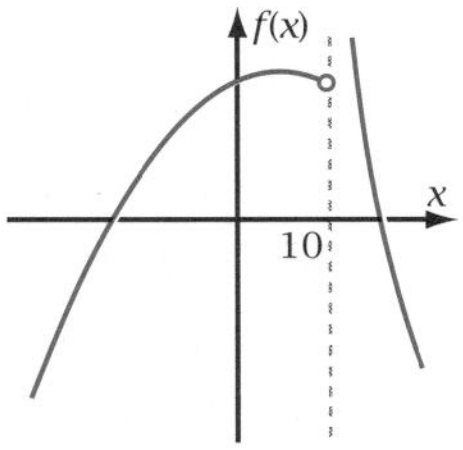


17.
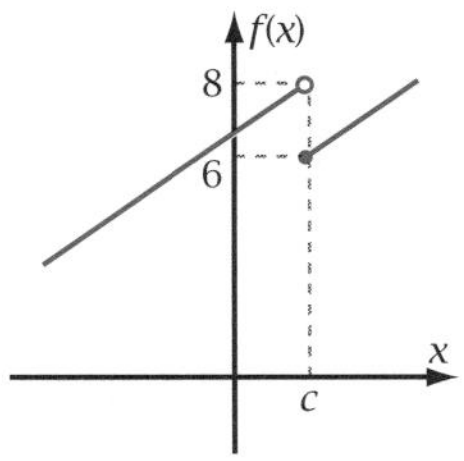


18.
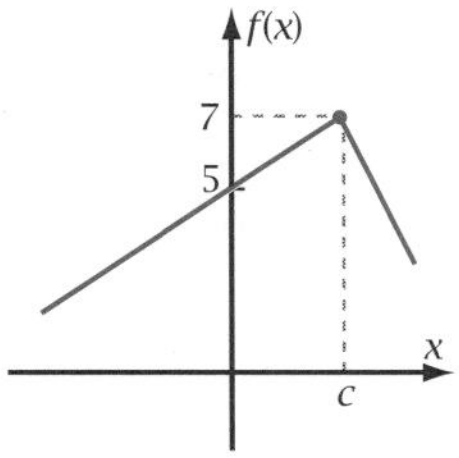


19.
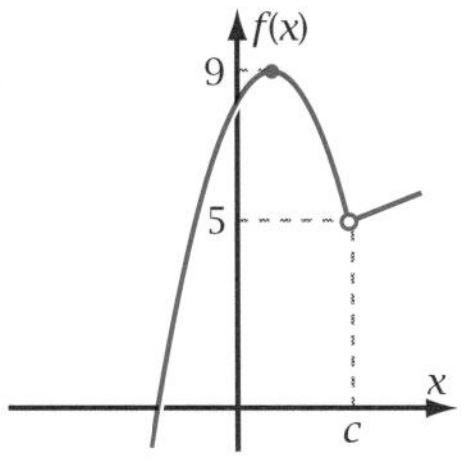


20.
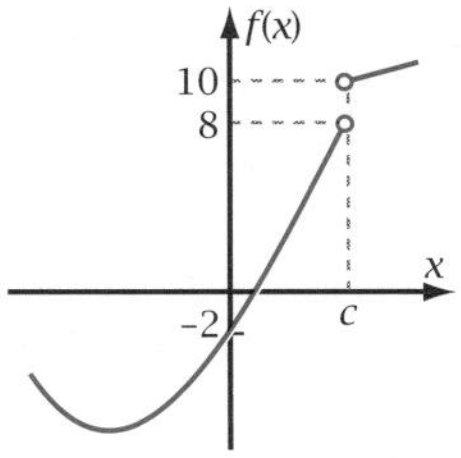


For Problems 21–42, sketch the graph of a function that has the indicated features.

21. Is continuous at $x = 3$ but has a cusp there.

22. Is continuous at $x = 4$ and is "smooth" there.

23. Has no value of $f(5)$ but has a limit as $x$ approaches 5.

24. Has a value of $f(-2)$ but has no limit as $x$ approaches $-2$.

25. Has a vertical asymptote at $x = -3$.

26. Has a vertical asymptote at $x = 6$.

27. Has a value of $f(2)$, a limit as $x$ approaches 2, but is not continuous at $x = 2$.

28. Has a negative value of $f(5)$ and a positive limit as $x$ approaches 5.

29. Has a step discontinuity at $x = -2$, and $f(-2) = 10$.

30. Has a step discontinuity at $x = -4$ and no value of $f(-4)$.

31. The value of $f(2) = 3$, the function is increasing slowly at $x = 2$, and the limit of $f(x)$ as $x$ approaches 5 is equal to 6, although there is no value of $f(5)$.

32. The value of $f(3) = 10$, the function is decreasing rapidly at $x = 3$, and the limit of $f(x)$ as $x$ approaches 7 is 1, although there is no value of $f(7)$.

33. The value of $f(4)$ is negative, but the function is increasing rapidly at $x = 4$.

34. The value of $f(-2)$ is positive, but the function is decreasing slowly at $x = -2$.

35. The limit of $f(x)$ as $x$ approaches $-4$ is 8, but there is no value of $f(-4)$.

36. The limit of $f(x)$ as $x$ approaches 5 is $-2$, and the value of $f(5)$ is also $-2$.

37. The limit of $f(x)$ as $x$ approaches 1 is 4, but $f(1) = 6$.

38. The limit of $f(x)$ as $x$ approaches 7 is 2, but $f(7) = -3$.

39. The value of $f(3) = 5$, but there is no limit of $f(x)$ as $x$ approaches 3 and no vertical asymptote there.

40. The value of $f(-3) = 2$, but there is no limit of $f(x)$ as $x$ approaches $-3$ and no vertical asymptote there.

41. The value of $f(x)$ has no limit as $x$ approaches $-9$, no value of $f(-9)$, and no vertical asymptote at $x = -9$, yet $f(x)$ is defined for all values of $x$ in a neighborhood of $-9$, not including $-9$ itself.

42. The value of $f(x)$ is increasing if $x < 6$ and decreasing if $x > 6$, but there is no limit of $f(x)$ as $x \to 6$.

For Problems 43–46, tell where, if anywhere, the function is discontinuous.

43. $f(x) = \dfrac{x-4}{x+3}$

44. $f(x) = \dfrac{x+5}{x-11}$

45. $g(x) = \tan x$

46. $g(x) = \cos x$

For Problems 47–52, the function is discontinuous at $x = 2$. Tell which part of the definition of continuity is not met at $x = 2$. You may plot the graph on your grapher. (Note: The symbol int ($n$) indicates the greatest integer less than or equal to $n$. Graph in dot mode.) Sketch the graph.

47. $f(x) = x + \text{int}(\cos \pi x)$

48. $g(x) = x + \text{int}(\sin \pi x)$

49. $s(x) = 3 + \sqrt{x-2}$

50. $p(x) = \text{int}(x^2 - 6x + 9)$

51. $h(x) = \dfrac{\sin(x-2)}{x-2}$

52. $f(x) = \begin{cases} x + (2-x)^{-1}, & \text{if } x \neq 2 \\ 3, & \text{if } x = 2 \end{cases}$

For Problems 53–58 do the following.

a. Sketch the graph of the function. Use the grapher only if necessary. Tell whether or not the function is continuous at the value of $x$ where the rule for the function changes.

b. Tell what the left- and right-limits are and whether or not the function has a limit at the value of $x$ where the rule for the function changes.

53. $d(x) = \begin{cases} 7 - x^2, & \text{if } x < 2, \\ 5 - x, & \text{if } x > 2 \end{cases}$

54. $h(x) = \begin{cases} 4 - x^2, & \text{if } x < 1 \\ x + 1, & \text{if } x \geq 1 \end{cases}$

55. $m(x) = \begin{cases} 3^x, & \text{if } x < 2 \\ 9 - x, & \text{if } x \geq 2 \end{cases}$

56. $q(x) = \begin{cases} 2^{-x}, & \text{if } x \leq -1 \\ x + 3, & \text{if } x > -1 \end{cases}$

57. $T(x) = \begin{cases} \dfrac{1}{x-2} & \text{if } x < 2 \\ 3, & \text{if } x = 2 \\ x + 1, & \text{if } x > 2 \end{cases}$

58. $Z(x) = \begin{cases} \dfrac{x^3 - x}{x^2 - x} & \text{if } x \neq 0 \text{ and } x \neq 1 \\ 3, & \text{if } x = 0 \\ 2, & \text{if } x = 1 \end{cases}$

For Problems 59–66, find the value of the constant $k$ that will make the function continuous where the defining rule changes by making the left limit of the left branch equal the right limit of the right branch. Sketch the graph, showing that the two branches "link up."

59. $f(x) = \begin{cases} -0.4x + 2, & \text{if } x \leq 1 \\ 0.3x + k, & \text{if } x > 1 \end{cases}$

60. $h(x) = \begin{cases} x^2, & \text{if } x < 2 \\ k - x, & \text{if } x \geq 2 \end{cases}$

61. $g(x) = \begin{cases} 9 - x^2, & \text{if } x < 2 \\ kx, & \text{if } x \geq 2 \end{cases}$

62. $f(x) = \begin{cases} 0.4x + 1, & \text{if } x < 1 \\ kx + 2, & \text{if } x \geq 1 \end{cases}$

63. $u(x) = \begin{cases} kx^2, & \text{if } x \leq 3 \\ kx - 3, & \text{if } x > 3 \end{cases}$

64. $v(x) = \begin{cases} kx + 5, & \text{if } x < -1 \\ kx^2, & \text{if } x \geq -1 \end{cases}$

65. $f(x) = \begin{cases} 0.4x + k^2, & \text{if } x < 1 \\ kx + 2.4, & \text{if } x \geq 1 \end{cases}$

66. $f(x) = \begin{cases} k^2 - x^2, & \text{if } x < 2 \\ 1.5kx, & \text{if } x \geq 2 \end{cases}$

67. *Two Constants Problem:* Let $a$ and $b$ stand for constants and let

$$f(x) = \begin{cases} b - x, & \text{if } x \leq 1 \\ a(x-2)^2, & \text{if } x > 1. \end{cases}$$

a. Find an equation relating $a$ and $b$ if $f$ is to be continuous at $x = 1$.

b. Find $b$ if $a = -1$. Show by graphing that $f$ is continuous at $x = 1$ for these values of $a$ and $b$.

c. Pick another value of $a$ and find $b$. Show that $f$ is continuous for these values of $a$ and $b$.

68. *Surprise Function Problem!* Let $f(x) = x + 3 + \dfrac{10^{-20}}{x-1}$.

a. Plot the graph on the grapher.

b. What appears to be the limit of $f(x)$ as $x$ approaches 1?

c. Show that $f(x)$ is very close to the number in 68b when $x = 1.0000001$.

d. Function $f$ is not continuous at $x = 1$ because there is no value for $f(1)$. What type of discontinuity is there at $x = 1$? Be careful!

69. *Continuity of Polynomial Functions:* The general polynomial function of degree $n$ has an equation of the form

$$P(x) = a_0 + a_1x + a_2x^2 + a_3x^3 + \cdots + a_nx^n.$$

Based on the closure axioms for real numbers and the properties of limits you have learned, explain why any polynomial function is continuous for all real values of $x$.

70. *The Signum Function:* Figure 2-4n shows the graph of the signum function, $f(x) = \text{sgn } x$. The value of the function is 1 when $x$ is positive, $-1$ when $x$ is negative, and 0 when $x$ is zero. This function is useful in computing for testing a value of $x$ to see what sign it has (hence the name *signum*). The formal definition is given below.

$$\text{sgn } x = \begin{cases} 1, & \text{if } x > 0 \\ 0, & \text{if } x = 0 \\ -1, & \text{if } x < 0 \end{cases}$$

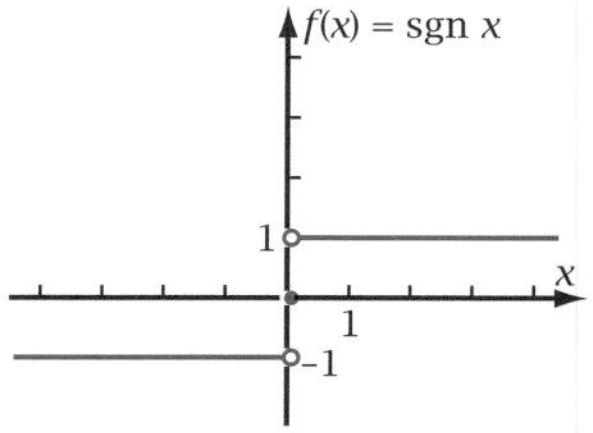

Figure 2-4n

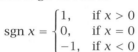

In this problem you will explore various compositions of the signum function.

a. Does $r(x) = |\text{sgn } x|$ have a limit as $x$ approaches zero? Does it have a function value at $x = 0$? Is it continuous at $x = 0$?

b. Sketch the graph of $g(x) = 3 \text{ sgn } (x - 2)$.

c. Sketch the graph of $h(x) = x^2 - \text{sgn } x$.

d. Show that the function $a(x) = |x|/x$ is equal to sgn $x$ for all $x$ except zero.

e. Sketch the graph of $f(x) = \cos x + \text{sgn } x$.

f. Suppose you want to plot $p(x) = x^{3/7}$ on a calculator or a computer that will not handle powers with negative bases. With the help of the signum function, write $x^{3/7}$ as a single expression in a form that will give the correct answer for both positive and negative $x$-values, but that does not involve raising a negative number to a power. Sketch the resulting graph on your paper.

# 2-5 Limits Involving Infinity

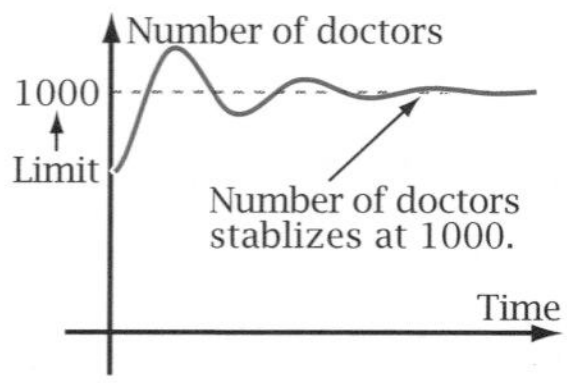

Figure 2-5a

Suppose that there is an increase in the demand for doctors in a particular community. The number of people who choose to pursue that career will increase to meet the demand. After a while there may be too many doctors, causing the number of people who want to enter the medical profession to decrease. Eventually the number of doctors stabilizes somewhere, say at 1000 (Figure 2-5a). This steady-state value is called the limit of the number of doctors as time approaches infinity.

Another type of limit involving infinity can be visualized by imagining you are pointing a flashlight straight at a wall (Figure 2-5b). If you begin to turn with the flashlight in your hand, the length of the light beam increases. When the angle is $\pi/2$ radians (90°), the beam is parallel to the wall, so its length becomes infinite.

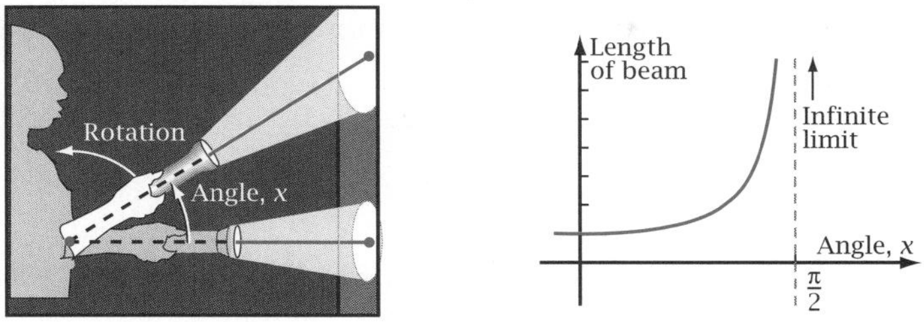


Figure 2-5b

In this section you will see how the definition of limit must be modified to take into account cases where $x$ approaches infinity or where the limit is infinite.

**OBJECTIVE**

Find limits of functions where either $x$ goes to infinity, the limit is infinite, or both.

The definition you have learned for limit tells what happens to the $y$-value of a function when $x$ is kept close to a certain number, $c$. If $x$ increases without bound, there is no such number it can be kept close to. Suppose the function value can be made to stay arbitrarily close to a given number $L$, like the 1000 in Figure 2-5a, just by making $x$ large enough. Then $L$ is the limit of the function as $x$ approaches infinity. The following definition records this fact.

### Definition: Limit as x Approaches Infinity

$L = \lim_{x\to\infty} f(x)$ if and only if for any number $\epsilon > 0$, there is a number $D > 0$ such that if $x > D$, then $f(x)$ is within $\epsilon$ units of $L$.

A similar definition holds for $\lim_{x\to-\infty} f(x)$, and the same type of reasoning can be applied if the function value becomes infinite as $x$ approaches $c$. There is no number $L$ that $f(x)$ can be kept close to, so the following definition is used.

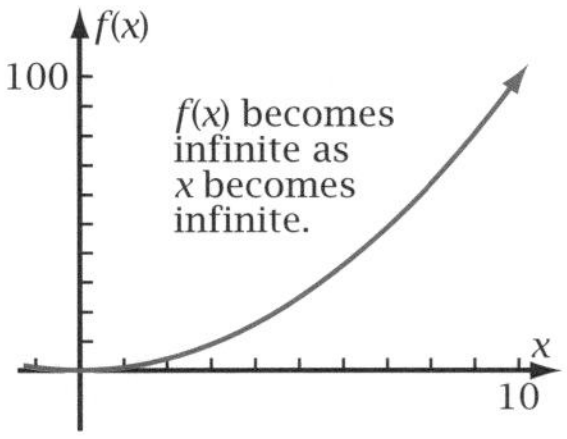


Figure 2-5c

### Definition: Infinite Limit

$\lim_{x\to c} f(x)$ is **infinite** if and only if for any number $E > 0$ there is a number $\delta > 0$ such that if $x$ is within $\delta$ units of, but not equal to, $c$, then $|f(x)|$ is greater than $E$.

If $f(x)$ becomes infinite as $x$ becomes infinite, both modifications to the usual definition of limit are used. Figure 2-5c shows the graph of $f(x) = x^2$, which illustrates this property. In plain English, this property says "If you can make $y$ as big as you like by making $x$ big enough, then the limit of $f(x)$ is infinite as $x$ approaches infinity."

**Definition: Infinite Limit as x Approaches Infinity**

$\lim_{x \to \infty} f(x)$ is infinite if and only if for any number $E > 0$, there is a number $D > 0$ such that if $x > D$, then $|f(x)| > E$.

A similar definition holds for $\lim_{x \to -\infty} f(x)$.

### A Note on Infinity, "Undefined," and the Proper Use of the = Sign

The = in mathematics is used to connect two equal numbers. Because infinity is not a real number, it is more appropriate to say "the limit of $f(x)$ is infinite" rather than saying it "equals infinity." Sometimes, when it is important to describe briefly the direction in which a function goes to infinity, the following statements are used.

$$\lim_{x \to c} f(x) = \infty \qquad \text{or} \qquad \lim_{x \to c} f(x) = -\infty$$

The symbols $\infty$ and $-\infty$ are convenient shorthand for describing the behavior of the function at $x = c$. You should realize that the limits still do not exist. The notation simply explains why the limits do not exist. They are **undefined** because they are **infinite**. Note that a limit may be undefined without being infinite. For instance, the limit $f(x) = |x|/x$ as $x$ approaches zero is **undefined** because of a **step discontinuity** there.

The statement "$x \to \infty$" is also somewhat misleading. Although pronounced "$x$ approaches infinity," the statement really means "$x$ gets infinitely far away from zero." No matter how large $x$ gets, it can never be close to infinity!

### Properties of Limits Involving Infinity

Two properties come directly from the above definitions. They concern what happens to the reciprocal of a function if the value of the function approaches either zero or infinity. For instance, suppose

$$f(x) = \frac{1}{x - 3}.$$

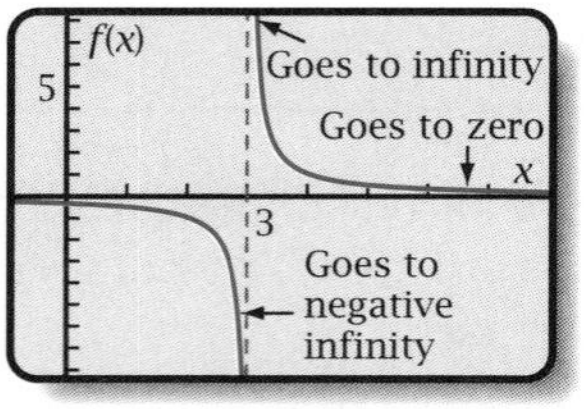

Figure 2-5d

As $x$ approaches 3, the denominator goes to zero. When you use a grapher (Figure 2-5d) you can see that the fraction itself becomes infinitely large in the positive direction if $x$ is to the right of 3, and infinitely large in the negative direction if $x$ is to the left of 3. On the other hand, if $x$ approaches infinity or negative infinity, the denominator becomes infinite and the fraction itself approaches zero. These properties are summarized in the following box.

**Property: Reciprocals of Zero and Infinity**

If $f(x) = \dfrac{1}{g(x)}$ and $\lim\limits_{x \to c} g(x) = 0$, then $\lim\limits_{x \to c} f(x)$ is infinite.

If $f(x) = \dfrac{1}{g(x)}$ and $\lim\limits_{x \to c} g(x)$ is infinite, then $\lim\limits_{x \to c} f(x) = 0$.

The same properties apply if $x$ approaches infinity.

Informal words: The form $\dfrac{1}{0}$ is infinite. The forms $\dfrac{1}{\infty}$ and $\dfrac{1}{-\infty}$ have a zero limit.

Note that the above property holds if $c$ is replaced by $\infty$ or $-\infty$.

**Example 1** If $f(x) = \tan^{-1} x$, find $\lim_{x \to \infty} f(x)$. Find a number $D$ such that $f(x)$ is within $\epsilon = 0.1$ unit of the limit whenever $x > D$. Illustrate by graph the meaning of $D$ and $\epsilon$.

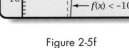

**Solution** You recall that the inverse tangent graph has a horizontal asymptote at $y = \pi/2$. Thus,

$$\lim_{x \to \infty} f(x) = \tfrac{\pi}{2}.$$

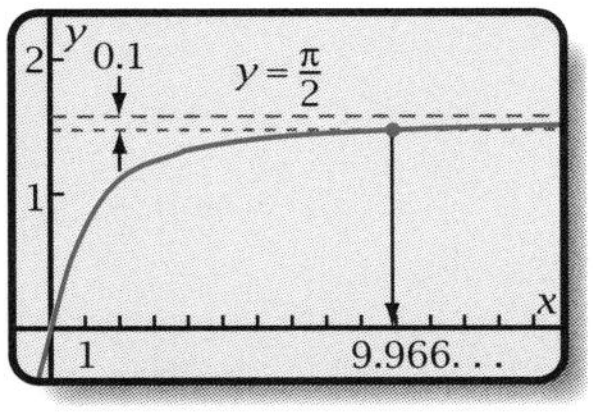


Figure 2-5e

To find $D$, let

$$\tan^{-1} D = \tfrac{\pi}{2} - 0.1 = 1.4707963\ldots$$

$$\therefore D = \tan 1.4707963\ldots = 9.966644\ldots$$

As indicated in Figure 2-5e, $\tan^{-1} x$ is closer than 0.1 unit to $\pi/2$ whenever $x$ is greater than 9.966.... Because this calculation could be done for any number $\epsilon > 0$, $\pi/2$ is the limit of $f(x)$ as $x$ approaches infinity. ■

**Example 2** For $f(x) = \dfrac{x-4}{x-2}$, show that $\lim_{x \to 2^+} f(x) = -\infty$. Find a value of $\delta$ such that $|f(x)| > 10$ whenever $x$ is within $\delta$ units of 2 on the positive side but not equal to 2.

**Solution** Figure 2-5f shows that there is a vertical asymptote at $x = 2$ because of division by zero, so the limit is infinite. Because $f(x)$ has the form (positive) ÷ (negative) when $x$ is close to 2 on the positive side, the limit is $-\infty$. To find the value of $\delta$, set $f(x) = -10$.

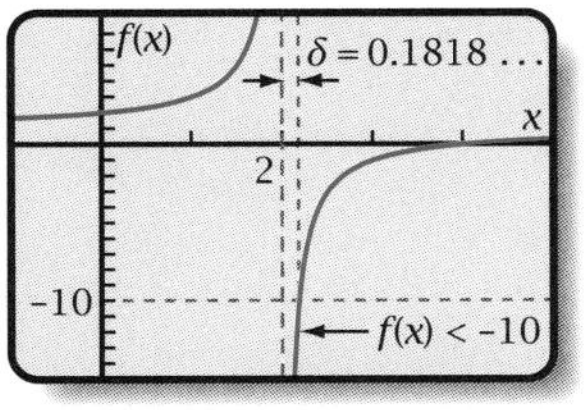


Figure 2-5f

$$-10 = \frac{x-4}{x-2}$$

$$-10x + 20 = x - 4 \Rightarrow x = \tfrac{24}{11} = 2.1818\ldots$$

$$\therefore \delta = 2.1818\ldots - 2 = 0.1818\ldots$$

Thus, $|f(x)| > 10$ whenever $x$ is within 0.1818... unit on the right of 2. ■

## Problem Set 2-5

### *Do These Quickly*

The following problems are intended to refresh your skills. You should be able to do all ten problems in less than five minutes. Refer to Figure 2-5g.

**Q1.** $\lim_{x\to 1} f(x) =$ -?-

**Q2.** $\lim_{x\to 2} f(x) =$ -?-

**Q3.** $\lim_{x\to 3} f(x) =$ -?-

**Q4.** $\lim_{x\to 4} f(x) =$ -?-

**Q5.** $\lim_{x\to 5} f(x) =$ -?-

**Q6.** Is $f$ continuous at $x = 1$?

**Q7.** Is $f$ continuous at $x = 2$?

**Q8.** Is $f$ continuous at $x = 3$?

**Q9.** Is $f$ continuous at $x = 4$?

**Q10.** Is $f$ continuous at $x = 5$?

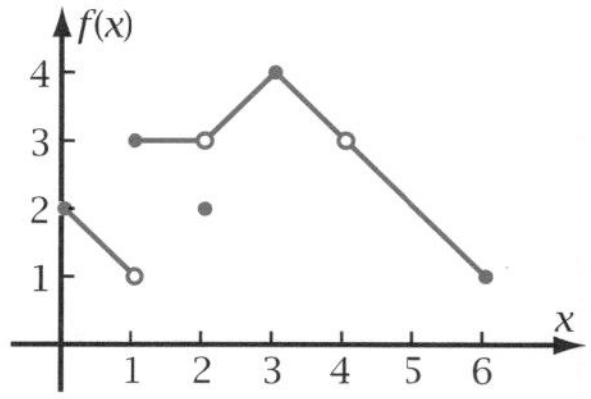


Figure 2-5g

For Problems 1–4, sketch the graph of a function that has the given features.

1. $\lim_{x\to 2^-} f(x) = \infty$ and $\lim_{x\to 2^+} f(x) = \infty$

2. $\lim_{x\to 2^-} f(x) = \infty$ and $\lim_{x\to 2^+} f(x) = -\infty$

3. $\lim_{x\to \infty} f(x) = -5$ and $\lim_{x\to -\infty} f(x) = 7$

4. $\lim_{x\to \infty} f(x) = \infty$ and $\lim_{x\to -\infty} f(x) = \infty$

5. Let $f(x) = 2 + \dfrac{1}{x-3}$.
   a. Sketch the graph of $f$.
   b. Find $\lim\limits_{x\to 3^+} f(x)$, $\lim\limits_{x\to 3^-} f(x)$, $\lim\limits_{x\to 3} f(x)$, $\lim\limits_{x\to \infty} f(x)$, and $\lim\limits_{x\to -\infty} f(x)$.
   c. Find a number $\delta > 0$ such that $f(x) > 100$ if $x$ is within $\delta$ units of 3 on the positive side.
   d. Find a number $D > 0$ such that $f(x)$ is within 0.001 unit of the limit as $x \to \infty$ whenever $x > D$.

6. Let $g(x) = \sec x$.
   a. Sketch the graph of $g$.
   b. Explain why $\lim_{x\to \pi/2} g(x)$ is infinite.
   c. Find a number $\delta > 0$ such that $g(x) > 1000$ if $x$ is within $\delta$ units of $\pi/2$ on the negative side.
   d. What does $\lim_{x\to \pi/2^+} g(x)$ equal? Using the value of $\delta$ from 6c, what can you say about the value of $g(x)$ if $x$ is kept within $\delta$ units of $\pi/2$ on the positive side?

7. Let $r(x) = 2 + \dfrac{\sin x}{x}$.
   a. Plot the graph of $r$. Use a friendly window with an $x$-range of about $-20$ to 20 for which $x = 0$ is a grid point. Sketch the result.
   b. Find the limit of $r(x)$ as $x$ approaches infinity.

c. You realize that sin $x$ ranges between $x = -1$ and $x = 1$. What, then, could you pick for $D$ so that $r(x)$ would be within $\epsilon = 0.001$ unit of the limit found in 7b whenever $x$ is greater than $D$?

d. If in 7b you draw a horizontal line at $y = \lim$, will it be an asymptote? Explain.

e. Make a conjecture about the limit of $r(x)$ as $x$ approaches zero. Give evidence to support your conjecture.

8. Let $h(x) = \left(1 + \dfrac{1}{x}\right)^x$.

a. Plot the graph of $h$. Use a friendly window with an $x$-range of 0 to about 100. You will have to explore to find a suitable $y$-range. Sketch the result.

b. As $x$ becomes large, $1/x$ approaches zero, so $h(x)$ takes on the form $1^\infty$. You realize that 1 to any power is 1, but the base is always greater than 1, and a number greater than 1 raised to a large positive power becomes infinite. Which phenomenon "wins" as $x$ approaches infinity, 1, infinity, or some "compromise" number in between?

9. Figure 2-5h shows the graph of

$$y = \log x.$$

Does the graph level off and approach a (finite) limit as $x$ approaches infinity, or is the limit infinite? Justify your answer. You might find that the definition of logarithm is helpful ($y = \log x$ if and only if $10^y = x$).

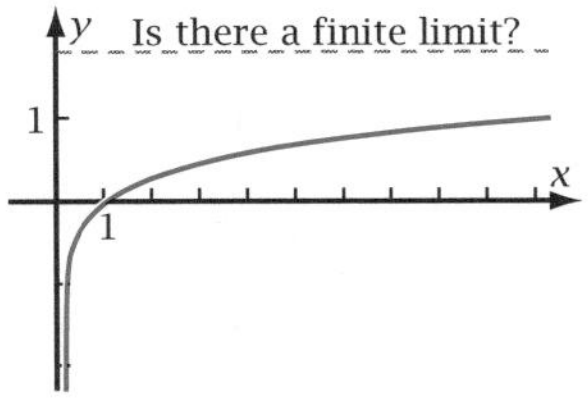

Figure 2-5h

10. Wanda Wye wonders why the form 1/0 is infinite and why the form $1/\infty$ is zero. Explain to her what happens to the size of fractions such as 1/0.1, 1/0.0001, etc., as the denominator gets close to zero. Explain what happens as the denominator becomes very large.

11. *Limits Applied to Integrals Problem:* Rhoda Huffy starts riding down the driveway on her tricycle. Being quite precocious, she figures her velocity, $v$, in feet per second is

$$v = \sqrt{t}$$

where $t$ is time in seconds since she started. Figure 2-5i shows $v$ as a function of $t$.

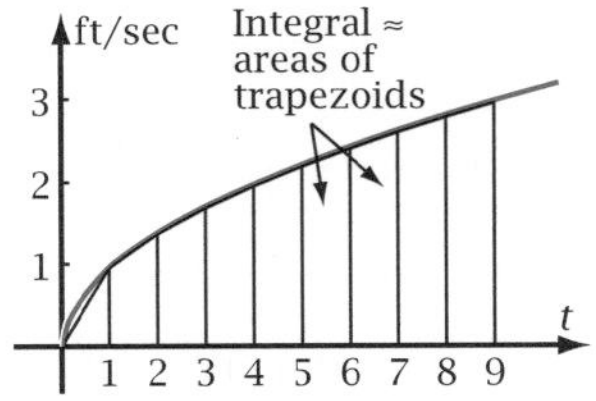

Figure 2-5i

a. Explain why the definite integral from $t = 0$ to $t = 9$ represents the distance Rhoda rode in the first 9 sec.

b. Estimate by trapezoids the integral in 11a, using 9, 45, 90, and 450 trapezoids. Record all the decimal places your program gives you.

c. What number (an integer in this case) do you think is the exact value of the integral? Explain why this number is a limit. Why are the approximate answers by trapezoids all smaller than this number?

d. Figure out how many trapezoids are needed so that the approximation of the integral is within 0.01 unit of the limit. Tell how you go about getting the answer.

12. *Work Problem:* The work done as you drag a box across the floor is equal to the product of the force you exert on the box and the distance the box moves. Suppose that the force varies, and is equal to

$$F(x) = 10 - 3\sqrt{x},$$

where $F(x)$ is force in pounds and $x$ is the number of feet the box is from its starting point. Figure 2-5j shows the graph of $F$.

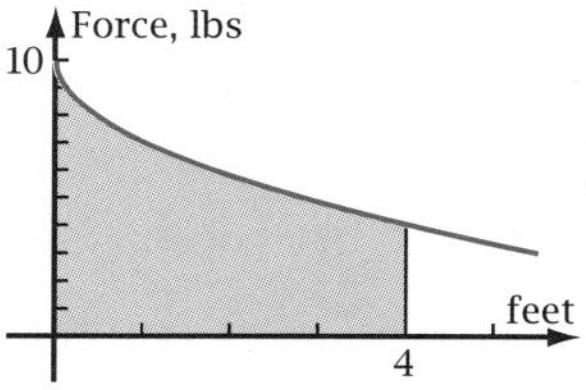

Figure 2-5j

a. Explain why a definite integral is used to calculate the amount of work done.

b. Use the trapezoidal rule with $n = 10$ and $n = 100$ increments to estimate the value of the integral. What are the units of work in this problem?

c. The exact amount of work is the limit of the trapezoidal sums as $n$ approaches infinity. In this case the answer is an integer. What do you suppose that the integer is?

d. What is the minimum number, $D$, such that the trapezoidal sums are closer than 0.01 unit to the limit in 12c whenever $n > D$?

13. *Searchlight Problem:* A searchlight shines on a wall as shown in Figure 2-5k. The perpendicular distance from the light to the wall is 100 ft. Write an equation for the length of the beam of light as a function of the angle (in radians) between the perpendicular and the beam. How close to $\pi/2$ must the angle be in order for the length of the beam to be at least 1000 ft, assuming that the wall is long enough?

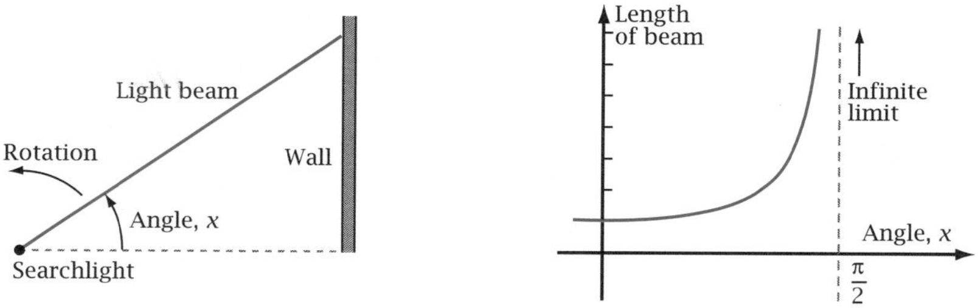

Figure 2-5k

14. *Zero Times Infinity Problem:* You have learned that 0/0 is called an indeterminate form. You can't determine what it equals just by looking at it. Similarly, $0 \cdot \infty$ is an indeterminate form. In this problem you will see three possibilities for the limit of a function whose form goes to $0 \cdot \infty$. Let $f$, $g$, and $h$ be functions defined as follows.

$$f(x) = 5x(x-2) \cdot \frac{1}{x-2} \qquad g(x) = 5x(x-2) \cdot \frac{1}{(x-2)^2} \qquad h(x) = 5x(x-2)^2 \cdot \frac{1}{x-2}$$

a. Show that each of the three functions takes the form $0 \cdot \infty$ as $x$ approaches 2.

b. Find the limit of each function as $x$ approaches 2.

c. Describe three things that the indeterminate form $0 \cdot \infty$ could approach.

# 2-6 The Intermediate Value Theorem and Its Consequences

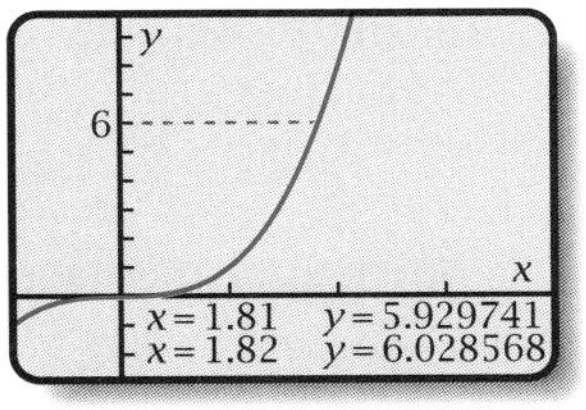


Figure 2-6a

Suppose you try to find a solution of the equation $x^3 = 6$ by tracing the graph of $y = x^3$ (Figure 2-6a). The cursor never quite hits a value of $x$ that makes $y$ equal exactly 6. That's because the grapher plots **discrete** points that represent only approximately the **continuous** graph. However, because $y = x^3$ is continuous, there really is a value of $x$ (an irrational number) which, when cubed, gives exactly 6.

The property of continuous functions that guarantees there is an exact value is called the **intermediate value theorem**. Informally, it says that if you pick a value of $y$ between any two values of $f(x)$, there is an $x$-value in the domain that gives exactly that $y$-value for $f(x)$. Because $1.81^3 = 5.929741$ and $1.82^3 = 6.028568$, and because 6 is between 5.929741 and 6.028568, there must be a number $x$ between 1.81 and 1.82 for which $f(x) = 6$ exactly. One must show that $y = x^3$ is continuous in order for the property to apply.

### *Property: The Intermediate Value Theorem*

If function $f$ is continuous for all $x$ in the closed interval $[a, b]$, and $y$ is a number between $f(a)$ and $f(b)$, then there is a number $x = c$ in $(a, b)$ for which $f(c) = y$.

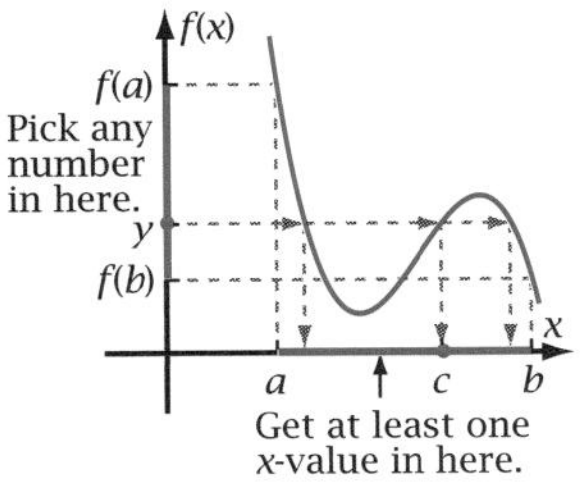


Figure 2-6b

Figure 2-6b illustrates the meaning of the theorem. Pick $y$ between $f(a)$ and $f(b)$. If $f$ is continuous, you can go over to the graph, then go down to the $x$-axis and find $c$, a corresponding value of $x$. The value of $f(c)$ will thus equal $y$ exactly. The proof of this theorem relies on the **completeness axiom**. This axiom, which comes in several forms, says that there is a real number corresponding to every point on the number line, and vice versa. Thus, the set of real numbers is "complete." It has no "holes," as does the set of rational numbers.

A formal proof of the intermediate value theorem usually appears in later courses on analysis of real numbers. The gist of the proof is that for any $y$-value you pick in the interval, there will be a point on the graph because the graph is continuous. Going vertically to the $x$-axis gives a point on the number line. This point corresponds to a real number $x = c$, because the set of real numbers is complete. Reversing the steps shows that $f(c)$ really does equal $y$.

***OBJECTIVE***

Given an equation for a continuous function $f$ and a value of $y$ between $f(a)$ and $f(b)$, find a value of $x = c$ between $a$ and $b$ for which $f(c) = y$.

In addition, you will be exposed to a corollary of the intermediate value theorem, called the **image theorem**, which relies for its proof on the **extreme value theorem**.

■ ***Example 1*** If $f(x) = x^3 - 4x^2 + 2x + 7$, find, approximately, a value of $x = c$ between 1 and 3 for which $f(c) = 5$. Prove that there is a value of $c$ for which $f(c)$ is exactly 5.

**Solution**

First plot the graph (Figure 2-6c). Use a friendly window. A line at $y = 5$ intersects the graph at three points. The one between 1 and 3 is approximately 1.3.

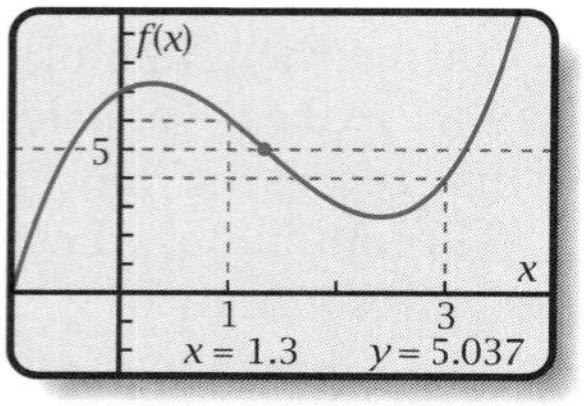


Figure 2-6c

To show that $f(c)$ can be exactly 5, first observe that $f$ is a polynomial function. Thus, $f$ is continuous. (See Problem 69 in Problem Set 2-4.) Therefore, one hypothesis of the intermediate value theorem is true for $x$ in [1, 3].

By tracing or by direct substitution, $f(1) = 6$ and $f(3) = 4$.

The number 5 is between 4 and 6, so the other hypothesis of the intermediate value theorem is true in the interval [1, 3].

$\therefore$ there is a number $x = c$ between 1 and 3 for which $f(c) = 5$ exactly, Q.E.D. ■

If desired, you can find a better approximation of $c$ by zooming in on your grapher or by using the solve feature of your calculator. The answer is $c = 1.31110781\ldots$.

## Problem Set 2-6

### *Do These Quickly*

The following problems are intended to refresh your skills. You should be able to do all ten problems in less than five minutes.

**Q1.** Evaluate $f(2)$ if $f(x) = 3x^4 + 5$.

**Q2.** Find $\lim_{x \to 2} f(x)$ if $f(x) = 3x^4 + 5$.

**Q3.** Evaluate $h(3)$ if $h(x) = 5(x - 3)/(x - 3)$.

**Q4.** Find $\lim_{x \to 3} h(x)$ if $h(x) = 5(x - 3)/(x - 3)$.

**Q5.** Evaluate $s(0)$ if $s(x) = |x|/x$.

**Q6.** Find $\lim_{x \to 0} s(x)$ if $s(x) = |x|/x$.

**Q7.** Evaluate: $\sin(\pi/2)$

**Q8.** Evaluate: $|13 - 7|$

**Q9.** Fill in the blank with the correct operation: $\log(xy) = \log x$ -?- $\log y$.

**Q10.** Solve: $-3x < 12$

For Problems 1 and 2, find, approximately, a value of $x = c$ in the given interval for which $f(c)$ equals the given $y$-value. Tell why each function is continuous , then prove that there is a value of $x = c$ for which $f(c)$ is exactly equal to the given $y$-value. Illustrate by graph.

1. $f(x) = (x - 3)^4 + 2,\ [1, 4],\ y = 8$

2. $f(x) = 0.001x^5 - 8,\ [0, 6],\ y = -1$

3. *Converse of the Intermediate Value Theorem?* The intermediate value theorem is not an "if and only if" theorem. The conclusion can be true even if the hypotheses are not met.

   a. The left figure of Figure 2-6d shows

$$f(x) = 2 + x + \frac{|x - 2|}{x - 2}.$$

   Explain why the conclusion of the intermediate value theorem could be true or false for the interval [1, 5], depending on the value of $y$ you pick in [2, 8].

b. The right figure of Figure 2-6d shows the graph of

$$g(x) = 2 + x - \frac{|x-2|}{x-2}.$$

Explain why the conclusion of the intermediate value theorem is always true for the interval [1, 5], no matter what value of $y$ you pick between $g(1)$ and $g(5)$, even though the function is discontinuous at $x = 2$.

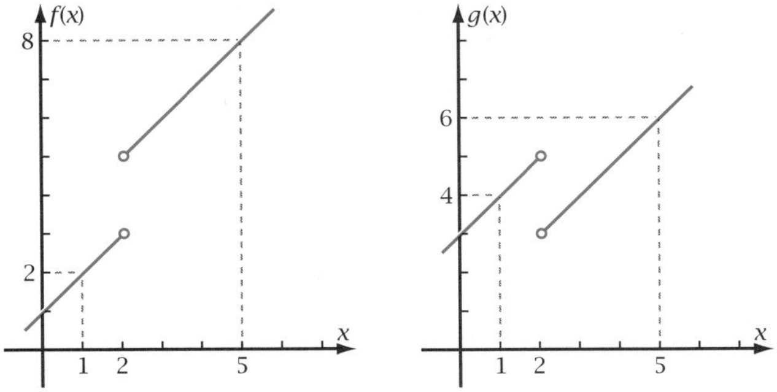


Figure 2-6d

4. Figure 2-6e shows the graph of the following.

$$f(x) = \begin{cases} 2^x, & \text{if } x \text{ is rational} \\ 8, & \text{if } x \text{ is irrational} \end{cases}$$

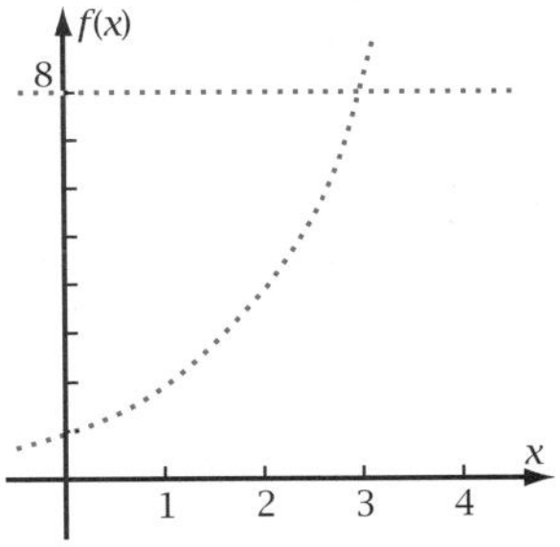


Figure 2-6e

a. Find $f(2)$, $f(3)$, $f(0.5)$, and $f(\sqrt{5})$.

b. Is $f$ continuous at $x = 3$? Explain.

c. Where else is $f$ continuous? Surprising?!

d. Because $f(0) = 1$ and $f(2) = 4$, is the conclusion of the intermediate value theorem true for all values of $y$ between 1 and 4? Explain.

5. Use the intermediate value theorem to prove that there is a real number equal to $\sqrt{3}$. That is, prove that there is a number $c$ such that $c^2 = 3$.

6. Use the intermediate value theorem to prove that if $f$ is continuous, and if $f(a)$ is positive and $f(b)$ is negative, then there is at least one zero of $f(x)$ between $x = a$ and $x = b$. (Recall that a zero of a function is a value of $x$ that makes $f(x) = 0$.)

7. The intermediate value theorem is an example of an **existence theorem**. Why do you suppose this term is used? What does an existence theorem *not* tell you how to do?

8. *Sweetheart Problem:* You wish to visit your sweetheart, but you don't want to go all the way over to his or her house if your sweetheart isn't home. What sort of "existence proof" could you do beforehand to tell whether or not it is worthwhile to make the trip? What sort of information will your proof *not* give you about making the trip? Why do you suppose mathematicians are so interested in doing existence proofs before they spend a lot of time searching for solutions?

9. *Foot Race Problem:* Jesse and Kay run the 1000-m race. One minute after the race begins, Jesse is running 20 km/hr and Kay is running 15 km/hr. Three minutes after the race begins, Jesse has slowed to 17 km/hr and Kay has speeded up to 19 km/hr. Assume that each runner's speed is a continuous function of time. Prove that there is a time between 1 min and 3 min after the race began at which each one is running exactly the same speed. Is it possible to tell what that speed is? Is it possible to tell when that speed occurred? Explain.

10. *Postage Stamp Problem:* United States postage rates in 1996 for first-class letters was 32¢ for the first ounce and 23¢ per ounce thereafter. Figure 2-6f, the classical example of a **step function**, shows the cost of mailing a first-class letter versus the number of ounces it weighs. Does the function meet the hypotheses of the intermediate value theorem? Is there a weight of letter that can be mailed for exactly \$1.00? Justify your answers.

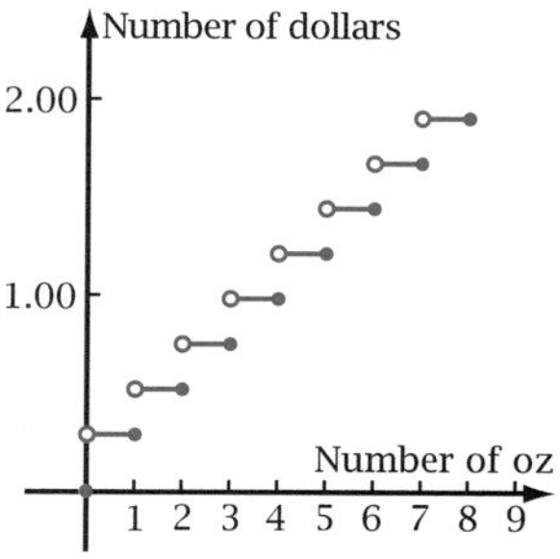


Figure 2-6f

11. *Cosine Function Problem:* Figure 2-6g shows $f(x) = \cos x$. From trigonometry you recall that $\cos 0 = 1$ and $\cos \pi = -1$. As shown in the figure, 0.6 is between $-1$ and 1. Can you use the intermediate value theorem to show that there really is a value of $x = c$ between 0 and $\pi$ for which $\cos c = 0.6$? If so, tell how you know and calculate it as accurately as possible. If not, tell why not.

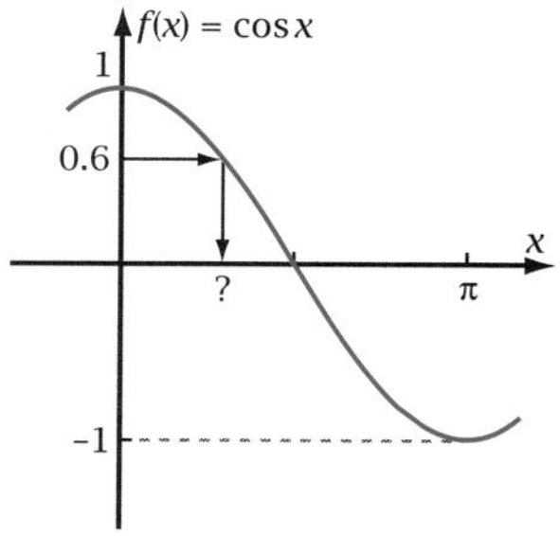


Figure 2-6g

12. *Exponential Function Problem:* Figure 2-6h shows $f(x) = 2^x$. Why does $f(0) = 1$? Because $f(2) = 4$ and 3 is between 1 and 4, does it necessarily follow that there is a value of $x = c$ between 0 and 2 for which $2^c = 3$? If so, tell how you know and find as accurate a value of $c$ as possible. If not, tell why not.

13. *The Extreme Value Theorem:* The **extreme value theorem** expresses the property that if $f$ is continuous on the closed interval $[a, b]$, then there are numbers $c_1$ and $c_2$ in $[a, b]$ for which $f(c_1)$ and $f(c_2)$ are the maximum and minimum values of $f(x)$ for that interval. Think about what this means, then draw a graph showing what you have thought. Draw a graph showing why the conclusion might not be true for a function that has a discontinuity somewhere in $[a, b]$.

14. *The Image Theorem:* The **image theorem** is a corollary of the intermediate value theorem, expressing the property that if $f$ is continuous on $[a, b]$, then the image (the set of $y$-values) is all real numbers between the minimum of $f(x)$ and the maximum of $f(x)$, inclusive. Use the extreme value theorem as a lemma (a preliminary result) to prove the image theorem.

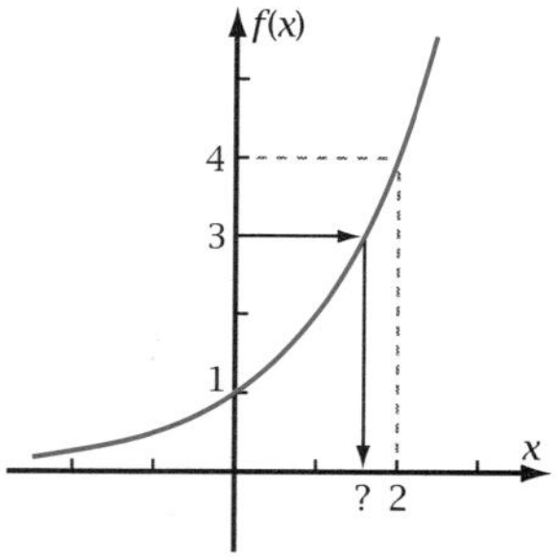


Figure 2-6h

# 2-7 Chapter Review and Test

In this chapter you have gained further insight into the meaning of limit. You have broadened the idea of limit to include right- and left-hand limits and infinite limits, and you have applied these ideas to make precise the concept of a continuous function. By now you should realize that a limit is a number $f(x)$ stays close to when $x$ is kept close enough, but not equal, to $c$. You should be able both to find a limit of a function given by graph or by equation and to show that $f(x)$ really does stay within $\epsilon$ units of the limit when $x$ is within $\delta$ units of $c(x \neq c)$. You should be able to use the limit properties to prove that the number you've found is the limit. If you think of "lim" as an operation that acts on functions, many of these properties can be thought of as distributive properties. The following box summarizes the properties.

**Limit Property Summary**

Limit distributes over addition, subtraction, multiplication, and division (denominator $\neq 0$) with any finite number of terms or factors.

Finally, you learned another major theorem of calculus, the intermediate value theorem, which expresses a property of continuous functions.

The Review Problems below are numbered according to the sections of this chapter. The Concepts Problems allow you to apply your knowledge to new situations. The Chapter Test is more like a normal classroom test your instructor might give you.

## Review Problems

R0. You have learned that calculus involves four concepts. Your goal for the course is to be able to do four things with each of these concepts.

| | Define it. | Understand it. | Do it. | Apply it. |
|---|---|---|---|---|
| Limit | | | | |
| Derivative | | | | |
| Integral | | | | |
| Integral | | | | |

Make a table like that shown and put it into your journal. Check each box you have worked on as you have studied this chapter. Make journal entries for such things as those listed below.

- The one most important thing you have learned in studying Chapter 2
- A statement telling what you now understand a limit to be
- How limits apply to derivatives and definite integrals
- Your understanding of continuity and the intermediate value theorem
- Anything you need to ask about in class before your test on Chapter 2

R1. a. Write the definition of limit.

b. Plot the graph of $f(x) = (x - 2)^{1/5} + 3$. Show that $f(2) = 3$. Make a table of values of $f(x)$ for each 0.0001 unit of $x$ from 1.9995 through 2.0005. Based on the table, find out how close to 2 you must keep $x$ in order for $f(x)$ to be within 0.2 unit of 3.

c. Plot and sketch the graph of $g(x) = (x - 2)^{2/5} + 3$. Tell what feature this graph has that the graph of $f$ in R1b doesn't have. Is there a limit as $x$ approaches 2?

R2. a. For $f(x) = (x - 2)^{1/5} + 3$ from Problem R1, calculate the maximum value that $\delta$ can be so that $f(x)$ is within 0.2 unit of 3 when $x$ is within $\delta$ units of 2. Sketch on a graph.

b. Show that there is a positive number $\delta$ for any positive value of $\epsilon$, no matter how small, such that $f(x)$ is within $\epsilon$ units of 3 whenever $x$ is within $\delta$ units of 2.

c. For the function in Figure 2-7a, write the limit of $f(x)$ as $x$ approaches 2. Estimate from the graph the largest possible value of $\delta$ that can be used to keep $f(x)$ within 0.4 unit of the limit when $x$ is within $\delta$ units of 2.

d. In R2c, $f(x) = 2 + \sqrt{x - 1}$. Calculate the maximum value of $\delta$ that you estimated in R2c.

e. For the function in R2d, show that there is a positive value of $\delta$ for any $\epsilon > 0$ for which $f(x)$ will be within $\epsilon$ units of the limit when $x$ is within $\delta$ units of 2.

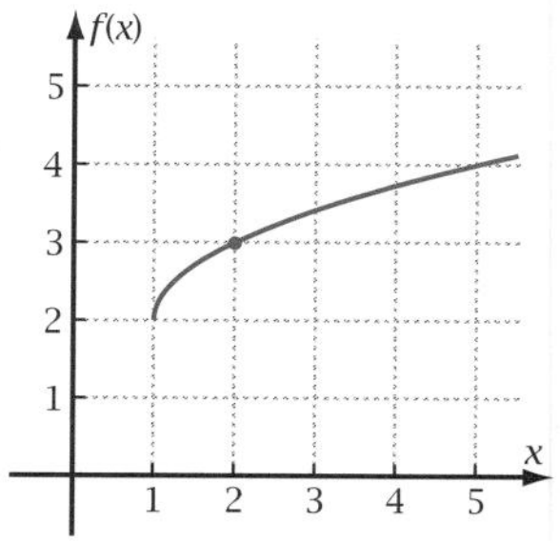


Figure 2-7a

R3. a. State the following limit properties.

i. Limit of a sum of two functions
ii. Limit of a constant times a function
iii. Limit of a quotient of two functions

b. For $g(x) = \dfrac{x^3 - 13x^2 + 32x - 6}{x - 3}$, plot the graph, using a friendly window that includes $x = 3$, then sketch. Use algebra and the appropriate limit properties to find $\lim_{x\to 3} g(x)$. Show that it agrees with your graph.

c. What part of the definition of limit allows you to cancel the $(x - 3)$ factor in the denominator in R3b without having to worry about dividing by zero?

d. Let $m(x) = \dfrac{(x + 3)(x - 2)}{x - 4}$. Find $\lim_{x\to 6} m(x)$. Prove that you are right by citing the appropriate limit properties. Explain why you cannot use the limit of a quotient property for $\lim_{x\to 4} m(x)$.

e. *Chuck's Rock Problem:* Chuck throws a rock high into the air. Its distance, $d(t)$ meters, above the ground is given by $d(t) = 35t - 5t^2$, where $t$ is the number of seconds since he threw it. Find the average velocity of the rock from time 5 sec to 5.1 sec. Write an equation for the average velocity from 5 sec to $t$ sec. By taking the limit of the expression in this equation, find the instantaneous velocity of the rock at $t = 5$. Was the rock going up or down at $t = 5$? How do you tell? What mathematical quantity is this instantaneous velocity?

R4. a. Write the definition of continuity at a point.

b. Sketch graphs of the functions described.

i. Has a removable discontinuity at $x = 1$.
ii. Has a step discontinuity at $x = 2$.
iii. Has a vertical asymptote at $x = 3$.
iv. Has a cusp at $x = 4$.
v. Is continuous at $x = 5$.
vi. Has a limit as $x \to 6$, a value of $f(6)$, but is discontinuous at $x = 6$.
vii. Has left-hand limit of $-2$ and right-hand limit of 5 as $x$ approaches 1.

c. Let $f(x) = \begin{cases} x^2, & \text{if } x \le 2 \\ x^2 - 6x + k, & \text{if } x > 2. \end{cases}$

i. Sketch the graph of $f$ if $k = 10$.
ii. Show that $f$ is discontinuous at $x = 2$ if $k = 10$.
iii. Find the value of $k$ that makes $f$ continuous at $x = 2$.

R5. a. Write the definition: $\lim_{x\to\infty} f(x)$ is infinite.

b. Sketch a single graph for which $\lim_{x\to 2^-} f(x) = \infty$, $\lim_{x\to 2^+} f(x) = -\infty$, and $\lim_{x\to\infty} f(x) = 3$ .

c. Let $f(x) = 6 - 2^{-x}$. Find the limit of $f(x)$ as $x$ approaches infinity. Sketch a graph showing that $f(x)$ can be kept within 0.1 unit of this limit by keeping $x$ large enough. What values of $x$ will ensure that $f(x)$ is within 0.001 unit of the limit?

d. The distance you travel at a variable velocity, $v(t)$, is the definite integral of $v(t)$ with respect to $t$. Suppose that your car's velocity is given by $v(t) = 40 + 6\sqrt{t}$, where $t$ is in seconds and $v(t)$ is in feet per second. Use the trapezoidal rule with varying numbers, $n$, of increments to estimate the distance traveled from $t = 0$ to $t = 9$. What limit do these sums seem to be approaching as $n$ approaches infinity? Find a number $D$ for which the trapezoidal sum is within 0.01 unit of this limit when $n > D$.

R6. a. State the intermediate value theorem. What axiom forms the basis for the proof of the intermediate value theorem? State the extreme value theorem. What word tells how the extreme value theorem is related to the intermediate value theorem?

b. For $f(x) = -x^3 + 5x^2 - 10x + 20$, find $f(3)$ and $f(4)$. Based on these two numbers, how can you tell immediately that there is a zero of $f(x)$ between $x = 3$ and $x = 4$? What property of polynomial functions allows you to make this conclusion? Find as accurate a value of this zero as possible.

c. Plot the function $f(x) = \dfrac{x^2 + 11x + 28}{x + 4}$. Use a friendly window that includes $x = -4$. Show that $f(-6) = 1$ and $f(-2) = 5$. Based on the intermediate value theorem, if you pick a number $y$ between 1 and 5, will you always get a value of $x = c$ between $-6$ and $-2$ for which $f(c) = y$? If so, tell why. If not, give a counterexample.

## Concepts Problems

C1. *Squeeze Theorem Introduction Problem:* Suppose that $g(x)$ and $h(x)$ both approach 7 as $x$ approaches 4, but that $g(x) < h(x)$ for all other values of $x$. Suppose another function, $f$, has a graph that is bounded above by the graph of $h$, and bounded below by the graph of $g$. That is, $g(x) \le f(x) \le h(x)$ for all values of $x$. Sketch possible graphs of the three functions on the same set of axes. Make a conjecture about the limit of $f(x)$ as $x \to 4$.

C2. *Derivatives and Continuity Problem:* Figure 2-7b shows the graph of

$$f(x) = \begin{cases} x^2 + 3, & \text{if } x < 1 \\ x^2 - 6x + 9, & \text{if } x \ge 1. \end{cases}$$

Find the value of $f(1)$. Is $f$ continuous at $x = 1$? Find the limit of $\dfrac{f(x) - f(1)}{x - 1}$ as $x \to 1^-$

and as $x \to 1^+$. Based on your work, explain how a function can be continuous at a point but not have a derivative there.

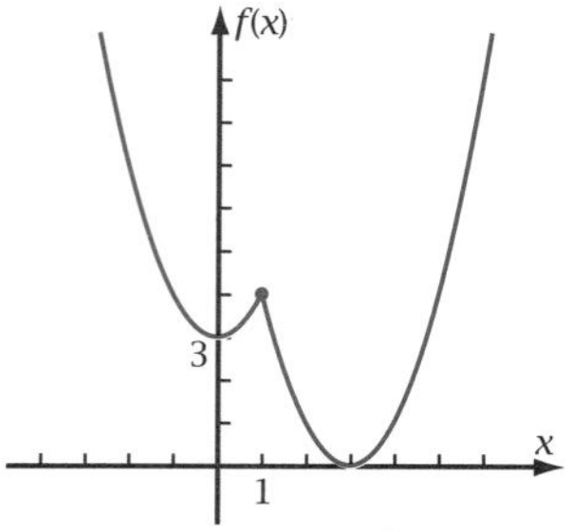


Figure 2-7b

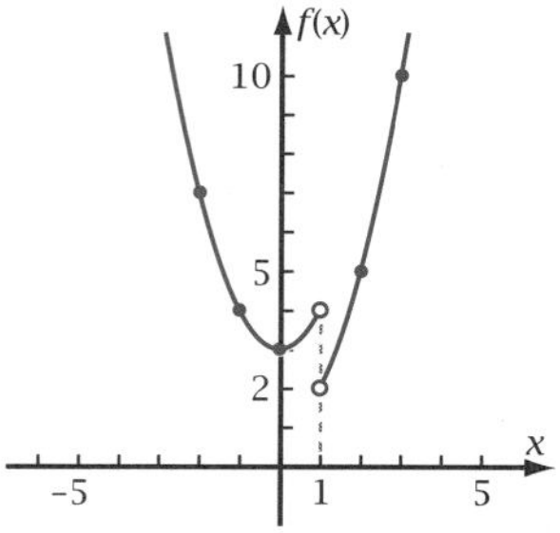


Figure 2-7c

C3. *Equation from Graph Problem:* Figure 2-7c is the graph of a discontinuous function. Write a single equation whose graph could be that shown in the figure.

C4. *Absolute Value Definition of Limit:* Later in your mathematical career, you may encounter the definition of limit written in the form shown in the box.

> **Algebraic (Absolute Value) Definition of Limit**
>
> $L = \lim_{x \to c} f(x)$ if and only if, for any $\epsilon > 0$, there is a $\delta > 0$ such that if $0 < |x - c| < \delta$, then $|f(x) - L| < \epsilon$.

Explain how this algebraic definition of limit is equivalent to the "within" definition you have learned.

## Chapter Test

T1. State the Limit of a Quotient Property.

For the functions graphed in Problems T2–T5, tell the following for $x = c$.

a. Left- and right-hand limits if they exist

b. The limit if it exists

c. Whether or not the function is continuous

T2.

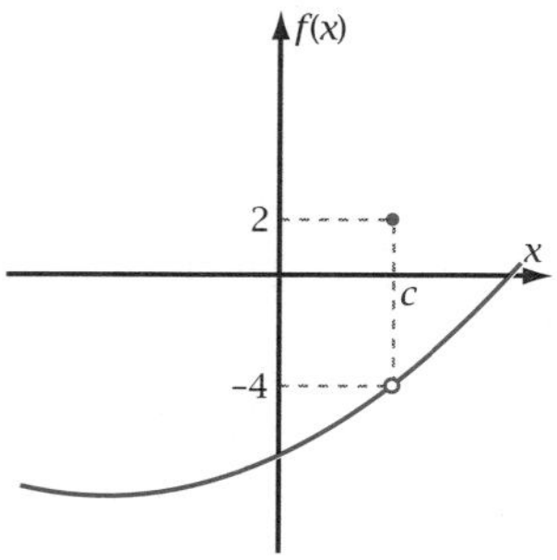


T3.

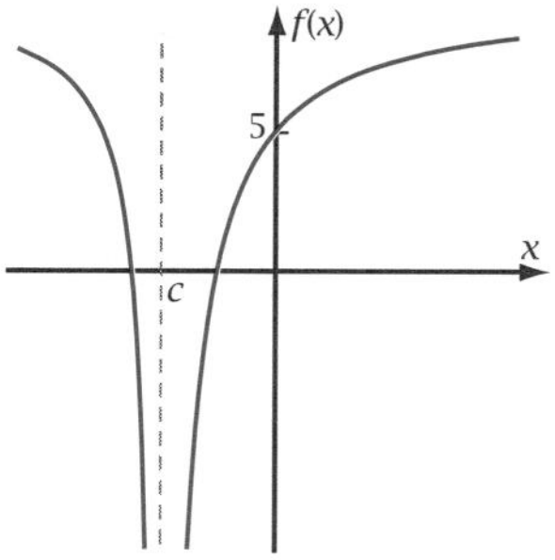

T4.

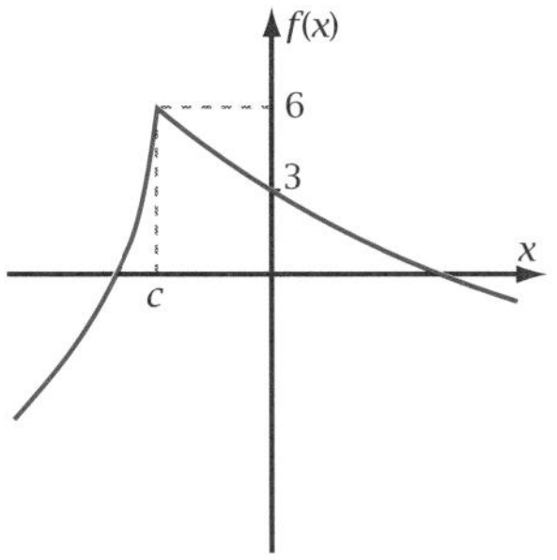


T5.

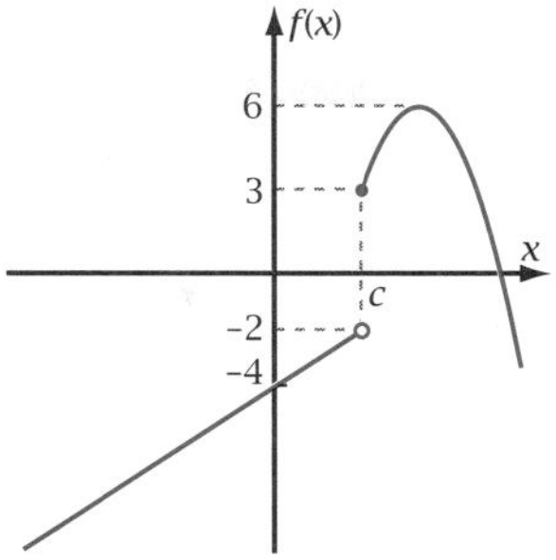


T6. Sketch graphs showing that you understand the difference in behavior of the following functions at $x = 0$.

a. $f(x) = \dfrac{1}{x^2}$  b. $g(x) = \dfrac{x}{x}$  c. $h(x) = \dfrac{|x|}{x}$  d. $s(x) = \sin \dfrac{1}{x}$

T7. Let $g(x) = \dfrac{4x^2 + 17x + 15}{x + 3}$.

a. Plot the graph, using a friendly window for which $x = -3$ is a grid point. Sketch.

b. Find the limit of $g(x)$ as $x$ approaches $-3$. Show the limit on your graph.

c. Make a table of values of $g(x)$ for each 0.01 unit of $x$ from $x = -3.05$ to $x = -2.95$.

d. Based on your table, for which values of $x$ is $g(x)$ within 0.1 unit of the limit?

e. What is the maximum value of $\delta$ that could be used to insure that $g(x)$ is within 0.1 unit of the limit whenever $x$ is within $\delta$ units of $-3$?

f. Show how to calculate $\delta$ for any $\epsilon > 0$, no matter how small, for which keeping $x$ within $\delta$ units of $-3$ will make $g(x)$ stay within $\epsilon$ units of the limit.

T8. Let $h(x) = x^3 - 10x^2 + 3x + 31$.

a. Prove that $h(2)$ is the limit of $h(x)$ as $x \to 2$ by citing the appropriate limit properties.

b. Based on the definition of continuity, explain why $h$ is continuous at $x = 2$.

c. Show that $h(3)$ has the opposite sign from $h(2)$. Use the result to explain why $h(x)$ has at least one zero between $x = 2$ and $x = 3$. Find this zero as accurately as possible.

T9. *Glacier Problem:* To determine how far a glacier has traveled in a given amount of time, naturalists drive a metal stake into the surface of the glacier. From a point not on the glacier, they measure the distance, $d(t)$ centimeters, the stake has moved in $t$ days from its original position. Every ten days they record this distance, getting the values shown in the table.

| $t$ days | $d(t)$ cm |
|---|---|
| 0 | 0 |
| 10 | 6 |
| 20 | 14 |
| 30 | 24 |
| 40 | 36 |
| 50 | 50 |

a. Show that the equation $d(t) = 0.01t^2 + 0.5t$ fits all the data points in the table. Use the most time-efficient way you can think of to do this problem.

b. Use the equation to find the average rate the glacier is moving for 20 days to 20.1 days.

c. Write an equation for the average rate from 20 days to $t$ days. Do the appropriate algebra, then find the limit of the average rate as $t$ approaches 20. What is the instantaneous rate the glacier is moving at $t = 20$? What mathematical name is given to this rate?

d. Based on the table, does the glacier seem to be speeding up or slowing down as time goes on? How do you reach this conclusion?

T10. *Calvin and Phoebe's Acceleration Problem:* Calvin and Phoebe are running side by side along the jogging trail. At time $t = 0$, each one starts speeding up. Their velocities are given by the following, where $p(t)$ and $c(t)$ are in feet per second and $t$ is in seconds.

$c(t) = 16 - 6(2^{-t})$ For Calvin.

$p(t) = 10 + \sqrt{t}$ For Phoebe.

Show that each is going the same speed when $t = 0$. What are the limits of their speeds as $t$ approaches infinity? Surprising?!

T11. Let $f(x) = \begin{cases} kx^2, & \text{if } x \le 2 \\ 10 - kx, & \text{if } x > 2. \end{cases}$ What value of $k$ makes $f$ continuous at $x = 2$? What feature will the graph of $f$ have at this point?

T12. Let $h(x) = x^3$. Show that the number 7 is between $h(1)$ and $h(2)$. Since $h$ is continuous on $[1, 2]$ what theorem allows you to conclude that there is a real number $\sqrt[3]{7}$ between 1 and 2?

CHAPTER

# 3 Derivatives, Antiderivatives, and Indefinite Integrals

During the free fall part of a skydiver's descent, her downward acceleration is influenced by gravity and by air resistance. The velocity increases at first, then approaches a limit called the terminal velocity. At any instant in time the acceleration is the derivative of the velocity. The distance she has fallen is the antiderivative or indefinite integral of the velocity. Velocity, acceleration, and displacement all vary, and depend on time.

# Mathematical Overview

In Chapter 3 you will apply the concept of *limit* to find formulas with which you can calculate exact values of derivatives. Then you will go backward to find the function equation if the derivative equation is given. The antiderivative you get will give you a clue as to why there are *two* concepts of calculus, both with the name "integral." You will work with these concepts four ways.

***Graphically*** The logo on each even-numbered page of this chapter shows the run, $\Delta x$, and the rise, $\Delta y$, from one point on a graph to another. The limit of $\Delta y/\Delta x$ is the instantaneous rate, or derivative of $f(x)$.

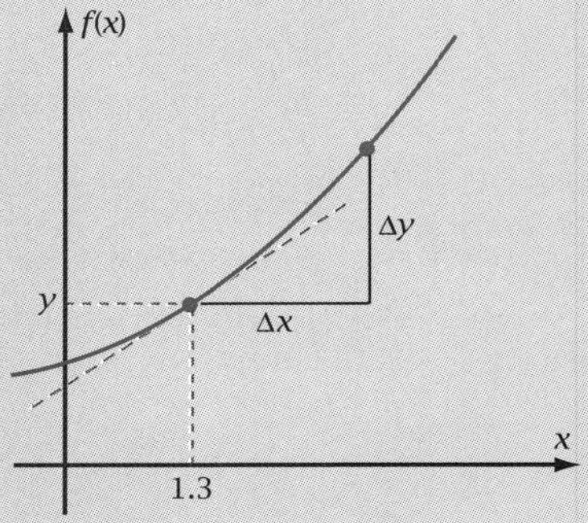


***Numerically***

| $\Delta x$ | $\Delta y/\Delta x$ |
|---|---|
| 0.1 | 0.705 |
| 0.01 | 0.6915 |
| 0.001 | 0.69015 |
| 0.0001 | 0.690015 |
| ... | ... |

***Algebraically*** $f'(1.3) = \lim_{x \to 1.3} \dfrac{f(x) - f(1.3)}{x - 1.3}$, the definition of derivative.

***Verbally*** *I had learned about limits, derivatives, and definite integrals already. But it wasn't until I learned how to find an algebraic equation for a derivative that I could understand the meaning of* indefinite integral, *which is a name for* antiderivative.

# 3-1 Graphical Interpretation of Derivative

You have learned the physical meaning of derivative: an instantaneous rate of change. In this section you will be exposed to a graphical meaning of derivative.

**OBJECTIVE**

Given the equation of a function, find the value of the derivative at a given point, and learn the meaning of the derivative as it relates to the graph of the function.

The problems in this section will allow you to accomplish this objective as an assignment after your test on Chapter 2, either on your own or with your study group.

## Exploratory Problem Set 3-1

*Spaceship Problem:* A spaceship approaches a far-off planet. At time $x$ minutes after its retrorockets fire, its distance, $f(x)$ kilometers, from the surface of the planet is given by

$$f(x) = x^2 - 8x + 18.$$

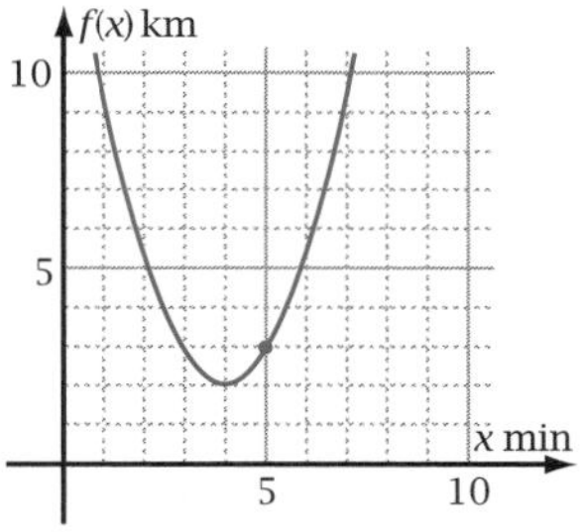

Figure 3-1a

1. Figure 3-1a shows the graph of $f$. Confirm by grapher that this graph is correct.
2. Find the average rate of change of $f(x)$ with respect to $x$ from $x = 5$ to 5.1. What are the units of this rate of change?
3. The average rate of change, $m(x)$, of $f(x)$ from 5 to $x$ is

   $$m(x) = \frac{f(x) - f(5)}{x - 5}.$$

   By appropriate substitution, express $m(x)$ in terms of $x$.
4. Find the limit of $m(x)$ in Problem 3 as $x$ approaches 5. This number is the *derivative* of $f$ at $x = 5$. What physical quantity does this number represent? What are its units?
5. What form does $m(5)$ take if you substitute 5 for $x$ without having canceled? What word describes this form? Why is $m(5)$ undefined?
6. Photocopy the graph or plot it accurately on graph paper. On your graph, plot a line with slope equal to the derivative you calculated in Problem 4, passing through the point on the graph of $f$ where $x = 5$.
7. What words can you use to describe the relationship between the line in Problem 6 and the graph of function $f$?
8. Plot the graph of $f$ and the line in Problem 6. Use a friendly window for which $x = 5$ is a grid point, then zoom in repeatedly on the point (5, 3). Describe the relationship between the line and the graph of $f$ as you zoom in.
9. Record in your journal what you learned as a result of doing this problem set.

# 3-2 Difference Quotients and One Definition of Derivative

You have been finding derivatives by taking a change in $x$, dividing it into the corresponding change in $y$, and taking the limit of the resulting fraction as the change in $x$ approaches zero. Figure 3-2a illustrates what you have been doing. The change in the $y$-value is equal to $f(x) - f(c)$. The change in the $x$-value is $x - c$. Thus, the derivative is approximately equal to

$$\frac{f(x) - f(c)}{x - c}.$$

This fraction is called a **difference quotient**.

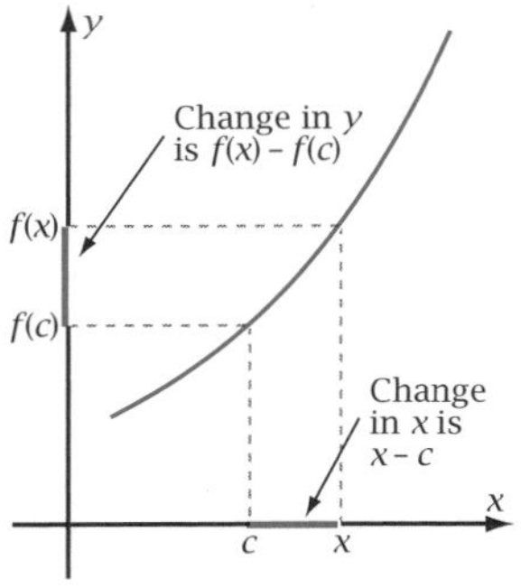

Figure 3-2a

The derivative is the function you get by taking the limit of the difference quotient as the denominator approaches zero. If the function's name is $f$, then the symbol $f'$ (pronounced "$f$ prime") is often used for the derivative function. The symbol shows that there is a relationship, yet a difference, between the original function and the function "derived" from it (hence the name *derivative*), which indicates its rate of change. One way to write the definition of derivative is shown in the box. An alternative way to state the definition is shown in Section 3-4.

> ***Definition of Derivative (derivative at x = c form)***
>
> $$f'(c) = \lim_{x \to c} \frac{f(x) - f(c)}{x - c}$$
>
> *Meaning:* The instantaneous rate of change of $f(x)$ with respect to $x$ at $x = c$.

***OBJECTIVE***

Given the equation of a function and a value of $x$, use the definition of derivative to calculate the value of the derivative at that point, and confirm your answer numerically and graphically.

Example 1 shows how the definition of derivative can be used to accomplish this objective.

■ ***Example 1*** If $f(x) = x^2 - 3x - 4$, find $f'(5)$, the value of the derivative if $x = 5$. Check by graphing the difference quotient and finding the limit.

***Solution***

$$f(5) = 5^2 - 3(5) - 4 = 6$$

$$\therefore f'(5) = \lim_{x \to 5} \frac{f(x) - f(5)}{x - 5} = \lim_{x \to 5} \frac{(x^2 - 3x - 4) - 6}{x - 5} = \lim_{x \to 5} \frac{x^2 - 3x - 10}{x - 5}$$

$$= \lim_{x \to 5} \frac{(x - 5)(x + 2)}{x - 5} = \lim_{x \to 5}(x + 2)$$ Why can you cancel without dividing by zero?

$$= 5 + 2 = 7$$ Use the limit of a sum and the limit of $x$ properties from Chapter 2.

As a check, plot $y = \dfrac{f(x) - f(5)}{x - 5} = \dfrac{x^2 - 3x - 10}{x - 5}$, the difference quotient (Figure 3-2b).

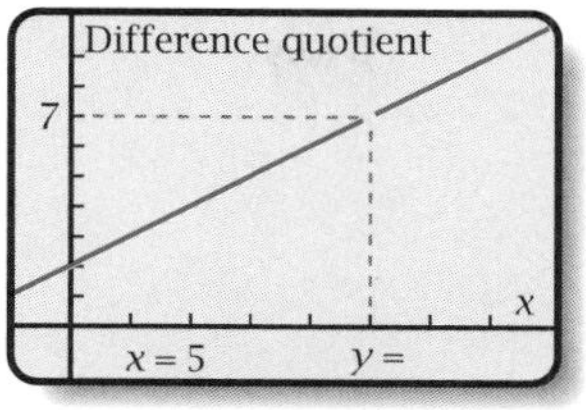


Figure 3-2b

| $x$ | quotient |
|---|---|
| 4.97 | 6.97 |
| 4.98 | 6.98 |
| 4.99 | 6.99 |
| 5.00 | (none) |
| 5.01 | 7.01 |
| 5.02 | 7.02 |
| 5.03 | 7.03 |

Use a friendly window for which $x = 5$ is a grid point. There is a removable discontinuity at $x = 5$.

Using the trace or table feature gives the values shown for $x$ on either side of 5. You should be able to see from the pattern that the limit of the quotient is 7 as $x$ approaches 5. ■

Another way to check the answer in Example 1 is to graph the original function, then draw a line with a slope of 7 (the derivative) through the point on the graph at $x = 5$ (that is, (5, 6)). To plot the line on the grapher, find its equation.

$$y = 7x + b \Rightarrow 6 = 7(5) + b \Rightarrow -29 = b$$

$$\therefore y = 7x - 29$$

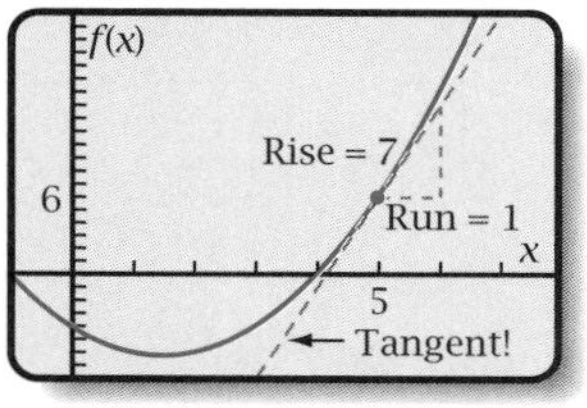


Figure 3-2c

Figure 3-2c shows that the line will be **tangent** to the graph of $f$.

You've already discovered this property from Problem Set 3-1. The fact that the line is tangent to the graph is a geometrical interpretation of the meaning of the derivative.

> ***Geometrical Interpretation of Derivative: Slope of a Tangent Line***
>
> The derivative of a function at a point equals the slope of the tangent line to the graph of the function at that point. Both equal the instantaneous rate of change.

# Problem Set 3-2

### *Do These Quickly*

The following problems are intended to refresh your skills. You should be able to do all ten problems in less than five minutes.

***Q1.*** Quick! What does derivative mean?

***Q2.*** Simplify: $(x^2 - 81)/(x - 9)$

***Q3.*** Find $\lim_{x \to 9} (x^2 - 81)/(x - 9)$.

***Q4.*** Sketch the graph of $y = 2^x$.

***Q5.*** Do the squaring: $(3x - 7)^2$

***Q6.*** Fill in the blank with the appropriate operation: $\log(x/y) = \log x$ -?- $\log y$.

**Q7.** Sketch a graph with a step discontinuity at $x = 3$.

**Q8.** Sketch a graph with a cusp at the point (5, 2).

**Q9.** Sketch: $y = 3x + |x - 2|$

**Q10.** Who invented calculus?

1. Write the definition of derivative.

2. What are the physical and the geometrical meanings of the derivative of a function?

For Problems 3 and 4, do the following.

a. Use the definition of derivative to calculate the value of $f'(c)$ exactly.

b. Plot the difference quotient in a neighborhood of $c$ and sketch the result.

c. Plot the graph of the function in a neighborhood of $c$.

d. Draw a line through $(c, f(c))$ with slope $f'(c)$. Sketch the graph and the line.

3. $f(x) = 0.6x^2,\ c = 3$

4. $f(x) = -0.2x^2,\ c = 6$

For Problems 5–12, use the definition of derivative to calculate $f'(c)$ exactly.

5. $f(x) = x^2 + 5x + 1,\ c = -2$

6. $f(x) = x^2 + 6x - 2,\ c = -4$

7. $f(x) = x^3 - 4x^2 + x + 8,\ c = 1$

8. $f(x) = x^3 - x^2 - 4x + 6,\ c = -1$

9. $f(x) = -0.7x + 2,\ c = 3$

10. $f(x) = 1.3x - 3,\ c = 4$

11. $f(x) = 5,\ c = -1$

12. $f(x) = -2,\ c = 3$

13. From the results of Problems 9 and 10, what can you conclude about the derivative of a linear function? How does this conclusion relate to derivatives and tangent lines?

14. From the results of Problems 11 and 12, what can you conclude about the derivative of a constant function? How does this conclusion relate to derivatives and tangent lines?

15. *Local Linearity Problem:* Figure 3-2d shows the graph of $f(x) = x^2$, along with a line of slope $f'(1)$ passing through the point on the graph of $f$ where $x = 1$.

a. Reproduce this graph on your grapher. Use a friendly window that includes the point (1, 1). Tell how you plotted the tangent line.

b. Zoom in on the point (1, 1). What do you notice about the line and the curve?

c. Zoom in several more times. How do the line and the curve seem to be related now?

d. The graph of $f$ possesses a property called **local linearity** at $x = 1$. Why do you suppose these words are used to describe this property?

e. Explain why you could say that the value of the derivative at a point equals the "slope of the graph" at that point if the graph has local linearity.

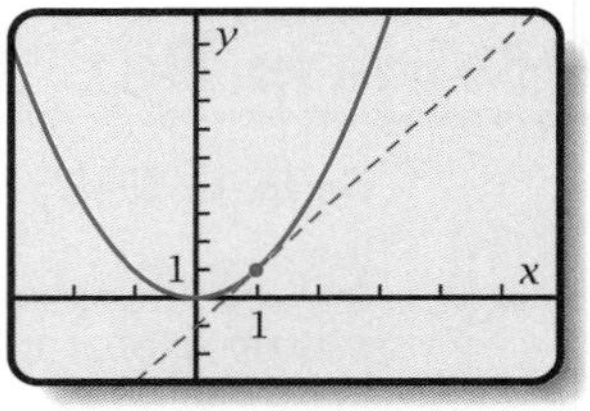


Figure 3-2d

16. *Local Nonlinearity Problem:* Figure 3-2e shows the graph of

$$f(x) = x^2 + 0.1\left(\sqrt[3]{x-1}\right)^2.$$

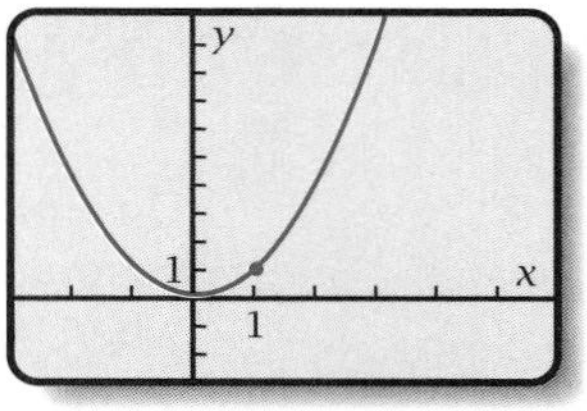

Figure 3-2e

a. Show that the point (1, 1) is on the graph of $f$. Does the graph seem to possess local linearity at that point? (See Problem 15.)

b. Zoom in on the point (1, 1) several times. Sketch what you see.

c. Explain why the graph of $f$ does not have local linearity at $x = 1$.

d. Explain why $f$ does not have a value for the derivative at $x = 1$.

17. Let

$$f(x) = \begin{cases} \dfrac{x^2 - x - 6}{x - 3}, & \text{if } x \neq 3 \\ 7, & \text{if } x = 3 \end{cases}$$

a. Plot the graph on your grapher, using a friendly window for which $x = 3$ is a grid point. Sketch the result, showing clearly what happens at $x = 3$.

b. Write the difference quotient for $f'(3)$ and plot it on the grapher. (See if you can find a time-efficient way to enter the equation!) Sketch the result.

c. Make a short table of values of the difference quotient for values of $x$ close to 3 on both sides of 3. Based on your work, tell why the function has no derivative at $x = 3$.

18. Let $s(x) = 2 + |\sin(x - 1)|$.

a. Plot the graph of $s$. Sketch the result.

b. Plot the difference quotient for $s'(1)$. Sketch the graph.

c. Explain why $s$ does not have a value for the derivative at $x = 1$.

19. *Tangent Lines as Limits of Secant Lines:* Figure 3-2f shows the graph of

$$f(x) = 0.25x^2 - 2.5x + 7.25.$$

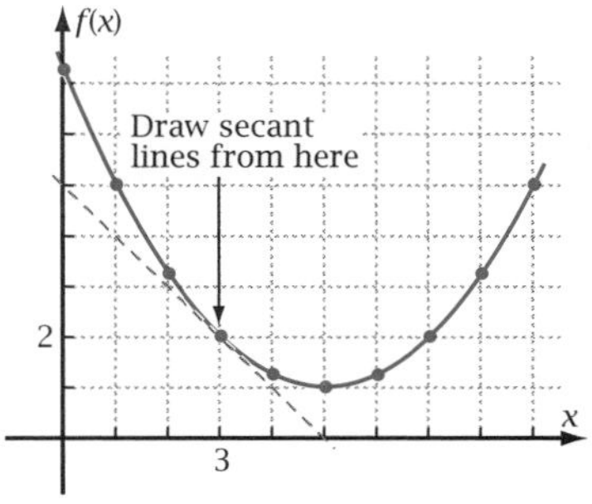

Figure 3-2f

a. Show that the tangent line on the diagram at $x = 3$ has slope equal to $f'(3)$.

b. On a photocopy of Figure 3-2f, draw secant lines starting at the point (3, 2) and going through the points on the graph where $x = 9, 8, 7, 6, 5,$ and 4. Tell what happens to the secant lines as the $x$-distance between those points and the point (3, 2) decreases.

c. Does the same thing happen with the secant lines from the point (3, 2) to the points on the graph where $x = 0, 1,$ and 2?

d. Figure 3-2g shows the graph of

$$g(x) = 4 - 6|\cos \tfrac{\pi}{6}x|.$$

On a photocopy of Figure 3-2g, draw secant lines from the cusp at the point (3, 4) through the points on the graph where $x = 8, 7, 6, 5$, and 4 and where $x = 0, 1$, and 2.

e. The slopes of the lines in 19d approach a different limit as $x$ approaches 3 from the left than they do when $x$ approaches 3 from the right. Explain why $g$ has no derivative at $x = 3$.

f. Make a conjecture about what numbers the two limits in 19e equal.

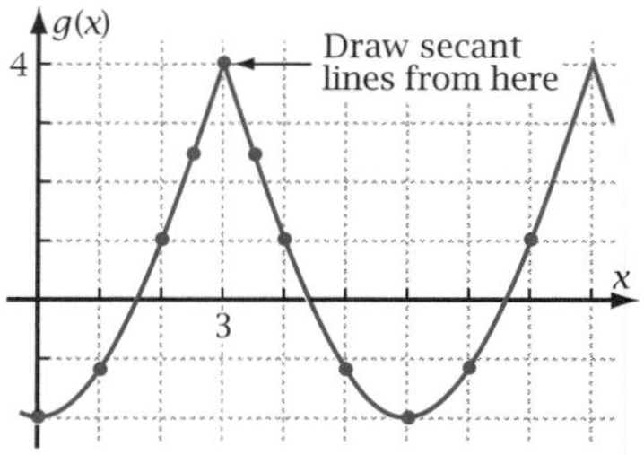


Figure 3-2g

20. Based on your work in Problem 19, explain why the following property is true.

> **Property: Tangent Line as a Limit of Secant Lines**
>
> The tangent to a graph at $(c, f(c))$ is the limit of the secant lines from $(c, f(c))$ to $(x, f(x))$ as $x$ approaches $c$. The slope of the tangent line equals $f'(c)$.

# 3-3 Derivative Functions, Numerically and Graphically

You have been calculating the derivative of a given function at one particular point, $x = c$. Now it is time to turn your attention to finding the derivative for *all* values of $x$. That is, you seek a new function whose values are the derivatives of the given function. In this section you will use the numerical derivative feature of your grapher to do this. In the next sections you will find formulas with which you can simply write down the derivative function for various types of given functions.

**OBJECTIVE**

> Given the equation for a function, graph the function and its (numerical) derivative function on the same set of axes, and make conjectures about the relationship between the derivative function and the original function.

Graphers calculate numerical derivatives by using difference quotients, just as you have been doing. Often they use a **symmetric difference quotient**. As illustrated in the third figure in Figure 3-3a, points on the graph $\pm h$ (meaning "horizontal" distance) units from $x$ are found. The corresponding difference in $y$-values, $\Delta y$ (pronounced "delta $y$," meaning difference between $y$-values), is divided by the difference in $x$-values, $2h$, to get an estimate of the rate of change of the function. You have used a **forward difference quotient** or a **backwards difference quotient**, as shown in the first and second figures of Figure 3-3a. A symmetric difference quotient usually gives a more accurate answer.

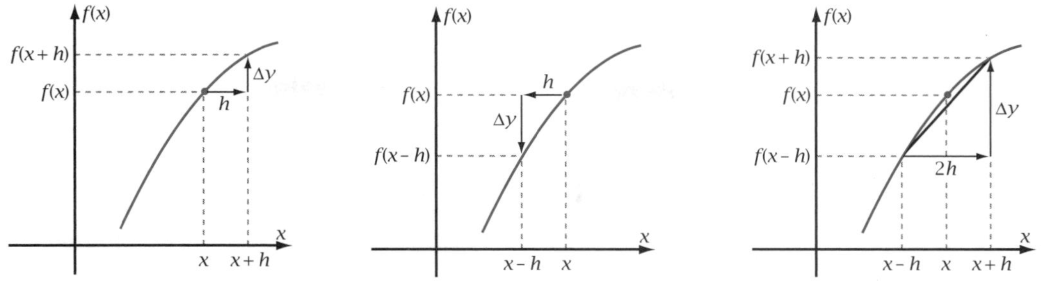


Forward difference quotient $\Delta y/h$ | Backward difference quotient $\Delta y/h$ | Symmetric difference quotient $\Delta y/(2h)$

Figure 3-3a

To see how to calculate forward, backward, and symmetric difference quotients, suppose you want to estimate the derivative of $f(x) = x^3$ at $x = 2$ (abbreviated $f'(2)$ and pronounced "$f$-prime of 2"). The $x$-increment, $h$, is often called the **tolerance.** If a tolerance of 0.01 is specified, for example, the calculations are as shown.

$$\text{Forward: } \frac{f(2.01) - f(2)}{2.01 - 2} = \frac{2.01^3 - 2^3}{0.01} = \frac{8.120601 - 8}{0.01} = 12.0601$$

$$\text{Backward: } \frac{f(1.99) - f(2)}{1.99 - 2} = \frac{1.99^3 - 2^3}{-0.01} = \frac{7.880599 - 8}{-0.01} = 11.9401$$

$$\text{Symmetric: } \frac{f(2.01) - f(1.99)}{2.01 - 1.99} = \frac{2.01^3 - 1.99^3}{0.02} = \frac{8.120601 - 7.880599}{0.02} = 12.0001$$

As you might guess from the answers, the exact value of the derivative is 12. The symmetric difference quotient really does give a more accurate answer.

The numerical derivative instruction on a typical grapher is shown here.

nDeriv($x^3$, $x$, 2)

It says to take the numerical derivative of $x^3$ with respect to $x$, evaluated where $x = 2$. You will need to check your grapher's manual to find out exactly how to write the instruction and how to specify the desired tolerance.

Because there will be a value of the derivative for each value of $x$, there is a *function* whose independent variable is $x$ and whose dependent variable is the value of the derivative. This function is called (obviously!) the **derivative function** and is usually abbreviated $f'(x)$. The grapher plots the (numerical) derivative function by using an instruction such as

$y_2$ = nDeriv($y_1$, $x$, $x$).

The instruction tells the grapher to find the numerical derivative of $y_1$ with respect to $x$ (the first $x$ in the parentheses) and evaluate it at whatever the value of $x$ happens to be (the second $x$ in the parentheses). Example 1 shows what you can learn.

■ ***Example 1*** Find $f(x) = x^3 - 5x^2 - 8x + 70$.

a. Plot the graphs of $f$ and $f'$ (the numerical derivative of $f$) on the same screen.

b. Function $f$ is a *cubic* function. What type of function does $f'$ appear to be?

c. Trace to find values of $f(3)$ and $f'(3)$. Describe how $f'(3)$ relates to the graph of $f$ at $x = 3$.

d. For what values of $x$ does $f'(x) = 0$? What feature does the $f$ graph have at these $x$-values?

e. Plot $g(x) = f(x) + 10$. On the same screen, plot $g'$. How is the graph of $g$ related to the graph of $f$? How is the graph of $g'$ related to the graph of $f'$?

**Solution**

a. Figure 3-3b shows the graphs of $f$ and $f'$ (dotted) on the same screen. Type in instructions such as those shown (depending on your grapher).

$$y_1 = x^3 - 5x^2 - 8x + 70$$
$$y_2 = \text{nDeriv}(y_1, x, x)$$

b. The $f'$ graph looks like a parabola. Conjecture: $f'$ is quadratic.

c. $f(3) = 28$ and the value of $f'(3) = -11$. The negative value of the derivative says that $f(x)$ is decreasing when $x = 3$, which the graph shows.

d. $f'(x) = 0$ for $x = 4$ and for $x \approx -0.7$. The graph of $f$ appears to have a high point or a low point when $f'(x) = 0$.

e. Figure 3-3c shows $y_3 = y_1 + 10$ along with the $f$ and $f'$ graphs. The graphs of $f$ and $g$ are congruent to each other, separated vertically by ten units space. The graphs of $f'$ and $g'$ are identical. This is to be expected because $f$ and $g$ are changing at the same rate. ■

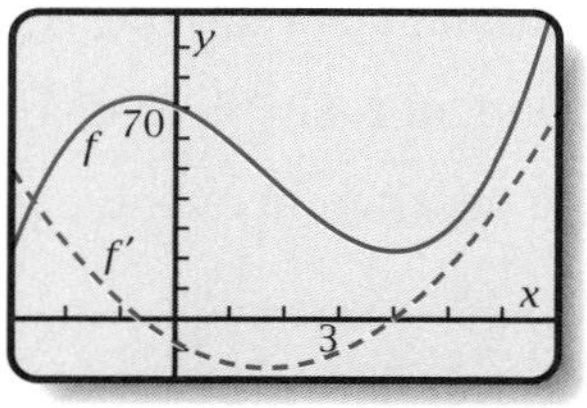

Figure 3-3b

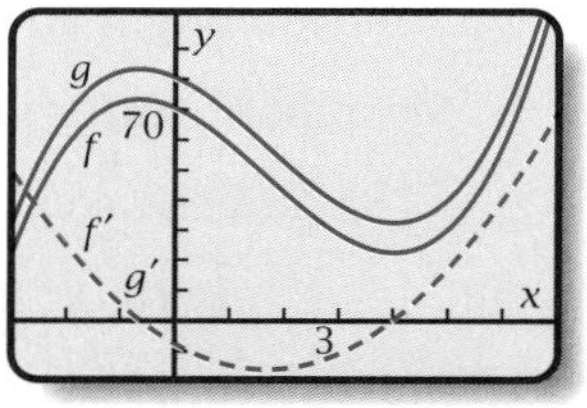

Figure 3-3c

**■ Example 2**

Explore on the grapher the cubic function $f(x) = -x^3 + 3x^2 + 9x + 20$ and its numerical derivative, $f'$. Make some conclusions about how certain features on the graph of $f'$, such as high and low points and $x$-intercepts, are related to features on the original function's graph. Write in your journal the conclusions you reach.

**Solution**

In this problem you have considerable freedom to explore, to conjecture, to discuss, and to write. Problems such as this are best done with your study group so that you may share ideas. Here is a typical (correct!) response to such a problem as it might appear in your journal.

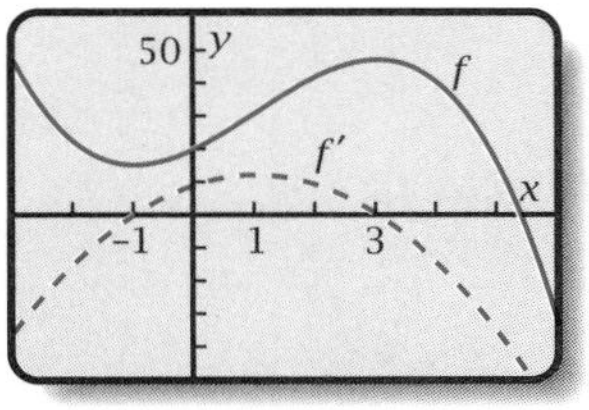

Figure 3-3d

*I plotted the graphs of f and f′ and got something like this (Figure 3-3d). The high and the low points of the cubic graph come where the derivative graph crosses the x-axis. I suppose this is reasonable. Where the derivative graph crosses the x-axis, the derivative is zero, meaning the rate of change of the function graph is zero. This would be true at a high or low point. One of the group members saw that wherever the derivative graph is positive, the function graph is going up. Another one saw that the high point on the derivative graph is at x = 1, where the function graph has its steepest up slope. I still don't understand why the derivative graph is going up at x = -2, for instance, but the function graph is decreasing.* ■

## Problem Set 3-3

### *Do These Quickly*

The following problems are intended to refresh your skills. You should be able to do all ten problems in less than five minutes.

**Q1.** Find $\lim_{x \to 0} 3x/x$.

**Q2.** Sketch a graph with a removable discontinuity at the point $(-2, 5)$.

**Q3.** Sketch the graph of $y = \tan x$.

**Q4.** What percentage of 70 is 14?

**Q5.** Multiply: $(3x + 4)(x - 2)$

**Q6.** Do the squaring: $(5x - 7)^2$

**Q7.** Write as the log of a single argument: $\log 36 - \log 12 + \log 2$.

**Q8.** Factor: $x^3 - 8$

**Q9.** Draw a tangent line to a circle.

**Q10.** Draw a secant line to a circle.

1. *Cubic Function Problem I:* Let $f(x) = -x^3 + 12x + 25$.
   a. Plot the graphs of $f$ and $f'$ (the numerical derivative of $f$) on the same screen.
   b. For what values of $x$ is $f'(x)$ positive? What is the graph of $f$ doing for these values of $x$?
   c. For what values of $x$ is $f(x)$ decreasing? What is true about $f'(x)$ for these values of $x$?
   d. What does the graph of $f$ do at values of $x$ where the $f'$ graph crosses the $x$-axis?
   e. Sketch the graphs of $f$ and $f'$, showing clearly the relationships you have stated in 1a through 1d.
   f. Make a conjecture about what type of function $f'$ is.
2. *Cubic Function Problem II:* Explore the cubic function $g(x) = x^3 - 2x^2 + 2x - 15$ and its numerical derivative, $g'$. Does the graph have a high point and a low point such as is typical for cubic functions? How does the graph of the derivative function reveal this behavior? When your study group has come to a consensus, write the conclusions in your journal.

3. *Quartic Function Problem I:* Let $h(x) = x^4 - 2x^3 - 9x^2 + 20x + 80$.
   a. Plot the graphs of $h$ and $h'$ on the same screen.
   b. What type of function has a graph that is the shape of the $h'$ graph? Make a conjecture about what type of function the derivative of a seventh-degree function would be.
   c. What do the zeros of $h'(x)$ equal? That is, what values of $x$ make $h'(x) = 0$?
   d. What features does the graph of $h$ have if $h'(x) = 0$? Based on the meaning of derivative, explain why this observation is reasonable.
   e. Sketch the graphs of $h$ and $h'$, consistent with your answers above.
4. *Quartic Function Problem II:* Explore the function $q(x) = -x^4 + 8x^3 - 24x^2 + 32x - 25$ and its numerical derivative, $q'$. Does the function have the shape you expect of a fourth-degree function (that is, three high or low points)? How does the derivative graph compare with the derivative graph for the quartic function in Problem 3? When your study group has come to a consensus, write the conclusions in your journal.
5. *Sinusoid Problem I:* Let $f(x) = 4 + \sin x$.
   a. Plot the graphs of $f$ and $f'$ on the same screen. Be sure your calculator is set in radian mode.
   b. The graph of $f$ is called a **sinusoid**. You recall that the amplitude of a sinusoid is the distance from the middle to a high point, and the period is the distance along the $x$-axis from one high point to the next. What are the amplitude and the period of the $f$ graph?
   c. The $f'$ graph is also a sinusoid. What are its amplitude and period?
   d. Let $g(x) = 3 + \sin x$. Plot the graphs of $g$ and $g'$ on the same screen, along with the graphs of $f$ and $f'$. How are the $f$ and $g$ graphs related to each other? How do you explain the relationship between the $f'$ and the $g'$ graphs?
6. *Sinusoid Problem II:* Let $f(x) = 4 + \sin x$, as in Problem 5. Make a conjecture about which one of the functions available on your grapher the numerical derivative turns out to be. Give both graphical and numerical evidence to support your conjecture. Record the results in your journal. You will be using this information later in this chapter.
7. *Exponential Function Problem:* Figure 3-3e shows the graphs of the exponential function $f(x) = 2^x$ and its numerical derivative $f'$. They have similar shape. For instance, each has $y$-values that are four times as large at $x = 2$ as they are at $x = 0$. By experimenting with bases other than 2, see if you can find an exponential function that is identical to its derivative. Write a paragraph in your journal, telling what you have learned.

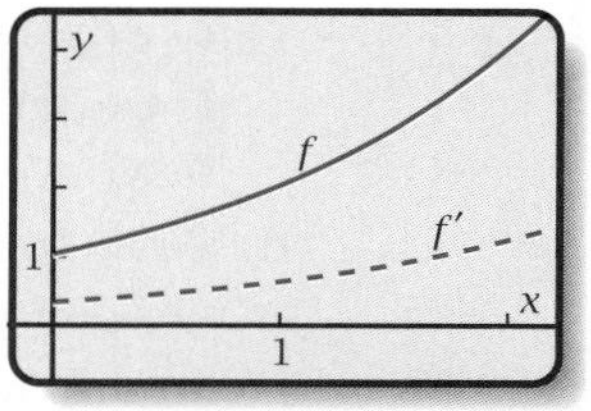

Figure 3-3e

8. *How the Grapher Works Problem:* The text in this section shows that by symmetric difference quotient, if $f(x) = x^3$, then $f'(2) \approx 12.0001$. Find $f'(2)$ by using the numerical derivative feature on your grapher. Set the tolerance for $x$ at 0.01, as you did with the text. Based on the result, tell whether your calculator seems to find numerical derivatives by symmetric difference quotient or by some other method.

9. *Tolerance Problem (Epsilon and Delta):* Figure 3-3f depicts a square floor tile that is to be manufactured to a certain tolerance. Suppose the dimensions are $12'' \times 12''$.
   a. If the tolerances on the dimensions are $\pm 0.01''$, what range of areas can the tile have? Within how many square inches of the nominal area (144 $\text{in}^2$) is the tile?
   b. If it is desired to manufacture tiles that are within 0.02 sq in. of the nominal area, to what tolerance must the dimensions of the tile be kept?
   c. How does your work in this problem relate to the epsilon and delta definition of limit?

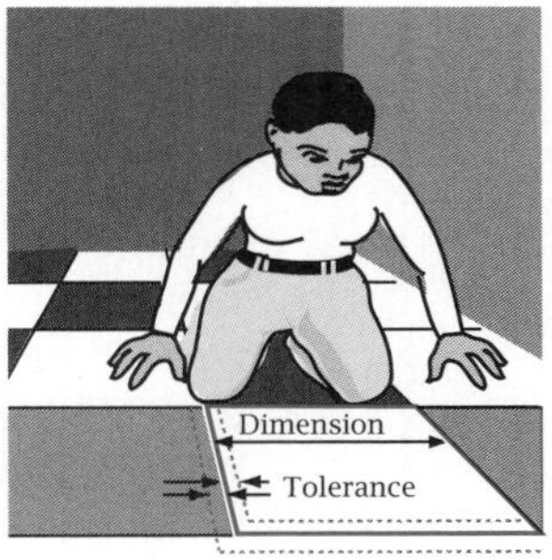

Figure 3-3f

10. *Symmetric Difference Quotient Problem:* In the box are formulas for forward, backward, and symmetric difference quotients. Show algebraically that the symmetric difference quotient is always the average of the forward and backward difference quotients.

**Formulas for Difference Quotients**

Forward difference quotient $= \dfrac{f(x+h) - f(x)}{h}$

Backward difference quotient $= \dfrac{f(x) - f(x-h)}{h}$

Symmetric difference quotient $= \dfrac{f(x+h) - f(x-h)}{2h}$

The tolerance, $h$, is positive in each case.

11. *Difference Quotient Accuracy Problem:* Figure 3-3g shows the graph of

$$f(x) = x^3 - x + 1.$$

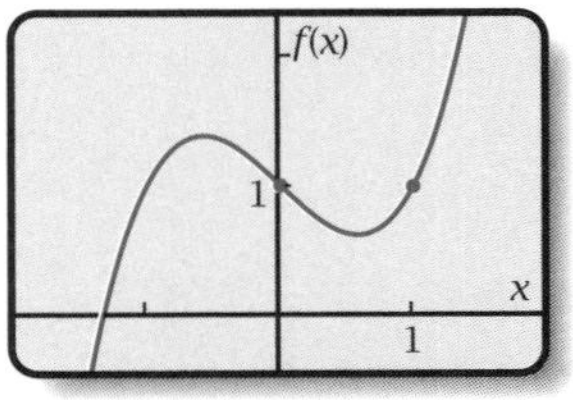

Figure 3-3g

   a. By the method of Section 3-2, find the exact value of $f'(1)$.
   b. Using a tolerance of $h = 0.1$, find the forward, backward, and symmetric difference quotients for $f'(1)$. Explain why the symmetric difference quotient is so much closer to the actual derivative than either the forward or backward difference quotient.
   c. Find the exact value of $f'(0)$.
   d. Using a tolerance of $h = 0.1$, find the forward, backward, and symmetric difference quotients for $f'(0)$. How do you explain the fact that all three are equal, and thus that the symmetric difference quotient is not more accurate than the other two?
   e. Write a paragraph in your journal, telling what you have learned about the relative accuracy of forward, backward, and symmetric difference quotients.

12. *Numerical Derivative Error Problem!* Figure 3-3h shows the graph of

$$f(x) = \left(\sqrt[3]{x-2}\right)^2 + x - 1.$$

Use various tolerances, $h$, to explore the forward, backward, and symmetric difference quotients at $x = 2$. Do all three values seem to be approaching the same number as $h$ approaches zero? What do you conclude about $f'(2)$? Does the numerical derivative function on your grapher give a value for $f'(2)$? Write a paragraph in your journal, describing what you have learned in this problem about symmetric difference quotients and numerical derivatives.

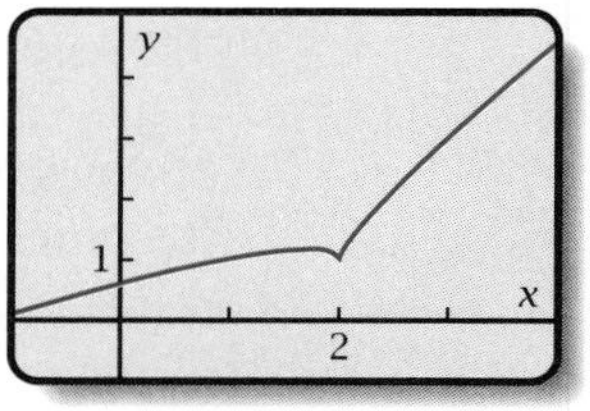

Figure 3-3h

13. *Journal Problem:* Update your journal with things you've learned since your last entry. Include such things as those listed here.
    - The one most important thing you have learned since the last journal entry
    - What you now better understand about the derivative of a function
    - How the grapher calculates numerical derivatives
    - How the grapher could give a wrong answer for a numerical derivative
    - Any conjectures you have made concerning derivatives of various types of functions
    - Anything you're still unsure of concerning derivatives and want to ask about during the next class period

# 3-4 Derivative of the Power Function and Another Definition of Derivative

In Section 3-2 you learned a definition of derivative. Another form of this definition lets you find an equation that will give the values of the derivative without having to resort to the definition each time. In this section you will find the derivative of a **power function**, such as

$$f(x) = x^5,$$

or a **linear combination** of power functions, such as

$$g(x) = 7x^{4/5} - 11x^{-2} + 13.$$

In each term the exponent is a **constant.** (Similar functions with variable exponents are called *exponential* functions. You will deal with these in Chapter 6.) If each exponent is a *nonnegative integer* constant, the function is called a **polynomial function.**

**OBJECTIVE**

Given a power function, $f(x) = x^n$, where $n$ stands for a constant, or given a linear combination of power functions, find an equation expressing $f'(x)$ in terms of $x$.

The derivative of a function at a point $x = c$ is

$$f'(c) = \lim_{x \to c} \frac{f(x) - f(c)}{x - c}.$$

This form of the definition is easy to remember because it ties in with the slope formula for a line you will recall from algebra, namely,

$$\text{slope} = \frac{\text{rise}}{\text{run}}.$$

It also calls attention to the fact that you are finding the derivative at the one fixed point where $x = c$ (Figure 3-4a).

Another form of the definition leads more directly to an equation for a derivative. As shown in Figure 3-4b, $c$ is replaced by $x$ and $x$ is replaced by $x + \Delta x$. The change in $x$ thus takes the simpler form $\Delta x$ (pronounced "delta $x$," meaning "difference between $x$-values"). The rise, $\Delta y$, can be written $\Delta y = f(x + \Delta x) - f(x)$. As $x$ approaches $c$ in Figure 3-4a, $\Delta x$ approaches zero in Figure 3-4b. The definition of derivative reduces to that shown in the box.

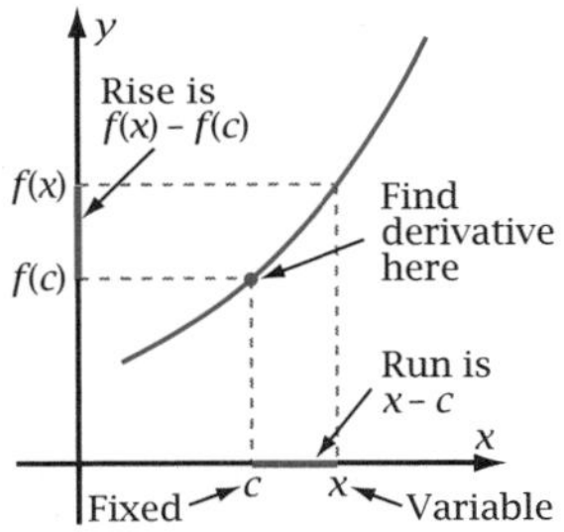

Figure 3-4a

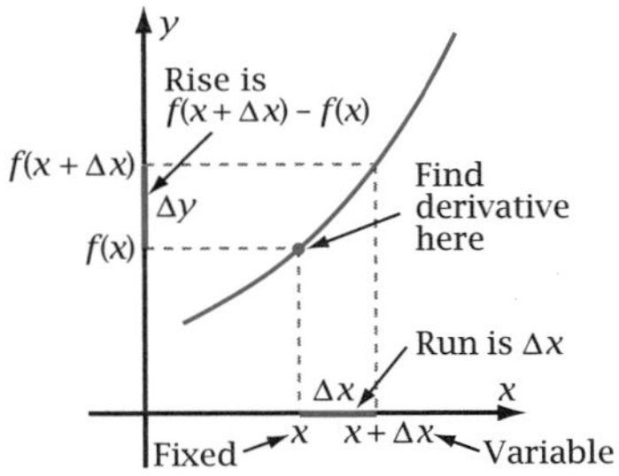

Figure 3-4b

**Definition of Derivative ($\Delta x$ or $h$ form)**

$$f'(x) = \lim_{\Delta x \to 0} \frac{\Delta y}{\Delta x} = \lim_{\Delta x \to 0} \frac{f(x + \Delta x) - f(x)}{\Delta x} = \lim_{h \to 0} \frac{f(x + h) - f(x)}{h}$$

Note that $\Delta$ is the uppercase form of the Greek letter delta, while $\delta$, which you have been using in notation for limits, is the lowercase form. Sometimes the single letter $h$ (for *horizontal*) is used in place of $\Delta x$ to make the algebra easier to write.

**Example 1** Given $f(x) = x^5$, use the definition of derivative to find an equation for $f'(x)$.

**Solution**

$$f'(x) = \lim_{h \to 0} \frac{(x+h)^5 - x^5}{h}$$ By the definition of derivative.

$$f'(x) = \lim_{h \to 0} \frac{(x^5 + 5x^4h + 10x^3h^2 + 10x^2h^3 + 5xh^4 + h^5) - x^5}{h}$$ Expand.

$$f'(x) = \lim_{h \to 0} \frac{5x^4h + 10x^3h^2 + 10x^2h^3 + 5xh^4 + h^5}{h}$$ Combine like terms.

$$f'(x) = \lim_{h \to 0}(5x^4 + 10x^3h + 10x^2h^2 + 5xh^3 + h^4)$$ Distribute $1/h$ to each term.

$$f'(x) = 5x^4 + 0 + 0 + 0 + 0 = 5x^4$$ Use the limit properties. ■

You should see both the source of the answer and a pattern.

$$\text{If } f(x) = x^5, \text{ then } f'(x) = 5x^4.$$

The answer, $5x^4$, is what remains of the second term in the binomial expansion of $(x + h)^5$.

*Source:* Answer comes from *second* term.

$$x^5 + \overbrace{5x^4}h + 10x^3h^2 + 10x^2h^3 + 5xh^4 + h^5$$

*Patterns:* One *less* than the original exponent.
The *original* exponent.

Generalizing these patterns gives a property for finding the derivative of any power function.

### Property: Derivative of the Power Function

If $f(x) = x^n$, then $f'(x) = nx^{n-1}$. Restriction: The exponent $n$ is a constant.

In Problem 28 of Problem Set 3-4 you will demonstrate that this property works for powers with constant exponents but not for variable exponents. In Chapter 4 you will prove that it works for negative and fractional exponents. In Chapter 6 you will deal with variable exponents.

The process of finding an equation for the derivative of a function is called **differentiation**. The word reflects the fact that $\Delta y/\Delta x$ is a *difference* quotient. The corresponding verb is **differentiate**. It may be easier to remember this property by what it allows you to do.

### Procedure: Differentiating the Power Function

To differentiate the power function, $f(x) = x^n$, you multiply by the old exponent, $n$, then reduce the exponent by 1 to get the new exponent.

To find a formula for differentiating a linear combination of powers, you must be able to differentiate a sum of two functions, and a constant times a function. An algebraic proof for a sum property is shown here. You will prove a property about the derivative of a constant times a function in Problem 35 of Problem Set 3-4.

**Theorem:**

If $f(x) = g(x) + h(x)$, where $g$ and $h$ are differentiable functions, then $f'(x) = g'(x) + h'(x)$.

**Algebraic Proof:**

By the definition of derivative,

$$f'(x) = \lim_{\Delta x \to 0} \frac{f(x + \Delta x) - f(x)}{\Delta x} \qquad \text{Definition of derivative.}$$

$$f'(x) = \lim_{\Delta x \to 0} \frac{[g(x + \Delta x) + h(x + \Delta x)] - [g(x) + h(x)]}{\Delta x} \qquad \text{Substitute for } f(x).$$

$$f'(x) = \lim_{\Delta x \to 0} \frac{[g(x + \Delta x) - g(x)] + [h(x + \Delta x) - h(x)]}{\Delta x}$$ Associate the $g$'s and the $h$'s.

$$f'(x) = \lim_{\Delta x \to 0} \left( \frac{g(x + \Delta x) - g(x)}{\Delta x} + \frac{h(x + \Delta x) - h(x)}{\Delta x} \right)$$ Reason?

$$f'(x) = \lim_{\Delta x \to 0} \frac{g(x + \Delta x) - g(x)}{\Delta x} + \lim_{\Delta x \to 0} \frac{h(x + \Delta x) - h(x)}{\Delta x}$$ Reason?

$$f'(x) = g'(x) + h'(x)$$ Definition of derivative (backward).

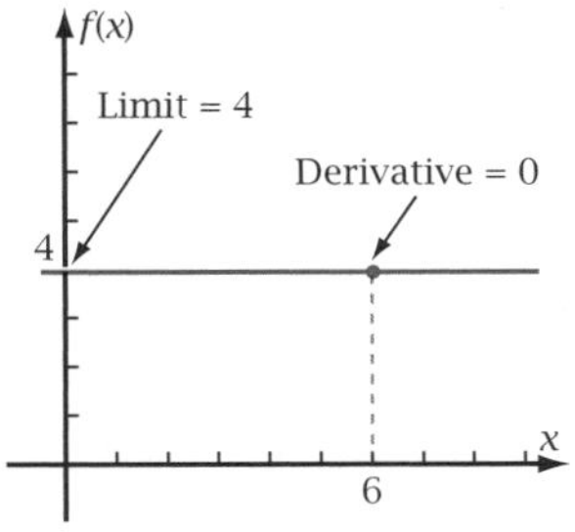


Figure 3-4c

The derivative of a constant function is zero. Figure 3-4c shows the function

$$f(x) = 4.$$

As you can see, the function value is always 4. It doesn't change, so its rate of change is zero. Don't confuse the derivative of a constant function with the limit of a constant function. The limit of $f(x)$ as $x$ approaches 6, for instance, is still 4, not zero.

### *Three Properties of Differentiation*

**Derivative of a Sum of Two Functions:** If $f(x) = g(x) + h(x)$, where $g$ and $h$ are differentiable functions of $x$, then $f'(x) = g'(x) + h'(x)$.

Words: The derivative of a sum equals the sum of the derivatives.
Differentiation distributes over addition.

**Derivative of a Constant Times a Function:** If $f(x) = kg(x)$, where $g$ is a differentiable function of $x$, then $f'(x) = kg'(x)$, provided $k$ is a constant.

Words: The derivative of a constant times a function equals the constant times the derivative of the function.

**Derivative of a Constant Function:** If $f(x) = C$, where $C$ stands for a constant, then $f'(x) = 0$ for all values of $x$.

Words: Constants don't change, so their rate of change is zero.

Combining these properties with the derivative of a power function allows you to differentiate any linear combination of power functions in one step!

***Example 2*** If $f(x) = 5x^7 - 11x^3 + 12x - 47$, find $f'(x)$.

***Solution***

$$f'(x) = 5(7x^6) - 11(3x^2) + 12(1) = 35x^6 - 33x^2 + 12$$

The answer to Example 2 is called the **algebraic derivative**, which distinguishes it from the numerical derivative found by difference quotients. The algebraic derivative gives the exact values. The values by numerical derivative are only approximate.

**Example 3** Check the answer to Example 2 by graphing both the algebraic derivative and the numerical derivative on the same screen.

**Solution**

Enter: $y_1 = 5x^7 - 11x^3 + 12x - 47$

$y_2 = 35x^6 - 33x^2 + 12$

$y_3 =$ numerical derivative of $y_1$

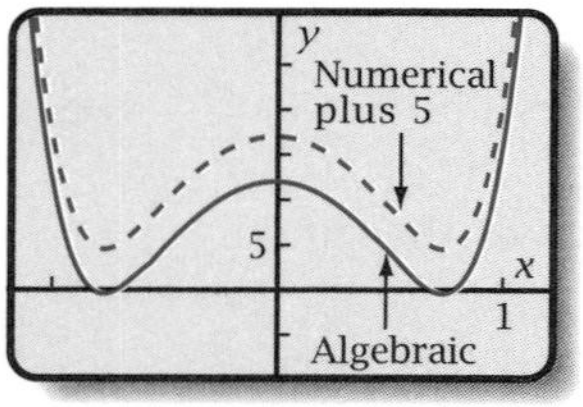


Figure 3-4d

Plot only $y_2$ and $y_3$. One graph appears on the screen. By using trace, you can find small differences between $y_2$ and $y_3$. Another option is to separate the graphs by adding a constant to $y_3$, as shown below.

$y_3 = \text{nDeriv}(y_1, x, x) + 5$

Figure 3-4d shows the two graphs, using a window of $[-1.2, 1.2]$ for $x$ and $[-10, 30]$ for $y$. The check comes by observing that the two graphs have the same shape. ■

There are other widely used symbols for the derivative, with which you should become familiar. Each has advantages and disadvantages, depending on where it is used.

> ### *dy/dx* and *y'* Terminology
>
> If $y = f(x)$, then instead of writing $f'(x)$ you can write any of the following.
>
> $y'$, pronounced "$y$ prime" (a short form of $f'(x)$)
>
> $\dfrac{dy}{dx}$, pronounced "dee $y$, dee $x$" (a single symbol, not a fraction)
>
> $\dfrac{d}{dx}(y)$, pronounced "dee, dee $x$, of $y$" (an operation done on $y$)

The symbol $dy/dx$ comes from the difference quotient $\Delta y/\Delta x$. It means that the limit is to be taken as both $\Delta y$ and $\Delta x$ go to zero. Mathematician Gottfried Leibniz (1646–1716) started using this terminology in about 1675. Later in this book you will learn that *dy* and *dx* are called *differentials.* For the time being, regard $dy/dx$ as a single symbol that cannot be taken apart—avoid saying "*dy* over *dx*."

The symbol $\dfrac{d}{dx}$ comes from rearranging the letters in $\dfrac{dy}{dx}$. It is an **operator** that acts on the expression $y$, similar to sin $y$ or log $y$. It tells you to take the derivative of $y$ with respect to $x$. It is useful if you want to show the expression for the function rather than just $y$. For example,

$$\frac{d}{dx}(x^5) = 5x^4.$$

**Example 4** If $y = 7x^{-4/5}$, write an equation for the derivative function, $dy/dx$. Assume the power rule works for negative and rational exponents.

**Solution**

Assume the power rule works for negative and fractional exponents.

$\dfrac{dy}{dx} = 7(-\tfrac{4}{5}x^{-9/5}) = -5.6x^{-9/5}$ Subtract 1 from $-4/5$ to get $-9/5$. ■

**Example 5** If $y = 7^5$, find $y'$.

**Solution** $y' = 0$ Because $7^5$ is a constant and the derivative of a constant is zero.

It is possible to sketch the graph of a derivative function just by looking at the graph of the function. For example, at a high or a low point in the function graph, the derivative will be zero. If the graph is going up, the derivative will be positive, and so forth. Example 6 shows how to sketch such a graph.

**Example 6** For the function in Figure 3-4e, sketch a reasonable graph of the derivative function.

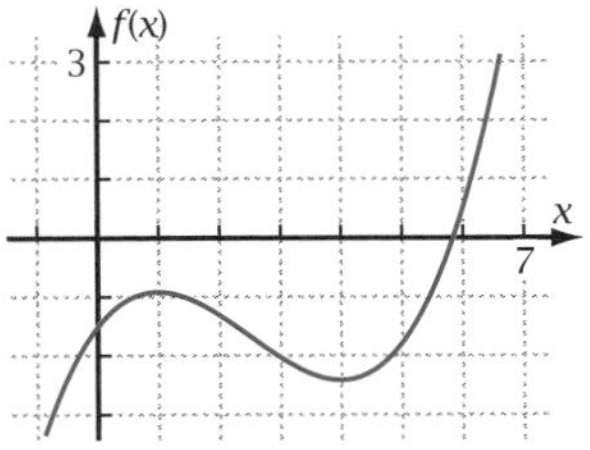


Figure 3-4e

**Solution** Photocopy Figure 3-4e or sketch the graph on graph paper. At $x = 1$ and at $x = 4$, the function has leveled off. Thus, it is not changing, and its derivative is zero. Mark these two points (Figure 3-4f).

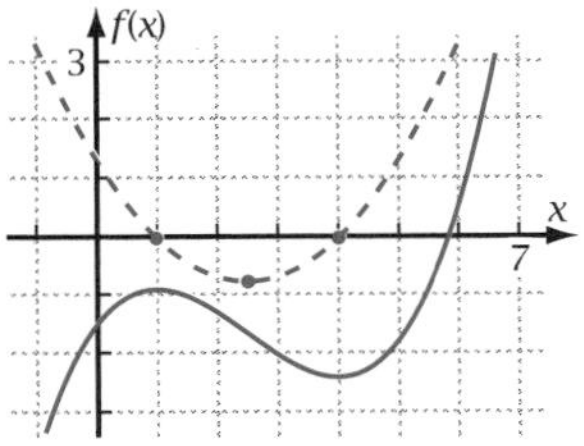


Figure 3-4f

Between $x = 1$ and $x = 4$, the function is decreasing. Its greatest downward slope comes at about $x = 2.5$. Mark a point below the $x$-axis at $x = 2.5$.

Above $x = 4$, the graph slopes up at an increasing rate. Draw the derivative graph as being positive and increasing.

Below $x = 1$, the graph is also sloping up but at a decreasing rate. Draw the derivative graph as being positive but coming down toward $y = 0$ at $x = 1$.

## Problem Set 3-4

### *Do These Quickly*

The following problems are intended to refresh your skills. You should be able to do all ten problems in less than five minutes.

**Q1.** Do the squaring: $(3x - 4)^2$

**Q2.** Do the cubing: $(a + b)^3$

**Q3.** Write the definition of derivative (either form).

**Q4.** Write the formula for a symmetric difference quotient.

**Q5.** Find $\lim_{x \to -3} (x - 5)/(x + 3)$.

**Q6.** Write as the log of a power: 3 log 7.

**Q7.** Write the exact value of $\tan(\pi/3)$.

**Q8.** Name the theorem whose conclusion is $r^2 = s^2 + t^2$.

**Q9.** Evaluate: $100^{1/2}$

**Q10.** Sketch the graph of a function that is continuous at $x = 4$.

For Problems 1–18, find the equation of the derivative function.

1. $f(x) = 5x^4$
2. $y = 11x^8$
3. $v = 0.007t^{-83}$
4. $v(x) = \dfrac{x^{-9}}{18}$
5. $M(x) = 1215$
6. $f(x) = 4.77^{23}$
7. $y = 0.3x^2 - 8x + 4$
8. $r = 0.2x^2 + 6x - 1$
9. $\dfrac{d}{dx}(13 - x)$
10. $f(x) = 4.5x^2 - x$
11. $y = x^{2.3} + 5x^{-2} - 100x + 4$
12. $\dfrac{d}{dx}(x^{2/5} - 4x^2 - 3x^{-1} + 14)$
13. $v = (3x - 4)^2$ (Do the squaring first.)
14. $u = (5x - 7)^2$ (Do the squaring first.)
15. $f(x) = (2x + 5)^3$ (Be clever!)
16. $f(x) = (4x - 1)^3$ (Be clever!)
17. $P(x) = \dfrac{x^2}{2} - x + 4$
18. $Q(x) = \dfrac{x^3}{3} + \dfrac{x^2}{2} - x + 1$

For Problems 19–22, use the definition of derivative in the $f(x + h)$ form to find the equation for the derivative function. In each case, show that the answer is consistent with the answer you would get if you used the formula for the derivative of the power function.

19. $f(x) = 7x^4$
20. $g(x) = 5x^3$
21. $v(t) = 10t^2 - 5t + 7$
22. $s(t) = t^4 - 6t^2 + 3.7$
23. *Misconception Problem:* Mae Danerror needs to find $f'(3)$, where $f(x) = x^4$. She substitutes 3 for $x$, gets $f(3) = 81$, differentiates 81, and gets zero for the answer. Explain why she also gets zero for her grade.
24. *Higher Math Problem:* Chuck stands atop a cliff (Figure 3-4g). He throws his math book into the air with an initial upward velocity of 20 m/sec. As a result, its height above where he threw it, $h(x)$ meters, after $x$ seconds is

$$h(x) = -5x^2 + 20x.$$

   a. The upward velocity of the book is the derivative of height with respect to time. Write an equation for the upward velocity.

   b. How fast was the book going at time $x = 3$? Was it going up or going down? Explain.

   c. At time $x = 3$, was the book above or below where Chuck threw it? How far?

   d. At what time is the book at its highest point? How do you know?

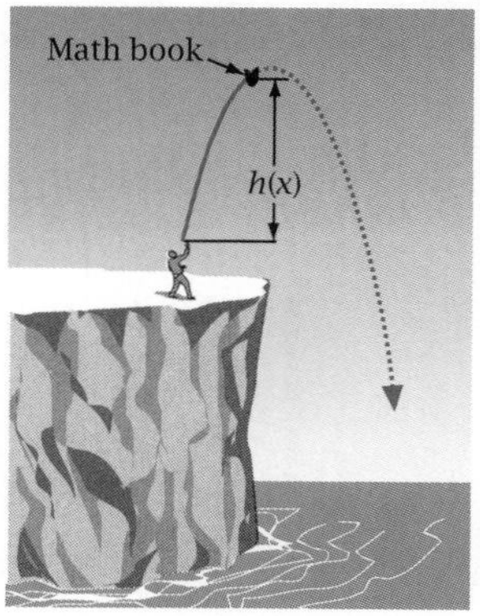

Figure 3-4g

For Problems 25 and 26, photocopy or sketch the graph of the function. On the same set of axes, sketch a reasonable graph of the derivative function.

25.

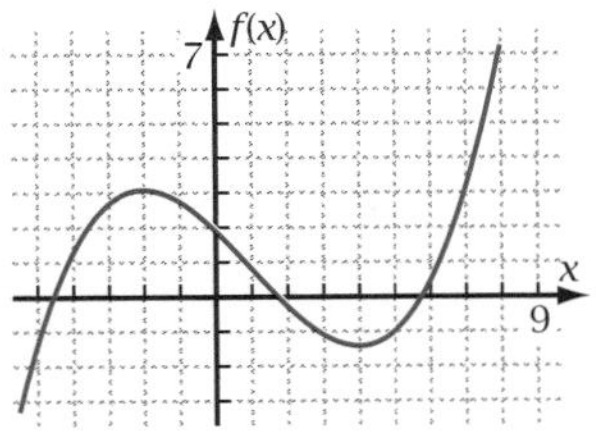


26.

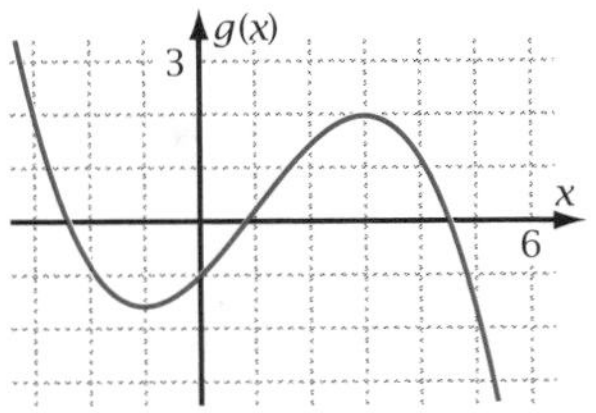


27. *Numerical Versus Exact Derivative Problem:* Figure 3-4h shows the graph of

$$f(x) = 0.4x^3 - 7x + 4,$$

along with two graphs of $f'(x)$. One derivative graph is found numerically as in Section 3-3. The other derivative graph is found algebraically using this section's technique.

a. Plot these graphs on your grapher.

b. Tell which graph is $f$ and which is $f'$.

c. Why do there appear to be only two graphs on the screen, not three?

d. Trace to $x = 3$. Write the $y$-value you get for each of the three graphs. How closely does the numerical derivative fit the algebraic derivative at $x = 3$?

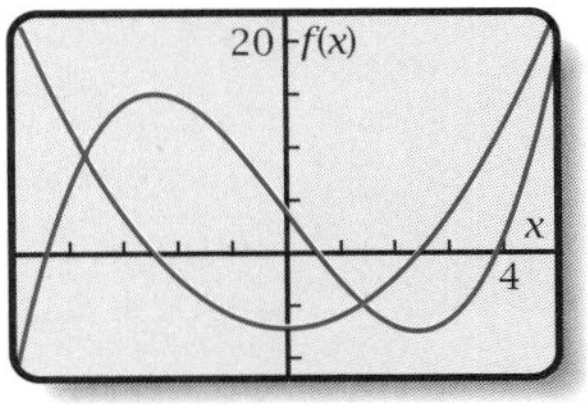


Figure 3-4h

28. *Power Formula for Various Types of Exponents:* The derivation of the power formula,

$$f(x) = x^n \text{ implies } f'(x) = nx^{n-1},$$

was based on an example (Example 1 of this section) from which a pattern was found. In Example 1, the binomial formula was used to expand $(x + h)^5$ as a sum. Unfortunately, such sums will have an infinite number of terms unless the exponent is a nonnegative integer. Your objective in this problem is to show by example that the power formula for derivatives works if the exponent is a negative or fractional constant but clearly does not work if the exponent is a variable. To accomplish the objective, predict the derivative for each function given below, assuming that the formula works for the type of exponent shown. Then show that the answer is correct or incorrect by plotting three graphs on the same screen.

$y_1$ = the given function

$y_2$ = your answer from using the derivative of a power formula

$y_3$ = the numerical derivative of $y_1$

a. $g(x) = x^{-1}$

b. $h(x) = x^{1/2}$

c. $e(x) = 2^x$

For Problems 29–32, tell quickly whether $f(x)$ is increasing or decreasing at $x = c$, and how fast.

29. $f(x) = x^{1/2} + 2x - 13, c = 4$

30. $f(x) = x^{-2} - 3x + 11,\ c = 1$

31. $f(x) = x^{1.5} - 6x + 30,\ c = 9$

32. $f(x) = -3\sqrt{x} + x + 1,\ c = 2$

For Problems 33 and 34, plot the graphs of $f$ and $f'$ on the same screen. Show that each place where the $f'$ graph crosses the $x$-axis corresponds to a high or low point on the $f$ graph.

33. $f(x) = \dfrac{x^3}{3} - x^2 - 3x + 5$

34. $f(x) = \dfrac{x^3}{3} - 2x^2 + 3x + 9$

35. *Formula Proof Problem I:* Use the definition of derivative to prove that if $g$ is a differentiable function of $x$, and $f(x) = k \cdot g(x)$, then $f'(x) = k \cdot g'(x)$.

36. *Formula Proof Problem II:* Given $f(x) = x^5$, derive the formula for $f'(c)$ directly from the $x = c$ form of the definition of derivative,

$$f'(c) = \lim_{x \to c} \frac{f(x) - f(c)}{x - c}.$$

It will be helpful to remember how to factor a difference of like, odd powers.

$$a^5 - b^5 = (a - b)(a^4 + a^3b + a^2b^2 + ab^3 + b^4)$$

37. *Derivative of a Power Formula:* Show that the formula for the derivative of a power, namely, $f'(x) = nx^{n-1}$, comes from the second term in the binomial series expansion of $(x + \Delta x)^n$.

38. *Derivative of a Sum of n Functions Problem:* Prove by mathematical induction that the derivative of a sum of $n$ functions is equal to the sum of the derivatives.

39. *Introduction to Antiderivatives:* Suppose you know the answer to a derivative problem, and you want to know just what function has been differentiated. For example, suppose that

$$f'(x) = 3x^2 - 10x + 5.$$

a. Figure out an equation for a function $f$ for which $f'(x)$ is the function shown above.

b. If $f(x)$ is the answer you found in 39a, explain why $g(x) = f(x) + 13$ is also an answer to 39a.

c. The functions $f$ and $g$ in 39a and b are called **antiderivatives** of $f'$. Why do you suppose they are called antiderivatives?

# 3-5 Displacement, Velocity, and Acceleration

You have found the velocity or acceleration of a moving object several times in this course. Now that you know an algebraic method to find derivatives, you can get an *equation* for the velocity or acceleration if you know an equation for the position of the object.

**OBJECTIVE**

Given an equation for the displacement of a moving object, find an equation for its velocity and an equation for its acceleration, and use the equations to analyze the motion.

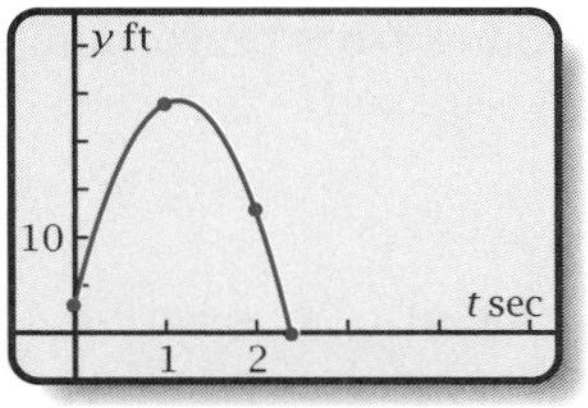


Figure 3-5a

Suppose that a football is punted into the air. As it rises and falls, its distance above the ground (its **displacement**) is a function of the number of seconds since it was punted. Suppose that by experiment it is found that

$$y = -16t^2 + 37t + 3,$$

where $y$ is its displacement in feet and $t$ is the number of seconds since it was punted. Figure 3-5a shows the graph of this function.

The **velocity** of the ball tells how fast it is going and in which direction. Because velocity is an instantaneous rate of change, it is a derivative. For the above equation,

$$\text{velocity} = \frac{dy}{dt} = -32t + 37. \qquad \text{Differentiate } y = -16t^2 + 37t + 3.$$

To find the velocity at any particular time, all you need to do is substitute for $t$. Here are some examples.

$$t = 1: \quad \frac{dy}{dt} = -32(1) + 37 = 5 \text{ ft/sec}$$

$$t = 2: \quad \frac{dy}{dt} = -32(2) + 37 = -27 \text{ ft/sec}$$

The $dy/dt$ symbol for the derivative helps you remember the units of velocity. Because $y$ is in feet and $t$ is in seconds, $dy/dt$ is in feet/second.

**Speed** is the absolute value of the velocity. Speed tells how fast an object is going, without regard to its direction. When $t = 1$, the ball is traveling 5 ft/sec. When $t = 2$, it is traveling faster at 27 ft/sec. The negative velocity when $t = 2$ indicates that the displacement is decreasing, which means that the ball is coming back down. Although the ball is traveling faster when $t = 2$, its velocity is less because $-27$ is less than 5.

The velocity changed from $t = 1$ to $t = 2$. The instantaneous rate of change of velocity is called **acceleration**. It is the derivative of the velocity. Using $v$ for velocity, $v = -32t + 37$. Thus,

$$\text{acceleration} = \frac{dv}{dt} = -32. \qquad \text{Differentiate } v = -32t + 37.$$

The $dv/dt$ symbol for the derivative tells you the units of acceleration. Because $v$ is in feet/second and $t$ is in seconds, $dv/dt$ is in (feet/second)/second. This quantity is pronounced, "feet per second, per second," with a pause at the comma. It is often pronounced "feet per second squared" and written "ft/sec $^2$."

The negative acceleration means that the velocity is decreasing. Be sure you know how to interpret this fact. In this instance, $v$ decreased from 5 ft/sec when $t = 1$ to $-27$ ft/sec when $t = 2$, even though the ball is traveling faster at $t = 2$. Note that the acceleration is *constant*, $-32$ (ft/sec)/sec, for an object acted on only by gravity.

The acceleration of a moving object is the derivative of a derivative. The words **second derivative** are used for the derivative of a derivative. The symbol for the second derivative of $y$ with respect to $t$ is

$$\frac{d^2y}{dt^2}$$

pronounced "dee squared $y$, dee tee squared." The symbol comes from performing $d/dt$ on $dy/dt$, then using "algebra" on the symbols.

$$\frac{d}{dt}\left(\frac{dy}{dt}\right) \quad \text{becomes} \quad \frac{d^2y}{dt^2}.$$

If $x = f(t)$, then the symbol $f''(t)$, pronounced "$f$ double prime of $t$," is used for the second derivative. Sometimes $y''$ is used if it is clear what the independent variable is.

**■ *Example 1*** An object moves in the $x$-direction in such a way that its displacement from the $y$-axis is

$$x = 3t^3 - 30t^2 + 64t + 57, \text{ for } t \geq 0,$$

where $x$ is in miles and $t$ is in hours. With your grapher in parametric mode, plot the path of the object. Hold or repeatedly press the trace key to find out how the object moves as time goes on. Write a paragraph describing the motion. Include the approximate times and places at which the object reverses direction, and the time intervals during which the object is traveling to the right and to the left. A sketch may help.

***Solution*** Enter the equation above for $x$, then enter some convenient value for $y$, such as 1. Use a friendly range from 0 to about 10 and an $x$ window from 0 to about 200. The graph is a straight line (Figure 3-5b). It is interesting to watch the line get generated! Your write-up might look something like this.

*The object starts out at $x = 57$ mi when $t = 0$. It goes right, slowing down until $t$ is about 1.3 hr, at which time it stops where $x$ is about 96 mi, as in Figure 3-5c. Then it turns around and starts off going to the left, speeding up for a while, then slowing down and stopping when $t$ is about 5.3 hr, at which time $x$ is about 0.1 mi. After that it starts off to the right again and continues speeding up.*

■

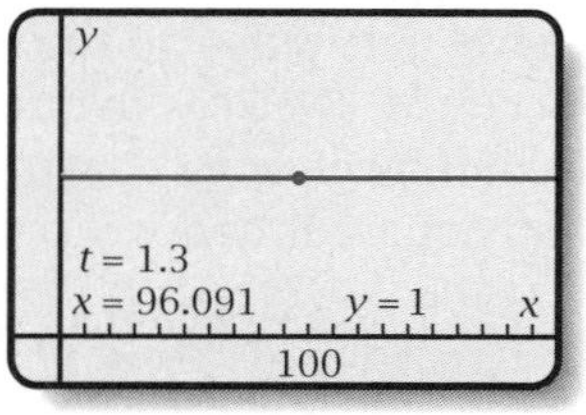


Figure 3-5b

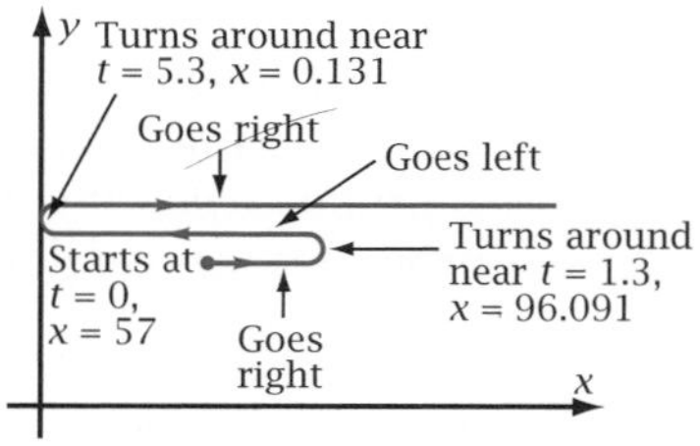


Figure 3-5c

In Example 2, you will use $y$ versus $t$ graphs to analyze the same motion.

**■ Example 2** The object in Example 1 moves in the $x$-direction with displacement from the $y$-axis given by

$$x = 3t^3 - 30t^2 + 64t + 57, \text{ for } t \geq 0,$$

where $x$ is in miles and $t$ is in hours.

a. Find equations for its velocity and acceleration.

b. At time $t = 2$, is $x$ increasing or decreasing? How fast?

c. At time $t = 2$, is the object speeding up or slowing down? At what rate?

d. At what times in the interval $[0, 8]$ is $x$ at a maximum? Justify your answer.

e. Is $x$ ever negative if $t$ is in the interval $[0, 8]$? Justify your answer.

**Solution**

a. $v = \dfrac{dx}{dt} = 9t^2 - 60t + 64$ Velocity equation.

$a = \dfrac{dv}{dt} = \dfrac{d^2x}{dt^2} = 18t - 60$ Acceleration equation.

b. At $t = 2$, $v = 9(2^2) - 60(2) + 64 = -20$. Thus, $x$ is decreasing at 20 mi/hr. The fact that $x$ is decreasing can be seen from a graph like that shown in Figure 3-5d. Note that $x$ is plotted vertically because it is the dependent variable.

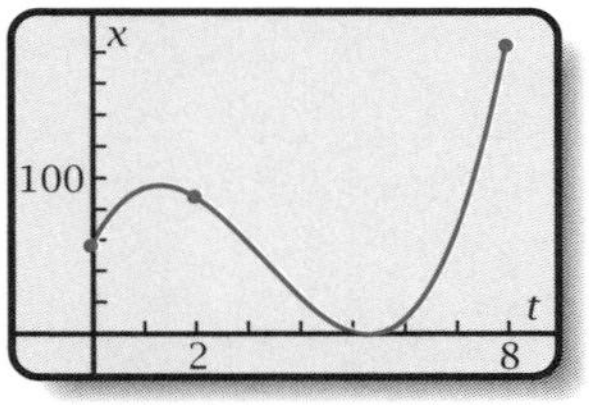


Figure 3-5d

c. At $t = 2$, $a = 18(2) - 60 = -24$, which means that the velocity is decreasing. However, the object is speeding up. As shown in Figure 3-5e, $v$ is negative at $t = 2$. If $t$ increases a bit, $v$ becomes larger in the negative direction. To check for speeding up or slowing down, ask yourself if $v$ is getting closer to the $t$-axis (slowing down) or farther from it (speeding up) as time increases. The object is speeding up in the negative direction at 24 (mi/hr)/hr when $t = 2$.

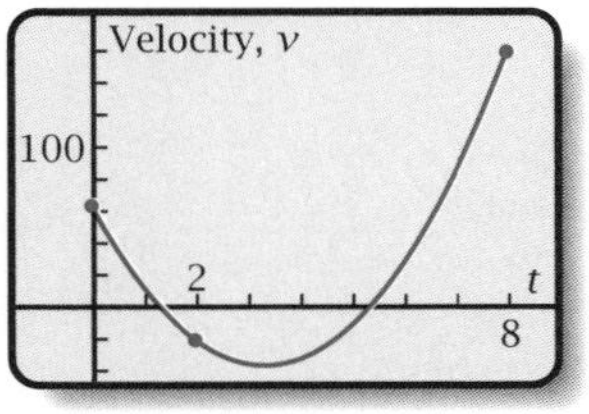


Figure 3-5e

d. The maximum value of a function occurs where it stops increasing and starts decreasing, or an endpoint of the domain. The closed interval [0, 8] means that $0 \leq t \leq 8$. From the graph in Figure 3-5d, you can see that $x$ is a maximum in this domain when $t = 8$. However, there is another relative maximum somewhere between $t = 1$ and $t = 2$. To find exactly this value of $t$, realize that the velocity will be zero then.

$9t^2 - 60t + 64 = 0$ Set the velocity equal to zero.

$\therefore t = \dfrac{60 \pm \sqrt{3600 - 4(9)(64)}}{2(9)}$ Use the quadratic formula.

$t = 5.3333\ldots$ or $1.3333\ldots$

A relative maximum occurs at $t \approx 1.33$ hr. Pick the value between 1 and 2.

The absolute maximum occurs at $t = 8$ hr. An endpoint maximum.

e. From Figure 3-5d it appears that $x$ is zero somewhere between $t = 5$ and $t = 6$. The lowest value of $x$ will occur where the object stops traveling in the negative direction and starts back in the positive direction. That is, the minimum will occur where the velocity is zero. In step d it was found that $v = 0$ when $t = 5.333\ldots$. Substituting this value for $t$ gives

$$x = 3(5.333\ldots)^3 - 30(5.333\ldots)^2 + 64(5.333\ldots) + 57 = 0.111\ldots.$$

Because $x$ is still positive at the lowest point in the interval [0, 8], it is never negative in that interval. ■

The following box summarizes what you should know about velocity and acceleration.

**Properties: Velocity and Acceleration**

If $x$ is the displacement of a moving object from a fixed plane (such as the ground), and $t$ is time, then the following are true.

$$\text{Velocity} = v = x' = \frac{dx}{dt}$$

$$\text{Acceleration} = a = \frac{dv}{dt} = x'' = \frac{d^2x}{dt^2}$$

## Problem Set 3-5

### Do These Quickly

The following problems are intended to refresh your skills. You should be able to do all ten problems in less than five minutes.

**Q1.** Quick! For what values of $t$ does $9t^2 - 30t + 64$ equal zero? (Be clever!)

**Q2.** Find an equation for $dy/dx$: $y = 5x^2$.

**Q3.** Find an equation for $y'$: $y = 17x^{-3}$.

**Q4.** Find an equation for $f'(x)$: $f(x) = x^{1.7}$.

**Q5.** Find $(d/dx)(3x + 5)$.

**Q6.** Find $f(3)$: $f(x) = 5x^2$.

**Q7.** Find $f'(3)$: $f(x) = 5x^2$.

**Q8.** Find $\lim_{x \to 3} 5x^2$.

**Q9.** In the definition of limit, which goes with $f(x)$, $\epsilon$ or $\delta$?

**Q10.** Which concept of calculus is used to find the product of $x$ and $y$ if $y$ varies?

For Problems 1 and 2, find equations for the velocity, $v$, and the acceleration, $a$, of a moving object if $y$ is its displacement.

1. $y = 5t^4 - 3t^{2.4} + 7t$

2. $y = 0.3t^{-4} - 5t$

For Problems 3 and 4, an object is moving in the $x$-direction with displacement, $x$ feet, from the $y$-axis given by the function of $t$ seconds. With your grapher in parametric mode, plot the path of the object. Hold or repeatedly press the trace key to find out how the object moves as time goes on. Write a paragraph describing the motion. Include the approximate times and places at which the object reverses direction, and the time intervals during which the object is traveling to the right and to the left. A sketch may help.

3. $x = -t^3 + 13t^2 - 35t + 27, t \ge 0$

4. $x = t^4 - 11t^3 + 38t^2 - 48t + 50, t \ge 0$

5. An object moves as in Problem 3, with displacement, $x$, given by

$$x = -t^3 + 13t^2 - 35t + 27,$$

where $x$ is in feet and $t$ is in seconds.

a. Find equations for the velocity and the acceleration.
b. At $t = 1$, is $x$ increasing or decreasing? How fast?
c. At $t = 1$, is the object speeding up or slowing down? At what rate?
d. At what times in the interval [0, 9] is $x$ a relative maximum? Justify your answer.
e. Is $x$ ever negative if $t$ is in the interval [0, 9]? Justify your answer.

6. A particle (a small object) moves as in Problem 4, with displacement, $x$, given by

$$x = t^4 - 11t^3 + 38t^2 - 48t + 50,$$

where $x$ is in meters and $t$ is in minutes.

a. Write equations for the velocity, $v$, and acceleration, $a$.
b. Find all values of $t$ for which $v = 0$. You may use the solve feature of your grapher.
c. Plot the graphs of $x$ and $v$ on the same screen, then sketch the results. Tell what is true about the displacement whenever $v = 0$.
d. Plot the graph of $a$ on the same screen you used in 6c. At each time the acceleration is zero, what is true about $v$? About $x$?

7. *Car Problem:* Calvin's car runs out of gas as it is going up a hill. The car rolls to a stop, then starts rolling backward. As it rolls, its displacement, $d(t)$ feet, from the bottom of the hill at $t$ seconds since Calvin's car ran out of gas is given by

$$d(t) = 99 + 30t - t^2.$$

a. Plot graphs of $d$ and $d'$ on the same screen. Use a window large enough to include the point where the $d$ graph crosses the positive $t$-axis. Sketch the result.
b. For what range of times is the velocity positive? How do you interpret this answer in terms of Calvin's motion up the hill?
c. At what time did Calvin's car stop rolling up and start rolling back? How far was it from the bottom of the hill at this time?
d. If Calvin doesn't put on the brakes, when will he be back down at the bottom of the hill?
e. How far was Calvin from the bottom of the hill when the car ran out of gas?

8. *Sky Diver's Acceleration Problem:* Phoebe jumps from an airplane. While she free-falls, her downward velocity, $v(t)$ feet per second, as a function of $t$ seconds since the jump, is

$$v(t) = 251(1 - 0.88^t).$$

a. Plot the velocity, $v$, and acceleration, $a$, on the same screen. Use an $x$-window (actually a $t$-window) of 0 sec to 30 sec. Sketch the results.
b. What is Phoebe's acceleration when she first jumps? Why do you suppose the acceleration decreases as she moves faster and faster?
c. What does the limit of $v(t)$ seem to be as $t$ approaches infinity? This limit is called the *terminal velocity.*

d. How many seconds does it take Phoebe to reach 90% of her terminal velocity? Explain how you got your answer.

e. When Phoebe reaches 90% of her terminal velocity, is her acceleration equal to 10% of its initial value? Justify your answer.

9. *Velocity from Displacement Problem:* If you place-kick a football, its displacement above the ground, $d(t)$ meters, is given by

$$d(t) = 18t - 4.9t^2,$$

where $t$ is time in seconds since it was punted (Figure 3-5f). (The coefficient 18 is the initial upward velocity in meters per second.)

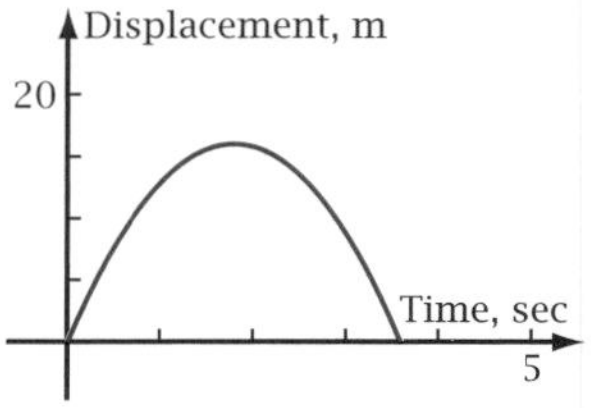

Figure 3-5f

a. Find $d'(1)$ and $d'(3)$. What name from physics is given to $d'$?

b. At times $t = 1$ and $t = 3$, is the football going up or down? How fast? How does the derivative tell you this? How do you know this from the graph?

c. Use the $d'$ equation to find the velocity at time $t = 4$. Explain why the answer has a meaning in the mathematical world but not in the real world.

10. *Displacement from Velocity Problem:* A sports car accelerates in such a way that its velocity as a function of time is given by

$$v(t) = 15t^{0.6},$$

where $v(t)$ is in feet per second and $t$ is in seconds. Figure out an equation for $x(t)$, the displacement of the car from a fixed point. Assume that the car is 50 ft from the fixed point at time $t = 0$. What concept of calculus have you used to find the displacement equation? Where is the car when $t = 10$? How far does it travel between $t = 0$ and $t = 10$?

11. *Average Versus Instantaneous Velocity Problem:* Suppose that $f(t)$ is the displacement of a moving object from a fixed plane. Explain why the difference quotient,

$$\frac{f(b) - f(a)}{b - a},$$

is the average velocity from $t = a$ to $t = b$. How is the instantaneous velocity at $t = a$ related to this average velocity? The definition of derivative should help you answer this question.

12. Figure 3-5g shows the displacement, $y$, in centimeters, from a tabletop for a mass bouncing up and down on a spring. Time $t$ is in seconds.

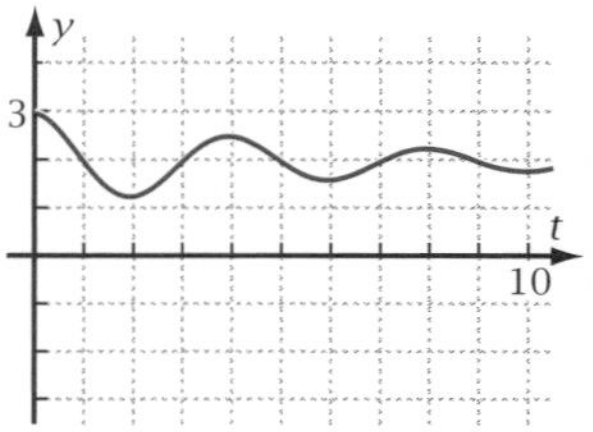

Figure 3-5g

a. Sketch or photocopy the graph. On the same axes, sketch the graph of the velocity.

b. For what values of $t$ is $y$ a relative maximum? For what values of $t$ is $y$ a relative minimum?

c. At what times is the velocity a relative maximum? Make some observations about the displacement graph at these times.

d. Just for fun, see if you can duplicate the graph in Figure 3-5g on your grapher. If you can, then check your answer to 12a by plotting the numerical derivative.

# 3-6 Introduction to Sine, Cosine, and Composite Functions

You have learned how to write down a formula for the derivative of a linear combination of power functions. Now you will do this for the *transcendental* functions sine and cosine.

Figure 3-6a shows the graph of $y = \sin x$ and its numerical derivative as they might appear on your grapher. Note that the derivative graph is *congruent* to the sine graph, just shifted sideways. Each graph is called a **sinusoid.** Recall from trigonometry that the cosine function has a graph that looks just like the derivative graph. A conjecture is as follows.

$$\text{If } f(x) = \sin x, \text{ then } f'(x) = \cos x.$$

Figure 3-6b shows similar relationships for the graphs of $g(x) = \cos x$ and its instantaneous rate of change. This time, the pattern seems to be the opposite of sin $x$, so the conjecture is as follows.

$$\text{If } g(x) = \cos x, \text{ then } g'(x) = -\sin x.$$

These two conjectures turn out to be true, as you will prove in Section 3-8.

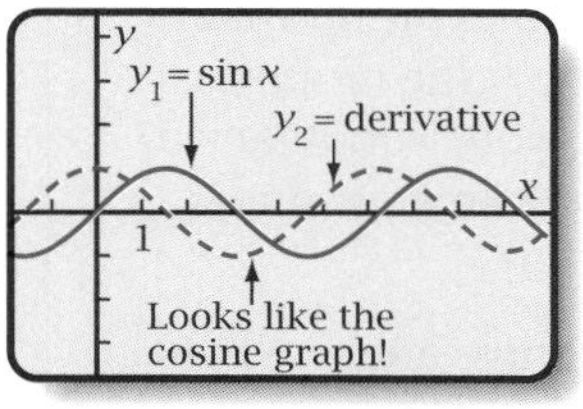


Figure 3-6a

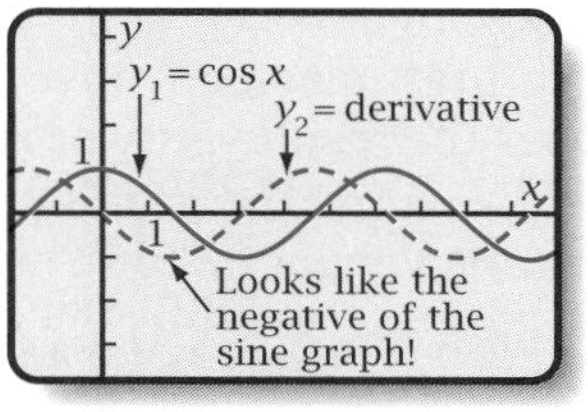


Figure 3-6b

**Properties: Derivatives of Sine and Cosine Functions**

$$\frac{d}{dx}(\sin x) = \cos x \qquad \frac{d}{dx}(\cos x) = -\sin x$$

In this section you will try to discover how to find the derivative of a **composite function**, such as

$$f(x) = \sin(x^5) \quad \text{or} \quad g(x) = (\cos x)^4,$$

where an operation is performed on the answer to another function. The function performed first is called the **inside function** (the fifth power function in $f$ and the cosine function in $g$, above). The function performed second, on the answer to the inside function, is called the **outside function** (the sine in $f$ and the fourth power in $g$, above).

**OBJECTIVE** Work with your study group to form conjectures on how to differentiate a composite function.

## Problem Set 3-6

1. Plot the graph of $y = \sin x$ on your grapher. Use a friendly window starting at $x = 0$ and ending at some convenient place around $x = 10$. Draw the resulting graph on graph paper, using scales such as those shown in Figure 3-6c.

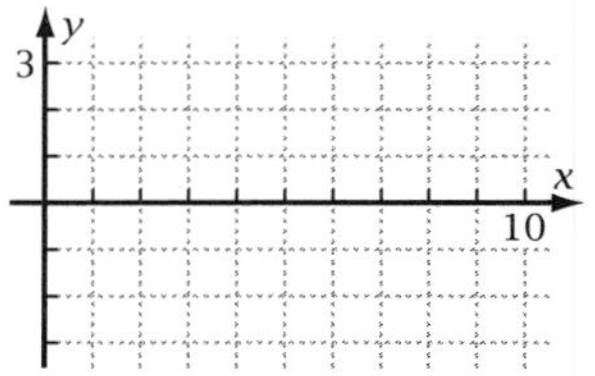


Figure 3-6c

2. You have assumed that the derivative of $f(x) = \sin x$ is $f'(x) = \cos x$. Based on this assumption, evaluate $f'(2)$. Then write the equation of the line through the point $(2, f(2))$ that has slope $f'(2)$. Plot that line as $y_2$ on your grapher and show it on the graph in Problem 1. What relationship does the line have to the sine graph? How does this relationship confirm that the derivative of the sine function really is the cosine function?

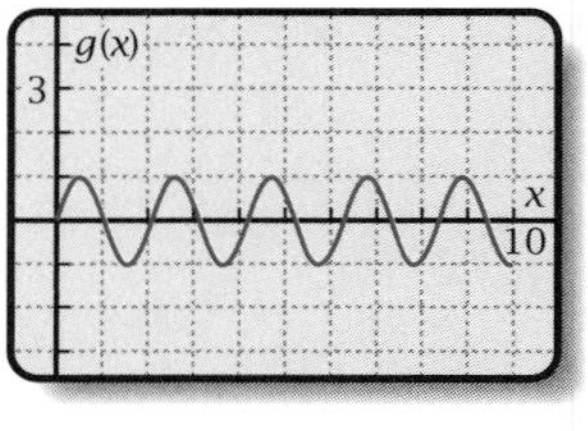


Figure 3-6d

3. Figure 3-6d shows $g(x) = \sin 3x$. Make a conjecture about what an equation for $g'(x)$ might be. Enter $g(x)$ as $y_1$ on your grapher. Then plot $y_2$ = your presumed derivative and $y_3$ = the numerical derivative of $g$. Does the result verify or refute your conjectured derivative? Sketch the correct $g'$ graph. If your conjecture was wrong, write the correct equation for $g'(x)$.

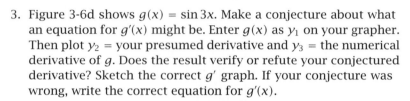

4. Figure 3-6e shows $h(x) = \sin x^2$. Make a conjecture about what an equation for $h'(x)$ might be. Then verify (or refute!) your conjecture by appropriately graphing on your grapher. Sketch the correct $h'$ graph. If your conjecture was wrong, see if you can figure out a correct equation for $h'(x)$.

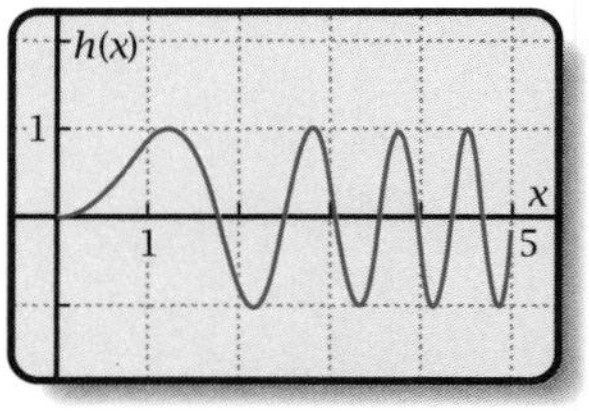


Figure 3-6e

5. You have assumed that the derivative of a power formula works for any constant exponent. Use this fact and the patterns you have observed in Problems 1–4 to make a conjecture about the derivative function for $t(x) = \sin x^{0.7}$. Verify your conjecture by plotting graphs as you did in Problems 3 and 4.

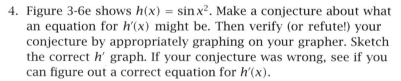

6. Suppose that $f(x) = \sin [g(x)]$ for some differentiable function $g$. What special name is given to function $f$ in this case? What special name is given to function $g$? What special name is given to the sine function in this case? Write a statement telling how you could find an equation for $f'(x)$.

7. For each function below, tell which is the inside function and which is the outside.

   a. $f(x) = \sin 3x$
   b. $h(x) = \sin^3 x$
   c. $g(x) = \sin x^3$
   d. $r(x) = 2^{\cos x}$
   e. $q(x) = \dfrac{1}{\tan x}$
   f. $L(x) = \log (\sec x)$

8. Write a paragraph in your journal, telling what you learned as a result of doing this problem set that you did not know before.

# 3-7 Derivatives of Composite Functions—The Chain Rule

A function with an equation such as

$$f(x) = \sin(x^2)$$

is called a **composite function.** It is composed of two other functions. The function $x^2$ in parentheses is called the **inside function**. The sine function outside the parentheses is called the **outside function.** It operates on the answer to the first function. Your purpose in this section is to learn how to find the derivative of a composite function.

***OBJECTIVE***

Given the equation for a composite function, write the equation for its derivative function.

Suppose you set out to differentiate

$$f(x) = \sin(x^2).$$

Your first reaction might be: This is just the derivative of the sine function, so the answer is $\cos(x^2)$. As you saw in Problem Set 3-6, the answer is really

$$f'(x) = \cos(x^2) \cdot 2x.$$

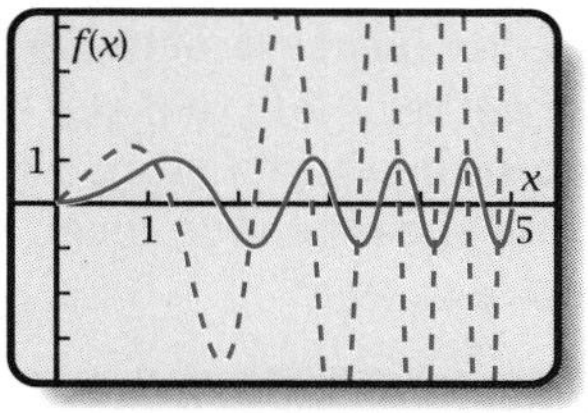


Figure 3-7a

The anticipated result, $\cos(x^2)$, is multiplied by the derivative of the inside function, $2x$. Figure 3-7a shows the graphs of $f$, $f'$, and the numerical derivative of $f$. The algebraic and numerical derivative (dashed) are the same. The property that tells you how to differentiate a composite function is called the **chain rule**.

To see why the chain rule works, realize that there are really three functions involved in $f(x) = \sin(x^2)$: the inside function, $x^2$; the outside function, sine; and the composite function, $\sin(x^2)$. Each one has its own derivative. For simplicity, let $u = x^2$ and let $y = \sin u$. Graphs of the three functions are shown in Figure 3-7b.

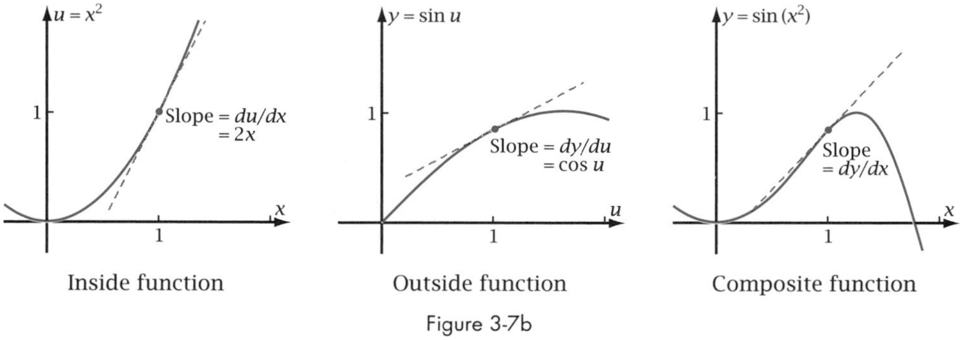


Figure 3-7b

Observe that $y$ depends on $u$ and that $u$ depends on $x$. The derivative of $u$ with respect to $x$, $du/dx$, is $2x$. It tells the slope of the $xu$-graph (left). Similarly, the derivative of $y$ with respect to $u$, $\cos u$, tells the slope of the $uy$-graph. You seek the slope of the $xy$-graph, $dy/dx$ (right). It is the limit of $\Delta y/\Delta x$. (The words *with respect to u,* for instance, mean that $u$ is the independent variable.)

Although derivatives are not fractions, you can use the definition of derivative to write them that way.

$$\frac{dy}{dx} = \lim_{\Delta x \to 0} \frac{\Delta y}{\Delta x} \qquad \frac{dy}{du} = \lim_{\Delta u \to 0} \frac{\Delta y}{\Delta u} \qquad \frac{du}{dx} = \lim_{\Delta x \to 0} \frac{\Delta u}{\Delta x}$$

To find the fraction for $dy/dx$ in terms of the fractions for $dy/du$ and $du/dx$, use some algebra. Multiplying by a clever form of 1, namely $\Delta u/\Delta u$, gives the following.

$$\frac{dy}{dx} = \lim_{\Delta x \to 0} \left( \frac{\Delta y}{\Delta x} \cdot \frac{\Delta u}{\Delta u} \right)$$

$$\frac{dy}{dx} = \lim_{\Delta x \to 0} \left( \frac{\Delta y}{\Delta u} \cdot \frac{\Delta u}{\Delta x} \right) \qquad \text{Reason?}$$

$$\frac{dy}{dx} = \lim_{\Delta x \to 0} \frac{\Delta y}{\Delta u} \cdot \lim_{\Delta x \to 0} \frac{\Delta u}{\Delta x} \qquad \text{Limit of a product of two functions.}$$

If $u$ is a *continuous* function of $x$, then $\Delta x \to 0$ implies $\Delta u \to 0$. By the limit of a composite function property (Section 2-3) you can replace $\Delta x \to 0$ with $\Delta u \to 0$.

$$\frac{dy}{dx} = \lim_{\Delta u \to 0} \frac{\Delta y}{\Delta u} \cdot \lim_{\Delta x \to 0} \frac{\Delta u}{\Delta x}$$

The two limits now fit the definition of derivative. Therefore,

$$\frac{dy}{dx} = \frac{dy}{du} \cdot \frac{du}{dx}.$$

The name *chain rule* is used because when a composite function has several inside functions, you get a whole "chain" of derivatives multiplied together. Note that since $\Delta u$ is a change in the dependent variable, it might go to zero somewhere before $\Delta x$ gets to zero. There is a way to get past this difficulty by using the extended mean value theorem, which you may learn later in your mathematical career.

### Property: The Chain Rule

**dy/dx Form:** If $y$ is a differentiable function of $u$ and $u$ is a differentiable function of $x$, then the derivative of $y$ with respect to $x$ is given by

$$\frac{dy}{dx} = \frac{dy}{du} \cdot \frac{du}{dx}.$$

**f(x) Form:** If $f(x) = g(h(x))$, then $f'(x) = g'(h(x)) \cdot h'(x)$

**Outside function, inside function form:** To differentiate a composite function, differentiate the outside function with respect to the inside function, then multiply by the derivative of the inside function with respect to $x$.

It is safest to remember the chain rule as a procedure, in its outside function, inside function form. This form indicates something to do. It is also easy to remember the $dy/dx$ form. Just think of "canceling" the *du*'s, and you are left with $dy/dx$.

With the chain rule at hand, you can accomplish this section's objective.

**Example 1** If $f(x) = (x^3 + 7)^2$, find $f'(x)$.

**Solution**

$f(x) = (x^3 + 7)^2$ — Write the given function's equation.

$f'(x) = \underline{2(x^3 + 7)^1} \cdot \underline{3x^2}$ — Apply the chain rule.

($3x^2$: Derivative of the inside function; $2(x^3+7)^1$: Derivative of the outside function)

$f'(x) = 6x^2(x^3 + 7)$ — Simplify. ■

**Example 2** If $y = \cos^4 x$, find $dy/dx$.

**Solution**

$y = \cos^4 x = (\cos x)^4$ — Write the fourth power as an outside function.

$\dfrac{dy}{dx} = 4(\cos x)^3 \cdot (-\sin x)$ — Differentiate the outside and inside functions.

$= -4\cos^3 x \sin x$ — Simplify. ■

# Problem Set 3-7

### *Do These Quickly*

The following problems are intended to refresh your skills. You should be able to do all ten problems in less than five minutes.

**Q1.** Write one condition for $f$ to be continuous at $x = c$.

**Q2.** Write another condition for $f$ to be continuous at $x = c$.

**Q3.** Write the third condition for $f$ to be continuous at $x = c$.

**Q4.** Is the signum function, $f(x) = \text{sgn } x$, continuous at $x = 0$?

**Q5.** Find $dy/dx$ if $y = 20x^{4/5}$.

**Q6.** Find $f(x)$ if $f'(x) = 30x^{-4}$.

**Q7.** Function $f$ in Problem Q6 is called a(n) —?—.

**Q8.** Sketch the graph of $y = \sin x$.

**Q9.** Sketch the graph of $y = \cos x$.

**Q10.** Sketch the graph of $y = -\sin x$.

1. State the chain rule in each form.
   a. Use $dy/dx$ terminology.
   b. Use $f'(x)$ terminology.
   c. State verbally, using the words *inside function* and *outside function.*

2. Given $f(x) = (x^2 - 1)^3$:
   a. Differentiate using the chain rule.
   b. Expand the power, then differentiate term by term.
   c. Show that the answers to a and b are equivalent.

For Problems 3–22, find an equation for the derivative function. You may check your answer by comparing its graph with the numerical derivative graph.

3. $f(x) = \cos 3x$

4. $f(x) = \sin 5x$

5. $g(x) = \cos(x^3)$

6. $h(x) = \sin(x^5)$

7. $y = (\cos x)^3$

8. $f(x) = (\sin x)^5$

9. $y = \sin^6 x$

10. $f(x) = \cos^7 x$

11. $y = -6 \sin 3x$

12. $f(x) = 4 \cos(-5x)$

13. $\dfrac{d}{dx}(\cos^4 7x)$

14. $\dfrac{d}{dx}(\sin^9 13x)$

15. $f(x) = 24 \sin^{5/3} 4x$

16. $f(x) = -100 \sin^{6/5}(-9x)$

17. $f(x) = (5x + 3)^7$

18. $f(x) = (x^2 + 8)^9$

19. $y = (4x^3 - 7)^{-6}$

20. $y = (x^2 + 3x - 7)^{-5}$

21. $y = [\cos(x^2 + 3)]^{100}$

22. $y = [\cos(5x + 3)^4]^5$

23. *Graphical Verification Problem:* For $f(x) = 5 \cos 0.2x$, plot the graph of function $f$. Where $x = 3$, plot a line on the graph with slope equal to $f'(3)$. Show that the line really is tangent to the graph.

Figure 3-7c

24. *Beanstalk Problem:* Jack's beanstalk grows in spurts (Figure 3-7c). Its height, $y$ feet, above the ground at time $t$ hours since he planted it is given by

$$y = 7 \sin \pi t + 12t^{1.2}.$$

Write an equation for $dy/dt$. Plot the graph of $y$ and the velocity graph on the same screen. Use a window from about $t = 0$ to $t = 10$. Do there appear to be times when the beanstalk is shrinking? Justify your answer.

25. *Balloon Volume Problem:* A spherical balloon is being inflated with air (see Figure 3-7d). The volume of the sphere depends on the radius, and the radius depends on time. Thus, the volume is a composite function of time.

a. The volume of a sphere is $V = (4\pi/3)r^3$, where $r$ is the radius in cm. Find an equation for $dV/dr$. What are the units of $dV/dr$?

b. At time $t = 0$, the radius is 10 cm. If $r$ increases at 6 cm/min, write $r$ as a function of $t$.

c. Find an equation for $dr/dt$. Surprising?! What are the units of $dr/dt$?

d. By appropriate use of the chain rule, find $dV/dt$ when $t = 5$ min. Based on the units of $dV/dr$ and $dr/dt$, explain why the units of $dV/dt$ are $\text{cm}^3/\text{min}$.

e. Find $dV/dt$ directly by substituting $r$ from 25b into the equation for $V$. Show that you get the same answer you did in 25d for $dV/dt$ when $t = 5$.

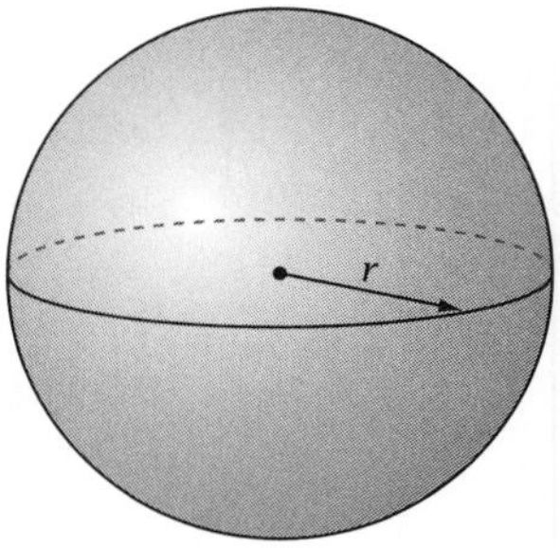


Figure 3-7d

26. *$\Delta u$ and $\Delta x$ Problem:* The derivation of the chain rule states that if $u$ is a continuous function of $x$, then $\Delta x \to 0$ implies $\Delta u \to 0$.

a. Sketch a graph showing that this may not be true if $u$ has a step discontinuity.

b. Sketch a graph showing why this is true if $u$ is continuous.

# 3-8 Proof and Application of Sine and Cosine Derivatives

In Section 3-6 you discovered that the derivative of the sine function is the cosine function, and the derivative of the cosine function is the opposite of the sine function. In this section you will prove algebraically and geometrically that these properties are true. You will also apply the derivatives of these sinusoidal functions to some problems from the real world.

**OBJECTIVE**

Be able to derive algebraically the formulas for the derivatives of sin $x$ and cos $x$. Find rates of change of sinusoidal functions in real-world problems.

### *Background: The Limit of (sin x)/x*

The function

$$y = \frac{(\sin x)}{x}$$

takes on the indeterminate form 0/0 as $x$ approaches zero. If you use a friendly window that includes $x = 0$ (Figure 3-8a) to graph the function, you will see that the fraction gets very close to 1 as $x$ gets close to zero. By using the appropriate geometry, it is possible to prove that 1 is the limit of $y$ as $x$ approaches zero.

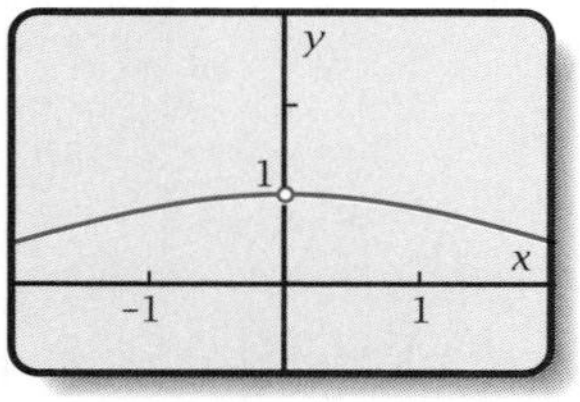

Figure 3-8a

Figure 3-8b shows a unit circle with an arc of length $x$ cut off by an angle of $x$ radians. The line segment tangent to the arc has length tan $x$ (hence the term *tangent*). The half-chord perpendicular to the $u$-axis has length sin $x$. The distance along the $u$-axis from the origin to this chord is cos $x$.

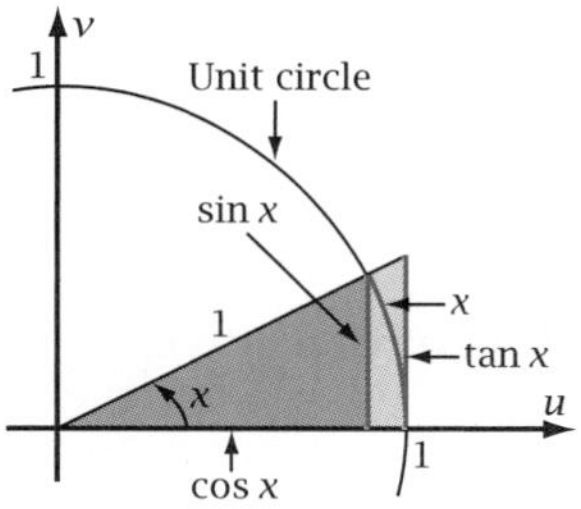

Figure 3-8b

Consider the areas of three regions shown in Figure 3-8b.

Large triangle: Area $= \frac{1}{2}(1)(\tan x)$   Area $= \frac{1}{2}$(base)(altitude).

Sector inscribed in the large triangle: Area $= \frac{1}{2}(x)$   A fraction of a unit circle, $(x/2\pi)\cdot(\pi\cdot 1^2)$

Small triangle inscribed in the sector: Area $= \frac{1}{2}(\sin x)(\cos x)$

From the areas of these figures, you can write the following three-member inequality, then use the appropriate algebra.

$$\tfrac{1}{2}(\sin x)(\cos x) < \tfrac{1}{2}(x) < \tfrac{1}{2}(1)(\tan x)$$

$$\cos x < \frac{x}{\sin x} < \frac{\tan x}{\sin x}$$   Divide all three members of the inequality by $\sin x$, then multiply by 2.

$$\frac{1}{\cos x} > \frac{\sin x}{x} > \frac{\sin x}{\tan x}$$   The order reverses because all three members of the inequality are the same sign.

$$\sec x > \frac{\sin x}{x} > \cos x$$   Because $1/(\cos x) = \sec x$, and $(\sin x)/(\tan x) = \cos x$.

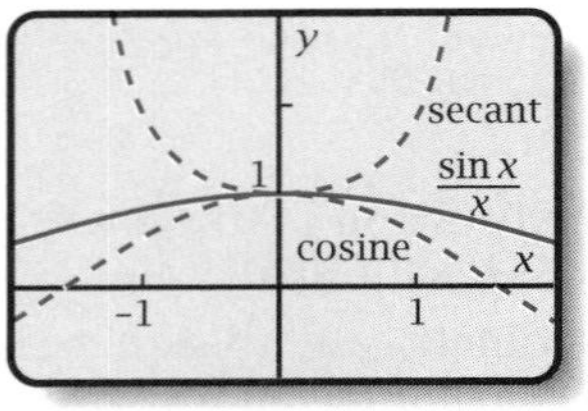

Figure 3-8c

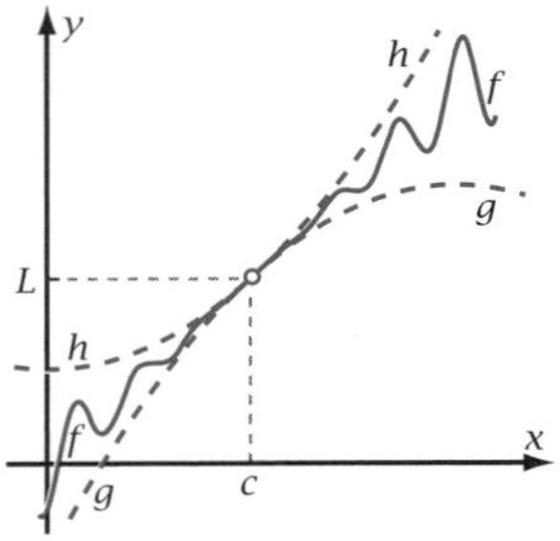

Figure 3-8d

Figure 3-8c shows how the graphs of the three members of this inequality would appear on your grapher. Sec $x$ and cos $x$ both approach 1 as $x$ approaches zero. So $(\sin x)/x$ is also "squeezed" to 1. Be careful not to read too much into this answer. (Sin 0)/0 is undefined, but has 1 for a limit as the argument, $x$, approaches zero. The indeterminate form 0/0 can approach numbers other than 1.

> **Property: Limit of (sin x)/x**
>
> $$\lim_{x\to 0} \frac{\sin x}{x} = 1$$

The function $(\sin x)/x$ approaches 1 because it stays between two other functions, each of whose limits equals 1. This fact is an example of the **squeeze theorem**. The theorem follows directly from the definition of limit. Figure 3-8d shows functions $f$, $g$, and $h$. If $g(x)$ and $h(x)$ can be kept within $\epsilon$ units of $L$ just by keeping $x$ close enough, but not equal to, $c$, and if $f(x)$ is always between $g(x)$ and $h(x)$, then $f(x)$ can also be kept within $\epsilon$ units of $L$. Hence, $L$ is also the limit of $f(x)$.

> **Property: The Squeeze Theorem**
>
> If: **1.** $g(x) \le h(x)$ for all $x$ in a neighborhood of $c$, where $x \ne c$,
>
> **2.** $\lim_{x\to c} g(x) = \lim_{x\to c} h(x) = L$, and
>
> **3.** $f$ is a function for which $g(x) \le f(x) \le h(x)$ for all $x$ in a neighborhood of $c$;
>
> then $\lim_{x\to c} f(x) = L$.

*Note:* A **neighborhood** of a number $c$ is an open interval containing $c$. Because the interval is open, $c$ cannot be at an endpoint. Thus, there are numbers in the interval on both sides of $c$.

### Derivative of the Sine Function

Let $f(x) = \sin x$. You suspect that $f'(x) = \cos x$. By the definition of derivative,

$$f'(x) = \lim_{h\to 0} \frac{\sin(x+h) - \sin x}{h}.$$

Algebra with fractions is usually easier if the numerator and the denominator have one term each, perhaps consisting of a product of several factors. The following property from trigonometry can be used to transform the numerator above from a sum to a product.

$$\sin A - \sin B = 2\cos\tfrac{1}{2}(A+B)\sin\tfrac{1}{2}(A-B)$$
A sum and a product property from trigonometry.

$$\therefore f'(x) = \lim_{h\to 0} \frac{2\cos\frac{1}{2}\left[(x+h)+x\right]\sin\frac{1}{2}\left[(x+h)-x\right]}{h}$$
Use $(x+h)$ for $A$ and $x$ for $B$.

$$f'(x) = \lim_{h\to 0} \frac{2\cos\left(x+\frac{h}{2}\right)\sin\frac{h}{2}}{h}$$

$$f'(x) = \lim_{h\to 0}\cos\left(x+\tfrac{h}{2}\right)\cdot\lim_{h\to 0}\frac{2\sin\frac{h}{2}}{h}$$
Limit of a product property.

$$f'(x) = (\cos x) \cdot \lim_{h \to 0} \frac{2 \sin \frac{h}{2}}{h}$$ Take limit of first factor, assuming cosine is continuous.

$$f'(x) = (\cos x) \cdot \lim_{h \to 0} \frac{\sin \frac{h}{2}}{\frac{h}{2}}$$ Express the second factor as $\frac{\sin(\text{argument})}{\text{argument}}$, whose limit is 1.

$f'(x) = (\cos x) \cdot (1) = \cos x$, which you discovered graphically in Section 3-6.

### Derivative of the Cosine Function

Using the cofunction properties from trigonometry, this new problem becomes an old problem.

$$y = \cos x = \sin\left(\frac{\pi}{2} - x\right) \Rightarrow y' = \cos\left(\frac{\pi}{2} - x\right) \cdot (-1) = -\cos\left(\frac{\pi}{2} - x\right) = -\sin x$$

So the property you discovered graphically in Section 3-6 is correct.

### Sinusoidal Equations from Real-World Information

The graph of a sine or a cosine function is called a **sinusoid**. Such functions occur in the real world, particularly with periodic motion. To write an equation for a given sinusoid, you must first recall the relationships between the equation and the graph. Figure 3-8e shows a sinusoid that is moved away from the origin. A **cycle** of the graph goes from one point to the point where the graph first starts repeating itself. The **period** is the number of $x$-units taken to complete one cycle (for instance, the $x$-distance between two high points).

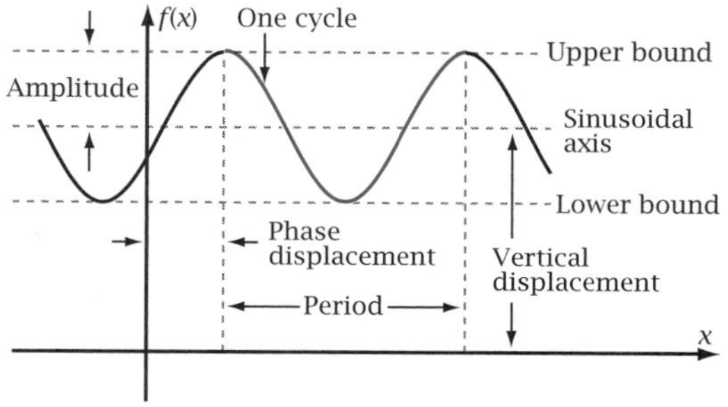

Figure 3-8e

The **phase displacement** is the $x$-coordinate of the beginning of the "first" cycle, where the argument of the sine or the cosine equals zero. The horizontal axis running along the middle of the graph is called the **sinusoidal axis**. The **amplitude** is the $y$-distance between the sinusoidal axis and a high point or a low point. The **vertical displacement** is the $y$-distance from the $x$-axis to the sinusoidal axis.

The general equation of a sinusoid is

$$f(x) = C + A \cos B(x - D),$$

where $A$, $B$, $C$, and $D$ stand for constants and the function can be either cosine or sine. To see the effects of these constants on the graph, plot a sinusoid such as

$$y = 5 + 3 \cos 2(x - 1)$$

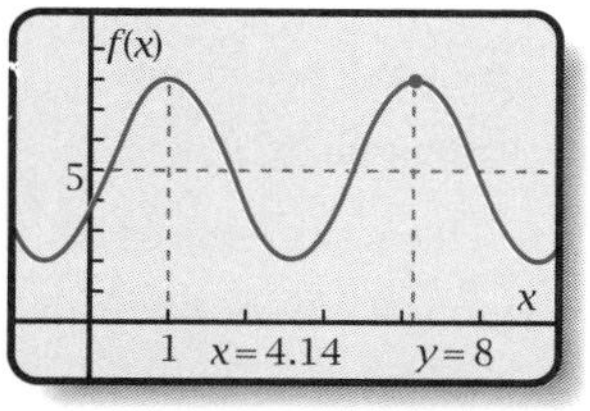

Figure 3-8f

on your grapher (Figure 3-8f). The 5 indicates how far the graph is shifted upwards and is thus equal to the vertical displacement (count up 5 spaces from the $x$-axis). The 3 indicates how far the graph is dilated in the $y$-direction and is thus equal to the amplitude (count $\pm 3$ spaces from the sinusoidal axis).

The argument of the cosine, $2(x - 1)$, is zero at $x = 1$. So the "first" cycle starts there, meaning the phase displacement is 1. To find the period, recall that $y = \cos x$ has a period of $2\pi$, the number of radians in a circle. The 2 in $2(x - 1)$ makes the argument change twice as fast. So the period is only 1/2 of $2\pi$, or simply $\pi$. Thus, the next high point comes at $x = 1 + \pi \approx 4.14$.

From the information above you can reach the following conclusions.

**Properties: Graph of a Sinusoid**

If $y = C + A\cos B(x - D)$, then the following are true.

1. The sinusoidal axis is along the line $y = C$.
2. The amplitude equals $|A|$.
3. The period equals $\dfrac{2\pi}{|B|}$.
4. The phase displacement equals $D$.

**Example 1**

A mass is bouncing up and down on a spring hanging from the ceiling (Figure 3-8g). Its distance, $y$ feet, from the ceiling varies sinusoidally with time $t$ seconds, making a complete cycle every 1.6 seconds. At $t = 0.4$, $y$ reaches its greatest value, 8 ft. The smallest $y$ gets is 2 ft.

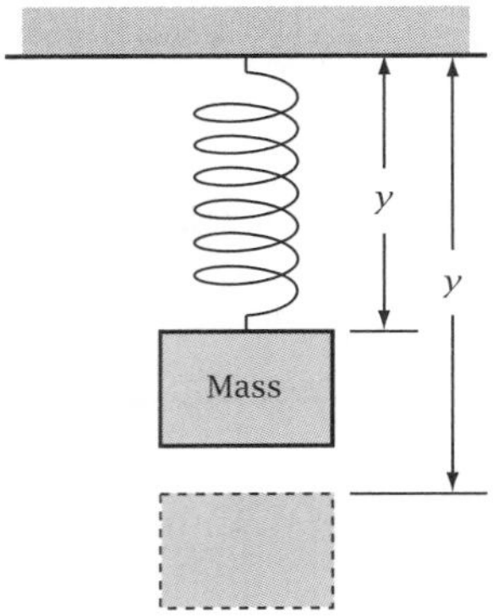

Figure 3-8g

a. Write an equation for $y$ in terms of $t$.

b. Write an equation for the derivative, $y'$.

c. How fast is the mass moving for these values of $t$?

   i. $t = 1$   ii. $t = 1.5$   iii. $t = 2.7$

d. At $t = 2.7$ sec, is the mass moving up or down? Justify your answer.

e. What is the fastest the mass moves? Where is the mass when it is moving this fast?

**Solution**

First sketch the graph. Show the high point at $t = 0.4$. The next high point will be at $t = 0.4$ plus the period, or 2.0. Halfway between the two high points, at $t = 1.2$ will be a low point. From these points you can sketch a reasonable graph, as shown in Figure 3-8h.

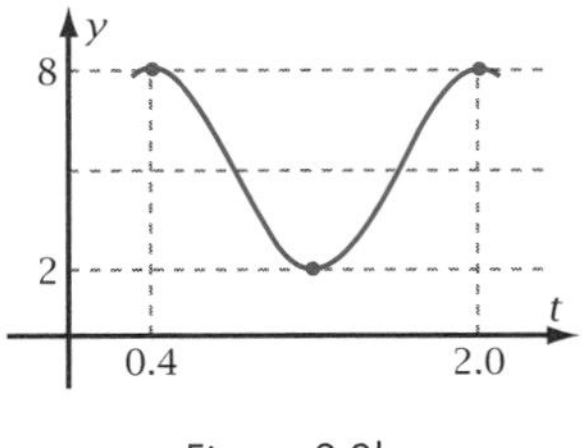

Figure 3-8h

a. $C = \frac{1}{2}(2 + 8) = 5$ — Sinusoidal axis is halfway between upper and lower bounds.

$A = 8 - 5 = 3$ — Amplitude is from sinusoidal axis to upper bound.

$B = \dfrac{2\pi}{1.6} = 1.25\pi$ — There are 1.25 $\pi$ cycles in $2\pi$ units of $x$ because the period is 1.6.

$D = 0.4$ — A high point occurs at $x = 0.4$.

$\therefore$ equation is $y = 5 + 3\cos 1.25\pi(t - 0.4)$.

b. $y' = -3\sin 1.25\pi(t - 0.4) \cdot 1.25\pi$ — Derivative of cos is −sin. Use the chain rule!

$y' = -3.75\pi \sin 1.25\pi(t - 0.4)$

c. Plot the graphs of $y$ and $y'$ on the same screen (Figure 3-8i), then trace the $y'$ graph to find the values.

i. $t = 1: \quad y' = -8.3304\ldots \approx -8.3$ ft/sec

ii. $t = 1.5: \quad y' = 10.884\ldots \approx 10.9$ ft/sec

iii. $t = 2.7: \quad y' = -4.508\ldots \approx -4.5$ ft/sec

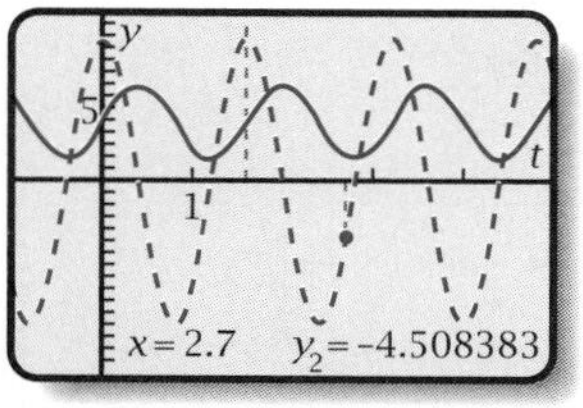

Figure 3-8i

d. At $t = 2.7$, the mass is going up; $y'$ is negative, meaning $y$ (the distance between the mass and the ceiling) is getting smaller.

e. The fastest the mass moves is $3.75\pi$, or about 11.8 ft/sec, which equals the amplitude of $y'$. Tracing shows a high point of $y'$ at $t = 1.6$ (dotted line in Figure 3-8i). At this time the mass is halfway between its high and low points. ■

# Problem Set 3-8

### *Do These Quickly*

The following problems are intended to refresh your skills. You should be able to do all ten problems in less than five minutes.

**Q1.** Differentiate: $f(x) = x^9$

**Q2.** Find $dy/dx$: $y = 3\cos x$.

**Q3.** Find $y'$: $y = (5x^6 + 11)^{2.4}$.

**Q4.** Find $s'(x)$: $s(x) = 2^{-13}$. (Be careful!)

**Q5.** Find $\lim_{x \to 7} \dfrac{(x+5)(x-7)}{x-7}$.

**Q6.** Find $\lim_{x \to 0} 2^x$.

**Q7.** Is $f(x) = 1/(x-3)$ continuous at $x = 4$?

**Q8.** If $f'(x) = 2x \cdot \sin x^2$, find $f(x)$.

**Q9.** Fill in the blank: $\cos^2 x + \sin^2 x =$ -?-.

**Q10.** Sketch the graph of the derivative of the function shown in Figure 3-8j.

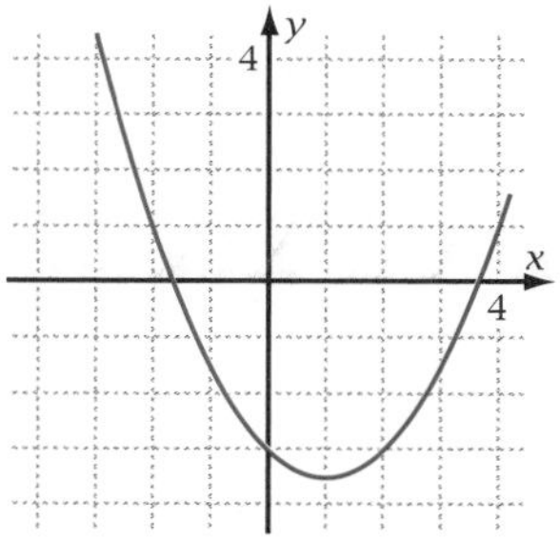

Figure 3-8j

1. *Ferris Wheel Problem:* When you ride a Ferris wheel, your distance, $y(t)$ feet, from the ground varies sinusoidally with time $t$ seconds since the wheel started rotating. Suppose that the Ferris wheel has a diameter of 40 ft and that its axle is 25 ft above the ground (see Figure 3-8k). Three seconds after it starts, your seat is at its high point. The wheel makes 3 rev/min.
   a. Sketch the graph of function $y$. From the sketch, figure out the particular equation for $y(t)$.
   b. Write an equation for $y'(t)$.
   c. When $t = 15$, is $y(t)$ increasing or decreasing? How fast? Where is the seat when $y(t)$ is changing the fastest?
   d. What is the fastest $y(t)$ changes?

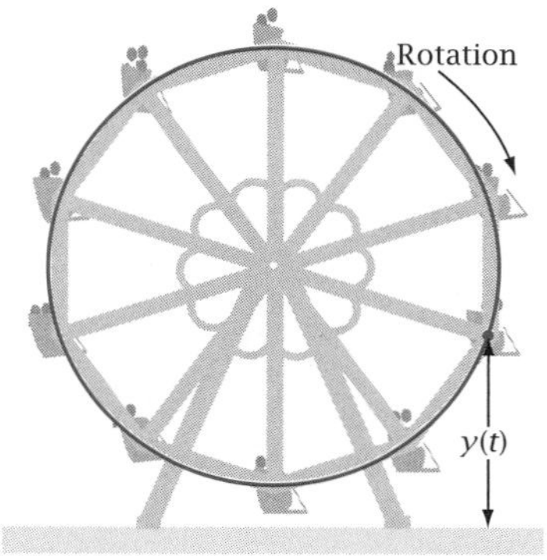

Figure 3-8k

2. *Pendulum Problem:* A pendulum hung from the ceiling makes a complete back-and-forth swing each 6 sec (see Figure 3-8l). As the pendulum swings, its distance, $d$ cm, from one wall of the room depends on the number of seconds, $t$, since it was set in motion. At $t = 1.3$ sec, $d$ is at its maximum of 110 cm from the wall. The lower bound of $d$ is 50 cm. Assume that $d$ is a sinusoidal function of $t$.
   a. Write an equation expressing $d$ as a function of $t$.
   b. Write an equation for the derivative function.
   c. How fast is the pendulum moving when $t = 5$? When $t = 11$? How do you explain the relationship between these two answers?
   d. When $t = 20$, is the pendulum moving toward or away from the wall? Explain.
   e. What is the fastest the pendulum swings? Where is the pendulum when it is swinging its fastest?
   f. What is the first positive value of $t$ at which the pendulum is swinging 0 cm/sec? Where is the pendulum at this time?

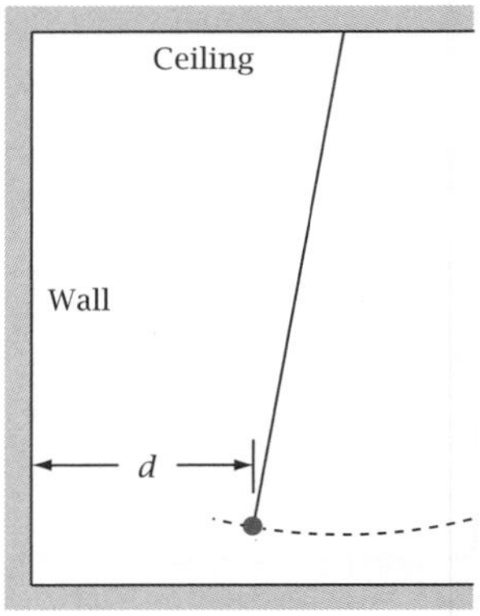


Figure 3-8l

3. *Playground Problem:* Opportunity Park, a playground in Midland, Texas, has a sinusoidal ramp for children to walk up (see photo). A brick curb starts 0.75 ft above the ground and slopes up to 3.25 ft above the ground, 44 ft away. The concrete walkway varies from 0.75 ft below this curb to 0.25 ft below it, as shown in Figure 3-8m. Let $x$ be the number of feet from the beginning of the ramp.
   a. Write an equation for $f(x)$, the distance from the ground to the top of the brick curb.
   b. Write an equation for $g(x)$, the distance from the ground to the top of the concrete walkway. Take into account the slope of the ramp.
   c. Write an equation for $g'(x)$. What is the slope of the ramp at $x = 9$? What is the slope at $x = 15$? What are the units of the slope? At these places, would a child walking up the ramp be going upward, downward, or on the level? Explain.
   d. As a child walks up the ramp, what are the steepest up and steepest down slopes?

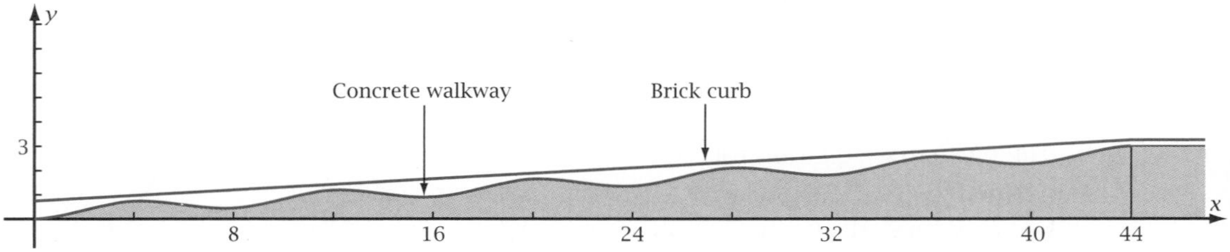


Figure 3-8m

4. *Daylight Problem:* The length of daylight (sunrise to sunset) is, approximately, a sinusoidal function of the day of the year. The longest day is around June 21, the 172nd day of the year. In San Antonio, Texas, the longest day has 14 hr, 3 min of daylight. The shortest day has 10 hr, 15 min of daylight.
   a. Write an equation expressing the length of daylight, in minutes per day, for San Antonio as a function of day of the year. How much daylight is there on August 7?
   b. Write an equation for the derivative of the function in 4a. At what rate is the length of daylight changing on August 7? What are the units of this rate of change?
   c. What is the greatest rate of change of daylight length? On what two days of the year is the rate equal to this number?
5. *Pendulum Experiment:* Swing a weight on a string from the ceiling of your classroom. Make appropriate measurements to find an equation for distance from the wall as a function of time since you let the pendulum go. Based on your equation, calculate the fastest the pendulum moves as it swings.
6. *Daylight Research Project:* Obtain a chart of sunrise and sunset times for various days of the year in your locality. Use this chart to derive a sinusoidal equation for the number of minutes of daylight in a day as a function of the day of the year. See Problem 4 for ideas. Draw a graph of predicted length of daylight versus day. Use your grapher to get the plotting data. On the same axes, plot the actual length of daylight derived from your chart. Discuss how well the sinusoidal model fits the real data. What is the greatest change in length of daylight from the table? How does this number compare with the derivative of the sinusoidal function at that time of year?
7. *Squeeze Theorem, Numerically:* Define functions $f$, $g$, and $h$ as shown.

$$f(x) = -2x^2 + 8x - 2$$
$$g(x) = 2x^2 + 2$$
$$h(x) = 4x$$

   a. Plot the three functions on your grapher. What is the limit of each function as $x$ approaches 1?
   b. Show that the squeeze theorem applies to the three functions. Which function is the upper bound, which is the lower bound, and which is in between?
   c. Make a table of values of $f(x)$, $g(x)$, and $h(x)$ for each 0.01 unit of $x$ from 0.95 to 1.05. Use a time-efficient method, such as the table or trace feature of your grapher.
   d. From your table, determine a value of $\delta$ that can be used to keep both the upper and lower bound functions within 0.1 unit of the limit when $x$ is within $\delta$ units of 1.
   e. Based on your table, explain how the conclusion of the squeeze theorem is true.
8. *Limit of* $(\sin x)/x$*, Numerically:* The adjacent table shows values of $(\sin x)/x$ as $x$ gets closer to zero. Don't forget to use radian mode!
   a. Use the table or trace feature to verify that these numbers are correct.
   b. Make a table of values for each 0.01 unit of $x$ from 0.05 to 0.01. Do the values seem to be getting closer to 1?
   c. Use smaller increments for $x$ to find the value of $x$ at which your grapher rounds the answer to exactly 1.

| $x$ | $(\sin x)/x$ |
|---|---|
| 0.5 | 0.9588510... |
| 0.4 | 0.9735458... |
| 0.3 | 0.9850673... |
| 0.2 | 0.9933466... |
| 0.1 | 0.9983341... |

d. The National Bureau of Standards lists the value of sin 0.001 to 23 places as

$$\sin 0.001 = 0.00099\ 99998\ 33333\ 34166\ 667.$$

(The spaces are left for ease of reading.) How close to 1 is $(\sin 0.001)/0.001$? How does this answer compare with what your calculator gives you?

e. Just for fun, see if you can explain why sin 0.001 has so many repeated digits.

9. *Limit of* $(\sin x)/x$ *Problem:* Without looking at the text, see if you can prove that 1 is the limit of $(\sin x)/x$ as $x$ approaches zero. If you get stuck, look at the text only enough to get going.

10. *Derivative of the Sine Function:* Without looking at the text, see if you can prove directly from the definition of derivative that cos $x$ is the derivative of sin $x$. If you get stuck, look at the text only enough to get started again.

11. *Derivative of the Cosine Function:* By a clever application of the chain rule and the appropriate trigonometry properties, prove that $-\sin x$ is the derivative of cos $x$.

12. *Squeeze Theorem Problem:*

a. State the squeeze theorem.

b. Prove directly from the definition of limit that the squeeze theorem is really true.

c. Sketch a graph that shows you understand what the squeeze theorem really means.

13. *Group Discussion Problem:* Figure 3-8n shows the graph of

$$y = 2 + (x - 1)\sin\left(\frac{1}{x-1}\right).$$

The function has a discontinuity at $x = 1$ because of division by zero.

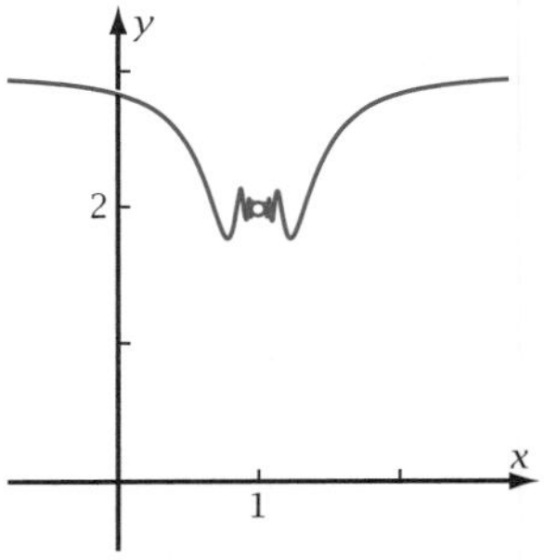

Figure 3-8n

a. What does the limit of $y$ seem to be as $x$ approaches 1?

b. Plot the graph using a friendly window that has $x = 1$ as a grid point and has bounds approximately as shown in Figure 3-8n. Then zoom in on the point $(1, 2)$ several times. Sketch the result.

c. Find two linear functions that are upper and lower bounds for the graph, and use the number in 13a for their limits as $x$ approaches 1. Plot these on your grapher, then sketch them.

d. Prove that your answer in 13a is correct. The squeeze theorem will help!

e. Why do you suppose the two linear functions are said to form an envelope for the $y$-graph?

f. If $x$ is far away from 1, $y$ seems to approach the constant 3. Based on what you have learned in this section, see if you can explain why this is true.

14. *Journal Problem:* Update your journal with things you have learned since the last entry. You should include such things as those listed here.
- The one most important thing you have learned since your last journal entry
- What you now better understand about formulas for derivatives of functions
- Properties you have learned and what they're named
- Any properties or techniques about which you are still unsure

# 3-9 Antiderivatives and Indefinite Integrals

If an object is falling freely under the action of gravity, it speeds up. From physics you may have learned that the velocity is given approximately by

$$v(t) = -9.8t,$$

where $v(t)$ is in meters per second and $t$ is in seconds. The negative sign indicates that as time increases, the distance the object is above the ground decreases. Velocity is the instantaneous rate of change of position. That is, the velocity is the derivative of position with respect to time. If $y$ is the number of meters the object is above the ground, then

$$\frac{dy}{dt} = -9.8t.$$

From this **differential equation** it is possible to find an equation for $y$ as a function of $t$. You have to go backward from the process of taking the derivative and ask yourself: "What could I differentiate to get $-9.8t$ for the answer?" If you differentiate $y = t^2$, you get $dy/dt = 2t$. The variable is correct, but its coefficient is not $-9.8$. So you ask, "What could I multiply 2 by to get $-9.8$?" The answer is $-9.8/2$, or $-4.9$. The function is thus

$$y = -4.9t^2.$$

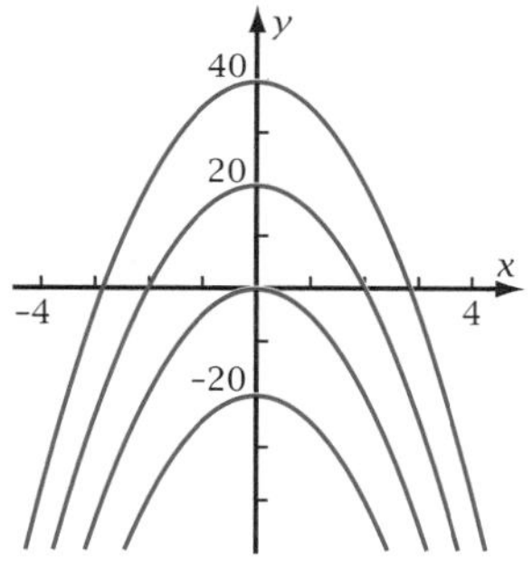


Some antiderivatives of $dy/dt = -9.8t$

Figure 3-9a

Interestingly, there are other functions you could differentiate to get $-9.8t$, such as

$$y = -4.9t^2 + 3.7,$$
$$y = -4.9t^2 - 1776,$$
$$y = -4.9t^2 + \pi, \text{ and}$$
$$y = -4.9t^2 + C,$$

where $C$ stands for a constant. Each function is an **antiderivative** of $-9.8t$. An antiderivative is also called an **indefinite integral** for reasons you will learn in Chapter 5. The equation

$$y = -4.9t^2 + C$$

is called the **general equation** for the antiderivative. Each of the other equations in which a particular value appears for the constant $C$ is called a **particular equation**. Figure 3-9a shows four particular equations in which $C = 40$, 20, 0, and $-20$.

**Definition: Antiderivative**

The function $f$ is an antiderivative of function $g$ if and only if $f'(x) = g(x)$ for all values of $x$ in their domains.

**OBJECTIVE**

Given the equation for the derivative of a function, find an equation for the function (that is, find an antiderivative).

**Example 1** If $f'(x) = x^7$, find the general equation for the antiderivative $f(x)$.

**Solution** Your thought process should go like this.

- The exponent is 7, so the function differentiated must have had an exponent of 8.
- The derivative of $x^8$ is $8x^7$, which is eight times too big.
- Therefore, the function differentiated must have been $(1/8)x^8$.
- The function differentiated could also have had some constant added to it. That constant does not show up in the derivative because the derivative of a constant is zero.
- Thus, the general equation for $f(x)$ would be

$$f(x) = \tfrac{1}{8}x^8 + C.$$

The particular equation of an antiderivative can be found if you know one point on the graph. The coordinates of this point are called an **initial condition**. The initial condition gives you the information you need to find the particular value of the constant $C$.

**Example 2** If $f'(x) = \sin 2x$, find the particular equation for the antiderivative, $f(x)$, using the initial condition $f(\pi/2) = 9$. Plot the antiderivative on your grapher. Show that it contains the point $(\pi/2, 9)$.

**Solution** Your thought process should go like this.

- The function differentiated must have been cosine.
- But the derivative of cosine is the opposite of sine.
- The argument of the cosine must have been $2x$ because the argument does not change when you differentiate.
- However, the derivative of $-\cos 2x$ is $2 \sin 2x$, which is twice what is needed.
- Thus, the general equation must be

$$f(x) = -\tfrac{1}{2}\cos 2x + C.$$

To find the particular equation, substitute $\pi/2$ for $x$ and 9 for $f(x)$.

$$\begin{aligned} 9 &= -\tfrac{1}{2}\cos(2\pi/2) + C \\ 9 &= -\tfrac{1}{2}(-1) + C \\ 8.5 &= C \\ \therefore f(x) &= -\tfrac{1}{2}\cos 2x + 8.5 \end{aligned}$$

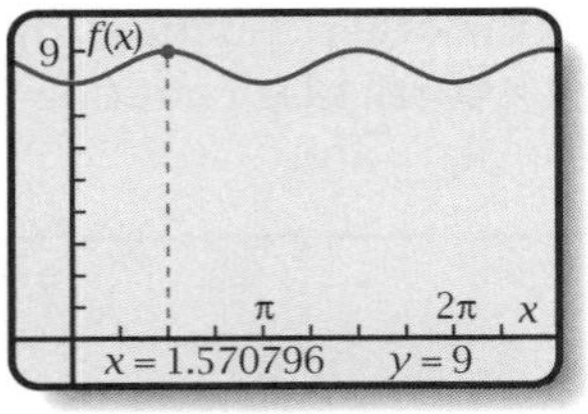

Figure 3-9b

Figure 3-9b shows the graph of this solution. If you use a friendly window with a multiple of $\pi$ as the scale factor, you can trace to $\pi/2$ exactly and find that $y$ actually does equal 9.

**Example 3** Galileo drops a cannonball from a leaning tower. Two seconds later the cannonball is at $y = 35$ m above the ground. Its velocity is given by $dy/dt = -9.8t$. Find the particular equation for the antiderivative, expressing $y$ as a function of $t$. Based on the equation, how tall is the leaning tower? When does the cannonball reach the ground?

**Solution**

$$\frac{dy}{dt} = -9.8t$$

$\therefore y = -4.9t^2 + C$ — See the beginning of this section.

$35 = -4.9(2^2) + C$ — Substitute the initial condition $y = 35$ when $t = 2$.

$54.6 = C$

$\therefore$ the particular equation is $y = -4.9t^2 + 54.6$.

The cannonball was dropped when $t = 0$. At that time, $y = 54.6$, so the tower is 54.6 m tall.

The cannonball reaches the ground when $y = 0$.

$$0 = -4.9t^2 + 54.6 \Rightarrow t = \left(\frac{54.6}{4.9}\right)^{1/2} = 3.338\ldots\text{, about 3.3 sec}$$ ■

## Problem Set 3-9

### *Do These Quickly*

The following problems are intended to refresh your skills. You should be able to do all ten problems in less than five minutes.

**Q1.** What theorem has a hypothesis that $f(x)$ is between $g(x)$ and $h(x)$ for all $x$ close to $c$?

**Q2.** What is the limit of $(\sin x)/x$ as $x$ approaches zero?

**Q3.** What is the derivative of $y = \cos x$?

**Q4.** If $y' = \cos x$, what function could $y$ equal?

**Q5.** If $g(x) = 2^x$, can $g'(x)$ be found using the power rule for derivatives?

**Q6.** Simplify: $x^{12}/x^4$

**Q7.** Simplify: $(x^{12})^4$

**Q8.** Write log 32 in terms of log 2.

**Q9.** Sketch the graph of $y = |x|$.

**Q10.** What is the outside function in $y = \sin^3 x$?

For Problems 1–16, find a function whose derivative is given. That is, write the general equation for the antiderivative.

1. $f'(x) = 7x^6$
2. $f'(x) = 10x^9$
3. $f'(x) = x^5$
4. $f'(x) = x^4$
5. $f'(x) = x^{-9}$
6. $f'(x) = x^{-1066}$
7. $f'(x) = \cos x$
8. $f'(x) = \sin x$
9. $f'(x) = 36x^{7/2}$
10. $f'(x) = 77x^{4/3}$
11. $f'(x) = \sin 5x$
12. $f'(x) = \cos 4x$

13. $f'(x) = (4x + 5)^7$ (Be clever!)

14. $f'(x) = (8x + 3)^5$ (Be clever!!)

15. $f'(x) = x^2 + 6x - 5$

16. $f'(x) = x^2 - 10x + 7$

For Problems 17–22, find the particular function $f(x)$ that has the given function $f'(x)$ for its derivative and contains the given point.

17. $f'(x) = x^4$ and $f(1) = 10$

18. $f'(x) = x^7$ and $f(-1) = 100$

19. $f'(x) = \cos x$ and $f(\pi/2) = 5$

20. $f'(x) = \sin x$ and $f(\pi) = 8$

21. $f'(x) = x^2 - 8x + 3$ and $f(-2) = 13$

22. $f'(x) = x^2 + 12x - 7$ and $f(3) = -10$

23. *Displacement Problem:* Ann Archer shoots an arrow into the air. Let $d(t)$ be its displacement above the ground at time $t$ seconds after she shoots it. From physics she knows that the velocity is given by

$$d'(t) = 70 - 9.8t.$$

a. Write the general equation for $d(t)$.

b. Write the particular equation for $d(t)$, using the fact that Ann is standing on a platform that puts the bow 6 m above the ground when she shoots the arrow.

c. How far is the arrow above the ground when $t = 5$? When $t = 6$? When $t = 9$? How do you explain the relationship among the three answers?

d. When is the arrow at its highest? How high is it at that time?

24. *Acceleration Problem:* Calvin is swinging on the playground. His velocity, $v(t)$ feet per second, gets larger and smaller as he swings. His girlfriend Phoebe tells him that his acceleration, $v'(t)$, is given by

$$v'(t) = 18 \sin 3t,$$

where $t$ is the number of seconds since he reached a low point on a backswing.

a. Write the general equation for $v(t)$.

b. Write the particular equation for $v(t)$ if Calvin's velocity is $-6$ ft/sec when $t = 0$. How do you interpret this negative velocity?

c. Make a table of values of $v(t)$ for each 0.2 sec from $t = 0$ through $t = 2$. Round to the nearest 0.1 ft/sec.

d. What is the maximum velocity Calvin reaches? What is his acceleration at this time? Surprising?!

25. *Derivative and Antiderivative Problem:* Let $g'(x) = 0.6x$.

a. Find the general equation for the antiderivative, $g(x)$.

b. Find the particular equation for $g(x)$ in each case.

i. $g(0) = 0$  ii. $g(0) = 3$  iii. $g(0) = 5$

c. Plot the graph of $g'(x)$ and the three graphs for $g(x)$ on the same screen, then sketch the results. Why are the three graphs of $g(x)$ called a family of functions?

# 3-10 Chapter Review and Test

In this chapter you have learned some algebraic techniques for differentiating functions. You can differentiate powers, sums, linear combinations, sine and cosine, and composite functions. You have learned formally about velocity and acceleration. You have also been exposed to the fourth concept of calculus, the indefinite integral, which is just an antiderivative.

The advantage of the algebraic techniques over the numerical and graphical ones is the ability to get the exact values of a derivative fairly quickly. The disadvantage of the algebraic techniques is that the way you calculate a derivative has nothing to do with what derivative means. You must always bear in mind that a derivative is an instantaneous rate of change.

The Review Problems below are numbered according to the sections of this chapter. The Concepts Problems allow you to apply your knowledge to new situations. The Chapter Test is more like a normal classroom test your instructor might give you.

## Review Problems

R0. Update your journal with things you've learned since your last entry. You should include such things as those listed here.

- The one most important thing you have learned in studying Chapter 3
- Which boxes you have been working on in the "define, understand, do, apply" table (See page 71.)
- Key words, such as *chain rule, difference quotient, sinusoid*
- Ways in which you have used graphs, tables, algebra, and writing to understand concepts
- Any ideas about calculus that you're still unclear about

R1. Let $f(x) = x^3$.

a. Calculate the numerical derivative of $f$ at $x = 2$.

b. Write an equation for $m(x)$, the slope of the line connecting the points $(x, x^3)$ and $(2, 8)$. What form does $m(2)$ take? What seems to be the limit of $m(x)$ as $x$ approaches 2?

c. Use algebra to simplify the expression for $m(x)$. You might recall how to factor a difference of two cubes, $a^3 - b^3 = (a - b)(a^2 + ab + b^2)$. Then take the limit of $m(x)$ as $x$ approaches 2.

d. Show that the result of R1c gives, exactly, the value of the derivative in R1a.

R2. a. Write the definition of derivative (derivative at $x = c$ form).

b. If $f(x) = 0.4x^2 - x + 5$, find $f'(3)$ directly from the definition of derivative.

c. Plot the difference quotient in a neighborhood of 3. Sketch the result.

d. Plot on the same screen the graph of function $f$ in R2b and a line through the point $(3, f(3))$ with slope $f'(3)$. Sketch the result.

e. What relationship does the line in R2d have to the graph?

f. Does function $f$ seem to have the property of local linearity at $x = 3$? How do you know?

R3. a. Plot $y_1 = x^4 - 4x^3 - 7x^2 + 34x - 24$. Use a window that goes from at least $x = -4$ to $x = 5$ and has a fairly large $y$-range. Sketch the result.

b. Plot $y_2$ = the numerical derivative of $y_1$. Sketch the result.

c. What feature does the $y_1$ graph have where the derivative graph equals zero?

d. *Leaky Tire Problem:* The air pressure in a leaky tire decreases according to the equation $p(t) = 35(0.9)^t$, where $p(t)$ is pressure in pounds per square inch and $t$ is time in hours since it was last inflated. Plot $p(t)$ and its numerical derivative on your grapher. Then sketch the result. At approximately what rate is the pressure changing when $t = 3$? When $t = 6$? When the tire was just filled? What are the units of pressure change? How do you explain the sign of the pressure change? Is the rate of change of pressure getting closer to zero as time goes on?

R4. a. Write the definition of derivative (the $h$ or $\Delta x$ form).

b. What word means "find the derivative"?

c. Write the property for the derivative of a power function.

d. Prove the property of the derivative of a constant times a function.

e. Prove the property of the derivative of a sum of two functions.

f. How do you pronounce $\dfrac{dy}{dx}$? How do you pronounce $\dfrac{d}{dx}(y)$? What do these symbols mean?

g. Find an equation for the derivative function.

i. $f(x) = 7x^{9/5}$

ii. $g(x) = 7x^{-4} - \dfrac{x^2}{6} - x + 7$

iii. $h(x) = 7^3$

h. Compare the exact value of $f'(32)$ in R4g with the numerical derivative at that point.

i. Sketch the derivative function's graph for the function shown in Figure 3-10a.

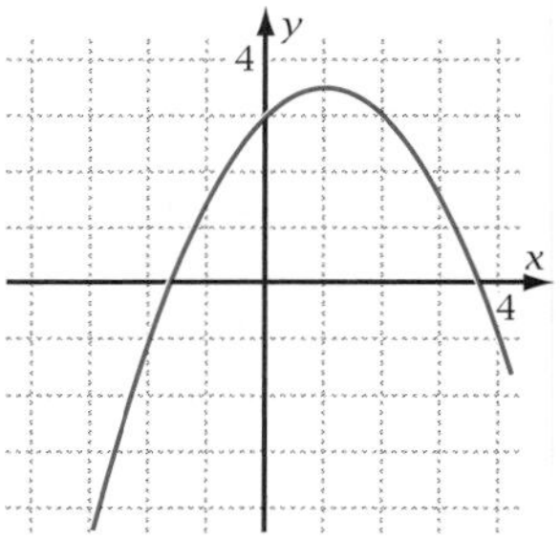

Figure 3-10a

R5. a. If $x$ is the displacement of a moving object from a fixed plane as a function of time, $t$, write the appropriate calculus symbol for the velocity, $v$. Write two forms of the symbol for the acceleration, $a$, one in terms of $v$ and the other in terms of $x$.

b. *Spaceship Problem:* A spaceship is approaching Mars. It fires its retrorockets, causing it to slow down, stop, rise up again, then come back down. Its displacement, $y$ kilometers, from the surface is found to be

$$y = -0.01t^3 + 0.9t^2 - 25t + 250,$$

where $t$ is time in seconds since the retrorocket was fired.

i. Write equations for the velocity and acceleration of the spaceship.

ii. Find the acceleration at time $t = 15$ sec. At that time is the spaceship speeding up or slowing down? How do you tell?

iii. Find by direct calculation the values of $t$ at which the spaceship is stopped.

iv. When does the spaceship touch the surface of Mars? What is its velocity at that time? Explain what you think will happen to the spaceship at that time.

R6. a. Plot and sketch $y_1 = \cos x$ and $y_2$ = the numerical derivative of $y_1$.

b. Explain how the graphs show that $\cos' x = -\sin x$.

c. Verify numerically that $\sin' 1 = \cos 1$.

d. What name is given to a function such as $f(x) = \cos(x^2)$ for which a function such as cosine is performed on an inside function, $x^2$? What does $f'(x)$ equal?

R7. a. State the chain rule in each form.
i. $dy/dx$
ii. $f(x)$
iii. Using outside function and inside function

b. Prove the chain rule. What assumption must be made about the quantity $\Delta u$ so that the proof is valid?

c. Differentiate $f(x) = (x^2 - 4)^3$ two ways and show that the two answers are equivalent.
i. Use the chain rule.
ii. Expand the binomial power first.

d. Differentiate.
i. $f(x) = \cos(x^3)$
ii. $g(x) = \sin 5x$
iii. $h(x) = \cos^6 x$
iv. $k(x) = \sin 3$

e. *Shark Problem:* The weight of a great white shark, $W$ pounds, is given approximately by $W = 0.6x^3$, where $x$ is the length of the shark in feet. Suppose that a baby shark is growing at the rate of $dx/dt = 0.4$ ft/day. How heavy is the shark when it is 2 ft long? 10 ft long? At what rate is it gaining weight (pounds per day) when it is these lengths? Tell how the chain rule allows you to calculate these answers.

R8. a. Evaluate: $\lim_{x \to 0} \frac{\sin x}{x}$

b. Make a table of values of $(\sin x)/x$ for each 0.01 unit of $x$ from $-0.05$ to $0.05$. Show from the table that $(\sin x)/x$ really does approach the limit in R8a as $x$ approaches zero.

c. State the squeeze theorem. Between what two quantities can $(\sin x)/x$ be "squeezed" to prove that the limit is the number you wrote in R8a?

d. Prove directly from the definition of derivative that $\sin' x = \cos x$.

e. Given that $\sin' x = \cos x$, use appropriate trigonometric properties to prove that $\cos' x = -\sin x$.

f. *Clock Problem:* A clock with a sweep second hand is fastened to the wall. As the sweep hand turns, the distance from its tip to the floor varies sinusoidally with time. The center of the clock is 180 cm from the floor, and the sweep hand is 20 cm long from the center to its tip. Write an equation for the distance from tip to floor as a function of the number of seconds since the hand was at the 12. Write an equation for the instantaneous rate of change of this distance with respect to time. How fast is the distance changing when the sweep hand points at the 2? At the 3? At the 7? How do you explain the signs you get for these rates?

R9. a. If $f'(x) = 36x^5$, find the general equation for $f(x)$.

b. If $dy/dx = \sin 0.2x$, and $y = 3$ when $x = 0$, find the particular equation for $y$.

c. *Distance Problem:* Iona Carr gets into her automobile, which is 100 ft from her house. She accelerates it in such a way that its velocity, $v(t)$ feet per second, is

$$v(t) = 6t^{1/2}.$$

Find the particular equation for $y(t)$, her displacement from the house $t$ seconds after she started accelerating. How far from the house is she 1 min after she starts? How fast is she going at that time?

d. What is the difference between an antiderivative and an indefinite integral?

## Concepts Problems

C1. *Introduction to the Derivative of a Product:* Let $f(x) = x^7$ and $g(x) = x^9$. Let

$$h(x) = f(x) \cdot g(x).$$

a. Write an equation for $h(x)$ in as simple a form as possible.

b. Find $h'(x)$.

c. Find $f'(x)$ and $g'(x)$. Does $h'(x) = f'(x) \cdot g'(x)$?

d. Show that for these particular functions, $h'(x) = f'(x) \cdot g(x) + f(x) \cdot g'(x)$.

C2. *Graph of an Interesting Function:* Let $f(x) = \dfrac{x - \sin 2x}{\sin x}$.

a. What form does $f(0)$ take? What name is given to a form like this? Explain why $f$ is discontinuous at $x = 0$.

b. The discontinuity in $f$ at $x = 0$ is removable. What number should $f(0)$ be defined to equal so that the function is continuous at $x = 0$?

c. Make a conjecture about whether or not the function as defined in C2b is differentiable at $x = 0$. If you think it is differentiable, make a conjecture about what $f'(0)$ equals. If you think it is not differentiable, tell why not.

d. Use the definition of derivative (derivative at $x = c$ form) to establish whether or not your conjecture in C2c is true.

## Chapter Test

T1. Write the formal definition of limit.

T2. Write the definition of derivative (either form).

T3. Prove directly from the definition of derivative that the derivative of $f(x) = 3x^4$ is $12x^3$.

T4. Is the function $t(x) = \cos 3x$ increasing or decreasing when $x = 5$? At what rate?

T5. Sketch the graph of a function for which $f'(5) = 2$. Sketch a line tangent to the graph at that point. What would happen to the graph and the tangent line if you were to zoom in on the point where $x = 5$? What is the name of the property that expresses this relationship between the graph and the tangent line?

T6. Amos Take must evaluate $f'(5)$ where $f(x) = 7x$. He substitutes 5 for $x$, getting $f(5) = 35$. Then he differentiates the 35 and gets $f'(5) = 0$ (which equals the score his instructor gives him for the problem!). What mistake did Amos make? What is the correct answer?

T7. Plot the graph of $f(x) = (\sin x)/x$. Then sketch the result. Show in particular what happens to $f(x)$ as $x$ approaches zero. In the proof of the limit of this function as $x$ approaches zero, the function is bounded below by $y = \cos x$ and bounded above by $y = \sec x$. Name and state (without proof) the theorem used in this proof.

For Problems T8–T12, find an equation for the derivative function.

T8. $f(x) = (7x + 3)^{15}$

T9. $g(x) = \cos(x^5)$

T10. $\dfrac{d}{dx}(\sin 5x)$

T11. $y = 60x^{2/3} - x + 2^5$

T12. $f(x) = \cos(\sin^5 7x)$

T13. Estimate the value of the derivative, $y'$, at $x = 1$ for the graph shown in Figure 3-10b.

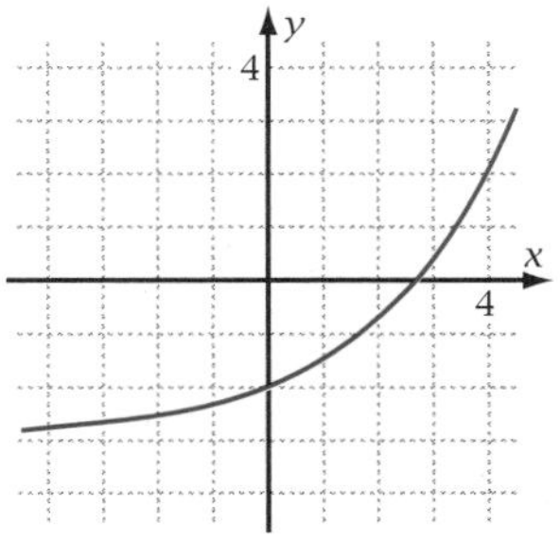

Figure 3-10b

T14. Find velocity and acceleration equations.

$$y = 3 + 5x^{-1.6}$$

T15. Find an equation for the antiderivative: $f'(x) = 72x^{5/4}$.

T16. Find an equation for $f(x)$ if $f'(x) = 5\sin x$ and $f(0) = 13$.

T17. *Carbon Dioxide Problem:* The concentration of carbon dioxide in the atmosphere fluctuates slightly. The concentration is at a minimum in the summer when tree leaves absorb the carbon dioxide and at a maximum in the winter when trees are bare. The fluctuation is only about ±2 ppm (parts per million) with an average concentration of 300 ppm. Assuming that the concentration varies sinusoidally with time, $t$ days since the first of the year, the concentration, $c(t)$, is

$$c(t) = 300 + 2\cos\frac{2\pi}{365}t,$$

whose graph is shown in Figure 3-10c.

a. Write an equation for $c'(t)$.

b. The greatest rate of increase occurs at $t = 273$, which is at the autumnal equinox. What is this rate in parts per million per day?

c. The earth's atmosphere contains a total of about $6 \times 10^{15}$ tons (t) of air. Show that the amount of carbon dioxide in the atmosphere is increasing by about 2390 tons/sec at $t = 273$. Surprising, isn't it!?

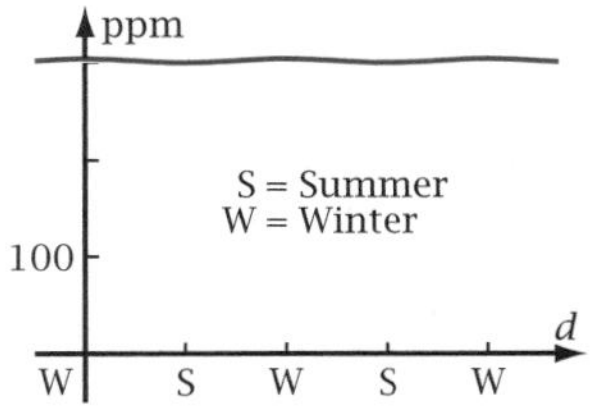

Figure 3-10c

CHAPTER

# 4 Products, Quotients, and Parametric Functions

Unlike the pendulum in a grandfather clock, this Foucault pendulum is free to swing in any direction. The path of the pendulum is as constant as possible with respect to space, and thus seems to move with respect to the earth as the earth rotates underneath it. Parametric functions are used as mathematical models of the path of an object whose $x$- and $y$-coordinates both vary with time.

# Mathematical Overview

You have already learned a way to differentiate power functions. In Chapter 4 you will learn algebraic methods for differentiating products and quotients. You will also apply these methods to parametric functions in which both $x$ and $y$ depend on some third variable such as time. You will gain this knowledge in four ways.

***Graphically*** The logo at the top of each even-numbered page of this chapter shows the path followed by a pendulum that is allowed to swing in both the $x$- and $y$-directions.

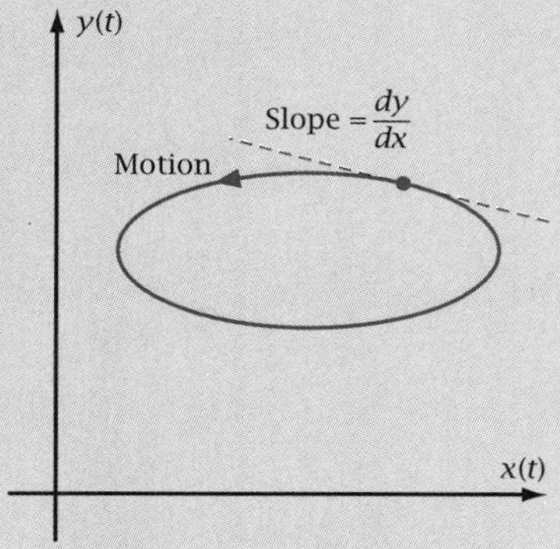


***Numerically***

| $t$ | $x$ | $y$ |
|---|---|---|
| 0 | 7 | 4 |
| 1 | 5.620 ... | 5.501 ... |
| 2 | 1.030 ... | 4.176 ... |
| 3 | 2.039 ... | 3.053 ... |
| ... | ... | ... |

***Algebraically*** $\dfrac{dy}{dx} = \dfrac{dy/dt}{dx/dt}$, the parametric chain rule.

***Verbally*** *I had my first major surprise in calculus! The derivative of a product of two functions is not the product of the two derivatives. The same thing goes for quotients. I also proved that the derivative property for power functions works when the exponent is negative and not an integer.*

# 4-1 Combinations of Two Functions

You have learned to differentiate algebraically a function that is a linear combination of two other functions, such as $f(x) = 3\cos x + 2\sin x$. In this section you will explore derivatives of a **product**, a **quotient**, and a **composition** of two other functions. For example,

$$p(x) = (3\cos x)(2\sin x), \quad q(x) = \frac{3\cos x}{2\sin x}, \quad \text{and} \quad \begin{aligned} x &= 3\cos t \\ y &= 2\sin t \end{aligned}$$

***OBJECTIVE***

Explore on your own or with your study group the derivatives of functions formed by multiplying, dividing, and composing two functions.

## Exploratory Problem Set 4-1

Let $f(x) = 3\cos x$ and let $g(x) = 2\sin x$, as shown in Figures 4-1a and 4-1b.

1. Find equations for $f'(x)$ and $g'(x)$.
2. *Derivative of a Product of Two Functions:* Plot $p(x) = f(x) \cdot g(x) = (3\cos x)(2\sin x)$. Use a friendly window that is about the size shown in Figures 4-1a and 4-1b. Sketch the result. Find $p'(2)$ numerically. How do you tell whether $p(x)$ is increasing or decreasing at $x = 2$? Does $p'(2)$ equal $f'(2) \cdot g'(2)$?
3. *Derivative of a Quotient of Two Functions:* Plot $q(x) = f(x)/g(x) = (3\cos x)/(2\sin x)$. Sketch the result. What familiar function is $q$? Find $q'(2)$ numerically. Is $q(x)$ increasing or decreasing at $x = 2$? Does $q'(2)$ equal $f'(2)/g'(2)$?
4. *Parametric Function:* Let $x = 3\cos t$ and $y = 2\sin t$. If you draw an $xy$-graph for various values of $t$, the result is called a parametric function. The elliptical path traced on the floor by the pendulum pictured on page 129 is an example of such a function. Put your grapher in parametric mode. Enter $x = 3\cos t$ and $y = 2\sin t$. Use a window with $x$- and $y$-ranges like those shown in Figure 4-1a. Use a window of $0 \le t \le 2\pi$, with a $t$-step of 0.1. Plot and sketch the graph. Does the graph really seem to be an ellipse?

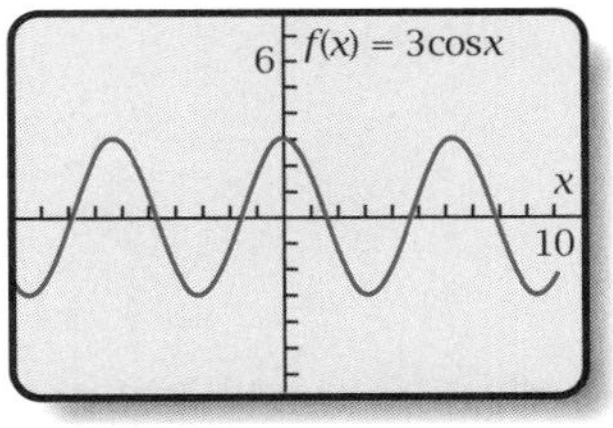


Figure 4-1a

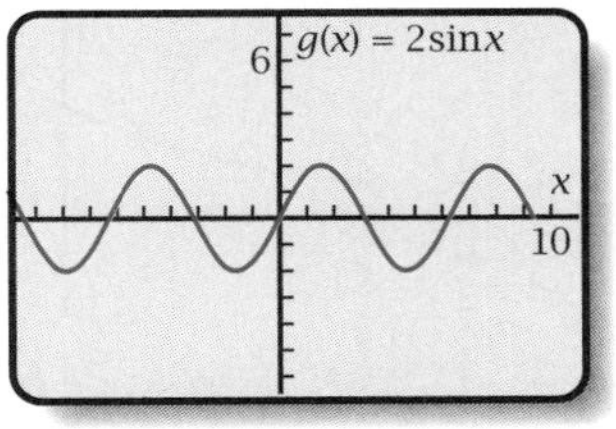


Figure 4-1b

5. *Derivative of a Parametric Function:* Trace the graph in Problem 4 to the point where $t = 2$. Find $\Delta x$ and $\Delta y$ as $t$ goes from 1.9 to 2.1 and use the results to find a symmetric difference quotient that approximates $dy/dx$ at $t = 2$. Give evidence to show that $dy/dx$ at this point could equal $(dy/dt)/(dx/dt)$ given that the derivatives are taken at $t = 2$.
6. *Conjectures?* Just for fun, see if you can calculate the correct values of $p'(2)$ and $q'(2)$ from Problems 2 and 3, using the values of $f'(2)$, $g'(2)$, $f(2)$, and $g(2)$.

# 4-2 Derivative of a Product of Two Functions

The derivative of a sum of two functions is equal to the sum of the two derivatives. As you learned in Exploratory Problem Set 4-1, there is no such distributive property for the derivative of a product of two functions. Here is an example.

| | | |
|---|---|---|
| Derivative of the product | ⟵ $f(x) = (x^5)(x^8)$ ⟶ | Product of the derivatives |
| $f(x) = x^{13}$ | | $(5x^4)(8x^7)$ |
| $f'(x) = 13x^{12}$ | ⟵ Not the same. ⟶ | $= 40x^{11}$ |

In this section you will learn how to differentiate a product of two functions without having to multiply first.

**OBJECTIVE**

Given a function that is a product of two other functions, find, in one step, an equation for the derivative function.

What follows involves some fairly complicated algebra. Therefore, it helps to streamline the symbols somewhat. Instead of writing $f(x) = g(x)\,h(x)$, write

$$y = uv,$$

where $u$ and $v$ stand for differentiable functions of $x$. The idea will be to find $dy/dx$ in terms of $du/dx$ and $dv/dx$.

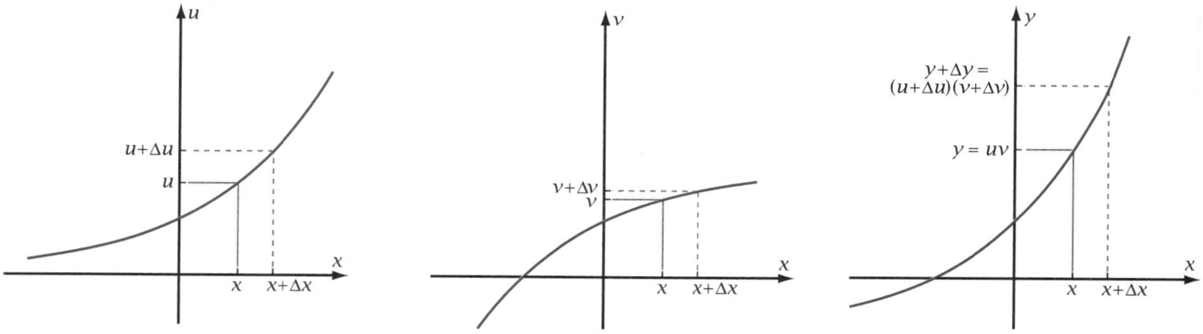


$u$ = one factor    $v$ = other factor    $y = uv$

Figure 4-2a

The graphs of two functions $u$ and $v$ and their product $y = uv$ are shown in Figure 4-2a. By the definition of derivative,

$$\frac{dy}{dx} = \lim_{\Delta x \to 0} \frac{(y + \Delta y) - y}{\Delta x}$$

Because $f(x) = g(x) \cdot h(x)$, $f(x + \Delta x)$ is equal to $g(x + \Delta x) \cdot h(x + \Delta x)$. Thus $(y + \Delta y)$ in the equation above can be replaced by $(u + \Delta u)(v + \Delta v)$, as indicated on the right side in Figure 4-2a, and $y$ can be replaced by $uv$. Therefore,

$$\frac{dy}{dx} = \lim_{\Delta x \to 0} \frac{(u + \Delta u)(v + \Delta v) - uv}{\Delta x}$$

$$\frac{dy}{dx} = \lim_{\Delta x \to 0} \frac{uv + \Delta uv + u\Delta v + \Delta u \Delta v - uv}{\Delta x}$$

$\Delta uv$ means $(\Delta u) \cdot v$.

$$= \lim_{\Delta x \to 0} \frac{\Delta uv + u\Delta v + \Delta u \Delta v}{\Delta x}$$

$$= \lim_{\Delta x \to 0} \left( \frac{\Delta uv}{\Delta x} + \frac{u\Delta v}{\Delta x} + \frac{\Delta u \Delta v}{\Delta x} \right)$$

$$= \lim_{\Delta x \to 0} \left( \frac{\Delta u}{\Delta x} v + u \frac{\Delta v}{\Delta x} + \Delta u \frac{\Delta v}{\Delta x} \right).$$

Using the limit of a sum and the limit of a product properties, and using the fact that the limits of $\Delta u/\Delta x$ and $\Delta v/\Delta x$ are $du/dx$ and $dv/dx$, respectively, gives

$$\frac{dy}{dx} = \frac{du}{dx} v + u \frac{dv}{dx} + 0 \frac{dv}{dx}$$

Because $u$ is a continuous function, $\Delta u \to 0$ as $\Delta x \to 0$.

$$= \frac{du}{dx} v + u \frac{dv}{dx}$$

Derivative of a product formula.

$$y' = u'v + uv'$$

Short form, where $u'$ and $v'$ are derivatives with respect to $x$.

The formula is best remembered as a procedure, as shown in the box.

### Property: Derivative of a Product of Two Functions

If $y = uv$, where $u$ and $v$ are differentiable functions of $x$, then $y' = u'v + uv'$.

*Words:* Derivative of first times second, plus first times derivative of second.

With this pattern you can accomplish the objective of differentiating a product in one step.

**Example 1** If $y = x^4 \cos 6x$, find $dy/dx$.

**Solution**

$$\frac{dy}{dx} = 4x^3 \cos 6x + x^4(-\sin 6x) \cdot 6$$
$$= 4x^3 \cos 6x - 6x^4 \sin 6x$$

■

As you write the derivative, say to yourself, "Derivative of first times second, plus first times derivative of second." Don't forget the chain rule!

**Example 2** If $y = (3x - 8)^7 (4x + 9)^5$, find $y'$ and simplify.

**Solution**

$$y' = 7(3x - 8)^6(3)(4x + 9)^5 + (3x - 8)^7(5)(4x + 9)^4(4)$$

The product rule and the chain rule have been used. Each term has common binomial factors. Simplification includes factoring out these common factors.

$$y' = (3x - 8)^6(4x + 9)^4[21(4x + 9) + 20(3x - 8)]$$
$$= (3x - 8)^6(4x + 9)^4(144x + 29)$$

■

Note that the factored form in Example 2 is considered simpler because it is easier to find values of $x$ that make the derivative equal zero.

# Problem Set 4-2

### *Do These Quickly*

The following problems are intended to refresh your skills. You should be able to do all ten problems in less than five minutes.

**Q1.** Differentiate: $y = x^{3/4}$

**Q2.** Find $y'$: $y = 17x$.

**Q3.** Find $dy/dx$: $y = (5x - 7)^{-6}$.

**Q4.** Find $\dfrac{d}{dx}(\sin 2x)$.

**Q5.** Differentiate: $v = \cos^3 t$

**Q6.** Differentiate: $L = m^2 + 5m + 11$

**Q7.** If $dy/dx = \cos x^3 \cdot 3x^2$, find $y$.

**Q8.** In Figure 4-2b, if $x = -2$, $y' \approx$ -?-

**Q9.** Sketch the graph $y = \cos x$.

**Q10.** If $u = v^2/6$, where $u$ is in feet and $v$ is in seconds, how fast is $u$ changing when $v = 12$?

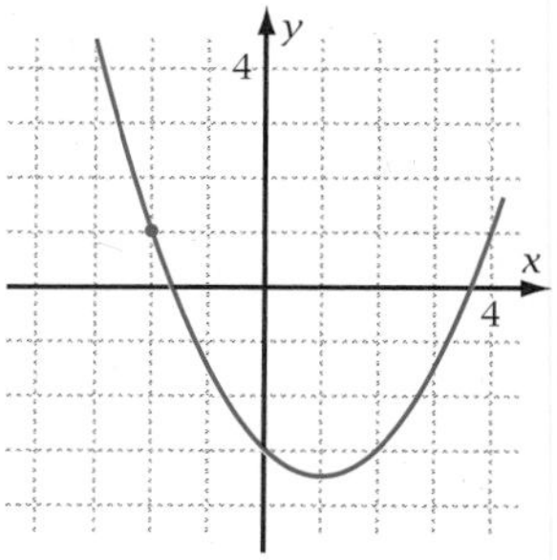


Figure 4-2b

For Problems 1–22, differentiate and simplify. You may check your answer by comparing its graph with the numerical derivative graph.

1. $f(x) = x^3 \cos x$
2. $f(x) = x^4 \sin x$
3. Find $g'(x)$: $g(x) = x^{1.5} \sin 7x$.
4. Find $h'(x)$: $h(x) = x^{-6.3} \cos 10x$.
5. Find $\dfrac{dy}{dx}$: $y = x^7(2x + 5)^{10}$.
6. Find $\dfrac{dy}{dx}$: $y = x^8(3x + 7)^9$.
7. Find $z'$: $z = x^4 \cos^5 3x$.
8. Find $v'$: $v = x^5 \sin^3 6x$.
9. Find $\dfrac{d}{dx}[(4x - 3)^6 \sin 5x]$.
10. Find $\dfrac{d}{dx}(p)$: $p = (7x - 4)^9 \cos 2x$.
11. $y = (6x + 11)^4(5x - 9)^7$
12. $y = (7x - 3)^9(6x - 1)^5$
13. $P = (x^2 - 1)^{10}(x^2 + 1)^{15}$
14. $P(x) = (x^3 + 6)^4(x^3 + 4)^6$
15. $a(t) = 4 \sin 3t \cos 5t$
16. $v = 7 \cos 2t \sin 6t$
17. $y = 10 \cos^8 5x \sin^5 8x$
18. $y = 7 \sin^3 4x \cos^4 3x$
19. $z = x^3(5x - 2)^4 \sin 6x$ (Be clever!)
20. $u = 3x^5(x^2 - 4) \cos 10x$ (Be clever!!)
21. $y = \cos(3 \sin x)$
22. $y = \sin(5 \cos x)$
23. *Product of Three Functions Problem:* Prove that if $y = uvw$, where $u, v$, and $w$ are differentiable functions of $x$, then $y' = u'vw + uv'w + uvw'$.
24. *Product of n Functions Conjecture Problem:* If $y = u_1u_2u_3 \ldots u_n$, where $u_1, \ldots, u_n$ are differentiable functions of $x$, make a conjecture about what an equation for $y'$ would be.

For Problems 25–28, differentiate and simplify.

25. $z = x^5 \cos^6 x \sin 7x$

26. $y = 4x^6 \sin^3 x \cos 5x$

27. $y = x^4(2x - 3)^5 \sin x \cos 2x$

28. $u = x^5(3x - 1)^2 \cos 2x \sin 3x$

29. *Odd Function and Even Function Derivative Problem:* A function is called an **odd function** if it has the property $f(-x) = -f(x)$. Similarly, $f$ is called an **even function** if $f(-x) = f(x)$. For instance, sine is odd because $\sin(-x) = -\sin x$, and cosine is even because $\cos(-x) = \cos x$. Use the chain rule appropriately to prove that the derivative of an odd function is an even function and that the derivative of an even function is an odd function.

30. *Double Argument Properties Problem:* Let $f(x) = 2 \sin x \cos x$ and let $g(x) = \sin 2x$. Find $f'(x)$ and $g'(x)$. Use the appropriate trigonometric properties to show that $f'(x)$ and $g'(x)$ are equivalent. Then show that $f(x)$ and $g(x)$ are also equivalent. Do the same for the functions $f(x) = \cos^2 x - \sin^2 x$ and $g(x) = \cos 2x$.

31. *Derivative of a Power Induction Problem:* Prove by mathematical induction that for any positive integer $n$, if $f(x) = x^n$, then $f'(x) = nx^{n-1}$.

32. *Derivative Two Ways Problem:* The function $y = (x + 3)^8(x - 4)^8$ can be differentiated by two methods: First, consider the function as a product of two composite functions; second, multiply and differentiate the result, $y = (x^2 - x - 12)^8$. Show that both methods give the same result for the derivative.

33. *Confirmation of the Product Property:* Let $f(x) = x^3 \cdot \sin x$. (See Figure 4-2c.)
    a. Sketch this graph, then draw what you think the derivative graph, $f'$, would look like. Show, especially, places where $f'(x)$ would equal zero.
    b. Write an equation for $f'(x)$. Plot $f$ and $f'$ on your grapher. How does the graph you predicted compare with the actual graph?
    c. Plot the numerical derivative on your grapher. How does this graph confirm that your equation for $f'(x)$ is correct?

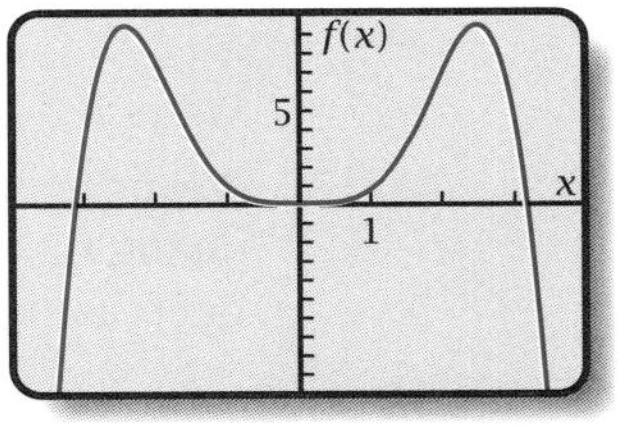

Figure 4-2c

34. *Repeated Roots Problem:* In this problem you will sketch the graph of the function $f(x) = (5x - 7)^4(2x + 3)^5$.
    a. Plot on your grapher the graph of $f$. Use an $x$-window from $-2$ to $2$ and a $y$-window that is tall enough to fit the graph. Sketch the result.
    b. Find $f'(x)$. Simplify. For example, factor out any common factors.
    c. Find all three values of $x$ for which $f'(x) = 0$. The factored form of $f'(x)$ from 34b should be convenient for this purpose.
    d. Find $f(x)$ for each of the values of $x$ in 34c. Show these three points on your graph.
    e. The graph of $f$ should have a horizontal tangent line at each of the points in 34d. State whether the following statement is true or false: The graph has a high point or a low point where $f'(x) = 0$.

35. *Pole Dance Problem:* In a variation of a Filipino pole dance, two pairs of bamboo poles are moved back and forth at floor level. The dancer steps into and out of the region between the poles (Figure 4-2d), trying to avoid being pinched between them as they come together. The area, $A = LW$, varies with time, $t$, where distances are in feet and time is in seconds.

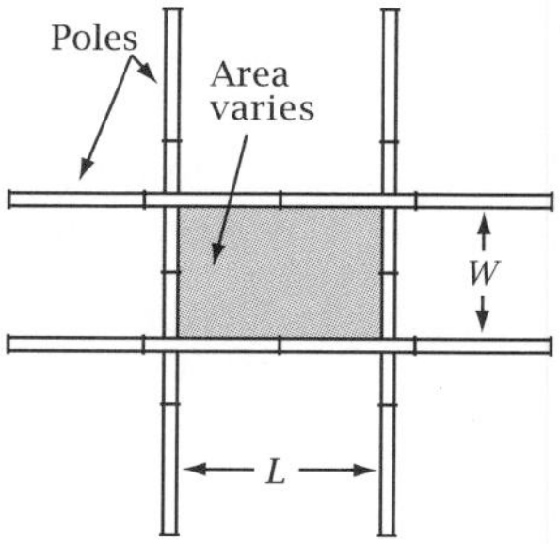


Figure 4-2d

a. Write $dA/dt$ in terms of $L, W, dL/dt$, and $dW/dt$.

b. Suppose that $W = 2 + 2\cos t$ and that $L = 3 + 2\sin 2t$. At what rate is the area changing when $t = 4$ sec? When $t = 5$ sec? At these times is the area increasing or decreasing?

## 4-3 Derivative of a Quotient of Two Functions

In this section you will learn how to find the derivative of a quotient of two functions. For example,

$$f(x) = \frac{\sin 5x}{8x - 3}.$$

**OBJECTIVE**

Given a function whose equation contains a quotient of two other functions, find an equation for the derivative function in one step and simplify the answer.

Suppose that $f(x) = g(x)/h(x)$. Using $y, u$, and $v$ for the three function values lets you write the equation in a simple form.

$$y = \frac{u}{v}$$

By the definition of derivative,

$$\frac{dy}{dx} = \lim_{\Delta x \to 0} \frac{\Delta y}{\Delta x} = \lim_{\Delta x \to 0} \left( \frac{\dfrac{u + \Delta u}{v + \Delta v} - \dfrac{u}{v}}{\Delta x} \right).$$

Multiplying the numerator and the denominator by $(v + \Delta v)(v)$ eliminates the complex fraction.

$$\frac{dy}{dx} = \lim_{\Delta x \to 0} \left( \frac{(u + \Delta u)v - u(v + \Delta v)}{\Delta x(v + \Delta v)(v)} \right)$$

Further algebra allows you to take the limit.

$$\frac{dy}{dx} = \lim_{\Delta x \to 0} \left( \frac{uv + \Delta uv - uv - u\Delta v}{\Delta x(v + \Delta v)(v)} \right)$$

$$= \lim_{\Delta x \to 0} \left( \frac{1}{(v + \Delta v)(v)} \cdot \frac{\Delta uv - u\Delta v}{\Delta x} \right)$$

Simplify, then associate $\Delta x$ with the numerator.

$$= \lim_{\Delta x \to 0} \left[ \frac{1}{(v + \Delta v)(v)} \cdot \left( \frac{\Delta u}{\Delta x} \cdot v - u \cdot \frac{\Delta v}{\Delta x} \right) \right]$$

Distribute $\Delta x$, then associate it with $\Delta u$ and $\Delta v$.

$$= \frac{1}{v^2} \cdot \left( \frac{du}{dx} \cdot v - u \cdot \frac{dv}{dx} \right)$$

Limits of products, quotient, and sum; definition of derivative; $\Delta v \to 0$ as $\Delta x \to 0$.

$$y' = \frac{1}{v^2}(u'v - uv') = \frac{u'v - uv'}{v^2}$$

Where $u'$ and $v'$ are derivatives with respect to $x$.

**Property: Derivative of a Quotient of Two Functions**

If $y = \dfrac{u}{v}$, where $u$ and $v$ are differentiable functions, and $v \neq 0$, then

$$y' = \frac{u'v - uv'}{v^2}.$$

Words: Derivative of top times bottom, minus top times derivative of bottom, all divided by bottom squared.

Note that the numerator has the same pattern as the derivative of a product, namely $u'v + uv'$, except that a subtraction sign $(-)$ is used instead of an addition sign $(+)$.

■ ***Example 1*** Differentiate: $f(x) = \dfrac{\sin 5x}{8x - 3}$

***Solution***

$$f'(x) = \frac{\cos 5x\,(5)(8x - 3) - \sin 5x\,(8)}{(8x - 3)^2}$$

$$f'(x) = \frac{5\cos 5x(8x - 3) - 8\sin 5x}{(8x - 3)^2}$$

■

As you differentiate, say to yourself, "Derivative of top times bottom, minus top times derivative of bottom, all divided by bottom squared." You must also, of course, apply the chain rule when necessary.

**Example 2** Differentiate: $y = \dfrac{(5x-2)^7}{(4x+9)^3}$

**Solution**

$$y' = \frac{7(5x-2)^6(5)\cdot(4x+9)^3 - (5x-2)^7\cdot 3(4x+9)^2(4)}{(4x+9)^6}$$

$$= \frac{(5x-2)^6(4x+9)^2[35(4x+9) - 12(5x-2)]}{(4x+9)^6} \qquad \text{Factor the numerator.}$$

$$= \frac{(5x-2)^6(80x+339)}{(4x+9)^4} \qquad \text{Cancel common factors.}$$

**Example 3** Differentiate: $\dfrac{d}{dx}\left(\dfrac{5}{7x^3}\right)$

**Solution** Although the quotient rule can be used here, it is simpler to transform to a power.

$$\frac{d}{dx}\left(\frac{5}{7x^3}\right) = \frac{d}{dx}\left(\frac{5}{7}x^{-3}\right) = -\frac{15}{7}x^{-4}$$

# Problem Set 4-3

### Do These Quickly

The following problems are intended to refresh your skills. You should be able to do all ten problems in less than five minutes.

**Q1.** Find $\dfrac{d}{dx}(x^{1066})$.

**Q2.** Antidifferentiate: $f'(x) = 60x^4$

**Q3.** Find $y'$: $y = x^3 \sin x$.

**Q4.** Find $\dfrac{dy}{dx}$: $y = \cos(x^7)$.

**Q5.** Differentiate: $f(x) = (3^5)(2^8)$

**Q6.** Find $a'(t)$: $a(t) = \sin 9t$.

**Q7.** Write the definition of derivative.

**Q8.** Write the physical meaning of derivative.

**Q9.** Factor: $(x-3)^5 + (x-3)^4(2x)$

**Q10.** Sketch the graph of the derivative of the function graphed in Figure 4-3a.

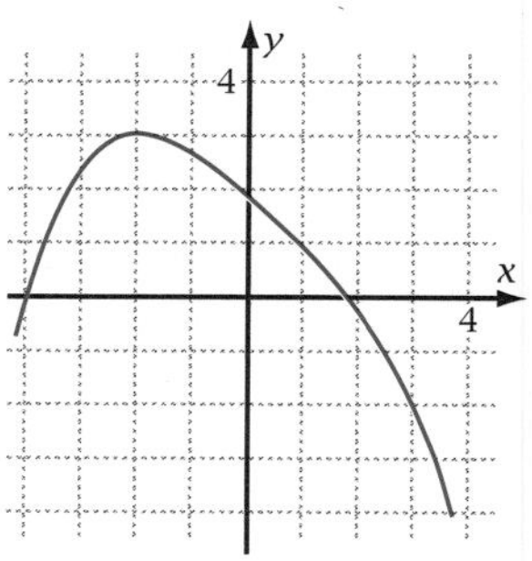

Figure 4-3a

For Problems 1–26, differentiate and simplify. You may check your answer by comparing its graph with the numerical derivative graph.

1. $f(x) = \dfrac{x^3}{\sin x}$

2. $f(x) = \dfrac{x^4}{\cos x}$

3. $g(x) = \dfrac{\cos^3 x}{x^5}$

4. $h(x) = \dfrac{\sin^5 x}{x^3}$

5. $y = \dfrac{\sin 10x}{\cos 20x}$

6. $y = \dfrac{\cos 12x}{\sin 18x}$

7. $y'$ if $y = \dfrac{3x - 7}{6x + 5}$

8. $y'$ if $y = \dfrac{10x + 9}{5x - 3}$

9. Find $\dfrac{dz}{dx}$ if $z = \dfrac{(8x + 1)^6}{(5x - 2)^9}$.

10. Find $\dfrac{dA}{dx}$ if $A = \dfrac{(4x - 1)^7}{(7x + 2)^4}$.

11. Find $P'$ if $P = \dfrac{5x^2 - 10x + 3}{3x^2 + 6x - 8}$.

12. Find $r'$ if $r = \dfrac{4x^2 + 8x + 1}{4x^2 - 8x + 3}$.

13. Find $\dfrac{d}{dx}(60x^{-4/3})$.

14. Find $\dfrac{d}{dx}(24x^{-7/3})$.

15. $r(x) = \dfrac{12}{x^3}$ (Be clever!)

16. $t(x) = \dfrac{51}{x^{17}}$ (Be clever!)

17. $v(x) = \dfrac{14}{\cos 0.5x}$

18. $a(x) = \dfrac{20}{\sin^2 x}$

19. $e(x) = \dfrac{1}{x}$

20. $s(x) = \dfrac{1}{x^2}$

21. Find $W'(x)$ if $W(x) = \dfrac{10}{(x^3 - 1)^{-5}}$.

22. Find $T'(x)$ if $T(x) = \dfrac{1}{\cos x \sin x}$.

23. $T(x) = \dfrac{\sin x}{\cos x}$

24. $C(x) = \dfrac{\cos x}{\sin x}$

25. Find $C'$ if $C = \dfrac{1}{\sin x}$.

26. Find $S'$ if $S = \dfrac{1}{\cos x}$.

27. *Black Hole Problem:* Ann Astronaut's spaceship gets trapped in the gravitational field of a black hole! Her velocity, $v(t)$ miles per hour, is given by:

$$v(t) = \frac{1000}{3 - t},$$

where $t$ is time in hours.

a. How fast is she going when $t = 1$? When $t = 2$? When $t = 3$?

b. Recall that acceleration is the instantaneous rate of change of velocity. Write an equation for the acceleration function, $a(t)$.

c. What is her acceleration when $t = 1$? When $t = 2$? When $t = 3$? What are the units of acceleration in this problem?

d. Using the same screen, plot graphs of velocity and of acceleration as functions of time. Sketch the results.

e. Ann is in danger if the acceleration exceeds 500 (mi/hr)/hr. For what range of times is Ann's acceleration below the danger point?

28. *Catch-Up Rate Problem:* Willie Ketchup is out for his morning walk. He sees Betty Wont walking ahead of him and decides to catch up to her. He quickly figures that she is walking at a rate of 5 ft/sec. He lets $x$ ft/sec stand for the rate he will go.

a. Explain why Willie catches up at a rate of $(x - 5)$ ft/sec.

b. Betty is 300 ft ahead of Willie when he first starts catching up. Recall that distance = rate × time and write an equation for $t(x)$, the number of seconds it will take him to catch up to her.

c. How long will it take Willie to catch up if he walks 6 ft/sec? 8 ft/sec? 10 ft/sec? 5 ft/sec? 4 ft/sec? 5.1 ft/sec? What is a reasonable domain for $x$?

d. At what instantaneous rate does Willie's catch-up time change with respect to speed if he is going 6 ft/sec? What are the units of this rate?

e. Explain why $t(x)$ has no value for the derivative at $x = 5$.

29. *Confirmation of Quotient Formula Problem:* Find $f'(x)$ for the function

$$f(x) = \frac{3x + 7}{2x + 5}.$$

Use the answer to evaluate $f'(4)$. Use $x = 4.1, 4.01$, and $4.001$ to show that the difference quotient $[f(x) - f(4)]/(x - 4)$ gets closer and closer to $f'(4)$.

30. *Derivative Graph and Table Problem:*

a. For the function $f$ in Figure 4-3b, sketch what you think the graph of the derivative, $f'$, looks like.

b. The equation for $f(x)$ is

$$f(x) = \frac{x^2 - 8}{x - 3}.$$

Make a table of values of $f(x)$ and $f'(x)$ for each 0.01 unit of $x$ from 2.95 to 3.05.

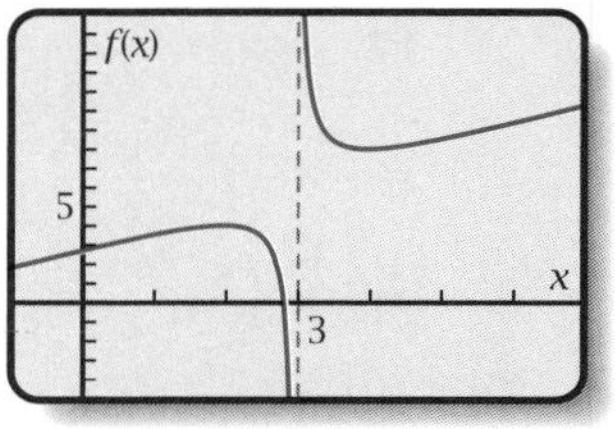


Figure 4-3b

c. Plot on your grapher the graph of $f'$. In what ways does your sketch in 30a differ from the actual derivative graph?

d. Based on your graphs and table, describe the way $f(x)$ changes as $x$ approaches 3.

e. Find the value of $x$ between 1 and 3 where $f(x)$ stops increasing and starts decreasing.

f. Find the value of $x$ between 3 and 5 where $f(x)$ stops decreasing and starts increasing.

g. What are the domain and the range of $f$? What are the domain and the range of $f'$?

31. *Proof of the Power Rule for Negative Exponents:* The proof you have used for the power rule for derivatives assumes that the exponent is a positive integer. You have seen by example that the rule also works for some powers with negative exponents. Suppose that $y = x^{-5}$. Use the quotient rule of this section and write $y$ as

$$y = \frac{1}{x^5}$$

to prove that $y' = 5x^{-6}$. Prove that, in general, if $y = x^n$, where $n$ is a negative constant, then $y' = nx^{n-1}$. To do this, it helps to write $y$ as

$$y = \frac{1}{x^p},$$

where $p$ is a positive number equal to the opposite of $n$.

*32. Figures 4-3c and 4-3d show the graphs of $y = \sec x$ and $y = \tan x$, respectively. Using a photocopy of each graph, sketch what you think the derivative graph looks like. Check your answers by grapher, using the numerical derivative feature.

---

*This problem prepares you for the next section.

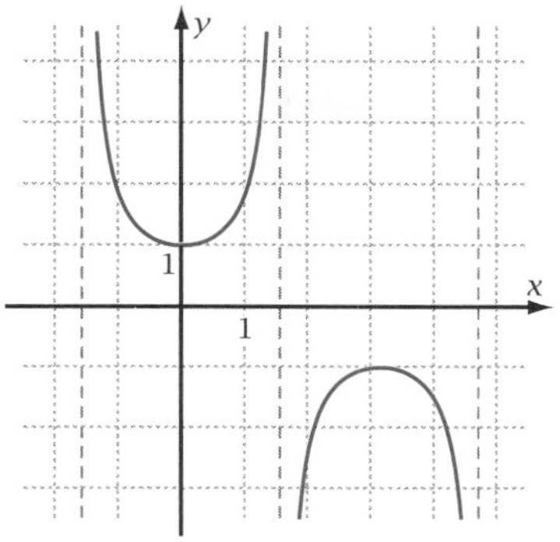


Figure 4-3c

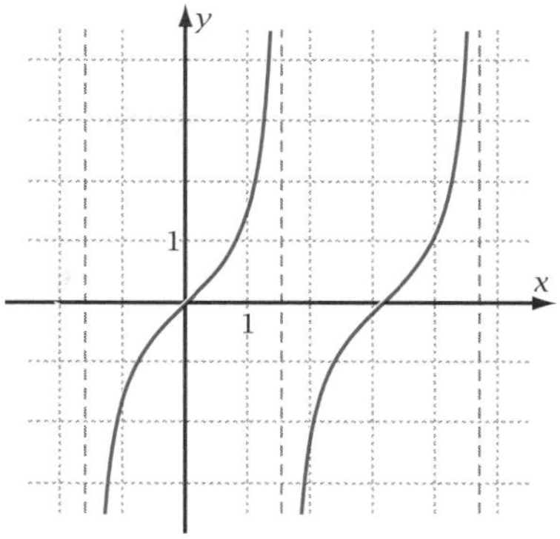


Figure 4-3d

33. *Journal Problem:* Update your journal with what you've learned since the last entry. Include such things as those listed here.
    - The one most important thing you have learned since your last journal entry
    - The primary difference between how to differentiate a sum of two functions and how to differentiate a product or a quotient of two functions
    - The meaning of a parametric function
    - What you better understand about the meaning of derivative
    - Any technique or idea about derivatives that is still unclear in your mind

# 4-4 Derivatives of the Other Trigonometric Functions

Recall from trigonometry that the tangent, cotangent, secant, and cosecant functions can be written in terms of sine and cosine.

$$\tan x = \frac{\sin x}{\cos x}, \quad \cot x = \frac{\cos x}{\sin x}, \quad \sec x = \frac{1}{\cos x}, \quad \csc x = \frac{1}{\sin x}$$

Each of the above is a quotient. Now that you can differentiate quotients, you can differentiate the other four trigonometric functions.

**OBJECTIVE**

Given a function whose equation contains any of the six trigonometric functions, find the equation for the derivative function in one step.

### *Derivative of Tangent and Cotangent Functions*

$$y = \tan x = \frac{\sin x}{\cos x}$$

$$\therefore y' = \frac{(\cos x)(\cos x) - (\sin x)(-\sin x)}{\cos^2 x} = \frac{\cos^2 x + \sin^2 x}{\cos^2 x} = \frac{1}{\cos^2 x}$$

$$= \sec^2 x$$

Derivative of tangent.

In Problem 37 of Problem Set 4-4, you will show that if $y = \cot x$, then $y' = -\csc^2 x$.

### *Derivative of Secant and Cosecant Functions*

$$y = \sec x = \frac{1}{\cos x}$$

$$\therefore\ y' = \frac{(0)(\cos x) - (1)(-\sin x)}{\cos^2 x} = \frac{\sin x}{\cos^2 x} = \frac{1}{\cos x} \cdot \frac{\sin x}{\cos x}$$

$$= \sec x \tan x$$ Derivative of secant.

In Problem 38 of Problem Set 4-4, you will show that if $y = \csc x$, then $y' = -\csc x \cot x$.

> **Properties: Derivatives of the Six Trigonometric Functions**
>
> $\sin' x = \cos x \qquad \cos' x = -\sin x$
>
> $\tan' x = \sec^2 x \qquad \cot' x = -\csc^2 x$
>
> $\sec' x = \sec x \tan x \qquad \csc' x = -\csc x \cot x$
>
> *Note:* $x$ must be in radians since this was assumed for the sine derivative.
>
> *Memory Aids:*
>
> a. The derivatives of the "co-" functions have a negative sign (−).
>
> b. To find the derivatives of the "co-" functions in the right column, replace each function in the left column with its cofunction (e.g., sec with csc).

**■ Example 1** Differentiate: $y = 3\tan^5 7x$

**Solution**

$$y' = 3(5\tan^4 7x)(\sec^2 7x)(7)$$
$$= 105\tan^4 7x \sec^2 7x$$ ■

Note that this example involves two applications of the chain rule. The outermost function is the fifth power function. This fact is easier to see if you write the original function as

$$y = 3(\tan 7x)^5.$$

The next function in is tan. Its derivative is $\sec^2$. The innermost function is $7x$; its derivative is 7. You should begin to see the "chain" of derivatives that gives the chain rule its name.

$$y' = 3(5\tan^4 7x) \cdot (\sec^2 7x) \cdot (7)$$
$$\uparrow \qquad\qquad \uparrow \qquad \uparrow$$

Here are the three "links" in the chain.

Problem Set 4-4 gives you practice differentiating all six trigonometric functions.

# Problem Set 4-4

***Do These Quickly***

The following problems are intended to refresh your skills. You should be able to do all ten problems in less than five minutes.

**Q1.** $(\sin x)/(\tan x) = $ —?—

**Q2.** $1/(\sec x) = $ —?—

**Q3.** $\cos^2 3 + \sin^2 3 = $ —?—

**Q4.** Differentiate: $f(x) = x \sin x$

**Q5.** Differentiate: $g(x) = x/(\cos x)$

**Q6.** Differentiate: $h(x) = (3x)^{-5/7}$

**Q7.** Find $dy/dx$: $y = (\cos x)^{-3}$.

**Q8.** Find $\lim_{x\to 2} (x^2 - 7x + 10)/(x - 2)$.

**Q9.** $\lim_{\Delta p\to 0} (\Delta j/\Delta p) = $ —?—

**Q10.** Sketch the graph of the derivative for the function graphed in Figure 4-4a.

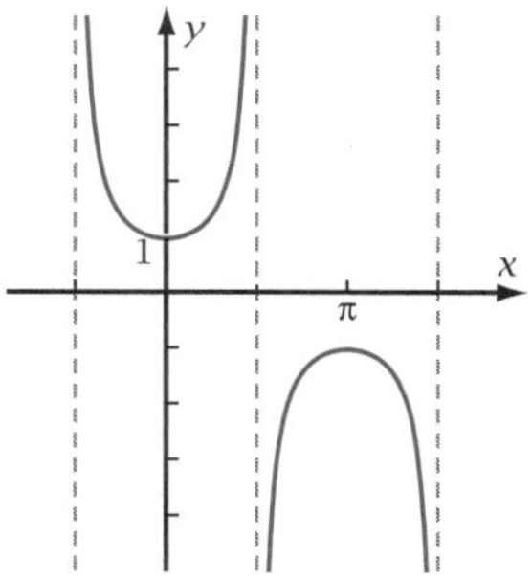

Figure 4-4a

For Problems 1–36, differentiate and do obvious simplification. You may check each answer by comparing its graph with the numerical derivative graph.

1. $f(x) = \tan 5x$
2. $f(x) = \sec 3x$
3. $y = \sec 7x$
4. $z = \tan 9x$
5. Find $g'(x)$: $g(x) = \cot 11x$.
6. Find $h'(x)$: $h(x) = \csc 10x$.
7. $r(x) = \csc 20x$
8. $p(x) = \cot 31x$
9. Find $\dfrac{d}{dx}(y)$: $y = \tan^5 4x$.
10. Find $\dfrac{d}{dx}(y)$: $y = \tan^7 9x$.
11. Find $\dfrac{d}{dx}(3 \cot^6 8x)$.
12. Find $\dfrac{d}{dx}(5 \sec^7 9x)$.
13. Find $y'$: $y = 8 \sec^{5/4} 4x$.
14. Find $y'$: $y = 88 \csc^{11/8} 2x$.
15. Find $v'$: $v = \csc(x^{-7})$.
16. Find $u'$: $u = \cot(3x^{-5})$.
17. Find $\dfrac{dp}{dx}$: $p = \sec x \tan x$.
18. Find $\dfrac{dm}{dx}$: $m = \csc x \cot x$.
19. $y = x^{-3} \cot x$
20. $y = x^{5/2} \sec x$
21. $y = \sec x \csc x$
22. $y = \tan x \cot x$
23. $y = \dfrac{\tan x}{\sin x}$
24. $y = \dfrac{\cot x}{\cos x}$
25. $y = \dfrac{5x^7}{\cot 14x}$
26. $y = \dfrac{4 \csc 10x}{x^{40}}$
27. $w = \tan(\sin 3x)$
28. $t = \sec(\cos 4x)$
29. $S(x) = \sec^2 x - \tan^2 x$
30. $m(x) = \cot^2 x - \csc^2 x$

31. $A(x) = \sin x^2$

32. $f(x) = \cos x^3$

33. $F(x) = \sin^2 x$

34. $g(x) = \cos^3 x$

35. $C(x) = \sin(\sin x)$

36. $h(x) = \cos(\cos x)$

37. *Derivative of Cotangent Problem:* Derive the formula for $y'$ if $y = \cot x$. You may write $\cot x$ either as $(\cos x)/(\sin x)$ or as $1/(\tan x)$.

38. *Derivative of Cosecant Problem:* Derive the formula for $y'$ if $y = \csc x$ by first transforming $\csc x$ into a function you already know how to differentiate.

39. *Confirmation of Tangent Derivative Formula:* Figure 4-4b shows the graph of $f(x) = \tan x$ as it might appear on your grapher.

    a. Sketch the graph. Without using the grapher, sketch what you think the derivative graph, $f'$, would look like.

    b. Find an equation for $f'(x)$. Plot the $f$ and $f'$ graphs on the same screen. Did the $f'$ you predicted look like the actual one? If not, write down where your thinking went astray and what you learned from this problem.

    c. Calculate the symmetric difference quotient for $f'(1)$, using $\Delta x = 0.01$. How close is the answer to the actual value of $f'(1)$?

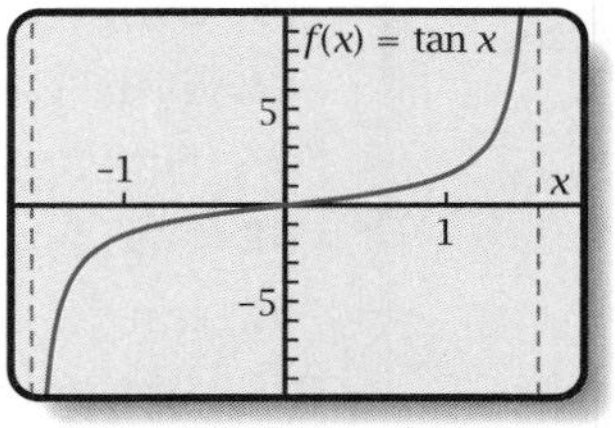

Figure 4-4b

40. *Confirmation of Secant Derivative Formula:* Figure 4-4c shows an accurate graph of $f(x) = \sec x$ in the closed interval $[-\pi/2, \pi/2]$.

    a. Write the formula for $f'(x)$. Use it to find the value of $f(1)$.

    b. Photocopy or trace the graph onto your own graph paper. At the point (1, sec 1), draw a line with slope $f'(1)$.

    c. How does your drawing confirm that the derivative formula for secant gives the correct answer at $x = 1$?

    d. Plot on the same screen the graphs of $f$ and $f'$. Copy the $f'$ graph onto the paper you used in 40b.

    e. What is happening to the $f$ graph at values of $x$ where the $f'$ graph is negative?

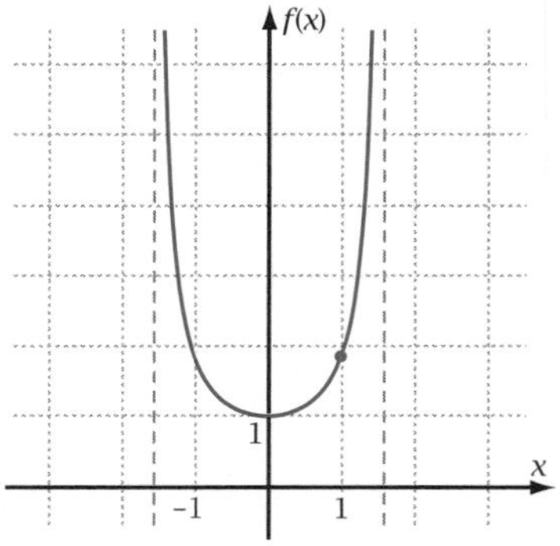

Figure 4-4c

41. *Light on the Monument Problem:* Suppose you stand 10 ft away from the base of the Washington Monument and shine a flashlight at it (Figure 4-4d). Let $x$ be the number of radians the light beam makes with a horizontal line. Let $y$ ft be the vertical distance from the flashlight to the spot of light on the wall.

    a. Show that $y = 10 \tan x$.

    b. As you rotate the flashlight upward, at what rate is $y$ increasing with respect to $x$ when $x = 1$? What are the units of this rate? What is this rate in feet per *degree*?

    c. At what rate does $y$ change when your light points at the top of the vertical monument wall, where $y = 535$ ft?

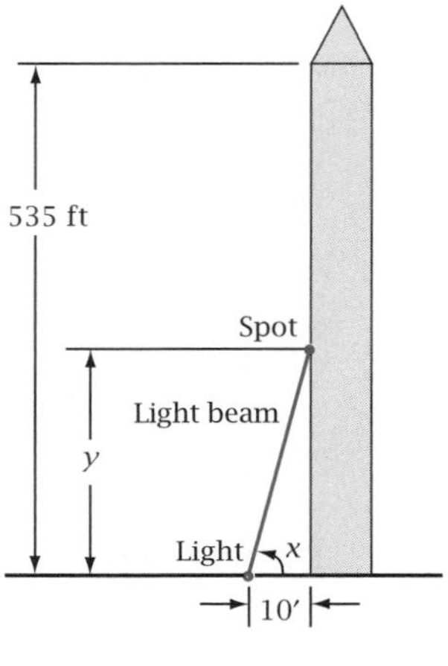

Figure 4-4d

42. *Point of Light Problem:* As the beacon light at an airport rotates, it casts a point of light onto objects it encounters. Suppose that a building is located northeast of the beacon and that the building's north-south wall is 500 ft east of the beacon (Figure 4-4e). Let $x$ be the angle (in radians) the light beam makes with the east-west line. Let $y$ be the number of feet north of this line where the point of light is shining when the angle is $x$.

    a. Show that $y = 500 \tan x$.

    b. Let $t$ be the number of seconds since the light was pointed due east. Find $dy/dt$. (Because $x$ depends on $t$, $x$ is an inside function. By the chain rule, the answer will contain $dx/dt$.)

    c. Suppose that the beacon is rotating counterclockwise at 0.3 rad/sec. What does $dx/dt$ equal? How fast is the point of light moving along the wall when it passes the window located at $y = 300$ ft?

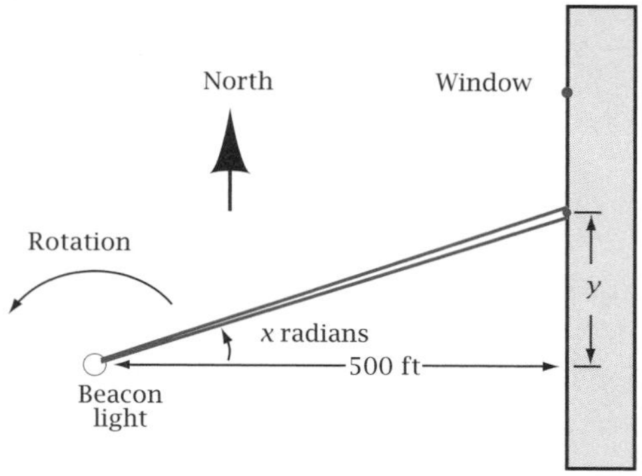


Figure 4-4e

43. *Antiderivative Problem:* For each function below, write an equation for the antiderivative. Remember "$+C$"!

    a. $y' = \cos x$

    b. $y' = \sin 2x$

    c. $y' = \sec^2 3x$

    d. $y' = \csc^2 4x$

    e. $y' = 5 \sec x \tan x$

44. *Journal Problem:* Update your journal with what you've learned since your last entry. Include such things as those listed below.
    - The one most important thing you have learned since your last journal entry
    - The extension you have made in the derivative of a power formula
    - How to differentiate all six trigonometric functions, using what you have recently learned
    - Anything you need to ask questions about during next class period

# 4-5 Derivatives of Inverse Trigonometric Functions

You have learned how to differentiate the six trigonometric functions. In this section you will explore the inverses of these functions.

**OBJECTIVE**

Differentiate each of the six inverse trigonometric functions.

### *Background Item Number 1: The Inverse of a Function*

The left-hand graph in Figure 4-5a shows how the population of a certain city may grow as a function of time. If you are interested in finding the time at which the population reaches a certain value, it may be more convenient to reverse the variables and write time as a function of population. The relation you get by interchanging the two variables is called the **inverse** of the original function. The graph of the inverse is shown on the right-hand graph in Figure 4-5a.

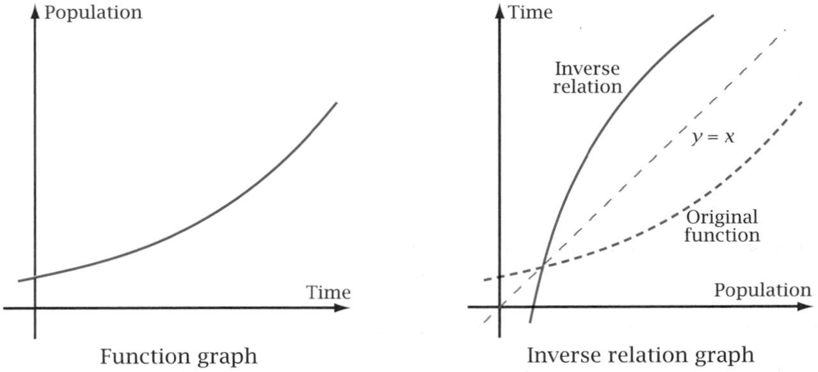


Figure 4-5a

For a linear function such as $y = 2x + 6$, interchanging the variables gives $x = 2y + 6$ for the inverse relation. Solving this equation for $y$ in terms of $x$ gives $y = 0.5x - 3$. The symbol $f^{-1}$, pronounced "$f$ inverse," is used for the inverse function of $f$. For this example,

$$\text{if } f(x) = 2x + 6, \text{ then } f^{-1}(x) = 0.5x - 3.$$

If $f^{-1}$ turns out to be a function (no two values of $f^{-1}(x)$ for the same value of $x$), then the original function $f$ is said to be **invertible**. Realize that the $-1$ exponent does *not* mean the reciprocal of $f(x)$. The inverse of a function undoes what the function did to x. That is, $f^{-1}(f(x)) = x$. For instance, the square root function is the inverse of the squaring function. If $f(x) = x^2$, then $f^{-1}(x) = \sqrt{x^2}$, and $\sqrt{x^2} = x$. Notice in Figure 4-5a that if the same scales are used for the two axes, then the graphs of $f$ and $f^{-1}$ are mirror images with respect to the 45° line $y = x$.

#### *Definition, Symbol, and Property: Inverse of a Function*

Definition: If $y = f(x)$, then the **inverse** of function $f$ has the equation $x = f(y)$.
Symbol: If $x = f(y)$, then $y = f^{-1}(x)$.
Definition: If $f^{-1}$ is a function, then $f$ is said to be **invertible**.
Property: If $f$ is invertible, then $f^{-1}(f(x)) = x$ and $f(f^{-1}(x)) = x$.

### *Background Item Number 2: The Inverse Trigonometric Functions*

The inverses of the trigonometric functions follow from the definition. For instance,

$y = \tan x$ Function.

$x = \tan y$ Inverse function.

In the equation $x = \tan y$, $y$ is called the inverse tangent of $x$, abbreviated

$$y = \tan^{-1} x$$

The symbol **arctan *x*** (for "the arc whose tangent is $x$") is sometimes used to help you distinguish $\tan^{-1}x$ from $1/\tan x$.

A clever way to plot the inverse of any function is to use the parametric mode on your grapher. For the tangent function you would use the following.

$x_1 = t$

$y_1 = \tan t$ Tangent function.

$x_2 = \tan t$

$y_2 = t$ Inverse tangent relation.

Figure 4-5b shows the two graphs on separate screens.

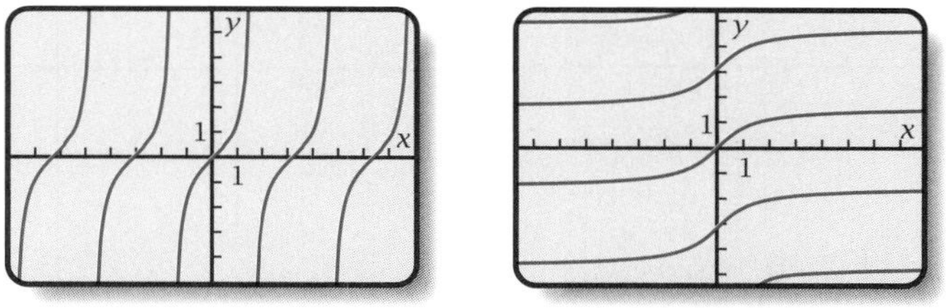

$y = \tan x$ $y = \tan^{-1} x = \arctan x$

Figure 4-5b

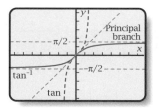



Figure 4-5c

Unfortunately, the inverse tangent relation is not a function. There are many values of $y$ for the same value of $x$. To make a function that is the inverse of $\tan x$, it is customary to restrict the range to $-\pi/2 < y < \pi/2$, or, briefly, $(-\pi/2, \pi/2)$. This restriction includes only the branch of the graph that is nearest the origin. Figure 4-5c shows this **principal branch**. The result is called the **inverse tangent function** (as opposed to the inverse tangent relation).

Figure 4-5c also shows that the function and inverse function graphs are symmetrical with respect to the line $y = x$. Everything that is an $x$-feature on the tangent graph is a $y$-feature on the inverse tangent graph.

The other five inverse trigonometric functions are defined the same way. For each, a principal branch is a function. The principal branch is near the origin, continuous if possible, and positive if there is a choice between two branches. The graphs are shown in Figure 4-5d.

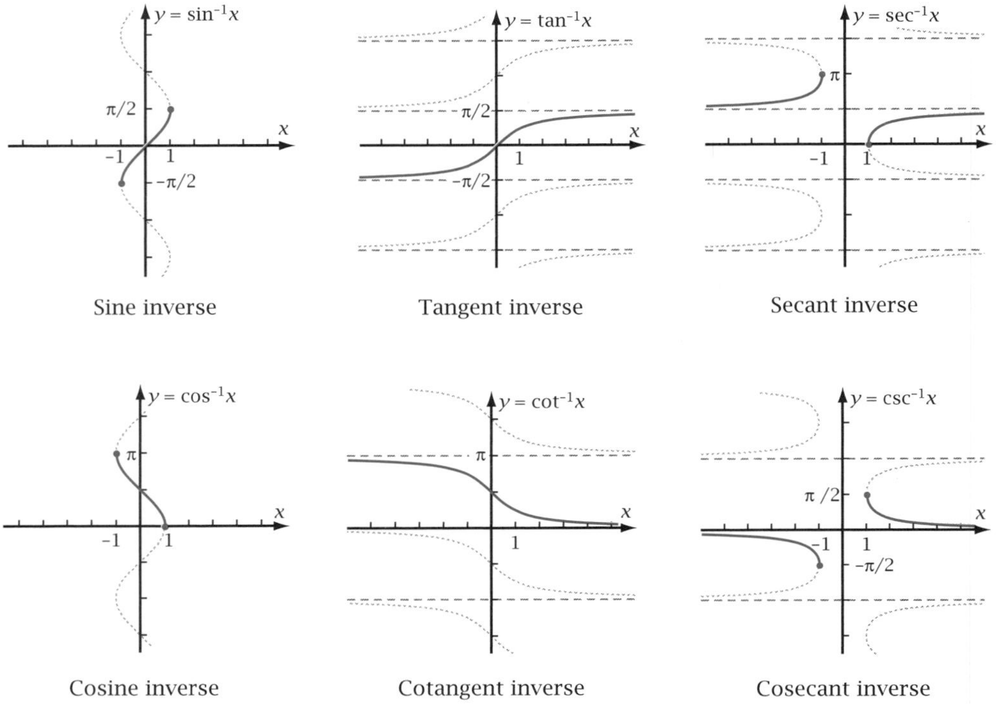


Figure 4-5d

The definitions and the ranges of the inverse trigonometric functions are summarized in the following table.

### *Definitions: Inverse Trigonometric Functions (Principal Branches)*

$y = \sin^{-1}x$ if and only if $\sin y = x$ and $y \in \left[-\frac{\pi}{2}, \frac{\pi}{2}\right]$

$y = \cos^{-1}x$ if and only if $\cos y = x$ and $y \in [0, \pi]$

$y = \tan^{-1}x$ if and only if $\tan y = x$ and $y \in \left(-\frac{\pi}{2}, \frac{\pi}{2}\right)$

$y = \cot^{-1}x$ if and only if $\cot y = x$ and $y \in (0, \pi)$

$y = \sec^{-1}x$ if and only if $\sec y = x$ and $y \in [0, \pi]$, but $x \neq \dfrac{\pi}{2}$

$y = \csc^{-1}x$ if and only if $\csc y = x$ and $y \in \left[-\frac{\pi}{2}, \frac{\pi}{2}\right]$, but $x \neq 0$.

*Note:* The names arcsin, arccos, arctan, arccot, arcsec, and arccsc can be used to help distinguish, for instance, $\tan^{-1}x$ from $1/\tan x$.

### *Algebraic Derivative of the Inverse Tangent Function*

Example 1 shows how to differentiate the inverse tangent function. The definition of inverse function lets you turn this new problem into the old problem of differentiating the tangent.

**Example 1** Differentiate $y = \tan^{-1}x$.

**Solution**

$y = \tan^{-1}x \Rightarrow \tan y = x.$ — Use the definition of $\tan^{-1}$ to write the equation in terms of tangent.

$\sec^2 y \cdot y' = 1$ — The derivative of tan is $\sec^2$. Because $y$ depends on $x$, it is an *inside* function. The $y'$ is the derivative of this inside function (from the chain rule).

$$y' = \frac{1}{\sec^2 y}$$
$$= \cos^2 y$$

Use algebra to solve for $y'$.

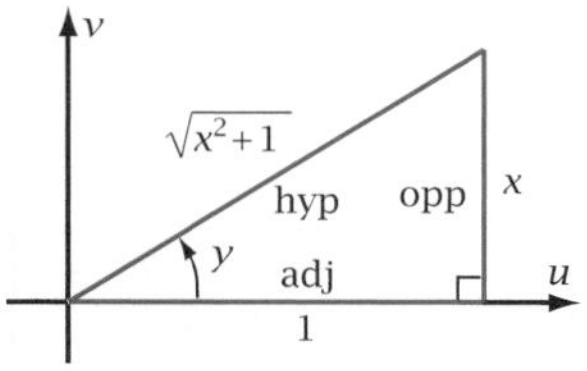

Figure 4-5e

To find $y'$ in terms of $x$, consider that $y$ is an angle whose tangent and cosine are being found. Draw a right triangle with angle $y$ in standard position (Figure 4-5e). By trigonometry,

$$\tan y = \frac{\text{opposite leg}}{\text{adjacent leg}}.$$

Because $\tan y = x$, which equals $x/1$, put $x$ on the opposite leg and 1 on the adjacent leg. The hypotenuse is thus $\sqrt{x^2 + 1}$. Because cosine equals (adjacent)/(hypotenuse), you can write

$$y' = \frac{1}{\left(\sqrt{x^2+1}\right)^2} = \frac{1}{x^2+1}.$$

■

In Example 1, both the left and right sides of the equation $\tan y = x$ are functions of $x$. The technique of differentiating both sides of such an equation with respect to $x$ is called **implicit differentiation.** You will study this technique more extensively in Section 4-8.

### *Derivative of the Inverse Secant Function*

The derivative of the inverse secant is tricky. Example 2 shows what happens.

**Example 2** Differentiate: $y = \sec^{-1}x$.

**Solution**

$y = \sec^{-1}x \Rightarrow \sec y = x$ — Transform the new problem into an old problem.

$\sec y \tan y \cdot y' = 1$ — Remember the chain rule! That's where $y'$ comes from.

$$y' = \frac{1}{\sec y \tan y}$$

Use algebra to solve for $y'$.

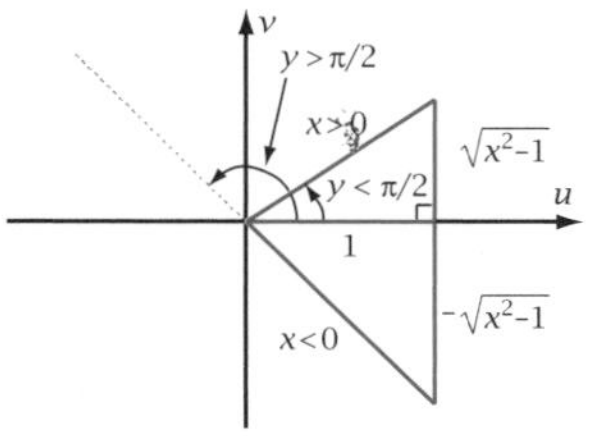

Figure 4-5f

Consider $y$ to be an angle. Draw a triangle with angle $y$ in the standard position (Figure 4-5f). Because secant equals (hypotenuse)/(adjacent) and $\sec y = x = x/1$, write $x$ on the hypotenuse and write 1 on the adjacent leg. Because the range of the inverse secant function is Quadrants I and II, $y$ will terminate in the second quadrant if $x$ is negative. In this case, $x$ must be drawn in the negative direction, as is done with negative radii in polar coordinates. By the Pythagorean theorem, the third side squared is $x^2 - 1$. This side is below the horizontal axis, so the radical for the third side is negative if $x$ is negative. Because tangent equals (opposite)/(adjacent), $\tan y = -\sqrt{x^2 - 1}$ in this case. Because you started with $\sec y = x$, the denominator of the derivative will be

$$x\sqrt{x^2 - 1} \quad \text{if } x > 0, \qquad \text{or} \qquad -x\sqrt{x^2 - 1} \quad \text{if } x < 0.$$

To avoid two different representations, use the notation $|x|$ and write the answer in this way.

$$y' = \frac{1}{|x|\sqrt{x^2 - 1}}$$ ■

The derivatives of the six inverse trigonometric functions are shown below. In the following problem set you will derive the other four properties.

**Properties: Derivatives of the Six Inverse Trigonometric Functions**

$$\frac{d}{dx}(\sin^{-1}x) = \frac{1}{\sqrt{1 - x^2}} \qquad \frac{d}{dx}(\cos^{-1}x) = -\frac{1}{\sqrt{1 - x^2}}$$

$$\frac{d}{dx}(\tan^{-1}x) = \frac{1}{1 + x^2} \qquad \frac{d}{dx}(\cot^{-1}x) = -\frac{1}{1 + x^2}$$

$$\frac{d}{dx}(\sec^{-1}x) = \frac{1}{|x|\sqrt{x^2 - 1}} \qquad \frac{d}{dx}(\csc^{-1}x) = -\frac{1}{|x|\sqrt{x^2 - 1}}$$

*Note:* Your grapher must be in the radian mode.

*Memory Aid:* The derivative of each "co-" inverse function is the *opposite* of the derivative of the corresponding inverse function because each co-inverse function is decreasing at $x = 0$ or 1 (Figure 4-5d).

**■ Example 3** Differentiate: $y = \cos^{-1}5x^7$

**Solution**

$$y = \cos^{-1}5x^7 \Rightarrow \cos y = 5x^7$$

$$-\sin y \cdot y' = 35x^6$$

$$y' = -\frac{35x^6}{\sin y} = -\frac{35x^6}{\sqrt{1 - 25x^{14}}} \quad \text{(Figure 4-5g)}$$

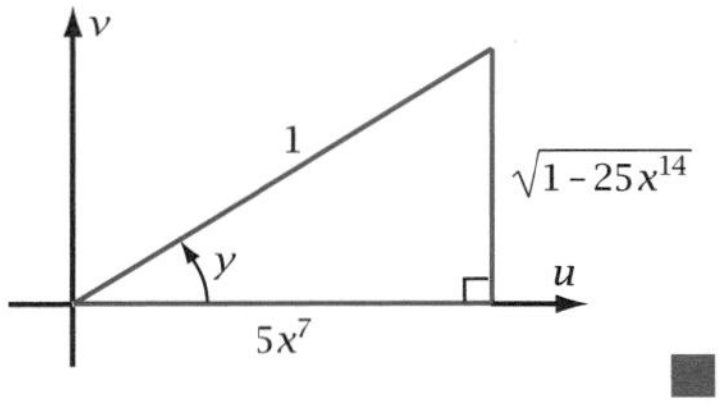

Figure 4-5g

■

## Problem Set 4-5

### *Do These Quickly*

The following problems are intended to refresh your skills. You should be able to do all ten problems in less than five minutes.

**Q1.** $\sin' x = $ —?—

**Q2.** $\cos' x = $ —?—

**Q3.** $\tan' x = $ —?—

**Q4.** $\cot' x = $ —?—

**Q5.** $\sec' x = $ —?—

**Q6.** $\csc' x = $ —?—

Refer to Figure 4-5h for Problems Q7–Q10.

**Q7.** $f'(1) = $ —?—

**Q8.** $f'(3) = $ —?—

**Q9.** $f'(4) = $ —?—

**Q10.** $f'(6) = $ —?—

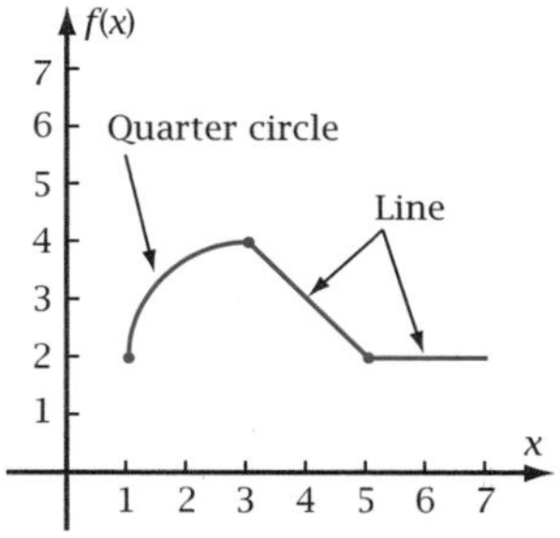


Figure 4-5h

For Problems 1–4, duplicate on your grapher the graphs in Figure 4-5d. For Problems 3 and 4, recall that $\csc y = 1/\sin y$ and that $\cot y = 1/\tan y$.

1. $y = \cos^{-1} x$
2. $y = \sin^{-1} x$
3. $y = \csc^{-1} x$
4. $y = \cot^{-1} x$
5. Explain why the principal branch of the inverse cotangent function goes from 0 to $\pi$ rather than from $-\pi/2$ to $\pi/2$.
6. Explain why the principal branch of the inverse secant function cannot be continuous.
7. Evaluate $\sin(\sin^{-1} 0.3)$.
8. Evaluate $\cos^{-1}(\cos 0.8)$.

For Problems 9–12, derive the formula shown.

9. $\dfrac{d}{dx}(\sin^{-1} x) = \dfrac{1}{\sqrt{1-x^2}}$
10. $\dfrac{d}{dx}(\cos^{-1} x) = -\dfrac{1}{\sqrt{1-x^2}}$
11. $\dfrac{d}{dx}(\csc^{-1} x) = -\dfrac{1}{|x|\sqrt{x^2-1}}$
12. $\dfrac{d}{dx}(\cot^{-1} x) = -\dfrac{1}{1+x^2}$

For Problems 13–24, find the derivative algebraically.

13. $y = \sin^{-1} 4x$
14. $y = \cos^{-1} 10x$
15. $y = \cot^{-1} x^{0.5}$
16. $y = \tan^{-1} x^{0.5}$
17. $y = \sec^{-1} \frac{x}{3}$
18. $y = \csc^{-1} \frac{x}{10}$
19. $y = \cos^{-1} 5x^2$
20. $f(x) = \tan^{-1} x^3$
21. $g(x) = (\sin^{-1} x)^2$
22. $u = (\sec^{-1} x)^2$

23. $v = x \sin^{-1} x + (1 - x^2)^{1/2}$ (Surprise!)

24. $I(x) = \cot^{-1}(\cot x)$ (Surprise!)

25. *Radar Problem:* An officer in a patrol car sitting 100 ft from the highway observes a truck approaching (Figure 4-5i).

    a. At a particular instant, $t$ seconds, the truck is $x$ ft down the highway. The line of sight to the truck makes an angle of $\theta$ radians to a perpendicular to the highway. Explain why $\theta = \tan^{-1}(x/100)$.

    b. Find $d\theta/dx$. Use the chain rule to write an equation for $d\theta/dt$.

    c. When the truck is at $x = 500$ ft, the angle is observed to be changing at a rate $d\theta/dt = -0.04$ rad/sec. How fast is the truck going? How many miles per hour is this?

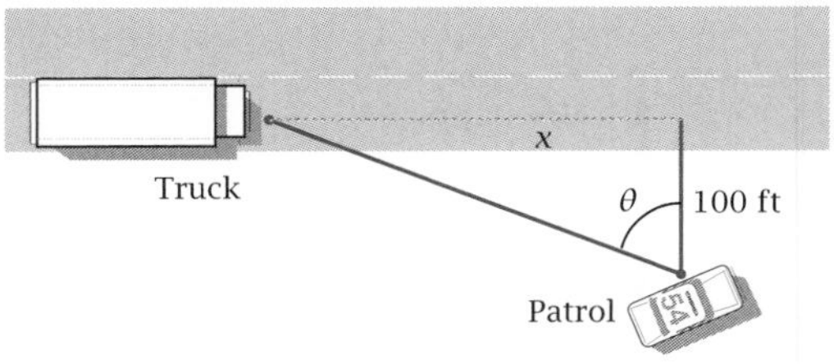

Figure 4-5i

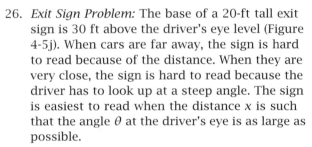

26. *Exit Sign Problem:* The base of a 20-ft tall exit sign is 30 ft above the driver's eye level (Figure 4-5j). When cars are far away, the sign is hard to read because of the distance. When they are very close, the sign is hard to read because the driver has to look up at a steep angle. The sign is easiest to read when the distance $x$ is such that the angle $\theta$ at the driver's eye is as large as possible.

    a. Write $\theta$ as the difference of two inverse cotangents.

    b. Write an equation for $d\theta/dx$.

    c. The sign will be easiest to read at the value of $x$ where $\theta$ stops increasing and starts decreasing. This happens when $d\theta/dx = 0$. Find this value of $x$.

    d. Confirm that your answer in 26c is correct by plotting $\theta$ as a function of $x$ and thus showing that the graph really does have a high point at that value.

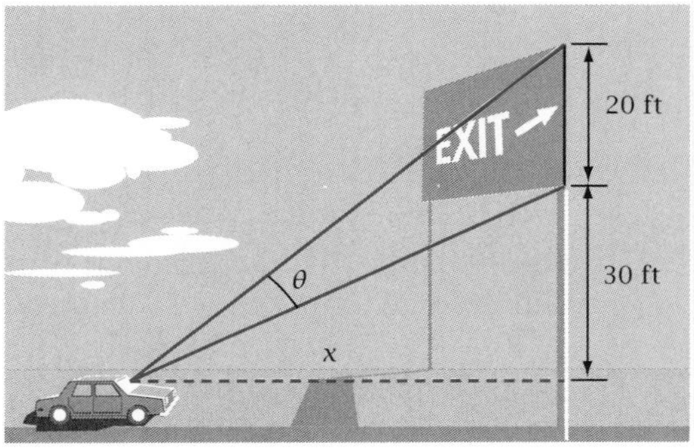

Figure 4-5j

27. *Numerical Answer Check Problem:* For $f(x) = \cos^{-1} x$, make a table of values that show $f'(x)$ numerically and $f'(x)$ by the formula. Start at $x = -0.8$ and go to $x = 0.8$, with $\Delta x = 0.2$. Show that the formula and the numerical derivative give the same answers for each value of $x$.

28. *Graphical Analysis Problem:* Figure 4-5k shows the graph of $y = \sec^{-1} x$.

    a. Calculate the derivative at $x = 2$. Based on what the graph shows, why is the answer reasonable?

    b. What does $y$ equal when $x$ is 2? What does $(d/dy)(\sec y)$ equal for this value of $y$?

    c. In what way is the derivative of the inverse secant function related to the derivative of the secant function?

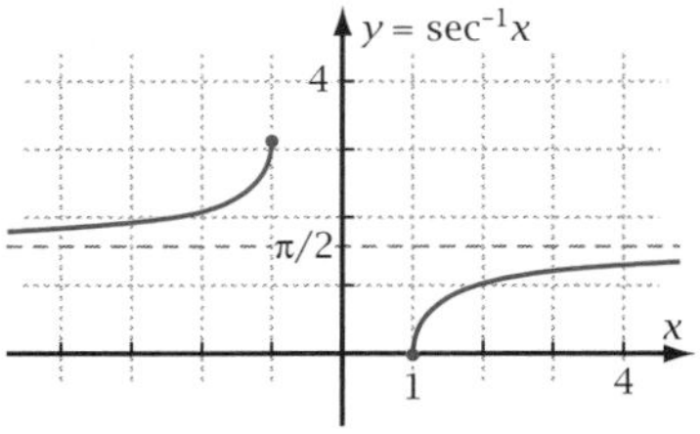

Figure 4-5k

29. *General Derivative of the Inverse of a Function:* In this problem you will derive a general formula for the derivative of the inverse of a function.

a. Let $y = \sin^{-1}x$. Show that $\dfrac{dy}{dx} = \dfrac{1}{\cos y}$.

b. By directly substituting $\sin^{-1}x$ for $y$ in 29a, you get $\dfrac{dy}{dx} = \dfrac{1}{\cos(\sin^{-1}x)}$. Show that the formula of this section and this problem's formula for $dy/dx$ give the same value when $x = 0.6$.

c. Show that the following property is true for the derivative of the inverse of a function.

**Property: Derivative of the Inverse of a Function**

If $y = f^{-1}(x)$, then $\dfrac{d}{dx}(f^{-1}(x)) = \dfrac{1}{f'(f^{-1}(x))}$.

d. Suppose that $f(x) = x^3 + x$. Let $h$ be the inverse function of $f$. Find $x$ if $f(x) = 10$. Use the result and the property given above to calculate $h'(10)$.

30. Quick! Which of the inverse trigonometric derivatives is preceded by a negative $(-)$ sign?

# 4-6 Differentiability and Continuity

It is time to pause in the study of derivatives and take care of some unfinished business. If a function $f$ has a value for $f'(c)$, then $f$ is said to be **differentiable** at $x = c$. If $f$ is differentiable at every value of $x$ in an interval, then $f$ is said to be differentiable on that interval.

**Definitions**

**Differentiability at a point:** Function $f$ is **differentiable at $x = c$** if and only if $f'(c)$ exists. (That is, $f'(c)$ is a real number.)

**Differentiability on an interval:** Function $f$ is **differentiable on an interval** if and only if it is differentiable for every $x$ value in the interval.

**Differentiability:** Function $f$ is **differentiable** if and only if it is differentiable at every value of $x$ in its domain.

In Section 2-4, you learned that a function $f$ is continuous at $x = c$ if $\lim_{x \to c} f(x) = f(c)$. A function can be continuous at $x = c$ without being differentiable at that point. But a function that is differentiable at $x = c$ is automatically continuous at that point. Figure 4-6a illustrates the two cases.

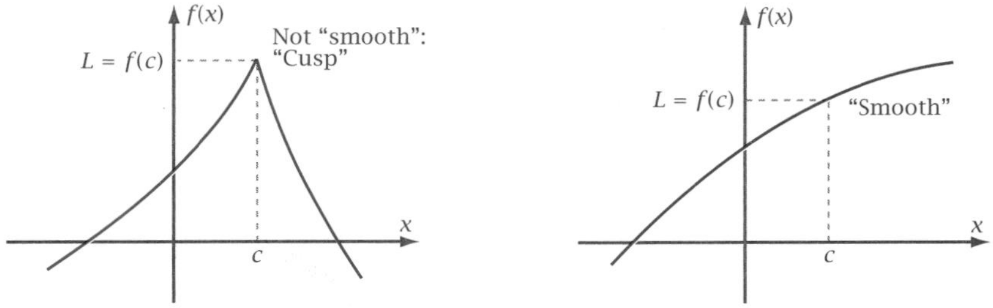


Continuous, but not differentiable | Differentiable, thus continuous

Figure 4-6a

***OBJECTIVE***

Prove that a differentiable function is continuous, and use this property to prove that certain functions are continuous.

To prove that a function $f$ is continuous at $x = c$, you must show that $\lim_{x \to c} f(x) = f(c)$. One form of the definition of derivative contains all these ingredients.

$$f'(c) = \lim_{x \to c} \frac{f(x) - f(c)}{x - c}$$

The trick is to perform some mathematically correct operations that lead from the hypothesis to the conclusion. In this case it is easier to start somewhere "in the middle" and pick up the hypothesis along the way. Here goes!

■ ***Property*** Prove that if $f$ is differentiable at $x = c$, then $f$ is continuous at $x = c$.

***Proof*** You must prove that $\lim_{x \to c} f(x) = f(c)$.

$$\lim_{x \to c} [f(x) - f(c)]$$ Start with something that contains limit, $f(x)$, and $f(c)$.

$$= \lim_{x \to c} \left[ \frac{f(x) - f(c)}{x - c} \cdot (x - c) \right]$$ Multiply by $\frac{x - c}{x - c}$.

$$= \lim_{x \to c} \frac{f(x) - f(c)}{x - c} \cdot \lim_{x \to c} (x - c)$$ Limit of a product.

$$= f'(c) \cdot 0$$ Definition of derivative and limit of a linear function.

$$= 0$$ Because $f$ is differentiable at $x = c$, $f'(c)$ is a real number; (number)$\cdot 0 = 0$.

$$\therefore \lim_{x \to c} [f(x) - f(c)] = 0$$ Transitive property.

But $\lim_{x \to c} [f(x) - f(c)] = [\lim_{x \to c} f(x)] - [\lim_{x \to c} f(c)] = [\lim_{x \to c} f(x)] - f(c)$.

$\therefore [\lim_{x \to c} f(x)] - f(c) = 0$, also. Transitive property again.

$$\therefore \lim_{x \to c} f(x) = f(c)$$

$\therefore f$ is continuous at $x = c$, Q.E.D. Definition of continuity. ■

The secret to this proof is to multiply by 1 in the form of $(x - c)/(x - c)$. This transformation causes the difference quotient $[f(x) - f(c)]/(x - c)$ to appear inside the limit sign. The rest of the proof involves algebra and limit properties and the definitions of derivative and continuity.

**Property: Differentiability Implies Continuity**

If function $f$ is differentiable at $x = c$, then $f$ is continuous at $x = c$.

**Contrapositive of the Property:** If function $f$ is not continuous at $x = c$, then $f$ is not differentiable at $x = c$.

(The converse and the inverse of this property are false.)

This property and its contrapositive provide a simple way to prove that a function is continuous or not differentiable, respectively.

**Example 1** Prove that $f(x) = x^2 - 7x + 13$ is continuous at $x = 4$.

**Solution**

$f'(x) = 2x - 7$

$f'(4) = 2(4) - 7 = 1$, which is a real number.

$\therefore f$ is differentiable at $x = 4$.

$\therefore f$ is continuous at $x = 4$, Q.E.D. Differentiability implies continuity. ■

Note that you could prove that $f$ is continuous by applying the limit theorems. The technique in Example 1 provides a faster way if you can find the derivative easily.

**Example 2** Is the function $g(x) = \dfrac{(x-2)(x+3)}{x-2}$ differentiable at $x = 2$? Justify your answer.

**Solution**

The function $g$ has a (removable) discontinuity at $x = 2$.

$\therefore g$ is not differentiable at $x = 2$. Contrapositive of differentiability implies continuity. ■

The most significant thing for you to understand is the distinction between the concepts of differentiability and continuity. To help you acquire this understanding, it helps to look at graphs of functions and state which, if either, of the two properties applies.

**Example 3** State whether or not the following functions are differentiable or continuous at $x = c$.

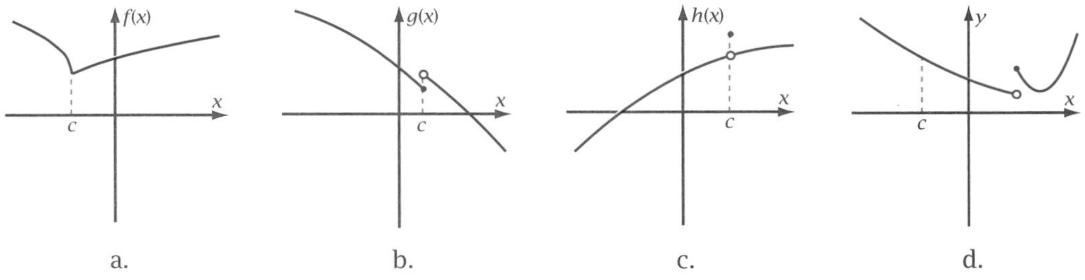


Figure 4-6b

**Solutions**

a. The function is continuous but not differentiable. At the cusp, the rate of change approaches a different number as $x \to c$ from the left side than it does as $x \to c$ from the right.

b. The function is neither continuous nor differentiable. There is no limit for $g(x)$ as $x \to c$.

c. The function is neither continuous nor differentiable. Although the graph appears "smooth" as $x$ goes through $c$, the difference quotient $[h(x) - h(c)]/(x - c)$ approaches $+\infty$ (positive infinity) as $x$ approaches $c$ from the left side, and approaches $-\infty$ as $x$ approaches $c$ from the right.

d. The function is continuous and differentiable. The discontinuity elsewhere has no effect on the behavior of the function at $x = c$. ■

**■ Example 4** Find values of the constants $a$ and $b$ that make function $f$ differentiable at $x = 2$. Check your answer by graphing.

$$f(x) = \begin{cases} ax^3, & \text{if } x \le 2 \\ b(x-3)^2 + 10, & \text{if } x > 2 \end{cases}$$

**Solution** Let $y_1 = ax^3$ and let $y_2 = b(x-3)^2 + 10$.

For $f$ to be differentiable at $x = 2$, it must also be continuous at that point. Thus, at $x = 2$, $y_1$ must equal $y_2$ and $y_1'$ must equal $y_2'$.

$y_1' = 3ax^2$ and $y_2' = 2b(x - 3)$

$\therefore 8a = b + 10$ — $y_1 = y_2$ at $x = 2$.

$12a = -2b \Rightarrow b = -6a$ — $y_1' = y_2'$ at $x = 2$.

$8a = -6a + 10$ — By substitution.

$a = \frac{5}{7}$

$b = -6 \cdot \frac{5}{7} = -\frac{30}{7}$

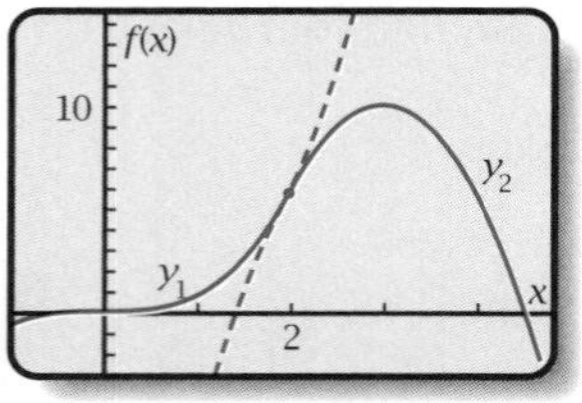


Figure 4-6c

Figure 4-6c shows the graph of $f$ with these values of $a$ and $b$. The broken end portions of the graph show $y_1$ and $y_2$ outside their respective domains. As you can see, the graphs have the same slope at $x = 2$, and they are continuous. This means that $f$ is differentiable at $x = 2$. ■

# Problem Set 4-6

### *Do These Quickly*

The following problems are intended to refresh your skills. You should be able to do all ten problems in less than five minutes.

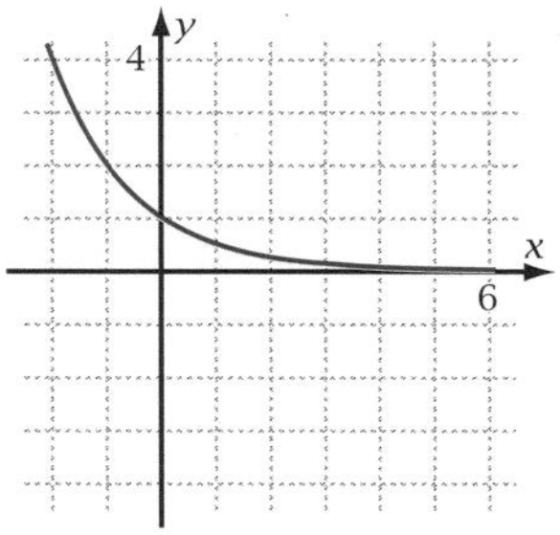

Figure 4-6d

**Q1.** Write the definition of continuity.

**Q2.** Write the definition of derivative.

**Q3.** Find $y$: $y' = 12x^{-3}$.

**Q4.** Find $\cos' x$.

**Q5.** Find $dy/dx$: $y = \tan x$.

**Q6.** Find $\dfrac{d}{dx} \sec^{-1} x$.

**Q7.** If $f(x) = x^4$, find $f'(2)$.

**Q8.** Find $dy/dx$: $y = (x^3 + 1)^5$.

**Q9.** Estimate the definite integral from $-2$ to 2 of the function in Figure 4-6d.

**Q10.** Sketch the derivative graph for the function in Figure 4-6d.

For Problems 1–12, state whether the function is continuous, differentiable, both, or neither at $x = c$.

1.
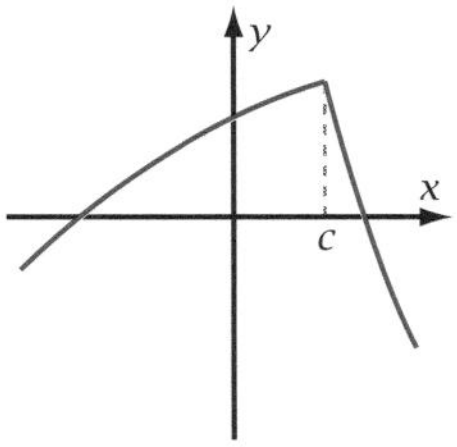


2.
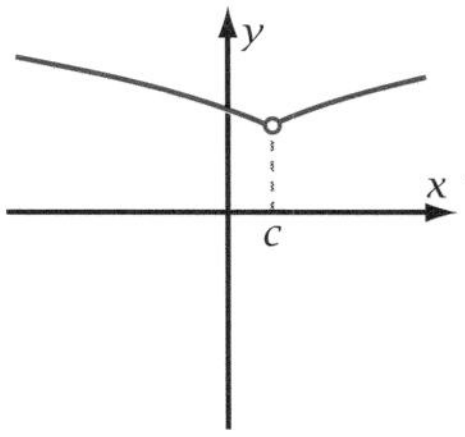


3.
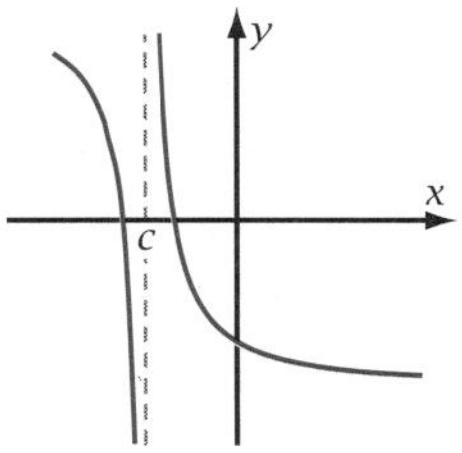


4.
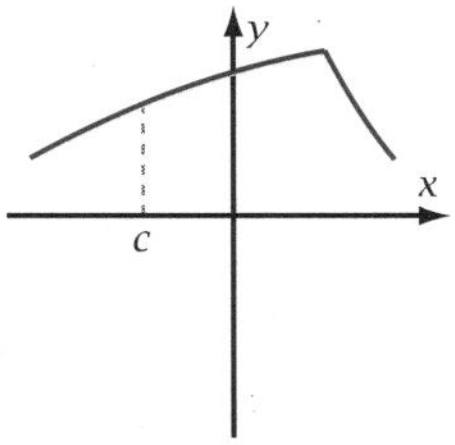


5.
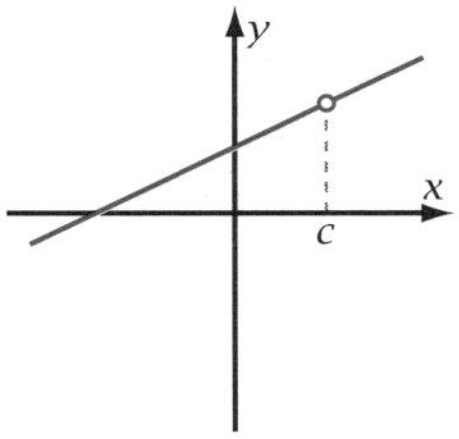


6.
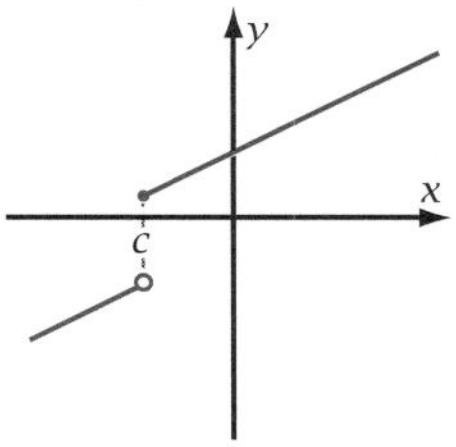


7.
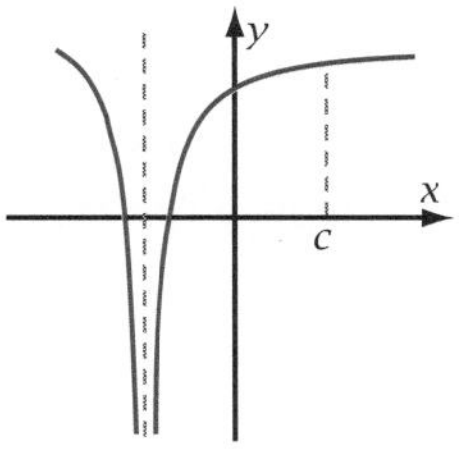


8.
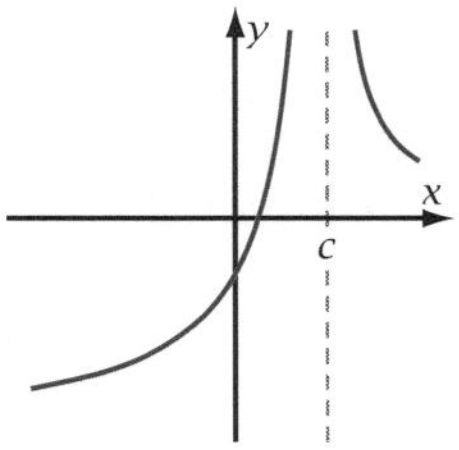


9.
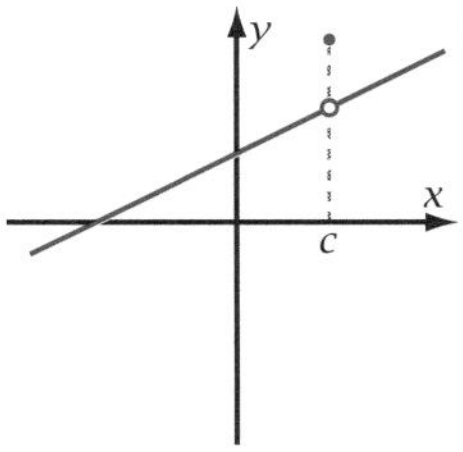


10.
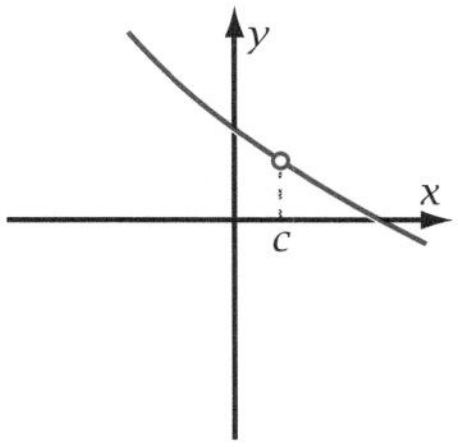


11.
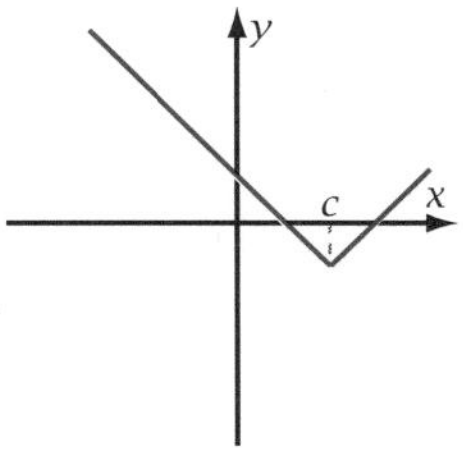


12.
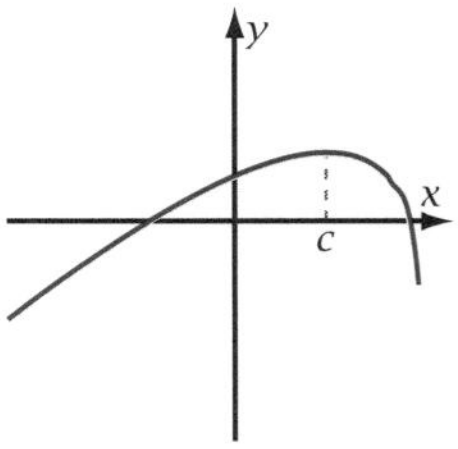

For Problems 13–20:

a. Sketch the graph of a function that has the indicated features.

b. Write the equation for a function that has these features.

13. Is differentiable and continuous at the point (3, 5)

14. Is differentiable and continuous at the point $(-2, 4)$

15. Has a finite limit as $x$ approaches 6, but is not continuous at that point because $f(6)$ is undefined

16. Has a finite limit as $x$ approaches 1, has a value for $f(1)$, but still is not continuous at that point

17. Has a value for $f(-5)$ but has no limit as $x$ approaches $-5$

18. Has a cusp at the point $(-1, 3)$

19. Is continuous at the point (4, 7) but is not differentiable at that point

20. Is differentiable at the point (3, 8) but is not continuous at that point

For Problems 21–30, sketch the graph. State whether the function is differentiable, continuous, neither, or both at the indicated value of $x = c$.

21. $f(x) = |x - 3|$, $c = 3$

22. $f(x) = 4 + |x|$, $c = 2$

23. $f(x) = \sin x$, $c = 1$

24. $f(c) = \tan x$, $c = \pi/2$

25. $$f(x) = \begin{cases} x^2 - 4x + 8, & \text{if } x \le 3 \\ 11 - x, & \text{if } x > 3 \end{cases}$$
$c = 3$

26. $$f(x) = \begin{cases} x^2 - 6x + 8, & \text{if } x \ge 1 \\ 7 - 4x, & \text{if } x < 1 \end{cases}$$
$c = 1$

27. $$f(x) = \begin{cases} x^2 - x + 1, & \text{if } x < 1 \\ x + 1, & \text{if } x \ge 1 \end{cases}$$
$c = 1$

28. $$f(x) = \begin{cases} x^2 - x + 1, & \text{if } x \le 1 \\ 2 - x, & \text{if } x > 1 \end{cases}$$
$c = 1$

29. $f(x) = \dfrac{x^3 - 8}{x - 2}$, $c = 2$

30. $f(x) = x^2 + 2x + 4 - \dfrac{|x - 2|}{x - 2}$, $c = 2$

For Problems 31–34, find values of the constants $a$ and $b$ that make the function differentiable at the point where the rule for the function changes. Check by grapher.

31. $$f(x) = \begin{cases} x^3, & \text{if } x < 1 \\ a(x - 2)^2 + b, & \text{if } x \ge 1 \end{cases}$$

32. $$f(x) = \begin{cases} -(x - 3)^2 + 7, & \text{if } x \ge 2 \\ ax^3 + b, & \text{if } x < 2 \end{cases}$$

33. $$f(x) = \begin{cases} ax^2 + 10, & \text{if } x < 2 \\ x^2 - 6x + b, & \text{if } x \ge 2 \end{cases}$$

34. $$f(x) = \begin{cases} a/x, & \text{if } x \le 1 \\ 12 - bx^2, & \text{if } x > 1 \end{cases}$$

35. *Railroad Curve Problem:* Curves on a railroad track are made in the shape of sections of cubic parabolas rather than arcs of circles. This ensures that locomotives are gradually eased into curved paths and are thus prevented from derailing. Suppose a track goes along the negative $x$-axis and starts curving at $x = 0$. By the time the curve reaches $x = 100$ yd, the track lies at a $45°$ angle to its original direction (Figure 4-6e).

a. The equation for the path of the track is

$$y = \begin{cases} 0, & \text{if } x < 0 \\ ax^3, & \text{if } 0 \le x \le 100 \\ x + b, & \text{if } x > 100 \end{cases}$$

Find the values of $a$ and $b$ that make the path differentiable at $x = 0$ and at $x = 100$.

b. Show that at $x = 0$ (where the train will first enter the curve) the rate of change of slope is zero. Also show that thereafter the slope increases uniformly with $x$.

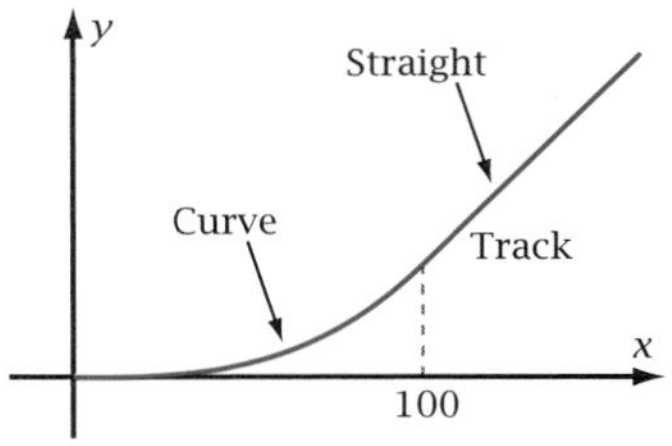

Figure 4-6e

36. *Bicycle Frame Design Problem:* Figure 4-6f shows a side view of a bicycle frame's front fork, holding the front wheel. To make the bike track properly, the fork curves forward at the bottom where the wheel bolts on. Assume that the fork is bent in the shape of a cubic parabola, $y = ax^3 + bx$. What should the constants $a$ and $b$ be so that the curve joins smoothly to the straight part of the fork at the point (10 cm, 20 cm) with slope equal to 5?

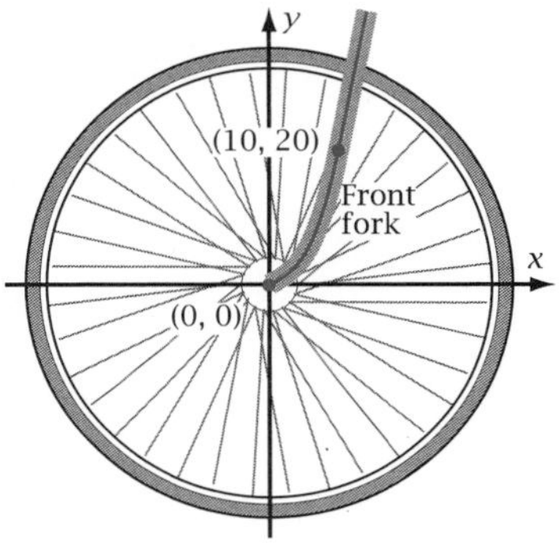

Figure 4-6f

37. Let $f(x) = \begin{cases} x^2 - \dfrac{|x-2|}{x-2}, & \text{if } x \ne 2 \\ 4, & \text{if } x = 2 \end{cases}$

Find an equation for $f'(x)$. Show that function $f$ is not differentiable at $x = 2$, even though the left and right limits of $f'(x)$ are equal as $x$ approaches 2.

38. *Baseball Line Drive Problem:* Milt Famey pitches his famous fastball. At time $t = 0.5$ sec after Milt releases the ball, Joe Jamoke hits a line drive to center field. The distance, $d(t)$ feet, of the ball from home plate is given by the two-rule function shown below.

$$d(t) = \begin{cases} 60.5\left(\dfrac{0.5 - t}{0.5 + t}\right), & \text{if } t \le 0.5 \\ 150\left(2 - \dfrac{1}{t}\right), & \text{if } t \ge 0.5 \end{cases}$$

Figure 4-6g shows the graph of function $d$.

a. Find an equation for $d'(t)$. Be careful about the inequality signs at $t = 0.5$.

b. Prove quickly that $d$ is continuous at $t = 1$.

c. Find the limit of $d'(t)$ as $t \to 0.5^-$ and as $t \to 0.5^+$. State the real-world meanings of these two numbers.

d. Explain why $d$ is continuous, but not differentiable, at $t = 0.5$.

e. What is the significance of the number 60.5 in the first rule for $d(t)$?

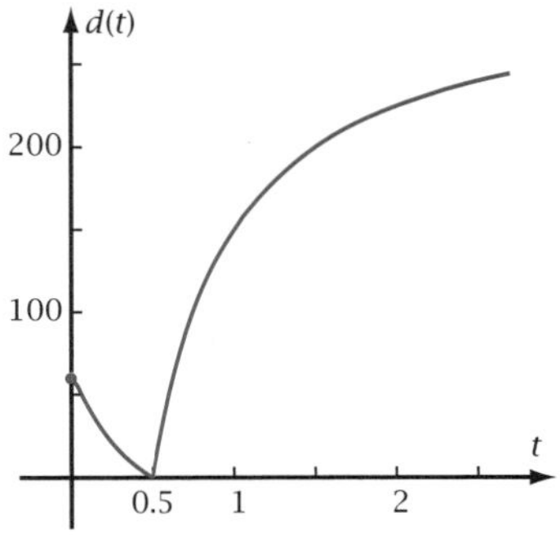

Figure 4-6g

39. *Continuity Proof Problem:* Use the fact that differentiability implies continuity to prove that the following kinds of functions are continuous.

a. Linear function, $y = mx + b$

b. Quadratic function, $y = ax^2 + bx + c$

c. Reciprocal function, $y = 1/x$, provided $x \ne 0$

d. Identity function, $y = x$

e. Constant function, $y = k$

40. *Differentiability Implies Continuity Proof:* Prove that if $f$ is differentiable at $x = c$, then it is continuous at that point. Try to do the proof without looking at the proof in the text. Consult the text only if you get stuck.

# 4-7 Derivative of a Parametric Function

Figure 4-7a shows how a pendulum hung from the ceiling of a room might move if it were to swing in both the $x$- and $y$-directions. It is possible to calculate its velocity in both the $x$- and $y$-directions, and along its curved path. These rates help you determine facts about the path of a moving object. In this section you will use **parametric functions** to make these determinations.

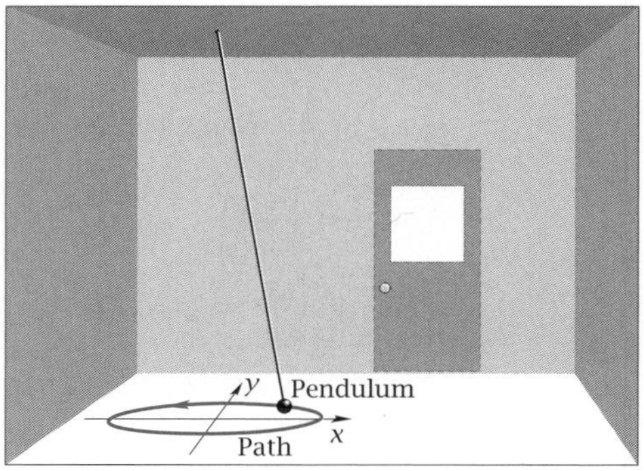


Figure 4-7a

**OBJECTIVE**

Given equations for $x$ and $y$ in terms of $t$, find $dx/dt$, $dy/dt$, and $dy/dx$.

As the pendulum in Figure 4-7a swings, it goes back and forth sinusoidally in both the $x$- and $y$-directions. By using the methods you learned in Section 3-8, you can find equations for these sinusoids. Suppose that the equations for a particular pendulum are

$$x = 50\cos 1.2t$$
$$y = 30\sin 1.2t,$$

where $x$ and $y$ are in centimeters and $t$ is time in seconds. The variable $t$ on which $x$ and $y$ both depend is called a **parameter**. (The word parameter means "parallel measure.") The two equations, one for $x$ and one for $y$, are called **parametric equations**.

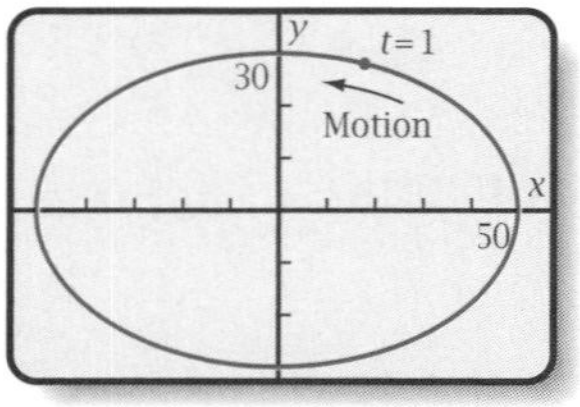


Figure 4-7b

You can use the parametric mode on your grapher to plot the $xy$-graph of the pendulum's path. The result is an ellipse, as shown in Figure 4-7b. The ellipse goes from $-50$ to $50$ cm in the $x$-direction and from $-30$ to $30$ cm in the $y$-direction. The points 50 and 30 appear in the parametric equations as the amplitudes of the two sinusoids. (If the pendulum were at rest, it would hang over the origin.)

The rates of change of $x$ and $y$ with respect to $t$ can be found by differentiating.

$$\frac{dx}{dt} = -60\sin 1.2t \qquad \text{and} \qquad \frac{dy}{dt} = 36\cos 1.2t$$

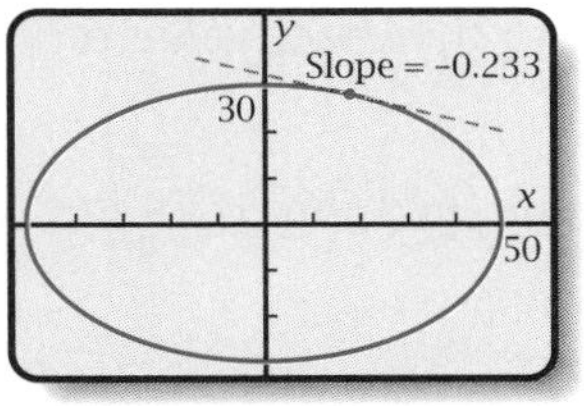

Figure 4-7c

Evaluating these derivatives at a certain value of $t$, say $t = 1$, shows that the pendulum is moving at about $-55.9$ cm/sec in the $x$-direction and at about 13.0 cm/sec in the $y$-direction. If you divide $dy/dt$ by $dx/dt$, the result is the slope of the ellipse, $dy/dx$, at the given point.

$$\frac{dy}{dx} = \frac{13.044\ldots}{-55.922\ldots} = -0.233\ldots$$

A line with this slope at the point where $t = 1$ is tangent to the graph (Figure 4-7c). The property illustrated by this example is called the **parametric chain rule**.

> ***Property: The Parametric Chain Rule***
>
> If $x$ and $y$ are differentiable functions of $t$, then the slope of the $xy$-graph is
>
> $$\frac{dy}{dx} = \frac{dy/dt}{dx/dt}.$$

**■ *Example 1*** Given: $x = 3\cos 2\pi t$
$y = 5\sin \pi t$,

a. Plot the $xy$-graph. Use a $t$-range that generates at least one complete cycle of $x$ and $y$. A $t$-step of 0.05 is reasonable. Sketch the result.

b. Describe the behavior of the $xy$-graph as $t$ increases.

c. Find an equation for $dy/dx$ in terms of $t$.

d. Calculate $dy/dx$ when $t = 0.15$. Show how the answer corresponds to the graph.

e. Show that $dy/dx$ is indeterminate when $t = 0.5$. Find the approximate limit of $dy/dx$ as $t$ approaches 0.5. How does the answer relate to the graph?

f. Make a conjecture about what geometrical figure the graph represents. Then confirm your conjecture by eliminating the parameter $t$ and analyzing the resulting Cartesian equation.

g. How do the range and the domain of the parametric function relate to the range and the domain of the Cartesian equation in part f?

***Solution***

a. Figure 4-7d shows the graph as it might appear on your grapher. The period for $x$ is $2\pi/2\pi = 1$; for $y$ it is $2\pi/\pi = 2$. Thus a minimal range is $0 \le t \le 2$.

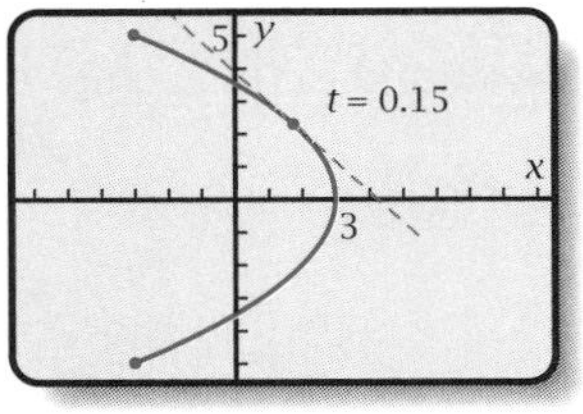

Figure 4-7d

b. If you watch the graph being generated, you will see that the points start at (3, 0), go upward to the left, stop, retrace the path through the point (3, 0), then go downward to the left, eventually coming back to the point (3, 0).

c. $$\frac{dx}{dt} = -6\pi\sin 2\pi t \qquad \text{and} \qquad \frac{dy}{dt} = 5\pi\cos\pi t$$

$$\therefore \frac{dy}{dx} = \frac{5\pi\cos\pi t}{-6\pi\sin 2\pi t} = \frac{5\cos\pi t}{-6\sin 2\pi t}$$

d. $t = 0.15 \Rightarrow \dfrac{dy}{dx} = \dfrac{5\cos 0.15\pi}{-6\sin 0.3\pi} = \dfrac{4.455\ldots}{-4.854\ldots} = -0.917\ldots$

As shown in Figure 4-7d, a tangent line to the graph at the point where $t = 0.15$ has slope of about $-1$, which corresponds to the exact value of $-0.917\ldots$.

e. $t = 0.5 \Rightarrow \dfrac{dy}{dx} = \dfrac{5\cos 0.5\pi}{-6\sin\pi} = \dfrac{0}{0}$, which is indeterminate. A graph of $dy/dx$ versus $t$ (Figure 4-7e) shows a removable discontinuity at $t = 0.5$.

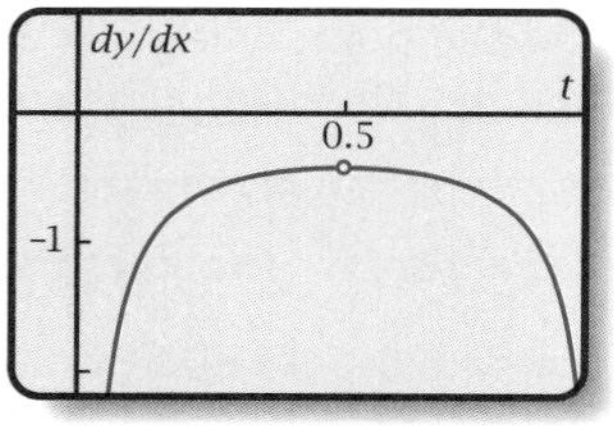


Figure 4-7e

| $t$ | $dy/dx$ |
|---|---|
| 0.498 | −0.4166749 |
| 0.499 | −0.4166687 |
| 0.500 | (no value) |
| 0.501 | −0.4166687 |
| 0.502 | −0.4166749 |

To find the limit of $dy/dx$ more precisely, either zoom in on the discontinuity or use the table feature. The limit appears to be $-0.4166666\ldots$, which equals $-5/12$.

f. The graph appears to be a parabola. Eliminating the parameter $t$ involves solving one equation for $t$ in terms of $x$ (or $y$) and substituting the result into the other equation. Sometimes there are shortcuts that will let you do this more easily, as shown below.

| | |
|---|---|
| $x = 3\cos 2\pi t$ and $y = 5\sin\pi t$ | The given parametric equations. |
| $x = 3(1 - 2\sin^2\pi t)$ | The double argument property gets $\cos 2\pi t$ in terms of $\sin\pi t$, which appears in the original parametric equation for $y$. |
| But $\sin\pi t = (y/5)$. | From the original parametric equations. |
| $\therefore x = 3(1 - 2(y/5)^2)$ | Substituting $y/5$ for $\sin\pi t$ eliminates the parameter $t$. |
| $x = -\dfrac{6}{25}y^2 + 3$ | By algebra. |

As conjectured, this is the equation of a parabola opening in the negative $x$-direction.

g. The Cartesian equation has domain $x \le 3$, which is unbounded in the negative $x$-direction. The parametric graph stops at $x = -3$. ■

# Problem Set 4-7

### *Do These Quickly*

The following problems are intended to refresh your skills. You should be able to do all ten problems in less than five minutes.

**Q1.** Differentiate: $y = 0.2x^{1215}$

**Q2.** Find $\dfrac{dy}{dx}$: $y = \dfrac{x-3}{x-1}$.

**Q3.** Find $f'(x)$: $f(x) = x\cos x$.

**Q4.** Find $y'$: $y = \sin(x^5)$.

**Q5.** Find $\dfrac{d}{dx}(y)$: $y = \dfrac{x^8}{x^5}$.

**Q6.** Differentiate: $y = \dfrac{\sin 8}{\cos 3}$

**Q7.** Find $\theta'$: $\theta = \cos^{-1}x$.

**Q8.** For Figure 4-7f, sketch the graph of $y'$.

**Q9.** If $v'(5) = -3$, what can you conclude about $v(t)$ at $t = 5$?

**Q10.** If $u'(7) = 4$, what can you conclude about $u(x)$ at $x = 8$?

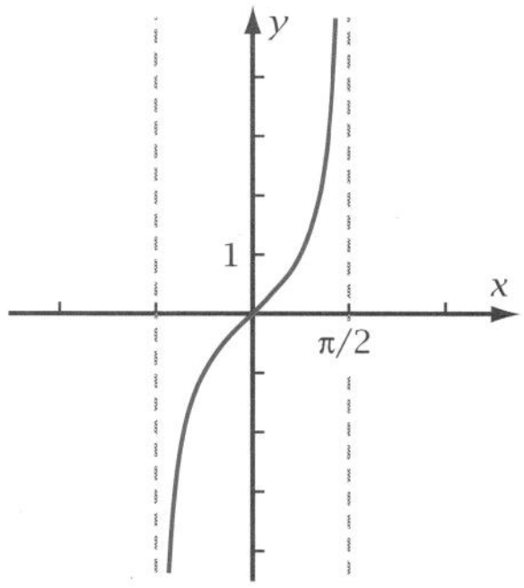


Figure 4-7f

1. *Parabola Problem:* A parametric function has the following equations.

$$x = 2 + t$$
$$y = 3 - t^2$$

   a. Make a table of values of $x$ and $y$ for each integer value of $t$ from $-3$ through 3.
   b. Plot the graph of this function on graph paper, using the points in 1a.
   c. Find $dy/dx$ when $t = 1$. Show that the line through the point $(x, y)$ from 1a, with slope $dy/dx$, is tangent to the graph at that point.
   d. Eliminate the parameter $t$ and show that the resulting Cartesian equation is that of a parabola.
   e. Find $dy/dx$ by direct differentiation of the equation in 1d. Show that the value of $dy/dx$ calculated this way is equal to the value you found in 1c by using the parametric chain rule.

2. *Semicubical Parabola Problem:* A parametric function has the following equations.

$$x = t^2$$
$$y = t^3$$

   a. Make a table of values of $x$ and $y$ for each integer value of $t$ from $-3$ through 3.
   b. Plot the graph of this function on graph paper, using the coordinate pairs found in 2a.
   c. Find $dy/dx$ when $t = 1$. Show that the line through the point $(x, y)$ from 2a, with slope $dy/dx$, is tangent to the graph at that point.
   d. Eliminate the parameter $t$. Find $y$ in terms of $x$. From the result, state why this graph is called a **semicubical parabola**.

e. Find $dy/dx$ by direct differentiation of the equation in 2d. Show that the value of $dy/dx$ calculated in this way is equal to the value you found in 2c by using the parametric chain rule.

3. *Ellipse Problem:* The ellipse in Figure 4-7g has the parametric equations

$$x = 3\cos t$$
$$y = 5\sin t.$$

a. Plot the graph on your grapher. Sketch the result or photocopy the text graph.

b. Find an equation for $dy/dx$.

c. Evaluate the point $(x, y)$ when $t = \pi/4$, and find $dy/dx$ when $t = \pi/4$. Plot a line on your graph at this point $(x, y)$ that has slope $dy/dx$. Is the line tangent to the graph?

d. Determine whether the following statement is true or false: When $t = \pi/4$, the point $(x, y)$ is on a line through the origin that makes a 45-degree angle with the $x$- and $y$-axes.

e. Use your equation for $dy/dx$ from 3b to find all the points where the tangent line is vertical or horizontal. Show these points on your graph.

f. Eliminate the parameter $t$ and thus confirm that your graph actually is an ellipse. This elimination may be done by cleverly applying the Pythagorean property for sine and cosine.

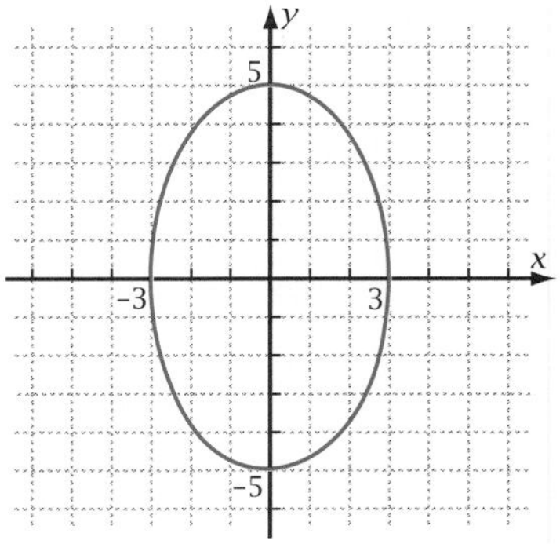


Figure 4-7g

4. *Astroid Problem:* The star-shaped curve in Figure 4-7h is called an **astroid**. Its parametric equations are

$$x = 8\cos^3 t$$
$$y = 8\sin^3 t.$$

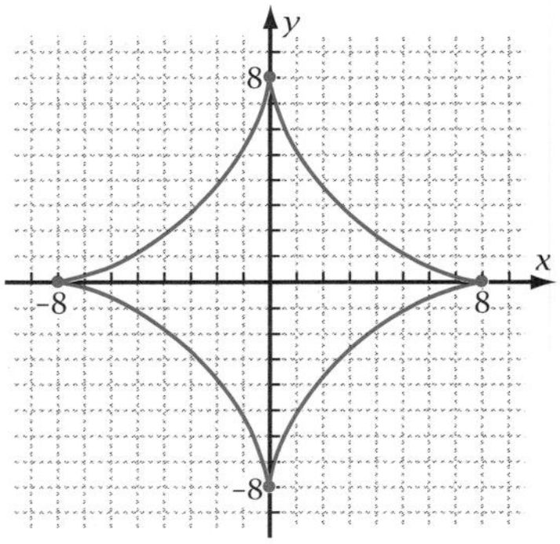


Figure 4-7h

a. Plot the graph on your grapher. Sketch the result or photocopy the text graph.

b. Find an equation for $dy/dx$.

c. Evaluate the point $(x, y)$ when $t = 1$, and find $dy/dx$ when $t = 1$. Plot a line on your graph at this point $(x, y)$ that has slope $dy/dx$. Is the line tangent to the graph?

d. At each cusp, $dy/dx$ has the indeterminate form $0/0$. Explain the difference in behavior at the cusp at the point $(8, 0)$ and at the cusp at the point $(0, 8)$.

e. Eliminate the parameter $t$. This transformation may be done by solving the two equations for the squares of $\cos t$ and $\sin t$ in terms of $x$ and $y$, then using the Pythagorean property for sine and cosine.

5. *Circle Problem:* A parametric function has the following equations.

$$x = 6 + 5\cos t$$
$$y = 3 + 5\sin t$$

a. Plot the graph of this function. Sketch the result.

b. Find an equation for $dy/dx$ in terms of $t$.

c. Find a value of $t$ that makes $dy/dx$ equal zero. Find a value of $t$ that makes $dy/dx$ infinite. Show a point on the graph for which $dy/dx$ is infinite. What is true about $dx/dt$ and about $dy/dt$ at a point where $dy/dx$ is infinite?

d. Eliminate the parameter $t$. This may be done by expressing the squares of cosine and sine in terms of $x$ and $y$, then by applying the Pythagorean property for sine and cosine.

e. From the equation in 5d, you should be able to tell that the graph is a circle. How can you determine the center and the radius of the circle just by looking at the original equations?

6. *Line Segment Problem:* Plot the graph of the parametric function

$$x = \cos^2 t$$
$$y = \sin^2 t.$$

Show that $dy/dx$ is constant. How does this fact correspond to what you observe about the graph? Confirm your observation by eliminating the parameter to get an $xy$-equation. Describe the difference in domain and range between the parametric function and the $xy$-equation.

7. *Deltoid Problem:* The graph of the parametric function

$$x = 2\cos t + \cos 2t$$
$$y = 2\sin t - \sin 2t$$

is shown in Figure 4-7i. It is called a **deltoid**, for reasons that should be obvious.

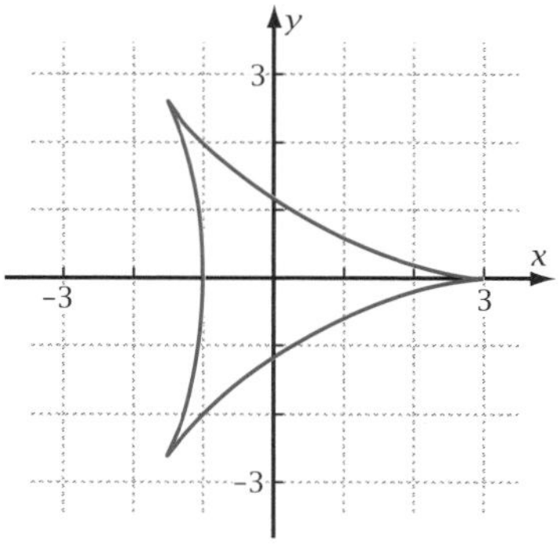

Figure 4-7i

a. Confirm by grapher that the equations shown above give the deltoid in Figure 4-7i.

b. Find an equation for $dy/dx$ in terms of $t$.

c. Show that at two of the cusps, the tangent line is neither horizontal nor vertical, yet the derivative $dy/dx$ fails to exist. Find the limit of $dy/dx$ as $t$ approaches the value at the cusp in Quadrant II.

8. *Witch of Agnesi Problem:* The **Witch of Agnesi**, named for Italian mathematician Maria Gaetana Agnesi (1718–1799), has the equations

$$x = 2a\tan t$$
$$y = 2a\cos^2 t,$$

where $a$ stands for a constant.

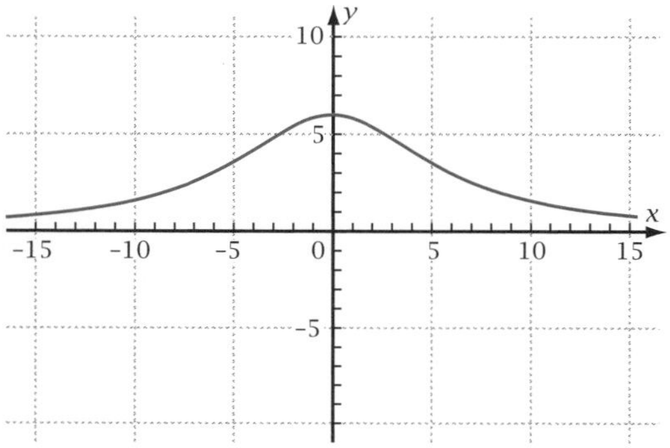

Figure 4-7j

a. Figure 4-7j shows a curve for which $a = 3$. Plot the graph. Sketch the result or photocopy the text graph.

b. Find $dy/dx$ in terms of $t$.

c. Eliminate the parameter to get an equation for $y$ in terms of $x$.

d. Differentiate the equation in 8c to get an equation for $dy/dx$ in terms of $x$.

e. Show that both equations for $dy/dx$ give the same answer at $t = \pi/4$, and that a line through the point where $t = \pi/4$ with this value of $dy/dx$ as its slope is tangent to the curve.

9. *Involute Problem:* A string is wrapped around a circle 1 in. in radius. As the string is unwound, its end traces a path called the **involute of a circle** (Figure 4-7k). The parametric equations of this involute are

$$x = \cos t + t \sin t$$
$$y = \sin t - t \cos t,$$

where $t$ is the number of radians from the positive $x$-axis to the radius drawn to the point of tangency of the string.

a. Use your grapher to confirm that these parametric equations give the graph shown in Figure 4-7k.

b. Find $dy/dx$ in terms of $t$. Simplify as much as possible.

c. Show that the value you get for $dy/dx$ at $t = \pi$ is consistent with the graph.

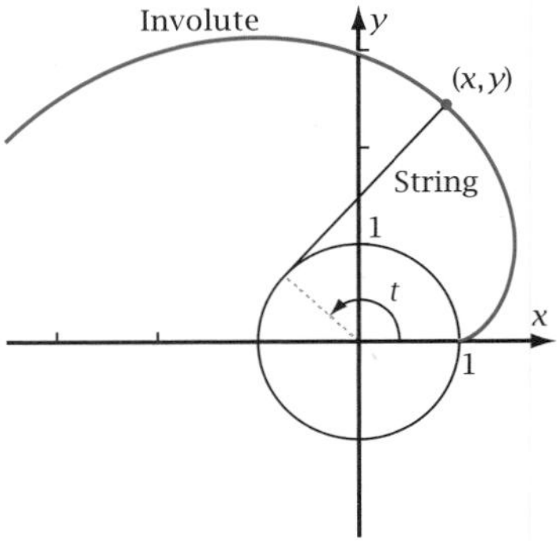

Figure 4-7k

10. *Clock Problem:* A clock sits on a shelf close to a wall (Figure 4-7l). As the second hand turns, its distances $x$ cm and $y$ cm from the wall and the shelf, respectively, depend on the number of seconds, $t$, since the second hand was pointing straight up.

a. Write parametric equations for $x$ and $y$ in terms of $t$.

b. At what rates are $x$ and $y$ changing when $t = 5$ sec?

c. What is the slope of the circular path traced by the second hand when $t = 5$?

d. Confirm that the path really is a circle by finding an $xy$-equation.

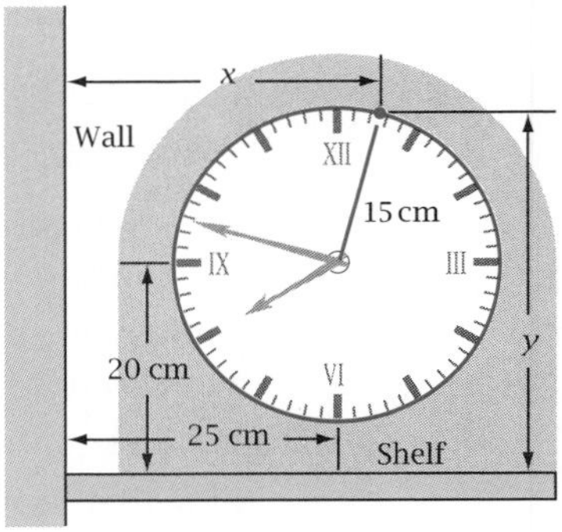

Figure 4-7l

11. *Pendulum Project:* Suspend a small mass from the ceiling on the end of a nylon cord. Place meter sticks on the floor, crossing them at the point below which the mass hangs at rest, as shown in Figure 4-7m. Determine the period of the pendulum by measuring

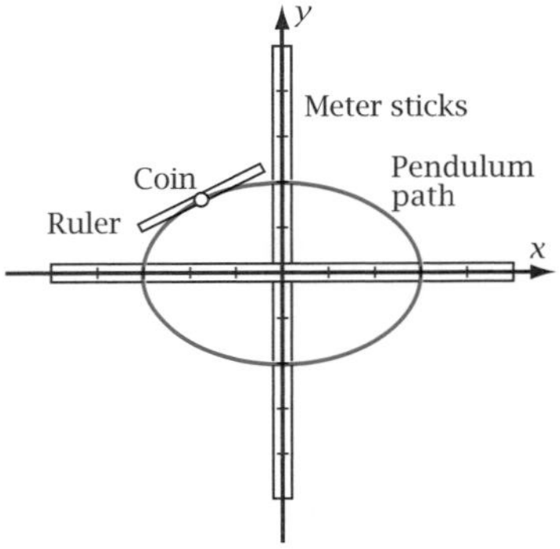

Figure 4-7m

the time for 10 swings. Then start the pendulum in an elliptical path by pulling it 30 cm in the $x$-direction and pushing it sideways just hard enough for it to cross the $y$-axis at 20 cm. Write parametric equations for the path this pendulum traces on the floor. Place a coin on the floor at the point at which you predict the pendulum will be at time $t = 5$ sec. (Lay the coin on top of a ruler tilted at an angle corresponding to the slope of the path at that time.) Then set the pendulum in motion again. How close do the predicted point and slope come to those you observe by experiment?

12. *Spring Problem:* Figure 4-7n shows a "spring" drawn by computer graphics. Figure out equations for a parametric function that will generate this graph. How did you verify that your equations are correct? Use your equations to find values of $x$ and $y$ at which the graph has interesting features, such as horizontal or vertical tangents and places where the graph seems to cross itself.

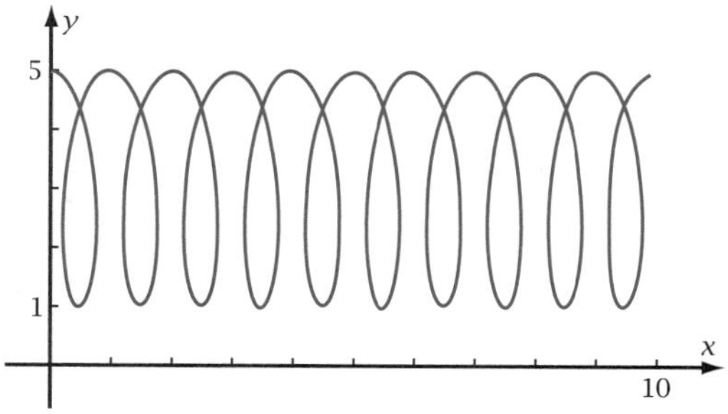

Figure 4-7n

13. *Lissajous Curves:* Graphs of parametric functions with the equations

$$x = \cos nt$$
$$y = \sin t,$$

where $n$ is (usually) an integer, are called **Lissajous curves**, or sometimes **Bowditch curves**. In this problem you will investigate some of these curves.

a. Figure 4-7o shows the Lissajous curve with the parametric equations

$$x = \cos 3t$$
$$y = \sin t.$$

Use your grapher to confirm that these equations generate this graph.

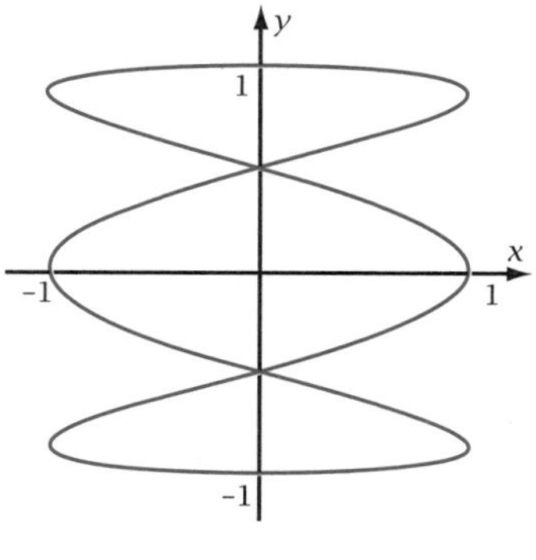

Figure 4-7o

b. Plot the Lissajous curve with the equations

$$x = \cos 4t$$
$$y = \sin t.$$

Sketch the resulting curve.

c. In what fundamental way do the curves differ for $n = 3$ (an odd number) and for $n = 4$ (an even number)?

d. Sketch what you think these curves would look like.

i. $x = \cos 5t$, $y = \sin t$

ii. $x = \cos 6t$, $y = \sin t$

e. Plot on your grapher the two curves in 13d. Did your predicted graphs match the actual ones in number of vertices and in behavior at the extreme points?

f. What two familiar curves are special cases of Lissajous curves when $n = 1$ and $n = 2$?

# 4-8 Graphs and Derivatives of Implicit Relations

If $y$ equals some function of $x$, such as $y = x^2 + \sin x$, then there is said to be an **explicit** relationship between $x$ and $y$. The word *explicit* comes from the same root as the word *explain.* If $x$ and $y$ appear in an equation such as

$$x^2 + y^2 = 25,$$

then there is an **implicit relation** between $x$ and $y$ because it is only "implied" that $y$ is a function of $x$. In this section you will see how to differentiate such an implicit relation without first solving for $y$ in terms of $x$. As a result, you will be able to prove that the power rule for derivatives works when the exponent is a rational number, not just an integer. In Section 4-5, you used **implicit differentiation** to find derivatives of the inverse trigonometric functions.

**OBJECTIVE**

Given the equation for an implicit relation, find the derivative of $y$ with respect to $x$, and show by graph that the answer is reasonable.

■ ***Example 1*** Consider the implicit relation $x^2 + y^2 = 25$ plotted in Figure 4-8a.

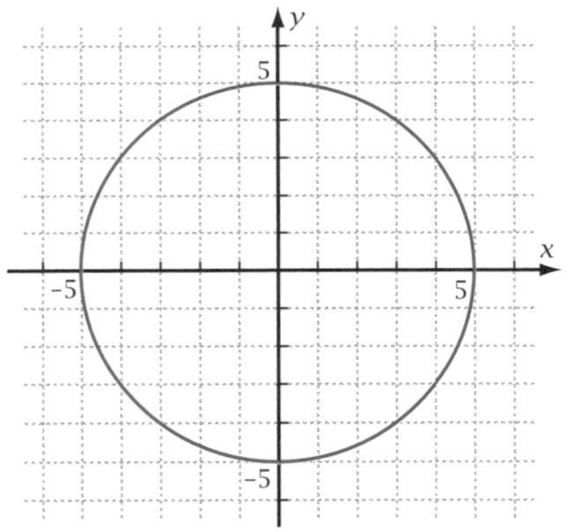

Figure 4-8a

a. Tell why the graph is a circle.

b. Differentiate implicitly to find $dy/dx$.

c. Calculate the two values of $y$ when $x = 3$.

d. Through the point determined in part c with the lower value of $y$, draw a line with slope $dy/dx$. How is this line related to the graph?

***Solutions***

a. The graph is a circle by the Pythagorean theorem. Because $x^2 + y^2 = 25 = 5^2$, all points on the graph are five units from the origin, implying that the graph is a circle.

b. For simplicity, use $y'$ for $dy/dx$.

$$2x + 2yy' = 0 \qquad \text{The } y' \text{ comes from the chain rule.}$$
$$2yy' = -2x$$
$$y' = \frac{-x}{y}$$

c. $x = 3 : 9 + y^2 = 25$
$y^2 = 16 \Rightarrow y = \pm 4$

d. At the point $(3, -4)$, slope $= y' = -\dfrac{-3}{4} = 0.75$. The line goes through the point $(3, -4)$ and is tangent to the graph (Figure 4-8b). ■

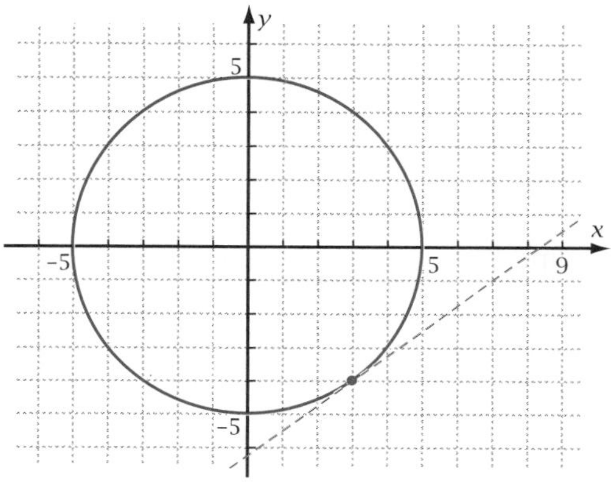


Figure 4-8b

■ ***Example 2*** For the implicit relation $y^4 + x^3y^5 - 2x^7 = 13$, find $dy/dx$.

***Solution*** For simplicity, use $y'$ for $dy/dx$. Be on the lookout for the derivative of a product property. Of course, you must also obey the chain rule wherever $y$ appears as an inside function.

$$4y^3y' + 3x^2y^5 + x^3 \cdot 5y^4y' - 14x^6 = 0$$

Note that $y'$ shows up as a result of the chain rule and is only to the first power, so you can use relatively easy algebra to isolate $y'$.

$$4y^3y' + x^3 \cdot 5y^4y' = -3x^2y^5 + 14x^6$$
$$(4y^3 + 5x^3y^4)y' = -3x^2y^5 + 14x^6$$
$$y' = \frac{-3x^2y^5 + 14x^6}{4y^3 + 5x^3y^4}$$ ■

The answer to Example 2 expresses $y'$ in terms of both $x$ and $y$, which is okay because the original relation had $x$ and $y$ together. Given a point $(x, y)$ on the graph, the answer above could be used to find $y'$. In practice, it is usually harder to find a point on the graph than it is to do the calculus! Thus you will work with problems like that in Example 2 mainly for practice in differentiating.

**Technique: Implicit Differentiation**

To find $dy/dx$ for a relation whose equation is written implicitly:

1. Differentiate both sides of the equation with respect to $x$. Observe the chain rule by multiplying by $dy/dx$ each time you differentiate an expression containing $y$.
2. Isolate $dy/dx$ by getting all of the $dy/dx$ terms onto one side of the equation, and all other terms onto the other side. Then factor, if necessary, and divide both sides by the coefficient of $dy/dx$.

**Example 3** If $y = x^{7/3}$, prove that the power rule for derivatives gives the right answer for $y'$.

**Solution**

$$y^3 = x^7$$ Cube both sides of the given equation.

$$3y^2y' = 7x^6$$ Use the power rule for integer exponents to differentiate implicitly with respect to $x$.

$$y' = \frac{7x^6}{3y^2}$$

$$y' = \frac{7}{3}\frac{x^6}{(x^{7/3})^2} = \frac{7}{3}\frac{x^6}{x^{14/3}} = \frac{7}{3}x^{4/3}$$

This is the answer you would get by direct application of the power rule using fractional exponents, Q.E.D. ■

In the following problem set you will prove, in general, the property proved in Example 3. You will also use implicit differentiation to verify the results you obtained by differentiating parametric functions from the preceding section.

## Problem Set 4-8

### Do These Quickly

The following problems are intended to refresh your skills. You should be able to do all ten problems in less than five minutes.

**Q1.** If $f(x) = \cos x$, then $f(\pi) =$ —?—

**Q2.** Differentiate: $y = x^{2001}$

**Q3.** $\lim_{x \to 5} (x^2 - 5x)/(x - 5) =$ —?—

**Q4.** Differentiate: $f(u) = \cot u$

**Q5.** A definite integral is a —?— of $x$ and $y$.

**Q6.** $y = \tan^{-1} 3x \Rightarrow y' =$ —?—

**Q7.** If $dy/dx = 3x^2$, what function could $y$ equal?

**Q8.** A derivative is an —?—

**Q9.** Sketch the derivative of the function graphed in Figure 4-8c.

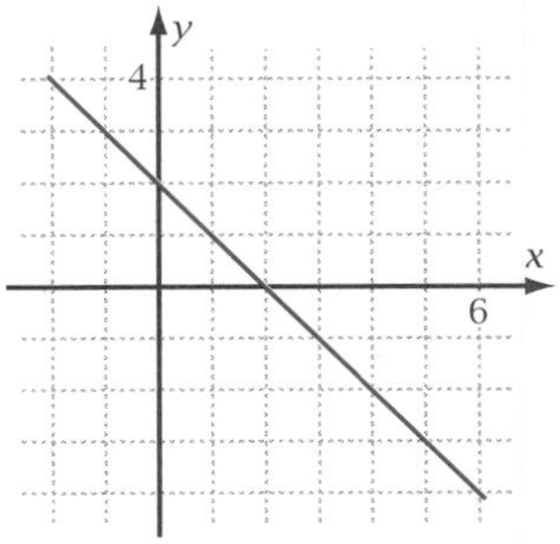

Figure 4-8c

**Q10.** If the position of a moving object is given by $x(t) = t \sin t$ feet, what is the velocity of the object when $t = 3$ sec?

For Problems 1–20, differentiate implicitly to find $y'$ in terms of $x$ and $y$.

1. $x^3 + 7y^4 = 13$
2. $3x^5 - y^4 = 22$
3. $x^6y^9 + 3x - y^3 = 10^4$
4. $4x + 8x^2y^6 + y^4 = 21^3$
5. $x + xy + y = \sin 2x$
6. $\cos(xy) = x - 2y$
7. $x^{0.5} - y^{0.5} = 13$
8. $x^{1.2} + y^{1.2} = 64$
9. $4y^2 + 9x^2 = 36$
10. $25y^2 - 16x^2 = 400$
11. $(x^3y^4)^5 = x - y$
12. $(xy)^6 = x + y$
13. $\cos^2 x + \sin^2 y = 1$
14. $\sec^2 y - \tan^2 x = 1$
15. $\tan(xy) = xy$
16. $\cos(xy) = xy$
17. $\sin y = x$
18. $\cos y = x$
19. $\csc y = x$
20. $\cot y = x$
21. By implicit differentiation, derive the formula for $y'$ if $y = \cos^{-1}x$. Express the answer explicitly in terms of $x$.
22. By implicit differentiation, derive the formula for $y'$ if $y = \tan^{-1}x$. Express the answer explicitly in terms of $x$.
23. If $y = x^{11/5}$, prove that the derivative of a power formula for powers with integer exponents gives the correct answer for $y'$.
24. *Derivative of a Rational Power:* Suppose that $y = x^n$, where $n = a/b$ for integers $a$ and $b$. Write the equation $y = x^{a/b}$ in the form $y^b = x^a$. Then use the derivative of a power formula for integer exponents to prove that the formula also works for rational constant exponents.
25. *Circle Problem:* Consider the circle $x^2 + y^2 = 100$ (Figure 4-8d).
    a. Show that the point $(-6, 8)$ is on the graph.
    b. Evaluate $dy/dx$ at the point $(-6, 8)$. Explain why your answer is reasonable.
    c. Show that the parametric equations

$$x = 10\cos t$$
$$y = 10\sin t$$

    give the same value for $dy/dx$ at $x = -6$.

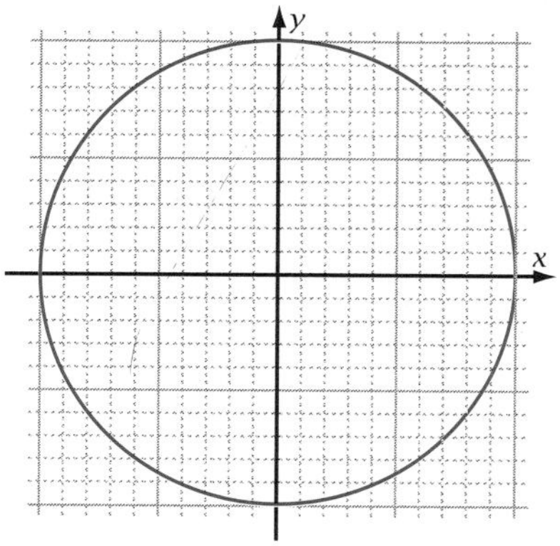

Figure 4-8d

26. *Hyperbola Problem:* Consider the hyperbola $x^2 - y^2 = 36$ (Figure 4-8e).
    a. Show that the point $(10, -8)$ is on the graph.
    b. Evaluate $dy/dx$ at the point $(10, -8)$. Explain why your answer is reasonable.

c. Show that the parametric equations

$$x = 6 \sec t$$
$$y = 6 \tan t$$

give the same value for $dy/dx$ at $x = 10$.

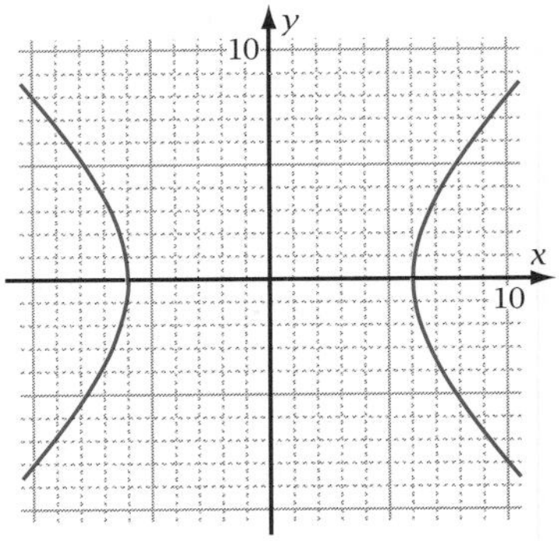

Figure 4-8e

27. *Cubic Circle Problem:* Figure 4-8f shows the **cubic circle**

$$x^3 + y^3 = 64.$$

a. Find $dy/dx$ at the points where $x = 0$, $x = 2$, and $x = 4$. Show that your answers are consistent with the graph.

b. Find $dy/dx$ at the point where $y = x$.

c. Find the limit of $dy/dx$ as $x$ approaches infinity.

d. Why do you suppose this graph is called a cubic circle?

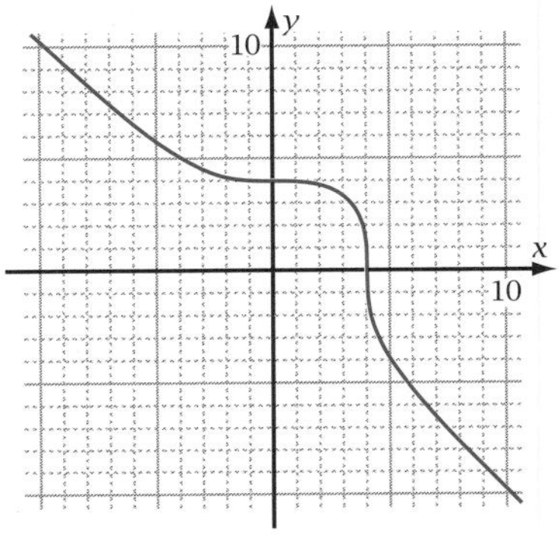

Figure 4-8f

28. *Ovals of Cassini Project:* Figure 4-8g shows the **ovals of Cassini**,

$$[(x - 6)^2 + y^2][(x + 6)^2 + y^2] = 1200.$$

In 1680, Italian astronomer Giovanni Domenico Cassini (1625–1712) used these figures for relative motions of the earth and the sun.

a. Find the two values of $dy/dx$ when $x = 8$. Show that your answers are reasonable.

b. Find the four $x$-intercepts. What does $dy/dx$ seem to be at these points? Confirm your conclusion for the largest intercept.

c. Starting with the original equation above, use the quadratic formula to find an equation for $y^2$ explicitly in terms of $x$. Use this equation to duplicate Figure 4-8g.

d. Replace the number 1200 in the original equation with the number 1400, then plot the graph. In what way or ways is this graph different from that shown in Figure 4-8g?

e. Show that for any point on the graph, the product of its distances from the points $(6, 0)$ and $(-6, 0)$ is constant.

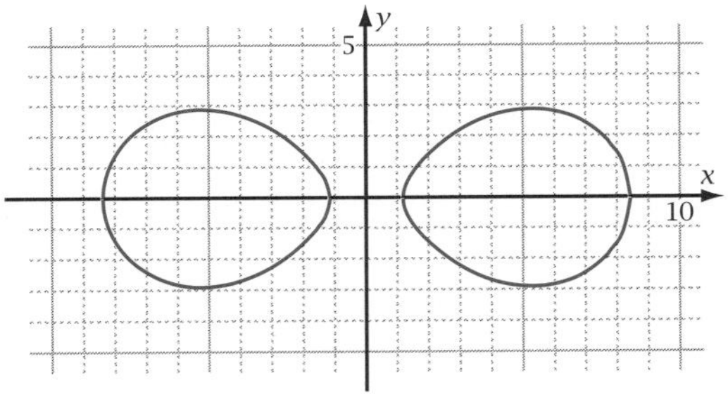

Figure 4-8g

# 4-9 Chapter Review and Test

In this chapter you have learned more algebraic techniques for differentiating functions. You can now differentiate products, quotients, parametric functions, and implicit relations. You can differentiate implicit relations, and all six trigonometric functions. The properties are sometimes surprising; for instance, for a product, $(uv)' = u'v + uv'$, not $u'v'$. Derivatives of parametric functions and of implicit relations allow you to analyze geometric figures that are much more complicated than those you've dealt with so far.

The Review Problems below are numbered according to the sections of this chapter. The Concepts Problems allow you to apply your knowledge to new situations. The Chapter Test is more like a typical classroom test your instructor might give you.

## Review Problems

R0. Update your journal with what you've learned since the last entry. Include such things as those listed here.

- The one most important thing you have learned by studying Chapter 4
- Which boxes you have been working on in the "define, understand, do, apply" table
- Key terms, such as *parametric function, implicit differentiation*, and *differentiability*
- Surprising properties, such as the derivative of a product and the parametric chain rule
- Ways in which you have used graphs, tables, algebra, and writing to understand concepts
- Any ideas about calculus that you're still unclear about

R1. Suppose that $x = g(t) = t^3$ and that $y = h(t) = \cos t$.

a. If $f(t) = g(t) \cdot h(t)$, show by counterexample that $f'(t)$ does not equal $g'(t) \cdot h'(t)$.

b. If $f(t) = g(t)/h(t)$, show by counterexample that $f'(t)$ does not equal $g'(t)/h'(t)$.

c. Show by example that $dy/dx$ equals $(dy/dt)/(dx/dt)$.

R2. a. State the property of the derivative of a product.

b. Prove the property of the derivative of a product, using the definition of derivative.

c. Differentiate and simplify.

i. $f(x) = x^7 \cos 3x$ ii. $g(x) = (\sin x)(\sin 2x)$

iii. $h(x) = (3x - 7)^5(5x + 2)^3$ iv. $s(x) = (5^3)(x^8)$

d. Differentiate $f(x) = (3x + 8)(4x + 7)$ in two ways.

i. As a product of two functions

ii. By multiplying the binomials, then differentiating

Show that your answers are equivalent.

R3. a. State the property of the derivative of a quotient.

b. Prove the property of the derivative of a quotient, using the definition of derivative.

c. Differentiate and simplify.

i. $f(x) = \dfrac{\sin 10x}{x^5}$ ii. $g(x) = \dfrac{(2x + 3)^9}{(9x - 5)^4}$ iii. $h(x) = (100x^3 - 1)^{-5}$

d. Differentiate $y = 1/x^{10}$ as a quotient and as a power with a negative exponent. Show that both answers are equivalent.

e. Find $t'(x)$ if $t(x) = \dfrac{\sin x}{\cos x}$. Use the result to find $t'(1)$.

f. Plot the difference quotient $[t(x) - t(1)]/(x - 1)$, using a window centered at $x = 1$, with $\Delta x = 0.001$. (Enter $t(1)$ as $(\sin 1)/(\cos 1)$ to avoid rounding errors.)

Sketch the result. Show that the difference quotient approaches $t'(1)$ by tracing the graph and making a table of values for several $x$-values on either side of 1.

R4. a. Differentiate.

i. $y = \tan 7x$  ii. $y = \cot(x^4)$  iii. $y = 3\sec x$  iv. $y = \csc x$

b. Derive the formula $\cot' x = -\csc^2 x$.

c. Plot the graph of $y = \tan x$. Make a connection between the slope of the graph and the fact that the derivative is equal to the square of a function.

d. Suppose that $f(t) = 7\sec t$. How fast is $f(t)$ changing when $t = 1$? When $t = 1.5$? When $t = 1.57$? How do you explain the dramatic increase in the rate of change of $f(t)$ even though $t$ doesn't change very much?

R5. a. Differentiate.

i. $y = \tan^{-1} 3x$  ii. $\dfrac{d}{dx}(\sec^{-1} x)$  iii. $c(x) = (\cos^{-1} x)^2$

b. Plot on your grapher the graph of $y = \sin^{-1} x$. Use parametric mode. Evaluate the derivative at $x = 0$, $x = 1$, and $x = 2$. How do your results agree with the graph?

R6. a. State the relationship between differentiability and continuity.

b. Sketch a graph for each of the following.

i. Function $f$ is neither differentiable nor continuous at $x = c$.
ii. Function $f$ is continuous but not differentiable at $x = c$.
iii. Function $f$ is differentiable but not continuous at $x = c$.
iv. Function $f$ is differentiable and continuous at $x = c$.

c. Let $f(x) = \begin{cases} x^2 + 1, & \text{if } x < 1 \\ -x^2 + 4x - 1, & \text{if } x \ge 1 \end{cases}$

i. Sketch the graph.
ii. Show that $f$ is continuous at $x = 1$.
iii. Is $f$ differentiable at $x = 1$? Justify your answer.

d. Let $g(x) = \begin{cases} \sin^{-1} x, & \text{if } 0 \le x \le 1 \\ x^2 + ax + b, & \text{if } x < 0 \end{cases}$

Find the values of the constants $a$ and $b$ that make $g$ differentiable at $x = 0$. Confirm your answer by graphing.

R7. a. Figure 4-9a shows the spiral with the parametric equations

$$x = (t/\pi)\cos t$$
$$y = (t/\pi)\sin t.$$

Write $dy/dx$ in terms of $t$. The graph appears to pass vertically through the point (6, 0). Does the graph contain this point? If not, why not? If so, is it really vertical at that point? Justify your answer.

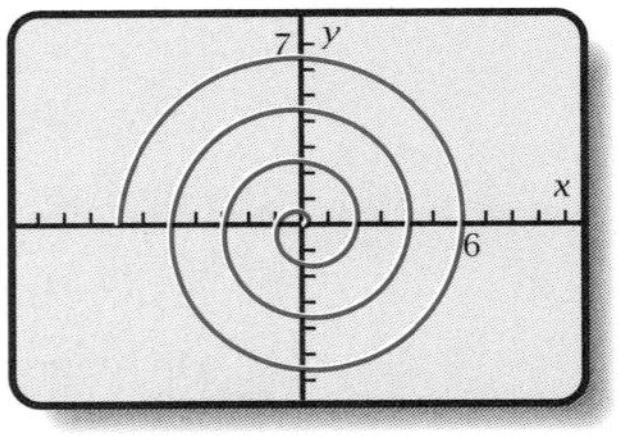

Figure 4-9a

b. *Ferris Wheel Problem:* Figure 4-9b shows a Ferris wheel of diameter 40 ft. Its axle is 25 ft above the ground. (The same Ferris wheel appeared in Problem 1 of Problem Set 3-8.) The seat shown is $y(t)$ feet from the ground and $x(t)$ feet out from the axle. The seat first reaches a high point when $t = 3$ sec. The wheel makes 3 rev/min. Given that $x$ and $y$ vary sinusoidally with time, $t$, as the Ferris wheel rotates clockwise, write parametric equations for $x$ and $y$ in terms of $t$. When $t = 0$, is the seat moving up or down? How fast? How can you determine these facts? When $t = 0$, is the seat moving to the left or to the right? How fast? How can you determine this? What is the first positive value of $t$ for which $dy/dx$ is infinite?

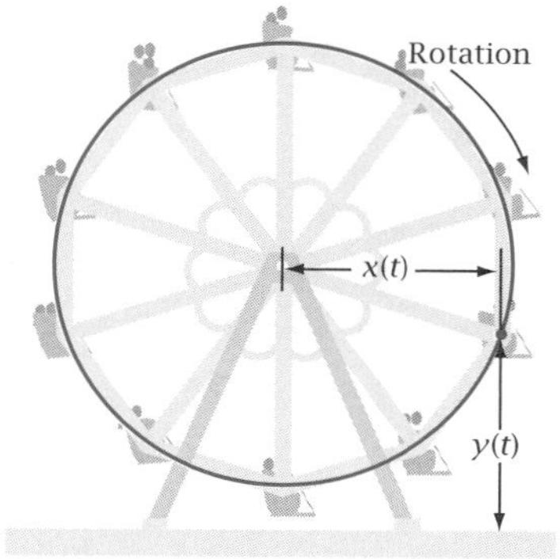

Figure 4-9b

R8. a. Find $y'$: $y = (12x^{1/3} + 7)^6$.

b. Find $dy/dx$: $y^3 \sin(xy) = x^{4.5}$.

c. *Cissoid of Diocles Problem:* The cissoid of Diocles in Figure 4-9c has the equation $4y^2 - xy^2 = x^3$. (The word cissoid comes from Greek and means "ivylike.") In *Curves and Their Properties* (National Council of Teachers of Mathematics, 1974) Robert C. Yates reports that the Greek mathematician Diocles (ca. 250–100 B.C.) used cissoids for finding cube roots.

i. Find $dy/dx$ when $x = 2$. Show that your answers are reasonable.

ii. Find $dy/dx$ at the point (0, 0). Interpret your answer.

iii. Find the vertical asymptote.

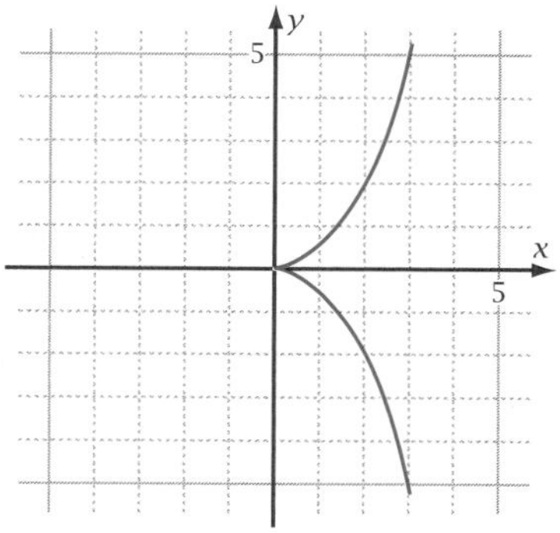

Figure 4-9c

## Concepts Problems

C1. *Historical Problem: Newton's Method:* Suppose you are trying to find a zero (an $x$-intercept) of function $f$, and you can't solve the equation $f(x) = 0$ by using algebra. English mathematician Isaac Newton (1642–1727) is credited with finding a way to solve such equations approximately by using derivatives. This process is called **Newton's method**. Figure 4-9d shows the graph of function $f$ for which a zero is to be found. Pick a convenient value $x = x_0$ close to the zero. Calculate $y_0 = f(x_0)$. The tangent line to the graph of $f$ at that point will have slope $m = f'(x_0)$. If you extend this tangent line to the $x$-axis, it should cross at a place $x_1$ that is closer to the desired zero than your original choice, $x_0$. By repeating this process, you can find the zero to as many decimal places as you like!

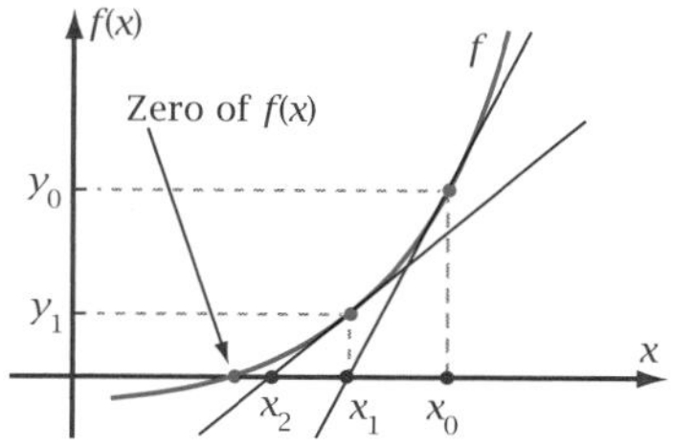

Figure 4-9d

a. Let $m$ be the slope of the tangent line at the point $(x_0, y_0)$. Write an equation for the tangent line.

b. The point $(x_1, 0)$ is on the tangent line. Substitute these coordinates for $x$ and $y$ in the equation from C1a. Use the result to show that $x_1 = x_0 - (y_0/m)$.

c. If a tangent line is drawn at $(x_1, y_1)$, it will cross the $x$-axis at $x_2$. Explain why

$$x_2 = x_1 - \frac{f(x_1)}{f'(x_1)}.$$

d. Write a program to use the formula from C1c to calculate values of $x$ iteratively. The equation for $f(x)$ can be stored in the $y =$ menu. You can use the numerical derivative feature to calculate the value of $f'(x)$. The input should be the value of $x_0$. The program should allow you to press ENTER, then read the next value of $x$. Test the program on $f(x) = x^2 - 9x + 14$. Start with $x_0 = 1$, then again with $x_0 = 6$.

e. Use the program to find the three zeros of $g(x) = x^3 - 9x^2 + 5x + 10$. Compare your answers with those you get by using your grapher's built-in solve feature.

f. The equation of the graph in Figure 4-9d is $f(x) = \sec x - 1.1$. Use Newton's method to estimate the zero shown in the figure. If you start with $x_0 = 1$, how many iterations, $n$, does it take to make $x_{n+1}$ indistinguishable from $x_n$ on the calculator?

## Chapter Test

T1. Is the function $c(x) = \cot 3x$ increasing or decreasing when $x = 5$? At what rate?

T2. If $f(x) = \sec x$, find $f'(2)$. Show that the difference quotient $\dfrac{\sec x - \sec 2}{x - 2}$ approaches $f'(2)$ by making a table of values from $x = 1.997$ through $x = 2.003$ with an $x$-step of 0.001.

T3. Sketch the graph of a function that has all these features.
- The value $f(-2) = 7$.
- The function $f(x)$ is increasing slowly at $x = -2$.
- The value $f(1)$ is positive, but $f(x)$ is decreasing fast at $x = 1$.
- The function $f(x)$ is continuous at $x = 2$ but is not differentiable at that point.

T4. State (without proof) the derivative of a quotient property.

T5. State (without proof) the parametric chain rule.

T6. Use the most time-efficient method to prove that the general linear function, $f(x) = mx + b$, is continuous for every value of $x = c$.

For problems T7–T14, find $f'(x)$ or $dy/dx$. Simplify.

T7. $f(x) = \sec 5x$

T8. $y = \tan^{7/3} x$

T9. $\dfrac{d}{dx}(3 \csc 11x)$

T10. $f(x) = (2x - 5)^6 (5x - 1)^2$

T11. $f(x) = \dfrac{\cot 3x}{\cos^2 3x}$

T12. $5x^3 y^7 = y^{1.6}$

T13. $x = \sec 2t$
$y = \tan 2t^3$

T14. $y = 4 \sin^{-1}(5x^3)$

T15. *Rotated Ellipse Problem:* Figure 4-9e shows the graph of

$$9x^2 - 20xy + 25y^2 - 16x + 10y - 50 = 0.$$

The figure is an ellipse that is rotated with respect to the $x$- and $y$-axes. Evaluate $dy/dx$ at both points where $x = -2$. Show that each answer is reasonable.

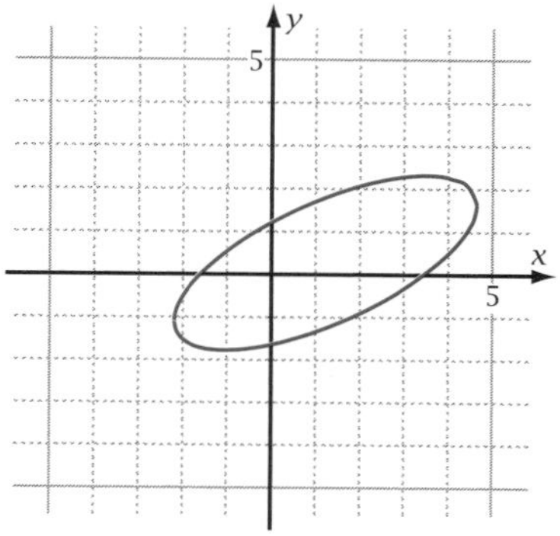


Figure 4-9e

T16. Let $y = x^{7/3}$. Transform this equation into an implicit relation involving only integer exponents. Then differentiate implicitly to find $y'$. Show that your answer agrees with the answer found directly, using the formula for the derivative of a power on the original equation.

T17. Let $f(x) = \begin{cases} x^3 + 1, & \text{if } x \le 1 \\ a(x-2)^2 + b, & \text{if } x > 1 \end{cases}$

What values of the constants $a$ and $b$ make function $f$ differentiable at $x = 1$? Show that the limits of $f(x)$ as $x$ approaches 1 from the right and from the left can equal each other but that $f$ is still not differentiable at $x = 1$.

CHAPTER

# 5 Definite and Indefinite Integrals

Cable cars are used for steep streets in San Francisco. For each 100 feet the car goes horizontally, it might rise as much as 20 feet vertically. The slope of the street is a derivative, $dy/dx$, a single quantity. The differentials $dy$ and $dx$ can be defined separately, in such a way that their ratio is the slope. These differentials play a crucial role in the definition, computation, and application of definite integrals.

# Mathematical Overview

In your study of calculus so far you have learned that a definite integral is a product of $x$ and $y$, where $y$ varies with $x$. In Chapter 5 you will learn the formal definition of definite integral, that an indefinite integral is an antiderivative, and that the two are related by the fundamental theorem of calculus. You will gain this knowledge in four ways.

***Graphically*** The logo at the top of each even-numbered page of this chapter shows how a definite integral can be analyzed by slicing a region into vertical strips.

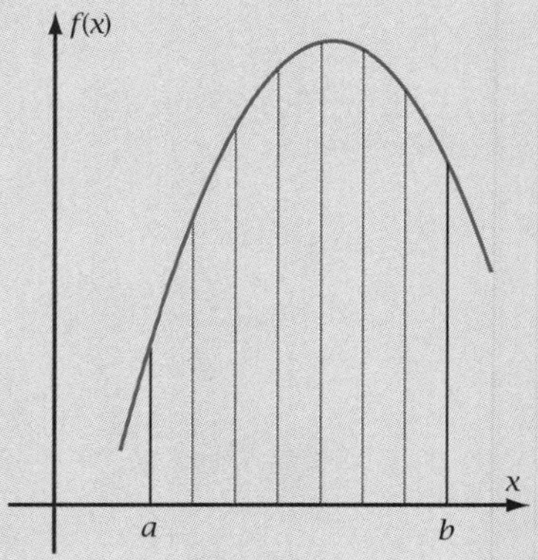


***Numerically***

| $x$ | $f(x)$ | integral |
|---|---|---|
| 1.0 | 5 | 0.0 |
| 1.5 | 8 | 2.5 |
| 2.0 | 10 | 7.0 |
| ... | ... | ... |

***Algebraically*** $\int_1^4 \cos x \, dx = \sin 4 - \sin 1$, the fundamental theorem.

***Verbally*** *Finally I found out why definite and indefinite integrals share a name. Indefinite integrals can be used to calculate definite integrals exactly. I also learned a way to analyze many different problems involving the product of x and y by slicing the region under the graph into vertical strips.*

# 5-1 A Definite Integral Problem

So far you have learned three of the four concepts of calculus. In this chapter you will learn about the fourth concept—indefinite integral—and why its name is so similar to that of definite integral. In this section you will refresh your memory about definite integrals.

**OBJECTIVE**

Work the problems in this section, on your own or with your study group, as an assignment after your last test on Chapter 4.

## Exploratory Problem Set 5-1

*Oil Well Problem:* An oil well that is 1000 ft deep is to be extended to a depth of 4000 ft. The drilling contractor estimates that the cost in dollars per foot, $c(x)$, for doing the drilling is

$$c(x) = 20 \cdot 1.0003^x,$$

where $x$ is the number of feet below the surface at which the drill is operating. Figure 5-1a shows an accurate graph of function $c$.

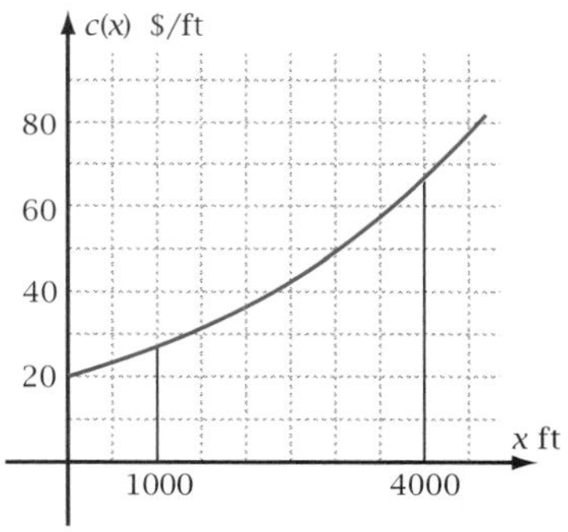

Figure 5-1a

1. How much does it cost per foot to drill at 1000 feet? At 4000 ft?
2. The actual cost of extending the well is the definite integral of $c(x)$ from $x = 1000$ to $x = 4000$. Estimate this integral by using the trapezoidal rule with $n = 6$ increments.
3. The average cost per foot is equal to the total cost from Problem 2 divided by the number of feet that were drilled (3000). Calculate the average cost per foot.
4. Estimate the definite integral again, this time assuming that each of the six strips is a rectangle instead of a trapezoid. Let the altitudes of the rectangles be the costs per foot at the midpoints of the six strips (that is, $c(1250)$, $c(1750)$, $c(2250)$, and so on). How close is your answer to the answer you got by using the trapezoidal rule?
5. Is the average cost per foot for extending the well from 1000 ft to 4000 ft equal to, more than, or less than the average of the two values in Problem 1?
6. What is the approximate instantaneous rate of change of the cost per foot at $x = 1000$? At $x = 4000$? What are the units of this rate?
7. The answer to Problem 6 is a rate of change of a rate of change. What mathematical word identifies such a rate? What other physical quantity is a rate of change of a rate of change?

# 5-2 Review of Antiderivatives

Recall from Section 3-9 that function $f$ is said to be an antiderivative of another function $g$ if and only if $g(x)$ is the derivative of $f(x)$. For instance, if

$$g(x) = 5x^4 \quad \text{and} \quad f(x) = x^5,$$

then $f$ is an antiderivative of $g$ because $f'(x)$ and $g(x)$ both equal $5x^4$. Note that $x^5 + 7$, $x^5 - 13.2$, and $x^5 + \pi$ are also antiderivatives of $g(x)$ because the derivative of a constant equals zero. In general, if $f(x)$ is an antiderivative of $g(x)$, then so is $f(x) + C$, where $C$ is an arbitrary constant. For reasons you will soon learn, the constant $C$ is called the **constant of integration**. The equation $f(x) = x^5 + C$ is called the **general equation for the antiderivative**. An equation such as $f(x) = x^5 - 1001$, where a particular value has been substituted for the constant of integration, is called a **particular equation for the antiderivative**.

In this section you will refresh your memory about how to find an antiderivative.

***OBJECTIVE*** Given the equation for the derivative of a function, write the general equation for the antiderivative function.

■ ***Example 1*** If $f'(x) = x^7$, find the general equation for $f(x)$.

***Solution*** $f(x) = \frac{1}{8}x^8 + C$ Because $f'(x) = x^7$. ■

## Problem Set 5-2

### *Do These Quickly*

The following problems are intended to refresh your skills. You should be able to do all ten problems in less than five minutes.

**Q1.** Find $dy/dx$: $x^3y^2 = 5$.

**Q2.** Find $dy/dx$: $x = \cos t$ and $y = 5t^{-1.7}$.

**Q3.** Differentiate: $f(x) = 3^7$

**Q4.** Find $f'(x)$: $f(x) = \sin^{-1} x$.

**Q5.** Find $y'$: $y = \sec x$.

**Q6.** Find the second derivative: $y = x^6$.

**Q7.** Find the velocity: $x(t) = \cos 3t$.

**Q8.** Find the acceleration: $x(t) = \cos 3t$.

**Q9.** $\log 5x + \log 3x = \log$ -?-

**Q10.** Sketch the graph of $y'$ for $y = |x| + 2$, shown in Figure 5-2a.

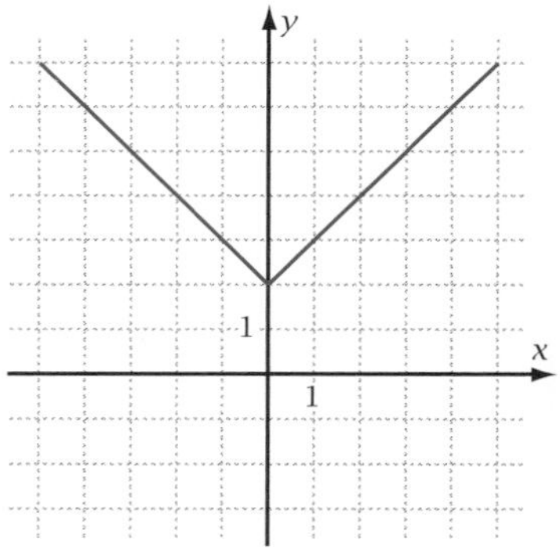

Figure 5-2a

Write the general equation for the antiderivative function.

1. $f'(x) = 7x^6$
2. $f'(x) = 10x^9$
3. $f'(x) = x^{-9}$
4. $f'(x) = x^{-1066}$
5. $f'(x) = \cos x$
6. $f'(x) = \sin x$
7. $f'(x) = \csc^2 x$
8. $f'(x) = \sec x \tan x$
9. $f'(x) = -\csc x \cot x$
10. $f'(x) = \sec^2 x$
11. $f'(x) = \sin 5x$
12. $f'(x) = \cos 4x$
13. $f'(x) = \sec^2 8x$
14. $f'(x) = \csc 2x \cot 2x$
15. $f'(x) = (4x + 5)^7$
16. $f'(x) = (8x + 3)^5$
17. *Family of Functions Problem:* Figure 5-2b shows the graphs of three functions.

$$y = x^5 + 0.3$$
$$y = x^5 + 0.7$$
$$y = x^5 + 1.1$$

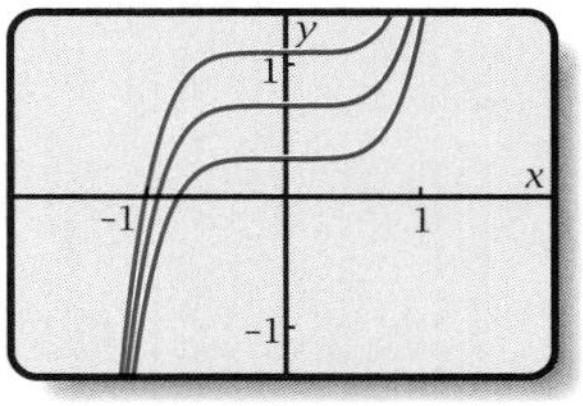

Figure 5-2b

a. Each of the functions is an antiderivative of the same function. Write an equation for that function.

b. What word from geometry (beginning with the letter *c*) describes the three graphs? In what way could it be said that the graphs are the same distance apart from one another? Why is it not strictly correct to say that the graphs are "parallel" to one another?

c. Suppose that $f'(x) = 3x^2 - 2$. Write the general equation for the antiderivative $f(x)$. Then write the equations for three particular solutions, the first containing the point (1, 0), the second containing the point (1, 1), and the third containing the point (1, 2).

d. Plot the graphs of the three particular solutions in 17c. Sketch the results.

e. Write a paragraph in your journal that describes how the constant of integration, *C*, affects the graph of the antiderivative. Explain why an antiderivative can be called a **family** of functions.

# 5-3 Linear Approximations and Differentials

You have learned how to find an equation for an antiderivative by asking "What did they differentiate to get this function?" but nowhere have you seen a symbol for an antiderivative.

In this section you will learn how to find a linear function that goes through a fixed value on the graph of a given function and that approximately fits the given function when $x$ is close to that fixed value. If you pick a point on the linear function graph, the changes in $x$ and $y$ from the fixed point are called **differentials** of $x$ and $y$, written $dx$ and $dy$ (Figure 5-3a). Differentials will appear in the antiderivative symbol, as you will see in Section 5-4.

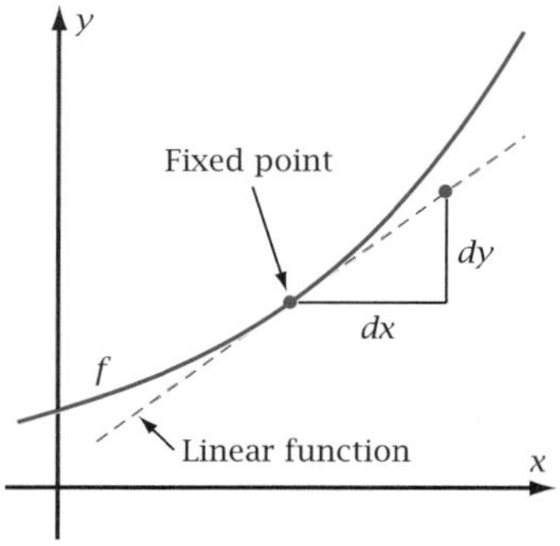


Figure 5-3a

***OBJECTIVE***

Given the equation for a function $f$ and a fixed point on its graph, find an equation for the linear function that best fits the given function. Use the equation to find approximate values for $f(x)$ and values for the differentials $dx$ and $dy$.

For the linear function $y = L(x) = mx + b$ to fit a given function $f$ close to $x = c$, two criteria should be met.

- The function values should be equal at $x = c$. That is, $L(c) = f(c)$.
- The slopes should be equal at $x = c$. That is, $L'(c) = f'(c)$.

Example 1 shows you a way to meet these criteria and find how good the fit is.

■ ***Example 1*** For $f(x) = 15 - x^3$, find an equation of the linear function that best fits $f$ at the fixed point (2, 7). Sketch the graphs of $f$ and of the linear function. Find the error in approximating $f(x)$ with the linear function for values of $x$ close to 2.

***Solution***

$f(2) = 15 - 2^3 = 7$, so $y = 7$ when $x = 2$.

$f'(x) = -3x^2 \Rightarrow f'(2) = -12$, so $m = -12$.

$\therefore$ the line has the equation $y - 7 = -12(x - 2) \Rightarrow y = 7 - 12(x - 2)$.

Figure 5-3b shows the graphs of $f$ and of the linear function. Using your grapher's table feature gives the following values of $f(x)$ and $y$, and the error, $f(x) - y$.

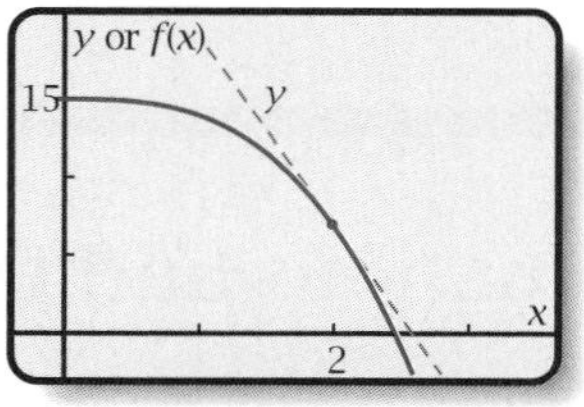


Figure 5-3b

| $x$ | $f(x)$ | $y$ | error, $f(x) - y$ |
|---|---|---|---|
| 1.7 | 10.087 | 10.6 | −0.513 |
| 1.8 | 9.168 | 9.4 | −0.232 |
| 1.9 | 8.141 | 8.2 | −0.059 |
| 2.0 | 7 | 7 | 0 |
| 2.1 | 5.739 | 5.8 | −0.061 |
| 2.2 | 4.352 | 4.6 | −0.248 |
| 2.3 | 2.833 | 3.4 | −0.567 |

The linear function fits $f(x)$ perfectly at $x = 2$, and $y \approx f(x)$ when $x$ is close to 2. The error, $f(x) - y$, gets larger in absolute value as $x$ gets farther from 2. ■

Parts of the linear equation $y = 7 - 12(x - 2)$ in Example 1 are significant.

- 7 is $f(2)$, the value of the original function at the fixed point.
- $-12$ is $f'(2)$, the value of the derivative there.
- $(x - 2)$ is the differential $dx$, the $x$-displacement from the fixed point (2, 7).
- $-12(x - 2)$ is the differential $dy$, the $y$-displacement from the point (2, 7) for the linear function.

**Property: Linearization of a Function**

The linear function that best fits function $f$ for values of $x$ close to $x = c$ is

$$y = f(c) + f'(c)(x - c) \text{ or, equivalently, } y = f(c) + f'(c)\,dx.$$

**Example 2** If $f(x) = \sin x$, write an equation for the linear function that best fits at $x = 1$. Use the linear function to approximate $f(1.02)$. What is the error in the approximation? What are the values of $dx, dy, \Delta x$, and $\Delta y$? Sketch a graph that shows these quantities and the error.

**Solution**

$$f(1) = \sin 1 = 0.84147\ldots$$

$$f'(x) = \cos x \Rightarrow f'(1) = \cos 1 = 0.54030\ldots$$

$$\therefore y = (\sin 1) + (\cos 1)(x - 1) \qquad y = f(c) + f'(c)(x - c)$$

$$y = 0.84147\ldots + 0.54030\ldots(x - 1).$$

If $x = 1.02$, then

$$y = 0.84147\ldots + 0.54030\ldots(1.02 - 1) = 0.852277030\ldots$$

$$f(1.02) = \sin 1.02 = 0.852108021\ldots$$

$$\therefore \text{error} = \sin 1.02 - 0.852277030\ldots = -0.000169008\ldots$$

Small error. 1.02 is close to 1.

$$dx = 1.02 - 1 = 0.02$$

$$dy = (\cos 1)(0.02) = 0.01080604\ldots$$

$$\Delta x = dx = 0.02$$

$$\Delta y = \sin 1.02 - \sin 1 = 0.01063703\ldots \approx dy.$$

Figure 5-3c illustrates the differentials $dx$ and $dy$, and shows their relationship to $\Delta x$ and $\Delta y$. The error is also equal to $\Delta y - dy$. ■

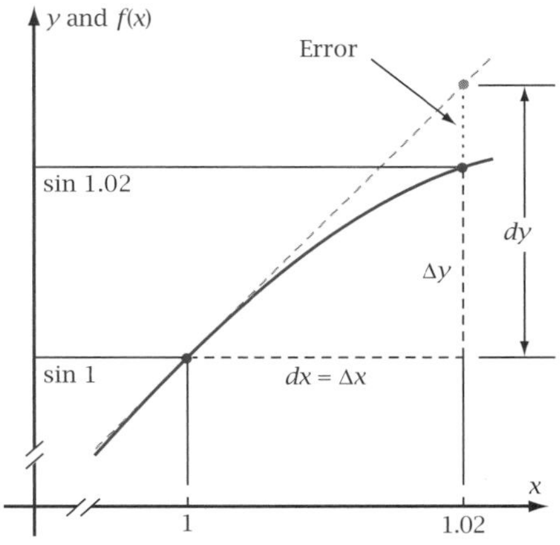


Figure 5-3c

In Example 2, $dy = (\cos 1)(x - 1)$. In general, $dy$ is given by

$$dy = f'(x)\,dx.$$

This fact can be used as a definition for the differential $dy$.

> **Definition: Differentials**
>
> The **differentials** $dx$ and $dy$ are defined as follows.
>
> $$dx = \Delta x$$
> $$dy = f'(x)\,dx$$
>
> Thus $dy \div dx$ is equal to $f'(x)$. Note that $dy$ is *not* usually equal to $\Delta y$.

An important aspect of the definition of differentials is that it allows for $dy$ and $dx$ in the symbol for derivative,

$$\frac{dy}{dx},$$

to be treated as separate quantities.

Example 3 shows you how to find the antiderivative when the differential of a function is given.

**Example 3** Given $dy = (3x + 7)^5\,dx$, find an equation for the antiderivative, $y$.

**Solution**

$$\frac{dy}{dx} = (3x + 7)^5$$

Divide both sides of the given equation by $dx$.

Thought process:

- It looks like someone differentiated $(3x + 7)^6$.
- But the differential of $(3x + 7)^6$ is $6(3x + 7)^5 \cdot 3 \cdot dx$, or $18(3x + 7)^5\,dx$.
- So the function must be only 1/18 as big as $(3x + 7)^6$, and the answer is:

$$y = \tfrac{1}{18}(3x + 7)^6 + C$$

Why is $+C$ needed? ■

The problems in the following problem set are designed to help you become comfortable with linear approximations for functions and with the differentials $dy$ and $dx$.

# Problem Set 5-3

### Do These Quickly

The following problems are intended to refresh your skills. You should be able to do all ten problems in less than five minutes.

**Q1.** Sketch a graph that illustrates the meaning of definite integral.

**Q2.** Write the physical meaning of derivative.

**Q3.** Differentiate: $f(x) = 3x^{-5}$

**Q4.** Find the antiderivative: $y' = \cos x$.

**Q5.** If $y = \tan t$ meters, how fast is $y$ changing when $t = \pi/3$ sec?

**Q6.** Find $\lim_{\Delta x \to 0}[f(x + \Delta x) - f(x)]/\Delta x$ if $f(x) = \sec x$.

**Q7.** Find $\lim_{x \to 0} \sec x$.

**Q8.** What is the limit of a constant?

**Q9.** What is the derivative of a constant?

**Q10.** If $\lim_{x \to c} g(x) = g(c)$, then $g$ is —?— at $x = c$.

1. For $f(x) = 0.2x^4$, find an equation of the linear function that best fits $f$ at $x = 3$. What is the error in this linear approximation of $f(x)$ if $x = 3.1$? If $x = 3.001$? If $x = 2.999$?

2. For $g(x) = \sec x$, find an equation of the linear function that best fits at $x = \pi/3$. What is the error in this linear approximation of $g(x)$ if $dx = 0.04$? If $dx = -0.04$? If $dx = 0.001$?

3. *Local Linearity Problem I:* In Problem Set 3-2, you learned that the function $f(x) = x^2$ has the property of *local linearity* at any point, such as $x = 1$. Figure 5-3d shows the graph of $f$ and the linear function that fits best at $x = 1$. Write an equation for this linear function. Plot $f$ and the linear function on the same screen, then zoom in repeatedly on the point (1, 1). Tell why the words *local linearity* describe the relationship between the linear graph and the graph of $f$ when $x = 1$.

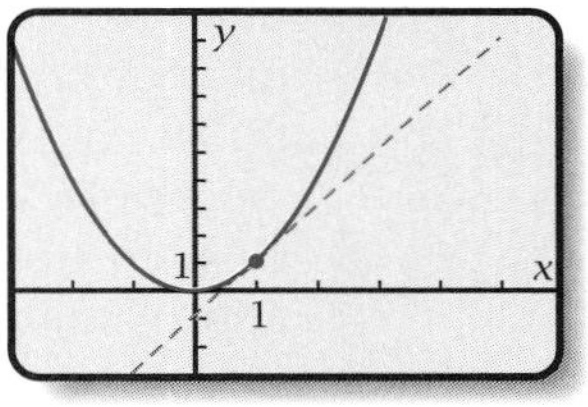

Figure 5-3d

4. *Local Linearity Problem II:* Figure 5-3e shows the graph of

$$f(x) = x^2 - 0.1(x - 1)^{1/3}.$$

Explore the graph for $x$ close to 1. Does the function have local linearity at $x = 1$? Is $f$ differentiable at $x = 1$? If $f$ is differentiable at $x = c$, is it locally linear at that point? Is the converse of this statement true or false? Explain.

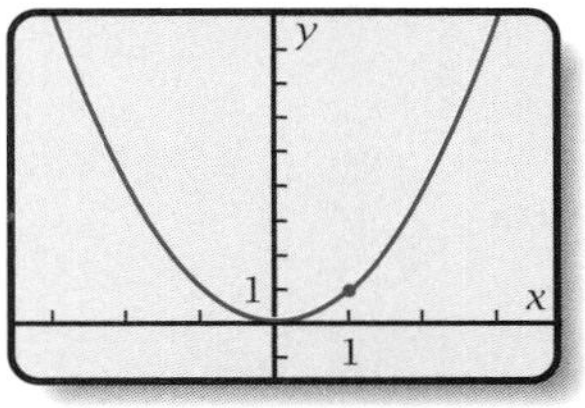

Figure 5-3e

5. *Steepness of a Hill Problem:* On roads in hilly areas, you sometimes see signs like this.

| Steep hill<br>20% grade |
|---|

The grade of a hill is the slope (rise/run) written as a percentage, or, equivalently, as the number of feet the hill rises per hundred feet horizontally. Figure 5-3f shows the latter meaning of grade.

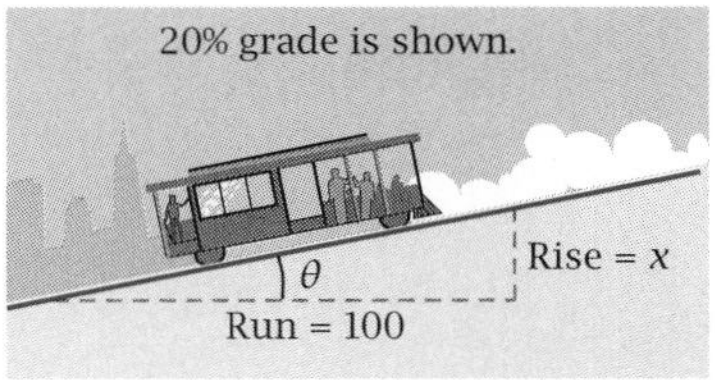

Figure 5-3f

a. Let $x$ be the grade of a hill. Explain why the angle, $\theta$ degrees, that a hill makes with the horizontal is given by

$$\theta = \frac{180}{\pi}\tan^{-1}\frac{x}{100}.$$

b. Find an equation for $d\theta$ in terms of $x$ and $dx$. Then find $d\theta$ in terms of $dx$ for grades of $x = 0\%$, 10%, and 20%.

c. You can estimate $\theta$ at $x = 20\%$ simply by multiplying $d\theta$ at $x = 0$ by 20. How much error is there in the value of $\theta$ found by using this method rather than by using the exact formula that involves the inverse tangent function?

d. A rule of thumb you can use to estimate the number of degrees a hill makes with the horizontal is to divide the grade by 2. Where in your work for 5c did you divide by approximately 2? When you use this method to determine the number of degrees for grades of 20% and 100%, how much error is there in the number?

6. *Table of Differentials Problem:* Figure 5-3g shows both the graph of $y = x^3$ and a tangent line drawn at $x = 1$. Plot this diagram on your grapher. Use TABLE or TRACE to make a table of values of $\Delta x, \Delta y$, and $dy$ and of the difference between $\Delta y$ and $dy$ for values of $x$ on both sides of 1. Pick some values of $x$ that are very close to 1 and some that are fairly far away. How well does $dy$ approximate $\Delta y$ for $x$ close to 1 and for $x$ farther away from 1?

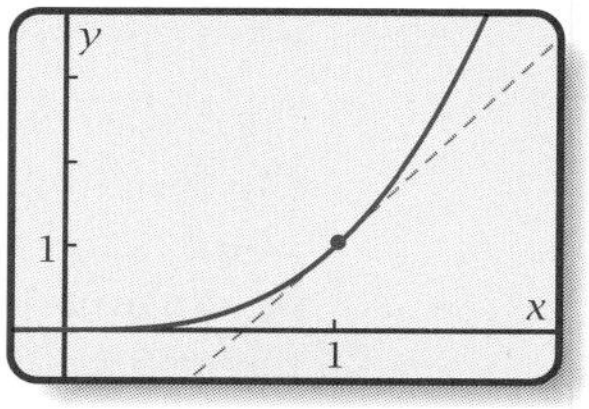

Figure 5-3g

For Problems 7–24, find an equation for the differential $dy$.

7. $y = 7x^3$

8. $y = -4x^{11}$

9. $y = (x^4 + 1)^7$

10. $y = (5 - 8x)^4$

11. $y = 3x^2 + 5x - 9$

12. $y = x^2 + x + 9$

13. $y = -5x^{-1.7}$

14. $y = 15x^{1/3}$

15. $y = \sin 3x$

16. $y = \cos 4x$

17. $y = \tan^3 x$

18. $y = \sec^3 x$

19. $y = 4x \cos x$

20. $y = 3x \sin x$

21. $y = \dfrac{x^2}{2} - \dfrac{x}{4} + 2$

22. $y = \dfrac{x^3}{3} - \dfrac{x}{5} + 6$

23. $y = \cos(\sec x)$

24. $y = \sin(\csc x)$

For Problems 25–38, find an equation for the antiderivative $y$.

25. $dy = 20x^3\,dx$

26. $dy = 36x^4\,dx$

27. $dy = \sin 4x\,dx$

28. $dy = \cos 0.2x\,dx$

29. $dy = (0.5x - 1)^6\,dx$

30. $dy = (4x + 3)^{-6}\,dx$

31. $dy = \sec^2 x\,dx$

32. $dy = \csc x \cot x\,dx$

33. $dy = 5\,dx$

34. $dy = -7\,dx$

35. $dy = (6x^2 + 10x - 4)\,dx$

36. $dy = (10x^2 - 3x + 7)\,dx$

37. $dy = \sin^5 x \cos x\,dx$ (Be clever!)

38. $dy = \sec^7 x \tan x\,dx$ (Be very clever!)

For Problems 39 and 40, do the following.

a. Find $dy$ in terms of $dx$.

b. Find $dy$ for the given values of $x$ and $dx$.

c. Find $\Delta y$ for the given values of $x$ and $dx$.

d. Show that $dy$ is close to $\Delta y$.

39. $y = (3x + 4)^2(2x - 5)^3,\ x = 1,\ dx = -0.04$

40. $y = \sin 5x,\ x = \pi/3,\ dx = 0.06$

# 5-4 Formal Definition of Antiderivative and Indefinite Integral

You have learned that an antiderivative is a function whose derivative is given. As you will learn in Section 5-8, the antiderivative of a function provides an algebraic way to calculate exact definite integrals. For this reason an antiderivative is also called an indefinite integral. The word *indefinite* is used because there is always a "$+C$" whose value is not determined until an initial condition is specified.

**_Relationship: Antiderivative and Indefinite Integral_**

Indefinite integral is another name for antiderivative.

In this section you will learn the symbol that is used for an indefinite integral or an antiderivative.

***OBJECTIVE***

Become familiar with the symbol used for an indefinite integral or an antiderivative by using this symbol to evaluate indefinite integrals.

In Section 5-3, you worked problems such as "If $dy = x^5\,dx$, find $y$." **Indefinite integration**, which you now know is the same thing as antidifferentiation, can be considered to be the operation performed on a differential to get the expression for the original function. The **integral sign** used for this operation is a stretched-out S like that shown here.

$$\int$$

As you will see in Section 5-5, the S shape comes from "sum." To indicate that you want to find the indefinite integral of $x^5\,dx$, write

$$\int x^5\,dx.$$

The whole expression, $\int x^5\,dx$, is the **integral**. The function $x^5$ "inside" the integral sign is called the **integrand**. These words are similar, for example, to the words *radical*, used for $\sqrt{7}$, and *radicand*, used for the number 7 inside. Note that although the $dx$ must appear in the integral, only the function $x^5$ is called the integrand.

Writing the answer to an indefinite integral is called **evaluating** it or **doing the integration**. Having seen the techniques of the last two sections, you should recognize that

$$\int x^5\,dx = \tfrac{1}{6}x^6 + C.$$

From the discussion above, the formal definition can be understood.

### Definition: Indefinite Integral

$$g(x) = \int f(x)\,dx \text{ if and only if } g'(x) = f(x).$$

That is, an indefinite integral of $f(x)\,dx$ is a function whose derivative is $f(x)$. The function $f(x)$ inside the integral sign is called the **integrand**.

Words: The expression $\int f(x)\,dx$ is pronounced "The integral of $f(x)$ with respect to $x$."

*Notes:* An indefinite integral is the same as an **antiderivative**. The symbol $\int$ is an **operator**, like "cos" or the minus sign, that acts on $f(x)\,dx$.

Another symbol for $g'(x) = f(x)$ is $\dfrac{d}{dx}\displaystyle\int f(x)\,dx = f(x)$.

### *Integral of a Constant Times a Function and of a Sum of Several Functions*

To develop a systematic way of integrating, it helps to know some properties of indefinite integrals, like those shown below.

$$\int 5\cos x\,dx \quad\text{and}\quad \int (x^5 + \sec^2 x - x)\,dx$$

$$= 5\int \cos x\,dx \qquad = \int x^5\,dx + \int \sec^2 x\,dx - \int x\,dx$$

$$= 5\sin x + C \qquad = \tfrac{1}{6}x^6 + \tan x - \tfrac{1}{2}x^2 + C$$

In the first case, 5, a constant, can be multiplied by the answer to $\int \cos x\,dx$. In the second case, the integral of each term can be evaluated separately and the answers can be added together. Because of the "only if" part of the definition of indefinite integral, all you have to do to prove these facts is differentiate the answers. The following is a proof of the integral of a constant times a function property. You will prove the integral of a sum property in Problem 45 of Problem Set 5-4.

**■ Property** If $k$ stands for a constant, then $\int kf(x)\,dx = k\int f(x)\,dx$.

**Proof**

| | |
|---|---|
| Let $g(x) = k\int f(x)\,dx$. | |
| Then $g'(x) = k \cdot \frac{d}{dx}\left(\int f(x)\,dx\right)$ | Derivative of a constant times a function. |
| $= kf(x)$ | Definition of indefinite integral (the "only if" part). |
| $\therefore\ g(x) = \int kf(x)\,dx$ | Definition of indefinite integral (the "if" part). |
| $\therefore\ \int kf(x)\,dx = k\int f(x)\,dx$, Q.E.D. | Transitive property of equality. ■ |

### *Two Properties of Indefinite Integrals*

**Integral of a Constant Times a Function:** If $f$ is a function that can be integrated and $k$ is a constant, then

$$\int kf(x)\,dx = k\int f(x)\,dx.$$

Words: "You can pull a constant multiplier out through the integral sign."

**Integral of a Sum of Two Functions:** If $f$ and $g$ are functions that can be integrated, then

$$\int (f(x) + g(x))\,dx = \int f(x)\,dx + \int g(x)\,dx.$$

Words: "Integration distributes over addition."

Be sure you don't read too much into these properties! You can't pull a variable through the integral sign. For instance,

$$\int x\cos x\,dx \quad \text{does not equal} \quad x\int \cos x\,dx.$$

The integral on the right is $x\sin x + C$. Its differential is $(\sin x + x\cos x)\,dx$, not $x\cos x\,dx$. The integral $\int x\cos x\,dx$ is the integral of a product of two functions. Recall that the derivative of a product does not equal the product of the derivatives.

### *The "dx" in an Indefinite Integral*

There is a relationship between the differential, $dx$, at the end of the integral and the argument of the function in the integrand. For example,

$$\int \cos x\,dx = \sin x + C.$$

It does not matter what letter you use for the variable.

$$\int \cos r\, dr = \sin r + C$$

$$\int \cos t\, dt = \sin t + C$$

$$\int \cos u\, du = \sin u + C$$

The words "with respect to" identify the variable in the differential that follows the integrand function. Note that in each case, $dx$, $dr$, $dt$, or $du$ is the *differential of the argument* of the cosine. This observation provides you with a way to integrate some composite functions.

**■ Example 1** Evaluate: $\int 5 \cos (5x + 3)\, dx$

**Solution**

$\int \cos (5x + 3)(5\, dx)$ — Commute the 5 on the left, and associate it with the $dx$.

$= \sin (5x + 3) + C$ — The differential of the inside function, $5x + 3$, is $5\, dx$. ■

**■ Example 2** Evaluate: $\int (7x + 4)^9\, dx$

**Solution**

This is the integral of the ninth power function. If the $dx$ were the differential of the inside function, $7x + 4$, then the integral would have the form

$$\int u^n\, du.$$

Transform the integral to *make* the $dx$ the differential of $(7x + 4)$. When you do so, the work looks like this.

$\int (7x + 4)^9\, dx$

$= \int (7x + 4)^9 \left(\frac{1}{7} \cdot 7\, dx\right)$ — Multiply by 1, using the form (1/7)(7).

$= \int \frac{1}{7}(7x + 4)^9 (7\, dx)$ — Associate $7\, dx$, the differential of the inside function. Commute 1/7.

$= \frac{1}{7} \int (7x + 4)^9 (7\, dx)$ — Integral of a constant times a function. (Pull the 1/7 out through the integral sign.)

$= \frac{1}{7} \cdot \frac{1}{10}(7x + 4)^{10} + C$ — Integral, $\int u^n\, du$.

$= \frac{1}{70}(7x + 4)^{10} + C$ ■

Once you understand the process you can leave out some of the steps, thus shortening your work. In Problem Set 5-4, you will practice evaluating indefinite integrals.

## Problem Set 5-4

***Do These Quickly***

The following problems are intended to refresh your skills. You should be able to do all ten problems in less than five minutes.

**Q1.** Find the antiderivative: $3x^2\,dx$.

**Q2.** Find the indefinite integral: $x^5\,dx$.

**Q3.** Find the derivative: $y = x^3$.

**Q4.** Differentiate: $y = (1/6)x^6$

**Q5.** Integrate: $\cos x\,dx$

**Q6.** Differentiate: $y = \cos x$

**Q7.** The "if" part of a theorem is called the —?— .

**Q8.** The "then" part of a theorem is called the —?— .

**Q9.** If $h(x) = r'(x)$, then $r$ is a(n) —?— or a(n) —?— of $h$.

**Q10.** $\lim_{j\to 0}(\sin j)/(j)$ = —?— .

For Problems 1–42, evaluate the indefinite integral.

1. $\int 6x^5\,dx$
2. $\int 5x^4\,dx$
3. $\int x^{10}\,dx$
4. $\int x^{20}\,dx$
5. $\int 4x^{-6}\,dx$
6. $\int 9x^{-7}\,dx$
7. $\int 102t^{4.1}\,dt$
8. $\int 72r^{-1.1}\,dr$
9. $\int 30p^{-2/5}\,dp$
10. $\int 56v^{-3/7}\,dv$
11. $\int \cos x\,dx$
12. $\int \sin x\,dx$
13. $\int \sin 3m\,dm$
14. $\int \cos 5u\,du$
15. $\int 4\cos 7x\,dx$
16. $\int 20\sin 9x\,dx$
17. $\int (4v + 9)^2\,dv$
18. $\int (3p + 17)^5\,dp$
19. $\int (8 - 5x)^3\,dx$
20. $\int (20 - x)^4\,dx$
21. $\int (6 + 7b)^{-4}\,db$
22. $\int (10 + 13t)^{-6}\,dt$
23. $\int (\sin x)^6 \cos x\,dx$
24. $\int (\cos x)^8 \sin x\,dx$
25. $\int \cos^4\theta \sin\theta\,d\theta$
26. $\int \sin^5\theta \cos\theta\,d\theta$
27. $\int \sin^3 \pi x \cos \pi x\,dx$
28. $\int \cos^8 \pi x \sin \pi x\,dx$
29. $\int (x^2 + 3x - 5)\,dx$
30. $\int (x^2 - 4x + 1)\,dx$

31. $\int (r^{-2} + r^2)\,dr$

32. $\int (u^3 - u^{-3})\,du$

33. $\int (x^2 + 5)^3\,dx$ (Beware!)

34. $\int (x^3 - 6)^2\,dx$ (Beware!)

35. $\int \sec^2 x\,dx$

36. $\int \csc^2 x\,dx$

37. $\int \csc 3x \cot 3x\,dx$

38. $\int \sec 5x \tan 5x\,dx$

39. $\int \tan^7 x \sec^2 x\,dx$

40. $\int \cot^8 x \csc^2 x\,dx$

41. $\int \csc^9 x \cot x\,dx$ (Be clever!)

42. $\int \sec^7 x \tan x\,dx$ (Be clever!)

43. *Distance from Velocity Problem:* As you drive along the highway, you step hard on the accelerator to pass a truck (Figure 5-4a). Assume that your velocity, $v(t)$ feet per second, is given by

$$v(t) = 40 + 5\sqrt{t},$$

where $t$ is the number of seconds since you started accelerating. Find an equation for $D(t)$, your displacement from the starting point, that is, from $D(0) = 0$. How far do you go in the 10 sec it takes to pass the truck?

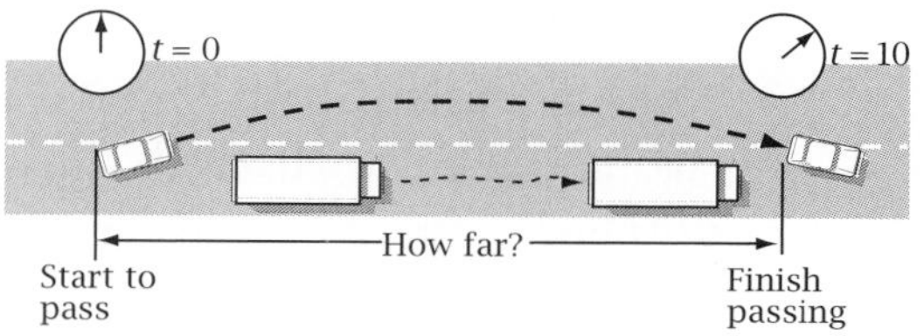

Figure 5-4a

44. *Definite Integral Surprise!* Figure 5-4b shows the region that represents the definite integral of $f(x) = 0.3x^2 + 1$ from $x = 1$ to $x = 4$.

a. Evaluate the integral by using the trapezoidal rule with $n = 100$ increments.

b. Let $g(x) = \int f(x)\,dx$. Integrate to find an equation for $g(x)$.

c. Evaluate the quantity $g(4) - g(1)$. What is interesting about your answer?

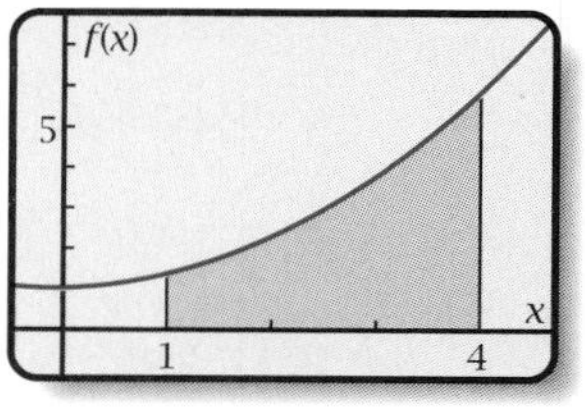

Figure 5-4b

45. *Integral of a Sum Property:* Prove that if $f$ and $g$ are functions that can be integrated, then $\int (f(x) + g(x))\,dx = \int f(x)\,dx + \int g(x)\,dx$.

46. *Integral Table Problem:* Calvin finds the formula $\int x \cos x\,dx = x \sin x + \cos x + C$ in a table of integrals. Phoebe says, "That's right!" How can Phoebe be sure the formula is right?

*47. *Introduction to Riemann Sums:* Suppose the velocity of a moving object is given by

$$v(t) = t^2 + 10,$$

where $v(t)$ is in feet per minute and $t$ is in minutes. Figure 5-4c shows the region that represents the integral of $v(t)$ from $t = 1$ to $t = 4$. Thus the area of the region equals the distance traveled by the object.

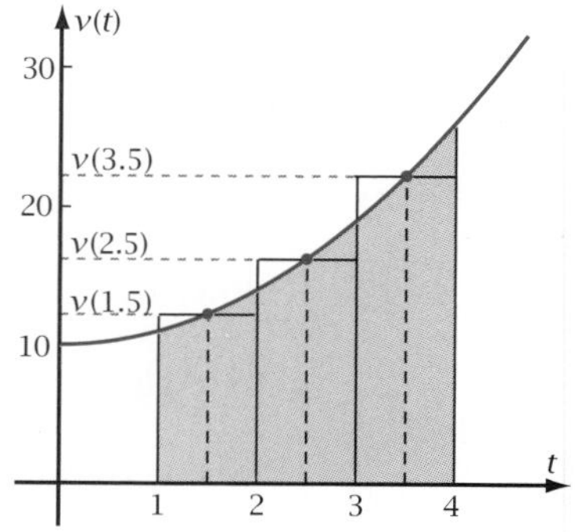

Figure 5-4c

*This problem prepares you for the next section.

In this problem you will find the integral, approximately, by dividing the region into rectangles instead of into trapezoids. The width of each rectangle will still be $\Delta t$, and each rectangle's length will be $v(t)$ found at the $t$-value in the middle of the strip. The sum of the areas of these rectangles is called a *Riemann sum*.

a. Use a Riemann sum with $n = 3$ strips, as shown in Figure 5-4c, to find an approximation for the definite integral of $v(t) = t^2 + 10$ from $t = 1$ to $t = 4$.

b. Use a Riemann sum with $n = 6$ strips, as shown in Figure 5-4d, to find another approximation for the definite integral. The altitudes of the rectangles will be values of $v(t)$ for $t$ at the midpoints of the intervals, namely, $t = 1.25$, $t = 1.75$, $t = 2.25$, $t = 2.75$, $t = 3.25$, and $t = 3.75$. The widths of the strips are, of course, $\Delta t = 0.5$.

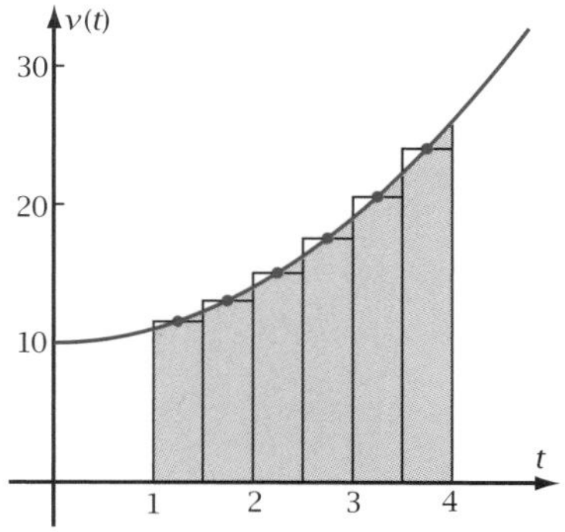

Figure 5-4d

c. Explain why the Riemann sum you used in 47b should be a better approximation for the integral than that used in 47a.

d. Make a conjecture about the exact value of the definite integral.

e. Check the conjecture you made in 47d by evaluating the integral using the trapezoidal rule with $n = 100$ increments.

f. How far did the object travel between $t = 1$ min and $t = 4$ min? What was its average velocity for that time interval?

48. *Journal Problem:* Update your journal with what you've learned since your last entry. Include such things as those listed here.
   - The one most important thing you've learned since your last journal entry
   - The difference, as you understand it so far, between definite integral and indefinite integral
   - The difference between a differential and a derivative
   - Any insight you may have gained about why two different concepts are both named *integral*, and how you gained that insight
   - Algebraic techniques you have learned for finding equations for indefinite integrals
   - Questions you plan to ask during the next class period

# 5-5 Riemann Sums and the Definition of Definite Integral

Recall that a definite integral is used for the product of $f(x)$ and $x$, such as (rate)(time). Thus the integral is equal to the area of the region under the graph of $f$, as shown in Figure 5-5a. The trapezoidal rule lets you find definite integrals by slicing the region under a graph into strips, then by approximating the area of each strip with the area of a trapezoid.

Another way to estimate a definite integral is to slice the region into strips and approximate the strips with rectangles instead of with trapezoids. Figure 5-5b shows the region in Figure 5-5a sliced into $n$ strips of variable width $\Delta x_1$, $\Delta x_2$, $\Delta x_3$, ... ($n = 6$, in this case). These strips are said to **partition** the interval $[a, b]$ into $n$ **subintervals**, or **increments**. Values of $x$ (called $c_1, c_2, c_3, \ldots$) are picked so that one value is in each (closed) subinterval. These $x$-values are called **sample points**.

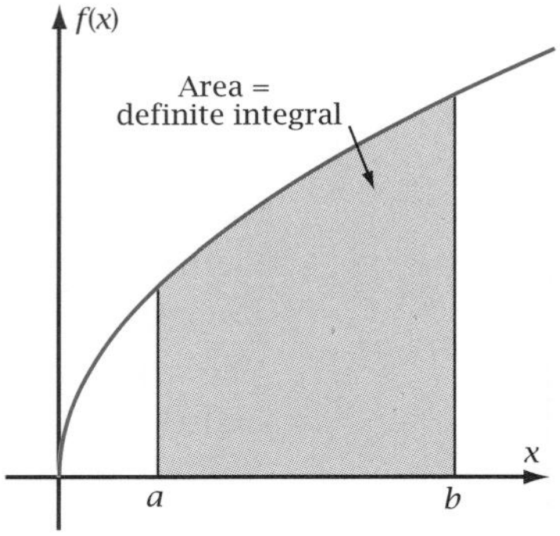


Figure 5-5a

At each of the sample points, the corresponding function values $f(c_1)$, $f(c_2)$, $f(c_3)$, ... are the altitudes of the rectangles. The area of any one rectangle is thus

$$A_{\text{rect}} = f(c_k)\,\Delta x_k,$$

where $k$ is 1, 2, 3, ..., up to $n$. The integral is approximately equal to the sum of the areas of the rectangles.

$$\text{Area} \approx \sum_{k=1}^{n} f(c_k)\,\Delta x_k$$

This sum is called a Riemann sum (pronounced "ree-mahn," with the accent on the first syllable) after G. F. Bernhard Reimann (1826–1866).

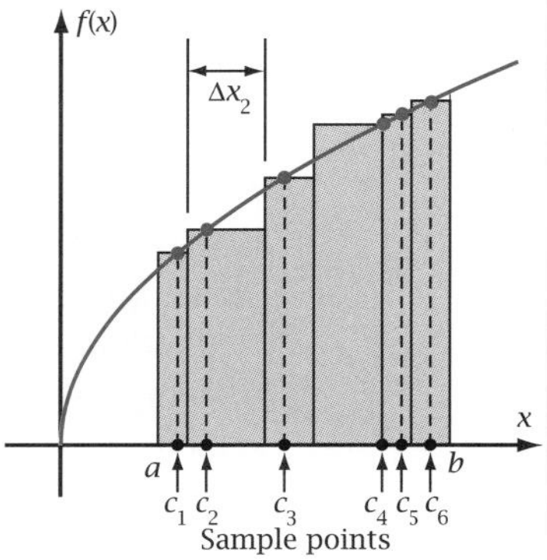


A Riemann sum

Figure 5-5b

> ### *Definition: Riemann Sum*
>
> A **Riemann sum**, $R_n$, for function $f$ on the interval $[a, b]$ is a sum of the form
>
> $$R_n = \sum_{k=1}^{n} f(c_k)\,\Delta x_k,$$
>
> where the interval $[a, b]$ is partitioned into $n$ subintervals of widths $\Delta x_k$, and the numbers $\{c_k\}$ are sample points, one in each subinterval.

If each sample point is picked so that $f(c)$ is the lowest in its respective subinterval, then each rectangle has an area that is less than the area of the strip. In this case, the Riemann sum is called a **lower sum**. Similarly, an **upper sum** is a Riemann sum with each sample point taken where $f(c)$ is the highest in its respective subinterval. A **midpoint sum** is formed by choosing each sample point at the midpoint of the respective subinterval. An upper sum is an *upper bound* for the area of the region, and a lower sum is a *lower bound*. A lower Riemann sum, an upper Riemann sum, and a midpoint Riemann sum are shown in Figure 5-5c. Equal values of $\Delta x$ have been used.

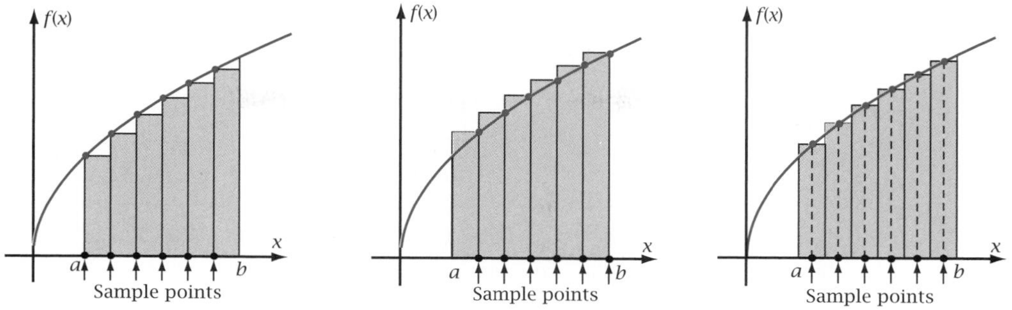


$L_n$: lower Riemann sum (inscribed rectangles)

$U_n$: upper Riemann sum (circumscribed rectangles)

$M_n$: midpoint Riemann sum (intermediate rectangles)

Figure 5-5c

The symbols $L_n$, $U_n$, $M_n$, and $R_n$ are used for lower, upper, midpoint, and general Riemann sums, respectively. Suppose that the limits of $L_n$ and $U_n$ are equal to each other as the largest value of $\Delta x$ approaches zero. If this is the case, function $f$ is said to be **integrable** on the interval $[a, b]$. The common limit of the upper and lower sums is defined to be the definite integral of $f$ on the interval $[a, b]$. The integral sign (a stretched S for "sum") with the $a$ and $b$ of $[a, b]$ attached to it is used for a definite integral, like this.

$$\int_a^b \qquad \text{The definite integral sign.}$$

Any Riemann sum, $R_n$, for a given partition of $[a, b]$ is bounded by the upper and lower sum.

$$L_n \le R_n \le U_n$$

Thus if function $f$ is integrable on $[a, b]$, then any Riemann sum will also have the definite integral as its limit. This result is a direct application of the squeeze theorem.

### *Definitions: Definite Integral and Integrability*

If the lower and upper sums for function $f$ on the interval $[a, b]$ have a common limit as $\Delta x$ approaches 0, then $f$ is said to be **integrable on $[a, b]$**. This common limit is defined to be the **definite integral of $f$ from $x = a$ to $x = b$**. The numbers $a$ and $b$ are called lower and upper **limits of integration**, or **bounds of integration**. In symbols,

$$\int_a^b f(x)\,dx = \lim_{\Delta x \to 0} L_n = \lim_{\Delta x \to 0} U_n.$$

*Note:* The differential symbol $dx$ is used in definite integrals instead of $\Delta x$.

> **Property: Limit of a Riemann Sum**
>
> If $f$ is integrable on $[a, b]$, and if $R_n$ is any Riemann sum for $f$ on $[a, b]$, then
>
> $$\int_a^b f(x)\,dx = \lim_{\Delta x \to 0} R_n.$$

**OBJECTIVE** Use Riemann sums to find approximate values of definite integrals.

**■ Example 1** For the integral $\int_1^4 (1/x)\,dx$, do the following.

a. Find $U_6$ for the integral.

b. Find $L_6$ for the integral.

c. Find $M_6$ for the integral. Show that $M_6$ is between $L_6$ and $U_6$.

d. Find $T_6$, the integral found by application of the trapezoidal rule using six increments. Show that $T_6$ is also between $L_6$ and $U_6$. Is $T_6$ higher or lower than the actual integral? Explain.

**Solutions**

a. Sketch the graph and the six subintervals of width $\Delta x = 0.5$ (Figure 5-5d). Because $f(x)$ is decreasing, the left ends of the subintervals will give the highest values of $f(x)$. Pick the sample points at the left ends.

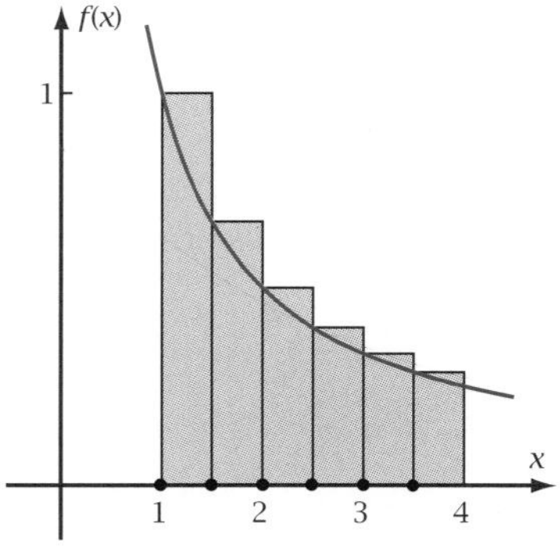

Upper Riemann sum

Figure 5-5d

| $x = c$ | $1/x$ | $(1/x)(\Delta x)$ |
|---|---|---|
| 1.0 | 1 | 0.5 |
| 1.5 | 0.6666666 . . . | 0.3333333 . . . |
| 2.0 | 0.5 | 0.25 |
| 2.5 | 0.4 | 0.2 |
| 3.0 | 0.3333333 . . . | 0.1666666 . . . |
| 3.5 | 0.2857142 . . . | 0.1428571 . . . |
| | | $U_6$ = 1.5928571 . . . |

b. For the lower sum, the sample points should be taken at the right ends of the subintervals (Figure 5-5e).

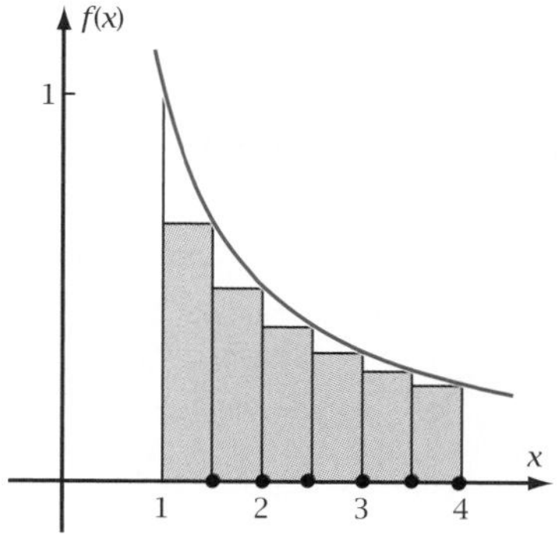


Lower Riemann sum

Figure 5-5e

| $x = c$ | $1/x$ | $(1/x)(\Delta x)$ |
|---|---|---|
| 1.5 | 0.6666666 . . . | 0.3333333 . . . |
| 2.0 | 0.5 | 0.25 |
| 2.5 | 0.4 | 0.2 |
| 3.0 | 0.3333333 . . . | 0.1666666 . . . |
| 3.5 | 0.2857142 . . . | 0.1428571 . . . |
| 4.0 | 0.25 | 0.125 |

$L_6 = 1.2178571\ldots$

c. For the midpoint sum, use sample points $c = 1.25$, $c = 1.75$, $c = 2.25$, and so on (Figure 5-5f).

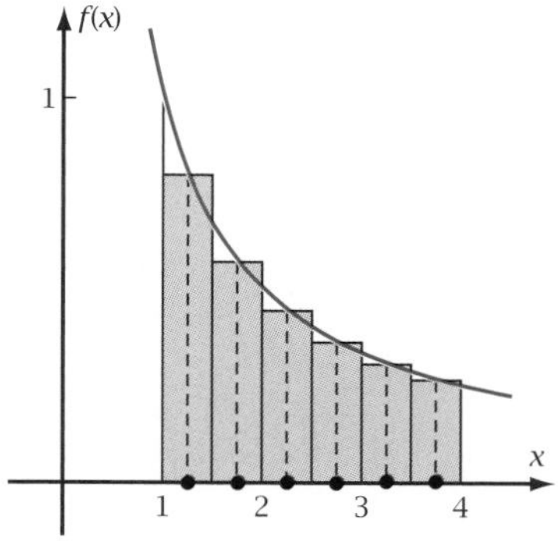


Midpoint Riemann sum

Figure 5-5f

| $x = c$ | $1/x$ |
|---|---|
| 1.25 | 0.8 |
| 1.75 | 0.5714285 . . . |
| 2.25 | 0.4444444 . . . |
| 2.75 | 0.3636363 . . . |
| 3.25 | 0.3076923 . . . |
| 3.75 | 0.2666666 . . . |

Sum = 2.7538683...

$M_6 = 0.5(2.7538683\ldots) = 1.3769341\ldots$

The table above shows a shortcut that allows you to take advantage of the fact that all the $\Delta x$'s are equal. See if you can figure out why it works! The midpoint sum is between the lower and upper sums,

$$1.2178571\ldots < 1.3769341\ldots < 1.5928571\ldots.$$

d. By using your trapezoidal rule program, you should find that $T_6 = 1.405357\ldots$. This value is also between the lower and upper sums.

$$1.2178571\ldots < 1.405357\ldots < 1.5928571\ldots$$

The trapezoidal sum $T_6$ is higher than the actual value of the integral. Figure 5-5g shows that the trapezoid is circumscribed around the outside of the strip, thus the trapezoid has a greater area. This happens because the graph is "concave upward," a property you will explore in Chapter 8. The sum of the areas of the trapezoids will therefore be greater than the area of the region that represents the integral. ■

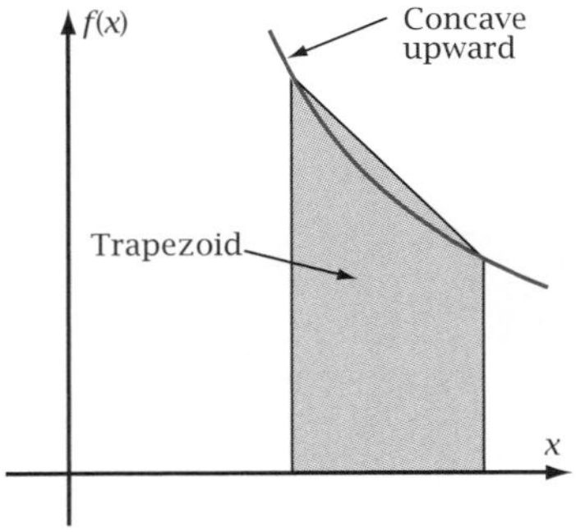


Figure 5-5g

# Problem Set 5-5

### *Do These Quickly*

The following problems are intended to refresh your skills. You should be able to do all ten problems in less than five minutes.

**Q1.** Differentiate: $y = x \sin x$

**Q2.** Integrate: $\int \sec^2 x\, dx$

**Q3.** Differentiate: $f(x) = \tan x$

**Q4.** Integrate: $\int x^3\, dx$

**Q5.** Differentiate: $z = \cos 7x$

**Q6.** Integrate: $\int \sin u\, du$

**Q7.** Find $\lim_{x \to 5} (x^2 - 2x - 15)/(x - 5)$.

**Q8.** Sketch a function graph with a cusp at the point (4, 7).

**Q9.** Write the converse of this statement: If $a = 2$ and $b = 3$, then $a + b = 5$.

**Q10.** The statement in Problem Q9 is true. Is the converse true?

For Problems 1–6, calculate approximately the given definite integral by using a Riemann sum with $n$ increments. Pick the sample points at the midpoints of the subintervals.

1. $\int_1^4 x^2\, dx,\ n = 6$
2. $\int_2^6 x^3\, dx,\ n = 8$
3. $\int_{-1}^3 3^x\, dx,\ n = 8$
4. $\int_{-1}^2 2^x\, dx,\ n = 6$
5. $\int_1^2 \sin x\, dx,\ n = 5$
6. $\int_0^1 \cos x\, dx,\ n = 5$

For Problems 7 and 8, calculate the Riemann sums $U_4$, $L_4$, and $M_4$, and the sum found by applying the trapezoidal rule, $T_4$. Show that $M_4$ and $T_4$ are between the upper and lower sums.

7. $\int_{0.4}^{1.2} \tan x\, dx$
8. $\int_1^3 (10/x)\, dx$

9. *Sample Point Problem:* Figure 5-5h shows the graph of the sinusoid

$$h(x) = 3 + 2 \sin x.$$

a. At what values of $x$ should the sample points be taken to get an upper sum for the integral of $h$ on [0, 6] with $n = 6$?

b. Where should the sample points be taken to get a lower Riemann sum for the integral?

c. Calculate these upper and lower sums.

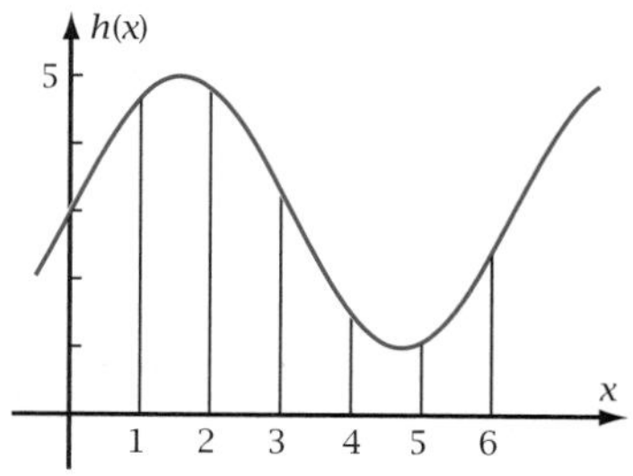

Figure 5-5h

10. *Program for Riemann Sums Problem:* Write a program to compute Riemann sums for a given function. If you write the program on your grapher, you can store the integrand as $y_1$, just as you did for the trapezoidal rule program. You should be able to input $a$ and $b$, the lower and upper bounds of integration; $n$, the number of increments to use; and $p$, the percentage of the way through each subinterval to take the sample point. For instance, for a midpoint sum, $p$ would equal 50. Test the program by using it for Problem 7 of this problem set. If your program gives you the correct answers for $U_4$, $L_4$, and $M_4$, you may assume that it is working properly.

11. *Limit of Riemann Sums Problem:* In Problem 1 of this problem set, you evaluated

$$\int_1^4 x^2\,dx$$

by using midpoint sums with $n = 6$. In this problem you will explore what happens to approximate values of this integral as $n$ gets larger.

a. Use your programs to show that $L_{10} = 18.795, U_{10} = 23.295, M_{10} = 20.9775$, and $T_{10} = 21.045$.

b. Calculate $L_{100}$ and $L_{500}$. What limit does $L_n$ seem to be approaching as $n$ increases?

c. Calculate $U_{100}$ and $U_{500}$. Does $U_n$ seem to be approaching the same limit as $L_n$? What words describe a function $f(x)$ on the interval [1, 4] if $L_n$ and $U_n$ have the same limit as $n$ approaches infinity (and thus $\Delta x$ approaches zero)?

d. See if you can figure out why the trapezoidal sums are always slightly greater than your conjectured value for the exact integral and why the midpoint sums are always less than your conjectured value.

12. *Exact Integral of the Square Function by Brute Force Project:* In this problem you will find, exactly, the integral $\int_0^3 x^2\,dx$ by actually calculating the limit of the upper sums.

a. Find, approximately, the value of the integral by calculating the upper and lower Riemann sums with 100 increments, $U_{100}$ and $L_{100}$. Make a conjecture about the exact value.

b. If you partition [0, 3] into $n$ subintervals, then each one will be $\Delta x = 3/n$ units wide. The partition points will be at $x$ equals

$$0,\ 1 \cdot \tfrac{3}{n},\ 2 \cdot \tfrac{3}{n},\ 3 \cdot \tfrac{3}{n},\ \ldots,\ n \cdot \tfrac{3}{n}.$$

Which of these partition points would you pick to find the upper sum?

c. The $y$-values will be the values of $f(x)$ at these sample points, namely, the squares of these numbers. For instance, at the end of the fifth increment, $x = 5(3/n)$ and $f(x) = [5(3/n)]^2$ (Figure 5-5i). Write a formula for $U_n$, an upper sum with $n$ increments.

d. The formula you wrote in 12c can be rearranged by factoring out common factors, leaving only the squares of the counting numbers inside parentheses. From algebra, this sum is

$$1^2 + 2^2 + 3^2 + \cdots + n^2 = \tfrac{n}{6}(n+1)(2n+1).$$

Use this information to write a closed formula (no ellipsis: ...) for $U_n$. Confirm that this formula gives the right answer for $U_{100}$.

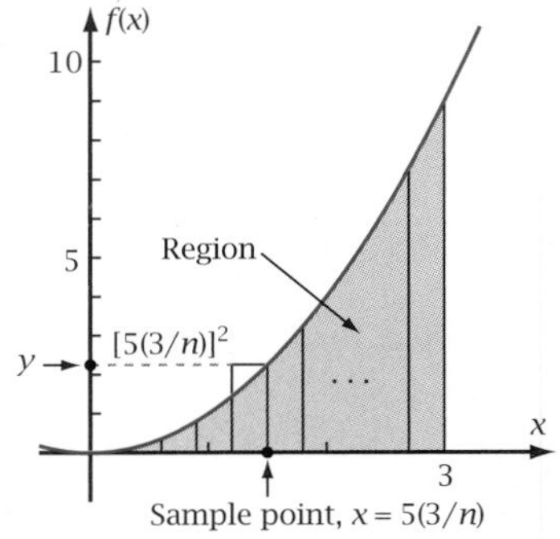

Figure 5-5i

e. Use the formula to predict $U_{1000}$. Does $U_n$ seem to be approaching the limit you conjectured in 12a?

f. Find algebraically the limit of $U_n$ from 12e as $n$ approaches infinity. This limit is the definite integral of $x^2$ from $x = 0$ to $x = 3$ and equals the exact area and integral!

13. *Exact Integral of the Cube Function Project:* Find the exact value of $\int_0^2 x^3\,dx$. Use as a guide the technique you used in Problem 12 of this problem set. Recall that the sum of the cubes of the counting numbers is given by

$$\sum_{k=1}^{n} k^3 = 1^3 + 2^3 + 3^3 + 4^3 + \cdots + n^3 = \left[\tfrac{n}{2}(n+1)\right]^2.$$

# 5-6 The Mean Value Theorem and Rolle's Theorem

Suppose that you go 500 ft in 10 sec as you slow down on a freeway exit. Your average velocity for the 10-sec time interval is 50 ft/sec. It seems reasonable to conclude that sometime in that interval, your instantaneous velocity was also equal to 50 ft/sec (Figure 5-6a). In this section you will learn the **mean value theorem**, which states conditions under which this conclusion is true. You will also learn **Rolle's theorem** and use it as a lemma to prove the mean value theorem. In Sections 5-7 and 5-8, you will see how the mean value theorem leads to an algebraic method for finding exact definite integrals.

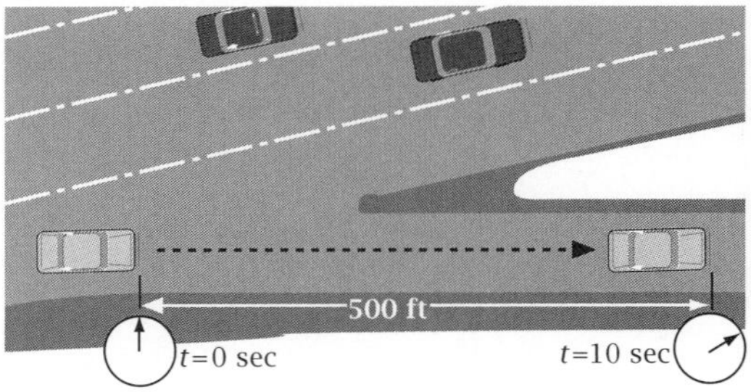

Figure 5-6a

**OBJECTIVE**

Learn the mean value theorem and Rolle's theorem and learn how to find the point in an interval at which the instantaneous rate of change of the function equals the average rate of change.

Let $f(x)$ be your displacement as you exit the freeway. As shown in Figure 5-6b, your average velocity from time $x = a$ to $x = b$ is displacement divided by time.

$$\text{Average velocity} = \frac{f(b) - f(a)}{b - a}$$

The average velocity is the slope of the secant line connecting two points on the graph. As you can see from the figure, there is a time $x = c$ between the points $a$ and $b$ at which the tangent line parallels the secant line. At this point the instantaneous velocity, $f'(c)$, equals the average velocity.

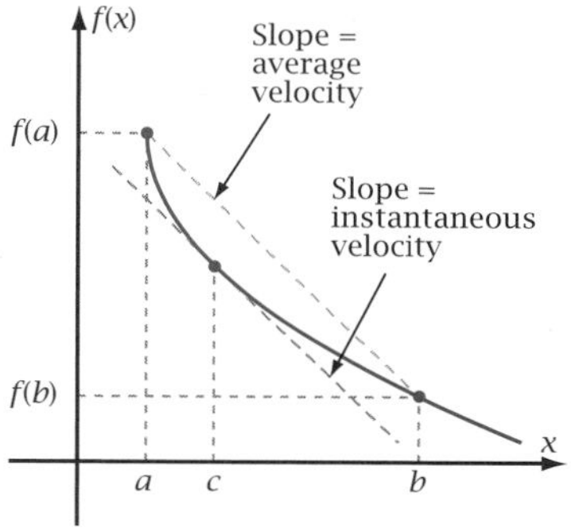


Figure 5-6b

The mean value theorem gives two **sufficient conditions** for there to be an instantaneous rate of change equal to the average rate from $x = a$ and $x = b$. First, the function is differentiable for all values of $x$ between $a$ and $b$. Second, the function is continuous at $x = a$ and $x = b$, even if it is not differentiable at these points. The function in Figure 5-6b meets these two conditions. Note that $f$ is not differentiable at $x = a$ because the tangent line would be vertical at that point.

### Property: The Mean Value Theorem

If **1.** $f$ is differentiable for all values of $x$ in the open interval $(a, b)$, and
**2.** $f$ is continuous at $x = a$ and at $x = b$,

then there is at least one number $x = c$ in $(a, b)$ such that

$$f'(c) = \frac{f(b) - f(a)}{b - a}.$$

The two conditions in the "if" part are the **hypotheses** of the mean value theorem. The "then" part is the **conclusion**. The left-hand and center graphs of Figure 5-6c show why the conclusion might not be true if the hypotheses are not met by a function. For the function on the left, there is a point between $a$ and $b$ at which the function is not differentiable. You cannot draw a unique tangent line at the cusp, and there is no other place at which the tangent line parallels the secant. In the center graph, the function is differentiable for all values of $x$ between $a$ and $b$, but the function is not continuous at $x = a$. At no place is there a tangent line parallel to the secant. The third function is continuous but not differentiable at $x = a$. There is a tangent line parallel to the secant.

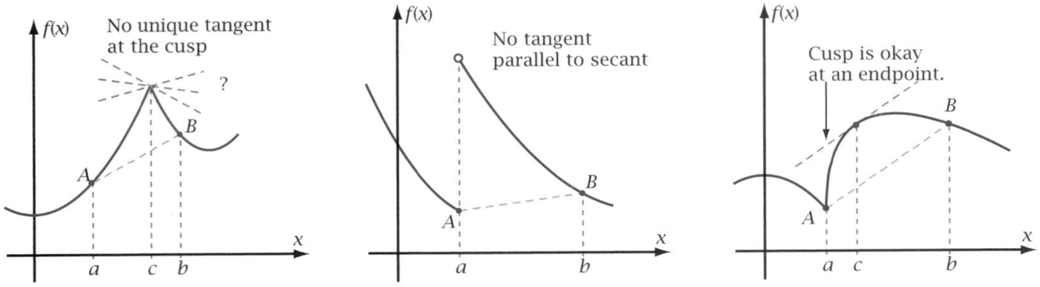


Not differentiable at an $x$ between $a$ and $b$

Not continuous at one of the endpoints

Not differentiable at one endpoint, but continuous there

Figure 5-6c

### Rolle's Theorem

The proof of the mean value theorem uses as a lemma another theorem from the analysis of real numbers, Rolle's theorem. Named after seventeenth-century French mathematician Michel Rolle (pronounced "roll"), the theorem states that between two consecutive zeros of a function, there is a place where the derivative is zero (Figure 5-6d). Sufficient conditions for this conclusion to be true are the same as the hypotheses of the mean value theorem, with the additional hypothesis $f(a) = f(b) = 0$.

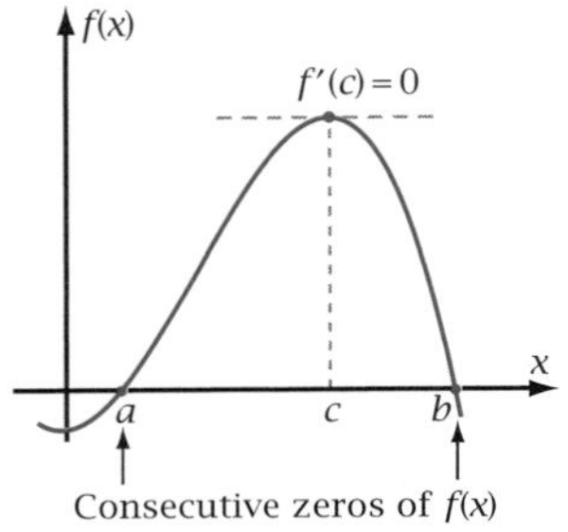


Rolle's theorem

Figure 5-6d

**Property: Rolle's Theorem**

If
1. $f$ is differentiable for all values of $x$ in the open interval $(a, b)$, and
2. $f$ is continuous at $x = a$ and at $x = b$, and
3. $f(a) = f(b) = 0$,

then there is at least one number $x = c$ in $(a, b)$ such that $f'(c) = 0$.

### Geometrical Proof of Rolle's Theorem

Suppose that $f(x)$ is positive somewhere between $x = a$ and $x = b$. As Figure 5-6e shows, $f(x)$ must reach a maximum for some value of $x$ ($x = c$) between $a$ and $b$. The fact that there is such a number relies on the **completeness axiom** (Section 2-6) and on the fact that $f$ is continuous (because it is differentiable). If $x$ is less than $c$, then $\Delta x$ is negative. If $x$ is greater than $c$, then $\Delta x$ is positive. Because $f(c)$ is the maximum value of $f(x)$, $\Delta y$ will always be negative (or possibly zero). Thus the difference quotient,

$$\frac{\Delta y}{\Delta x} = \frac{f(x) - f(c)}{x - c},$$

is positive (or zero) when $x$ is less than $c$ and negative (or zero) when $x$ is greater than $c$. The limit of this difference quotient is, of course, $f'(c)$. Thus

$$0 \le f'(c) \le 0.$$

By the squeeze theorem, $f'(c) = 0$.

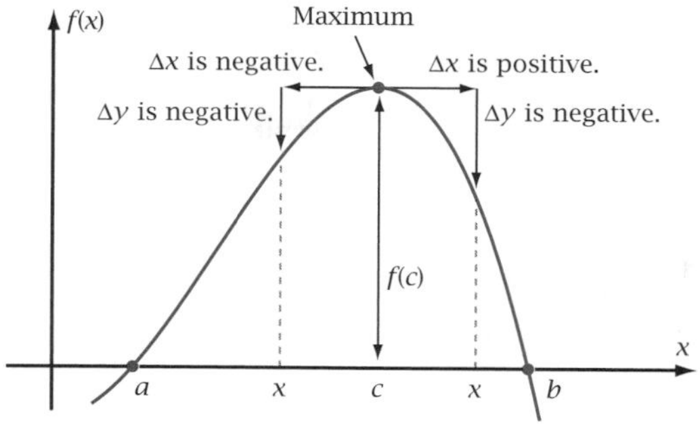

Figure 5-6e

A similar case can be made if $f(x)$ is negative for some $x$ between $a$ and $b$, or if $f(x)$ is always zero. In conclusion, if the three hypotheses are true, then there is always a number $x = c$ between $a$ and $b$ such that $f'(c) = 0$, Q.E.D.

### *Algebraic Proof of the Mean Value Theorem*

The mean value theorem can be proved using Rolle's theorem as a lemma. The left-hand graph in Figure 5-6f shows function $f$, the secant line through points $A$ and $B$ on the graph of $f$, and the tangent line you hope to prove is parallel to the secant line.

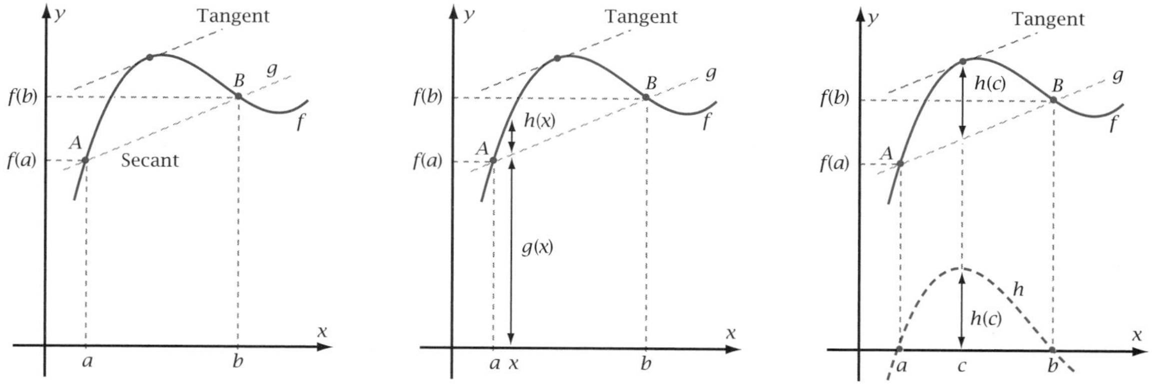

Secant line through $A$ and $B$

Define functions $g$ and $h$

$c$ is at maximum of $h(x)$.

Figure 5-6f

Let $g$ be the linear function whose graph is the secant line through points $A$ and $B$.

Let $h$ be the function defined by

$$h(x) = f(x) - g(x).$$

As shown in the center graph of Figure 5-6f, the values of $h(x)$ are the vertical distances between the $f$ graph and the $g$ graph. Because the $f$ and $g$ graphs coincide at both $x = a$ and $x = b$, it follows that $h(a) = h(b) = 0$. The graph of $h$ is shown in the right-hand graph of Figure 5-6f.

Function $h$ is continuous and differentiable at the same places as function $f$. This is true because $g$ is a linear function, which is continuous and differentiable everywhere, and because a difference such as $h(x)$ between continuous, differentiable functions is also continuous and differentiable.

Therefore $h$ satisfies the three hypotheses of Rolle's theorem. Function $h$ is differentiable on $(a, b)$, continuous at $x = a$ and $x = b$, and has $h(a) = h(b) = 0$. By the conclusion of Rolle's theorem, there is a number $x = c$ in $(a, b)$ such that $h'(c) = 0$. All that remains to be done is the algebra.

$h'(c) = 0$

However, $h'(x) = f'(x) - g'(x)$, which implies that $h'(c) = f'(c) - g'(c) = 0$.

Therefore $f'(c) = g'(c)$.

However, $g$ is a linear function. Thus $g'(x)$ is everywhere equal to the slope of the graph. This slope is $[f(b) - f(a)]/(b - a)$. Hence

$$f'(c) = \frac{f(b) - f(a)}{b - a}, \quad \text{Q.E.D.}$$

Be careful! Do not read more into the mean value theorem and Rolle's theorem than they say. The hypotheses of these theorems are *sufficient* conditions to imply the conclusions. They are not necessary conditions. Figure 5-6g shows two functions that satisfy the conclusions of the mean value theorem even though the hypotheses are not true.

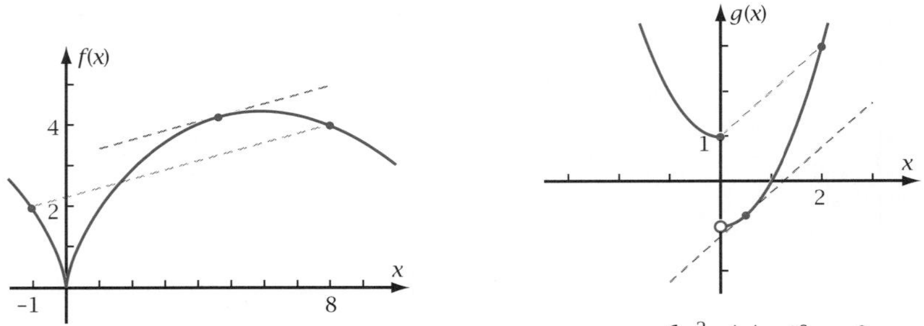

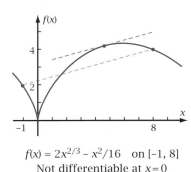

$f(x) = 2x^{2/3} - x^2/16$ on $[-1, 8]$
Not differentiable at $x = 0$

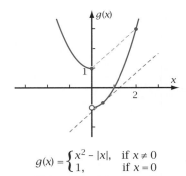

$g(x) = \begin{cases} x^2 - |x|, & \text{if } x \neq 0 \\ 1, & \text{if } x = 0 \end{cases}$
Not continuous at $x = 0$

Figure 5-6g

**■ Example 1** Given $f(x) = x^{1/3}$, plot the graph. Explain why $f$ satisfies the hypotheses of the mean value theorem on [0, 8]. Find a value of $x = c$ in the open interval (0, 8) at which the conclusion of the theorem is true, and show on your graph that the tangent really is parallel to the secant.

***Solutions*** Figure 5-6h suggests that $f$ is differentiable everywhere except, perhaps, at $x = 0$. Because

$$f'(x) = \tfrac{1}{3}x^{-2/3},$$

$f'(0)$ would be $0^{-2/3} = 1/0^{2/3} = 1/0$, which is infinite. But $f$ is differentiable on the *open* interval (0, 8). Function $f$ is continuous at $x = 0$ and $x = 8$ because the

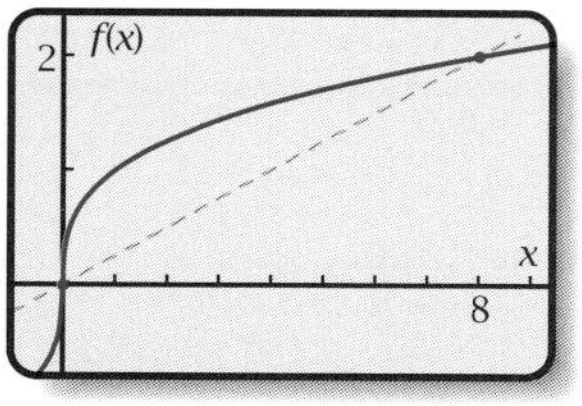


Figure 5-6h

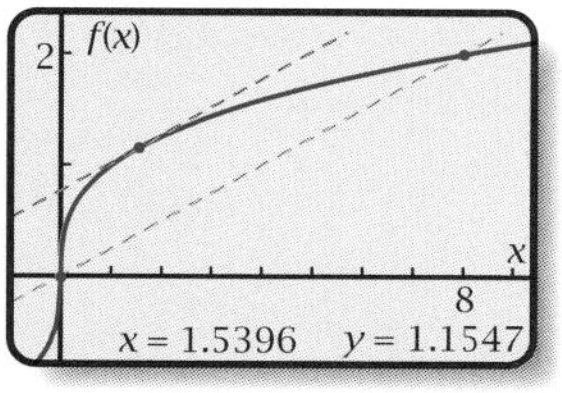


Figure 5-6i

limits of $f(x)$ as $x \to 0$ and as $x \to 8$ are 0 and 2, the values of $f(0)$ and $f(8)$, respectively.

Thus $f$ satisfies the hypotheses of the mean value theorem on [0, 8]. The slope of the secant line (Figure 5-6h) is

$$m_{\text{sec}} = \frac{8^{1/3} - 0^{1/3}}{8 - 0} = \frac{1}{4}.$$

Setting $f'(c) = 1/4$ gives

$$\tfrac{1}{3}c^{-2/3} = \tfrac{1}{4} \Rightarrow c^{-2/3} = \tfrac{3}{4}$$

$$\therefore c = \pm\left(\tfrac{3}{4}\right)^{-3/2} = \pm 1.5396\ldots$$

Only the positive value of $c$ is in (0, 8). Thus the answer is $c = 1.5396\ldots.$

To plot the tangent line, find the particular equation of the line with slope 1/4 through the point $(1.5396\ldots, f(1.5396\ldots))$.

$$f(1.5396\ldots) = (1.5396\ldots)^{1/3} = 1.1547\ldots$$

$$\therefore y - 1.1547\ldots = 0.25(x - 1.5396\ldots) \Rightarrow y = 0.25x + 0.7698\ldots$$

Enter this equation as $y_2$ into your grapher. Figure 5-6i shows that the line really is tangent to the graph and that it is also parallel to the secant line. ■

**■ Example 2**

Given $f(x) = x \sin x$, find the first interval of nonnegative $x$-values on which the hypotheses of Rolle's theorem are true. Then find the point $x = c$ in the corresponding open interval at which the conclusion of Rolle's theorem is true. Illustrate with a graph.

**Solutions**

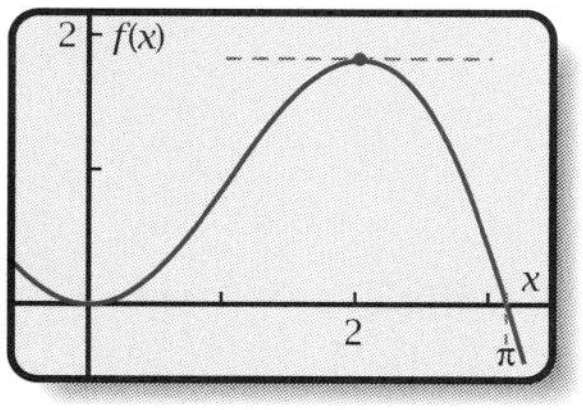


Figure 5-6j

As Figure 5-6j shows, $f(x) = 0$ at $x = 0$ and at $x = \pi$ because $\sin x$ is zero at those points. To establish differentiability,

$$f'(x) = \sin x + x\cos x,$$

which exists for all $x$. Thus $f$ is differentiable on $(0, \pi)$. The function is continuous at 0 and $\pi$ because it is differentiable there. So the hypotheses are met for the interval $[0, \pi]$.

$$f'(c) = 0 \Longleftrightarrow \sin c + c\cos c = 0$$

$$\therefore c = 2.02875$$ Use your grapher's solve feature.

Note that $f'(0)$ is also zero, but $c \neq 0$ because 0 is not in the open interval $(0, \pi)$. ■

## Problem Set 5-6

### *Do These Quickly*

The following problems are intended to refresh your skills. You should be able to do all ten problems in less than five minutes.

**Q1.** Integrate: $\int (x + 2)\, dx$

**Q2.** Integrate: $\int 10t\, dt$

**Q3.** Integrate: $\int \csc^2 x\, dx$

**Q4.** Differentiate: $g(x) = \csc x$

**Q5.** Differentiate: $p(x) = \sin^5 x$

**Q6.** Sketch a graph that shows $\int_1^2 x^2\, dx$.

**Q7.** Sketch a graph with a removable discontinuity at the point (3, 5).

**Q8.** Sketch a graph of a function that is continuous at the point (2, 1) but not differentiable at that point.

**Q9.** Find $\lim_{x\to 0} 1/x$.

**Q10.** If $f(x) = 2x + 6$, then $f^{-1}(x) =$ —?—

1. State the mean value theorem. If you have to refer to the definition in this book to find out what it says, then practice stating it until you can do so without looking.
2. State Rolle's theorem. If you have to refer to its definition in this book to find out what it says, then practice stating it until you can do so without looking.

For Problems 3–6, plot the graph. Find a point $x = c$ in the given interval at which the mean value theorem conclusion is true. Plot the secant line and the tangent line, showing that they are really parallel. Sketch the resulting graphs.

3. $g(x) = \frac{6}{x}$, $[1, 4]$
4. $f(x) = x^4$, $[-1, 2]$
5. $c(x) = 2 + \cos x$, $\left[0, \frac{\pi}{2}\right]$
6. $h(x) = 5 - \sqrt{x}$, $[1, 9]$

For Problems 7–10, plot the graph. Find an interval on which the hypotheses of Rolle's theorem are met. Then find a point $x = c$ in that interval at which the conclusion of Rolle's theorem is true. Plot a horizontal line through the point $(c, f(c))$ and show that the line really is tangent to the graph. Sketch the result.

7. $f(x) = x\cos x$ $\left(\text{Use } \left[0, \frac{\pi}{2}\right]\right)$
8. $f(x) = x^2 \sin x$
9. $f(x) = (6x - x^2)^{1/2}$
10. $f(x) = x^{4/3} - 4x^{1/3}$
11. *Compound Interest Problem:* Suppose you invest \$1000 in a retirement account. The account pays interest continuously at a rate that makes the annual percentage rate (APR) equal 9%. Thus the number of dollars, $d(t)$, in your account at time $t$ years is given by

$$d(t) = 1000(1.09^t).$$

   a. When you retire 50 years from now, how much money will be in the account? Surprising?!

   b. At what average rate does your money increase?

c. Differentiate numerically to calculate the instantaneous rate at which your money is increasing now, at $t = 0$, and when you retire, at $t = 50$. Is the average of these two rates equal to the average rate you found in 11b?

d. Solve numerically to find the time at which the instantaneous rate equals the average rate. Is this time halfway between now and the time you retire?

12. *Baseball Line Drive Problem (Second Inning):* In Problem 38 of Problem Set 4-6, the displacement, $d(t)$, of a baseball from home plate was given to be

$$d(t) = \begin{cases} 60.5\left(\dfrac{0.5 - t}{0.5 + t}\right), & \text{if } t \le 0.5 \\ 150\left(2 - \dfrac{1}{t}\right), & \text{if } t \ge 0.5 \end{cases}$$

where $t$ is the number of seconds since the ball was pitched (Figure 5-6k). Discuss the way in which the mean value theorem applies to function $d$. For instance, do the hypotheses apply on the interval $[0, 1]$? $[0, 2]$? $[0.5, 2]$? Is the conclusion true anywhere in $(0, 1)$? $(0, 2)$? $(0.5, 2)$? How do your answers illustrate the fact that the hypotheses of the mean value theorem are sufficient conditions, not necessary ones?

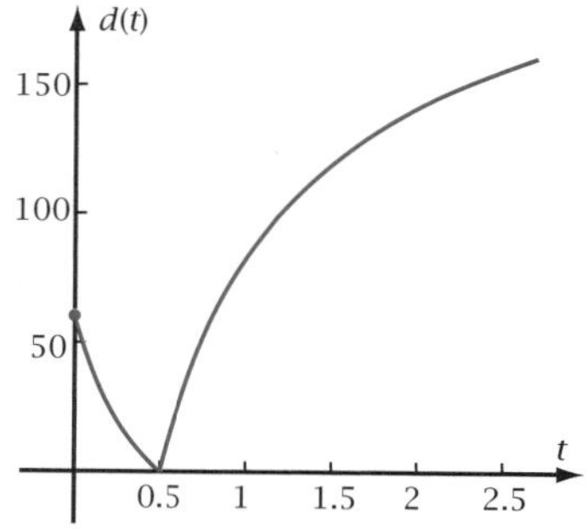

Figure 5-6k

13. Sketch a graph that clearly shows you understand both the hypotheses and the conclusion of Rolle's theorem.

For Problems 14–16, sketch a graph that shows why the conclusion of Rolle's theorem might not be true if $f$ meets all the hypotheses of the theorem on the interval $[a, b]$ except the following.

14. The function $f$ is discontinuous at $x = b$.

15. The function $f$ is continuous, but not differentiable, at $x = d$ in $(a, b)$.

16. The value of $f(a)$ is not equal to zero.

17. Sketch a graph that shows that a function may satisfy the conclusion of Rolle's theorem even though the function does not meet all of the hypotheses.

18. What was Rolle's first name? When did he live? In what country?

For Problems 19–28, plot (if necessary) and sketch the graph. State which of the hypotheses of Rolle's theorem are not met on the given interval. Then state whether or not the conclusion of Rolle's theorem is true on the corresponding open interval.

19. $f(x) = x^2 - 4x$ on $[0, 1]$

20. $f(x) = x^2 - 6x + 5$ on $[1, 2]$

21. $f(x) = x^2 - 4x$ on $[0, 2]$

22. $f(x) = x^2 - 6x + 5$ on $[1, 4]$

23. $f(x) = x^2 - 4x$ on $[0, 3]$

24. $f(x) = |x - 2| - 1$ on $[1, 3]$

25. $f(x) = \dfrac{1}{x}$ on $[0, 5]$

26. $f(x) = x - [x]$ on $[1, 2]$ ($[x]$ is the greatest integer less than or equal to $x$.)

27. $f(x) = 1 - (x - 3)^{2/3}$ on $[2, 4]$

28. $f(x) = \dfrac{x^3 - 6x^2 + 11x - 6}{x - 2}$ on $[1, 3]$

29. Given $g(x) = \dfrac{x^3 - 7x^2 + 13x - 6}{x - 2}$, explain why the hypotheses of the mean value theorem are not met on any interval containing $x = 2$. Is the conclusion true if the theorem is applied on [1, 3]? On [1, 5]? Justify your answers. A graph may help.

30. Given $h(x) = x^{2/3}$, explain why the hypotheses of the mean value theorem are met on [0, 8] but are not met on [−1, 8]. Is the conclusion of the mean value theorem true for any $x = c$ in $(-1, 8)$? Justify your answer. A graph may help.

31. Suppose that $f(x) = |x - 3| + 2x$.
    a. Use the definition of absolute value to write two equations for $f(x)$, one that works if $x \geq 3$ and one that works if $x < 3$.
    b. Sketch the graph of $f$.
    c. Is $f$ continuous at $x = 3$? Justify your answer.
    d. Is $f$ differentiable at $x = 3$? Justify your answer.
    e. Which hypothesis of the mean value theorem is not met on the interval [1, 6]?
    f. Show that there is no point $x = c$ in (1, 6) at which the conclusion of the mean value theorem is true.
    g. Is $f$ integrable on [0, 5]? If not, why not? If so, evaluate $\int_0^5 f(x)\,dx$ geometrically.

32. *New Jersey Turnpike Problem:* When you enter the New Jersey Turnpike you receive a card that indicates your entrance point and the time at which you entered. When you exit, therefore, it can be determined how far you went and how long it took, and thus what your average speed was.
    a. Let $f(t)$ be the number of miles you traveled in $t$ hours. What assumptions must you make about $f$ so that it satisfies the hypotheses of the mean value theorem on the interval from $t = a$, when you entered the turnpike, to $t = b$, when you exited?
    b. Suppose that your average speed is 60 mi/hr. If $f$ meets the hypotheses of the mean value theorem, prove that your speed was exactly 60 mi/hr at some time between $t = a$ and $t = b$.

33. *Rolle's Theorem Proof Illustrated by Graph and by Table:* The proof of Rolle's theorem shows that at a high point, $f(c)$, for the open interval $(a, b)$, the difference quotient

$$\frac{f(x) - f(c)}{x - c}$$

is always positive (or zero) when $x < c$ and always negative when $x > c$. In this problem you will show graphically and numerically that this fact is true for a fairly complicated function.

    a. Figure 5-61 shows the graph of

$$f(x) = 25 - (x - 5)^2 + 4\cos(2\pi(x - 5)).$$

    Plot the graph as $y_1$. Use a friendly window that includes $x = 5$, with $\Delta x = 0.1$.

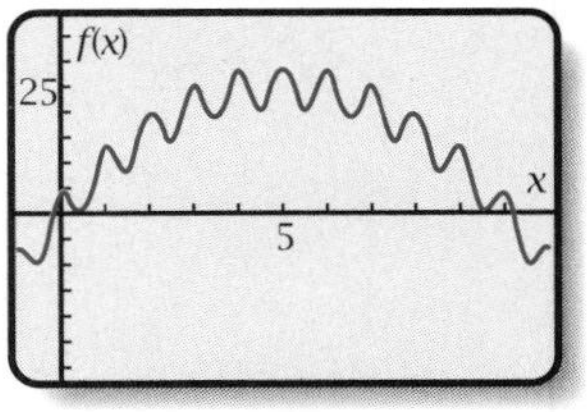

Figure 5-61

    b. Explain why the high point of the graph is at $x = 5$. What does $f(5)$ equal?
    c. Find $f'(x)$. What does $f'(5)$ equal?

d. Let $y_2$ be the difference quotient

$$y_2 = \frac{y_1 - f(5)}{x - 5}.$$

Plot on your grapher the graph of $y_2$. Sketch the result.

e. Make a table of values of the difference quotient for each 0.5 units of $x$ from $x = 2$ to $x = 8$.

f. Read the proof of Rolle's theorem, which appears in this section. Explain how the work you've done in this problem relates to this proof. Tell which hypothesis of Rolle's theorem has not been mentioned so far in this problem. Is this hypothesis true for function $f$? Can the conclusion of Rolle's theorem be true for a function if the hypotheses aren't? Explain.

34. *Mean Value Theorem Proof Illustrated by Graph and by Table:* In the proof of the mean value theorem, a linear function, $g$, and a difference function, $h$, were created. Rolle's theorem was then applied to function $h$. In this problem you will derive equations for $g(x)$ and $h(x)$, and you'll illustrate the proof by graph and by table of values.

a. Figure 5-6m shows the graph of

$$f(x) = 1 + x + \cos \pi x$$

and a chord drawn between the endpoints of the graph for the interval [2, 4.5]. Plot the graph as $y_1$. Use a friendly window with $\Delta x$ no larger than 0.05.

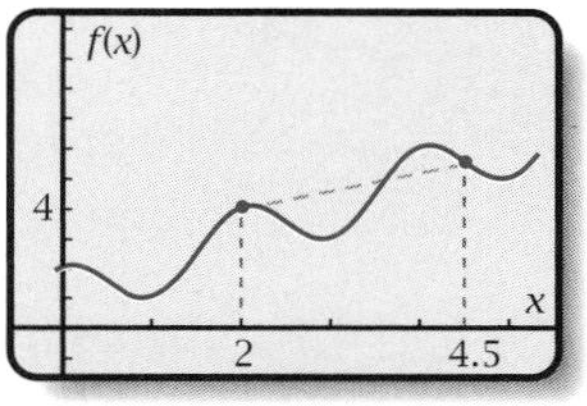

Figure 5-6m

b. Figure out an equation for the linear function $g(x)$ and plot it as $y_2$.

c. Use a time-efficient way to plot the function $h(x)$ mentioned in the proof of the mean value theorem.

d. Find a point $x = c$ in (2, 4.5) at which the conclusion of the mean value theorem is true.

e. Make a table of ten values of $h(x)$ for values of $x$ around $c$, spaced 0.05 units apart. Show that $h(c)$ is an upper (or lower) bound for the values of $h(x)$ in the table.

f. Read the proof of the mean value theorem, which appears in this section. Show how functions $g$ and $h$ in this problem are used with Rolle's theorem to prove the mean value theorem.

g. Show that function $f$ meets the hypotheses of the mean value theorem on [2, 4.5].

35. *Corollary of the Mean Value Theorem:* A **corollary** of a theorem is another theorem that follows easily from the first one. Explain why the corollary of the mean value theorem shown in the box below is true.

**Property: Corollary of the Mean Value Theorem**

If $f$ is differentiable on the closed interval $[a, b]$,
then there is at least one number $x = c$ in $(a, b)$ such that

$$f'(c) = \frac{f(b) - f(a)}{b - a}.$$

36. *Converse of a Theorem:* It is easy to show that if two differentiable functions differ by a constant, then their derivatives are equal for all values of $x$ in the domain. For instance, if

$$f(x) = \sin x \quad \text{and} \quad g(x) = 2 + \sin x,$$

then $f'(x) = g'(x)$ for all $x$ (Figure 5-6n). The **converse** of a theorem is the statement that comes from interchanging the hypothesis and the conclusion, as shown in the box below.

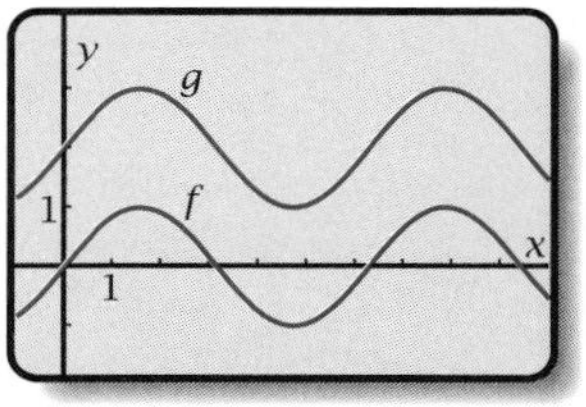

Figure 5-6n

**Property: Converse of Equal-Derivative Theorem**

**Theorem:** If $f(x) = g(x) + D$ for all $x$ in the domain, where $D$ is a constant, then $f'(x) = g'(x)$ for all $x$ in the domain.

**Converse of the Theorem:** If $f'(x) = g'(x)$ for all $x$ in the domain, then $f(x) = g(x) + D$ for all $x$ in the domain, where $D$ is a constant.

As you realize, the converse of a theorem is not necessarily true. For instance, the converse of the mean value theorem is false. However, the above converse *is* true and can be proved by contradiction with the help of the mean value theorem.

a. Suppose that there are two values of $x$ such that $f(a) = g(a) + D_1$ and $f(b) = g(b) + D_2$, where $D_1 \neq D_2$. Let $h(x) = f(x) - g(x)$. Explain why the mean value theorem applies to $h$ on the interval $[a, b]$.

b. The mean value theorem lets you conclude that there is a number $x = c$ in $(a, b)$ such that

$$h'(c) = \frac{h(b) - h(a)}{b - a}.$$

Show that $h'(c)$ also equals $(D_2 - D_1)/(b - a)$.

c. Show that $h'(x) = 0$ for all $x$ in $(a, b)$, and thus $h'(c) = 0$. Use the result to show that $D_1$ and $D_2$ are equal, which proves the converse by contradicting the assumption made in 36a.

37. *Antiderivative of Zero:* Prove as a corollary of the property in Problem 36 that if $f'(x) = 0$ for all values of $x$, then $f(x)$ is a constant function.

38. Let $f(x) = (\cos x + \sin x)^2$. Let $g(x) = \sin 2x$. On the same screen, plot graphs of $f$ and $g$. Sketch the result. Make a table of values of the two functions for convenient values of $x$, say 0, 1, 2, .... What seems to be true about values of $f(x)$ and $g(x)$ at the same values of $x$? Prove algebraically that $f'(x) = g'(x)$ for all values of $x$.

39. *Maximum and Minimum Values of Continuous Functions:* When you study the analysis of real numbers you will show that if a function $f$ is continuous on a closed interval $[a, b]$, then $f(x)$ has a maximum value and a minimum value at values of $x$ in that interval. Explain why a function that meets the hypotheses of Rolle's theorem automatically meets these requirements.

40. *Intermediate Value Theorem versus Mean Value Theorem:* The words *intermediate* and *mean* both connote the concept of betweenness. Both the intermediate value theorem and the mean value theorem assert the existence of a number $x = c$ that is between two numbers $a$ and $b$. However, the hypotheses and conclusions of the theorems are

quite different. Write a paragraph or two describing how the two theorems differ and how they are alike. Graphs will help.

41. *Journal Problem:* Update your journal with what you've learned since the last entry. Include such things as those listed here.
    - The one most important thing you have learned since your last journal entry
    - The fact that you can now fill in one more square in your chart of calculus concepts
    - The two new theorems you have just learned and how they are related to each other
    - The difference between the mean value theorem and the intermediate value theorem
    - The difference between definite integral and indefinite integral
    - The different kinds of Riemann sums
    - Any technique or idea about which you plan to ask at the next class period

# 5-7 Some Very Special Riemann Sums

In Sections 5-5 and 5-6, you learned that a definite integral is the limit of Riemann sums and that there is a mean value theorem, which equates the slope of a tangent line to the slope of a secant line. In this section you will explore Riemann sums in which the sample points are picked very cleverly based on the mean value theorem. The conclusions you reach will pave the way to evaluating exact definite integrals, without using Riemann sums or the trapezoidal rule.

**OBJECTIVE**

Calculate Riemann sums for given sets of sample points and reach some conclusions about how the sample points were chosen.

## Problem Set 5-7

Note: Your instructor might have you work these problems in groups so that you can consult your classmates about what you are discovering.

For Problems 1–7, let $f(x) = x^{1/2}$ (Figure 5-7a).

1. Find an estimate for the integral

$$I = \int_1^4 x^{1/2}\,dx$$

by using the trapezoidal rule with $n = 3$ subintervals. Write down all the decimal places your calculator will give you. Does this value overestimate or underestimate the actual integral? Explain.

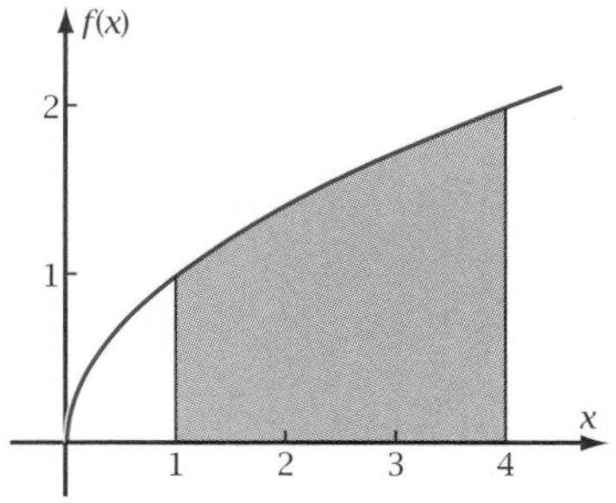

Figure 5-7a

2. Find a midpoint Riemann sum for integral $I$ in Problem 1. Use $n = 3$ increments. Show that this sum is not equal to the value you found by using the trapezoidal rule. Does the midpoint sum overestimate or underestimate the actual integral? Explain.

3. Find a Riemann sum for integral $I$ by using the subintervals in Problem 1, but use the following sample points. (Let $k$ stand for the subinterval number.)

| $k$ | $x = c$ |
|---|---|
| 1 | 1.48584256 |
| 2 | 2.49161026 |
| 3 | 3.49402722 |

How does this sum compare with your answers to Problems 1 and 2?

4. Find a Riemann sum for $I$ by using six subintervals of equal width and the following sample points.

| $k$ | $x = c$ |
|---|---|
| 1 | 1.24580513 |
| 2 | 1.74701361 |
| 3 | 2.24768040 |
| 4 | 2.74810345 |
| 5 | 3.24839587 |
| 6 | 3.74861006 |

How does the integral approximated by this Riemann sum compare with other values in this problem set?

5. Let $g(x) = (2/3)x^{3/2}$. Find the point in the open interval $(1, 1.5)$ at which the conclusion of the mean value theorem is true for function $g$. Where have you seen this number in this problem set?

6. How is function $g$ related to function $f$?

7. Make a conjecture about the exact value of the integral in Problem 1.

For Problems 8–12, let $f(x) = x^3$ (Figure 5-7b).

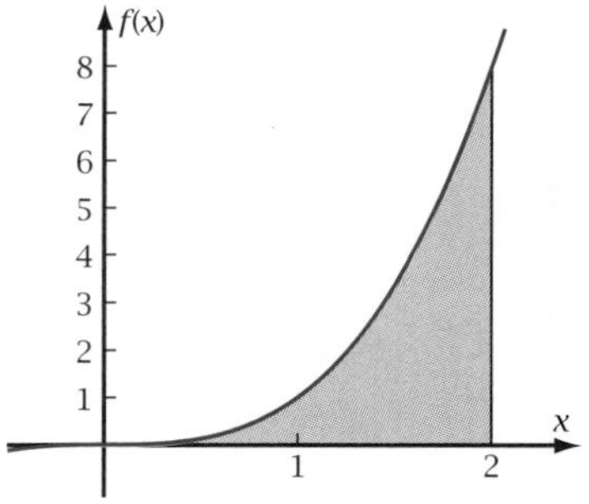

Figure 5-7b

8. Find an approximate value of the integral

$$I = \int_0^2 f(x)\,dx$$

by using a midpoint Riemann sum with $n = 100$ subintervals. Do not round off. Does this sum underestimate or overestimate the integral?

9. Find another approximate value for integral $I$ using the trapezoidal rule with $n = 100$. Do not round off. Based on your answer to Problem 8, make a conjecture about what integer the exact value of integral $I$ is.

10. Let $g(x) = \int f(x)\,dx$. Assuming that the constant of integration is $C = 0$, find $g(0)$, $g(0.5), g(1), g(1.5)$, and $g(2)$. Use these values to find the slopes of the secant lines connecting $(0,\ g(0))$ to $(0.5,\ g(0.5))$, and so forth.

11. The mean value theorem applies to function $g$ on each interval (0, 0.5), (0.5, 1), (1, 1.5), and (1.5, 2). Find the values of $x = c_1$, $c_2$, $c_3$, and $c_4$ in each interval for which $g'(c)$ equals the slope of the respective secant line in Problem 10. Do not round off.

12. Find the Riemann sum for the integral in Problem 8, using as sample points the values of $c$ you found in Problem 10. Keep all the decimal places. How does this sum compare with the exact (integer) answer you conjectured in Problem 9?

13. Make a conjecture about how you could calculate the exact value of the integral by using a Riemann sum with just one increment and a judiciously-chosen sample point. Then test your conjecture to see whether or not it works.

# 5-8 The Fundamental Theorem of Calculus

Riemann sums tend to get closer to the actual value of the corresponding integral as the number of intervals increases. The value of a Riemann sum also depends on just where you pick the sample points in each interval. For instance, a midpoint sum should be closer to the actual value of the integral than a sum for which sample points are taken at one end of the interval.

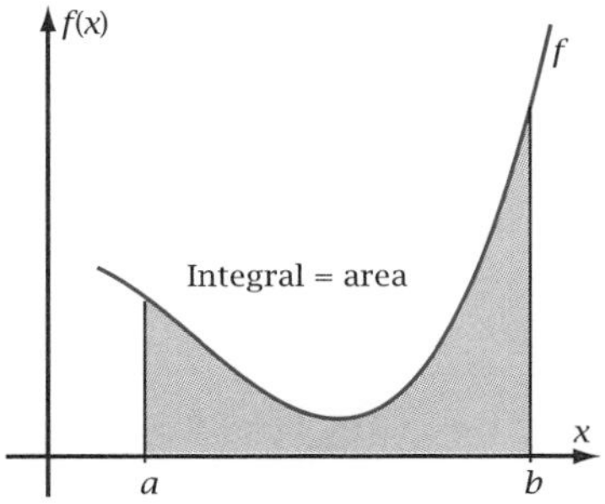


Figure 5-8a

What if you could pick the sample points in such a way that the Riemann sum is independent of the number of intervals? The Riemann sum would be the same no matter how many or how few intervals you used. In Section 5-7, you discovered a way to do this. In this section you will use what you discovered to put together the **fundamental theorem of calculus**. This theorem lets you evaluate definite integrals exactly, by algebra, using indefinite integrals.

Figure 5-8a shows a function $f$ for which it is desired to find the definite integral

$$\int_a^b f(x)\,dx.$$

The top graph in Figure 5-8b is function $g$, an indefinite integral of $f$. That is, $g(x) = \int f(x)\,dx$. By the definition of indefinite integral, $g'(x) = f(x)$. Because $g$ is differentiable, the mean value theorem applies to it on $[a, b]$ or on any subinterval of $[a, b]$.

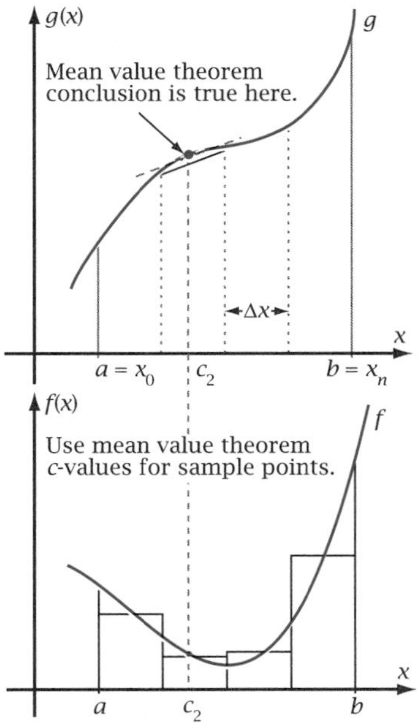


Figure 5-8b

Divide the interval $[a, b]$ into $n$ subintervals of equal width $\Delta x$. Let $c_1, c_2, c_3, \ldots, c_n$ be the points in the first, second, third, ..., $n$th subinterval at which the conclusion of the mean value theorem is true for function $g$ on that subinterval. Thus

$$\begin{aligned} g'(c_1) &= \frac{g(x_1) - g(a)}{\Delta x} \\ g'(c_2) &= \frac{g(x_2) - g(x_1)}{\Delta x} \\ g'(c_3) &= \frac{g(x_3) - g(x_2)}{\Delta x} \\ &\ldots \\ g'(c_n) &= \frac{g(b) - g(x_{n-1})}{\Delta x}. \end{aligned}$$

Now, use the points $c_1, c_2, c_3, \ldots, c_n$ as sample points for a Riemann sum of the original definite integral, as shown in the bottom graph of Figure 5-8b. That is,

$$R_n = f(c_1)\,\Delta x + f(c_2)\,\Delta x + f(c_3)\,\Delta x + \cdots + f(c_n)\Delta x.$$

However, $f(x) = g'(x)$ for any value of $x$. Therefore,

$$R_n = g'(c_1)\,\Delta x + g'(c_2)\,\Delta x + g'(c_3)\,\Delta x + \cdots + g'(c_n)\Delta x.$$

Replacing the $g'(c_1)$ with $\dfrac{g(x_1) - g(a)}{\Delta x}$, and so forth, canceling the $\Delta x$'s, and arranging in column form gives

$$\begin{aligned} R_n = {} & g(x_1) - g(a) \\ & + g(x_2) - g(x_1) \\ & + g(x_3) - g(x_2) \\ & \ldots \\ & + g(b) - g(x_{n-1}) \\ \hline R_n = {} & g(b) - g(a). \end{aligned}$$

All the middle terms "telescope," leaving only $-g(a)$ from the first term and $g(b)$ from the last. The result is *independent* of the number of increments. The quantity $g(b) - g(a)$ is, in fact, the exact value of the definite integral. This is what the fundamental theorem of calculus says. The definite integral can be calculated by evaluating the antiderivative at the upper limit of integration and then subtracting from it the value of the antiderivative at the lower limit of integration. The formal statement of this theorem and its proof follow.

> **Property: The Fundamental Theorem of Calculus**
>
> If $f$ is an integrable function, and if $g(x) = \int f(x)\,dx$, then $\int_a^b f(x)\,dx = g(b) - g(a)$.

***Proof:***

Partition the interval $[a, b]$ into $n$ subintervals of equal width $\Delta x$. Let $L_n$ and $U_n$ be lower and upper sums for $\int_a^b f(x)\,dx$. Let $R_n$ be the Riemann sum equal to

$g(b) - g(a)$, as derived above. Because any Riemann sum is between the upper and lower sum, you can write

$$L_n \le R_n \le U_n.$$

By the definition of integrability, the limits of $L_n$ and $U_n$ as $\Delta x$ approaches zero are equal to each other. By the squeeze theorem, therefore, the limit of $R_n$ as $\Delta x$ approaches zero is also equal to this common limit. The common limit is defined to be the definite integral. Therefore

$$\int_a^b f(x)\,dx = \lim_{\Delta x \to 0} R_n = \lim_{\Delta x \to 0} [g(b) - g(a)] = g(b) - g(a), \text{ Q.E.D.}$$

The last equality is true because the quantity $g(b) - g(a)$ is a constant with respect to $\Delta x$.

***OBJECTIVE***

Learn what the fundamental theorem of calculus says. Show that it produces reasonable answers by comparing them with approximations obtained by using the familiar techniques of Riemann summing and the trapezoidal rule.

You—perhaps with your study group members—will accomplish this objective by working the problems in the following problem set. In Problem 10, you will record in your journal what you have learned. In Section 5-9, you will see examples of how to use the fundamental theorem, and you'll practice evaluating definite integrals.

## Problem Set 5-8

### *Do These Quickly*

The following problems are intended to refresh your skills. You should be able to do all ten problems in less than five minutes.

**Q1.** $r(x) = \int m(x)\,dx$ if and only if —?—

**Q2.** Write the definition of derivative.

**Q3.** How fast is $f(x) = x^2$ changing when $x = 3$?

**Q4.** Find $dy$: $y = \sec x$.

**Q5.** Find $y'$: $y = (x^2 + 3)^4$.

**Q6.** Find $dz/du$: $z = \sin u$.

**Q7.** Find $f'(x)$: $f(x) = 7^3$.

**Q8.** Solve for the minimum positive value of $x$: $\cos x = 0.5$.

**Q9.** $\cos^2 x + \sin^2 x$ = -?-

**Q10.** Sketch a graph that shows the conclusion of the mean value theorem.

1. For the integral $I = \int_4^9 10x^{-1.5}\,dx$, do the following:
   a. Find the exact value of $I$ by using the fundamental theorem. What happens to "+$C$" from the indefinite integral?
   b. Sketch a graph that shows an upper sum with $n = 5$ increments for this integral.

c. Find $U_5$, $L_5$, and the average of these two sums. Does the average overestimate or underestimate the integral? Explain.

d. Find midpoint Riemann sums $M_{10}, M_{100}$, and $M_{1000}$ for $I$. Do the Riemann sums seem to be converging to the exact value of $I$?

2. Let $I = \int_0^{1.5} \sin x\, dx$. Find the exact value of $I$ by using the fundamental theorem. Show that midpoint Riemann sums approach this value as the number of increments approaches infinity. Sketch an appropriate graph to show why midpoint Riemann sums overestimate the value of the definite integral.

3. State the fundamental theorem of calculus.

4. Prove that if $f$ is an integrable function, then for any partition of the interval $[a,\ b]$ into $n$ subintervals of equal width there is a Riemann sum for $\int_a^b f(x)\, dx$ whose value is independent of the number $n$.

5. Prove the fundamental theorem of calculus by using the result of Problem 4 as a lemma.

6. You have proved that it is possible to pick a Riemann sum whose value is independent of the number of increments. Suppose that the interval $[a,\ b]$ is taken as a whole. That is, suppose there is just one "subinterval." Where should the sample point for this interval be picked so that the corresponding Riemann "sum" is exactly equal to the definite integral from $a$ to $b$? How does your answer relate to the fundamental theorem?

7. *Freeway Exit Problem:* In the design of freeway exit ramps it is important to allow enough room for cars to slow down before they enter the frontage road. Suppose that the velocity is given by $v(t) = 100 - 20(t + 1)^{1/2}$, where $v(t)$ is in feet per second and $t$ is the number of seconds since you started slowing down. Write a definite integral equal to the number of feet the car goes from $t = 0$ to $t = 8$. Evaluate the integral exactly by using the fundamental theorem.

8. *The Fundamental Theorem Another Way:* Let $h$ be the square root function $h(x) = x^{1/2}$. Let $P$ be the region under the graph of $h$ from $x = 4$ to $x = 9$ (Figure 5-8c).

a. Evaluate the Riemann sum $R_{10}$ for $P$, picking sample points at the midpoints of the subintervals. Don't round the answer.

b. Let $u$ be a value of $x$ in the interval [4, 9]. Let $A(u)$ be the area of the portion of the region from $x = 4$ to $x = u$ (Figure 5-8d). Let $\Delta u$ be a small change in $u$. The area of the strip from $x = u$ to $x = u + \Delta u$ equals $A(u + \Delta u) - A(u)$. Explain why this area is between $h(u)\,\Delta u$ and $h(u + \Delta u)\Delta u$. Write the result as a three-member inequality.

c. Use the inequality you found in 8b to prove that $dA/du = h(u)$. This equation is called a **differential equation**.

d. Multiply both sides of the differential equation given in 8c by $du$. Then take the indefinite integral of both sides. Find the constant of integration by observing that $A(4)$ must equal zero.

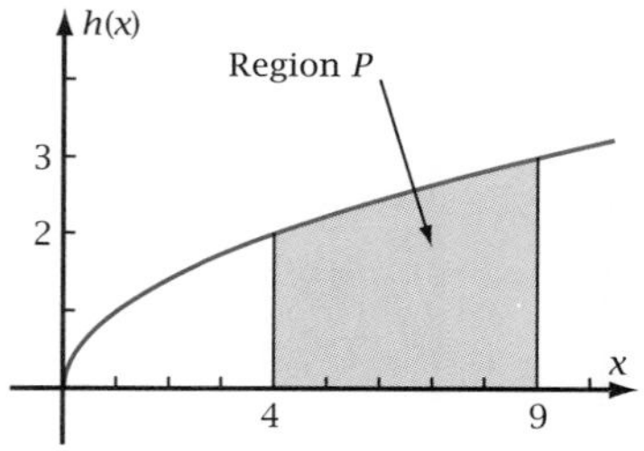

Figure 5-8c

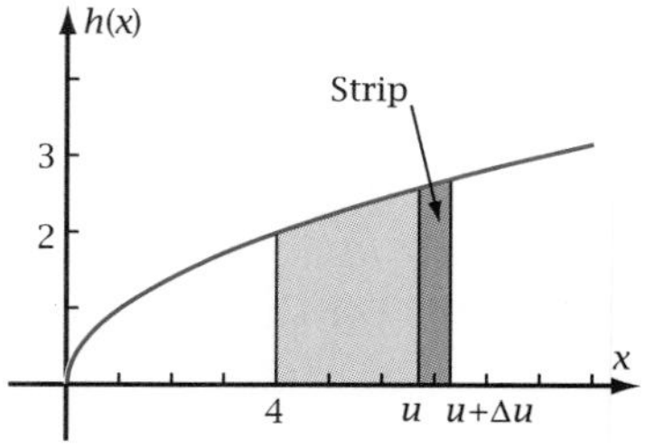

Figure 5-8d

e. Find the area of region $P$ by evaluating $A(9)$. Explain why your answer to 8a is consistent with your answer to this problem.

9. *Riemann Sum Sketching Problem:* Sketch appropriate rectangles to show the following.
   a. An upper sum with four increments, where the sample points are taken at the left endpoint of each subinterval
   b. A lower sum with three increments, where the sample points are taken at the left endpoint of each subinterval
   c. A Riemann sum with five increments, where the sample points are taken at the midpoint of each subinterval
   d. A Riemann sum with four increments, where no sample point is taken at the middle or at either end of a subinterval
   e. A Riemann sum with three increments, where two different sample points are at the same $x$-value
   f. A subinterval for an upper sum in which the sample point must be somewhere between the two endpoints

10. *Journal Problem:* Update your journal with what you've learned as a result of doing this problem set. Include such things as those listed here.
    - A statement of the fundamental theorem of calculus
    - How sample points can be chosen so that a Riemann sum is independent of the number of increments, and how this fact leads to the fundamental theorem
    - Evidence to show that Riemann sums really do get close to the value of a definite integral found by the fundamental theorem and as $n$ approaches infinity
    - What you now better understand about the meaning of Riemann sum
    - Anything about the fundamental theorem that you're still unclear about

# 5-9 Definite Integral Properties and Practice

You now know precise definitions of the four concepts in calculus, and you know what you should be able to do with each concept.

| | Define it. | Understand it. | Do it. | Apply it. |
|---|---|---|---|---|
| Limit | | | | |
| Derivative | | | | |
| Definite integral | | | | |
| Indefinite integral | | | | |

In this section you will work on the "Do it" box for definite integrals. Because you will be using the fundamental theorem, you will also be working on the "Do it" box for indefinite integrals.

**OBJECTIVE**

Be able to evaluate quickly a definite integral, in an acceptable format, using the fundamental theorem of calculus.

To evaluate a definite integral such as

$$\int_1^4 x^2\, dx,$$

you could start by writing an indefinite integral, $g(x) = \int x^2\, dx$, integrating, then finding $g(4) - g(1)$. Here is a compact format that is customarily used.

$$\int_1^4 x^2\, dx$$

$$= \frac{1}{3}x^3 \Big|_1^4 \qquad \text{Pronounced "(1/3)}x^3\text{ evaluated from } x = 1 \text{ to } x = 4.\text{"}$$

$$= \frac{1}{3} \cdot 4^3 - \frac{1}{3} \cdot 1^3$$

$$= 21$$

In the first step you find the indefinite integral. The vertical bar at the right reminds you that the upper and lower limits of integration are to be substituted into the expression at its left.

As mentioned in Section 5-5, the values 1 and 4 are called **limits of integration**. This terminology is unfortunate because these values have nothing to do with the concept of limit as you have defined it. The term *lower and upper bounds of integration* would be more suitable. However, the word *limit* is firmly entrenched in mathematical literature, so you should get used to the ambiguity and interpret the word in its proper context.

The following are some properties of definite integrals that are useful both for evaluating definite integrals and for understanding what they mean.

### Integral with a Negative Integrand

Suppose you must evaluate $\int_1^4 (x^2 - 5x + 2)\, dx$. The result is

$$\left(\frac{1}{3}x^3 - \frac{5}{2}x^2 + 2x\right)\Big|_1^4$$

$$= \left(\frac{64}{3} - 40 + 8\right) - \left(\frac{1}{3} - \frac{5}{2} + 2\right)$$

$$= -10.5.$$

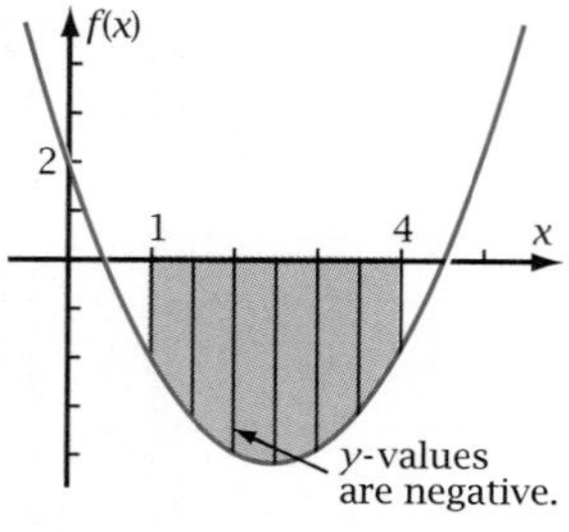

Figure 5-9a

The answer should be surprising. How could an area be negative? Figure 5-9a reveals the reason why. The region lies below the $x$-axis. The Riemann sum has the form

$$\sum f(x)\, \Delta x.$$

Each value of $f(x)$ is negative, and each $\Delta x$ is positive. Thus each term in the sum is negative, and as a result the integral is negative.

### *Integral from a Higher Number to a Lower Number*

Suppose an integral has a lower limit of integration that is greater than the upper limit, such as

$$\int_{\pi/3}^{0} \cos x\, dx.$$

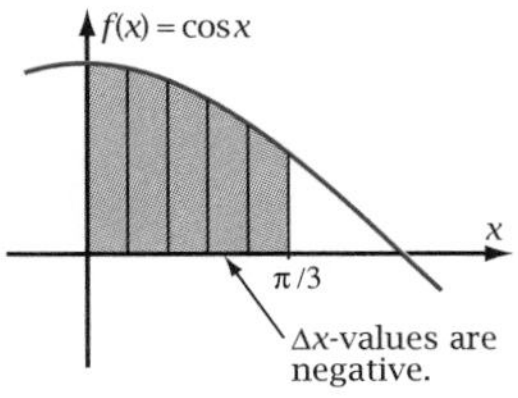

Figure 5-9b

Evaluating the integral gives

$$\sin x \Big|_{\pi/3}^{0}$$
$$= \sin 0 - \sin \tfrac{\pi}{3}$$
$$= 0 - \tfrac{\sqrt{3}}{2}$$
$$= -0.86602\ldots$$

The integral is negative, yet the integrand is positive, as shown in Figure 5-9b. The reason why is the same as that shown in the previous property but more subtle. In this case each $\Delta x$ is negative. Because $\Delta x = (b - a)/n$, $\Delta x$ will be negative whenever $b$ is less than $a$. Thus each term in the sum

$$\sum f(x)\, \Delta x$$

will be negative, making the integral itself negative. Combining the observations above leads you to conclude that if both $f(x)$ and $\Delta x$ are negative, the integral is positive. For instance,

$$\int_{3}^{1} -x\, dx = -\tfrac{1}{2}x^2 \Big|_{3}^{1} = -\tfrac{1}{2} + \tfrac{9}{2} = 4.$$

### *Sum of Integrals with the Same Integrand*

Suppose you integrate a function such as $x^2 + 1$ from $x = 1$ to $x = 4$, then integrate the same function from $x = 4$ to $x = 5$. Figure 5-9c shows the two regions whose areas equal the two integrals. The sum of the two areas equals the area of the region from $x = 1$ all the way to $x = 5$. This fact suggests that the two integrals should add up to the integral of $x^2 + 1$ from $x = 1$ to $x = 5$. This turns out to be true, as you can see below.

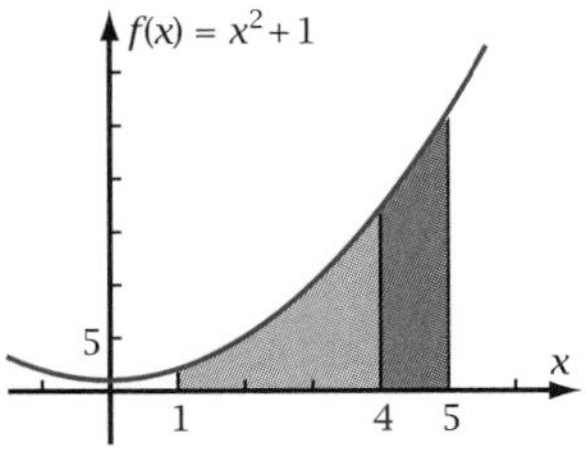

Figure 5-9c

$$\int_{1}^{4} (x^2 + 1)\, dx = \left(\tfrac{1}{3}x^3 + x\right)\Big|_{1}^{4} = \tfrac{64}{3} + 4 - \tfrac{1}{3} - 1 = 24$$

$$\int_{4}^{5} (x^2 + 1)\, dx = \left(\tfrac{1}{3}x^3 + x\right)\Big|_{4}^{5} = \tfrac{125}{3} + 5 - \tfrac{64}{3} - 4 = 21\tfrac{1}{3}$$

$$\int_{1}^{5} (x^2 + 1)\, dx = \left(\tfrac{1}{3}x^3 + x\right)\Big|_{1}^{5} = \tfrac{125}{3} + 5 - \tfrac{1}{3} - 1 = 45\tfrac{1}{3}, \text{ which equals } 24 + 21\tfrac{1}{3}.$$

In general, $\int_a^b f(x)\, dx = \int_a^c f(x)\, dx + \int_c^b f(x)\, dx$.

### *Integrals between Symmetric Limits*

$\int_{-a}^{a} f(x)\, dx$ is called an **integral between symmetric limits**. If $f$ happens to be either an odd function (such as $\sin x$ or $x^5$) or an even function (such as $\cos x$ or $x^6$), then the integral has properties that make it easier to evaluate.

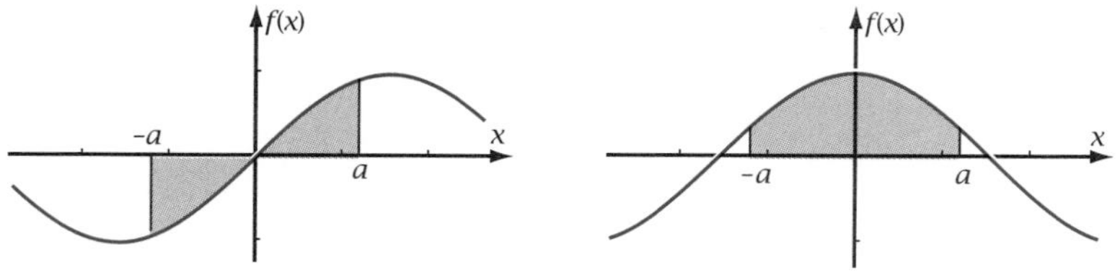

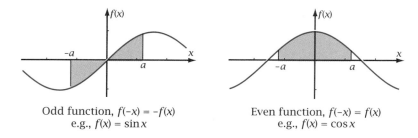

Odd function, $f(-x) = -f(x)$
e.g., $f(x) = \sin x$

Even function, $f(-x) = f(x)$
e.g., $f(x) = \cos x$

Figure 5-9d

The left-hand graph in Figure 5-9d shows an **odd function**, where $f(-x) = -f(x)$. The area of the region from $x = -a$ to $x = 0$ equals the area from $x = 0$ to $x = a$, but the signs of the integrals will be opposite. Thus the integral equals zero! For instance,

$$\int_{-2}^{2} x^3\,dx = \tfrac{1}{4}x^4 \Big|_{-2}^{2} = \tfrac{1}{4}(2)^4 - \tfrac{1}{4}(-2)^4 = 0.$$

The right-hand graph in Figure 5-9d shows an **even function**, where $f(-x) = f(x)$. The areas of the regions from $x = -a$ to 0 and from $x = 0$ to $a$ are again the same. This time the integrals have the same sign. Thus you can integrate from zero to $a$, then double the result. For instance,

$$\int_{-3}^{3} x^4\,dx = \tfrac{1}{5}x^5 \Big|_{-3}^{3} = \tfrac{1}{5}(3)^5 - \tfrac{1}{5}(-3)^5 = 48.6 - (-48.6) = 97.2, \text{ and}$$

$$2\int_{0}^{3} x^4\,dx = 2 \cdot \tfrac{1}{5}x^5 \Big|_{0}^{3} = 2 \cdot \tfrac{1}{5}(3)^5 - 2 \cdot \tfrac{1}{5}(0)^5 = 2(48.6) = 97.2$$

### *Integral of a Sum, and Integral of a Constant Times a Function*

In Section 5-4, you learned that the indefinite integral of a sum of two functions equals the sum of the integrals and that the integral of a constant times a function is the constant times the integral of the function. By the fundamental theorem, these properties apply to definite integrals, too.

$$\int_{a}^{b} (f(x) + g(x))\,dx = \int_{a}^{b} f(x)\,dx + \int_{a}^{b} g(x)\,dx, \text{ and}$$

$$\int_{a}^{b} k f(x)\,dx = k\int_{a}^{b} f(x)\,dx.$$

Figures 5-9e and 5-9f show geometrically what these two properties say. In Figure 5-9e the regions representing the two integrals are shaded differently. The second region sits down on top of the first without a change in area. Thus the integral of the sum of the two functions is represented by the sum of the two areas. In Figure 5-9f, the region representing the integral of $f$ is magnified by a factor of $k$ in the vertical direction. The region representing the integral of $kf$ thus has $k$ times the area of the region representing $f$.

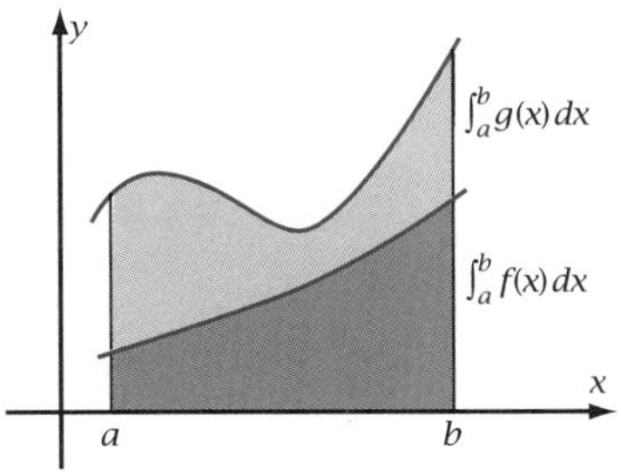


Figure 5-9e

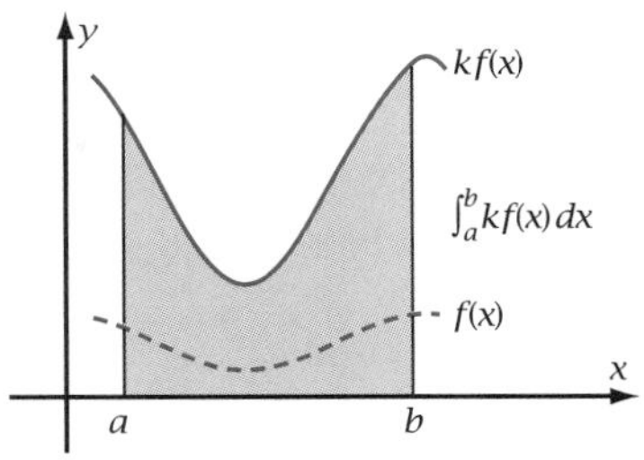


Figure 5-9f

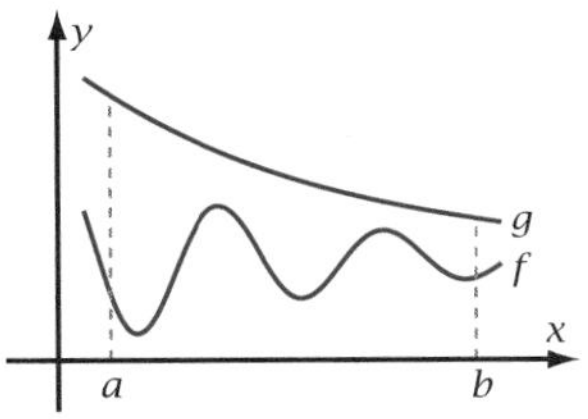


Figure 5-9g

### *Upper Bounds for Integrals*

Suppose that the graph of one function is always below the graph of another. Figure 5-9g shows functions for which

$$f(x) < g(x) \quad \text{for all} \quad x \text{ in } [a, b].$$

The area of the region corresponding to the integral of $f$ is smaller than that for $g$. Thus

$$\int_a^b f(x)\,dx < \int_a^b g(x)\,dx.$$

The properties shown above are summarized in the following table.

#### *Properties of Definite Integrals*

1. **Positive and Negative Integrands:** The integral $\int_a^b f(x)\,dx$ is positive if $f(x)$ is positive for all values of $x$ in $[a, b]$ and negative if $f(x)$ is negative for all values of $x$ in $[a, b]$, provided $a < b$.
2. **Reversal of Limits of Integration:** $\int_b^a f(x)\,dx = -\int_a^b f(x)\,dx$
3. **Sum of Integrals with the Same Integrand:** $\int_a^b f(x)\,dx = \int_a^c f(x)\,dx + \int_c^b f(x)\,dx$
4. **Integrals between Symmetric Limits:** If $f$ is an odd function, then $\int_{-a}^a f(x)\,dx = 0$. If $f$ is an even function, then $\int_{-a}^a f(x)\,dx = 2\int_0^a f(x)\,dx$.
5. **Integral of a Sum and of a Constant Times a Function:**
   $\int_a^b (f(x) + g(x))\,dx = \int_a^b f(x)\,dx + \int_a^b g(x)\,dx$
   $\int_a^b kf(x)\,dx = k\int_a^b f(x)\,dx$
6. **Upper Bounds for Integrals:** If $f(x) < g(x)$ for all $x$ in $[a, b]$, then $\int_a^b f(x)\,dx < \int_a^b g(x)\,dx$.

## Problem Set 5-9

***Do These Quickly***

The following problems are intended to refresh your skills. You should be able to do all ten problems in less than five minutes.

**Q1.** Evaluate: $\int x^5\,dx$

**Q2.** Evaluate: $\int (3x + 7)^5\,dx$

**Q3.** Evaluate: $\int x^{-4}\,dx$

**Q4.** Evaluate: $\int \sin^5 x \cos x\,dx$

**Q5.** Evaluate: $\int \cos 5x\,dx$

**Q6.** Evaluate: $\int (\cos^2 x + \sin^2 x)\,dx$

**Q7.** Evaluate: $\int \sec^2 x\,dx$

**Q8.** Find $y'$: $y = x^2 \sec x$.

**Q9.** $\int_a^b f(x)\,dx$ is a(n) —?— integral.

**Q10.** $\int f(x)\,dx$ is a(n) —?— integral.

For Problems 1–26, evaluate the integral exactly by using the fundamental theorem. You may check your answer by Riemann sum or by trapezoidal rule.

1. $\int_1^4 x^2\,dx$

2. $\int_2^5 x^3\,dx$

3. $\int_{-2}^3 (1 + 3x)^2\,dx$

4. $\int_{-1}^4 (5x - 2)^2\,dx$

5. $\int_1^8 60x^{2/3}\,dx$

6. $\int_1^4 24x^{3/2}\,dx$

7. $\int_2^8 5\,dx$

8. $\int_{20}^{50} dx$

9. $\int_{-2}^0 (x^2 + 3x + 7)\,dx$

10. $\int_{-3}^0 (x^2 + 4x + 10)\,dx$

11. $\int_{-1}^1 \sqrt{4x + 5}\,dx$

12. $\int_{-3}^3 \sqrt{2x + 10}\,dx$

13. $\int_0^\pi 4 \sin x\,dx$

14. $\int_{-\pi/2}^{\pi/2} 6 \cos x\,dx$

15. $\int_{\pi/6}^{\pi/3} (\sec^2 x + \cos x)\,dx$

16. $\int_0^{\pi/3} (\sec x \tan x + \sin x)\,dx$

17. $\int_{1.2}^{1.4} (5x + 1)^6\,dx$

18. $\int_{0.4}^{0.7} (4x - 1)^5\,dx$

19. $\int_1^2 \sin^3 x \cos x\,dx$

20. $\int_{-3}^3 (1 + \cos x)^4 \sin x\,dx$

21. $\int_{0.1}^{0.2} \cos 3x\,dx$

22. $\int_0^{0.4} \sin 2x\,dx$

23. $\int_{-5}^5 (x^7 - 6x^3 + 4 \sin x + 2)\,dx$ (Be clever!)

24. $\int_{-1}^1 (\cos x + 10x^3 - \tan x)\,dx$ (Be very clever!!)

25. $\int_{-1}^1 x^{-2}\,dx$ (Beware!)

26. $\int_{-2}^2 \sqrt{x}\,dx$ (Beware!)

For the functions in Problems 27–30, state whether or not the definite integral equals the area of the region bounded by the graph and the $x$-axis. A graph may help.

27. $\int_3^6 (x^2 - 10x + 16)\,dx$

28. $\int_5^7 \cos x\,dx$

29. $\int_0^7 \sin \frac{\pi}{6}x\,dx$

30. $f(x) = \int_1^8 \left(\frac{1}{x^2} - \frac{1}{4}\right) dx$

For Problems 31–36, suppose that

$$\int_a^b f(x)\,dx = 7, \quad \int_a^b g(x)\,dx = 12, \quad \text{and} \quad \int_b^c g(x)\,dx = 13.$$

Evaluate the given integral or state that it cannot be evaluated from the given information.

31. $\int_b^a f(x)\,dx$

32. $\int_a^b 4f(x)\,dx$

33. $\int_a^c g(x)\,dx$

34. $\int_a^c f(x)\,dx$

35. $\int_a^c (f(x) + g(x))\,dx$

36. $\int_a^b (f(x) + g(x))\,dx$

37. The property of the upper bound of an integral states: If $f(x) < g(x)$ for all $x$ in $[a, b]$, then $\int_a^b f(x)\,dx < \int_a^b g(x)\,dx$. Write the converse of this statement, then show by example that the converse is false.

38. *"Plus C" Problem:* When you write an indefinite integral, you always write "$+C$," but you don't do this with a definite integral. Evaluate the integral

$$\int_1^4 x^2\,dx$$

by using the indefinite integral $\int x^2\,dx = \frac{1}{3}x^3 + C$. Then explain what happens to $C$ and why one does not write $+C$ for a definite integral.

# 5-10 A Way to Apply Definite Integrals

You have learned that a definite integral has a physical meaning as the product of $x$ and $y$, and has a geometric meaning as the area of a region under a graph. In this section you will put these two ideas together to arrive at a systematic method for applying definite integrals.

**OBJECTIVE**

Given a problem in which a quantity $y$ varies with $x$, learn a systematic way to write a definite integral for the product of $y$ and $x$, and evaluate the integral by using the fundamental theorem.

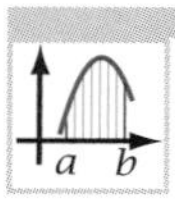

Suppose you are driving 60 ft/sec (about 40 mi/hr). You speed up to pass a truck. Assume that $t$ seconds after you start accelerating, your velocity is given by

$$v = 60 + 6t^{1/2}.$$

The "big" problem of finding the distance you have gone from $t = 0$ sec to $t = 10$ sec can be solved by dividing it into little problems. Divide the time interval $[0, 10]$ into subintervals, each of width $dt$ units. Figure 5-10a shows a representative subinterval and a narrow strip of width $dt$. Pick a sample point $(t, v)$ on the graph within the subinterval. If $dt$ is small, the velocity throughout the subinterval will be almost the same as it is at the sample point. Let $y$ be the number of feet your car has gone. The distance $dy$ it goes in the time interval $dt$ is approximately

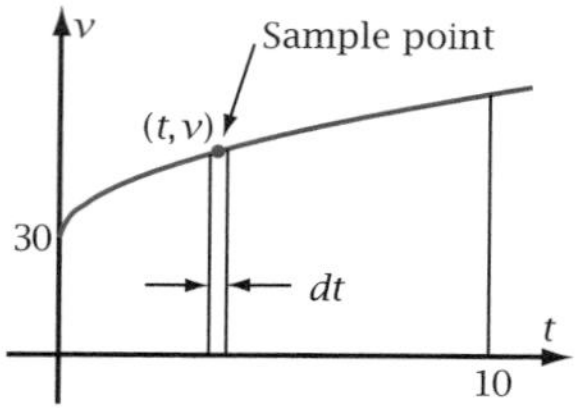

Figure 5-10a

$$dy = v\,dt$$
$$dy = (60 + 6t^{1/2})\,dt.$$

The total distance is approximately equal to the sum of the distances $dy$. Thus

$$y \approx \sum dy = \sum (60 + 6t^{1/2})\,dt.$$

This sum is a Riemann sum. Its limit as $dt$ approaches zero is a definite integral. So the distance traveled between $t = 0$ and $t = 10$ is

$$y = \int_0^{10} (60 + 6t^{1/2})\,dt$$

The definite integral is the exact distance.

$$= (60t + 4t^{3/2})\Big|_0^{10} = 600 + 4(10^{3/2}) - 0 - 0$$

$$= 726.49\ldots \approx 726 \text{ ft}.$$

The thought process in the problem above can be applied to any problem involving a definite integral. The process is summarized below.

### Technique: Application of a Definite Integral

To find the product of $P = y$ times $x$, where $y = f(x)$ and $x$ goes from $a$ to $b$, do the following.

a. Divide the interval $[a, b]$ into subintervals. Draw a strip of width $dx$, corresponding to one representative subinterval.

b. Pick a sample point $(x, y)$ on the graph in that subinterval.

c. Write $dp$ as a function of $x$ and $dx$, using the fact that $y$ is essentially constant throughout the subinterval.

d. Add up the $dP$'s and take the limit; that is, integrate.

## Problem Set 5-10

### *Do These Quickly*

The following problems are intended to refresh your skills. You should be able to do all ten problems in less than five minutes.

**Q1.** Evaluate: $\int 72x^{1.4}\,dx$

**Q2.** Evaluate: $\int_1^4 72x^{1.4}\,dx$

**Q3.** Find $y'$: $y = \cos^{-1} x$.

**Q4.** Find $f'(x)$: $f(x) = x^3 \sin x$.

**Q5.** Sketch $f'(x)$ for Figure 5-10b.

**Q6.** Is $g(x) = 2 + |x - 1|$ continuous at $x = 1$?

**Q7.** Is $f(x) = \sin x$ increasing or decreasing at $x = 7$?

**Q8.** What hypothesis of Rolle's theorem is not a hypothesis of the mean value theorem?

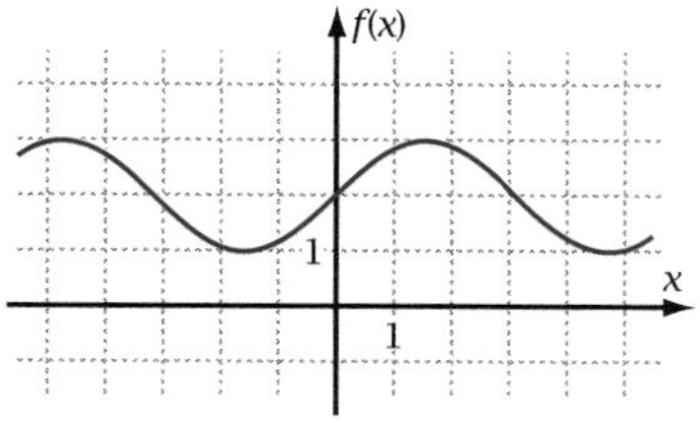

Figure 5-10b

**Q9.** How fast are you going at time $t = 9$ sec if your displacement is $d(t) = 100t^{1.5}$ ft?

**Q10.** In Problem Q9, what is your acceleration at time $t = 9$ sec?

1. *Displacement Problem:* Suppose you take a long trip. You are impatient to arrive at your destination, so you gradually let your velocity increase according to the equation

$$v = 55 + 12t^{0.6},$$

where $v$ is in miles per hour and $t$ is in hours (Figure 5-10c). Your displacement equals (velocity)(time), but velocity varies.

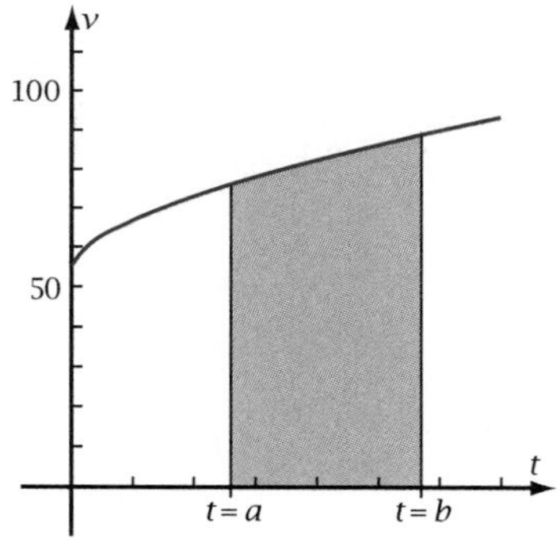

Figure 5-10c

a. On a copy of the graph, draw a narrow vertical strip of width $dt$. Show a sample point, $(t, v)$, on the graph within the strip.

b. The distance you go in time $dt$ is approximately equal to the value of $v$ at the sample point times $dt$. Write an equation for $dy$, the number of miles you go in $dt$ hours.

c. Write a Riemann sum for your approximate displacement, $y$, between $t = a$ and $t = b$.

d. Write an expression for the exact displacement you get by adding up all the $dy$'s and taking the limit as $dt$ approaches zero.

e. How far did you travel in the first hour ($t = 0$ to $t = 1$)? How far did you travel in the second hour? Show that the property of the sum of two integrals with the same integrand applies to your answers.

f. How fast were you going at the end of 2 hr?

g. Just for fun, see if you can figure out how long it would take to make the entire 300-mi trip, assuming you don't stop for food, fuel, speeding tickets, and so on.

2. *Area Problem:* In this problem you will find the area of a region whose length varies.

   a. Sketch the graph of the parabolic region under the graph of $y = 6x - x^2$ and between the two $x$-intercepts. Show a narrow vertical strip of the region of width $dx$. Show a sample point $(x, y)$ on the graph within the strip.

   b. The area of the strip, $dA$, is approximately equal to its length, $y$, at the sample point times its width, $dx$. Write an equation for $dA$ in terms of $x$ and $dx$.

   c. Write a Riemann sum for the total area of the region.

   d. Find the definite integral of $dA$ from 2b. Explain why this integral is the exact area.

   e. Show that the area of this parabolic region is two-thirds of the area of the circumscribed rectangle.

3. *Work Problem:* The amount of work needed to stretch a spring equals the force exerted on the spring times the displacement of the end of the spring where the force is being exerted. According to **Hooke's law**, this force is proportional to the displacement. Suppose that for a particular spring, the force is given by

$$F = 0.6x,$$

where $F$ is in pounds and $x$ is in inches. Figure 5-10d shows the graph of $F$ versus $x$.

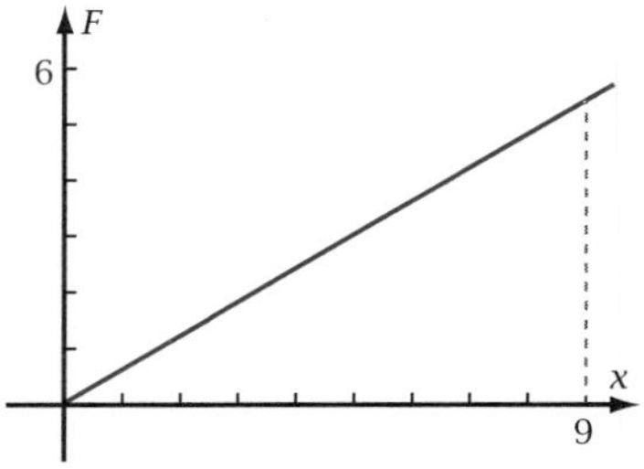


Figure 5-10d

   a. On a copy of the graph, draw a narrow vertical strip of width $dx$ in the region under the graph. Pick a sample point $(x, F)$ on the graph within the strip.

   b. The work, $dW$, done in stretching the spring by $dx$ is approximately equal to the force at the sample point times the displacement $dx$. Write $dW$ in terms of $x$ and $dx$.

   c. The definite integral can be interpreted as: "Add up the $dW$'s and take the limit as $dx$ goes to zero." Use a definite integral to find the exact number of inch-pounds of work done in stretching the spring from $x = 0$ to $x = 9$.

   d. Is the force at $x = 9$ twice that at $x = 4.5$? Is the work done in stretching the spring from 0 in. to 9 in. twice that done in stretching it from 0 in. to 4.5 in.?

4. *Degree-Days Problem:* A quantity used to measure the expense of air-conditioning a building is the degree-day. If the outside temperature is 20 degrees above that inside for two days, then there have been 40 degree-days. Usually the temperature difference varies. Suppose the temperature difference, $T$, is

$$T = 20 - 12\cos 2\pi(x - 0.1),$$

where $x$ is time in days (Figure 5-10e).

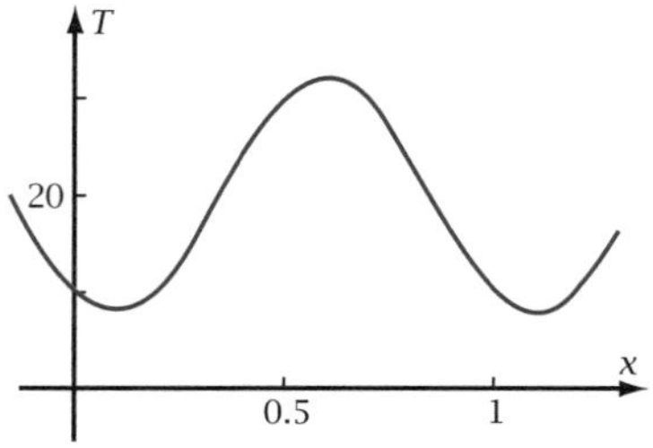


Figure 5-10e

   a. On a copy of the graph, sketch a narrow vertical strip of width $dx$ days. Show a sample point $(x, T)$ on the graph within the strip.

   b. The number of degree-days, $dD$, during the time interval $dx$ is approximately the value of $T$ at the sample point times the length of time, $dx$. Write $dD$ in terms of $x$ and $dx$.

c. To find the total number of degree-days, $D$, from $x = 0$ to $x = 0.5$, add up all of the $dD$'s and find the limit. That is, find the definite integral from $x = 0$ to $x = 0.5$.

d. The answer to 4c is the number of degree-days from midnight to noon. Find the number of degree-days from noon to the next midnight. What is the total number of degree-days from one midnight till the next?

5. *Heat Problem:* The amount of heat needed to warm a substance equals the heat capacity of the substance times the number of degrees the substance is warmed. From experimental data it is found that the heat capacity for 1 lb mol (a pound mole equals about 18 lb) of steam at normal atmospheric pressure is approximately

$$C = -0.016T^3 + 0.678T^2 + 7.45T + 796, \quad \text{for} \quad T \text{ in the interval } [0, 30],$$

where $T$ is in hundreds of degrees Fahrenheit and $C$ is in Btu per 100 degrees. (A Btu, or British thermal unit, is the amount of heat needed to warm one pound of water by one Fahrenheit degree.)

a. Plot the graph of $C$ and sketch the result. Show a narrow vertical strip of width $dT$ for the region under the graph. Show a sample point on the graph within the strip.

b. The heat, $dH$, needed to warm the steam by $dT$ degrees is approximately equal to the heat capacity at the sample point times $dT$. Write an equation for $dH$ in terms of $T$ and $dT$.

c. Write an integral equal to the amount of heat needed to warm one pound mole of steam from 1000 degrees to 3000 degrees. Evaluate the integral by using the fundamental theorem.

d. The amount of heat needed to warm 2000 mol of steam is $2000C$. How much heat would it take to warm this amount from 1000 degrees to 3000 degrees? What property of definite integrals lets you easily find this answer without doing any more calculus?

e. The actual heat capacity of steam rises at a slower and slower rate beyond 3000 degrees ($T = 30$). Does this mathematical model give reasonable answers beyond the given domain?

6. *Total Cost Problem:* A mining company wants to dig a silver mine horizontally into the side of a mountain. The price per meter for digging the mine increases as the mine shaft gets longer because it is more expensive to bring out the dirt and the rock and to shore up the tunnel. Suppose the price, $P$, in dollars per meter for digging at a point $x$ meters from the entrance is given by

$$P = 100 + 0.06x^2.$$

a. On a graph of $P$, draw a narrow strip of width $dx$. Show a sample point $(x, P)$ on the graph within the strip.

b. Write an equation for $dC$, the number of dollars it costs to dig $dx$ meters. Write an equation for $C$, the total cost of digging from $x = 0$ to $x = b$.

c. How much would it cost to dig from 0 m to 100 m? From 100 m to 200 m? From 0 m to 200 m? Show that the property of a sum of two integrals with the same integrand applies to the three answers.

7. *Golf Course Problem:* Adolph Ball Company is constructing a golf course in Scorpion Gulch. The plot for one of the putting greens is shown in Figure 5-10f. To estimate the area of the green, Mr. Ball draws parallel lines 10 (scale) ft apart and measures their lengths (feet). From the information given in the table, figure out about how many square feet of grass sod Mr. Ball must purchase to cover the green. Describe how you find the answer. Why can't the fundamental theorem of calculus be used to find this area?

| $x$ | width |
|---|---|
| 20 | 0 |
| 30 | 38 |
| 40 | 50 |
| 50 | 62 |
| 60 | 60 |
| 70 | 55 |
| 80 | 51 |
| 90 | 30 |
| 100 | 3 |

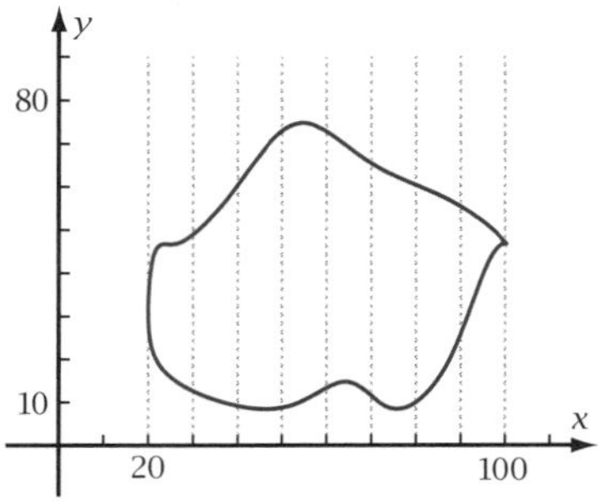

Figure 5-10f

# 5-11 Numerical Integration by Simpson's Rule and a Grapher

Before you learned the fundamental theorem of calculus, you found approximate values of definite integrals by using the trapezoidal rule or Riemann sums. In both methods the actual graph is replaced by segments of other function graphs, constant functions for Riemann sums and linear functions for the trapezoidal rule (Figure 5-11a). The areas of the rectangles or the trapezoids can be found by using only the $y$-values at various points in the domain and $\Delta x$.

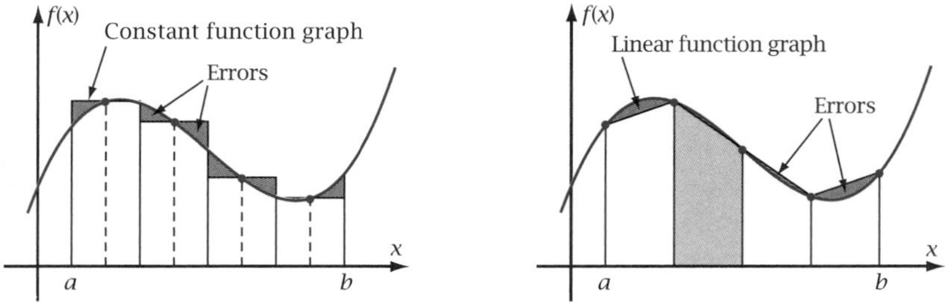

Riemann sum
Graph is approximated by zero-degree functions.

Trapezoidal rule
Graph is approximated by first-degree functions.

Figure 5-11a

In this section you will learn a similar numerical technique in which the graph of a function is approximated by *parabolas*. This technique is called **Simpson's rule**. Like the trapezoidal rule, it is useful if the function you want to integrate is specified only by a table of data. You will also learn how to use your grapher's built-in numerical integration feature for functions specified by equation.

***OBJECTIVE***

Use Simpson's rule or your grapher's built-in integrate feature to approximate a given definite integral.

### *Integrals by Simpson's Rule*

Figure 5-11b shows the function from Figure 5-11a, with parabolas approximating the graph. As you can see, there is less error than there would be either for Riemann sums or for the trapezoidal rule.

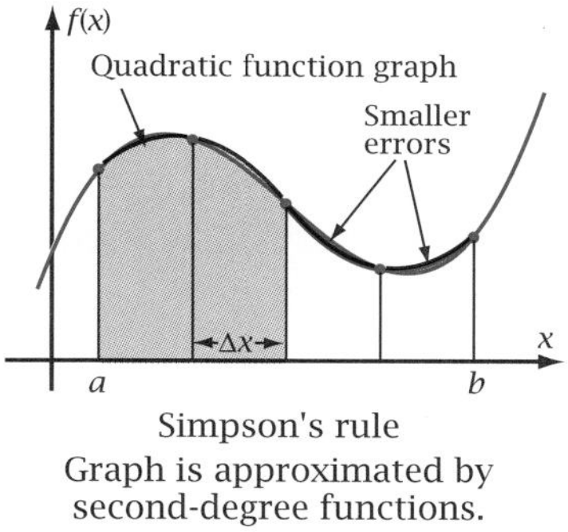


Figure 5-11b

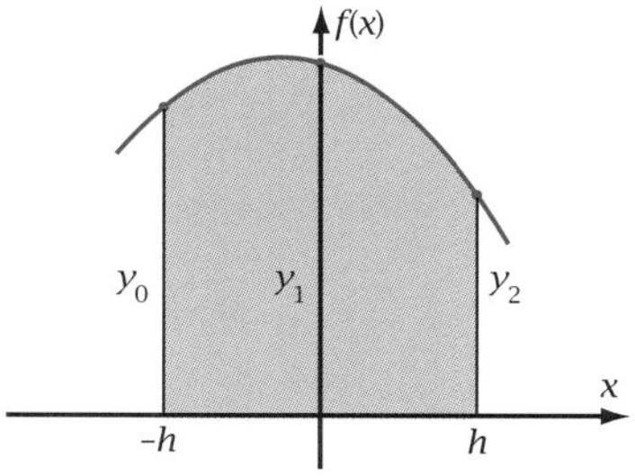


Figure 5-11c

It is possible to find the area of a parabolic region in terms of three $y$-values, one at the left, one at the middle, and one at the right of the region. Figure 5-11c shows the region under the parabola

$$y = ax^2 + bx + c,$$

from $x = -h$ to $x = h$. The area of the region is

$$A = \int_{-h}^{h} (ax^2 + bx + c)\, dx$$

$$= \tfrac{2}{3}ah^3 + 2ch$$

$$= \tfrac{1}{3}(h)(2ah^2 + 6c).$$

Factor (cleverly!). The area is in terms of $h$.

Set this result aside for a moment while you substitute $-h$, 0, and $h$ for $x$ in $y = ax^2 + bx + c$.

$$y_0 = ah^2 - bh + c$$

$$y_1 = \qquad\qquad + c$$

$$y_2 = ah^2 + bh + c$$

Adding the first and third equations gives

$$y_0 + y_2 = 2ah^2 + 2c,$$

which is interesting because the quantity $(2ah^2 + 6c)$ appears in the equation for $A$ by integration. Substituting $(y_0 + y_2)$ for the quantity $(2ah^2 + 2c)$ and substituting $4y_1$ for the remaining four $c$'s gives

$$A = \frac{1}{3}h(y_0 + y_2 + 4y_1)$$

$$A = \frac{1}{3}h(y_0 + 4y_1 + y_2). \qquad \text{Area in terms of three } y\text{-values.}$$

So the area of a parabolic region may be found by adding the first $y$-value, four times the middle value, and the last value, then by multiplying by one third of the spacing between $x$-values. Using this property, you can approximate by parabolas the area of a region under a graph, using only the $y$-values at regularly-spaced points. Suppose that integral $I$ is

$$I = \int_a^b f(x)\,dx.$$

Let $x_0, x_1, x_2, \ldots, x_n$ be values of $x$ spaced $\Delta x$ units apart, where $x_0 = a$ and $x_n = b$. Let $y_0, y_1, y_2, \ldots, y_n$ be the corresponding values of $f(x)$ (Figure 5-11d). Because it takes three points to determine a parabola, group the strips in pairs and draw parabolic arcs, as shown in the figure. Integral $I$ is equal to the area of the region under the graph, and this area is approximately equal to the sum of the areas of the parabolic regions.

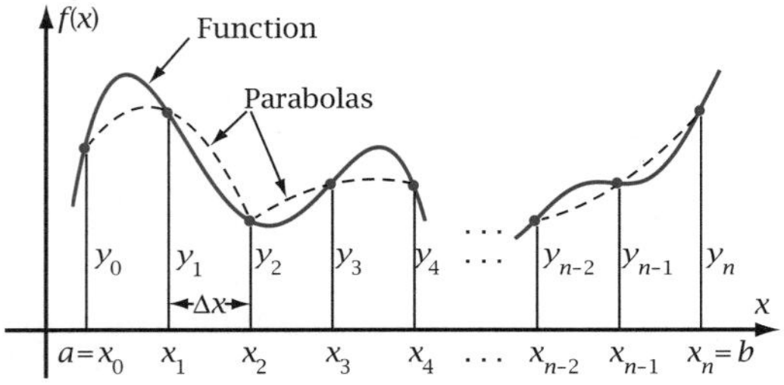


Figure 5-11d

By using the areas of the parabolic regions in terms of $y$, you can write

$$I \approx \frac{1}{3}h(y_0 + 4y_1 + y_2) + \frac{1}{3}h(y_2 + 4y_3 + y_4)$$

$$+ \frac{1}{3}h(y_4 + 4y_5 + y_6) + \cdots + \frac{1}{3}h(y_{n-2} + 4y_{n-1} + y_n).$$

Factoring out $(1/3)(h)$ from each term, combining like terms inside the parentheses, and replacing $h$ with $\Delta x$ gives the following formula, called Simpson's rule.

**Property: Simpson's Rule**

If the interval $[a, b]$ is divided into an even number, $n$, of subintervals of equal width $\Delta x$, then the integral of $f(x)$ from $x = a$ to $x = b$ is approximately equal to

$$\frac{1}{3}(\Delta x)(y_0 + 4y_1 + 2y_2 + 4y_3 + 2y_4 + \cdots + 2y_{n-2} + 4y_{n-1} + y_n).$$

Simpson's rule is applied by multiplying each $y$-value by the appropriate weighting factor, adding them up, then multiplying the result by one third of the spacing between $x$-values.

**■ Example 1** The given data express $y$ as a function of $x$. Use Simpson's rule with as many increments as possible to evaluate

$$\int_{30}^{70} y\,dx.$$

| $x$ | $y$ |
|---|---|
| 30 | 83 |
| 35 | 79 |
| 40 | 74 |
| 45 | 68 |
| 50 | 61 |
| 55 | 49 |
| 60 | 37 |
| 65 | 31 |
| 70 | 33 |

**Solution** Assume the function has a smooth graph that can be approximated by parabolic segments. For a small number of data points, such as those in this example, write down the weighting factor by each point. Then multiply the factor by the $y$-value and add the results. The following table shows a reasonable way to present your solution.

| $x$ | $y$ | factor | $y \times$ factor |
|---|---|---|---|
| 30 | 83 | 1 | 83 |
| 35 | 79 | 4 | 316 |
| 40 | 74 | 2 | 148 |
| 45 | 68 | 4 | 272 |
| 50 | 61 | 2 | 122 |
| 55 | 49 | 4 | 196 |
| 60 | 37 | 2 | 74 |
| 65 | 31 | 4 | 124 |
| 70 | 33 | 1 | 33 |
| | | Sum | 1368 |

Integral $\approx \frac{5}{3}(1368) = 2280.$ ■

You need only write out the $x$-values and the appropriate weighting factors. Accumulate the rest on your calculator. For larger numbers of data points, write a program that multiplies, accumulates, and does the final calculation.

**Example 2** The data shown express $y$ as a function of $x$. Use Simpson's rule with as many increments as possible to evaluate

$$\int_1^7 f(x)\,dx.$$

| $x$ | $y$ |
|---|---|
| 1 | 192 |
| 3 | 249 |
| 5 | 398 |
| 7 | 544 |

**Solution** The problem cannot be worked by Simpson's rule—there must be an even number of increments. Because there are four data points, there are only three increments between them. The integral can be approximated by the trapezoidal rule. ■

### *Integrals by a Grapher*

Your grapher has a built-in feature that will allow it to evaluate approximately an indefinite integral. Internally, the method used may resemble Simpson's rule. Example 3 shows two ways to evaluate an integral with a typical grapher. You may need to consult your instruction manual to find out how to evaluate on your grapher.

**Example 3** Evaluate: $\displaystyle\int_{0.3}^{4} \frac{\sin x}{x}\,dx$

**Solution** The numerical integration feature on a typical grapher might look like this.

fnInt((sin $x$)/$x$, $x$, 0.3, 4)

The integrand appears first, followed by a comma. The name of the variable of integration appears next; $x$, in this case. The third and fourth numbers are the lower and upper limits of integration, respectively. These four quantities are in the same order you would use in pronouncing "The integral of (sin $x$)/$x$, with respect to $x$, from 0.3 to 4."

Upon executing this command, the answer is 1.459699....

Some graphers have a numerical integrator that can be used directly from the graphing screen. The equation is stored on the $y$-menu. Then the graph is plotted, using a friendly window containing the two limits of integration. Upon accessing the integral command on a menu such as CALCULATE, the grapher allows you to trace to the lower limit, press ENTER, trace to the upper limit, and press ENTER.

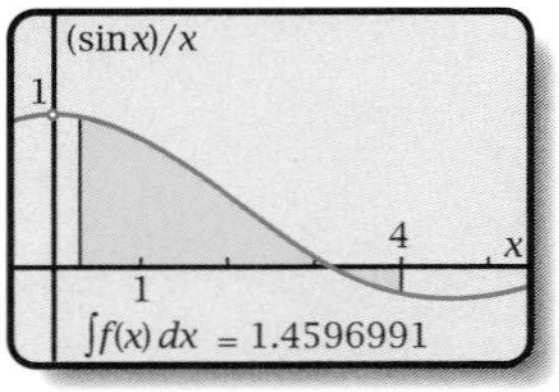

Figure 5-11e

The grapher will display the answer and may shade the region on the graph, as shown in Figure 5-11e. The answer, shown on the screen, is 1.4596991.... ■

Example 3 illustrates an instance in which the fundamental theorem cannot be used. There is no elementary transcendental function equal to the indefinite integral $\int(\sin x)/dx$. Later in your mathematical career, you will learn that this is an example of the **sine-integral function.** The next example shows you how to graph a function defined by a definite integral.

**Example 4** Let $f(x) = \int_1^x \frac{1}{t}\,dt$.

a. Explain why $1/t$ is not the derivative of a power function, and thus why you cannot yet use the fundamental theorem to evaluate the integral.

b. Use your grapher's numerical integration feature to plot the graph of $f$ from $x = 0.1$ to about $x = 10$.

c. Make a table of values of $f(x)$ for $x = 1, 2, 3, \ldots, 6$.

d. Why is $f(x)$ negative for values of $x$ less than 1?

e. See if you can find any relationship among $f(2)$, $f(3)$, and $f(6)$.

**Solutions**

a. $1/t$ equals $t^{-1}$. If this were the derivative of a power, the antiderivative's exponent would be zero. Its coefficient would thus be $1/0$, which is infinite. Because the antiderivative of $1/t$ is not known yet, the fundamental theorem cannot be used.

b. On the $y=$ menu, enter the equation. The instruction on a typical grapher would be

$$y_1 = \text{fnInt}(t^{-1}, t, 1, x).$$

The graph is shown in Figure 5-11f.

c. Use your grapher's table or trace feature to get the table shown.

d. The values of $f(x)$ are negative for $x < 1$ because the upper limit of integration is less than the lower limit. This makes all the values of $dt$ negative while the values of $t^{-1}$ are positive. Thus each $t^{-1}\,dt$ is negative.

e. You should discover from the table that

$$f(6) = f(2) + f(3).$$

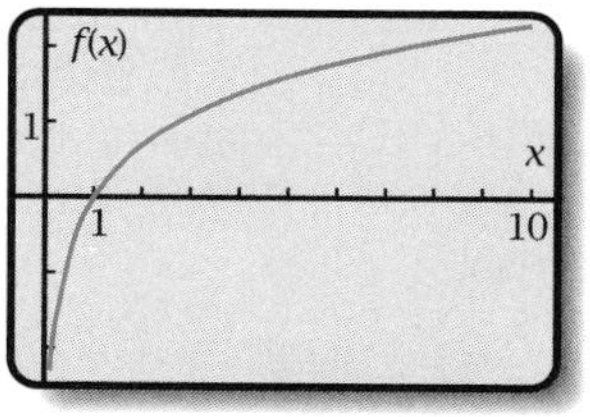


Figure 5-11f

| $x$ | $f(x)$ |
|---|---|
| 1 | 0 |
| 2 | 0.693147 ... |
| 3 | 1.098612 ... |
| 4 | 1.386294 ... |
| 5 | 1.609437 ... |
| 6 | 1.791759 ... |

# Problem Set 5-11

### *Do These Quickly*

The following problems are intended to refresh your skills. You should be able to do all ten problems in less than five minutes.

**Q1.** Evaluate: $\int (x^2 + 1)\,dx$

**Q2.** Evaluate: $\int_{-3}^{3} (x^2 + 1)\,dx$

**Q3.** Evaluate: $\int \sec^2 x\,dx$

**Q4.** Evaluate: $\dfrac{d}{dx}(\sec^2 x)$

**Q5.** Sketch a velocity versus time graph for a moving object.

**Q6.** Show a strip of width $dt$ on the graph you sketched in Q5.

**Q7.** Show a sample point $(t, v)$ on the graph within the strip in Q6.

**Q8.** Write the displacement of the object in Q5 for the time interval $dt$.

**Q9.** Write a Riemann sum for the approximate displacement of the object from $t = a$ to $t = b$.

**Q10.** Write an expression for the exact displacement of the object from $t = a$ to $t = b$.

1. *Velocity Problem:* People who sail ships at sea use dead reckoning to calculate the distance a ship has gone. (The term *dead reckoning* comes from "ded-reckoning," which is short for "deduced reckoning.") Suppose that a ship is maneuvering by changing speed rapidly. The table shows its speeds at 2-min intervals. (A knot—abbreviated kn—is a nautical mile per hour. A nautical mile is about 2000 yd.)

| time (min) | speed (kn) |
|---|---|
| 0 | 33 |
| 2 | 25 |
| 4 | 27 |
| 6 | 13 |
| 8 | 21 |
| 10 | 5 |
| 12 | 9 |

   a. Use Simpson's rule to find the distance traveled in the 12-min time interval.

   b. Find the distance again by using the trapezoidal rule.

   c. Which answer should be closer to the actual distance? Explain.

2. *Spleen Mass Problem:* Figure 5-11g is a CAT scan that shows a cross section of an eleven-year-old girl's body, looking up from below. The spleen is located at the right of the cross section (the girl's left). Doctors want to know whether or not the spleen has a mass that is within the normal range, 150 g to 200 g. Using the information contained in this and other CAT scans taken at 0.8-cm intervals up and down the girl's body, the doctors measure the spleen's cross-sectional areas.

| *D* (cm) | *A* (cm$^2$) | *D* (cm) | *A* (cm$^2$) |
|---|---|---|---|
| 0 | 6.8 | 4.8 | 38.4 |
| 0.8 | 6.8 | 5.6 | 33.9 |
| 1.6 | 20.1 | 6.4 | 15.8 |
| 2.4 | 25.3 | 7.2 | 6.1 |
| 3.2 | 29.5 | 8.0 | 2.3 |
| 4.0 | 34.6 | | |

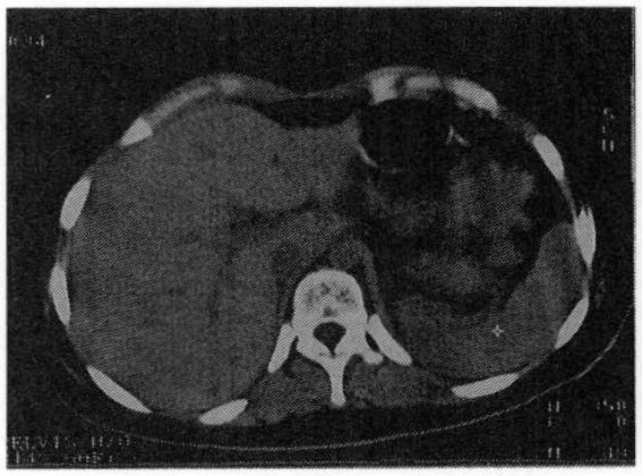

Figure 5-11g

a. The volume of an object equals its cross-sectional area times its thickness. If the cross section's area varies, the volume is the integral of the area with respect to the thickness. Use Simpson's rule to estimate the volume of the spleen.

b. The density of the spleen is about the same as that of water, namely, 1.0 g/cm$^3$. Is the girl's spleen within the normal mass range?

3. *Tensile Strength Test Problem:* The tensile strength of a metal bar is measured by the amount of force needed to stretch the bar until it breaks (Figure 5-11h). At first the force varies directly with the distance stretched. After a certain point, the bar begins to deform (to yield) and the force goes down. The amount of work done in breaking the bar is equal to the force times displacement (the distance stretched). Suppose the following data is measured.

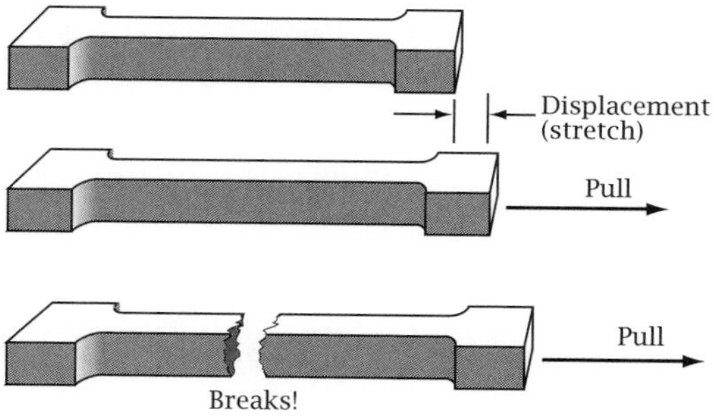

Figure 5-11h

| inches | pounds | inches | pounds |
|---|---|---|---|
| 0.00 | 0 | 0.30 | 290 |
| 0.05 | 120 | 0.35 | 280 |
| 0.10 | 240 | 0.40 | 270 |
| 0.15 | 360 | 0.45 | 270 |
| 0.20 | 370 | 0.50 | 190 (breaks) |
| 0.25 | 330 | | |

a. Draw a scatter plot of force versus displacement.

b. Work equals force times displacement. If the force varies, the work must be found by integration. Use Simpson's rule to find the inch-pounds of work done in breaking the bar.

4. *Heat Capacity Problem:* The amount of heat needed to warm a mole of gas by 1 degree is called the molal heat capacity of the gas. The amount of heat added to a mole of gas in warming it by a certain number of degrees is, then, equal to the heat capacity times the number of degrees. Most gases have heat capacities that change as they are heated. For example, steam at the normal boiling point of water has a heat capacity just over 8 (Btu/lb mol)/F°. (The abbreviation Btu stands for British thermal unit, which is the amount of heat needed to warm one pound of water by one Fahrenheit deg.) However, if the steam is at 5000°F, its heat capacity is over 13 (Btu/lb mol)/F°. Therefore calculus must be used to find the amount of heat added! Figure 5-11i (next page) shows graphs—from Hougen and Watson's *Chemical Process Principles Charts* (John Wiley, 1946)—of heat capacity versus temperature. Use the chart to find the heat capacity of steam ($H_2O$) for each 500 degrees from 500°F to 4500°F. Then use Simpson's rule to find the number of Btu needed to warm a pound mole of steam from 500°F to 4500°F.

5. *Sine-Integral Function Problem:* The sine-integral function, Si $x$, is defined by

$$\text{Si } x = \int_0^x \frac{\sin t}{t}\, dt.$$

a. Use your grapher's integrate feature to plot the graph of Si $x$ from about $x = -20$ to $x = 20$ and a $y$ window of $-2$ to 2. Sketch the result.

b. (Sin $x$)/($x$) takes on the indeterminate form 0/0 at $x = 0$. What limit does $(\sin x)/(x)$ seem to approach as $x$ approaches zero?

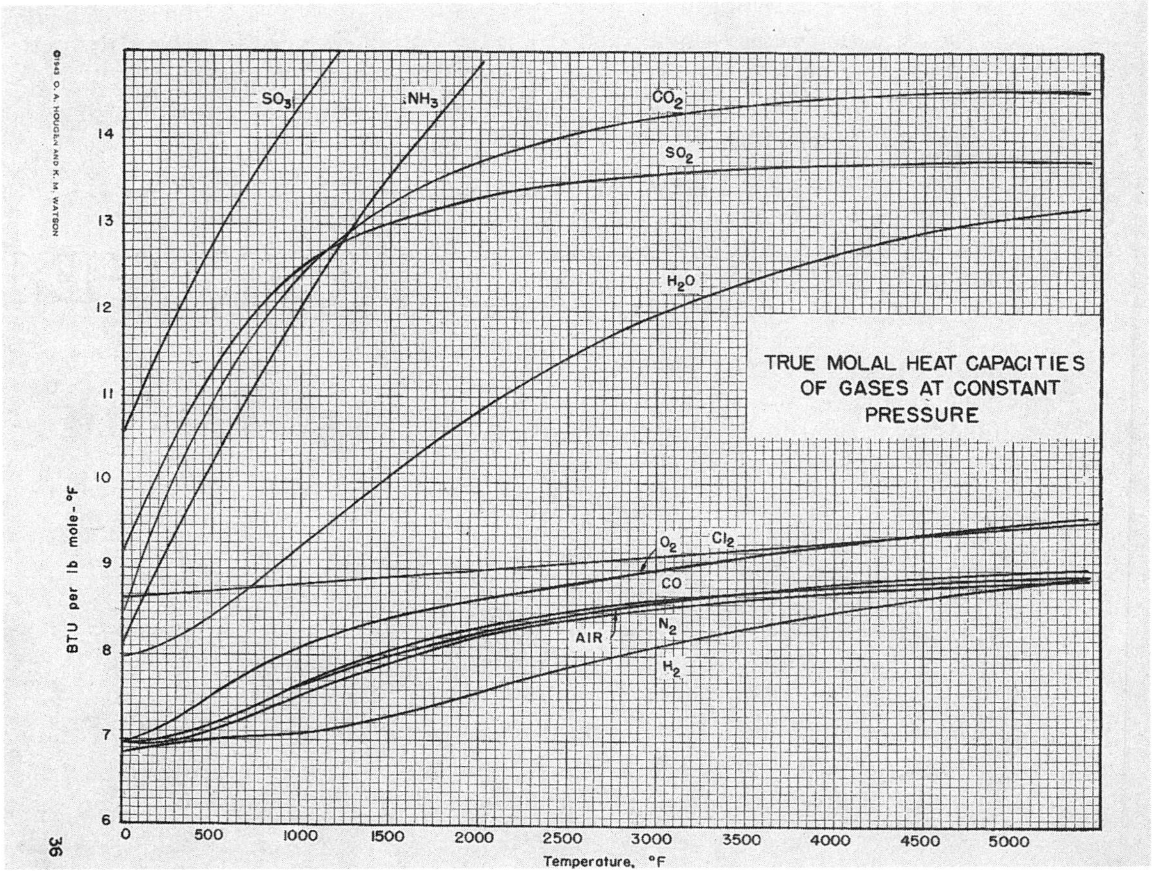


Figure 5-11i

c. The National Bureau of Standards *Handbook of Mathematical Functions* lists Si 0.6 as 0.5881288096. How close does your grapher's value come to this number?

d. Does Si $x$ seem to approach a limit as $x$ approaches infinity? If so, what number do you conjecture this limit is? If not, explain how you know why not.

e. Compare the graphs of Si $x$ and $f(x) = (\sin x)/(x)$. How do you know from the graphs that one is the derivative of the other?

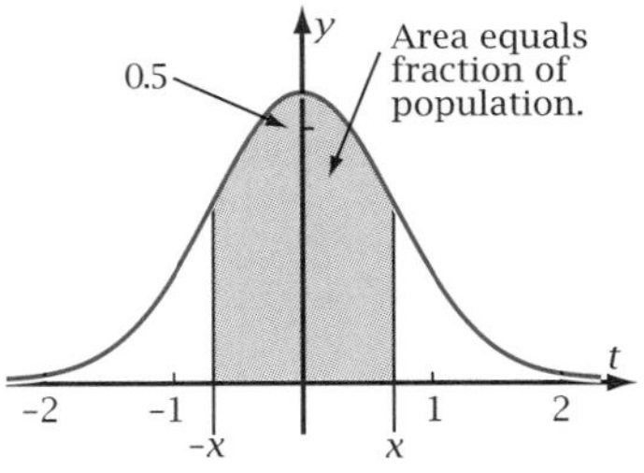


Figure 5-11j

6. *Error Function Problem:* If you measure statistics on a large population, such as test scores or peoples' heights, the numbers are often **normally distributed**. That is, most of the data points are close to the mean and fewer are farther away. In statistics courses, you will learn that for a normal (or **Gaussian**) distribution, the relative frequency with which a particular data point occurs is given by

$$y = \frac{1}{\sqrt{\pi}}e^{-t^2},$$

where $t$ is the number of **standard deviations** the data point is from the mean and $e$ is the base of natural logarithms (approximately 2.718, as you will learn in Chapter 6). The area under the graph from $t = -x$ to $t = x$ is equal to the fraction of the population within $x$ standard deviations of the mean. This area is called the **error function of $x$** (erf $x$).

$$\text{erf } x = \frac{2}{\sqrt{\pi}} \int_0^x e^{-t^2}\,dt$$

a. What property of definite integrals explains the fact that the coefficient in the integral is $2/\sqrt{\pi}$ but that the coefficient in the equation for $y$ is only $1/\sqrt{\pi}$?

b. Plot the graph of erf $x$ for $x = 0$ to $x = 2$. Use your grapher's built-in function $e^x$. Sketch the result.

c. If $x$ is enough standard deviations from the mean, virtually all the data should be within that number of standard deviations. How do the values of erf $x$ confirm this fact?

d. The National Bureau of Standards *Handbook of Mathematical Functions* lists erf 0.5 as 0.5204998778. How close does your grapher's value come to this number?

e. Compare the graphs of erf $x$ and $f(x) = 2/\sqrt{\pi}e^{-x^2}$. How do you know from the graphs that one is the derivative of the other?

For Problems 7–10, evaluate the integral approximately by using your grapher's built-in integrate feature.

7. $\int_{0.3}^{1.4} \cos x\,dx$

8. $\int_1^4 (x^2 - 3x + 5)\,dx$

9. $\int_0^3 2^x\,dx$

10. $\int_{0.1}^{1.4} \tan x\,dx$

11. *Answer Check Problem:* Evaluate the integral in Problem 7 exactly by using the fundamental theorem. Find a decimal approximation for your answer. How closely does your grapher's numerical answer match the exact answer?

12. *Simpson's Rule from Equation Problem:* Use Simpson's rule with $n = 4$ increments to estimate the integral given in Problem 9. You should be able to figure out how to do this without having seen an example! Estimate the integral again by using the trapezoidal rule. Assuming that your grapher's answer is the actual answer, does Simpson's rule really seem to give a more accurate approximation than the trapezoidal rule? Justify your answer.

13. *Program for Simpson's Rule from Data:* Write a program to evaluate integrals by using Simpson's rule. Data for the $y$-values may be entered into a table such as $L_1$ before the program is run. Input should include the number of increments, $n$, (one less than the number of data points) and the value of $\Delta x$. An easy way to calculate the terms is to start a counter $k$ at 2, then have the program evaluate $L_1(k - 1) + 4L_1(k) + L_1(k + 1)$. Then increment $k$ by 2 and repeat the calculation, each time adding the result to the sum of the previous calculations. When $k$ exceeds $n$, the program should leave the loop and evaluate the integral by multiplying by $\Delta x$ and dividing by 3. The output should be this value of the integral. Test your program by using the data given in Problem 1.

14. *Program for Simpson's Rule from Equation:* Write another program to evaluate integrals by using Simpson's rule. This time, the $y$-values should be calculated by equation rather than from a table of data. The equation can be stored in the $y$-menu, say at $y_1$. The input should be the upper and lower limits of integration and the number of increments, $n$. The program should then calculate $\Delta x$ as $(b - a)/n$. The computations can be done by

finding $y_1(x - \Delta x) + 4y_1(x) + y_1(x + \Delta x)$. Again, the output should be the approximate value of the integral. Test your program by using $n = 100$ increments to evaluate the integral given in Problem 5. The answer should be 0.6899295234.

15. *Relative Accuracy Problem:* In this problem you will investigate the relative accuracy of integrals found by Simpson's rule, the trapezoidal rule, and your grapher's built-in integrate feature.
    a. Evaluate $\int_0^{\pi} \sin x \, dx$ in four ways.
        i. By Simpson's rule, with $n = 50$ increments
        ii. By the trapezoidal rule, with $n = 50$ increments
        iii. By the built-in integrate feature
        iv. Exactly, using the fundamental theorem
    b. Which of the first three techniques in 15a give you an answer closest to the actual value in part iv of 15a? By what percentage does each answer differ from the actual answer?

# 5-12 Chapter Review and Test

In previous chapters, you learned about definite integrals and antiderivatives. In this chapter, you learned about the symbols and formal definitions for these concepts. The mean value theorem and Rolle's theorem led to the fundamental theorem of calculus, which allows you to find definite integrals exactly, by algebra, rather than just numerically or graphically. This connection between the antiderivative and the definite integral explains why the word *integral* is used also for the antiderivative. You learned a method for applying definite integrals by slicing a region under a graph, picking a sample point, forming a Riemann sum, then integrating. Finally you learned two more ways of evaluating definite integrals numerically: Simpson's rule and your grapher's built-in integrate feature.

The Review Problems below are numbered according to the sections of this chapter. The Concepts Problems allow you to apply your knowledge to new situations. The Chapter Test is more like a typical classroom test your instructor might give you.

## Review Problems

R0. Update your journal with what you've learned since the last entry. Include such things as those listed here.
- The one most important thing you have learned in your study of Chapter 5
- Which boxes you have been working on in the "define, understand, do, apply" table
- The difference between definite integral and indefinite integral
- The fundamental theorem of calculus, how it is proved, and what it is useful for
- Application of definite integrals to real-world problems involving a product of variables
- Simpson's rule and your grapher's numerical integration feature
- Any ideas about calculus you're still unclear about

R1. *Heat Capacity Problem:* The amount of heat it takes to heat a pound of a substance from one temperature to another equals the heat capacity of the substance (British thermal units per degree) times the number of degrees by which the substance is heated. Most substances have a heat capacity that depends on temperature. For instance, the heat capacity of steam at high temperatures is given approximately by

$$C(T) = -0.4 + 0.3 \log T,$$

where $C(T)$ is in Btu/deg, $T$ is temperature in Fahrenheit, and log is the common base-10 logarithm. A graph of this function is shown in Figure 5-12a.

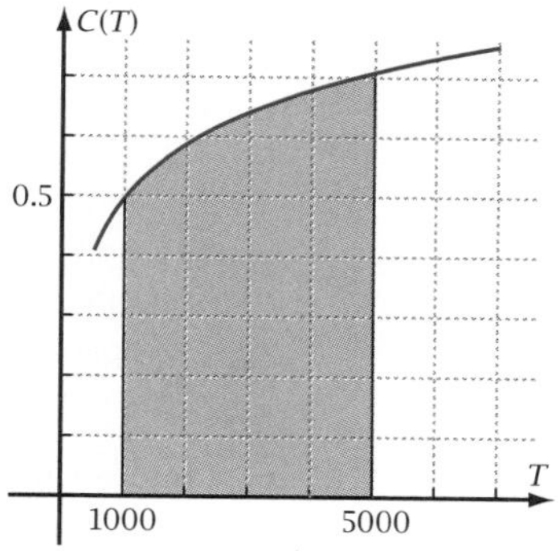


Figure 5-12a

a. Explain why the number of Btu needed to heat steam is equal to a definite integral.

b. Find the approximate number of Btu needed to heat a pound of steam from 1000°F to 5000°F. Show how you arrive at your answer.

c. Find the average heat capacity for the interval 1000 deg to 5000 deg. That is, find the number of Btu/deg you could multiply by (5000 − 1000) to get the number of Btu you found in R1b.

R2. Find the general equation for $f(x)$, the antiderivative function.

a. $f'(x) = 4x^{3/7}$ b. $f'(x) = 10\cos 2x$ c. $f'(x) = (12x + 5)^{-3}$

R3. a. For $f(x) = \sin \pi x$, find an equation of the linear function that best fits $f$ at $x = 1$. What is the error in approximating $f(x)$ by this linear function if $x = 1.1$? If $x = 1.001$?

b. Find $dy$.

i. $y = \csc^5 2x$ ii. $y = \dfrac{x^5}{5} - \dfrac{x^{-3}}{3}$ iii. $y = (7 - 3x)^4$

c. Find the general equation for the antiderivative, $y$.

i. $dy = \sec x \tan x\, dx$ ii. $dy = (3x + 7)^5\, dx$ iii. $dy = 5\, dx$

d. For $y = (2x + 5)^{1/2}$, do the following.

i. Find $dy$ in terms of $dx$.

ii. Find $dy$ if $x = 10$ and $dx = 0.3$.

iii. Find $\Delta y$ if $x = 10$ and $dx = 0.3$.

iv. Show that $dy$ is approximately equal to $\Delta y$.

R4. a. Write the definition of indefinite integral.

b. Evaluate the indefinite integral.

i. $\int 12x^{2/3}\, dx$ ii. $\int \sin^6 x \cos x\, dx$ iii. $\int (x^2 - 8x + 3)\, dx$

R5. a. Write the definition of integrability.

b. Write the definition of definite integral.

c. Use the following to evaluate approximately $\int_{0.2}^{1.4} \sec x\, dx$.

i. The upper Riemann sum with six increments

ii. The lower Riemann sum with six increments

iii. The midpoint Riemann sum with six increments

iv. The trapezoidal rule with six increments

d. Draw a diagram that shows the meaning of each of the sums in R5c.

e. Let $I = \int_0^5 x\,dx$.

i. Divide the interval [0, 5] into $n$ subintervals, each of equal width $5/n$. Write a formula for the upper sum of $I$ in terms of $n$.

ii. Transform the formula in R5e.i to eliminate the ellipsis (...). Recall from algebra that $(1 + 2 + 3 + \cdots + n) = (0.5n)(n + 1)$.

iii. Evaluate $I$ exactly by taking the limit of the formula given in R5e.ii as $n$ approaches infinity (and thus $\Delta x$ approaches zero).

iv. Use appropriate geometry to show that your answer to R5e.iii is correct.

R6. a. What is the difference between the hypotheses of a theorem and the conclusion?

b. A long pendulum swings slowly back and forth. Its displacement, $d(t)$ meters, from one wall of the museum in which it hangs is

$$d(t) = 20 + 3\sin\tfrac{\pi}{4}t,$$

where $t$ is time in seconds. What is its average velocity from $t = 0$ sec to $t = 2$ sec? At what time in the interval (0, 2) does the instantaneous velocity equal this average velocity?

c. Find an interval $[a, b]$ on which the hypotheses of Rolle's theorem are satisfied for the function $g(x) = x^{4/3} - 4x^{1/3}$. Then find the value of $x$ in $(a, b)$ at which the conclusion of the theorem is true. Show that $g$ is not differentiable at one of the two endpoints of $[a, b]$, and explain why this fact is consistent with the hypotheses of the theorem.

d. Sketch a graph that shows why the conclusion of the mean value theorem might not be true for $[a, b]$ if the function is not differentiable at some value of $x$ in $(a, b)$.

e. Sketch a graph that shows why the conclusion of the mean value theorem might be true in $(a, b)$ even though the function is discontinuous at one of the endpoints of $[a, b]$.

f. In the proof of the mean value theorem for $f(x)$ on $[a, b]$, two new functions were defined, $g$ and $h$. Tell how they were defined and how, as a consequence, you can use Rolle's theorem as a lemma to prove the mean value theorem.

g. Let $f(x) = 3 + 5\cos 8\pi x$. Plot the graph on your grapher. Quickly find all the points in the interval (0, 1) at which the conclusion of Rolle's theorem is true.

h. What can you conclude about the values of $r(x)$ and $s(x)$ if $r'(x) = s'(x)$ for all values of $x$ in an interval?

R7. Find a Riemann sum, $R_3$, for $\int_1^4 x^{1.5}\,dx$ by choosing the sample points in a special way: Let $g(x) = \int x^{1.5}\,dx$, the indefinite integral. Let $c_1$, $c_2$, and $c_3$ be the values of $x$ in the three subintervals, (1, 2), (2, 3), and (3, 4), at which the conclusion of the mean value theorem is true for the integral, function $g$. Use these numbers as sample points for $R_3$ for the given integral. If the sample points are picked in this way, what can you conclude about the answer you get for the Riemann sum?

R8. a. Evaluate $\int_{-1}^3 (10 - x^2)\,dx$ exactly by using the fundamental theorem of calculus.

b. Check your answer to R8a by using the trapezoidal rule with a reasonable number of increments. Show that the answer is close to the exact answer.

c. Find the midpoint Riemann sums $M_{10}$, $M_{100}$, and $M_{1000}$ for the integral in R8a. Show that the greater the number of terms in the Riemann sum, the closer the sum gets to the actual value of the integral.

R9. a. Evaluate the following integrals by using the fundamental theorem of calculus. Check your answers by using a Riemann sum or the trapezoidal rule.

i. $\int_1^5 x^{-2}\,dx$    ii. $\int_3^4 (x^2+3)^5(x\,dx)$    iii. $\int_0^{\pi} (\sin x - 5)\,dx$

b. Sketch a graph of R9a.iii to show why you get a negative answer.

c. Quick! Evaluate $\int_{-10}^{10} (4\sin x + 6x^7 - 8x^3 + 4)\,dx$.

d. Sketch a graph to illustrate the property $\int_a^b f(x)\,dx = \int_a^c f(x)\,dx + \int_c^b f(x)\,dx$.

R10. *Displacement Problem:* Suppose that as a rocket rises from its launching pad, its upward velocity, $v$ feet per second, is given as a function of time, $t$ seconds, by

$$v = 150t^{0.5}.$$

a. Sketch the graph of $v$ versus $t$. Show a narrow strip of width $dt$ for the region under the graph. Show a sample point $(t, v)$ on the graph within the strip.

b. The displacement, $dy$, of the rocket in this time interval is approximately equal to the velocity at the sample point times the time, $dt$. Write $dy$ in terms of $t$ and $dt$.

c. Write a Riemann sum for the vertical displacement of the rocket in the time interval [0, 9].

d. Find the limit of the Riemann sum given in R10c as $dt$ approaches zero. What mathematical quantity is this?

e. Show that the displacement of the rocket for the time interval [0, 9] is the sum of the displacements for the intervals [0, 4] and [4, 9].

R11. a. Sketch a graph to illustrate the idea behind Simpson's rule and why you need to use an even number of increments.

b. Sketch a graph to show why Simpson's rule is expected to give a more accurate value of an integral than the trapezoidal rule.

c. The table below shows the velocity, $v(t)$ meters per minute, of a moving object. Write an integral to represent the displacement of the object from its position at time $t = 3$ min. Use Simpson's rule appropriately to calculate the distance the object travels between $t = 3$ min and $t = 5$ min.

| $t$ | $v(t)$ | $t$ | $v(t)$ |
|---|---|---|---|
| 3.0 | 29 | 4.2 | 28 |
| 3.2 | 41 | 4.4 | 20 |
| 3.4 | 50 | 4.6 | 11 |
| 3.6 | 51 | 4.8 | 25 |
| 3.8 | 44 | 5.0 | 39 |
| 4.0 | 33 | | |

d. You can't yet evaluate $\int_1^{10} \log x\,dx$ using the fundamental theorem because you haven't learned an algebraic way to find the indefinite integral. Use your grapher's built-in integrate feature to find the value of this integral. Sketch the graph of the integrand and use the graph to explain why your answer is reasonable.

## Concepts Problems

C1. In this problem you will investigate $\int_0^b \frac{1}{x^2+1}\,dx$ for various values of $b$.

a. Evaluate the integral approximately, using midpoint Riemann sums with 100 terms for $b = 1$, $b = 2$, $b = 3$, $b = 4$, and $b = 5$.

b. Evaluate the integral given in C1a for $b = 100$ by using the midpoint Riemann sum with $n = 1000$ terms.

c. Plot the graph of the value of the integral as a function of $b$. Use the same scale on both axes. What value does the integral seem to be approaching as $b$ gets very large?

d. On another piece of graph paper, plot $y = \tan x$. Use the same scales on this graph as you used in C1c.

e. Turn over the graph paper you used for C1d and look at the graph by holding the paper up to a light. Rotate the paper if necessary. What do you notice?

C2. *Mean Value Theorem for Quadratic Functions:* Let $f$ be the general quadratic function, $f(x) = ax^2 + bx + c$. Given any interval $[d, e]$, show that the point $x = k$ in $(d, e)$ at which the conclusion of the mean value theorem is true is the midpoint of that interval.

C3. *Sum of the Squares Problem:* In Problem 12 of Problem Set 5-5, you found that the exact value of $\int_0^3 x^2\,dx$ can be found by using the sum of the squares of the whole numbers. You also learned that the indefinite integral $\int x^2\,dx$ is a cubic function of $x$. In this problem you will see that the sum of the squares of the whole numbers is also a cubic function. Let $S(n)$ be the sum of the squares of the integers from zero through $n$. That is,

$$S(n) = 0^2 + 1^2 + 2^2 + 3^2 + \cdots + n^2.$$

a. Find $S(0)$, $S(1)$, $S(2)$, and $S(3)$.

b. Assume that $S(n)$ is a cubic function of $n$. That is,

$$S(n) = an^3 + bn^2 + cn + d,$$

where $a$, $b$, $c$, and $d$ are constants. Find the particular equation for $S(n)$ by finding these constants.

c. The constants in the equation turn out to be fractions. Factor out the appropriate fraction, leaving a polynomial with integer coefficients inside the parentheses. Then factor the polynomial. You can check a table of mathematical functions, such as CRC Tables, to see if you are correct.

d. Use the equation you found in C3c to predict $S(4)$ and $S(5)$. Show that your answers are correct by actually adding the squares of the integers.

e. Predict the value of $S(1000)$.

f. Use mathematical induction to prove that the equation given in C3c works for any positive integer $n$.

C4. *Sum of the Cubes Problem:* Let $S(n) = 0^3 + 1^3 + 2^3 + 3^3 + \cdots + n^3$ be the sum of the cubes of the integers from zero through $n$. Find $S(0)$, $S(1)$, $S(2)$, $S(3)$, and $S(4)$. You should find that all these numbers are perfect squares! Then derive a closed formula (no ellipsis) for $S(n)$ in terms of $n$, as you did in Problem C3. You may assume that the formula is quartic: $S(n) = an^4 + bn^3 + cn^2 + dn + e$. Find values of the constants $a$, $b$, $c$, $d$, and $e$, then use mathematical induction to prove that your formula is right.

C5. *Radio Wave Integral Problem:* AM radio signals are transmitted by sending a high-frequency wave whose amplitude varies in the pattern of the sound being carried. (The amplitude is modulated, hence the abbreviation AM.) Figure 5-12b shows

$$f(x) = 4 \sin x \sin 10x,$$

where $f(x)$ is the strength of the signal at any instant, $x$, in time. The sound represented by $y = 4 \sin x$, with a frequency of 1 cycle per $2\pi$ $x$-units, is being "carried" by the signal $y = \sin 10x$, with a frequency of 10 cycles per $2\pi$ $x$-units.

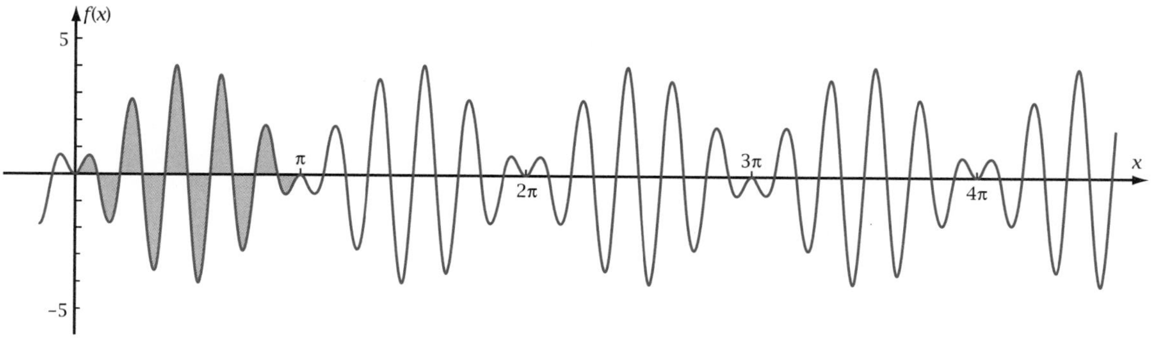


Figure 5-12b

a. Evaluate approximately the integral

$$\int_0^{\pi} 4 \sin x \sin 10x \, dx.$$

Show that the integral is very close to zero.

b. You do not yet know how to use the fundamental theorem to evaluate the integral because it is the integral of a product. However, the integrand can be changed to a sum by using the trigonometric property

$$2 \sin A \sin B = -\cos (A + B) + \cos (A - B).$$

Make the transformation, then show that the integral is exactly equal to zero by using the fundamental theorem to evaluate it.

c. The integral given in C5a is represented by the shaded region in Figure 5-12b. What is the geometrical interpretation of the fact that this integral equals zero?

d. Show that the integral

$$\int_0^{\pi} 4 \sin x \sin nx \, dx$$

is equal to zero for any integer $n > 1$.

e. Record in your journal the fact that this kind of integral is related to **Fourier series,** which you will study later in your mathematical career.

C6. *Riemann Sums with Unequal Increments:* Figure 5-12c shows the graph of $f(x) = 1.2^x$. The interval [1, 9] is partitioned into subintervals of unequal width. The largest value of $\Delta x$ is called the **norm of the partition**, written $\|P\|$. An upper and lower sum, $U_n$ and $L_n$, are shown.

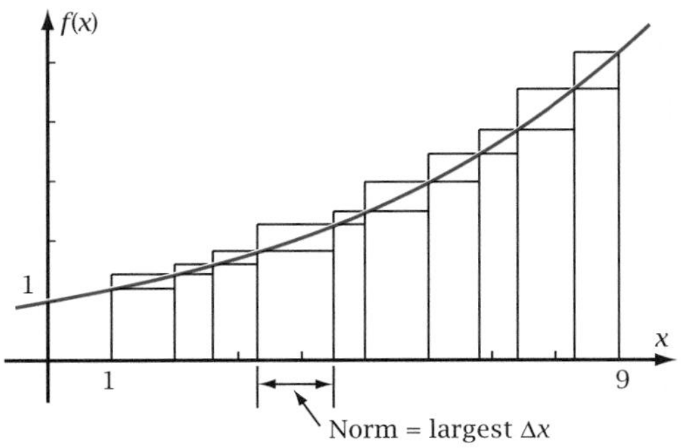

Figure 5-12c

a. Why is the difference $U_n - L_n$ no greater than $\|P\|(1.2^9 - 1.2^1)$?

b. Suppose that the number of subintervals is allowed to approach infinity in such a way that the limit of $\|P\|$ is zero. Use the observation you made in C6a to conclude that $f$ is integrable on [1, 9].

c. Prove that $g(x) = 1/x$ is integrable on [1, 4].

d. Could the reasoning of this problem be used to prove that $h(x) = \sin x$ is integrable on the interval [0, 3]? State why or why not.

## Chapter Test

T1. Write the definition of indefinite integral.

T2. Write the definition of definite integral.

T3. State the fundamental theorem of calculus.

T4. Given $\int_0^2 3^x\,dx$, do the following.

a. Find the upper and lower sums $U_4$ and $L_4$ for this integral and find their average. How does this average compare with the integral by trapezoidal rule with $n = 4$? Does this average overestimate or underestimate the actual value of the integral? Explain.

b. Find the midpoint Riemann sum $M_4$ for this integral. Explain why this Riemann sum underestimates the actual value of the integral.

c. Evaluate the integral approximately by using Simpson's rule with $n = 4$ increments.

d. Evaluate the integral by using your grapher's numerical integration feature.

Evaluate the indefinite integrals.

T5. $\int (3x - 11)^{17}\,dx$

T6. $\int (\cos 2x)^4 \sin 2x\,dx$

For Problems T7–T10, evaluate the integral exactly by using the fundamental theorem. You may check your answers by using a numerical method if you have time.

T7. $\int_{\pi/6}^{\pi/4} \cos 2x\,dx$

T8. $\int_{-1}^{1} \sec^2 x\,dx$

T9. $\int_{2}^{-2} (12x^3 + 10x^2)\,dx$

T10. $\int_{1}^{8} 7x^{-2/3}\,dx$

T11. Sketch a graph that clearly shows that you know the hypotheses and the conclusion of Rolle's theorem.

T12. Let $f(x) = 0.3x^2$ and let $g(x) = \int f(x)\,dx$.

a. Integrate to find an equation for $g(x)$. Set the constant of integration, $C$, equal to zero.

b. On graph paper, plot graphs of $f$ and $g$ in the domain [0, 4]. Plot them on different sets of axes, but use the same scales for both graphs.

c. Draw the secant line on the $g$ graph from $(1, g(1))$ to $(4, g(4))$. Find its slope. Then find the point $x = c$ in (1, 4) at which the conclusion of the mean value theorem is true for function $g$. Draw a line through the point $(c, g(c))$ parallel to the secant line and thus show that it is tangent to the graph of $g$ at that point.

d. Using the value of $c$ you calculated in T12c, find the point $(c, f(c))$ on the graph of $f$. Draw a rectangle whose base is the segment from $x = 1$ to $x = 4$ and whose altitude is $f(c)$. How does the graph show that the area of this rectangle is equal to the value of the definite integral of $f(x)\,dx$ from $x = 1$ to $x = 4$?

CHAPTER

# 6 The Calculus of Exponential and Logarithmic Functions

Rabbits introduced into Australia in the middle 1800s had no natural enemies. Their population grew unchecked. Such unrestricted population growth can be modeled by exponential functions, in which the exponent is a variable. Exponential functions and their inverses, the logarithmic functions, do not behave the same way as the power functions you have analyzed in calculus so far.

# Mathematical Overview

Exponential functions, where the variable is an exponent, model population growth. In Chapter 6 you will learn the calculus of these functions by exploring the integral of the reciprocal function, which turns out to be a logarithmic function. You will learn the calculus of these functions in four ways.

***Graphically*** The logo at the top of each even-numbered page of this chapter shows the natural logarithm function and its inverse, the base $e$ exponential function.

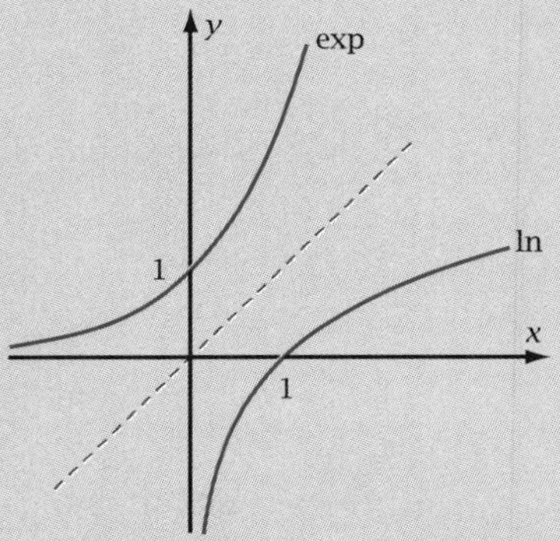


***Numerically***

| $x$ | $\exp x$ | $\ln x$ |
|---|---|---|
| 1 | 2.718 ... | 0 |
| 2 | 7.389 ... | 0.693 ... |
| 3 | 20.085 ... | 1.098 ... |
| ... | ... | ... |

***Algebraically*** $\ln x = \int_1^x \frac{1}{t}\,dt$, the definition of natural logarithm.

***Verbally*** *I didn't realize that it was possible to define a function to be the definite integral of another function. The advantage of doing this is that you know immediately the derivative of that new function. I was surprised to find out that the integral of 1/t from t = 1 to t = x turns out to be a logarithm function. I shall have to remember that derivatives and integrals of exponential functions are not the same as for powers.*

# 6-1 Integral of the Reciprocal Function: A Population Growth Problem

You have learned how to differentiate power functions with constant exponents, such as

$$f(x) = x^5.$$

You have also shown by example that functions with variable exponents, such as

$$f(x) = 5^x$$

cannot be differentiated by using the same rule as used for power functions. A frontal assault on finding the derivatives of such exponential functions is rather difficult. The method of choice, then, is to approach the exponential function through its inverse, the logarithmic function. In this section you will develop some background needed for this approach.

**OBJECTIVE**

Work the problems in this section, on your own or with your study group, as an assignment after your last test on Chapter 5.

## Exploratory Problem Set 6-1

*Population Problem:* A population (such as people, wildlife, or bacteria) tends to grow at a rate proportional to the number of individuals present. For example, the more people there are in a community, the more babies are born per year. Assume that a small town has a population of $P = 1000$ people now (time $t = 0$ yr) and that the population is growing at an instantaneous rate of 5% per year. In the following questions you will predict the population after various numbers of years.

1. Explain why the **differential equation** $dP/dt = 0.05P$ expresses the information above.
2. What are the units of $dP/dt$?
3. The differential equation in Problem 1 can be transformed by **separating the variables.**

   $$\frac{1}{P}\,dP = 0.05\,dt$$

   If $N$ is the value of $P$ when $t = 10$ yr, then integrating both sides gives

   $$\int_{1000}^{N} \frac{1}{P}\,dP = \int_{0}^{10} 0.05\,dt$$

   Evaluate the right-hand integral. Explain why the indefinite integral $\int (1/P)\,dP$, which equals $\int P^{-1}\,dP$, cannot be evaluated by using the normal method for power functions.

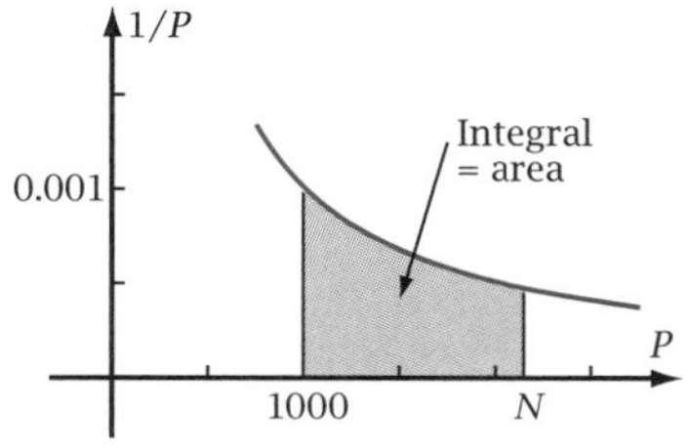

Figure 6-1a

4. Figure 6-1a shows the integrand $1/P$. The integral on the left in Problem 3 equals the area of the region under this graph. Evaluate this integral numerically for $N = 1500$ and $N = 2000$.
5. Find, numerically, the value of $N$ that makes the two integrals in Problem 3 equal to each other. Write a paragraph that describes how you accomplished this computation.
6. Predict the population of the town when $t = 20$ yr.
7. Is the $P$-versus-$t$ graph linear or nonlinear? Justify your answer.

# 6-2 Antiderivative of the Reciprocal Function

In Section 6-1, you saw that the integral of the reciprocal function can appear in problems of population growth. Although $\int (1/x)\,dx$ can be written as the integral of a power, $\int x^{-1}\,dx$, you cannot use the pattern "Increase the exponent by 1, divide by the new exponent, and add $C$." This pattern would result in division by zero.

$$\int x^{-1}\,dx = \frac{1}{0}x^0 + C$$

In Section 5-11, you were introduced to the sine-integral function and the error function, which were defined by definite integrals. In this section you will investigate another such function,

$$g(x) = \int_1^x \frac{1}{t}\,dt$$

and you will see how this problem leads to the antiderivative of $1/x$.

**OBJECTIVE**

Investigate the function $g(x) = \int_1^x (1/t)\,dt$ and reach some conclusions about its values, graph, and derivative.

You may work in groups, with guidance from your instructor as necessary.

## Problem Set 6-2

1. Let $g(x) = \int_1^x (1/t)\,dt$. Figure 6-2a shows that $g(x)$ is the area of a region under the graph of $y = 1/t$. Explain why this area is a function of $x$.

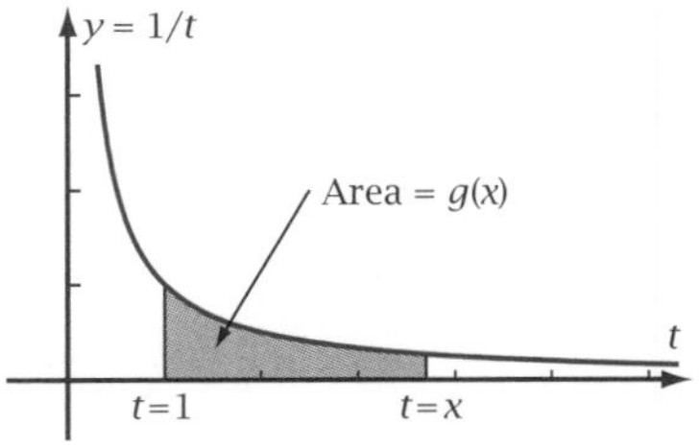


Figure 6-2a

2. Use a suitable numerical method to make a table of values of $g(x)$ for $x = 8, 7, 6, 5, 4, 3, 2, 1$, and $0.5$. Keep six decimal places.
3. Explain why $g(x)$ is negative if $x$ is less than 1. A graph may help.
4. Figure 6-2b shows the graph of function $g$. Use your grapher's numerical integration feature to plot this graph. To avoid division-by-zero errors, set the minimum value of $x$ at 0.1 rather than at 0. Use your grapher's trace feature to confirm that the value for $g(5)$ you found in Problem 2 is correct.
5. Show that the following are true for the values you calculated in Problem 2.
   a. $g(6) = g(3) + g(2)$
   b. $g(4) = g(8) - g(2)$
   c. $g(8) = 3 \cdot g(2)$
   d. $g(\frac{1}{2}) = -g(2)$

6. Recall the properties of logarithms.

$$\log_b 1 = 0$$
$$\log_b (xy) = \log_b x + \log_b y$$
$$\log_b (\tfrac{x}{y}) = \log_b x - \log_b y$$
$$\log_b (x^y) = y \cdot \log_b x$$
$$\log_b (\tfrac{1}{x}) = -\log_b x$$

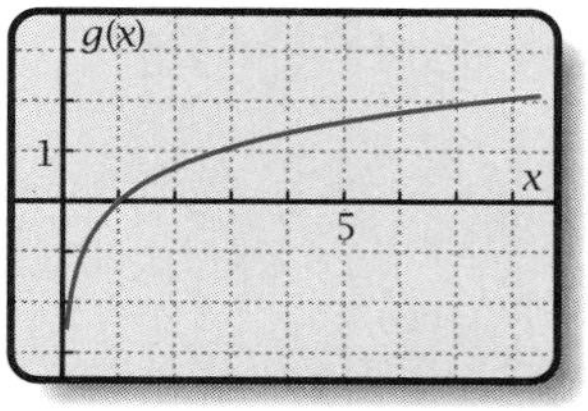

Figure 6-2b

Show that the values given in Problems 2 and 5 are examples of these properties.

7. Plot on the same screen you used in Problem 4 the graph of $y = \log x$ (that is, the base-10 log). Sketch the two graphs. Describe the similarities and the differences between them.

8. Plot on the same screen you used in Problem 4 the graph of the natural logarithm function. This function will appear on your grapher as ln $x$. The *l* stands for *logarithm,* and the *n* stands for *natural.* Describe the results. Surprising?!

9. Conjecture: $g(x) = \ln x$. Test this conjecture by finding $g'(3)$ numerically. How does your result confirm the conjecture?

10. By the definition of indefinite integral, $g(x) = \int f(x)\,dx$ if and only if $g'(x) = f(x)$. Which part of the definition, "if" or "only if," explains why

$$\int \frac{1}{x}\,dx = \ln x + C?$$

11. If $g(x)$, as defined in Problem 1, is really a logarithm function, then it has a base, $b$, such that $g(b) = 1$. Solve numerically to find $b$. Where have you seen this number before?

12. In the population problem of Problem Set 6-1, you evaluated

$$\int_{1000}^{N} \frac{1}{P}\,dP.$$

Use the result of Problem 10 in this problem set to evaluate the integral by using the fundamental theorem of calculus. Show that the answers you find for $N = 1500$ and $N = 2000$ agree with the answers you found in Problem 4 of Problem Set 6-1.

# 6-3 Natural Logarithms, and Another Form of the Fundamental Theorem

The function $g$ from Problem Set 6-2 is called the natural logarithm function. As you have shown, this function has the properties of logarithms. It arose "naturally" out of a population problem. The abbreviation for this function is ln, pronounced "el en." The letter *l* stands for the word *logarithm,* and the letter *n* stands for the word *natural.*

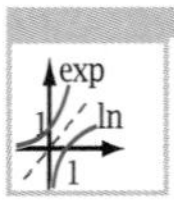


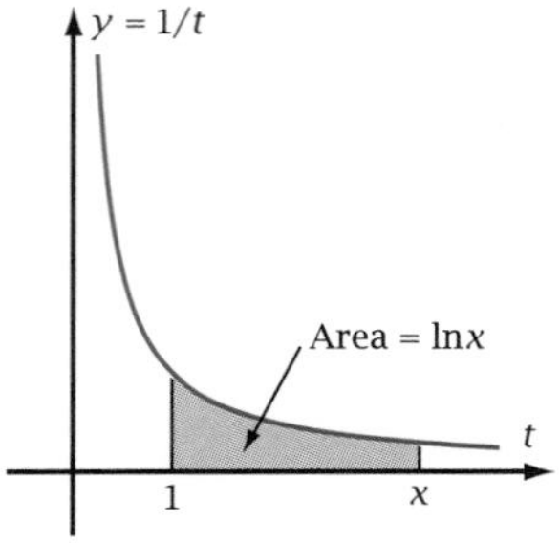


Figure 6-3a

**Definition: The Natural Logarithm Function**

$$\ln x = \int_1^x \frac{1}{t}\,dt,$$

where $x$ is a positive number.

The geometric meaning of the natural logarithm is illustrated in Figure 6-3a. The natural logarithm of $x$ equals the area of the region under the graph of $y = 1/t$ from $t = 1$ to $t = x$. In this section you will learn to do calculus with the ln function. Specifically, you will show that the derivative of $\ln x$ is $1/x$. Along the way you will learn another form of the fundamental theorem of calculus. This new form will enable you to find the derivative of a function defined as a definite integral.

**OBJECTIVE**

Given a function involving ln, find its derivative function; and given an integral of the form $\int (1/u)\,du$, do the integration.

### Background: Functions Defined as Definite Integrals

Suppose a definite integral has a variable for its upper limit of integration, for instance

$$\int_1^x \sin t\,dt.$$

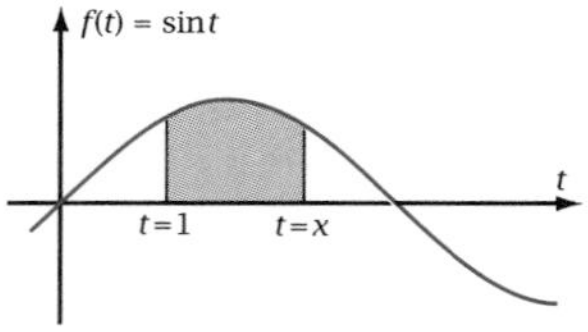


Figure 6-3b

Evaluating the integral gives

$$-\cos t\Big|_1^x = -\cos x + \cos 1$$
$$= -\cos x + 0.5403\ldots.$$

The answer is an expression involving the upper limit of integration, $x$. Thus the integral is a function of $x$. Figure 6-3b shows what is happening. The integral equals the area of the region under the graph of $y = \sin t$ from $t = 1$ to $t = x$. Clearly (as mathematicians like to say!) the area is a function of the value you pick for $x$. Let $g(x)$ stand for this function.

The interesting thing is what results when you find the derivative of $g$.

$$g(x) = \int_1^x \sin t\,dt = -\cos x + 0.5403\ldots$$
$$\therefore\ g'(x) = \sin x$$

The answer is the integrand, evaluated at the upper limit of integration, $x$. Here's why this result happens. Because $g(x)$ equals the area of the region, $g'(x)$ is the rate of change of this area. Its value, $\sin x$, is equal to the altitude of the region at the boundary where the change is taking place. Figure 6-3c shows this situation for three values of $x$.

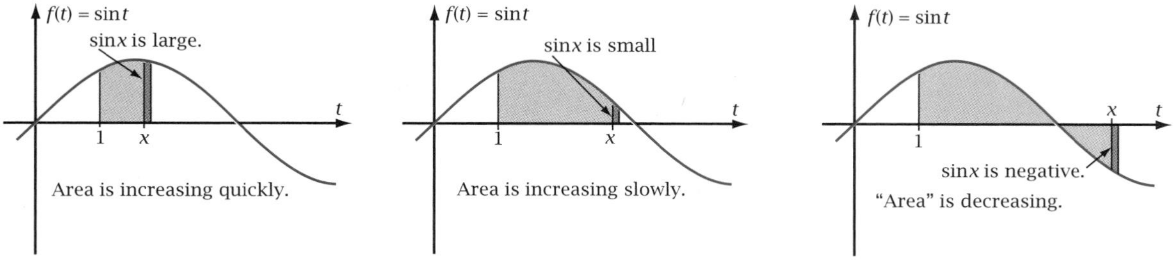

Figure 6-3c

The taller the region is, the faster its area increases as $x$ changes. Think of painting horizontally with a brush whose width is the altitude of the region at $x$. The wider the paint brush, the faster the region gets painted for each inch the brush moves. If $\sin x$ is negative, the "area" decreases because the integrand is negative. This property is called the **second form of the fundamental theorem of calculus**, and it is stated below.

> **Property: Fundamental Theorem of Calculus: Derivative of an Integral Form**
>
> If $g(x) = \int_a^x f(t)\,dt$, where $a$ is a constant, then $g'(x) = f(x)$.

This form of the fundamental theorem can be proved algebraically, using as a lemma the form of the theorem you already know.

**Proof:**

Let $g(x) = \int_a^x f(t)\,dt$.
Let $h$ be an antiderivative of $f$. That is, let $h(x) = \int f(x)\,dx$.

$\therefore g(x) = h(x) - h(a)$ — Fundamental theorem (first form).

$\therefore g'(x) = h'(x) - 0$ — Derivative of a constant is zero.

$\therefore g'(x) = f(x)$, Q.E.D. — Definition of indefinite integral.

The derivative of the natural logarithm function follows directly from the second form of the fundamental theorem.

$$\ln x = \int_1^x \frac{1}{t}\,dt \qquad \text{(where } x \text{ is a positive number)}$$

$$\therefore \ln' x = \frac{1}{x},$$

> **Property: Derivative of ln x**
>
> $$\frac{d}{dx}(\ln x) = \frac{1}{x}$$

To find derivatives involving ln, all you have to remember is that the derivative of $\ln x$ is $1/x$. You must also observe such rules as the chain rule and the product, power, and quotient rules.

**Example 1** If $y = \ln(7x^5)$, find $dy/dx$.

**Solution**

$$y = \ln(7x^5)$$

$$\frac{dy}{dx} = \frac{1}{7x^5}(35x^4) \qquad \text{Find the derivative of ln (argument), then use the chain rule.}$$

$$= \frac{5}{x} \qquad \text{Simplify.}$$

In Section 6-4, you will find out why the answer above is so simple.

**Example 2** If $y = \csc(\ln x)$, find $dy/dx$.

**Solution**

$$y = \csc(\ln x)$$

$$\frac{dy}{dx} = -\csc(\ln x)\cot(\ln x)\cdot\frac{1}{x}$$

Observe that Example 2 is a straight application of the derivative of cosecant, a method you learned earlier, followed by the application of the chain rule on the inside function, $\ln x$.

**Example 3** If $f(x) = x^3 \ln x$, find an equation for $f'(x)$. Then show graphically and numerically that your answer is correct.

**Solution**

$$f(x) = x^3 \ln x$$

$$f'(x) = 3x^2 \ln x + x^3 \cdot \frac{1}{x} = x^2(3\ln x + 1). \qquad \text{Equation for derivative.}$$

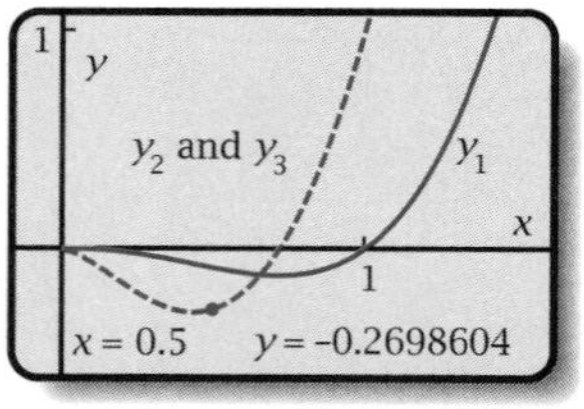


Figure 6-3d

*Graphical Check:* First plot the following.

$y_1 = x^3 \ln x$

$y_2 =$ numerical derivative of $y_1$

$y_3 = x^2(3\ln x + 1)$

Only two graphs appear on the screen, as shown in Figure 6-3d. Tracing the $y_2$ and $y_3$ graphs shows that their values are almost identical.

*Numerical Check:* Use your grapher's table feature to generate values of these three functions.

| $x$ | $y_1$ | $y_2$ | $y_3$ |
|---|---|---|---|
| 0.5 | −0.0866 . . . | −0.2698 . . . | −0.2698 . . . |
| 1.0 | 0 | 1 | 1.0000 . . . |
| 1.5 | 1.3684 . . . | 4.9869 . . . | 4.9869 . . . |
| 2.0 | 5.5451 . . . | 12.3177 . . . | 12.3177 . . . |
| 2.5 | 14.3170 . . . | 23.4304 . . . | 23.4304 . . . |

The numerical and algebraic derivatives give essentially the same values.

### Integral of the Reciprocal Function

Because $\ln' x = 1/x$, the integral $\int (1/x)\,dx$ equals $\ln x + C$. But this works only for positive values of the variable. The function $\ln x$ is undefined for negative values of

$x$ because finding $\ln x$ would require integrating across a discontinuity in the graph (Figure 6-3e). However, it is possible to find $\int (1/x)\,dx$ if $x$ is a negative number.

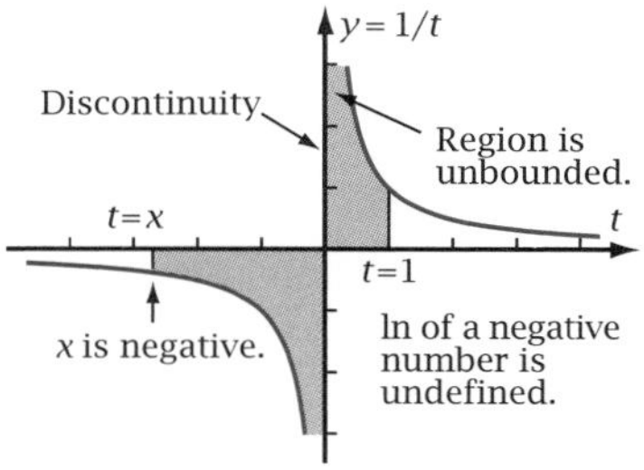


Figure 6-3e

Let $x = -u$. If $x$ is negative, then $u$ is a positive number. The differential, $dx$, is

$$dx = d(-u) = -du.$$

$$\therefore \int \frac{1}{x}\,dx = \int \frac{1}{-u}(-du)$$ Substitute for $x$ and $dx$.

$$= \int \frac{1}{u}\,du.$$ By algebra.

$$= \ln u + C.$$ The integral has the same form as $\int (1/x)\,dx$, and $u$ is a positive number.

$$= \ln(-x) + C.$$ Reverse substitution.

Putting this result together with the original result gives

$$\int \frac{1}{x}\,dx = \begin{cases} \ln x + C \text{ if } x \text{ is positive} \\ \ln(-x) + C \text{ if } x \text{ is negative} \end{cases}.$$

The two answers can be combined with the aid of the absolute value function, as follows.

**Integral of the Reciprocal Function**

$$\int \frac{1}{u}\,du = \ln |u| + C$$

The variable $u$, rather than $x$, has been used above to indicate that the integral of the reciprocal of a function, $u$, can be found in this way as long as the rest of the integrand is $du$, the *differential of the denominator.*

**Example 4** Integrate: $\int \frac{\sec^2 5x}{\tan 5x}\,dx$

**Solution**

$$\int \frac{\sec^2 5x\,dx}{\tan 5x}$$

$$= \frac{1}{5}\int \frac{1}{\tan 5x} \cdot 5\sec^2 5x\,dx$$ Write the fraction as a reciprocal. Multiply the other factor by 5 to make it equal to the differential of the denominator.

$$= \frac{1}{5}\ln|\tan 5x| + C$$ Integrate the reciprocal function. ■

Example 5 shows a case in which the absolute value comes into action. The argument is often negative when the integral has negative limits of integration.

**■ *Example 5*** Use the fundamental theorem to evaluate exactly. Check numerically.

$$\int_{-4}^{-5} \frac{x^2\,dx}{1+x^3}$$

***Solution***

$$\int_{-4}^{-5} \frac{x^2\,dx}{1+x^3}$$

$$= \frac{1}{3}\int_{-4}^{-5} \frac{1}{1+x^3}\cdot 3x^2\,dx$$

Make the numerator equal to the differential of the denominator.

$$= \tfrac{1}{3}\ln|1+x^3|\Big|_{-4}^{-5}$$

Integrate the reciprocal function.

$$= \tfrac{1}{3}\ln|-124| - \tfrac{1}{3}\ln|-63| = \tfrac{1}{3}\ln 124 - \tfrac{1}{3}\ln 63$$

Exact answer.

$$= 0.225715613\ldots$$

Decimal value of exact answer.

Using your grapher's numerical integration feature gives 0.225715613..., or an answer very close to this, which checks!. ■

Note that the answer is a positive number. Figure 6-3f reminds you that a definite integral is a limit of a Riemann sum. The terms have the form $f(x)\,dx$. The integrand function is negative, and so are the $dx$'s because $-5$ is less than $-4$. If both $f(x)$ and $dx$ are negative, the terms in the Riemann sum are positive.

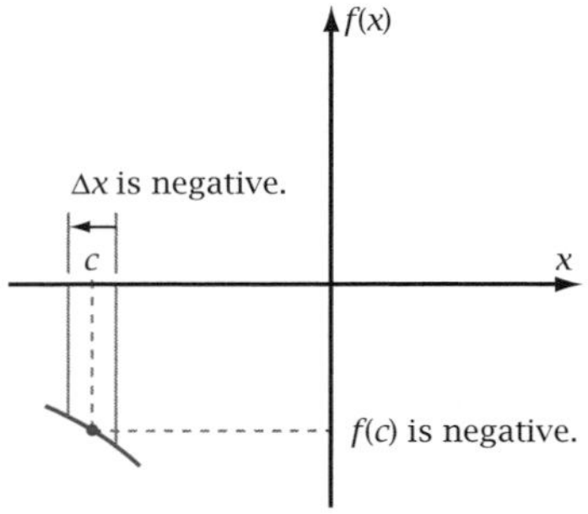


Figure 6-3f

Example 6 shows how to differentiate an integral when the upper limit of integration is a function of $x$ rather than $x$ itself.

**■ *Example 6*** Find $f'(x) : f(x) = \int_2^{5x} \sec t\,dt$.

***Solution***

Let $g(x) = \int \sec x\,dx$.

Then $g'(x) = \sec x$. — Definition of indefinite integral (antiderivative).

$\therefore f(x) = g(5x) - g(2)$ — Fundamental theorem, $g(b) - g(a)$ form.

$\therefore f'(x) = g'(5x)\cdot 5 - 0$ — Chain rule and derivative of a constant.

$= 5\sec 5x$ ■

Once you see the pattern that appears in Example 6, you can write down the answer quickly, in one step. The $\sec 5x$ is the integrand, evaluated at the upper limit of integration. This is the result you would expect from the fundamental theorem in its derivative of the integral form. The 5 is the derivative of $5x$, which is the inside function.

## Problem Set 6-3

### *Do These Quickly*

The following problems are intended to refresh your skills. You should be able to do all ten problems in less than five minutes.

**Q1.** Integrate: $\int x^{-0.3}\,dx$

**Q2.** Integrate: $\int_0^3 x^2\,dx$

**Q3.** Differentiate: $f(x) = \cos^2 x$

**Q4.** $\lim_{x\to 100} \cos x = \cos 100$, so cos is —?— at $x = 100$.

**Q5.** If $f(x) = x^3$, then $f'(2) = 12$. Thus $f$ is —?— at $x = 2$.

**Q6.** Find $y'$: $y = \sin^{-1} x$.

**Q7.** Find $y'$: $y = \csc x$.

**Q8.** $\sum f(x)\Delta x$ is called a(n) —?—.

**Q9.** $\int f(x)\,dx$ is called a(n) —?—.

**Q10.** $\log 3 + \log 4 = \log$ —?—.

0. *Look Ahead Problem:* Look at the derivatives and the integrals in Problem Set 6-9. Make a list, by problem number, of those you presently know how to do.

For Problems 1–26, find the derivative.

1. $y = \ln 7x$
2. $y = \ln 4x$
3. $f(x) = \ln x^5$
4. $f(x) = \ln x^3$
5. $h(x) = 6 \ln x^{-2}$
6. $g(x) = 13 \ln x^{-5}$
7. $r(t) = \ln 3t + \ln 4t + \ln 5t$
8. $v(z) = \ln 6z + \ln 7z + \ln 8z$
9. $y = (\ln 6x)(\ln 4x)$
10. $z = (\ln 2x)(\ln 9x)$
11. $y = \dfrac{\ln 11x}{\ln 3x}$
12. $y = \dfrac{\ln 9x}{\ln 6x}$
13. $p = (\sin x)(\ln x)$
14. $m = (\cos x)(\ln x)$
15. $y = \cos(\ln x)$
16. $y = \sin(\ln x)$
17. $y = \ln(\cos x)$ (Surprise?!)
18. $y = \ln(\sin x)$ (Surprise?!!)
19. $T(x) = \tan(\ln x)$
20. $S(x) = \sec(\ln x)$
21. $y = (3x + 5)^{-1}$
22. $y = (x^3 - 2)^{-1}$

23. $y = x^4 \ln 3x$

24. $y = x^7 \ln 5x$

25. $y = \ln(1/x)$

26. $y = \ln(1/x)^4$

For Problems 27–46, integrate.

27. $\int 7/x\,dx$

28. $\int 5/x\,dx$

29. $\int \frac{1}{3x}\,dx$

30. $\int \frac{1}{8x}\,dx$

31. $\int \dfrac{x^2}{x^3+5}\,dx$

32. $\int \dfrac{x^5}{x^6-4}\,dx$

33. $\int \dfrac{x^5\,dx}{9-x^6}$

34. $\int \dfrac{x^3\,dx}{10-x^4}$

35. $\int \dfrac{\sec x \tan x\,dx}{1+\sec x}$

36. $\int \dfrac{\sec^2 x\,dx}{1+\tan x}$

37. $\int \dfrac{\cos x\,dx}{\sin x}$

38. $\int \dfrac{\sin x\,dx}{\cos x}$

39. $\int_{0.5}^{4} (1/w)\,dw$

40. $\int_{0.1}^{10} (1/v)\,dv$

41. $\int_{-0.1}^{-3} (1/x)\,dx$

42. $\int_{-0.2}^{-4} (1/x)\,dx$

43. $\int_4^9 \dfrac{x^{1/2}\,dx}{1+x^{3/2}}$

44. $\int_1^8 \dfrac{x^{-1/3}\,dx}{2+x^{2/3}}$

45. $\int (\ln x)^5 \dfrac{dx}{x}$ (Be clever!)

46. $\int \dfrac{\ln x}{x}\,dx$ (Be very clever!)

For Problems 47–54, find the derivative.

47. $f(x) = \int_2^x \cos 3t\,dt$

48. $f(x) = \int_5^x (t^2 + 10t - 17)\,dt$

49. $\dfrac{d}{dx}\left(\int_2^x \tan^3 t\,dt\right)$

50. $\dfrac{d}{dx}\left(\int_{-1}^x 2^t\,dt\right)$

51. $f(x) = \int_1^{x^2} 3^t\,dt$

52. $g(x) = \int_0^{\cos x} \sqrt{t}\,dt$

53. $h(x) = \int_0^{3x-5} \sqrt{1+t^2}\,dt$

54. $p(x) = \int_{-1}^{x^3} (t^4+1)^7\,dt$

55. Evaluate $\int_1^3 (5/x)\,dx$ by using the fundamental theorem in its $g(b) - g(a)$ form. Then verify your answer numerically. Indicate which numerical method you used.

56. *Look Ahead Problem Follow Up:* In Problem 0 you were asked to look at Problem Set 6-9 and indicate which problems you knew how to do. Go back and make another list of the problems in Problem Set 6-9 that you know how to do now but that you didn't know how to do before you worked on Problems 1-54 in this problem set.

57. *Population Problem:* In the population problem of Problem Set 6-1, you evaluated

$$\int_{1000}^{N} \frac{1}{P}\,dP,$$

where $P$ stood for population as a function of time, $t$. Use what you have learned in this section to evaluate this integral by using the fundamental theorem of calculus, getting an answer in terms of $N$. Use the result to solve numerically for $N$, the number of people when $t = 10$ yr, in the equation

$$\int_{1000}^{N} \frac{1}{P}\,dP = \int_{0}^{10} 0.05\,dt.$$

58. *Tire Pump Work Problem:* Figure 6-3g shows a bicycle tire pump. To compress the inside air, you exert a force of $F$ lb on the movable piston by pushing the pump handle. The outside air exerts a force of 30 lb, so the total force on the piston is $F + 30$. By Boyle's law, this total force varies inversely with $h$, the distance between the top of the pump base and the bottom of the movable piston. Consequently, the general equation is

$$F + 30 = \frac{k}{h},$$

where $k$ is a constant of proportionality.

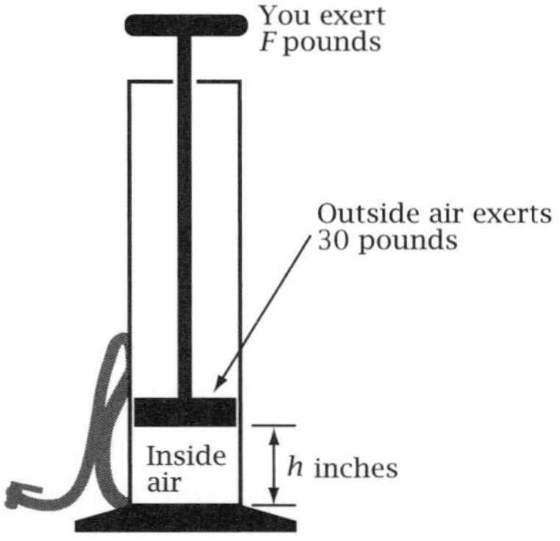


Figure 6-3g

a. Assume that the inside air is not compressed when $h = 20$ in., so that $F = 0$ when $h = 20$. Find the proportionality constant, $k$, and write the particular equation expressing $F$ as a function of $h$.

b. Draw a sketch that shows the region under the graph of $F$ between $h = 10$ and $h = 20$.

c. The amount of work done in compressing the air is defined to be the product of the force exerted on the piston and the distance the piston moves. Explain why this work can be found by using a definite integral.

d. Calculate the work done by compressing the air from $h = 20$ to $h = 10$. What is the mathematical reason why your answer is negative? (If you study physics or engineering, you will learn a scientific reason why the answer is negative.)

e. The units of work in this problem are inch-pounds (in-lb). Why is this name appropriate?

59. *Radio Dial Derivative Problem:* Figure 6-3h shows a typical AM radio dial. As you can see, the distances between numbers decrease as the frequency increases. If you study

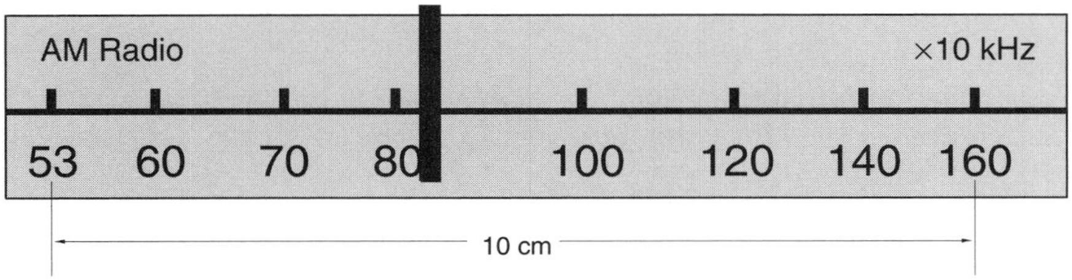


Figure 6-3h

the theory behind the tuning of radios, you will learn that the distance from the left end of the dial to a particular frequency varies logarithmically with the frequency. That is,

$$d(f) = a + b\ln f,$$

where $d(f)$ is the number of centimeters from the number 53 to the frequency number $f$ on the dial, and where $a$ and $b$ stand for constants.

a. Figure out the constants $a$ and $b$ to find the particular equation for this logarithmic function.

b. Use the equation you found in 59a to make a table of values of $d(f)$ for each of the frequencies shown in Figure 6-3h. Then measure the distances with a ruler to the nearest 0.1 cm. If your calculated and measured answers do not agree, go back and fix your errors.

c. Write an equation for $d'(f)$. Put a new column in the table you made in 59b that shows the instantaneous rates of change of distance with respect to frequency.

d. The numbers on the dial in Figure 6-3h are given in tens of kilohertz. (One hertz equal one cycle per second.) What are the units of $d'(f)$?

e. Do the values of $d'(f)$ increase or decrease as $f$ increases? Explain how this fact is consistent with the way the numbers are spaced on the dial.

*60. *Properties of* ln *Problem:* In this problem you will explore some properties of ln that you will prove in Section 6-4.

a. Evaluate ln 2, ln 3, and ln 6 by calculator. How are your results related to one another?

b. Make a conjecture: $\ln(ab)$ = -?-. Test your conjecture with two other values of $a$ and $b$.

c. Evaluate $\ln(10/2)$, ln 10, and ln 2. What do you observe?

d. Make a conjecture: $\ln(a/b)$ = -?-. Test your conjecture with two other values of $a$ and $b$.

e. Evaluate $\ln(2^{10})$ and ln 2. How are the results related to each other?

f. Make a conjecture: $\ln(a^b)$ = -?-. Test your conjecture on two other values of $a$ and $b$.

g. Find ln 5 and log 5, where log is the base-10 logarithm. Assuming that $\ln x = k \log x$, find the value of $k$.

h. Test the assumption you made in 60g by using a different value of $x$. In the equation $\ln k = k \log x$, does $k$ seem to be a constant or is it definitely not a constant?

61. *Journal Problem:* Update your journal with what you've learned since the last entry. Include such things as those listed here.
- The one most important thing you have learned since your last journal entry.
- The difference between the graph of $y = \ln x$ and the graph of $y = 1/t$, from which $\ln x$ is defined.
- The second form of the fundamental theorem of calculus, as the derivative of a definite integral. You might give an example such as $g(x) = \int_1^x \sin t\, dt$, where you actually do the integrating, then show that $g'(x) = \sin x$.
- The algebraic proof of the fundamental theorem in its second form.
- The geometric interpretation of the fundamental theorem, second form, as the rate at which the area of a region changes.
- Evidence (numerical, graphical, and algebraic) you have encountered so far to indicate that ln really is a logarithm.

---

*This problem prepares you for Section 6-4.

# 6-4 ln *x* Really *Is* a Logarithmic Function

In Section 6-3, you defined the function

$$\ln x = \int_1^x \frac{1}{t}\,dt,$$

where *x* is a positive number, and called it the natural logarithm of *x*. In this section you will see why you are justified in calling this function a logarithm.

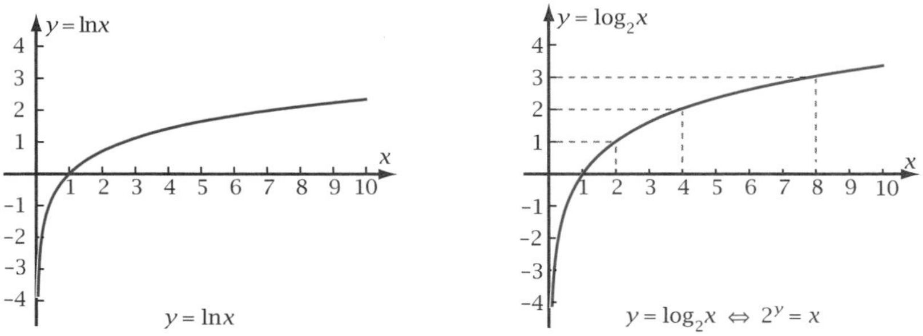


Figure 6-4a

Figure 6-4a shows the graphs of $y = \ln x$ and $y = \log_2 x$. The graphs look remarkably similar. In each, 1 is the *x*-intercept and the *y*-axis is an asymptote. Each is increasing and concave downward. It is the similarity that suggests ln might actually be a log. If you can show that ln also has the properties of logs, you will be justified in calling it a log.

**OBJECTIVE**

Prove that ln has the properties of logarithms.

### *Background Item I: Properties of Logarithms*

*Logarithm* is just a fancy name for *exponent*. The name was picked some 300 years ago because converting numbers to powers of 10 gave a *log*ical way to do *arithm*etic before calculators were invented. For instance, a product of several factors could be computed quickly by adding their logs (that is, exponents) columnwise in one step instead of by multiplying each pair of factors one at a time.

The three major properties of logarithms come from the corresponding properties of exponents.

## Properties of Exponents

1. Product of powers
   $b^c \cdot b^d = b^{c+d}$
2. Quotient of powers
   $b^c / b^d = b^{c-d}$
3. Power of a power
   $(b^c)^d = b^{cd}$

## Properties of Logarithms

1. Log of a product
   $\log_b(cd) = \log_b c + \log_b d$
2. Log of a quotient
   $\log_b(c/d) = \log_b c - \log_b d$
3. Log of a power
   $\log_b(c^r) = r \cdot \log_b c$

For the log properties, $b > 0, b \neq 1, c > 0, d > 0$, and $r$ is any real number.

The properties are proved by transforming logarithms to exponential form using the following definition.

## Algebraic Definition of Logarithm

$a = \log_b c$ if and only if $b^a = c$

Words: A logarithm is an exponent.

Here is the thought process in transforming $y = \log_2 x$ to exponential form.

- $\log_2 x$ is pronounced "log to the base 2 of $x$," so 2 is the base. Write down 2.
- A logarithm is an exponent. Because $y$ equals a log, $y$ must be the exponent. Write $2^y$.
- The only other number in $y = \log_2 x$ is $x$, so $x$ must be the "answer." Write $2^y = x$.

### Background Item II: The Uniqueness Theorem for Derivatives

In Problem 36 of Problem Set 5-6, you may have seen that if $f'(x) = g'(x)$ for all $x$, then $f(x)$ and $g(x)$ differ at most by a constant. Figure 6-4b shows two such functions. If $f(x)$ and $g(x)$ also have a point in common, then they are actually just one ("unique") function. This property is called the **uniqueness theorem for derivatives**. Intuition tells you that if functions start at the same point and change the same way, they are the same function. The property can be proved algebraically by using the mean value theorem as a lemma.

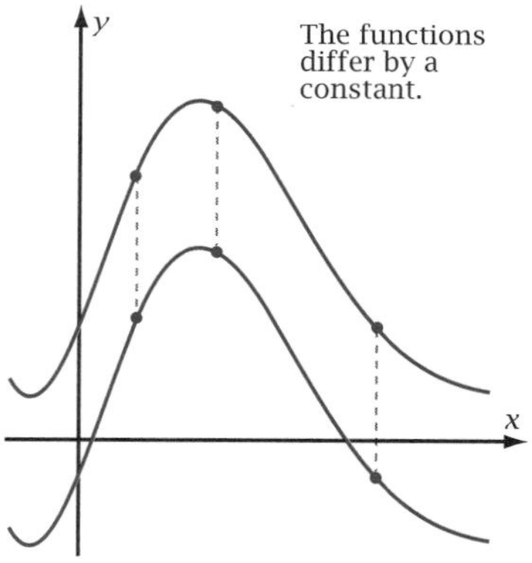


Figure 6-4b

### *Property: The Uniqueness Theorem for Derivatives*

If: **1.** $f'(x) = g'(x)$ for all values of $x$ in the domain, and

**2.** $f(a) = g(a)$ for one value, $x = a$, in the domain, then $f(x) = g(x)$ for all values of $x$ in the domain.

Words: If two functions have the same derivative everywhere and they also have a point in common, then they are the same function.

*Proof (by contradiction):* Assume that the conclusion is false. Then there is a number $x = b$ in the domain for which $f(b) \neq g(b)$ (Figure 6-4c, left side). Let $h$ be the difference function, $h(x) = f(x) - g(x)$ (Figure 6-4c, right side).

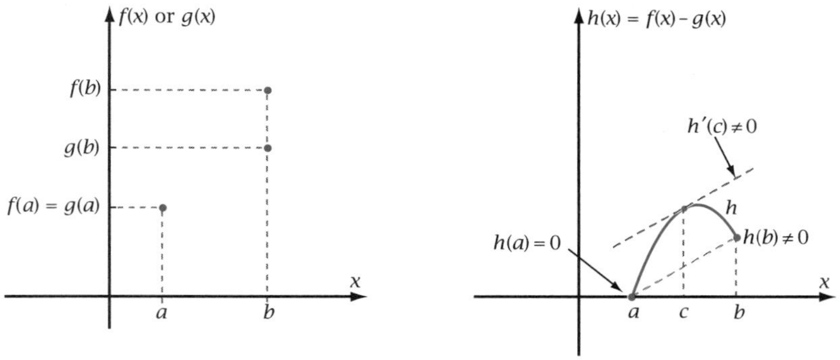


Figure 6-4c

Because $f(a) = g(a)$ and $f(b) \neq g(b)$, it follows that $h(a) = 0$ and $h(b) \neq 0$.

Thus the secant line through the points $(a, h(a))$ and $(b, h(b))$ will have a slope not equal to zero.

Because both $f$ and $g$ are given to be differentiable for all $x$ in the domain, $h$ is also differentiable, and thus the mean value theorem applies to function $h$ on $[a, b]$.

Therefore there is a number $x = c$ in $(a, b)$ such that $h'(c)$ equals the slope of the secant line. Thus $h'(c) \neq 0$.

But $h'(x) = f'(x) - g'(x)$. Because $f'(x)$ is given to be equal to $g'(x)$ for all $x$ in the domain, $h'(x) = 0$ for all $x$. Thus $h'(c)$ does equal zero.

This is a contradiction. Therefore the assumption is false, and $f(x)$ does equal $g(x)$ for all $x$ in the domain, Q.E.D.

### *Logarithm Properties of ln*

Four properties of logarithms for natural logs are given in the box below.

**Property: Logarithm Properties of ln**

($a$ and $b$ are positive, and $r$ is any real number.)

Product: $\ln(ab) = \ln a + \ln b$

Quotient: $\ln(a/b) = \ln a - \ln b$

Power: $\ln(a^r) = r \ln a$

Intercept: $\ln 1 = 0$ because $\int_1^1 (1/t)\, dt = 0$

The uniqueness theorem can be used to show that ln actually does have these properties. The proof for a product is shown below. You will prove the other properties in Problem Set 6-4.

### *Proof of the ln of a Product Property*

Prove that $\ln(ab) = \ln a + \ln b$ for all $a > 0$ and $b > 0$.

*Proof:* Let $b$ stand for a positive constant, and replace $a$ with the variable $x$.

Let $f(x) = \ln(xb)$, and let $g(x) = \ln x + \ln b$.

Then $f'(x) = \dfrac{1}{xb} \cdot b = \dfrac{1}{x}$ for all $x > 0$, and $g'(x) = \dfrac{1}{x} + 0 = \dfrac{1}{x}$ for all $x > 0$.
Substituting 1 for $x$ gives
$f(1) = \ln(1b) = \ln b$ and $g(1) = \ln 1 + \ln b = 0 + \ln b = \ln b$.

Thus $f'(x) = g'(x)$ for all $x > 0$ and $f(1) = g(1)$. Thus, by the uniqueness theorem for derivatives, $f(x) = g(x)$ for all $x > 0$.

That is, $\ln(xb) = \ln x + \ln b$ for any positive number $x$ and any positive number $b$. Replacing $x$ with $a$ gives

$\ln(ab) = \ln a + \ln b$ for all $a > 0$ and all $b > 0$, Q.E.D.

### *Summary*

Because the function ln has the three major properties of a logarithm, and because its graph looks like that of a logarithm function—including an $x$-intercept of 1 and the $y$-axis as an asymptote—you are justified in calling ln a logarithm. In Problem Set 6-4, you will prove the rest of these properties, and you'll find the number $e$ that is the base of the natural logarithm function.

## Problem Set 6-4

### *Do These Quickly*

The following problems are intended to refresh your skills. You should be able to do all ten problems in less than five minutes.

**Q1.** Differentiate: $y = \tan^{-1}x$

**Q2.** Integrate: $\int (4x + 1)^5\, dx$

**Q3.** Find $\lim_{x\to 0} (\sin x)/(x)$.

**Q4.** Find $\lim_{x\to 3} 7$.

**Q5.** $\log 12 - \log 48 = \log$ -?-

**Q6.** $\log 7 + \log 5 = \log$ -?-

**Q7.** $3 \log 2 = \log$ -?-

**Q8.** Sketch the graph of $\int_2^x y\, dx$ for the function shown in Figure 6-4d.

**Q9.** Write one hypothesis of the mean value theorem.

**Q10.** Write the other hypothesis of the mean value theorem.

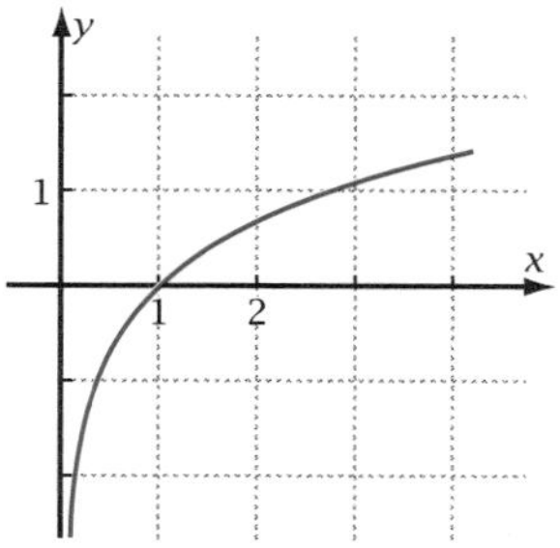

Figure 6-4d

For Problems 1–6, show that the properties of ln actually work by evaluating both sides of the given equation.

1. $\ln 24 = \ln 6 + \ln 4$
2. $\ln 35 = \ln 5 + \ln 7$
3. $\ln \frac{2001}{667} = \ln 2001 - \ln 667$
4. $\ln \frac{1001}{77} = \ln 1001 - \ln 77$
5. $\ln (1776^3) = 3 \ln 1776$
6. $\ln (1066^4) = 4 \ln 1066$
7. Prove the uniqueness theorem for derivatives. Try doing so without looking at the proof given in this text. If you get stuck, look at the text proof just long enough to get going again.
8. Prove by counterexample that $\ln (a + b)$ does not equal $\ln a + \ln b$.
9. Prove that $\ln (a/b) = \ln a - \ln b$ for all $a > 0$ and $b > 0$.
10. Prove that $\ln (a^b) = b \ln a$ for all $a > 0$ and for all $b$.
11. Prove that $\ln (a/b) = \ln a - \ln b$ again, using the property given in Problem 10 as a lemma.
12. Write the definition of ln.
13. *Base of Natural Logarithms Problem:* Because you have demonstrated that ln is a logarithm, it must have some number for its base. The question is, *what* number. In this problem you will investigate what that number could be. Let $y = \ln x = \log_b x$.
    a. Explain why $x = b^y$.
    b. Based on your answer to 13a, what would $x$ equal if $y = 1$?
    c. Figure 6-4e shows $y = \ln x$ with a line drawn across at $y = 1$. Use your grapher's trace or solve feature to find, approximately, what $x$ equals when $y = 1$.
    d. Have you seen the number you found in 13c before? If so, where? What letter is commonly used for this number?

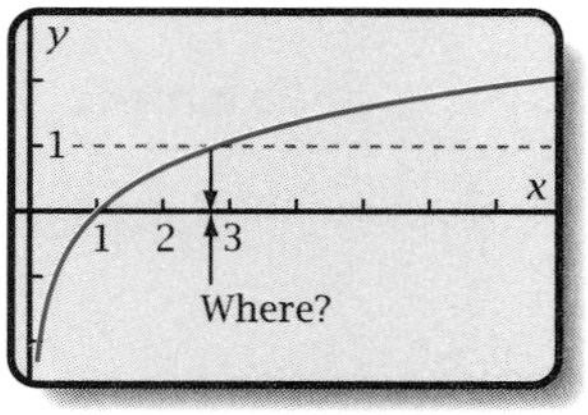

Figure 6-4e

# 6-5 Derivatives of Exponential Functions—Logarithmic Differentiation

So far, the only way you have been able to find derivatives of exponential functions such as

$$f(x) = 2^x$$

is by using numeric techniques. Now it is time to learn an algebraic technique that will let you find the derivative exactly. This technique is called **logarithmic differentiation**, and it uses the properties of ln to transform an equation to one that you can differentiate implicitly. The technique also provides an algebraic way to find derivatives of products and quotients more easily.

**OBJECTIVE**

Differentiate algebraically a function whose equation has a variable exponent. Use the properties of ln to differentiate products, powers, and quotients.

To find $f'(x)$ for the function above, start by taking the ln of both sides of the equation. This is the easiest thing you could ever do—you just write "ln" in front of each side!

$$\ln f(x) = \ln 2^x$$

The expression on the right is the ln of a power, so you can write

$$\ln f(x) = x(\ln 2).$$

Now, differentiate both sides implicitly with respect to $x$. Observe that ln 2 is a constant.

$$\frac{1}{f(x)} f'(x) = 1(\ln 2)$$

The $f'(x)$ on the left side comes from the chain rule. Finally, use algebra to isolate $f'(x)$.

$$f'(x) = f(x)(\ln 2) = 2^x \ln 2$$

The answer is simply the original function multiplied by a constant, ln 2 in this case. The same procedure can be used if the equation has more complicated variable exponents.

■ ***Example 1*** Find $f'(x)$ if $f(x) = (x^3 + 4)^{\cos x}$.

***Solution***

$$f(x) = (x^3 + 4)^{\cos x}$$

$$\ln f(x) = \ln (x^3 + 4)^{\cos x} \qquad \text{Take ln of both sides.}$$

$$\ln f(x) = \cos x[\ln (x^3 + 4)] \qquad \text{ln of a power.}$$

$$\frac{1}{f(x)} f'(x) = -\sin x[\ln (x^3 + 4)] + \cos x \left[\frac{3x^2}{x^3 + 4}\right] \qquad \text{Differentiate implicitly on the left. Derivative of a product on the right.}$$

$$f'(x) = (x^3 + 4)^{\cos x} \left(-\sin x[\ln (x^3 + 4)] + \cos x \left[\frac{3x^2}{x^3 + 4}\right]\right)$$ ■

### *Logarithmic Differentiation for Products and Quotients*

The properties of logarithms allowed you to turn a power into a product, which you know how to differentiate. The other properties let you transform products and quotients to sums and differences, which are even easier to differentiate. Example 2 shows you how this is done.

■ ***Example 2*** If $f(x) = \dfrac{(3x+7)^5}{\sin 4x}$, find $f'(x)$.

***Solution***

$$\ln f(x) = \ln \frac{(3x+7)^5}{\sin 4x}$$ Take ln of both sides.

$$\ln f(x) = 5\ln(3x+7) - \ln(\sin 4x)$$ Log of a quotient and a power.

$$\frac{1}{f(x)} f'(x) = \frac{5}{3x+7}\cdot 3 - \frac{1}{\sin 4x}\cdot \cos 4x \cdot 4$$ Differentiate implicitly (use the chain rule).

$$f'(x) = f(x)\left(\frac{5}{3x+7}\cdot 3 - \frac{1}{\sin 4x}\cdot \cos 4x\cdot 4\right)$$

$$= \frac{(3x+7)^5}{\sin 4x}\cdot\left(\frac{15}{3x+7} - 4\cot 4x\right)$$ ■

# Problem Set 6-5

### *Do These Quickly*

The following problems are intended to refresh your skills. You should be able to do all ten problems in less than five minutes.

**Q1.** Differentiate: $y = \ln 7x^3$

**Q2.** Integrate: $\int (5x)^{-3}\,dx$

**Q3.** Differentiate: $y = \cos^{-1} x$

**Q4.** Integrate: $\int (-x)^6\,dx$

**Q5.** Differentiate: $y = \sec x$

**Q6.** Integrate: $\int -\sin x\,dx$

**Q7.** Differentiate: $y = \tan x \cot x$

**Q8.** ln 12 + ln 3 = ln -?-

**Q9.** 3 ln 2 = ln -?-

**Q10.** 0/0 is called a(n) —?— form.

0. *Look Ahead Problem:* Look at the derivatives and the integrals in Problem Set 6-9. Make a list, by problem number, of those you presently know how to do.

For Problems 1–18, find an equation for the derivative of the given function.

1. $f(x) = 0.4^{2x}$
2. $f(x) = 10^{-0.2x}$
3. $g(x) = 4(7^x)$
4. $h(x) = 1000(1.03^x)$
5. $c(x) = x^5 \cdot 3^x$
6. $m(x) = 5^x \cdot x^7$
7. $y = (\cos x)^{0.7x}$
8. $y = (\tan x)^{4x}$
9. $y = (\csc 5x)^{2x}$
10. $y = (\cos 2x)^{3x}$

11. $f(t) = t^{\sec t}$

12. $r(u) = u^{\ln u}$

13. $v = (x^4 - 1)^x$

14. $z = (\sin t)^{\csc t}$

15. $y = 2^x \ln x$

16. $y = x(3^{x^2})$

17. $y = 5(3x - 4)^x$

18. $y = 8(4x - 5)^x$

For Problems 19–24, find an equation for the derivative function by applying the following methods: (a) Differentiate directly, using the chain rule and so on. (b) First apply the logarithm properties of ln, then differentiate. Show that both answers are equivalent.

19. $y = \ln 3x^7$

20. $y = \ln 10x^8$

21. $y = \ln[(3x + 4)(2x - 9)]$

22. $y = \ln[(4x - 7)(x + 10)]$

23. $y = \ln \dfrac{5x + 2}{7x - 8}$

24. $y = \ln \dfrac{6x - 5}{3x + 1}$

25. For $y = \ln 3x^7$ (Problem 19), show that your answer for $y'$ gives the right value when $x = 2$ by evaluating the difference quotient $\Delta y/\Delta x$ for $\Delta x = 0.001$.

26. For $y = \ln 10x^8$ (Problem 20), show that your answer for $y'$ gives the right value when $x = 2$ by evaluating the difference quotient $\Delta y/\Delta x$ for $\Delta x = 0.001$.

For Problems 27–30, find an equation for the derivative function by logarithmic differentiation.

27. $y = (5x + 11)^7(7x - 3)^5$

28. $y = (4x + 3)^8(8x - 9)^4$

29. $y = (3 - 4x)^5(7 + 5x)^4$

30. $y = (10 + 3x)^{10}(4 - 5x)^3$

31. $y = \dfrac{(4x + 1)\csc x}{\sin^5 x}$

32. $y = \dfrac{x^7 \cos x}{5x + 6}$

33. *Integral Review Problem:* Evaluate $\int_5^9 \dfrac{5}{3 - x}\,dx$ by using the fundamental theorem.

34. *Look Ahead Problem Follow-Up:* In Problem 0, you were asked to look at Problem Set 6-9 and indicate which problems you knew how to do. Go back and make another list of the problems in Problem Set 6-9 that you know how to do now but that you didn't know how to do before you worked on Problems 1-30 in this problem set.

35. *Continued Exponentiation Problem:*

    a. Let $f(x) = x^x$. Find an equation for $f'(x)$. Simplify as much as possible.

    b. Let $g(x) = x^{x^x}$. Find an equation for $g'(x)$. Simplify as much as possible. Observe that the $x^x$ in the exponent is the innermost function.

36. *Derivative with Variable Base and Exponent Generalization Problem:* Let $f(x) = x^3$, $g(x) = 3^x$, and $h(x) = x^x$.

    a. Differentiate function $f$ logarithmically, as you have for variable exponent functions in this section. Show that the answer reduces to the familiar form $nx^{n-1}$ from the derivative of the power function.

    b. Write an equation for $g'(x)$. In what ways is your equation similar to the equation for $f'(x)$. In what ways is it different?

    c. Write an equation for $h'(x)$. Show that your answer can be written as a sum of two terms, one of which is similar to the derivative of $f$ (constant exponent), the other of which is similar to the derivative of $g$ (constant base).

37. *Compound Interest Problem:* In a real-world situation that is driven by internal forces, the variables are often related by an exponential function. For instance, the more money there is in a savings account, the faster the amount in the account grows (Figure 6-5a).

If \$1000 is invested with interest compounded continuously, and the interest is enough to make the annual percentage rate (APR) equal 6%, then the amount of money, $m(t)$ dollars, in the account at time $t$ years after it is invested is

$$m(t) = 1000(1.06)^t.$$

a. Find an equation for the derivative, $m'(t)$. At what rate is the amount growing at the instant $t = 0$ yr? At $t = 5$ yr? At $t = 10$ yr? What are the units of these rates?

b. Find the amount of money in the account at $t = 0$, $t = 5$ yr, and $t = 10$ yr. Does the rate of increase seem to be getting larger as the amount increases?

c. Show that the rate of increase of money is directly proportional to the amount present. One way to do so is to show that $m'(t)/m(t)$ is constant.

d. Show that you earn exactly \$60 the first year. Then explain why the rate of increase at time $t = 0$ is less than \$60/yr.

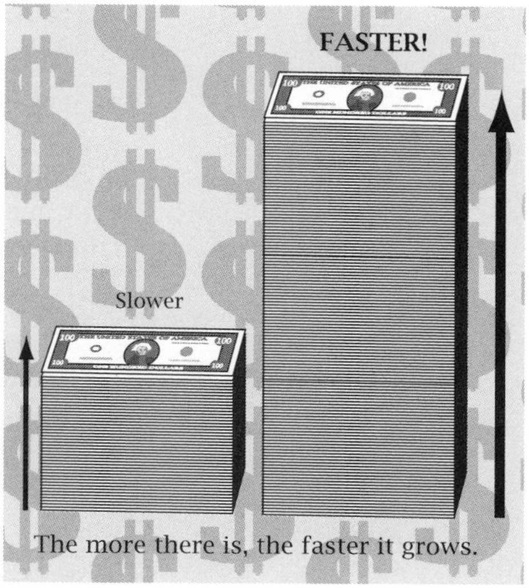


Figure 6-5a

38. *Door-Closer Problem:* In Section 1-1, you were introduced to a problem in which a door was pushed open. As the automatic door-closer slowed the door down, the number of degrees, $d(t)$, the door was open after $t$ seconds was given to be

$$d(t) = 200t \cdot 2^{-t}, 0 \le t \le 7.$$

Use what you have learned about derivatives of exponential functions to analyze the motion of the door. For instance, how fast is it opening at $t = 1$ and at $t = 2$? At what time is it open the widest, and what is the derivative at that time? A graph might help.

*39. *Limit of an Interesting Expression:* Figure 6-5b shows $f(n) = (1 + 1/n)^n$. As the exponent $n$ gets large, the base gets closer and closer to 1. And 1 raised to a large power is still 1. But a number greater than 1 raised to a large power is very large. Investigate what happens to $f(n)$ as $n$ gets very large. Go to at least $n = 1{,}000{,}000$. Where have you seen this number before?

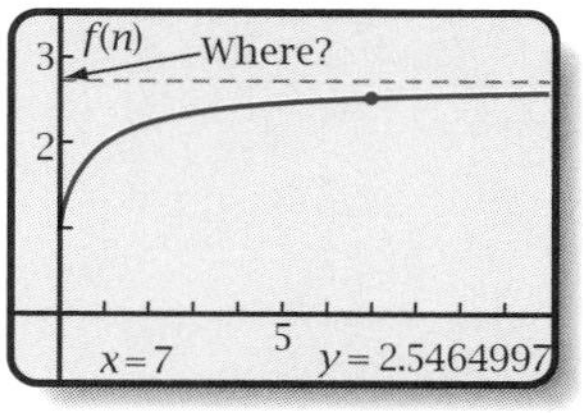


Figure 6-5b

40. *Journal Problem:* Update your journal with what you've learned since the last entry. Include such things as those listed here.
- The one most important thing you have learned since your last journal entry
- The way to differentiate algebraically an exponential function
- How you know that ln really is a logarithmic function
- What you now better understand about logarithms
- Any technique or idea you plan to ask about at the next class period

---

*This problem sets the stage for Section 6-6.

# 6-6 The Number *e*, and the Derivative of Base *b* Logarithm Functions

You defined ln $x$ to be a function whose derivative is $1/x$. You then found that the resulting function has the properties of logarithms. In this section you will attack the problem from the other end, starting with a base $b$ logarithm and using the definition of derivative. This task, though difficult to do, will lead you to the number that is the base of the natural logarithm.

**OBJECTIVE**

Find out algebraically what number is the base of the ln function.
Differentiate algebraically a logarithm function with any permissible number as its base.

### *Background Item I: Limit of $(1+n)^{1/n}$ as n Approaches Zero*

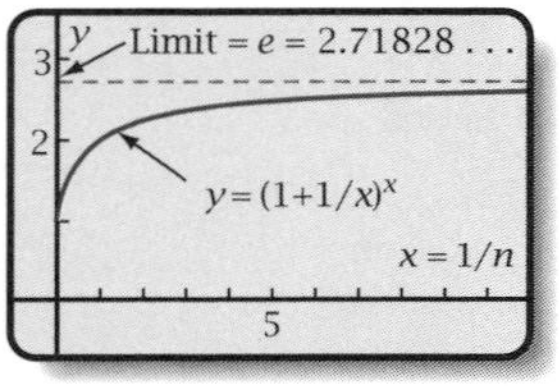

Figure 6-6a

The expression $(1+n)^{1/n}$ assumes interesting values if $n$ is close to zero. The base, $(1+n)$, is close to 1 and the exponent, $1/n$, is very large. As Figure 6-6a shows, the values approach an asymptote a bit above 2.7. If you trace the graph, here are some values.

| $1/n$ | $(1+n)^{1/n}$ | answer |
|---|---|---|
| 10 | $1.1^{10}$ | = 2.593742 . . . |
| 100 | $1.01^{100}$ | = 2.704813 . . . |
| 10,000 | $1.0001^{10{,}000}$ | = 2.718145 . . . |

The value of $(1+n)^{1/n}$ is caught between two opposing properties.

- $(1)^{\text{any exponent}} = 1$
- $(\text{greater than } 1)^{\text{large positive exponent}} = \text{large number}$.

The result is a stand off. The limit, named $e$, is 2.7182818284.... With $1/n = 10{,}000{,}000$, you should get 2.718281816..., which is close to $e$. Problem 43 in Problem Set 6-5 introduced you to $e$. It is a naturally-occurring constant, like $\pi$. The letter $e$ is used because it is the base of the natural *e*xponential function, as you will see in Section 6-7.

**Definition of e**

$$e = \lim_{n\to 0}(1+n)^{1/n} = \lim_{n\to\infty}(1+1/n)^n$$

$e = 2.7182818284\ldots$ (a nonrepeating decimal)

In spite of the fact that 1828 repeats once in the decimal part of $e$, $e$ is a nonterminating, nonrepeating decimal that cannot be expressed exactly by using only the operations of algebra. Like $\pi$, $e$ is a transcendental number. The proof of this fact appears in abstract algebra courses.

### *Background Item II: Limit-Function Interchange for Continuous Functions*

If you take the limit of a continuous function that has another function inside, such as

$$\lim_{x\to c} \sin(\tan x),$$

it is possible to interchange the limit and the outside function,

$$\sin\left(\lim_{x\to c} \tan x\right).$$

To see why continuity is sufficient for this interchange, consider a simpler case. The definition of continuity states that if $g$ is continuous at $x = c$, then

$$\lim_{x\to c} g(x) = g(c).$$

But $c$ is the limit of $x$ as $x$ approaches $c$. Replacing $c$ with the limit gives

$$\lim_{x\to c} g(x) = g\left(\lim_{x\to c} x\right),$$

which shows that the limit and the outside function have been interchanged.

> **Property: Limit-Function Interchange for Continuous Functions**
>
> For the function $f(x) = g(h(x))$, if $h(x)$ has a limit, $L$, as $x$ approaches $c$ and if $g$ is continuous at $L$, then $\lim_{x\to c} g(h(x)) = g\left(\lim_{x\to c} h(x)\right)$.

### *Derivative of the Base b Logarithm Function from the Definition of Derivative*

Suppose that $f(x) = \log_b x$, where $b$ is a positive constant not equal to 1. The graph is shown in Figure 6-6b. By the definition of derivative,

$$f'(x) = \lim_{h\to 0} \frac{\log_b(x+h) - \log_b x}{h}.$$

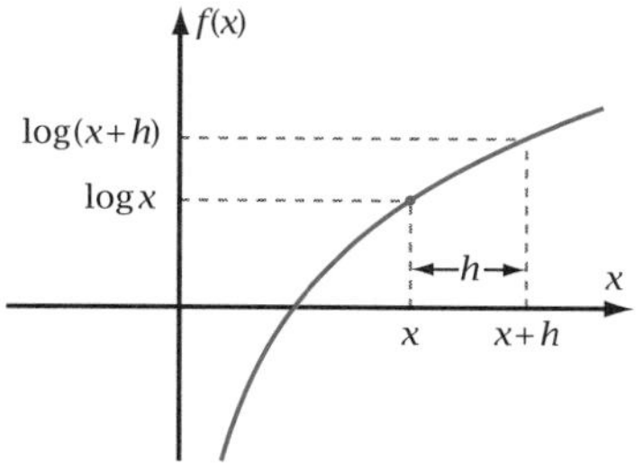


Figure 6-6b

The following sequence of steps shows how this difference quotient can be transformed into the form $(1 + n)^{1/n}$, whose limit is $e$ as $n$ approaches zero.

$$f'(x) = \lim_{h \to 0} \frac{\log_b\left(\dfrac{x+h}{x}\right)}{h}$$

Log of a quotient property, applied in reverse.

$$= \lim_{h \to 0} \left[\frac{1}{h}\log_b\left(1 + \frac{h}{x}\right)\right]$$

Algebra, used to get (1 + something) into the argument of the log.

$$= \lim_{h \to 0} \left[\frac{1}{x} \cdot \frac{x}{h}\log_b\left(1 + \frac{h}{x}\right)\right]$$

Multiply by $x/x$ and rearrange.

$$= \frac{1}{x} \cdot \lim_{h \to 0} \left[\frac{x}{h}\log_b\left(1 + \frac{h}{x}\right)\right]$$

Limit of a constant times a function. $1/x$ is independent of $h$.

$$= \frac{1}{x} \cdot \lim_{h \to 0} \left[\log_b\left(1 + \frac{h}{x}\right)^{x/h}\right]$$

Log of a power property, applied in reverse.

$$= \frac{1}{x} \cdot \log_b\left[\lim_{h \to 0}\left(1 + \frac{h}{x}\right)^{x/h}\right]$$

Interchange log and limit, assuming log is continuous.

$$f'(x) = \frac{1}{x} \cdot \log_b e$$

The expression in parentheses has the form $(1 + n)^{1/n}$, whose limit is $e$ as $n \to 0$.

Finding the limit in the last step depends on the fact that $h \to 0$ implies $h/x \to 0$, because $x$ is restricted away from zero by the definition of logarithm.

Now, suppose you choose $e$ as the base of the logarithm function. The derivative is

$$f(x) = \log_e x \Rightarrow f'(x) = \frac{1}{x} \cdot \log_e e = \frac{1}{x} \cdot 1 = \frac{1}{x}$$

$\log_b b = 1$ for any permissible base $b$.

The derivative is simpler because it involves no logarithms. But, more importantly, it is identical to the derivative of $\ln x$, namely, $1/x$. Because $\ln 1 = \log_e 1 = 0$, the two functions meet the hypotheses of the uniqueness theorem for derivatives. Therefore ln and $\log_e$ are the same function!

**Property: Equivalence of Natural Logs and Base e Logs**

$\ln x = \log_e x$ for all $x > 0$.

### *Algebraic Differentiation Technique for Base b Logarithm Functions*

It would be possible for you to memorize the formula above for the derivative of base $b$ logs. However, because calculators include an ln key, and because the derivative of ln is so simple, it is better to first transform the base $b$ log into a natural log. To do so, recall from algebra the change-of-base property.

**Property: Change-of-Base Property for Logarithms**

$$\log_b x = \frac{\log_a x}{\log_a b} \text{ in general, and}$$

$$\log_b x = \frac{\log_e x}{\log_e b} = \frac{\ln x}{\ln b} = \frac{1}{\ln b} \cdot \ln x \text{ in particular.}$$

In Problem 21 of Problem Set 6-6, you will prove this property. Examples 1 and 2 demonstrate how to differentiate algebraically some base $b$ log functions.

**Example 1** Find an equation for $f'(x)$ if $f(x) = \log_{10}x$. Check the formula by evaluating $f'(2)$ and showing that the line at the point $(2, \log_{10}2)$, with slope $f'(2)$, is tangent to the graph.

**Solution**

$$f(x) = \log_{10}x = \frac{1}{\ln 10} \cdot \ln x \qquad \text{Use the change-of-base property.}$$

$$f'(x) = \frac{1}{\ln 10} \cdot \frac{1}{x} = \frac{1}{x \ln 10} \qquad \text{Derivative of a constant times a function.}$$

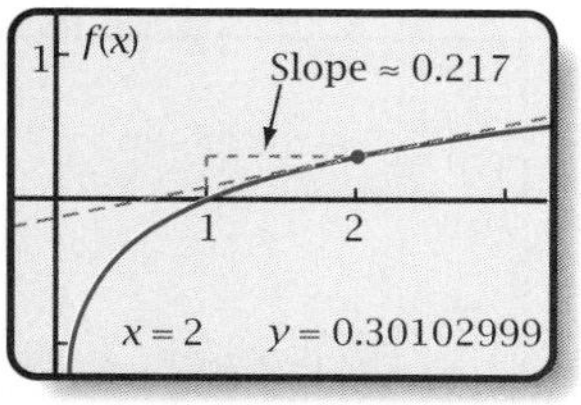


Figure 6-6c

The line through the point $(2, \log_{10}2)$, which equals $(2, 0.3010\ldots)$, has slope

$$f'(2) = \frac{1}{2.302585\ldots} \cdot \frac{1}{2} \approx 0.217.$$

Thus the line's equation is

$$y - 0.3010 \approx 0.217(x - 2), \text{ or } y \approx 0.217x - 0.133.$$

Figure 6-6c shows the log graph and the line. The line really is tangent to the graph, Q.E.D. ■

**Example 2** If $f(x) = \log_4 3x$, find $f'(x)$ algebraically and find an approximation for $f'(5)$. Show that your answer is reasonable by plotting $f$ on your grapher and by showing that $f'(5)$ has a sign that agrees with the slope of the graph.

**Solution**

$$f(x) = \log_4 3x = \frac{\ln 3x}{\ln 4} = \frac{1}{\ln 4} \cdot \ln 3x$$

$$f'(x) = \frac{1}{\ln 4} \cdot \left(\frac{1}{3x} \cdot 3\right)$$

$$= \frac{1}{x \ln 4}$$

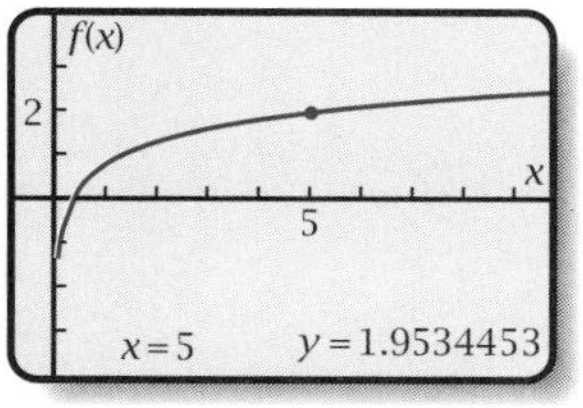


Figure 6-6d

By calculator, $f'(5) = 0.144269\ldots$.

To plot the graph, enter the transformed equation involving ln, shown above. As Figure 6-6d shows, $f(x)$ is increasing slowly at $x = 5$, which agrees with the small positive value of the derivative. ■

# Problem Set 6-6

### *Do These Quickly*

The following problems are intended to refresh your skills. You should be able to do all ten problems in less than five minutes.

**Q1.** Differentiate: $f(x) = \cos^2 x$

**Q2.** Differentiate: $g(x) = \cos x^2$

**Q3.** Differentiate: $h(x) = \cos 2^x$

**Q4.** Differentiate: $c(x) = \cos 2^5$

**Q5.** Differentiate: $L(x) = \ln x$

**Q6.** Differentiate: $M(x) = \ln x^5$

**Q7.** Differentiate: $N(x) = \ln^5 x$

**Q8.** Differentiate: $O(x) = \tan^{-1} x$

**Q9.** Sketch the graph of $y'$ for the function shown in Figure 6-6e.

**Q10.** State the conclusion of the uniqueness theorem for derivatives.

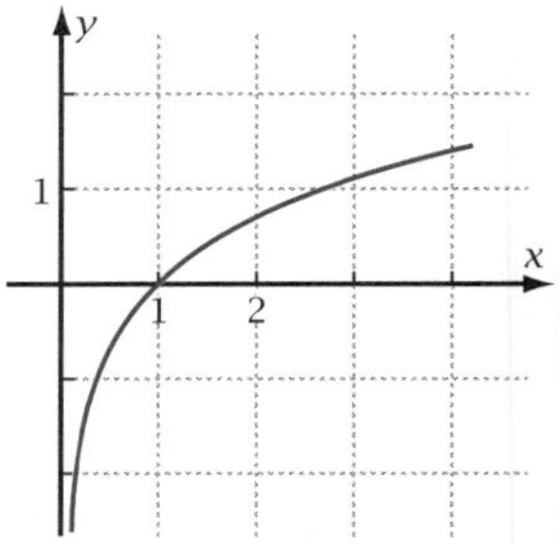

Figure 6-6e

For Problems 1–4, find an equation for the derivative of the given function, and show numerically or graphically that the equation gives a reasonable value for the derivative at the given value of $x$.

1. $f(x) = \log_3 x, \quad x = 5$
2. $f(x) = \log_7 x, \quad x = 3$
3. $f(x) = \log_{0.6} x, \quad x = 9$
4. $f(x) = \log_{0.8} x, \quad x = 4$

For Problems 5–12, find an equation for the derivative of the given function.

5. $f(x) = 13 \log_e x$
6. $f(x) = 5 \log_e x$
7. $g(x) = 8 \log_e (x^5)$
8. $h(x) = 10 \log_e (x^{0.4})$
9. $T(x) = \log_5 (\sin x)$
10. $R(x) = \log_4 (\sec x)$
11. $p(x) = (\log_e x)(\log_5 x)$
12. $q(x) = \dfrac{\log_9 x}{\log_3 x}$

For Problems 13 and 14, find the derivative at the given value of $x$, then show that your answer is correct by finding the numerical derivative.

13. $y = \log_{10} x, \quad x = 4$
14. $y = \log_{0.2} x, \quad x = 5$

For Problems 15 and 16, plot the graph of the given function, then find the derivative at the given value of $x = c$. Plot a line through the point $(c, f(c))$, with slope $f'(c)$. Explain why your results are reasonable.

15. $f(x) = \log_{0.9} x, \quad c = 2$
16. $f(x) = \log_{1.4} x, \quad c = 3$
17. *Derivative of Logarithm Proof:* Derive the formula for $f'(x)$ if $f(x) = \log_b x$, starting with the definition of derivative. Try to do this without looking at the proof in this text. If you need to look, do so just long enough to get moving again.
18. *Equivalence of Natural Logs and Base e Logs:* Use the uniqueness theorem for derivatives to prove that $\log_e x = \ln x$ for all $x > 0$.

19. *Lava Flow Problem:* Velocities are measured in miles per hour. When a velocity is low, people sometimes prefer to think of how many hours it takes to go a mile. Lava flowing down the side of a volcano flows more slowly as it cools. Assume that the distance, $y$ miles, from the crater to the tip of the flowing lava is given by

$$y = 7 \cdot (2 - 0.9^x),$$

where $x$ is the number of hours since the lava started flowing (Figure 6-6f).

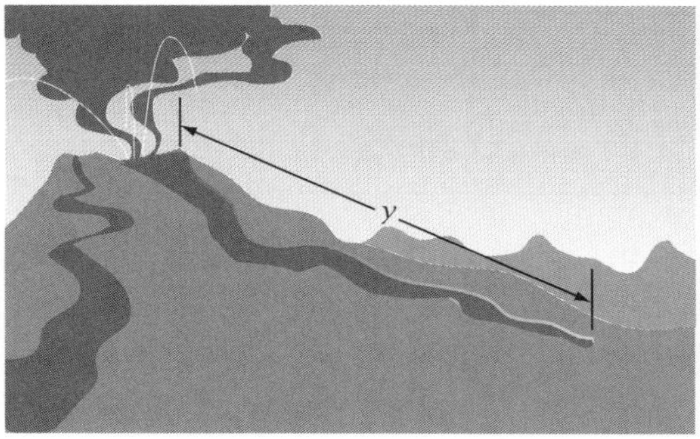


Figure 6-6f

Geologist collecting data about lava flow

a. Find an equation for $dy/dx$. Use the equation to find out how fast the lava tip is moving when $x = 0, 1, 5$, and 10 hr. Is the lava speeding up or slowing down as time passes?

b. Transform the equation $y = 7 \cdot (2 - 0.9^x)$ (from 19a) so that $x$ is in terms of $y$. Take the log of both sides, using some appropriate base for the logs.

c. Differentiate the equation given in 19b with respect to $y$ to find an equation for $dx/dy$. Calculate $dx/dy$ when $y = 10$ mi. What are the units of $dx/dy$?

d. Calculate $dx/dy$ for the value of $y$ when $x = 10$ hr.

e. Naive reasoning suggests that $dy/dx$ and $dx/dy$ are reciprocals of each other. Based on your answers above, in what way is this reasoning true and in what way is it not true?

20. *Compound Interest Problem:* If interest on a savings account is compounded continuously, and the interest is enough to make the annual percentage rate APR equal 6%, then the amount of money, $M$, after $t$ years is given by the exponential function $M = 1000 \times 1.06^t$. This equation can be solved for $t$ in terms of $M$.

$$t = \log_{1.06}\left(\frac{M}{1000}\right)$$

a. Show how the transformations are done to get $t$ in terms of $M$.

b. Write an equation for $dt/dM$.

c. Evaluate $dt/dM$ when $M = 1000$. What are the units of $dt/dM$? What real-world quantity does $dt/dM$ represent?

d. Does $dt/dM$ increase or decrease as $M$ increases? How do you interpret the real-world meaning of your answer?

21. *Proof of the Change-of-Base Property:* The following is a proof of the change-of-base property for logarithms. For each step in the proof, write a reason to justify that step.

Prove that $\log_a x = \dfrac{\log_b x}{\log_b a}$.

*Proof:*
Let $y = \log_a x$.

| | |
|---|---|
| $\therefore a^y = x$ | a. ________________________ |
| $\therefore \log_b (a^y) = \log_b x$ | b. ________________________ |
| $\therefore y \log_b a = \log_b x$ | c. ________________________ |
| $\therefore y = \dfrac{\log_b x}{\log_b a}$ | d. ________________________ |
| $\therefore \log_a x = \dfrac{\log_b x}{\log_b a}$, Q.E.D. | e. ________________________ |

22. *The Two Forms of the Definition of e:* Let $f(n) = (1 + n)^{1/n}$ and let $g(n) = (1 + 1/n)^n$ as in the definition of $e$. Show that the limit of $g(n)$ as $n$ approaches infinity is equal to the limit of $f(n)$ as $n$ approaches zero and thus that the two forms of the definition are equivalent.

23. *Definition of e Journal Problem:* Write in your journal what you understand about the number $e$. Include such things as those listed here.
    - The definition given in this text, and why $e = \lim_{x\to\infty}(1 + 1/x)^x$ is equivalent to this definition.
    - The graph of $y_1 = (1 + 1/x)^x$, using windows of [0, 10] and [0, 100,000] for $x$ and [0, 3] for $y$. Include a discussion about how you can tell that, even though the graph looks like a horizontal straight line for the larger window, it is actually increasing slightly. Explain why your grapher gives no value of $y$ if $x$ is zero.
    - What is meant by the fact that $e$ is a transcendental number.

24. *Population Problem Revisited:* In Section 6-1, and at several intervening times, you have worked with the population problem in which

$$\int_{1000}^{N} \frac{1}{P}\,dP = \int_0^{10} 0.05\,dt,$$

where $P = N$ is the number of people at time $t = 10$ yr. Integrating gives

$$\ln|N| - \ln 1000 = 0.5.$$

Use the fact that $\ln x = \log_e x$ to solve this equation explicitly for $N$. Show that the answer is approximately 1649 people, which you found numerically in Problem 57 of Problem Set 6-3.

25. *Limit and Function Interchange Journal Problem:* Write an entry in your journal about the property that lets you interchange the function name and the limit sign. Include the following.
    - What the property says
    - How the definition of continuity makes the property work
    - An example applied to a function you know is continuous
    - How the property is used in finding the derivative of base $b$ logarithms algebraically

# 6-7 The Natural Exponential Function: The Inverse of ln

In Section 6-6, you learned that the natural logarithm function, ln, has the number $e$ as its base. From Section 4-5, recall that the inverse of a function is the relation you get when you interchange the two variables. Thus, the inverse of $y = \ln x = \log_e x$ is

$$x = \log_e y.$$

By the algebraic definition of logarithm (Section 6-4),

$$y = e^x.$$

This function is called the **natural exponential function** because the constant $e$ arose "naturally" in differentiating logarithmic functions. In this section you will learn to differentiate and integrate quickly the natural exponential function.

***OBJECTIVE***

Given a function whose equation involves a variable power of $e$, find equations for its derivative and its integral functions.

In Section 6-5, you learned how to use logarithmic differentiation to find the equation for the derivative of a function with a variable exponent. The derivative of $f(x) = e^x$ is as follows.

$f(x) = e^x$

$\ln f(x) = \ln e^x = x \cdot \ln e = x \cdot 1 = x \Rightarrow \ln f(x) = x$ — Take ln of both sides and simplify.

$\therefore \dfrac{1}{f(x)} \cdot f'(x) = 1$ — Differentiate implicitly. Observe the chain rule.

$f'(x) = f(x)$ — Algebra.

$f'(x) = e^x$ — Substitute $f(x) = e^x$.

The natural exponential function has a remarkable property: It is its own derivative!! Figure 6-7a shows that the slope of the graph at any point is equal to the $y$-value at that point.

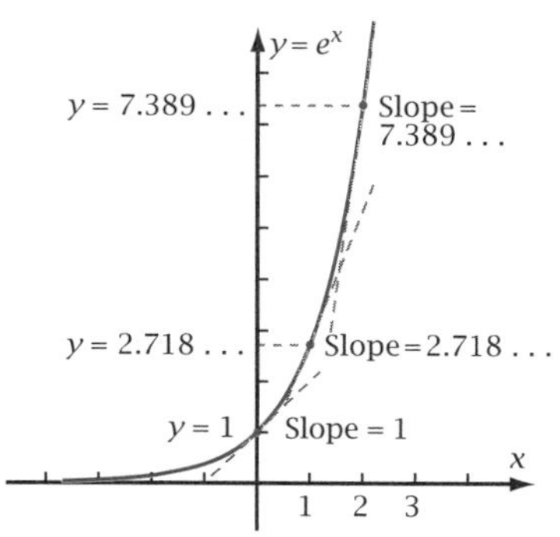


Figure 6-7a

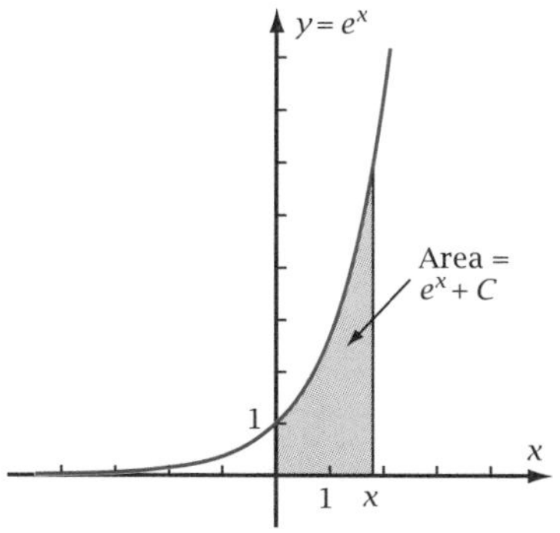


Figure 6-7b

Because $e^x$ is the derivative of $e^x$, you can find an equation for the integral of $e^x\,dx$.

$$\int e^x\,dx = e^x + C$$

The natural exponential function is practically indestructible! Differentiate it or integrate it—the answer comes out the same! Figure 6-7b shows that the area under the graph from a constant lower limit to the variable upper limit $x$ is

$$\text{Area} = e^x + C.$$

The number $e$, although it is a "messy decimal," is the base of choice in calculus for logarithmic and exponential functions because the derivatives and the integrals are so simple. The calculus of the natural exponential function is summarized below.

> **Properties: Calculus of the Natural Exponential Function**
>
> Derivative: If $f(x) = e^x$, then $f'(x) = e^x$.
> Integral: $\int e^x\,dx = e^x + C$

**Example 1** If $f(x) = 7e^{5x}$, find an equation for $f'(x)$. Use the equation to find the value of $f'(0.3)$. Use numerical differentiation to show that your answer is correct.

**Solution**

$$f(x) = 7e^{5x}$$

$$f'(x) = (7)(e^{5x})(5)$$ The $5x$ in the exponent is the inside function for the exponential function.

$$= 35e^{5x}$$

$$f'(0.3) = 35e^{5(0.3)} = 156.8591\ldots$$

Finding the numerical derivative of $7e^{5x}$ at $x = 0.3$ gives an answer close to $156.8591\ldots$. Your grapher may show something like $156.8597\ldots$, depending on the tolerance to which it is set. ■

**Example 2** Find an equation for the indefinite integral $\int e^{0.2x}\,dx$.

**Solution**

The key is recognizing that in $\int e^x\,dx$, the variable could be any letter.

$$\int e^t\,dt = e^t + C, \quad \int e^u\,du = e^u + C, \quad \text{etc.}$$

The only thing that is important is for the $d\ldots$ to be the *differential of the inside function*, namely, the exponent. In the given integral, the differential of $0.2x$ is $0.2\,dx$. The $dx$ is already there, but not the 0.2, so the first step is to multiply and divide by 0.2.

$$\int e^{0.2x}\,dx$$

$$= \frac{1}{0.2}\int e^{0.2x}(0.2\,dx)$$ Make the $dx$ the differential of the inside function.

$$= \frac{1}{0.2}e^{0.2x} + C$$ $\int e^u\,du = e^u + C$

$$= 5e^{0.2x} + C$$ ■

The symbol $\exp(x)$, or just $\exp x$, is often used in place of $e^x$. Using this symbol has several advantages.

- It uses the more familiar $f(x)$ terminology.
- It helps you realize that the exponent of an exponential is really an inside function.
- It makes exponentials easier to read if the exponent is a complicated expression, such as

$$e^{\sin x/(3x+7)} = \exp\left(\frac{\sin x}{3x+7}\right).$$

- It gives the function a name, exp, which can be used as ln, cos, and others are used.
- It appears in some computer languages.

### *Inverse Properties of ln and exp*

The fact that ln and exp are inverses of each other can sometimes be used to simplify an expression before you differentiate or integrate. For instance,

$$\ln e^x = x \ln e = x \cdot 1 = x.$$

This result is an example of the more general relationship between a function and its inverse, which you saw in Section 4-5. Specifically if $f$ is an invertible function, then

$$f(f^{-1}(x)) = x \quad \text{and} \quad f^{-1}(f(x)) = x.$$

**Property: Inverse Relationship Between ln and exp Functions**

$$\exp(\ln x) = x \quad \text{and} \quad \ln(\exp x) = x, \text{ or}$$
$$e^{\ln x} = x \quad \text{and} \quad \ln e^x = x$$

**■ Example 3** Differentiate: $y = \cos(\ln e^{7x})$

**Solution**

$y = \cos(\ln e^{7x}) \Rightarrow y = \cos 7x$   Function of an inverse function property.

$\therefore y' = -7 \sin 7x$ ■

# Problem Set 6-7

### *Do These Quickly*

The following problems are intended to refresh your skills. You should be able to do all ten problems in less than five minutes.

**Q1.** Differentiate: $y = \ln x$

**Q2.** Differentiate: $y = \log_e x$

**Q3.** Evaluate: $\ln 1$

**Q4.** Evaluate: $\log_3 1$

**Q5.** Evaluate: $\ln e^5$

**Q6.** Integrate: $\int \sec^2 x\, dx$

**Q7.** $(d/dx)(\sec x) = $ -?-

**Q8.** $(d/dx)(\sec^{-1} x) = $ -?-

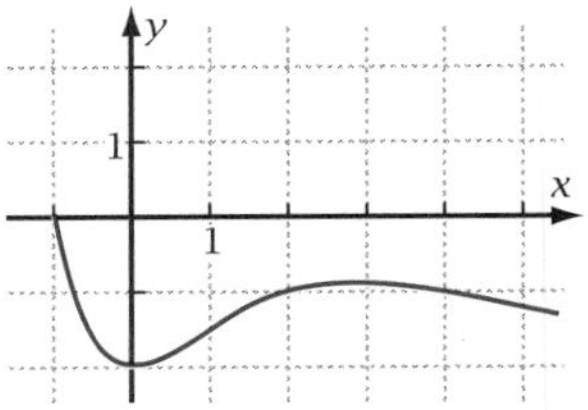


Figure 6-7c

**Q9.** Sketch the graph of the derivative for the function shown in Figure 6-7c.

**Q10.** True or false: Continuity implies differentiability.

0. *Look Ahead Problem:* Look at the derivatives and integrals in Problem Set 6-9. Make a list, by problem number, of those you presently know how to do.

For Problems 1–36, find an equation for the derivative function. Simplify your answer.

1. $y = e^{4x}$
2. $y = e^{9x}$
3. $y = 17e^{-5x}$
4. $y = 667e^{-3x}$
5. $f(x) = e^{-x}$
6. $f(x) = 3e^{-x}$
7. $h(x) = x^3 e^x$
8. $g(x) = x^{-6} e^x$
9. $r(t) = e^t \sin t$
10. $s(t) = e^t \tan t$
11. $u = 3e^x e^{-x}$
12. $v = e^{-4x} e^{4x}$
13. $y = e^{2u} \ln 3u$
14. $y = e^{-5u} \ln 4u$
15. $y = \dfrac{\exp x}{\ln x}$
16. $y = \dfrac{\ln x}{\exp x}$
17. $y = 4e^{\sec x}$
18. $y = 7e^{\cos x}$
19. $f(x) = \csc e^x$
20. $f(x) = \cot e^x$
21. $y = 3 \ln e^{2x}$
22. $y = 4 \ln e^{5x}$
23. $y = (\ln e^{3x})(\ln e^{4x})$
24. $y = (\ln e^{-2x})(\ln e^{5x})$
25. $g(x) = 4e^{\ln 3x}$
26. $h(x) = 6e^{\ln 7x}$
27. $y = 2001(e^{3x})^5$
28. $y = 1001(e^{4x})^7$
29. $y = e^x + e^{-x}$
30. $y = e^x - e^{-x}$
31. $u = (5 + e^{2t})^7$
32. $v = (3 + e^{-t})^5$

33. $y = \exp(5x^3)$

34. $y = 8\exp(x^5)$

35. $y = (\sin 3)(\ln 5)(e^2)$

36. $y = (\tan 4)(e^6)(\ln 2)$

For Problems 37 and 38, find $f'(x)$ algebraically for the given value of $x$, then confirm your answer numerically.

37. $f(x) = e^{0.4x}, \quad x = 2$

38. $f(x) = e^{-2x}, \quad x = 0.6$

For Problems 39 and 40, find $f'(x)$ algebraically for the given value of $x$. Then confirm your answer by graphing a line through the given point with the appropriate slope.

39. $f(x) = 5xe^x, \quad x = -1$

40. $f(x) = 6x^2e^{-x}, \quad x = 2$

For Problems 41–54, evaluate the indefinite integral.

41. $\int e^{5x}\,dx$

42. $\int e^{7x}\,dx$

43. $\int 6\exp x\,dx$

44. $\int \exp(0.2x)\,dx$

45. $\int 3e^{-2x}\,dx$

46. $\int -4e^{-6x}\,dx$

47. $\int e^{\sin x}\cos x\,dx$

48. $\int e^{\tan x}\sec^2 x\,dx$

49. $\int e^{3\ln x}\,dx$

50. $\int 60e^{\ln 5x}\,dx$

51. $\int (1 + e^{2x})^{50}e^{2x}\,dx$

52. $\int (1 - e^{4x})^{100}e^{4x}\,dx$

53. $\int (3 + e^x)^2\,dx$

54. $\int (2 + e^x)^3\,dx$

For Problems 55–58, evaluate the definite integral by using the fundamental theorem. Show by numerical integration that your answer is correct.

55. $\int_1^2 e^{0.4x}\,dx$

56. $\int_1^3 e^{0.2x}\,dx$

57. $\int_0^2 (e^x - e^{-x})\,dx$

58. $\int_{-1}^2 (e^x + e^{-x})\,dx$

59. *Rabbit Population Problem:* When rabbits were introduced to Australia in the middle of the nineteenth century, they had no natural enemies. As a result, their population grew exponentially with time. The photograph at the beginning of this chapter shows what happened. The general equation of the exponential function for the number of rabbits, $R(t)$, is

$$R(t) = ae^{kt}.$$

a. Suppose there were 60,000 rabbits in 1865, when $t = 0$, and that the population had grown to 2,400,000 by 1867. Substitute these values of $t$ and $R(t)$ to get two equations involving the constants $a$ and $k$. Use these equations to find values of $a$ and $k$, then write the particular equation expressing $R(t)$ as a function of $t$.

b. How many rabbits does your model predict there would have been in 1870?

c. According to your model, when was the first pair of rabbits introduced into Australia?

d. See George Laycock's *The Alien Animals* (Ballantine Books, 1966) for the eventual outcome of the rabbit problem.

60. *Depreciation Problem:* The value of a major purchase, such as a house, depreciates (decreases) each year because the purchase gets older. Assume that the value of Richard Holmes's house is given by

$$v(t) = 85{,}000\,e^{-0.05t},$$

where $v(t)$ is the number of dollars the house is worth at $t$ years after it was built.

a. How much was it worth when it was built?

b. How much did it depreciate during its eleventh year (from $t = 10$ to $t = 11$)?

c. What is the instantaneous rate of change (in dollars per year) of the value at $t = 10$? Why is this answer different from the answer you found in 60b?

d. When will the value have dropped to \$30,000?

61. *An Exponential Function is Not a Power Function!* Figure out a way to show that the formula for the derivative of a power function (that is, variable base and constant exponent) does *not* work for an exponential function (that is, constant base and variable exponent).

62. *Proof of the Function of an Inverse Function Property:* Prove the function of an inverse function property, mentioned in this section and in Section 4-5. The author's student Leighton Ku developed an easy proof that uses the definition of inverse function, namely,

$$y = f^{-1}(x) \quad \text{if and only if} \quad x = f(y).$$

*63. *Zero/Zero Problem:* Let $f(x) = \dfrac{\ln x + \sin(x-1)}{1 - e^{x-1}}$.

a. Show that $f(x)$ takes on the indeterminate form $0/0$ as $x$ approaches 1.

b. Plot the graph of $f$. Use a friendly window that includes 1.

c. What limit does $f(x)$ seem to be approaching as $x$ approaches 1?

d. Find the derivative of the numerator and the derivative of the denominator. Evaluate each derivative at $x = 1$. What does the ratio of the two derivatives equal? Surprising?!

64. *Journal Problem:* Update your journal with what you've learned since the last entry. Include such things as those listed here.
    - The one most important thing you have learned since your last journal entry
    - The reasons for using e as a base for logs and exponential functions
    - The algebraic techniques for finding derivatives and integrals of the natural exponential function and for finding the derivatives of any log function
    - Some instances in which exponential or log functions are used as mathematical models
    - Anything about logs or exponentials that you plan to ask about at the next class meeting

---

*This problem prepares you for Section 6-8.

# 6-8 Limits of Indeterminate Forms: l'Hospital's Rule

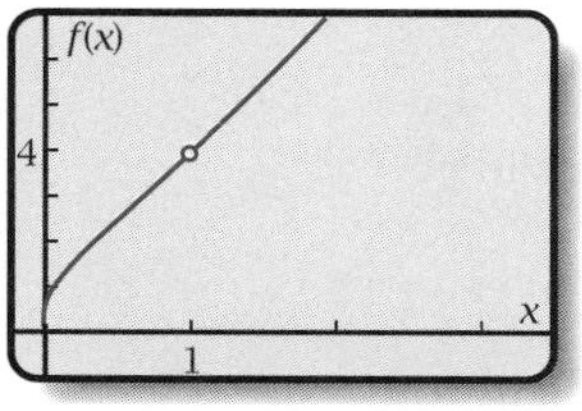

Figure 6-8a

When you use one of the formulas to find a derivative, you are really using a shortcut to find the limit of the indeterminate form 0/0. These formulas can be used to help you evaluate other expressions of the form 0/0. Figure 6-8a shows the graph of

$$f(x) = \frac{x^2 + 2x - 3}{\ln x}.$$

If you try to evaluate $f(1)$, you get

$$f(1) = \frac{1 + 2 - 3}{\ln 1} = \frac{0}{0}.$$

The graph suggests that the limit of $f(x)$ is 4 as $x$ approaches 1.

The technique you will use to evaluate such limits is called **l'Hospital's rule**, named after G. F. A. de l'Hospital (1661-1704), although it was probably known earlier by the Bernoulli brothers. This French name is pronounced "lo-pee-tal'." In older writing, it is sometimes spelled l'Hôpital, with a circumflex placed over the letter *o*. You will also learn how to use l'Hospital's rule to evaluate other indeterminate forms such as $\infty/\infty$, $1^\infty$, $0^0$, $\infty^0$, and $\infty - \infty$.

**OBJECTIVE**

Given an expression with an indeterminate form, find its limit using l'Hospital's rule.

L'Hospital's rule is easy to use but tricky to derive. Therefore you will start out by seeing how it works, then get some insight into why it works. The procedure for finding the limit of a fraction that has the form 0/0 or $\infty/\infty$ is to take the derivatives of the numerator and the denominator, then find the limit. For instance, if $g(x)/h(x) = (x^2 + 2x - 3)/(\ln x)$ (given above),

$$\lim_{x\to 1} \frac{g(x)}{h(x)} = \lim_{x\to 1} \frac{g'(x)}{h'(x)} = \lim_{x\to 1} \frac{2x + 2}{1/x} = \frac{4}{1} = 4,$$

which agrees with Figure 6-8a. The following is a formal statement of l'Hospital's rule.

**Property: l'Hospital's Rule**

If $f(x) = \dfrac{g(x)}{h(x)}$ and if $\lim_{x\to c} g(x) = \lim_{x\to c} h(x) = 0$,

then $\lim_{x\to c} f(x) = \lim_{x\to c} \dfrac{g'(x)}{h'(x)}$, provided the latter limit exists.

Corollaries of the rule lead to the same conclusion if $x \to \infty$ or if both $g(x)$ and $h(x)$ approach infinity.

Here's why l'Hospital's rule works. Because $g(x)$ and $h(x)$ both approach zero as $x$ approaches $c$, $g(c)$ and $h(c)$ either equal zero or can be defined to equal zero by removing a removable discontinuity. The fraction for $f(x)$ can be transformed to a ratio of difference quotients by subtracting $g(c)$ and $h(c)$, which both equal zero, and by multiplying by clever forms of 1.

$$f(x) = \frac{g(x)}{h(x)} = \frac{g(x) - g(c)}{h(x) - h(c)} = \frac{\dfrac{g(x) - g(c)}{x - c}}{\dfrac{h(x) - h(c)}{x - c}}$$

$$\therefore \lim_{x \to c} f(x) = \frac{\displaystyle\lim_{x \to c} \frac{g(x) - g(c)}{x - c}}{\displaystyle\lim_{x \to c} \frac{h(x) - h(c)}{x - c}} = \frac{g'(c)}{h'(c)}$$ Limit of a quotient. Definition of derivative.

If the derivatives of $f$ and $g$ are also continuous at $x = c$, you can write

$$g'(c) = g'(\lim_{x \to c} x) = \lim_{x \to c} g'(x) \quad \text{and} \quad h'(c) = h'(\lim_{x \to c} x) = \lim_{x \to c} h'(x).$$

Therefore

$$\lim_{x \to c} f(x) = \frac{\lim_{x \to c} g'(x)}{\lim_{x \to c} h'(x)} = \lim_{x \to c} \frac{g'(x)}{h'(x)}, \quad \text{Q.E.D.,}$$

where the last step is justified by the limit of a quotient property used "backwards." A formal proof of l'Hospital's rule must avoid the difficulty that $[h(x) - h(c)]$ might be zero somewhere other than at $x = c$. This proof and the proofs of the corollaries are not shown here because they would distract you from what you are learning. A geometric derivation of l'Hospital's rule is presented in Problem 34 of Problem Set 6-8.

Example 1 shows you a reasonable format to use when you apply l'Hospital's rule. The function is that given at the beginning of this section.

**Example 1** Find $L = \lim_{x \to 1} \dfrac{x^2 + 2x - 3}{\ln x}$.

**Solution**

$\lim_{x \to 1} \dfrac{x^2 + 2x - 3}{\ln x} \to \dfrac{0}{0}$ L'Hospital's rule applies because the limit has the form 0/0.

$= \lim_{x \to 1} \dfrac{2x + 2}{1/x} \to \dfrac{4}{1}$ L'Hospital's rule is no longer needed because the limit is no longer indeterminate.

$= 4$ ■

Example 2 shows how to use l'Hospital's rule for an indeterminate form other than 0/0.

**Example 2** Evaluate $\lim_{x \to \infty} x^2 e^{-x}$.

**Solution**

As $x$ goes to infinity, $x^2$ gets infinitely large and $e^{-x}$ goes to zero. A graph of $y = x^2 e^{-x}$ suggests that the expression goes to zero as $x$ becomes infinite (Figure 6-8b). To show this by l'Hospital's rule, first transform the expression into a fraction.

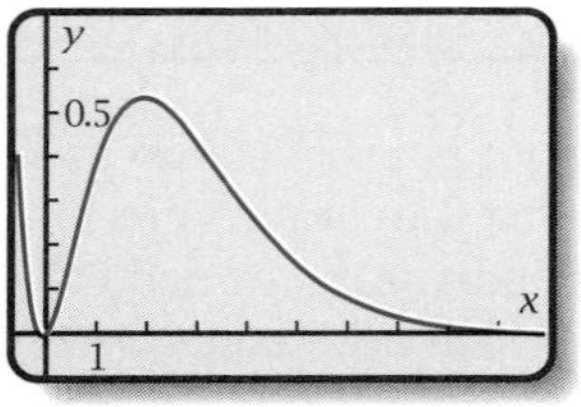


Figure 6-8b

$\lim_{x \to \infty} x^2 e^{-x} \to \infty \cdot 0$ L'Hospital's rule doesn't apply yet.

$= \lim_{x \to \infty} \dfrac{x^2}{e^x} \to \dfrac{\infty}{\infty}$ L'Hospital's rule does apply now. Find the derivative of the numerator and the denominator.

$= \lim_{x \to \infty} \dfrac{2x}{e^x} \to \dfrac{\infty}{\infty}$ L'Hospital's rule applies again.

$= \lim_{x \to \infty} \dfrac{2}{e^x} \to \dfrac{2}{\infty}$ L'Hospital's rule is no longer needed.

$= 0$ (finite)/(infinite) → 0 ■

### *Indeterminate Exponential Forms*

If you raise a number greater than 1 to a large power, the result is very large. A positive number less than 1 raised to a large power is close to zero. For instance,

$$\lim_{x\to\infty} 1.01^x = \infty \quad \text{and} \quad \lim_{x\to\infty} 0.99^x = 0.$$

If an expression approaches $1^\infty$, the answer is indeterminate. You saw such a case with the definition of $e$, which is the limit of $(1 + 1/x)^x$ as $x$ approaches infinity. Expressions that take on the form $\infty^0$ and $0^0$ are also indeterminate. Example 3 shows you how to evaluate an indeterminate form with a variable base and exponent. Like logarithmic differentiation shown earlier in this chapter, the secret is to take the log of the expression. Then you can transform the result to a fraction and apply l'Hospital's rule.

**Example 3** Evaluate $\lim_{x\to 1} x^{1/(1-x)}$.

**Solution** The function $f(x) = x^{1/(1-x)}$ takes on the indeterminate form $1^\infty$ at $x = 1$. The graph of $f$ (Figure 6-8c) shows a removable discontinuity at $x = 1$ and shows that the limit of $f(x)$ as $x$ approaches 1 is a number less than 0.5. The limit can be found by using l'Hospital's rule after taking the log.

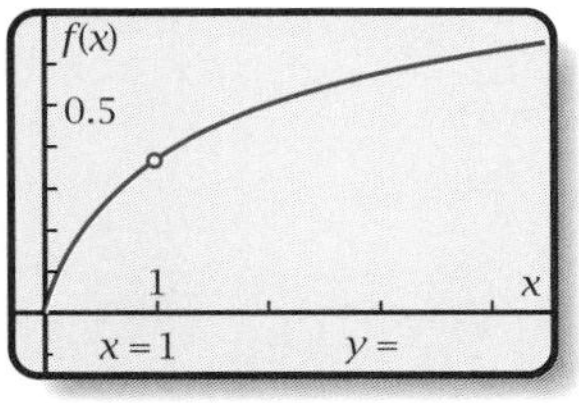


Figure 6-8c

Let $L = \lim_{x\to 1} x^{1/(1-x)}$.

Then $\ln L = \ln[\lim_{x\to 1} x^{1/(1-x)}] = \lim_{x\to 1}[\ln x^{1/(1-x)}]$ — Reverse ln and lim.

$= \lim_{x\to 1}\left[\dfrac{1}{1-x}\cdot \ln x\right] = \lim_{x\to 1}\dfrac{\ln x}{1-x} \to \dfrac{0}{0}$ — L'Hospital's rule applies now.

$= \lim_{x\to 1}\dfrac{1/x}{-1} = -1$ — Find the derivative of the numerator and the denominator.

$\therefore L = e^{-1} = 0.367879\ldots$ — $\ln L = -1 \Rightarrow L = e^{-1}$ ■

The answer to Example 2 agrees with the graph in Figure 6-8c.

# Problem Set 6-8

### *Do These Quickly*

The following problems are intended to refresh your skills. You should be able to do all ten problems in less than five minutes.

**Q1.** $e \approx$ -?- (as a decimal)

**Q2.** $e^{-1}$ = -?- (without negative exponents)

**Q3.** $\ln e$ = -?-

**Q4.** $\ln(\exp x)$ = -?-

**Q5.** $e^{\ln x}$ = -?-

**Q6.** If $\log_b x = \ln x$, then $b$ = -?-.

**Q7.** $\log_b x$ = -?- (in terms of the function ln)

**Q8.** If $f(x) = e^x$, then $f'(x)$ = -?-.

**Q9.** $\int e^{-x}\,dx$ = -?-

**Q10.** If $f(x) = \int_1^{\tan x} \sin t\,dt$, then $f'(x)$ = -?-.

For Problems 1 and 2, estimate graphically the limit of $f(x)$ as $x$ approaches zero. Sketch the graph. Then confirm your estimate by using l'Hospital's rule.

1. $\lim_{x\to 0} \dfrac{2\sin 5x}{3x}$

2. $\lim_{x\to 0} \dfrac{4\tan 3x}{5x}$

For Problems 3–30, find the indicated limit. Use l'Hospital's rule if necessary.

3. $\lim_{x\to 0} \dfrac{\tan x}{x}$

4. $\lim_{x\to 0} \dfrac{\sin x}{x}$

5. $\lim_{x\to 0} \dfrac{1-\cos x}{x^2}$

6. $\lim_{x\to 0} \dfrac{x^2}{\cos 3x - 1}$

7. $\lim_{x\to 0^+} \dfrac{\sin x}{x^2}$

8. $\lim_{x\to 0} \dfrac{1-\cos x}{x+x^2}$

9. $\lim_{x\to 0^+} \dfrac{\ln x}{1/x}$

10. $\lim_{x\to 0} \dfrac{e^{3x}}{x^2}$

11. $\lim_{x\to 1} \dfrac{e^x - e}{5\ln x}$

12. $\lim_{x\to 1} \dfrac{\ln x - x + 1}{x^2 - 2x + 1}$

13. $\lim_{x\to 2} \dfrac{3x+5}{\cos x}$

14. $\lim_{x\to 2} \dfrac{\tan x}{x-2}$

15. $\lim_{x\to \infty} \dfrac{e^x}{x^2}$

16. $\lim_{x\to \infty} \dfrac{x^3}{e^x}$

17. $\lim_{x\to \infty} \dfrac{3x+17}{4x-11}$

18. $\lim_{x\to \infty} \dfrac{2-7x}{3+5x}$

19. $\lim_{x\to \infty} \dfrac{x^3 - 5x^2 + 13x - 21}{4x^3 + 9x^2 - 11x - 17}$

20. $\lim_{x\to \infty} \dfrac{3x^5+2}{7x^5-8}$

21. $\lim_{x\to 0^+} x^x$

22. $\lim_{x\to 0^+} (\sin x)^{\sin x}$

23. $\lim_{x\to \pi/2^-} (\sin x)^{\tan x}$

24. $\lim_{x\to 1^+} x^{1/(x-1)}$

25. $\lim_{x\to \infty} (1+ax)^{1/x}$ (where $a$ = positive constant)

26. $\lim_{x\to 0} (1+ax)^{1/x}$ (where $a$ = constant)

27. $\lim_{x\to 0^+} x^{3/(\ln x)}$

28. $\lim_{x\to 0^+} (7x)^{5/(\ln x)}$

29. $\lim_{x\to 0} \left(\dfrac{1}{x} - \dfrac{1}{e^x - 1}\right)$

30. $\lim_{x\to 0} \left(\dfrac{1}{x} - \dfrac{1}{\sin x}\right)$

31. *Infinity Minus Infinity Problem:* Let $f(x) = \sec^2 \frac{\pi}{2}x - \tan^2 \frac{\pi}{2}x$. Because both sec $(\pi/2)$ and tan $(\pi/2)$ are infinite, $f(x)$ takes on the indeterminate form $\infty - \infty$ as $x$ approaches 1. Naive thinking might lead you to suspect that $\infty - \infty$ is zero because the difference between two equal numbers is zero. But $\infty$ is not a number. Plot the graph of $f$. Sketch the result, showing what happens at $x = 1, 3, 5, \ldots$. Explain the graph based on what you recall from trigonometry.

32. *l'Hospital's Surprise Problem!* Try to evaluate $\lim_{x\to \pi/2} \dfrac{\sec x}{\tan x}$ by using l'Hospital's rule. What happens? Find the limit by using some other method.

33. *Zero to the Zero Problem:* Often, the indeterminate form $0^0$ equals 1. For instance, the expression $(\sin x)^{\sin x}$ approaches 1 as $x$ approaches 0. But a function of the form

$$f(x) = x^{k/(\ln x)}$$

(where $k$ stands for a constant) that goes to $0^0$ does not, in general, approach 1. Apply l'Hospital's rule appropriately to ascertain the limit of $f(x)$ as $x$ approaches zero. On your grapher, investigate the graph of $f(x)$. Explain your results.

34. *L'Hospital's Rule, Geometrically:* In this problem you will investigate

$$f(x) = \frac{g(x)}{h(x)} = \frac{0.3x^2 - 2.7}{0.2x^2 - 2x + 4.2},$$

which approaches 0/0 as $x$ approaches 3. You will see l'Hospital's rule geometrically.

a. Confirm that $g(3) = h(3) = 0$.

b. Figure 6-8d shows the graphs of $g$ and $h$, along with the tangent lines at $x = 3$. Find equations of the tangent lines. Leave the answers in terms of $(x - 3)$.

c. Because $g$ and $h$ are differentiable at $x = 3$, they have local linearity in a neighborhood of $x = 3$. Thus the ratio $g(x)/h(x)$ is approximately equal to the ratio of the two linear functions you found in 34b. Show that this ratio is equal to $g'(3)/h'(3)$.

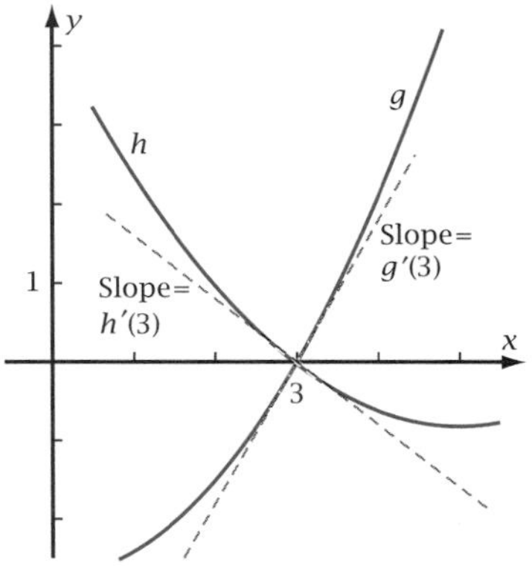

Figure 6-8d

d. Explain the connection between the conclusion you made in 34c and l'Hospital's rule. Explain why the conclusion might not be true if either $g(3)$ or $h(3)$ were not equal to zero.

e. Plot the graph of $f$. Sketch the result, showing its behavior at $x = 3$.

35. *Continuous Compounding of Interest Problem:* Suppose that \$1000 is earning interest at 6% per year, compounded annually (once a year). At the end of the first year, it will earn (0.06)(1000), or \$60, so there will be \$1060 in the account. This number can be easily found by multiplying the original \$1000 by 1.06, which is (1 + interest rate). At the end of each subsequent year, the amount in the account at the beginning of that year is multiplied again by 1.06, giving the following.

| year | total at end of year |
|---|---|
| 0 | 1000 |
| 1 | 1000(1.06) |
| 2 | $1000(1.06)^2$ |
| 3 | $1000(1.06)^3$ |
| ... | ... |
| $t$ | $1000(1.06)^t$ |

a. If the interest is compounded semiannually (twice a year), the account gets half the interest rate for twice as many time periods. If $m(t)$ is the number of dollars in the account after $t$ years, explain why

$$m(t) = 1000\left(1 + \frac{0.06}{2}\right)^{2t}.$$

b. Write an equation for $m(t)$ if the interest is compounded $n$ times a year. Then find the limit of this equation as $n$ approaches infinity to find $m(t)$ if the interest is compounded continuously. Treat $t$ as a constant, because it is $n$ that is varying as you find the limit.

c. How much more money will you have with continuous compounding rather than with annual compounding after 5 yr? After 20 yr? After 50 yr?

d. Quick! Write an equation for $m(t)$ if the interest is 7% per year compounded continuously.

36. *Order of Magnitude of a Function:* Let $L$ be the limit of $f(x)/g(x)$ as $x$ approaches infinity. If $L$ is infinite, then $f$ is said to be of a **higher order of magnitude** than $g$. If $L = 0$, then $f$ is said to be of a **lower order of magnitude** than $g$. If $L$ is a finite nonzero number, then $f$ and $g$ are said to have the **same order of magnitude.**

a. Rank each kind of function according to its order of magnitude.
   i. Power function, $f(x) = x^n$, where $n$ is a positive constant
   ii. Logarithmic function, $g(x) = \ln x$
   iii. Exponential function, $h(x) = e^x$

b. Quick! Without using l'Hospital's rule, evaluate the following limits.

i. $\lim_{x\to\infty} \frac{\ln 3x}{x^5}$ ii. $\lim_{x\to\infty} \frac{x^{100}}{e^{0.01x}}$ iii. $\lim_{x\to\infty} \frac{e^{0.3x}}{100\ln x}$ iv. $\lim_{x\to\infty} \frac{\sqrt{x}}{x}$ v. $\lim_{x\to\infty} \frac{e^x}{e^{0.2x}}$

37. *Journal Problem:* In your journal, write something about various indeterminate forms. Include examples of functions that approach the following forms.

**Kinds of Indeterminate Form**

Limits that take the following forms can equal different numbers at different times and thus cannot be found just by looking at the form:

$$\frac{0}{0},\quad \frac{\infty}{\infty},\quad \infty\cdot 0,\quad \infty-\infty,\quad 1^{\infty}, \infty^{0},\quad \text{and}\quad 0^{0}.$$

Try to pick examples for which the answer is not obvious. For instance, pick a function that goes to 0/0 but for which the limit does not equal 1. Show how other indeterminate forms can be algebraically transformed to 0/0 or to $\infty/\infty$ so that l'Hospital's rule can be used.

# 6-9 Derivative and Integral Practice for Transcendental Functions

The properties you have learned in this and previous chapters allow you to differentiate and integrate algebraically almost all of the elementary transcendental functions. These functions include trigonometric, inverse trigonometric, logarithmic, and inverse logarithmic (exponential) functions. In this section you will learn how to integrate exponential functions with any base (not just $e$) and how to integrate the remaining four trigonometric functions (sec, csc, tan, and cot). In Chapter 9, you will learn integration by parts, which will let you integrate logarithmic and inverse trigonometric functions algebraically.

**OBJECTIVE**

Be able to differentiate and integrate algebraically functions involving logs and exponentials quickly and correctly so that you can concentrate on the applications in the following chapters.

### Integrals of Base b Exponential Functions

In Section 6-7, you learned an algebraic method for integrating exponential functions with $e$ as the base. Exponentials with other bases can be integrated by transforming them to base $e$ first. Suppose you must integrate

$$\int 8^x\,dx.$$

Any positive number, such as 8, can be written as a power of $e$.

Let $8 = e^k$, where $k$ stands for a positive constant.

| | |
|---|---|
| Then $\ln 8 = \ln e^k$ | Take ln of both sides. |
| $= k(\ln e)$ | Reason? |
| $= k$ | Reason? |
| $\therefore 8 = e^{\ln 8}.$ | Substitute ln 8 for $k$. |

This equation is an example of the general relationship between a function and its inverse,

$$f(f^{-1}(x)) = x \quad \text{and} \quad f^{-1}(f(x)) = x.$$

The relationship leads to a definition of exponentials with bases other than $e$.

| | |
|---|---|
| $b^x = (e^{\ln b})^x$ | Replace $b$ with $e^{\ln b}$. |
| $= e^{x \ln b}$ | Multiply the exponents. |

**Definition: Exponential with Base b**

$$b^x = e^{x \ln b}$$

Using this definition, the integral above can be transformed and integrated as follows.

| | |
|---|---|
| $\int 8^x\,dx = \int e^{x \ln 8}\,dx$ | Definition of $8^x$. |
| $= \dfrac{1}{\ln 8}\int e^{x \ln 8}(\ln 8\,dx)$ | Transform to the differential of the inside function. |
| $= \dfrac{1}{\ln 8}e^{x \ln 8} + C$ | $\int e^u\,du = e^u + C$ |
| $= \dfrac{1}{\ln 8}8^x + C$ | Substitute back $8 = e^{\ln 8}$. |

Once you see the pattern, you can integrate or differentiate exponentials quickly.

> **Properties: Derivative and Integral of an Exponential Function**
>
> Derivative: $\frac{d}{dx}(b^x) = b^x \ln b$ — Multiply $b^x$ by $\ln b$.
>
> Integral: $\int b^x\,dx = b^x \frac{1}{\ln b} + C$ — Divide $b^x$ by $\ln b$.

### *Integrals of tan, cot, sec, and csc*

The tangent function can be integrated by first transforming it to sine and cosine, using the quotient properties from trigonometry.

$$\int \tan x\,dx = \int \frac{\sin x}{\cos x}\,dx$$

$$= -\int \frac{1}{\cos x}(-\sin x\,dx)$$ Transform to the integral of the reciprocal function.

$$= -\ln|\cos x| + C$$

$$= +\ln\left|\frac{1}{\cos x}\right| + C$$ $\ln n = -\ln(1/n)$

$$= \ln|\sec x| + C$$

The cotangent function is integrated the same way. The integral of secant and cosecant are trickier! A clever transformation is required to turn the integrand into the reciprocal function. The key to the transformation is that the derivative of $\sec x$ is $\sec x \tan x$ and the derivative of $\tan x$ is $\sec^2 x$. Here's how it works.

$$\int \sec x\,dx = \int \sec x \cdot \frac{\sec x + \tan x}{\sec x + \tan x}\,dx$$ Multiply by a "clever" form of 1.

$$= \int \frac{1}{\sec x + \tan x} \cdot (\sec^2 x + \sec x \tan x)\,dx$$ Write as the reciprocal function.

$$= \ln|\sec x + \tan x| + C$$ $(\sec^2 x + \sec x \tan x)\,dx$ is the differential of the denominator.

The formulas for $\int \cot x\,dx$ and for $\int \csc x\,dx$ are derived similarly. These integrals are listed, along with sine and cosine, in the box below.

> **Properties: Integrals of the Six Trigonometric Functions**
>
> $\int \sin x\,dx = -\cos x + C$
>
> $\int \cos x\,dx = \sin x + C$
>
> $\int \tan x\,dx = -\ln|\cos x| + C = \ln|\sec x| + C$
>
> $\int \cot x\,dx = \ln|\sin x| + C = -\ln|\csc x| + C$
>
> $\int \sec x\,dx = \ln|\sec x + \tan x| + C$
>
> $\int \csc x\,dx = -\ln|\csc x + \cot x| + C = \ln|\csc x - \cot x| + C$

The following boxes contain properties of logs and exponentials for doing calculus algebraically.

## *Properties: Natural Logs and Exponentials*

**Definition of the Natural Logarithm Function:**

$$\ln x = \int_1^x \frac{1}{t}\,dt \quad \text{(where } x \text{ is a positive number)}$$

**Calculus of the Natural Logarithm Function:**

$$\frac{d}{dx}(\ln x) = \frac{1}{x}$$

$$\int \ln x\,dx \quad \text{(to be introduced in Chapter 9)}$$

**Integral of the Reciprocal Function (from the definition):**

$$\int \frac{1}{u}\,du = \ln|u| + C$$

**Logarithm Properties of ln:**

Product: $\ln(ab) = \ln a + \ln b$

Quotient: $\ln(a/b) = \ln a - \ln b$

Power: $\ln(a^b) = b\ln a$

Intercept: $\ln 1 = 0$

**Calculus of the Natural Exponential Function:**

$$\frac{d}{dx}(e^x) = e^x$$

$$\int e^x\,dx = e^x + C$$

**Inverse Properties of Log and Exponential Functions:**

$$\ln(e^x) = x \quad \text{and} \quad e^{\ln x} = x$$

**Function Notation for Exponential Functions:**

$$\exp(x) = e^x$$

**Definition of *e*:**

$$e = \lim_{n \to 0}(1+n)^{1/n} = \lim_{n \to \infty}(1 + 1/n)^n$$

$e = 2.7182818284\ldots$ (a transcendental number, a nonrepeating decimal)

### *Properties: Base b Logs and Exponentials*

**Equivalence of Natural Logs and Base *e* Logs:**

$$\ln x = \log_e x \text{ for all } x > 0$$

**Calculus of Base *b* Logs:**

$$\frac{d}{dx}(\log_b x) = \frac{1}{\ln b} \cdot \frac{1}{x}$$

$$\int \log_b x\, dx \quad \text{(to be introduced in Chapter 9)}$$

**Calculus of Base *b* Exponential Functions:**

$$\frac{d}{dx}(b^x) = (\ln b)b^x$$

$$\int b^x\, dx = \frac{1}{\ln b}b^x + C$$

**Change of Base Property for Logarithms:**

$$\log_a x = \frac{\log_b x}{\log_b a} = \frac{\ln x}{\ln a}$$

## Problem Set 6-9

For Problems 1–56, find $y'$. Work all the problems in the order they appear, rather than just the odds or just the evens. (This is why they are numbered down the page instead of across.)

1. $y = \ln(3x + 4)$
2. $y = \ln(3x^5)$
3. $y = \ln(e^{3x})$
4. $y = \ln(\sin 4x)$
5. $y = \ln(\cos^5 x)$
6. $y = \ln(e^5)$
7. $y = \ln(\cos(\tan x))$
8. $y = \ln\sqrt{x^2 - 2x + 3}$
9. $y = \cos(\ln x)$
10. $y = \sin x \cdot \ln x$
11. $y = e^{7x}$
12. $y = e^{x^3}$
13. $y = e^{5 \ln x}$
14. $y = e^{\cos x}$
15. $y = \cos(e^x)$
16. $y = (\cos^3 x)(e^{3x})$
17. $y = \exp(x^5)$
18. $y = \exp(e^x)$
19. $\sin y = e^x$
20. $y = e^x \cdot \ln x$
21. $y = \int_1^x \frac{1}{t}\, dt$
22. $\tan y = e^x$
23. $y = \ln(e^{\ln x})$
24. $y = 2^x$

25. $y = e^{x \ln 2}$

26. $y = e^{2 \ln x}$

27. $y = x^2$

28. $y = e^{x \ln x}$

29. $y = x^x$

30. $y = x \ln x - x$

31. $y = e^x(x - 1)$

32. $y = \frac{1}{2}(e^x + e^{-x})$

33. $y = \frac{1}{2}(e^x - e^{-x})$

34. $y = \dfrac{e^x}{1 + e^x}$

35. $y = 5^x$

36. $y = \log_5 x$

37. $y = x^{-7}\log_2 x$

38. $y = 2^{-x}\cos x$

39. $y = e^{-2x} \ln 5x$

40. $y = \dfrac{7^x}{\ln 7}$

41. $y = \dfrac{\log_3 x}{\log_3 e}$

42. $y = \dfrac{\log_{10} x}{\log_{10} e}$

43. $y = (\log_8 x)(\ln 8)$

44. $y = (\log_4 x)^{10}$

45. $y = \log_5 x^7$

46. $y = \tan e^x$

47. $y = e^{\sin x}$

48. $y = \ln \csc x$

49. $y = 3^5$

50. $y = \ln(\cos^2 x + \sin^2 x)$

51. $y = \sin x$

52. $y = \sin^{-1} x$

53. $y = \csc x$

54. $y = \tan^{-1} x$

55. $y = \tan x$

56. $y = \cot x$

For Problems 57–80, integrate. Work all the problems in the order they appear, rather than just the odds or just the evens.

57. $\int e^{4x}\, dx$

58. $\int e^4\, dx$

59. $\int x^3 e^{x^4}\, dx$

60. $\int \cos x \cdot e^{\sin x}\, dx$

61. $\int \dfrac{(\ln x)^5}{x}\, dx$

62. $\int 5^x\, dx$

63. $\int e^{x \ln 5}\, dx$

64. $\int \dfrac{1}{2}(e^x + e^{-x})\, dx$

65. $\int_1^x \dfrac{1}{t}\, dt$

66. $\int e^{-x}\, dx$

67. $\int 2^x\, dx$

68. $\int (x^{-0.2} + 3^x)\, dx$

69. $\int \dfrac{3}{x}\, dx$

70. $\int_1^2 4^x\, dx$

71. $\int (\ln x)^9 \dfrac{1}{x}\, dx$

72. $\int \cos x\, dx$

73. $\int e^{\ln x}\, dx$

74. $\int \ln(e^{3x})\, dx$

75. $\int 0\, dx$

76. $\int \cos x \sec x\, dx$

77. $\int \sec 2x\,dx$

78. $\int \tan 3x\,dx$

79. $\int \cot 4x\,dx$

80. $\int \csc 5x\,dx$

For Problems 81–90, find the limit of the given expression.

81. $\lim\limits_{x\to 0} \dfrac{1-\cos x}{x}$

82. $\lim\limits_{x\to 0} \dfrac{x}{1-\cos x}$

83. $\lim\limits_{x\to \pi/2} \dfrac{x}{1-\cos x}$

84. $\lim\limits_{x\to \pi} \dfrac{x}{1+\cos x}$

85. $\lim\limits_{x\to 0} \dfrac{5x-\sin 5x}{x^3}$

86. $\lim\limits_{x\to \infty} \left(1+\dfrac{0.03}{x}\right)^x$

87. $\lim\limits_{x\to \infty} (1+0.03x)^{1/x}$

88. $\lim\limits_{x\to \infty} \dfrac{2^x}{x^2}$

89. $\lim\limits_{x\to 2} (0.5x)^{3/(2-x)}$

90. $\lim\limits_{x\to 0} \left(\dfrac{1}{e^{3x}-1}-\dfrac{1}{3x}\right)$

# 6-10 Chapter Review and Test

In this chapter you have studied the calculus of logarithmic and exponential functions. It all started with a real-world population problem in which $dP/dt$ was directly proportional to $p$. In solving this differential equation for $P$, you encountered $\int P^{-1}\,dP$, which you could integrate numerically but not algebraically.

The problem was solved by definition. The function $\ln x$ was defined as a definite integral whose derivative is $1/x$. This function was found to have the properties of logarithms, giving credence to the term *natural logarithm.* By starting at the other end, you found that the derivative of the function $y = \log_e x$ is also $1/x$ and thus concluded that $\ln x = \log_e x$. This fact allowed you to differentiate the inverse function, $y = e^x$. As a result, you became able to differentiate and integrate exponential functions such as $y = 2^x$, another problem you had been able to solve numerically but not algebraically.

The Review Problems below are numbered according to the sections of this chapter. The Concepts Problems allow you to apply your knowledge to new situations. The Chapter Test is like a typical classroom test your instructor might give you.

## Review Problems

R0. Update your journal with what you've learned since the last entry. Include such things as those listed here.

- The one most important thing you have learned in studying Chapter 6
- Which boxes you have been working on in the "define, understand, do, apply" table
- Your ability to do calculus algebraically, not just numerically, on logs and exponentials

- The new techniques and properties you have learned
- Any ideas about logs and exponentials you must ask about before the test on Chapter 6

R1. a. If money in a savings account earns interest compounded continuously, the rate of change of the amount of money in the account is directly proportional to the amount of money there. Suppose that for a particular account, $dM/dt = 0.06M$, where $M$ is the number of dollars and $t$ is the number of years the money has been in the account. Separate the variables so that $M$ is on one side and $t$ is on the other. If \$100 is in the account at time $t = 0$, show that when $t = 5$ yr,

$$\int_{100}^{x} M^{-1}\,dM = \int_{0}^{5} 0.06\,dt = 0.3,$$

where $x$ is the number of dollars in the account after five years.

b. Use your grapher's numerical integration and solve features to find, approximately, the value of $x$ for which the left-hand integral equals 0.3.

c. To the nearest cent, how much interest will the account have earned when $t = 5$ yr?

R2. a. Explain why $\int x^{-1}\,dx$ cannot be evaluated by using the power rule for integrals.

b. Let $L(x) = \int_1^x (1/t)\,dt$. Evaluate $L(2)$, $L(3)$, $L(4)$, $L(8)$, and $L(12)$ by using numerical integration. Show that these values are equal to the natural logarithms ln 2, ln 3, ln 4, ln 8, and ln 12 you can find on your grapher.

c. Show that the values of function $L$ in R2b have the properties of logarithms, namely, $L(ab) = L(a) + L(b)$, $L(a/b) = L(a) - L(b)$, and $L(a^b) = b \ln a$.

R3. a. Differentiate.

i. $y = (\ln 5x)^3$  ii. $f(x) = \ln x^9$  iii. $y = \csc(\ln x)$

iv. $g(x) = \int_1^{x^2} \csc t\,dt$

b. Integrate.

i. $\int \dfrac{\sec x \tan x}{\sec x}\,dx$  ii. $\int_{-2}^{-3} \dfrac{10}{x}\,dx$  iii. $\int x^2(x^3 - 4)^{-1}\,dx$

c. *Memory Retention Problem:* Paula Tishan prides herself on being able to remember names. She knows that the number of names she can remember at an event is a logarithmic function of the number of people she meets there, and she figures that her particular equation is

$$y = 1 - 101 \ln 101 + 101 \ln(100 + x),$$

where $y$ is the number of names she remembers when she meets $x$ people. The graph is shown in Figure 6-10a.

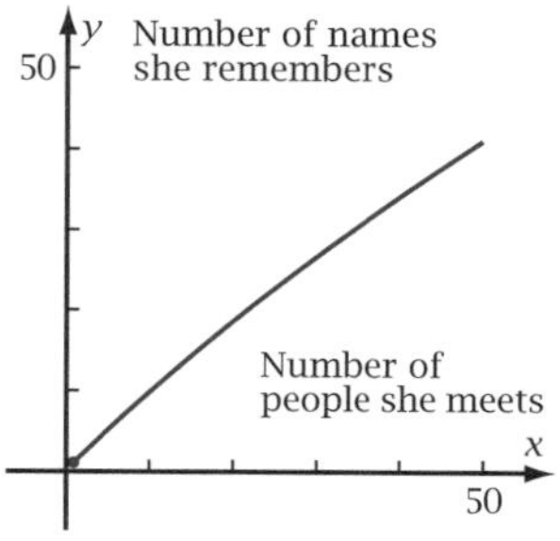

Figure 6-10a

i. How many names can she remember if she meets 100 people? Just 1 person? What percentage of the people she meets do these two numbers represent?

ii. At what rate does she remember names if she has met 100 people? Just 1 person?

iii. What is the greatest number of names she is likely to be able to remember without forgetting any? What assumptions do you make in coming up with your answer?

R4. a. State the definition of ln.

b. State the algebraic definition of logarithm.

c. State the uniqueness theorem for derivatives.

d. State the property of the ln of a power.

e. State and prove the property of the ln of a quotient.

R5. a. Write the equation of the derivative function.

i. $y = 100^x$ ii. $f(x) = 3.7 \cdot 10^{0.2x}$ iii. $r(t) = t^{\tan t}$

b. Differentiate logarithmically: $y = (5x - 7)^3(3x + 1)^5$

c. *Vitamin C Problem:* When you take vitamin C, its concentration, $C(t)$ parts per million, in your bloodstream rises rapidly, then drops off gradually. Assume that if you take a 500 mg tablet, the concentration is given by

$$C(t) = 200t \times 0.6^t,$$

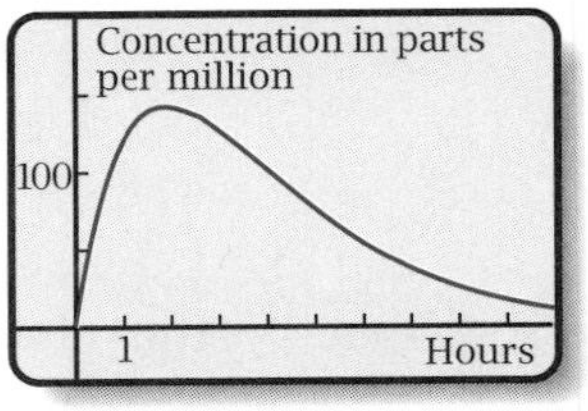


Figure 6-10b

where $t$ is time in hours since you took the tablet. Figure 6-10b shows the graph of $C$.

i. Approximately what is the highest concentration, and when does it occur?

ii. How fast is the concentration changing when $t = 1$? When $t = 5$? How do you interpret the signs of these rates?

iii. For how long a period of time will the concentration of the vitamin C be above 50 ppm?

iv. If you take the vitamin C with a cola drink, the vitamin C decomposes more rapidly. Assume that the base in the equation changes from 0.6 to 0.3. What effect will this change have on the highest concentration and when it occurs? What effect will this change have on the length of time the concentration is above 50 ppm?

R6. a. Write the definition of $e$.

b. Write an equation relating base $e$ logs and natural logs.

c. Write an equation expressing $\log_b x$ in terms of ln.

d. Differentiate.

i. $y = \log_4 x$ ii. $f(x) = \log_2(\cos x)$ iii. $y = \log_5 9^x$

e. Check your journal for Section 6-6. What is one important thing you wrote?

R7. a. Sketch the graph.

i. $y = e^x$ ii. $y = \exp(-x)$ iii. $y = \ln x$

b. Differentiate.

i. $f(x) = x^{1.4}\exp(5x)$ ii. $g(x) = \sin e^{-2x}$ iii. $y = e^{\ln x}$

c. Integrate.

i. $\int 10e^{-2x}\,dx$ ii. $\int e^{\cos x}\sin x\,dx$ iii. $\int_{-2}^{2} \exp(-0.1x)\,dx$

d. Tell why it is convenient in calculus to use the (untidy!) number $e$ as a base.

e. *Radioactive Decay Problem:* Strontium 90 is a radioactive isotope formed when uranium fissions. The percentage of the isotope remaining after $t$ years is given by

$$p(t) = 100e^{-0.025t}.$$

i. How much of the original strontium 90 is left after 5 yr?

ii. At what rate is the percentage of strontium 90 changing after 0 yr? After 5 yr?

iii. What is the half-life of strontium 90 (the time required for it to decay to 50%)?
iv. How long would it take for only 0.001% of the strontium 90 to remain?

f. *Chemotherapy Problem:* When a patient receives chemotherapy, the concentration, $C(t)$ parts per million, of chemical in the blood decreases exponentially with time. Assume that

$$C(t) = 150e^{-0.16t},$$

where $t$ is the number of days since the treatment (Figure 6-10c).

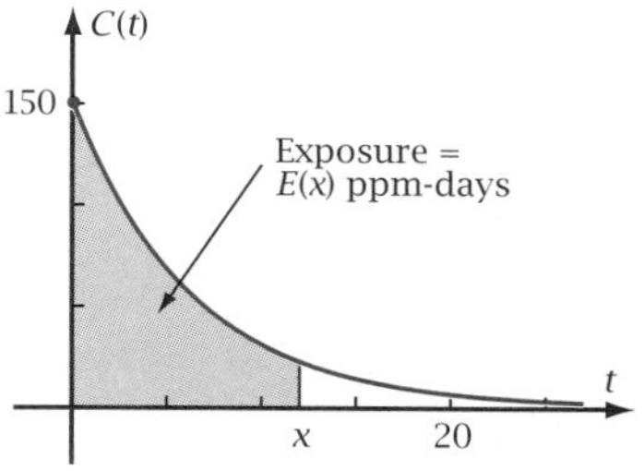

Figure 6-10c

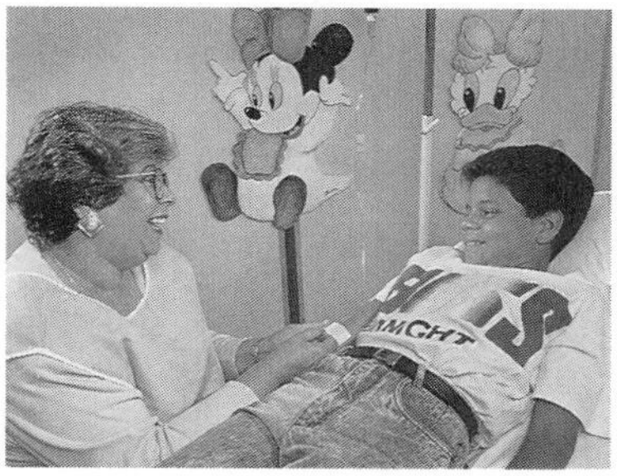

i. The amount of exposure to the treatment, $E(x)$, after $t = x$ days may be expressed as the product of the concentration and the number of days. Explain why a definite integral must be used to calculate the amount of exposure.
ii. Write an equation for $E(x)$. How much exposure has the patient received in 5 days? In 10 days? Does there seem to be a limit to the amount of exposure as $x$ becomes very large? If so, what is the limit? If not, why not?
iii. Quick! Write an equation for $E'(x)$. At what rate is $E(x)$ changing when $x = 5$? When $x = 10$?

R8. Evaluate the limits.

a. $\lim_{x\to\infty} \dfrac{2x^2 - 3}{7 - 5x^2}$  b. $\lim_{x\to 0} \dfrac{x^2 - \cos x + 1}{e^x - x - 1}$  c. $\lim_{x\to\infty} x^3 e^{-x}$

d. $\lim_{x\to 1} x^{\tan(\pi x/2)}$  e. $\lim_{x\to 2} 3x^4$  f. $\lim_{x\to\pi/2} (\tan^2 x - \sec^2 x)$

g. Write as many indeterminate forms as you can think of.

R9. a. Differentiate.

i. $y = \ln(\sin^4 7x)$  ii. $y = x^{-3}e^{2x}$  iii. $y = \cos(2^x)$  iv. $y = \log_3(x^4)$

b. Integrate.

i. $\int e^{-1.7x}\,dx$  ii. $\int 2^{\sec x}(\sec x \tan x\,dx)$

iii. $\int (5 + \sin x)^{-1}\cos x\,dx$  iv. $\int_1^5 \frac{1}{z}\,dz$

c. Find the following limits.

i. $\lim_{x\to 0} \dfrac{\tan 3x}{x^2}$  ii. $\lim_{x\to\infty} \left(1 - \dfrac{3}{x}\right)^x$

## Concepts Problems

C1. *Derivation of the Memory Equation:* In Problem R3c, the number of names, $y$, remembered as a function of people met, $x$, was said to be

$$y = 1 - 101 \ln 101 + 101 \ln(100 + x).$$

Suppose that, in general,

$$y = a + b \ln(x + c).$$

State why the following conditions are reasonable for $y$ and $y'$. Calculate the constants $a, b$, and $c$ so that these conditions will be met.

$$y = 1 \text{ when } x = 1$$
$$y' = 1 \text{ when } x = 1$$
$$y = 80 \text{ when } x = 100$$

C2. *Integral of ln Problem:* In Chapter 9 you will learn how to antidifferentiate $y = \ln x$. In this problem you are to try to discover what this antiderivative equals by examining graphs and a table of values. Figure 6-10d shows

$$y_1 = \ln x$$
$$y_2 = \int \ln x\, dx, \text{ with } C = 0.$$

The table shows values of $x, y_1$, and $y_2$. From the tables and the graph, see if you can figure out an equation for $y_2$. Write a description of methods you tried and whether or not these methods helped you get the answer.

| $x$ | $\ln x$ | $\int \ln x\, dx$ |
|---|---|---|
| 0.5 | −0.6931427 | −0.8465736 |
| 1.0 | 0 | −1 |
| 2.0 | 0.6931427 | −0.6137056 |
| 3.0 | 1.0986123 | 0.2958369 |
| 4.0 | 1.3862944 | 1.5451774 |
| 5.0 | 1.6094379 | 3.0471896 |
| 6.0 | 1.7917595 | 4.7505568 |
| 10.0 | 2.3025851 | 13.025851 |

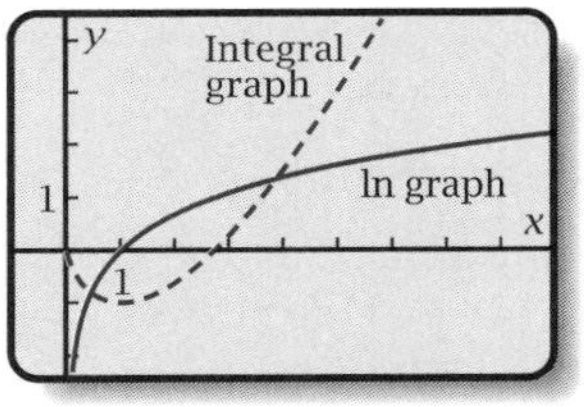

Figure 6-10d

C3. *Continued Exponentiation Function Problem:* Let $g(x) = x^x$, a function for which both the base and the exponent are variable. Find $g'(x)$. Then suppose that the number of $x$'s in the exponent is also variable. Specifically, define the **continued exponentiation** function, cont($x$), as follows:

$$\text{cont}(x) = x^{x^{x^{x^{\cdot^{\cdot^{\cdot}}}}}},$$

where there is a total of $x$ $x$'s in the exponent. For instance,

$$\text{cont}(3) = 3^{3^{3^3}} = 3^{3^{27}} = 3^{7625597484987},$$

which has over 3.6 billion digits. Figure out how to define cont($x$) for noninteger values of $x$. Try to do so in such a way that the resulting function is well defined, continuous, and differentiable for all positive values of $x$, including the integer values of $x$.

C4. *Every Real Number Is the* ln *of Some Positive Number:* Figure 6-10e shows the graph of $f(x) = \ln x$. The graph seems to be increasing, but slowly. In this problem you will prove that there is no horizontal asymptote and that the range of the ln function is all real numbers.

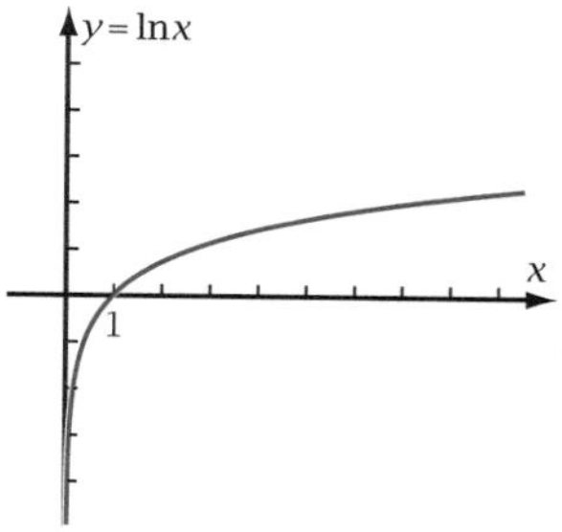


Figure 6-10e

a. Prove by contradiction that ln is unbounded above. That is, suppose that there is a positive number $M$ such that $\ln x \le M$ for all values of $x > 0$. Then pick a clever value of $x$ and show that you get an answer greater than $M$ for $\ln x$.

b. Prove (quickly!) that ln is unbounded below.

c. Prove (quickly!) that ln is continuous for all positive values of $x$.

d. Prove that for any two numbers $a$ and $b$, if $k$ is between $\ln a$ and $\ln b$, then there is a number $c$ between $a$ and $b$ such that $\ln c = k$. You should find that sketching a graph and using the intermediate value theorem are helpful.

e. Use the connections among C5a–d to prove that any real number, $k$, is the natural log of some positive number. That is, the range of ln is {real numbers}.

f. Use the fact that ln and exp are inverses of each other to show that the domain of exp is the set of all real numbers and that its range is the set of positive numbers.

C5. *Derivative of an Integral with Both Variable Upper and Lower Limits:* You have learned how to differentiate an integral such as $g(x) = \int_1^x \sin t\,dt$ between a fixed lower limit and a variable upper limit. In this problem you will see what happens if both limits of integration are variable.

a. Find $g'(x)$ if $g(x) = \int_{x^2}^{4} \sin t\,dt$.

b. Find $g'(x)$ if $g(x) = \int_{x^2}^{\tan x} \sin t\,dt$.

c. Write a generalization: If $g(x) = \int_{u(x)}^{v(x)} f(t)\,dt$, then $g'(x) =$ -?-. Include this generalization in your journal.

C6. What does $\int \dfrac{d(\text{cabin})}{\text{cabin}}$ equal?

## Chapter Test

T1. Write the definition of natural logarithm.

T2. Evaluate ln 1.8 approximately by using a midpoint Riemann sum with $n = 4$ increments. Show that your answer is close to the value of ln 1.8 you would get by calculator.

T3. If $g(x) = \int_2^x \sin t\,dt$, write an equation for $g'(x)$. What theorem tells you how to get this answer quickly?

T4. The uniqueness theorem for derivatives states that if $f(a) = g(a)$ for some number $x = a$, and if $f'(x) = g'(x)$ for all values of $x$, then $f(x) = g(x)$ for all values of $x$. In the proof of the theorem, you assume that there is a number $x = b$ for which $f(b)$ does not equal $g(b)$. Show how this assumption leads to a contradiction of the mean value theorem.

T5. Use the uniqueness theorem to prove that $\ln x = \log_e x$ for all positive numbers $x$.

T6. Let $f(x) = \ln(x^3 e^x)$. Find $f'(x)$ in the following two ways. Show that the two answers are equivalent.

a. Without first simplifying the equation for $f(x)$

b. First simplifying the equation for $f(x)$ by using ln properties

For Problems T7–T11, find an equation for the derivative. Simplify.

T7. $y = e^{2x} \ln x^3$

T8. $v = \ln(\cos 10x)$

T9. $f(x) = (\log_2 4x)^7$

T10. $t(x) = \ln(\cos^2 x + \sin^2 x)$

T11. $p(x) = \int_1^{\ln x} e^t \sin t \, dt$

For Problems T12–T15, evaluate the integral.

T12. $\int e^{5x}\, dx$

T13. $\int (\ln x)^6 \dfrac{dx}{x}$

T14. $\int \sec 5x \, dx$

T15. $\int_0^2 5^x \, dx$ (algebraically)

T16. Find $\displaystyle\lim_{x\to\infty} \frac{5 - 3x}{\ln 4x}$.

T17. Find $\displaystyle\lim_{x\to\pi/2^-} (\tan x)^{\cot x}$.

T18. *Force and Work Problem:* If you pull a box across the floor, you must exert a certain force. The amount of force needed may increase with distance if the bottom of the box becomes damaged as it moves. Assume that the force needed to move a particular box is given by

$$F(x) = 60e^{0.1x},$$

where $F(x)$ is the number of pounds that must be exerted when the box has moved $x$ feet (Figure 6-10f). Answer the following questions.

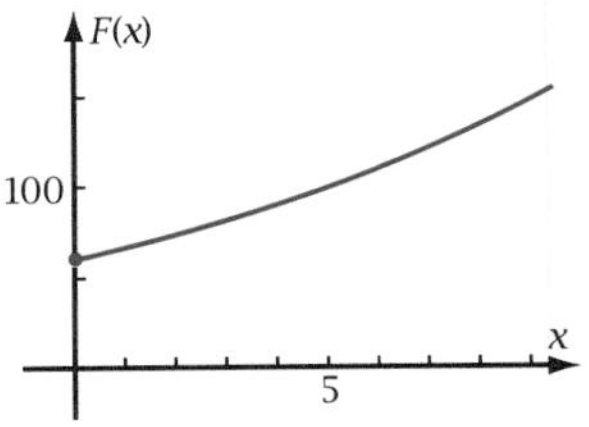


Figure 6-10f

a. At what rate is the force changing when $x = 5$? When $x = 10$?

b. Recall that work (foot-pounds) equals force times distance moved. Explain why a definite integral is used to find the work done moving the box to $x = 5$ from $x = 0$.

c. Write an integral for the work done in moving the box from $x = 0$ to $x = 5$. Evaluate the integral by using the appropriate form of the fundamental theorem to get a mathematical-world answer (exact). Then write a real-world answer, rounded appropriately.

# 6-11 Cumulative Review: Chapters 1–6

The following problems constitute a "semester exam" that will allow you to demonstrate your mastery of the concepts as you have studied them so far. Another cumulative review appears at the end of Chapter 7.

## Problem Set 6-11

1. The **derivative** of a function at a point is its instantaneous rate of change at that point. For the function

   $$f(x) = 2^x,$$

   show that you can find a derivative numerically by calculating $f'(3)$, using a **symmetric difference quotient** with $\Delta x = 0.1$.

2. A **definite integral** is a product of $x$ and $y$, where $y$ is allowed to vary with $x$. Show that you can calculate a definite integral graphically by estimating the integral of $g(x)$, shown in Figure 6-11a, from $x = 10$ to $x = 50$.

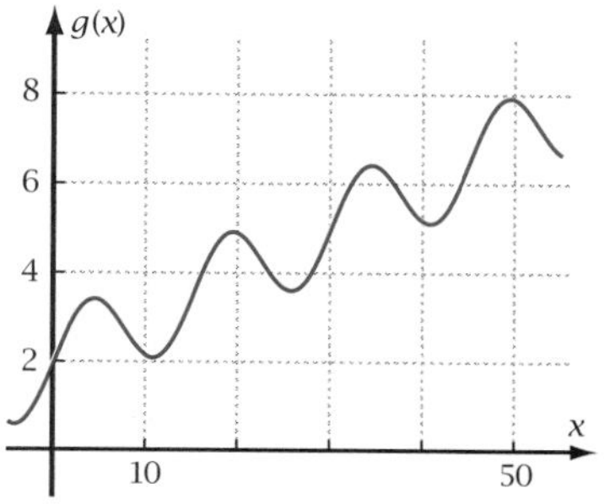


Figure 6-11a

3. Derivatives and definite integrals are defined precisely by using the concept of limit. Write the **definition of limit**.

4. Intuitively, a limit is a $y$-value that $f(x)$ stays close to when $x$ is close to a given number $c$. Show that you understand the symbols for, and the meaning of, limit by sketching the graph of one function for which both of the following are true.

   $$\lim_{x \to 3^-} f(x) = 4 \quad \text{and} \quad \lim_{x \to 3^+} f(x) = -\infty$$

5. Limits are the basis for the formal **definition of derivative**. Write this definition.

6. Show that you can operate with the definition of derivative by using it to show that if $f(x) = x^3$, then $f'(x) = 3x^2$.

7. Properties such as that in Problem 6 allow you to calculate derivatives *algebraically*, thus getting exact answers. Find $f'(5)$ for the function in Problem 6. Then find symmetric difference quotients for $f'(5)$ by using $\Delta x = 0.01$ and $\Delta x = 0.001$. Show that the difference quotients really get closer to the exact answer as $\Delta x$ decreases.

8. When **composite functions** are involved, you must remember the **chain rule**. Find the exact value of $f'(7)$ for

   $$f(x) = \sqrt{3x - 5}.$$

9. Derivatives can be interpreted *graphically*. Show that you understand this graphical interpretation by constructing an appropriate line on a copy of the graph in Figure 6-11b for the function in Problem 8.

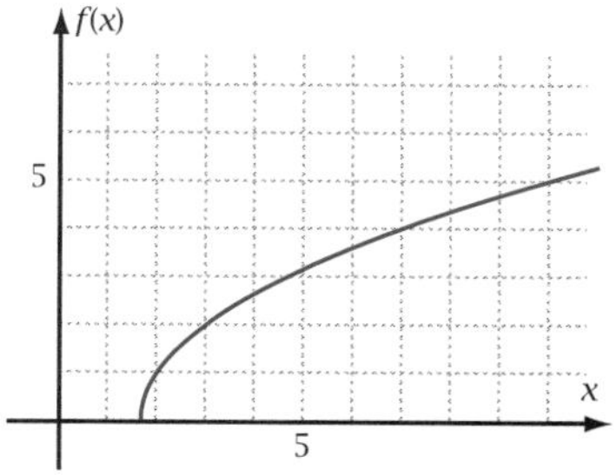


Figure 6-11b

10. Definite integrals can be calculated *numerically* by using **Riemann sums**. Show that you understand what a Riemann sum is by finding an upper sum, using $n = 6$ subintervals for

    $$\int_1^4 x^2\,dx.$$

11. The **definition of definite integral** involves the limit of a Riemann sum. For the integral in Problem 10, find midpoint Riemann sums with $n = 10$ and $n = 100$ increments. What limit do these sums seem to be approaching?

12. **Indefinite integrals** are **antiderivatives**. Evaluate the following.

a. $\int \cos^5 x \sin x \, dx$ b. $\int \frac{1}{x} \, dx$ c. $\int \tan x \, dx$

d. $\int \sec x \, dx$ e. $\int (3x - 5)^{1/2} \, dx$

13. The **fundamental theorem of calculus** gives an *algebraic* way to calculate definite integrals exactly, using indefinite integrals. Use the fundamental theorem to evaluate

$$\int_1^4 x^2 \, dx$$

from Problem 10. Show that your answer is the number you conjectured in Problem 11 for the limit of the Riemann sums.

14. The fundamental theorem is proved by using the **mean value theorem** as a lemma. State the mean value theorem. Draw a graph that clearly shows you understand its conclusion.

15. Much of calculus involves learning how to do *algebraically* the things you have learned how to do graphically or numerically. Use **implicit differentiation** to find $dy/dx$ if

$$y = x^{9/7},$$

thereby showing how the power rule for the derivative of functions with integer exponents is extended to functions with noninteger exponents.

16. Explain why the power rule for derivatives never gives $x^{-1}$ as the answer to a differentiation problem.

17. The **fundamental theorem** in its other form lets you take the derivative of a function defined by a definite integral. Find $f'(x)$ if

$$f(x) = \int_1^{\tan x} \cos 3t \, dt.$$

18. Show how the fundamental theorem in its second form lets you write a function whose derivative is $x^{-1}$.

19. The function you should have written in Problem 18 is the **natural logarithm** function. Use the **uniqueness theorem for derivatives** to show that this function has the property of the log of a power. That is, show that

$$\ln x^a = a \ln x$$

for any constant $a$ and for all values of $x > 0$.

20. Using the **parametric chain rule**, you can find $dy/dx$ for functions such as

$$x = 5 \cos t$$
$$y = 3 \sin t.$$

Write a formula for $dy/dx$ in terms of $t$.

21. The ellipse in Figure 6-11c has the parametric equations given in Problem 20. Find $dy/dx$ if $t = 2$. Show *graphically* that your answer is reasonable.

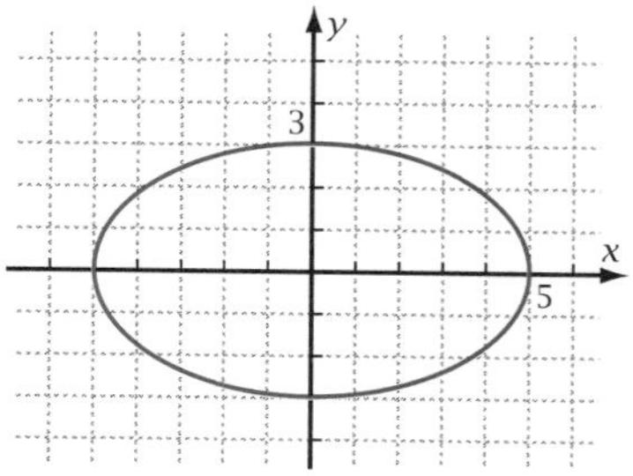

Figure 6-11c

22. Derivatives can be applied to **real-world** problems. Suppose that a car's position is

$$y = \tan^{-1} t,$$

where $y$ is in feet and $t$ is in seconds. The **velocity** is the instantaneous rate of change of position, and the **acceleration** is the instantaneous rate of change of velocity. Find an equation for the velocity and an equation for the acceleration, both as functions of time.

23. Derivatives can also be applied to problems from the **mathematical world.** For instance, derivatives can be used to calculate limits by using **l'Hospital's rule.** Find

$$\lim_{x \to 0} \frac{e^{3x} - 1}{\sin 5x}.$$

24. In the differentiation of the base $b$ logarithm function, the limit

$$L = \lim_{n \to 0} (1 + n)^{1/n}$$

appears. By appropriate use of l'Hospital's rule, show that this limit equals $e$, the **base of natural logarithms.**

25. **Simpson's rule** can be used to find definite integrals numerically if the integrand is specified only by a table of data. Use Simpson's rule to find the integral of $f(x)$ from $x = 2$ to $x = 5$.

| $x$ | $f(x)$ |
|---|---|
| 2.0 | 100 |
| 2.5 | 150 |
| 3.0 | 170 |
| 3.5 | 185 |
| 4.0 | 190 |
| 4.5 | 220 |
| 5.0 | 300 |

26. For the solid cone in Figure 6-11d, cross sections perpendicular to the $x$-axis, $x$ units from the vertex, are circles of radius $y = (r/h)x$, where $r$ is the radius of the cone's base and $h$ is its altitude (both constants). The volume of an object equals (cross-sectional area)(height). Definite integrals provide a way in which to evaluate (dependent variable)(independent variable). Use this information to derive the geometric formula for the volume of a cone,

$$V = \tfrac{1}{3}\pi r^2 h.$$

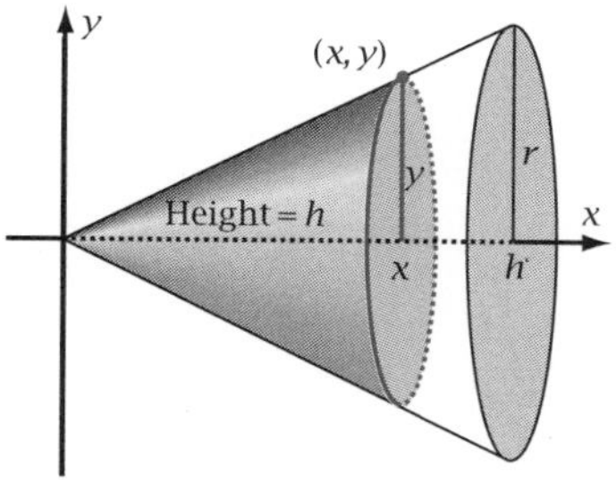

Figure 6-11d

27. It is important for you to be able to write about mathematics. Has writing in your journal helped you better understand calculus? If so, give an example. If not, why not?

CHAPTER

# 7 The Calculus of Growth and Decay

Bristlecone pine trees in California's White Mountains are still alive after thousands of years. Their ages can be found by counting the growth rings and by measuring carbon 14, absorbed when the tree grew. The rate of decay of carbon 14 is proportional to the amount remaining. Integrating the differential equation expressing this fact shows that the amount remaining is an exponential function of time.

## Mathematical Overview

If you know the rate at which a population grows, you can use antiderivatives to find the population as a function of time. In Chapter 7 you will learn ways to solve differential equations for population growth and other related real-world phenomena. You will solve these differential equations in four ways.

**Graphically** The logo at the top of each even-numbered page of this chapter shows three particular solutions of the same differential equation. The graph here also shows the slope field for this differential equation.

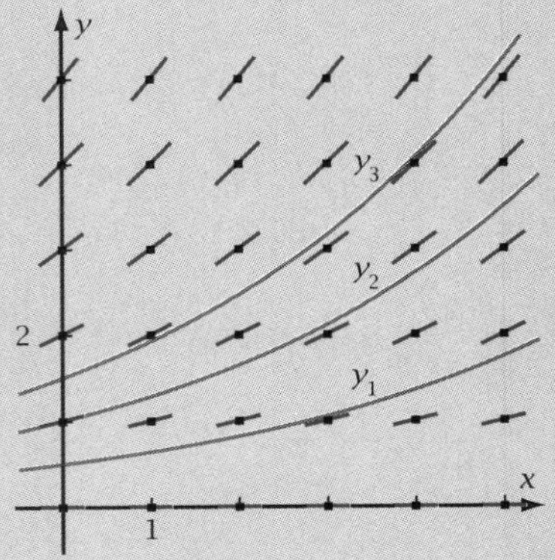


**Numerically**

| $x$ | $y_1$ | $y_2$ | $y_3$ |
|---|---|---|---|
| 0 | 0.5 | 1.0 | 1.5 |
| 1 | 0.64 ... | 1.28 ... | 1.92 ... |
| 2 | 0.82 ... | 2.64 ... | 2.47 ... |
| 3 | 1.05 ... | 2.11 ... | 3.17 ... |
| ... | ... | ... | ... |

**Algebraically** $\dfrac{dy}{dx} = 0.25y \Rightarrow y = Ce^{0.25x}$, a differential equation.

**Verbally** *I learned that the constant of integration is of vital importance in the solution of differential equations. Different values of C give different particular solutions. So I must always keep in mind, "Remember +C!"*

# 7-1 Direct Proportion Property of Exponential Functions

In Chapters 1–6, you learned the heart of calculus. You now know precise definitions and techniques for calculating limits, derivatives, indefinite integrals, and definite integrals. In this chapter you will solve *differential equations*, which express the rate at which a function grows. The function can represent population, money in a bank, water in a tub, radioactive atoms, or other quantities. A *slope field*, shown in the graph on this chapter's facing page, will let you solve complicated differential equations graphically. *Euler's method* provides you with a way to solve them numerically. Antiderivatives let you solve them algebraically. The experience you gain in this chapter will equip you to make intelligent application of these calculus concepts when they arise in your study of such fields as biology, economics, physics, chemistry, engineering, medicine, history, and law.

**OBJECTIVE**

Discover, on your own or with your study group, a property of exponential functions by working a real-world problem.

## Exploratory Problem Set 7-1

1. Suppose the number of dollars, $D(t)$, in a savings account after $t$ years is

   $$D(t) = 500(1.06^t).$$

   Calculate the number of dollars at $t = 0$ yr, $t = 10$ yr, and $t = 20$ yr.

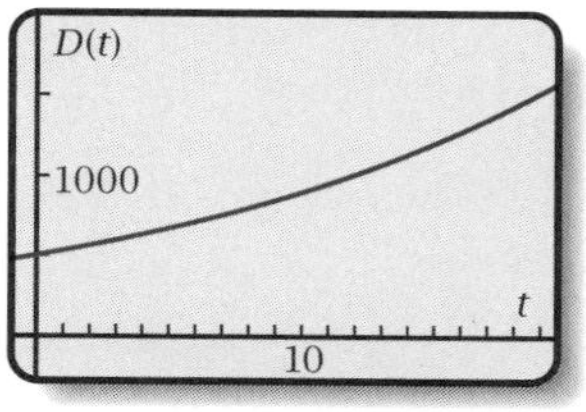

Figure 7-1a

2. For Problem 1, calculate $D'(0)$, $D'(10)$, and $D'(20)$. What are the units of $D'(t)$? Does the rate increase, decrease, or stay the same as the amount in the account increases?
3. For the account described in Problem 1, let $R(t)$ be the instantaneous rate of change of money in dollars per year *per dollar in the account.* Calculate $R(0)$, $R(10)$, and $R(20)$.
4. The values of $R(t)$ you found in Problem 3, when multiplied by 100, are percentage interest rates for the savings account. Does the percentage interest rate go up, go down, or stay the same as the amount of money in the account increases?
5. Recall that if $y$ is directly proportional to $x$, then $y = kx$, where $k$ stands for a constant (called the constant of proportionality). Show that the following property is true.

**Direct Proportion Property of Exponential Functions**

If $f$ is an exponential function, $f(x) = a \cdot b^x$, where $a$ and $b$ are positive constants, then $f'(x)$ is directly proportional to $f(x)$.

6. Just for fun, see if you can prove the converse of the property given in Problem 5. That is, prove that if $f'(x)$ is directly proportional to $f(x)$, then $f$ is an exponential function of $x$.

# 7-2 Exponential Growth and Decay

At the beginning of Chapter 6, you encountered a population growth problem in which the rate of change of the population, $dP/dt$, is directly proportional to that population. Recall from Section 3-9 that an equation such as $dP/dt = kP$ is called a **differential equation**. Finding an equation for $P$ as a function of $t$ is called **solving the differential equation**. In this section you will learn an efficient procedure for solving this sort of differential equation.

**OBJECTIVE**

Given a real-world situation in which the rate of change of $y$ with respect to $x$ is directly proportional to $y$, write and solve a differential equation and use the resulting solution as a mathematical model to make predictions and interpretations of that real-world situation.

**■ Example 1**

*Population Problem:* The population of the little town of Scorpion Gulch is now 1000 people. The population is presently growing at about 5% per year. Write a differential equation that expresses this fact. Solve it to find an equation that expresses population as a function of time.

**Solution**

Let $P$ be the number of people $t$ years after the present. The differential equation is

| | |
|---|---|
| $\dfrac{dP}{dt} = 0.05P.$ | The growth rate is $dP/dt$. Five percent of the population is 0.05 times the population. |
| $\dfrac{dP}{P} = 0.05dt$ | Use algebra to separate the variables on opposite sides of the differential equation. |
| $\int \dfrac{dP}{P} = \int 0.05dt$ | Integrate both sides of the differential equation. |
| $\ln\lvert P\rvert = 0.05t + C$ | Do the integrating. |
| $e^{\ln\lvert P\rvert} = e^{0.05t+C}$ | Exponentiate both sides of the integrated equation. |
| $\lvert P\rvert = e^{0.05t} \cdot e^{C}$ | Exponential of an ln on the left, product of powers with equal bases on the right. |
| $P = C_1e^{0.05t}$ | $e^C$ is a positive constant. Let $C_1 = \pm e^C$. This is the general solution. |
| $1000 = C_1e^{(0.05)(0)} = C_1$ | Substitute 0 for $t$ and 1000 for $P$. |
| $\therefore P = 1000\,e^{0.05t}$ | Substitute 1000 for $C_1$. This gives the particular solution. ■ |

The differential equation above was solved by **separating the variables**. The **general solution** represents a **family** of functions (Figure 7-2a), each with a different constant of integration. The population of 1000 at $t = 0$ is called an **initial condition**, or sometimes a **boundary condition**. The solution of a differential that meets a given initial condition is called a **particular solution**. Figure 7-2a shows the particular solution from Example 1. It also shows two other particular solutions, with $C_1 = 500$ and $C_1 = 1500$.

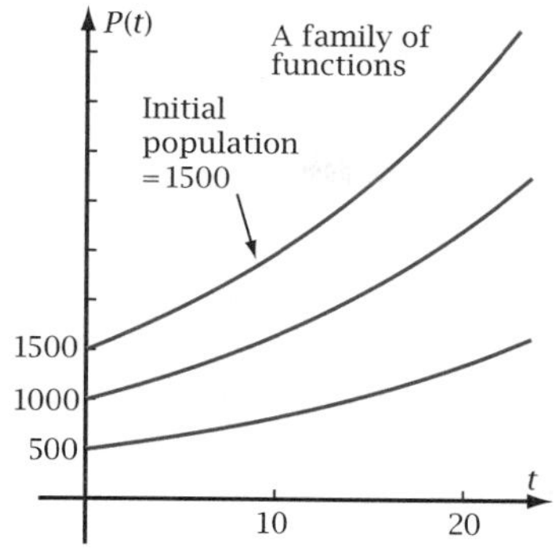


Figure 7-2a

Example 2 involves a differential equation for something other than population. The air pressure in a car or bicycle tire can be measured in pounds per square inch (psi). If the pressure in each of the four tires of a 3000-lb vehicle is 30 psi, the tires would flatten enough on the bottoms to have "footprints" totaling 100 in$^2$. Lower tire pressure would cause the tires to deform more so that pressure times area would still equal 3000.

**Example 2** *Punctured Tire Problem:* You run over a nail. As the air leaks out of your tire, the rate of change of air pressure inside the tire is directly proportional to that pressure.

a. Write a differential equation that states this fact. Evaluate the proportionality constant if the pressure was 35 psi and decreasing at 0.28 psi/min at time zero.

b. Solve the differential equation subject to the initial condition implied in step a.

c. Sketch the graph of the function. Show its behavior a long time after the tire is punctured.

d. What will the pressure be at 10 min after the tire was punctured?

e. The car is safe to drive as long as the tire pressure is 12 psi or greater. For how long after the puncture will the car be safe to drive?

**Solutions**

a. Let $p$ = no. of psi pressure.
Let $t$ = no. of minutes since the puncture.

$\frac{dp}{dt} = kp$ — Rate of change of pressure is directly proportional to pressure.

$-0.28 = k(35)$ — Substitute for $dp/dt$ and $p$. Because $p$ is decreasing, $dp/dt$ is negative.

$-0.008 = k$

$\therefore \frac{dp}{dt} = -0.008p$

b. $\dfrac{dp}{p} = -0.008\,dt$ — Separate the variables.

$\displaystyle\int \frac{dp}{p} = \int -0.008\,dt$ — Integrate both sides.

$\ln|p| = -0.008t + C_1$ — Use $C_1$ here in anticipation of using the simpler symbol $C$ later on.

$e^{\ln|p|} = e^{(-0.008t+C_1)}$

$|p| = e^{C_1}e^{-0.008t}$

$p = Ce^{-0.008t}$ — Replace $e^{C_1}$ with $C$. Replace $|p|$ with $p$ because pressure is a positive quantity.

$35 = Ce^{-0.008(0)} \Rightarrow 35 = C$ — Substitute the initial condition.

$\therefore p = 35e^{-0.008t}$ — Write the particular solution.

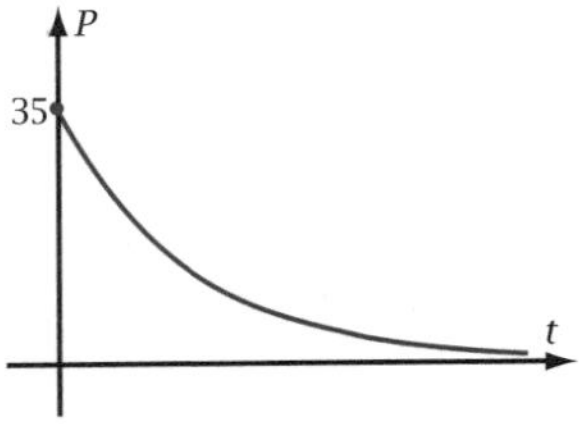


Figure 7-2b

c. The graph is shown in Figure 7-2b. The $t$-axis is a horizontal asymptote. You should be able to sketch the graph of a decreasing exponential function such as this one without having to plot it on your grapher first.

d. $p = 35e^{-0.008(10)} = 32.30907\ldots$
The pressure will be about 32.3 psi.

e. $12 = 35e^{-0.008t}$ — Substitute 12 for $p$.

$\frac{12}{35} = e^{-0.008t}$

$\ln(\frac{12}{35}) = -0.008t$

$t = \dfrac{\ln(\frac{12}{35})}{-0.008} = 133.805\ldots$

The car will be safe to drive for about 134 min, or a bit less than two and a quarter hours. ■

In Problem Set 7-2, you will work more problems in which differential equations lead to exponential functions.

# Problem Set 7-2

### *Do These Quickly*

The following problems are intended to refresh your skills. You should be able to do all ten problems in less than five minutes.

***Q1.*** Sketch: $y = e^x$

***Q2.*** Sketch: $y = e^{-x}$

***Q3.*** Sketch: $y = \ln x$

***Q4.*** Sketch: $y = x^2$

***Q5.*** Sketch: $y = x^3$

***Q6.*** Sketch: $y = 1/x$

***Q7.*** Sketch: $y = x$

***Q8.*** Sketch: $y = 3$

***Q9.*** Sketch: $x = 4$

***Q10.*** Sketch: $y = 3 - x$

1. *Bacteria Problem:* Bacteria in a lab culture (Figure 7-2c) grow in such a way that the instantaneous rate of change of bacteria is directly proportional to the number of bacteria present.

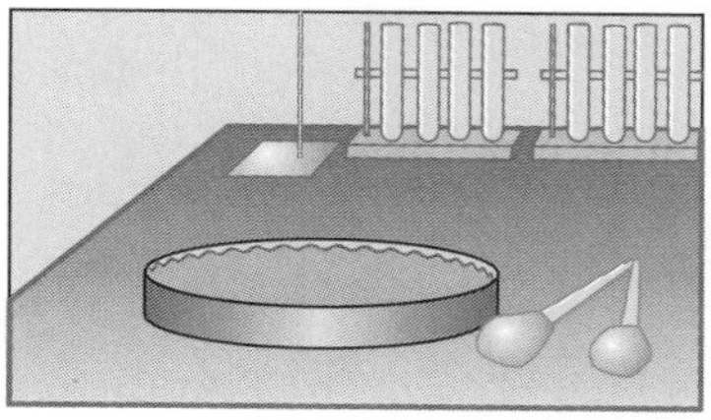

Figure 7-2c

   a. Write a differential equation that expresses the relationship. Separate the variables and integrate the equation, solving for the number of bacteria as a function of time.
   b. Suppose that initially there are 5 million bacteria. Three hours later, the number has grown to 7 million. Write the particular equation that expresses the number of millions of bacteria as a function of the number of hours.
   c. Sketch the graph of bacteria versus time.
   d. What will the bacteria population be one full day after the first measurement?
   e. When will the population reach 1 billion (1000 million)?

2. *Nitrogen 17 Problem:* When a water-cooled nuclear power plant is operating, oxygen in the water is transmuted to nitrogen 17. After the reactor is shut down, the radiation from this nitrogen 17 decreases in such a way that the rate of change in the radiation level is directly proportional to the radiation level.

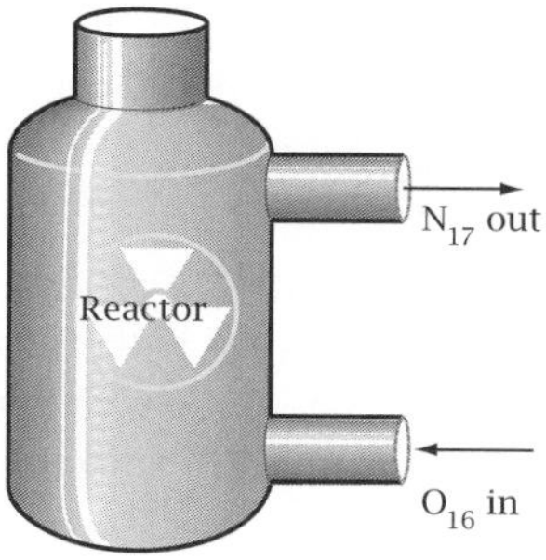


Figure 7-2d

   a. Write a differential equation that expresses the rate of change of the radiation level in terms of the radiation level. Solve the equation to find an equation that expresses the radiation level in terms of time.
   b. Suppose that when the reactor is first shut down, the radiation level is $3 \times 10^{17}$ units. After 60 sec the level has dropped to $5.6 \times 10^{13}$ units. Write the particular equation.
   c. Sketch the graph of radiation level versus time.
   d. It is safe to enter the reactor compartment when the radiation level has dropped to $7 \times 10^{-3}$ units. Will it be safe to enter the reactor compartment 5 min after the reactor has been shut down? Justify your answer.

3. *Chemical Reaction Problem:* Calculus foeride (a rare substance) reacts in such a way that the rate of change in the amount of foeride left unreacted is directly proportional to that amount.
   a. Write a differential equation that expresses this relationship. Integrate it to find an equation that expresses amount in terms of time. Use the initial conditions that the amount is 50 mg when $t = 0$ min, and 30 mg when $t = 20$ min.
   b. Sketch the graph of amount versus time.
   c. How much foeride remains an hour after the reaction starts?
   d. When will the amount of foeride equal 0.007 mg?

4. *Car Trade-in Problem:* Major purchases, like cars and houses, depreciate in value. That is, as time goes on, their value goes down. A reasonable mathematical model for the value of an object that depreciates assumes that the instantaneous rate of change of the object's value is directly proportional to the value.

   a. Write a differential equation that says that the rate of change of a car's trade-in value is directly proportional to that trade-in value. Integrate the equation and express the trade-in value as a function of time.
   b. Suppose you own a car whose trade-in value is presently \$4200. Three months ago its trade-in value was \$4700. Find the particular equation that expresses the trade-in value as a function of time since the car was worth \$4200.
   c. Plot the graph of trade-in value versus time. Sketch the result.
   d. What will the trade-in value be a year after the time the car was worth \$4700?
   e. You plan to get rid of the car when its trade-in value drops to \$1200. When will this be?
   f. At the time your car was worth \$4700, it was 31 mo old. What was its trade-in value when it was new?
   g. The purchase price of the car when it was new was \$16,000. How do you explain the difference between this number and your answer to 4f?

5. *Biological Half-Life Problem:* You accidentally inhale some mildly poisonous fumes (Figure 7-2e). Twenty hours later you still feel a bit woozy, so you go to a doctor. From blood samples, she measures a poison concentration of 0.00372 mg/ml and tells you to come back in 8 hr. On the second visit, she measures a concentration of 0.00219 mg/ml.

   Let $t$ be the number of hours that have elapsed since you first visited the doctor and let $C$ be the concentration of poison in your blood (in milligrams per milliliter). From biology, you realize that the instantaneous rate of change of $C$ with respect to $t$ is directly proportional to $C$.

Figure 7-2e

   a. Write a differential equation that relates these two variables.
   b. Solve the differential equation subject to the initial conditions specified. Express $C$ as a function of $t$.
   c. The doctor says you might have had serious body damage if the poison concentration had ever been as high as 0.015 mg/ml. Based on your mathematical model, was the concentration ever that high? Justify your answer.
   d. Plot the graph of this function. Sketch the results.
   e. The **biological half-life** of a poison is the length of time it takes for the concentration to drop to half of its present value. Find the biological half-life of this poison.

6. *Carbon 14 Dating Problem:* Carbon 14 is an isotope of carbon that is formed when radiation from the sun strikes ordinary carbon dioxide in the atmosphere. Thus plants

such as trees, which get their carbon dioxide from the atmosphere, contain small amounts of carbon 14. Once a particular part of a plant has been formed, no more new carbon 14 is taken in by that part. The carbon 14 in that part decays slowly, transmuting into nitrogen 14. Let $P$ be the percentage of carbon 14 that remains in a part of a tree that grew $t$ years ago.

a. The instantaneous rate of change of $P$ with respect to $t$ is directly proportional to $P$. Use this fact to write a differential equation that relates these two variables.

b. Solve the differential equation for $P$ in terms of $t$. Use the fact that the half-life of carbon 14 is 5750 yr. That is, if $P = 100$ when $t = 0$, then $P = 50$ when $t = 5750$.

c. The oldest living trees in the world are the bristlecone pines in the White Mountains of California. Four thousand growth rings have been counted in the trunk of one of these trees, meaning that the innermost ring grew 4000 years ago. What percentage of the original carbon 14 would you expect to find remaining in this innermost ring?

d. A piece of wood claimed to have come from Noah's Ark is found to have 48.37% of the carbon 14 remaining. It has been suggested that the Great Flood occurred in 4004 B.C. Is the wood old enough to have come from Noah's Ark? Explain.

e. Plot the graph of $P$ versus $t$ for times from 0 yr through at least 20,000 yr. Use your grapher's trace function to demonstrate that your answers to 6c-e are correct by showing that they lie on this graph. Sketch the results.

f. See Colin Renfrew's article "Carbon 14 and the Prehistory of Europe," *Scientific American*, (October, 1971) for some surprising results of slight inaccuracies in the carbon 14 dating technique!

7. *Compound Interest Problem I:* Banks compound interest on savings continuously, meaning that the instant the interest is earned, it starts earning more interest. Thus the instantaneous rate at which the amount in your account changes is directly proportional to the amount in the account. As a result, the amount of money, $M$, increases at a rate proportional to the amount of money in the account (Figure 7-2f),

$$\frac{dM}{dt} = kM,$$

where $M$ is in dollars, $t$ is in years, and $k$ is a proportionality constant.

Based on what you have learned thus far in calculus, figure out how $M$ varies with $t$. To find the value of $k$ for a particular savings account, realize that if \$100 is invested at an interest rate of 7% per year, then $M$ is increasing at a rate of \$7 per year at the instant $M = 100$. Once you have found a function that expresses $M$ in terms of $t$, investigate the effects of leaving various amounts for various times at various interest rates. For instance, which option gives you more money in the long run: investing twice the amount of money, leaving the money twice as long, or finding an interest rate twice as high?

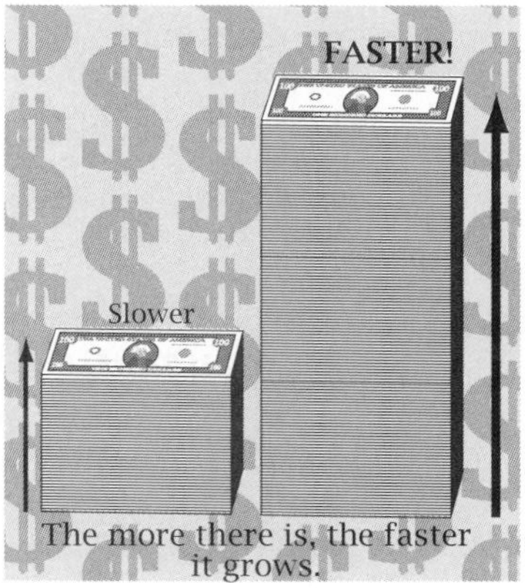
FASTER!
Slower
The more there is, the faster it grows.

Figure 7-2f

8. *Compound Interest Problem II:* If interest in a savings account is compounded at discrete intervals rather than continuously, then the amount of money, $M$, in the account is

$$M = M_0\left(1 + \frac{k}{n}\right)^{nt},$$

where $M$ is the number of dollars at time $t$ years after the investment was made, $M_0$ is the number of dollars invested when $t = 0$, $k$ is the interest rate as a decimal, and $n$ is the number of times per year the interest is compounded. The ideas behind this equation are shown in Problem 35 of Problem Set 6-8. Compare the amount, $M$, you would have after a specified time if the money were compounded yearly, quarterly (four times a year), monthly, and daily. Compare these amounts with that which you would get if the interest were compounded continuously, as in Problem 7. Reach some conclusions about the relative effects of higher interest rate versus more frequent compounding of interest. See if you can show that the function from Problem 7 for continuous compounding is a logical consequence of taking the limit of the compound interest formula in this problem as $n$ approaches infinity.

9. *Generalization Problem:* In this section you have worked problems in which the rate of change of $y$ is directly proportional to $y$. Solving this differential equation has always led to an exponential function. Good mathematicians are quick to spot possible generalizations that will shorten the problem-solving process. Prove the following theorem.

**Theorem: Converse of the Direct Proportion Property of Exponential Functions**

If $\dfrac{dy}{dx} = ky$, where $k$ stands for a constant, then $y = Ce^{kx}$.

# 7-3 Other Differential Equations for Real-World Applications

In Section 7-2, you worked real-world problems in which $dy/dx$ is directly proportional to $y$. In this section you will work real-world problems in which the derivative has a more complicated property than being directly proportional to $y$. Some of the resulting functions will be exponential and others will not.

**OBJECTIVE**

Given the relationship between a function and its rate of change, write a differential equation, solve it to find an equation for the function, and use the function as a mathematical model.

■ ***Example 1*** *Tin Can Leakage Problem:* Suppose you fill a tall (topless) tin can with water, then punch a hole near the bottom with an ice pick (Figure 7-3a). The water leaks quickly at first, then more slowly as the depth of the water decreases. In engineering or physics, you will learn that the rate at which water leaks out is directly proportional to the square root of its depth. Suppose that at time $t = 0$ min, the depth is 12 cm and $dy/dt$ is $-3$ cm/min.

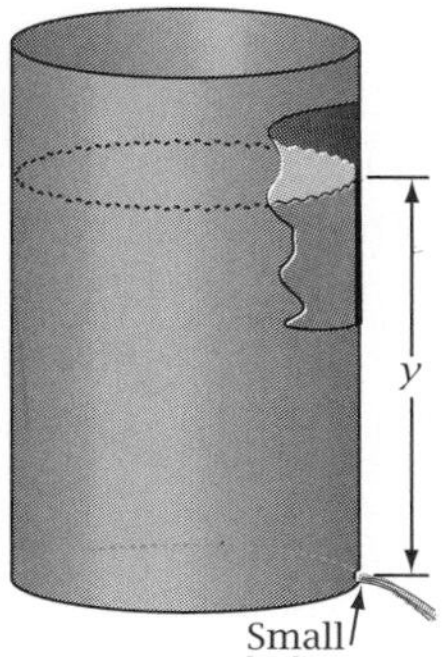

Figure 7-3a

a. Write a differential equation stating that the instantaneous rate of change of $y$ with respect to $t$ is directly proportional to the square root of $y$. Find the proportionality constant.

b. Solve the differential equation to find $y$ as a function of $t$. Use the given information to find the particular solution. What kind of a function is this?

c. Plot the graph of $y$ as a function of $t$. Sketch the graph. Consider the domain of $t$ in which the function gives reasonable answers.

d. Solve algebraically for the time at which the can becomes empty. Compare your answer with the time it would take at the initial rate of $-3$ cm/min.

***Solutions***

a. $$\frac{dy}{dt} = ky^{1/2}$$

$k$ is the proportionality constant. The 1/2 power is equivalent to the square root.

At $t = 0, y = 12$ and $\dfrac{dy}{dt} = -3.$

$\dfrac{dy}{dt}$ is negative because $y$ is decreasing as $t$ increases.

$$\therefore\ -3 = k(12^{1/2}) \Rightarrow k = -3(12^{-1/2})$$

b. $$y^{-1/2}\,dy = k\,dt$$

Separate the variables. It is simpler to write $k$ instead of $-3(12^{-1/2})$.

$$\int y^{-1/2}\,dy = \int k\,dt$$

$$2y^{1/2} = kt + C$$

$$2(12^{1/2}) = k \cdot 0 + C = C$$

Substitute the initial condition $y = 12$ when $t = 0$.

$$y = \tfrac{1}{4}(kt + C)^2 = \tfrac{1}{4}(k^2t^2 + 2kCt + C^2)$$

Do the algebra before substituting for $k$ and $C$.

$$y = \tfrac{3}{16}t^2 - 3t + 12$$

Use your pencil and paper to see how to get this!

This is a *quadratic* function.

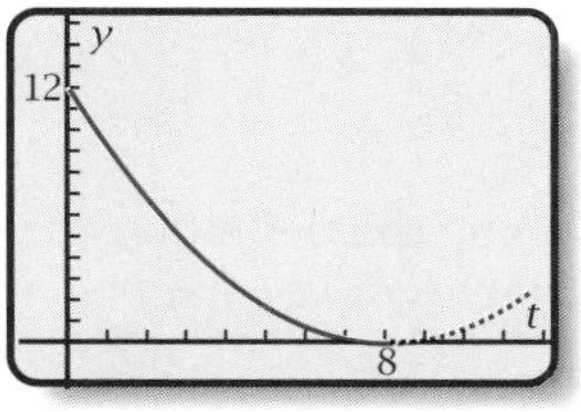

Figure 7-3b

c. Figure 7-3b shows the graph of this function. At time $t = 8$, the can becomes empty. Beyond that time the model would indicate that the can is filling back up. Before $t = 0$, the can was not draining. Thus the domain in which the mathematical model gives reasonable answers is $0 \le t \le 8$. The part of the graph beyond $t = 8$ is dotted to show the quadratic nature of the function.

d. $$0 = \tfrac{3}{16}t^2 - 3t + 12$$

$$t = \frac{3 \pm \sqrt{9 - 4(\frac{3}{16})(12)}}{2(\frac{3}{16})} = 8$$

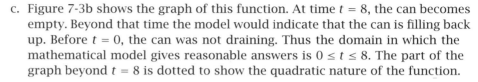

The can takes 8 min to drain, which is just twice as long as it would take at the original rate of $-3$ cm/min. ■

Example 2 shows what can happen if a population is growing at a constant rate because of one influence and decaying at another rate because of a second influence. The "population" is water in a lake behind a dam.

**■ Example 2** *Dam Leakage Problem:* A new dam is constructed across Scorpion Gulch (Figure 7-3c). Engineers want to predict the amount of water in the lake behind the dam as a function of time. At time $t = 0$ days the water starts flowing in at a fixed rate $F$ $\text{ft}^3/\text{hr}$. Unfortunately, as the water level rises, some leaks out. The leakage rate, $L$, is directly proportional to the amount of water, $W$ $\text{ft}^3$, present in the lake. Thus the instantaneous rate of change of $W$ is equal to $F - L$.

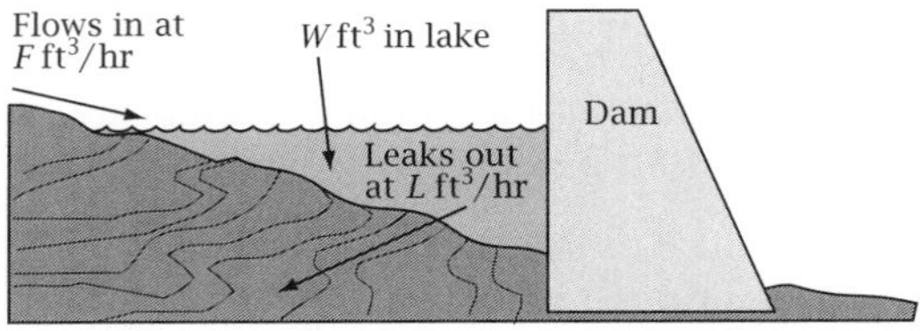


Figure 7-3c

a. What does $L$ equal in terms of $W$? Write a differential equation that expresses $dW/dt$ in terms of $F$, $W$, and $t$.

b. Solve for $W$ in terms of $t$, using the initial condition $W = 0$ when $t = 0$.

c. Water is known to be flowing in at $F = 5000$ $\text{ft}^3/\text{hr}$. Based on geological considerations, the proportionality constant in the leakage equation is assumed to be $0.04/\text{hr}$. Write the equation for $W$, substituting these quantities.

d. Predict the amount of water after 10 hr, 20 hr, and 30 hr. After these numbers of hours, how much water has flowed in and how much has leaked out?

e. When will the lake have 100,000 $\text{ft}^3$ of water?

f. Find the limit of $W$ as $t$ approaches infinity. State the real-world meaning of this number.

g. Draw the graph of $W$ versus $t$. Clearly show the asymptote.

**Solutions**

a. In a problem this complicated, it helps to start by writing the definitions of the letters being used and whether they stand for variables or constants.

$W =$ no. of $\text{ft}^3$ of water in the lake (dependent variable)

$t =$ no. of hours since water started flowing (independent variable)

$F =$ no. of $\text{ft}^3/\text{hr}$ the water flows in (a constant)

$L =$ no. of $\text{ft}^3/\text{hr}$ the water leaks out (a variable)

Then you proceed by putting together the information asked for in the problem.

$L = kW$ — Meaning of "directly proportional." $k$ stands for the constant of proportionality.

$dW/dt = F - L$ — $dW/dt$ is the instantaneous rate of change of $W$.

$\therefore\ dW/dt = F - kW$

b. Separating the variables appears to be tricky. Recall that $F$ and $k$ are constants.

$$\frac{dW}{F - kW} = dt \qquad \text{Multiply by } dt\text{. Divide by } F - kW.$$

$$\int \frac{dW}{F - kW} = \int dt \qquad \text{Integrate both sides.}$$

The differential of the denominator, $d(F - kW)$, equals $-kdW$. You can make the numerator equal to $-kdW$ by multiplying and dividing by $-k$.

$$\frac{1}{-k}\int \frac{-kdW}{F - kW} = \int dt$$

$$-\frac{1}{k}\ln|F - kW| = t + C \qquad \text{Integral of the reciprocal function.}$$

$$\ln(F - kW) = -kt - kC \qquad F > kW \text{ because water comes in faster than it goes out.}$$

$$e^{\ln(F-kW)} = e^{-kt-kC} \qquad \text{Exponentiate both sides.}$$

$$F - kW = e^{-kt}e^{-kC} \qquad \text{Do suitable algebra.}$$

$$W = \frac{1}{k}(F - e^{-kt}e^{-kC})$$

$$W = \frac{1}{k}(F - C_1e^{-kt}) \qquad \text{Use } C_1 \text{ for } e^{-kC} \text{ (general solution).}$$

Substituting the initial condition $W = 0$ when $t = 0$,

$$0 = \frac{1}{k}(F - C_1e^0).$$

$$0 = \frac{1}{k}(F - C_1), \text{ which implies that } C_1 = F.$$

$$\therefore W = \frac{1}{k}(F - Fe^{-kt})$$

$$W = \frac{F}{k}(1 - e^{-kt})$$

c. Substituting 5000 for $F$ and 0.04 for $k$ gives

$$W = 125000(1 - e^{-0.04t}). \qquad \text{This is the particular solution.}$$

d. Try using your grapher's trace or table feature to find values of $W$. Round to some reasonable value, such as to the nearest cubic foot. The values of $F$ are calculated by multiplying 5000 by $t$. The values of leakage are found by subtraction.

| $t$ | $W$ | $F$ | $L$ |
|---|---|---|---|
| 10 | 41,210 | 50,000 | 8,790 |
| 20 | 68,834 | 100,000 | 31,166 |
| 30 | 87,351 | 150,000 | 72,649 |

e. Substituting 100,000 for $W$ and using the appropriate algebra gives the following.

$$100000 = 125000(1 - e^{-0.04t})$$

$$0.8 = 1 - e^{-0.04t} \Rightarrow e^{-0.04t} = 0.2$$

$$-0.04t = \ln 0.2 \qquad \text{Take ln of both sides.}$$

$$t = 40.2359\ldots$$

Thus it will take a bit more than 40 hr for the lake to fill up to 100,000 $\text{ft}^3$.

f. $\lim\limits_{t\to\infty} W = \lim\limits_{t\to\infty} 125000(1 - e^{-0.04t})$

$= 125000(1 - 0)$

$= 125000$

$W$ is 125,000 $\text{ft}^3$ at most.
Note that $e^{-0.04t} = 1/e^{0.04t}$ (which has the form $1/\infty$ as $t$ approaches infinity) thus approaches zero.

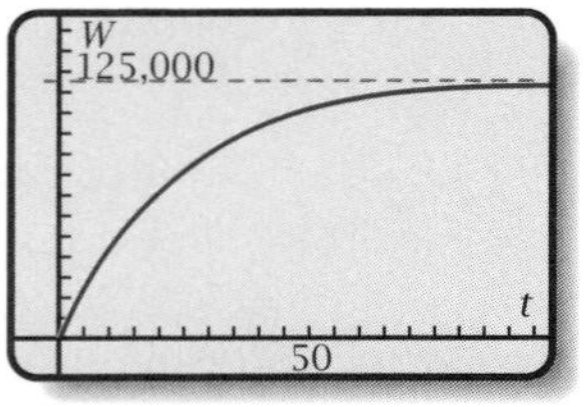

Figure 7-3d

g. The graph is shown in Figure 7-3d. ■

■ ***Example 3*** The lake in Example 2 starts filling with water. The actual amount of water at time $t = 10$ hr is exactly 40,000 $\text{ft}^3$. The flow rate is still 5000 $\text{ft}^3$/hr, as predicted. Use this information to find a more precise value of the leakage constant $k$.

***Solution*** Substituting $F = 5000$ and the ordered pair $(t, W) = (10, 40000)$ gives

$$40000 = \frac{5000}{k}(1 - e^{-10k}).$$

This equation cannot be solved analytically for $k$ because $k$ appears both algebraically (by division) and transcendentally (as an exponent). Fortunately, your grapher will allow you to evaluate $k$ as precisely as you like. You might first divide both sides by 5000 to make the numbers more manageable.

$$8 = \tfrac{1}{k}(1 - e^{-10k})$$

Then use your grapher's solve or intersect feature to find the value of $k$. The result is

$$k \approx 0.046421\ldots.$$

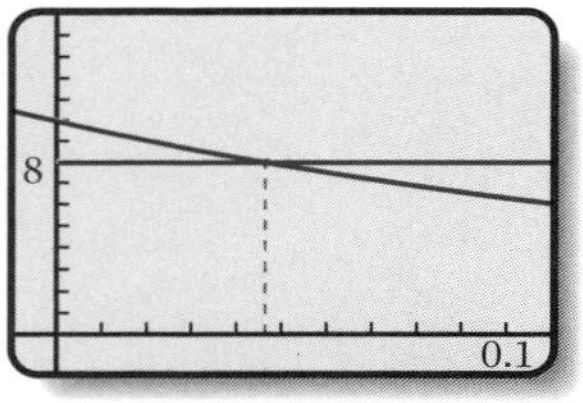

Figure 7-3e

The value of $k$ can also be found by plotting and tracing (Figure 7-3e). It is close to the 0.04 assumed in Example 2. ■

# Problem Set 7-3

### *Do These Quickly*

The following problems are intended to refresh your skills. You should be able to do all ten problems in less than five minutes.

**Q1.** If $dy/dx = ky$, then $y$ = -?-

**Q2.** If $dy/dx = kx$, then $y$ = -?-

**Q3.** If $dy/dx = k$, then $y$ = -?-

**Q4.** If $dy/dx = \sin x$, then $y$ = -?-

**Q5.** If $y = \sin^{-1} x$, then $dy/dx$ = -?-

**Q6.** $\ln(e^{5\cos x})$ = -?-

**Q7.** $e^{\ln \tan x}$ = -?-

**Q8.** Sketch a $y$-graph (Figure 7-3f) if $y(1) = 0$.

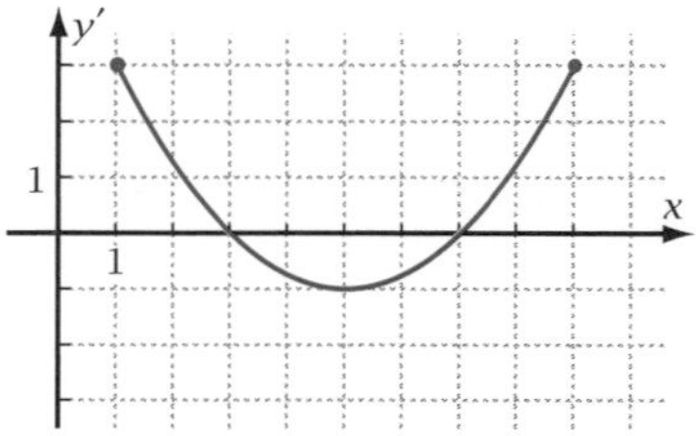

Figure 7-3f

**Q9.** What does it mean for $f$ to be integrable on $[a, b]$?

**Q10.** If $\int_1^4 v(t)\,dt = 17$ and $\int_1^7 v(t)\,dt = 33$, then $\int_4^7 v(t)\,dt$ = -?-

1. *Sweepstakes Problem I:* You win a well-known national sweepstakes! Your award is an income of \$100 a day for the rest of your life! You decide to put the money into a fireproof filing cabinet (Figure 7-3g) and let it accumulate there. But temptation sets in, and you start spending the money at $S$ dollars per day.

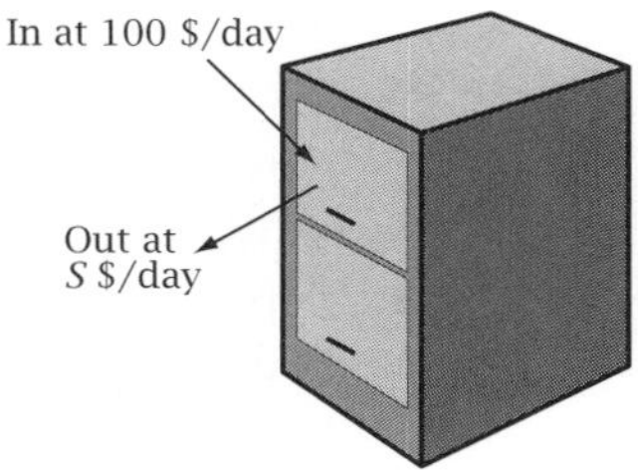

Figure 7-3g

   a. Let $M$ be the number of dollars you have in the filing cabinet and let $t$ be the number of days you have been receiving the money. Assuming that the rates are continuous, write a differential equation that expresses $dM/dt$ in terms of $S$.
   b. Your spending rate, $S$, is directly proportional to the amount of money, $M$. Write an equation that expresses this fact, then substitute the result into the differential equation.
   c. Separate the variables and integrate the differential equation in 1b to get an equation for $M$ in terms of $t$. As the initial condition, realize that $M = 0$ when $t = 0$.
   d. Suppose that each day you spend 2% of the money kept in the filing cabinet. That is, the proportionality constant in the equation for $S$ is 0.02. Substitute this value into the equation you found in 1c to get $M$ explicitly in terms of $t$.
   e. Plot the graph of $M$ versus $t$. Sketch the result.
   f. After 30 days, 60 days, and 90 days, how much money will you have in the filing cabinet? How much has come in? How much has been spent?
   g. After a year, how much money is in the filing cabinet? At what rate is the amount increasing at this time?
   h. What is the limit of $M$ as $t$ approaches infinity?

2. *Sweepstakes Problem II:* You win a well-known national sweepstakes! Your award is an income of \$100 a day for the rest of your life! You put the money into a savings account at a bank (Figure 7-3h), where it earns interest at a rate directly proportional to the amount, $M$, which is in the account. Assuming that the \$100 rate is continuous, $dM/dt$ equals $100 + kM$, where $k$ is a proportionality constant. Solve this differential equation subject to the initial condition that there was no money in the account at $t = 0$ days. Find the proportionality constant if the interest rate is 0.02% (*not* 2%!) per day, or roughly 7% per year. Transform the solution so that $M$ is in terms of $t$. Use the result to explore the way $M$ varies with $t$. A graph might help. Consider such information as how much of $M$ and of $dM/dt$ comes from the \$100 per day and how much comes from interest after various numbers of days. What is the limit of $M$ as $t$ approaches infinity?

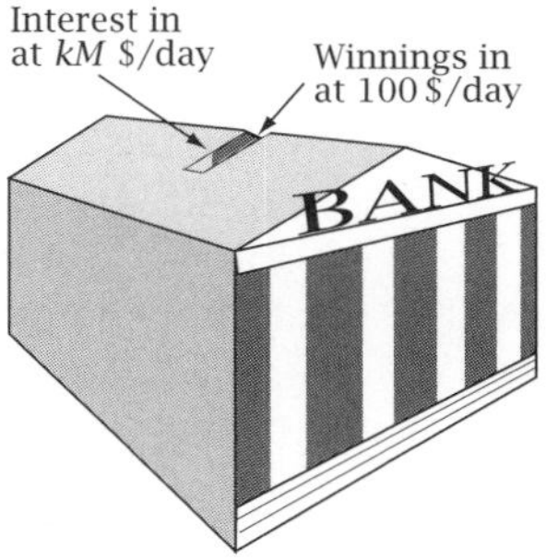

Figure 7-3h

3. *Electrical Circuit Problem:* When you turn on the switch in an electric circuit (Figure 7-3i), a constant voltage (electrical "pressure"), $E$, is applied instantaneously to the circuit. This voltage causes an electrical current to begin to flow through the circuit. The current is $I = 0$ amp (ampere) when the switch is turned on at time $t = 0$ sec. The part of this voltage that goes into overcoming the electrical resistance of the circuit is directly proportional to the current, $I$. The proportionality constant, $R$, is called the **resistance** of the circuit. The rest of the voltage is used to get the current moving through the circuit in the first place and varies directly with the

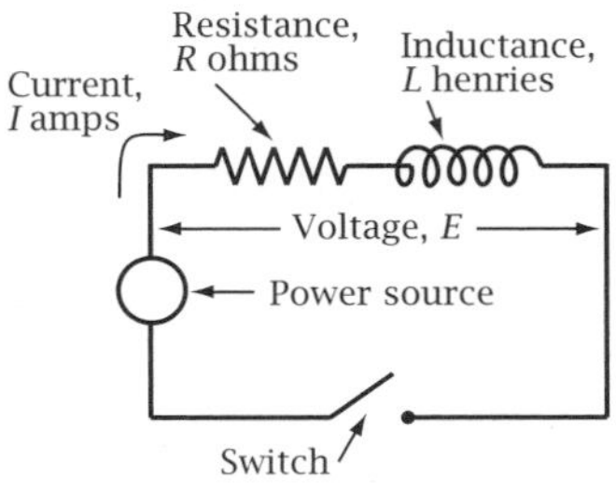

Figure 7-3i

instantaneous rate of change of the current with respect to time. The constant for this proportionality, $L$, is called the **inductance** of the circuit.

a. Write a differential equation stating that $E$ is the sum of the resistive voltage and the inductive voltage.
b. Solve this differential equation subject to the initial condition that $I = 0$ when $t = 0$. Write the resulting equation with $I$ as a function of $t$.
c. Suppose that the circuit has a resistance of 10 ohms and an inductance of 20 H (henries). If the circuit is connected to a normal 110-v (volt) outlet, write the particular equation and plot the graph. Sketch the result. Show any asymptotes.
d. Predict the current for the following times.
   i. 1 sec after the switch is turned on
   ii. 10 sec after the switch is turned on
   iii. At a steady state, after many seconds
e. At what time, $t$, will the current reach 95% of its steady-state value?

4. *Newton's Law of Cooling Problem:* When you turn on an electric heater, such as a "burner" on a stove (Figure 7-3j), its temperature increases rapidly at first, then more slowly, and finally approaches a constant high temperature. As the burner warms up, heat supplied by the electricity goes to two places.
   i. Storage in the heater materials, thus warming the heater
   ii. Losses to the room

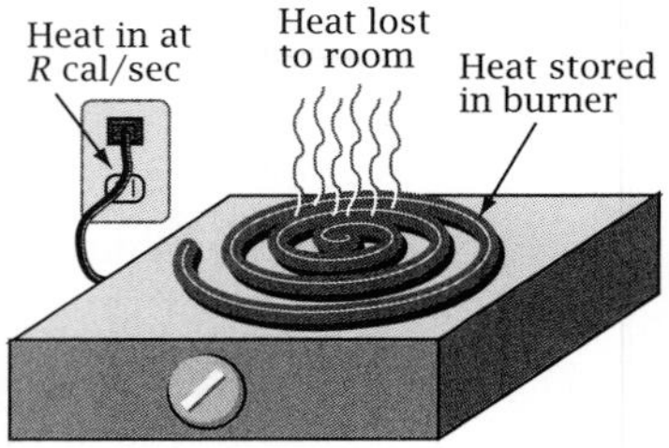

Figure 7-3j

Assume that heat is being supplied at a constant rate, $R$. The rate at which heat is stored is directly proportional to the rate of change of temperature. Let $T$ be the number of degrees above room temperature. Let $t$ be time in seconds. Then the storage rate is $C(dT/dt)$. The proportionality constant, $C$ (calories per degree), is called the **heat capacity** of the heater materials. According to Newton's law of cooling, the rate at which heat is lost to the room is directly proportional to $T$. The (positive) proportionality constant, $h$, is called the **heat transfer coefficient**.

a. The rate at which heat is supplied to the heater is equal to the sum of the storage rate and the loss rate. Write a differential equation that expresses this fact.
b. Separate the variables and integrate the differential equation. Explain why the absolute value sign is not necessary in this case. Transform the answer so that temperature, $T$, is in terms of time, $t$. Use the initial condition that $T = 0$ when $t = 0$.
c. Suppose that heat is supplied at a rate, $R = 50$ cal/sec. Assume that the heat capacity is $C = 2$ cal/degC, and that the heat transfer coefficient is $h = 0.04$ (cal/sec)/degC. Substitute these values to get $T$ in terms of $t$ alone.
d. Plot the graph of $T$ versus $t$. Sketch the result.
e. Predict $T$ at times of 10, 20, 50, 100, and 200 sec after the heater was turned on.
f. Find the limit of $T$ as $t$ approaches infinity. This is called the steady-state temperature.
g. How long does it take the heater to reach 99% of its steady-state temperature?

5. *Hot Tub Problem:* Figure 7-3k shows a cylindrical hot tub that is 8 ft in diameter and 4 ft deep. At time $t = 0$ min, the drain is opened and water flows out. The rate at which it flows is proportional to the square root of the depth, $y$ feet. Because the tub has vertical sides, the rate is also proportional to the square root of the volume, $V$ cubic feet, of water left.

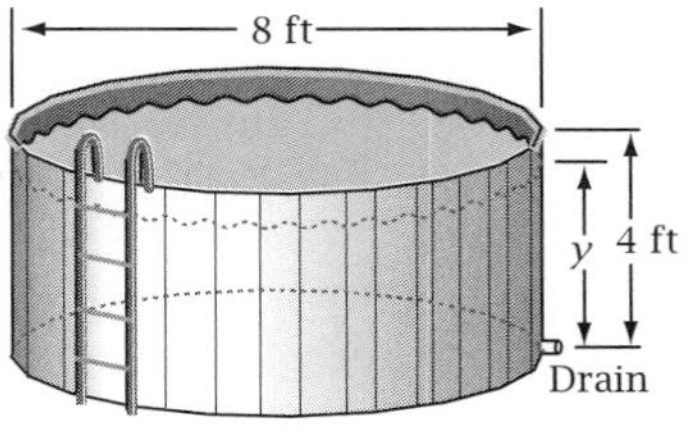

Figure 7-3k

   a. Write a differential equation for the rate at which water flows from the tub. That is, write an equation for $dV/dt$ in terms of $V$.
   b. Separate the variables and integrate the differential equation you wrote in 5a. Transform the result so that $V$ is expressed explicitly in terms of $t$. Tell how $V$ varies with $t$.
   c. Suppose that the tub initially (that is, when $t = 0$) contains 196 $ft^3$ of water and that when the drain is first opened the water flows out at 28 $ft^3$/min (that is, when $t = 0$, $dV/dt = -28$). Find the particular solution of the differential equation that fits these initial conditions.
   d. Naive thinking suggests that the tub would be empty after 7 min since it contained 196 $ft^3$ and the water flowed out at 28 $ft^3$/min. Show that this conclusion is false. Justify your answer.
   e. Does this mathematical model predict a time when the tub is completely empty, or does the volume, $V$, approach zero asymptotically? If there is a time, tell what time.
   f. Draw a graph of $V$ versus $t$ in a suitable domain.
   g. See Problem C4 in Section 7-7 to see what would happen if a hose were left running into the hot tub while it was draining.

6. *Burette Experiment:* In this problem you will simulate the Hot Tub Problem in this problem set and the Tin Can Leakage Problem in Example 1. Obtain a burette (see Figure 7-3l) from a chemistry lab. Fill the burette with water, then open the stopcock so that water runs out fairly slowly. Record the level of water in the burette at various times as it drains. Plot volume versus time on graph paper. Does the volume seem to vary quadratically with time, as it did in Example 1? Find the best-fitting quadratic function for the data. Discuss the implications of the fact that the volume read on the burette equals zero before the depth, $y$, of the water equals zero.

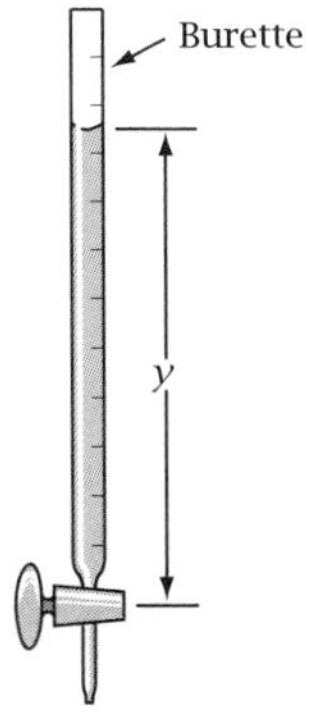

Figure 7-3l

7. *Differential Equation Generalization Problem:* The solutions of $dy/dx = ky^n$ are functions with different behaviors, depending on the value of the (constant) exponent $n$. If $n = 1$, then $y$ varies exponentially with $x$. If $n = 0.5$, as in the *Hot Tub Problem*, then $y$ varies quadratically with $x$. In this problem you will explore the graphs of various solutions of this equation.
   a. Write the solution of the equation for $n = 1$. Let $k = 1$ and let the constant of integration $C = -3$. Graph the solution and sketch the graph.
   b. Solve the equation for $n = 0.5$. Let $k = 1$ and $C = -3$, as in 7a. Graph the solution.
   c. Show that if $n = -1$, then $y$ is a square root function of $x$, and if $n = -2$, then $y$ is a cube root function of $x$. Plot both graphs, using $k = 1$ and $C = -3$, as in 7a.
   d. Show that if $n > 1$, then there is a vertical asymptote at $x = -C/k$. Plot two graphs that show the difference in behavior for $n = 2$ and for $n = 3$. Use $k = 1$ and $C = -3$, as in 7a.

e. What kind of function is $y$ when $n = 0$? Graph this function, using $k = 1$ and $C = -3$, as in 7a–d.

8. *Advertising Project:* A soft-drink manufacturing company introduces a new product. The company's salespeople want to predict the number of bottles per day they will sell as a function of the number of days since the product was introduced. One of the parameters will be the amount per day spent on advertising. Here are some assumptions the salespeople make about the sales.

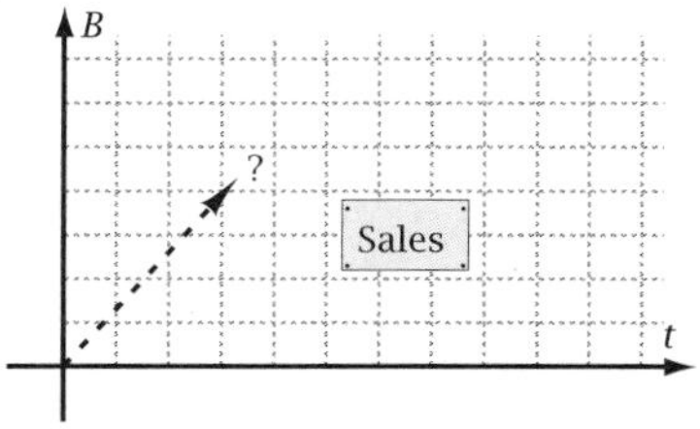


Figure 7-3m

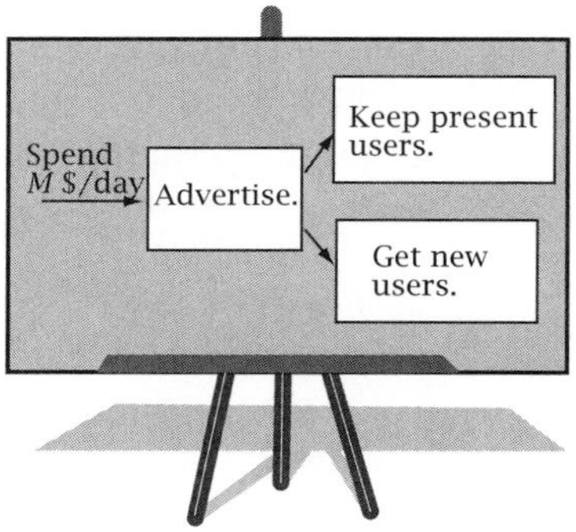


Figure 7-3n

- The dependent variable is $B$ bottles per day; the independent variable is $t$ days (Figure 7-3m).
- They will spend a fixed amount, $M$ dollars per day, on advertising.
- Part of $M$, an amount proportional to $B$, maintains present sales (Figure 7-3n).
- The rate of change of $B$, $dB/dt$, is directly proportional to the rest of $M$.
- Advertising costs need to be \$80 per day to maintain sales of 1000 bottles per day.
- Due to advance publicity, $dB/dt$ will be 500 bottles per day when $t = 0$, independent of $M$.

Use what you have learned in this section to find an equation for $B$ as a function of $t$. Then show the effect of spending various amounts, $M$, on advertising. Calculations and graphs would be convincing. You might include such information as whether sales will continue to go up without bound or will eventually level off. You could also make an impression on management by assuming a certain price per bottle and by indicating how long it will take before the product starts making a profit.

9. *Water Heater Project:* Suppose you have been hired by a water-heater manufacturer to determine some characteristics of a new line of water heaters (Figure 7-3o). Specifically, they want to know how long it will take to warm up a tank of cold water to various temperatures, and how long it takes from the time the thermostat turns off the heat to the time the thermostat turns on the heat again. Here are some things you learn from the engineering and design departments.

- Heat will be supplied at a constant rate of 1200 Btu (British thermal units) per minute.
- Heat will be lost to the surroundings at a rate, $L$, proportional to the difference between the heater temperature and the room temperature. That is,

$$L = h(T - 70),$$

  where $L$ is loss rate in Btu/min, $T$ is the water temperature, 70 deg is the room temperature, and $h$ is a proportionality constant called the heat transfer coefficient.
- the water will warm at a rate, $dT/dt$, proportional to $(1200 - L)$.

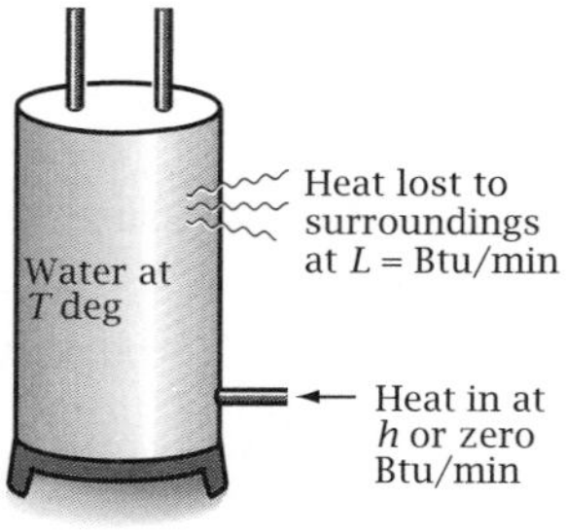


Figure 7-3o

- the water would warm up at 3 deg/min if there were zero losses to the surroundings.
- in 10 min the heater will warm water to 96 deg from the room temperature of 70 deg.

Use this information to derive an equation that expresses temperature, $T$, in terms of the number of minutes, $t$, since the heater was turned on. Use the equation to find the information the manufacturer is seeking (see the beginning of this problem). For instance, you might investigate how long it would take to warm water to 140 deg, to 160 deg, or to 180 deg. You can find out how long it takes, when the heat is off, for the water to cool from 160 deg to, say, 155 deg (when the heat turns on again). You can impress your boss by pointing out any inadequacies in the proposed design of the heater and by suggesting which of the parameters might be changed to improve the design.

10. *Vapor Pressure Project:* The vapor pressure, $P$, of a liquid or a solid (Figure 7-3p) increases as the temperature increases. The rate of change of the vapor pressure, $dP/dT$, is directly proportional to $P$ and inversely proportional to the square of the Kelvin temperature, $T$. In physical chemistry you will learn that this relationship is called the Clausius-Clapeyron equation.

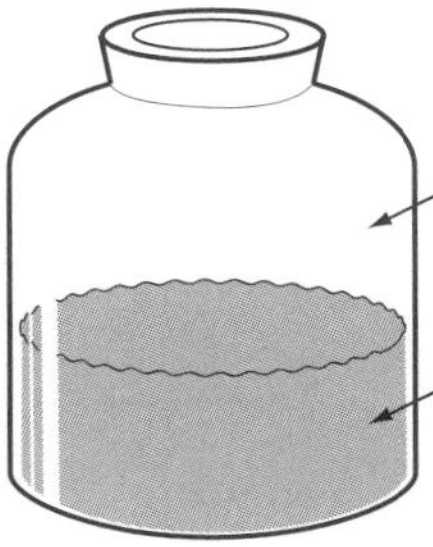


Figure 7-3p

a. Write a differential equation that expresses $dP/dT$ in terms of $P$ and $T$. Integrate the equation, then solve for $P$ in terms of $T$.

b. The table shows the vapor pressure (millimeters of mercury, or mm Hg) of naphthalene (moth balls, $C_{10}H_8$) from an old edition of Lange's *Handbook of Chemistry*. Use the data for 293 deg K (20 deg C) and 343 deg K (70 deg C) to find the two constants in the equation you wrote in 10a. You may solve the system of simultaneous equations either in their logarithmic form or in their exponential form, whichever is more convenient. Don't be afraid of large numbers! And don't round them off!!

| deg C | deg K | mm Hg | deg C | deg K | mm Hg |
|---|---|---|---|---|---|
| 10 | 283 | 0.021 | 70 | 343 | 3.95 |
| 20 | 293 | 0.054 | 80 | 353 | 7.4 (melting point) |
| 30 | 303 | 0.133 | 90 | 363 | 12.6 |
| 40 | 313 | 0.320 | 100 | 373 | 18.5 |
| 50 | 323 | 0.815 | 110 | 383 | 27.3 |
| 60 | 333 | 1.83 | 200 | 473 | 496.5 |

c. How well does your function fit the actual data? Does the same equation fit well above the melting point? If so, give information to support your conclusion. If not, find an equation that fits better above the melting point. Do any other types of functions available on your grapher seem to fit the data better than the function from the Clausius-Clapeyron equation?

d. Predict the boiling point of naphthalene, which is the temperature at which the vapor pressure equals atmospheric pressure, or 760 mm Hg.

e. What extensions can you think of for this project?

# 7-4 Graphical Solution of Differential Equations by Using Slope Fields

The function $y = e^{0.3x}$ is a particular solution of the differential equation $dy/dx = 0.3y$. The left-hand graph in Figure 7-4a shows this solution, with a tangent line through the point $(2, e^{0.6})$. In the right-hand graph of this figure, the curve and most of the tangent line have been deleted, leaving only a short segment of the tangent, centered at the point $(2, e^{0.6})$. This segment could have been drawn without ever having solved the differential equation. Its slope is $0.3e^{0.6} \approx 0.55$, the number you get by substituting $e^{0.6}$ for $y$ in the original differential equation.

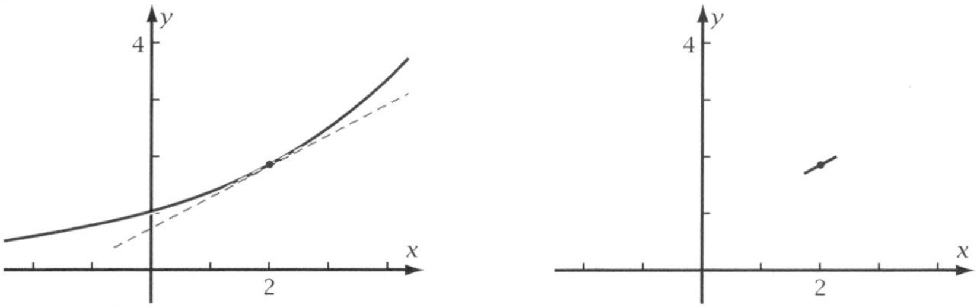


$y = e^{0.3x}$ Tangent segment at $x = 2$

Figure 7-4a

The left-hand graph in Figure 7-4b shows what results if you draw a short segment of slope $0.3y$ at every grid point (point with integer coordinates) on the plane. The result is called a **slope field** or sometimes a **direction field**. The right-hand graph in Figure 7-4b shows the solution $y = e^{0.3x}$, from Figure 7-4a, drawn on the slope field. The line segments show the direction the graph takes. As a result, you can draw the graph of another particular solution just by picking a starting point and going to the left and to the right "parallel" to the line segments. The dotted curves on the right-hand graph of Figure 7-4b show three such graphs.

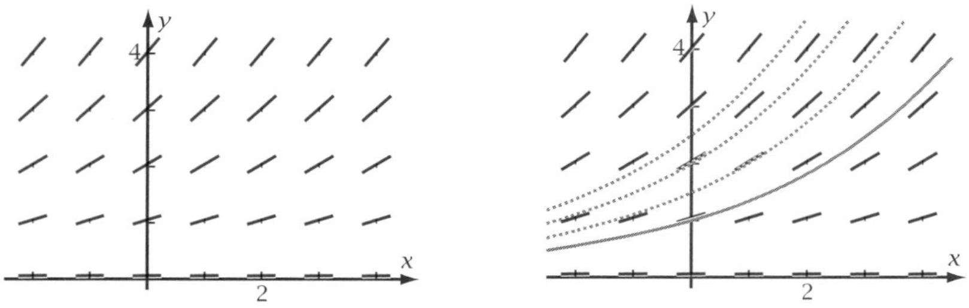


Slope field $y = e^{0.3x}$ and other particular solutions

Figure 7-4b

Slope fields are tedious to draw by hand and are best done by grapher. Once you get a slope field, however, it allows you to graph any particular solution without ever solving the differential equation. As you can appreciate from difficulties you may have had integrating the differential equations in Section 7-3, such an approximate solution method is welcome! In this section you will sketch the graphs by hand. However, you will compare some of the graphical solutions with exact, algebraic solutions. In Section 7-5, you will learn a numerical method for plotting such approximate graphs on the grapher itself.

**OBJECTIVE**

Given a slope field for a differential equation, graph an approximate particular solution by hand and, if possible, confirm the solution algebraically.

**Example 1** Figure 7-4c shows the slope field for the differential equation

$$\frac{dy}{dx} = -\frac{0.36x}{y}.$$

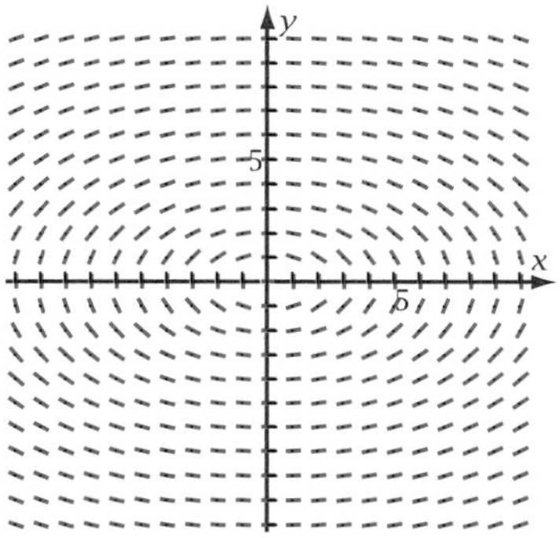

Figure 7-4c

a. From the differential equation, find the slope at the points (5, 2) and (−8, 9). Mark these points on the figure. Tell why the calculated slopes are reasonable.

b. Start at the point (0, 6) and draw a graph that represents the particular solution of the differential equation that contains that point. Go both to the right and to the left. Where does the curve seem to go after it touches the $x$-axis? What geometric figure does the graph seem to be?

c. Start at the point (5, 2), from part a, and draw another particular solution of the differential equation. How is this solution related to that in part b?

d. Solve the differential equation algebraically. Find the particular solution that contains the point (0, 6). Verify that the graph really is the figure indicated in part b.

**Solutions**

a. At the point (5, 2), $\frac{dy}{dx} = -\frac{0.36(5)}{2} = -0.9$.

At the point (−8, 9), $\frac{dy}{dx} = -\frac{0.36(-8)}{9} = 0.32$.

The circled points in Figure 7-4d show slopes of about −1 and 0.3, which agree with the calculations.

b. Figure 7-4d shows the graph. Start at the boxed point (0, 6). Where the graph goes between grid points, make its slope an average of the slopes shown. Don't try to head for the grid points themselves! The graph may not pass through these points. The graph appears to be an ellipse. The dotted line shows the same elliptical pattern below the $x$-axis.

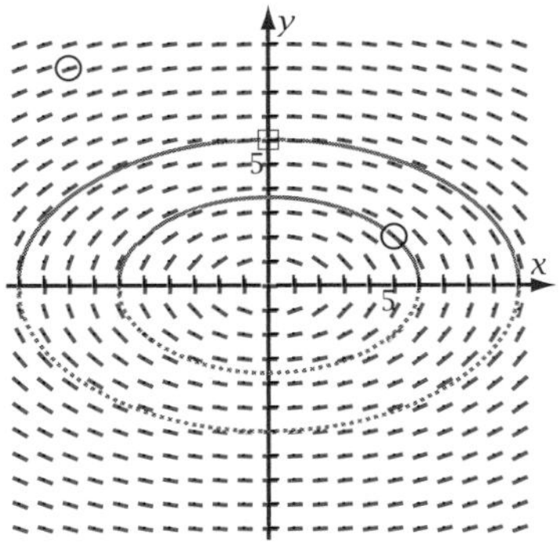

Figure 7-4d

c. The solution that contains the point (5, 2) is the inner ellipse in Figure 7-4d. It is similar (has the same proportions) to the ellipse described in part b.

d. $y\,dy = -0.36x\,dx \Rightarrow \int y\,dy = -0.36\int x\,dx \Rightarrow 0.5y^2 = -0.18x^2 + C$

Substituting the point (0, 6) gives $0.5(36) = 0 + C \Rightarrow C = 18$.

$\therefore\ 0.5y^2 = -0.18x^2 + 18 \Rightarrow 9x^2 + 25y^2 = 900$

This is the equation of an ellipse centered at the origin, as shown in part b.

■

Figure 7-4e shows slope fields for three simple differential equations. For each slope field or its differential equation, three particular solutions are shown, along with the corresponding initial conditions. Note that the graph follows the pattern but usually goes between lattice points rather than through them.

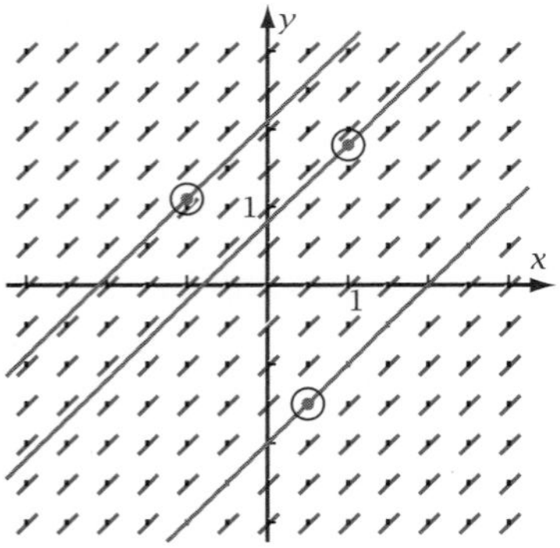

$\frac{dy}{dx} = 1$

(-1, 1.1), (1, 1.8), (0.5, -1.5)

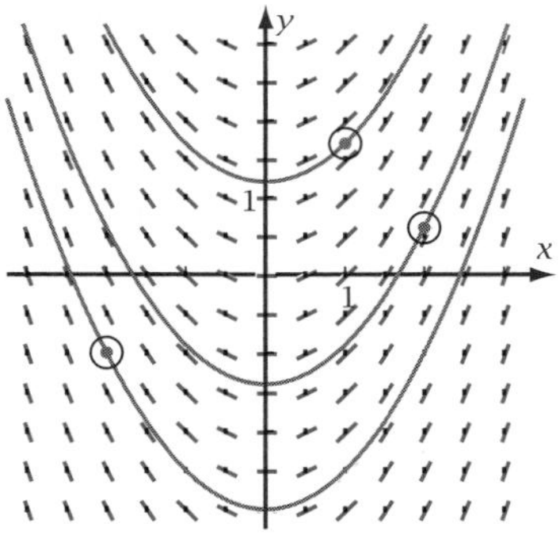

$\frac{dy}{dx} = x$

(1, 1.7), (2, 0.6), (-2, -1)

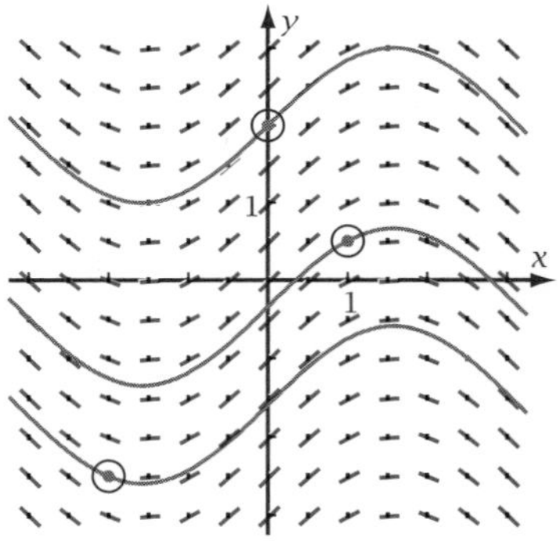

$\frac{dy}{dx} = \cos x$

(0, 2), (1, 0.5), (-2, -2.5)

Figure 7-4e

# Problem Set 7-4

***Do These Quickly***

The following problems are intended to refresh your skills. You should be able to do all ten problems in less than five minutes.

**Q1.** Differentiate: $y = x^5$

**Q2.** Differentiate: $y = 5^x$

**Q3.** Integrate: $\int x^7\,dx$

**Q4.** Integrate: $\int 7^x\,dx$

**Q5.** Differentiate: $xy = 3$

**Q6.** For Figure 7-4f, $\int_2^7 f(x)\,dx =$ -?-.

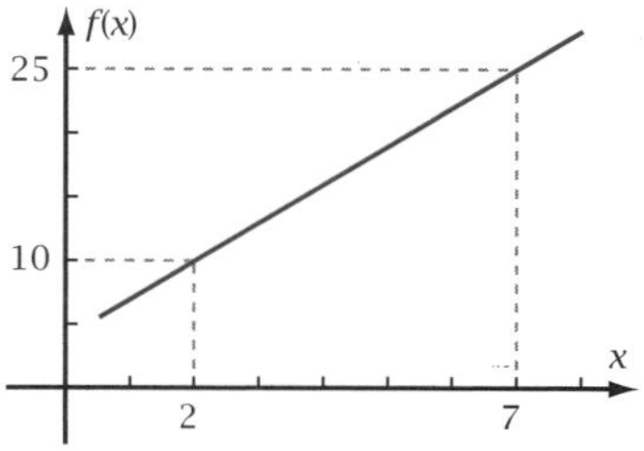


Figure 7-4f

**Q7.** Sketch the graph: $y = x^2$

**Q8.** Sketch the graph: $y = 2^x$

**Q9.** If $g(x) = \int f(x)\,dx$, then $\int_1^5 f(x)\,dx =$ -?-.

**Q10.** Find the slope of the line perpendicular to $y = x^2$ at the point (3, 9).

1. Figure 7-4g shows the slope field for the differential equation

$$\frac{dy}{dx} = \frac{x}{2y}.$$

Use a photocopy of this figure to answer the following questions.

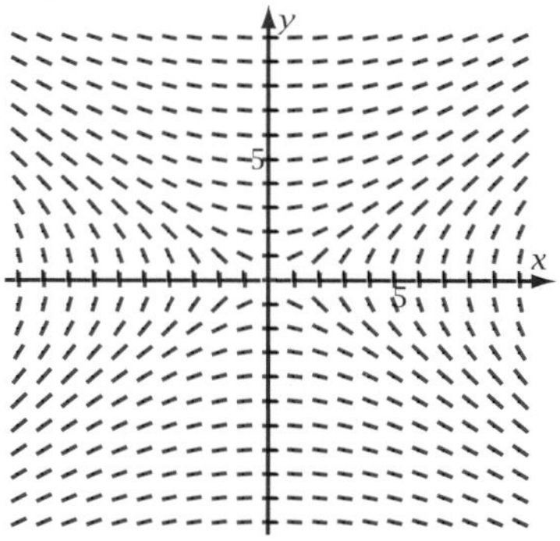


Figure 7-4g

a. Show that you understand the meaning of slope field by calculating $dy/dx$ at the points (3, 5) and (−5, 1) and by showing that the results agree with the figure.

b. Sketch the graph of the particular solution of the differential equation that contains the point (1, 2). Draw on both sides of the $y$-axis. What geometric figure does the graph seem to be?

c. Sketch the graph of the particular solution that contains the point (5, 1). Draw on both sides of the $x$-axis.

d. Solve the differential equation algebraically. Find the particular solution that contains the point (5, 1). How well does your graphical solution from 1b agree with the algebraic solution?

2. On dot paper, like that shown in Figure 7-4h, draw the slope field for the differential equation

$$\frac{dy}{dx} = -\frac{x}{2y}.$$

Then solve the differential equation algebraically. Find the particular solution that contains the point (5, 1). Plot this solution on the figure. What geometric figure is the graph?

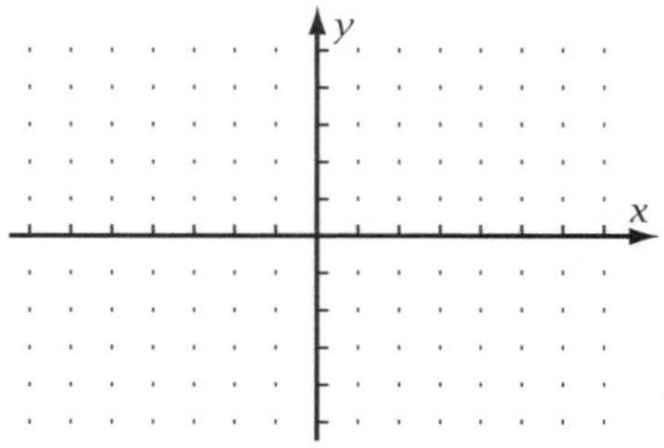


Figure 7-4h

3. a. On a photocopy of the slope field shown in Figure 7-4i, sketch two particular solutions: one that contains the point (3, 2), and one that contains the point (1, −2).

b. In Quadrant I, the slope is always negative and gets steeper as $x$ or $y$ increases. The slope at the point (1, 1) is about $-0.2$. Make a conjecture about a differential equation that could generate this slope field. Give evidence to support your conjecture.

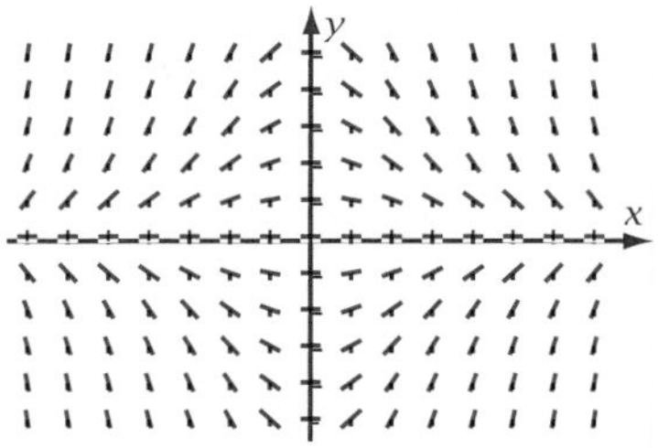


Figure 7-4i

4. *Dependence on Initial Conditions Problem:* Figure 7-4j shows the slope field for

$$\frac{dy}{dx} = 0.1x + 0.2y.$$

a. On a photocopy of this figure, draw the particular solution that contains the point (0, 2). Show the graph on both sides of the $y$-axis.

b. Show that the particular solution containing the point (0, $-5$) exhibits a different behavior from that in 4a.

c. The solution to 4a curves upward, and that to 4b curves downward. It seems reasonable that somewhere between these two solutions there is one that has a straight-line graph. Draw this solution. Where does the graph cross the $y$-axis?

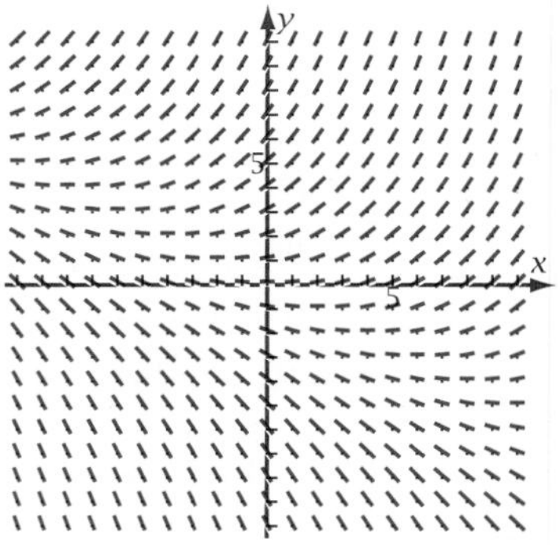


Figure 7-4j

5. On a photocopy of the slope field shown in Figure 7-4k, draw the particular solutions that contain the points (0, 1), (3, 4), (0, $-4$), and ($-8$, $-2$).

6. On a photocopy of the slope field shown in Figure 7-4l, draw the particular solutions that contain the points (0, 4), (0, 8), (0, 10), and (0, 15). How does the change from (0, 8) to (0, 10) for an initial condition affect the graph?

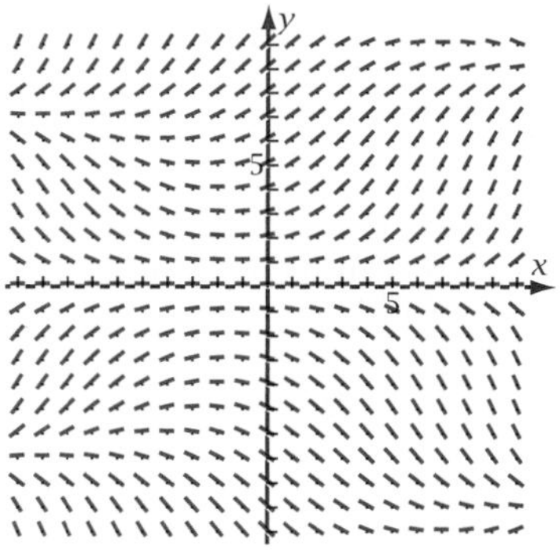


Figure 7-4k

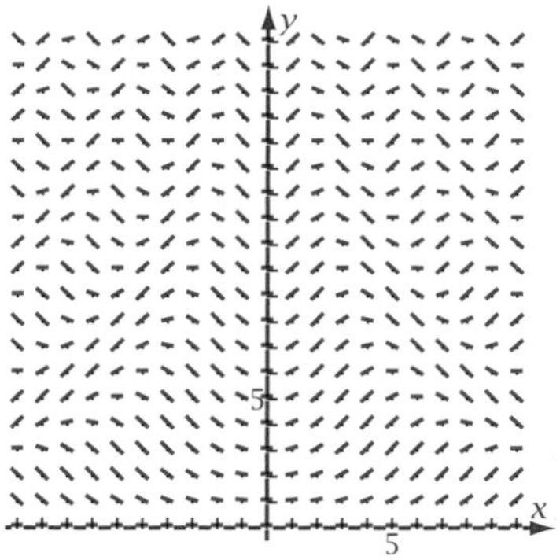


Figure 7-4l

7. *Rabbit Population Overcrowding Problem:* In the population problems of Section 7-2, the rate of change of population is proportional to the population. In the real world, overcrowding limits the size of the population. One mathematical model, the

**logistic equation**, says that $dP/dt$ is proportional to the product of the population and a constant minus the population. Suppose that rabbits are introduced to a small uninhabited island in the Pacific. Naturalists find that the differential equation for population growth is

$$\frac{dP}{dt} = 0.038P(10.5 - P),$$

where $P$ is in hundreds of rabbits and $t$ is in months. Figure 7-4m shows the slope field.

a. Suppose that 200 rabbits arrive at time $t = 0$. On a photocopy of Figure 7-4m, graph the particular solution.

b. Draw another particular solution if the 200 rabbits had been introduced at time $t = 4$. What would be the differences and the similarities in the population growth?

c. Draw a third particular solution if 1800 rabbits had been introduced at time $t = 0$. With this initial condition, what is the major difference in population growth? What similarity does this scenario have to those in 7a and b?

d. Think of a real-world reason to explain the horizontal asymptote each graph approaches. Where does this asymptote appear in the differential equation?

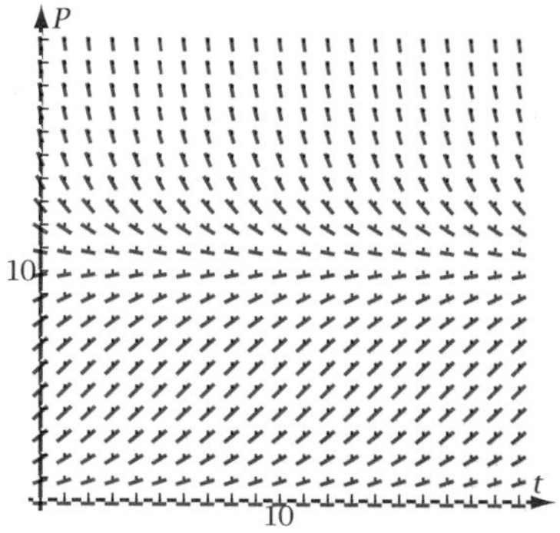


Figure 7-4m

8. *Terminal Velocity Problem:* A sky diver jumps from an airplane. During the free-fall stage, her speed increases at the acceleration of gravity, about 32.16 (ft/sec)/sec. But wind resistance causes a force that reduces the acceleration. The resistance force is proportional to the square of the velocity. Assume that the constant of proportionality is 0.0015, so that

$$\frac{dv}{dt} = 32.16 - 0.0015v^2,$$

where $v$ is in feet per second and $t$ is in seconds. The slope field for this differential equation is shown in Figure 7-4n.

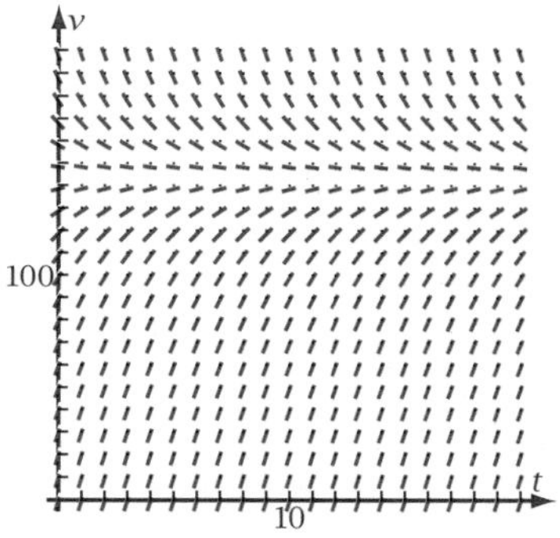


Figure 7-4n

a. What does the slope appear to be at the point (5, 120)? What does it actually equal? Explain any discrepancy between your two answers.

b. The diver starts at time $t = 0$ with zero initial velocity. On a photocopy of Figure 7-4n, sketch her velocity as a function of time.

c. The velocity approaches an asymptote. What does this **terminal velocity** appear to equal? About how long does it take her to fall until she is essentially at this velocity?

d. A second diver started 5 sec later with zero initial velocity. Sketch the velocity-time graph. What similarities does this graph have to the graph you sketched in 8b?

e. Suppose that the plane is going down steeply as a third diver jumps, giving him an initial downward velocity of 180 ft/sec. Sketch this diver's velocity-time graph. How is it different from the graphs you sketched in 8b and d?

f. The mathematical models for free fall in this problem and for population in Problem 7 have some similarities. Write a paragraph that discusses the similarities and the differences. Do you find it remarkable that two different phenomena have similar mathematical models?

9. *Escape Velocity Problem:* If a spaceship has a high enough initial velocity, it will escape the earth's gravity and be free to go elsewhere. Otherwise it will stop and fall back to earth.

a. By Newton's third law of motion, the force, $F$, on the spaceship equals its mass, $m$, times the acceleration, $a$. By his law of gravitation, $F$ is also equal to $mg/r^2$, where $g$ is the gravitational constant and $r$ is the distance from the center of the earth to the spaceship. Give reasons for each step in the following transformations.

$$ma = \frac{mg}{r^2}$$

$$\frac{dv}{dt} = \frac{g}{r^2}$$

$$\frac{dv}{dr} \cdot \frac{dr}{dt} = \frac{g}{r^2}$$

$$\frac{dv}{dr} \cdot v = \frac{g}{r^2}$$

$$\frac{dv}{dr} = \frac{g}{r^2 v}$$

b. If $r$ is in earth-radii (1 earth-radius = 6380 km) and $v$ is in kilometers per second, then

$$\frac{dv}{dr} = \frac{-62.44}{r^2 v}.$$

The sign is negative because gravity acts opposite to the direction of motion. Figure 7-4o shows the slope field for this differential equation. Confirm that the differential equation produces the slopes shown at the points $(r, v)$ =(5, 2), (1, 10), and (10, 4).

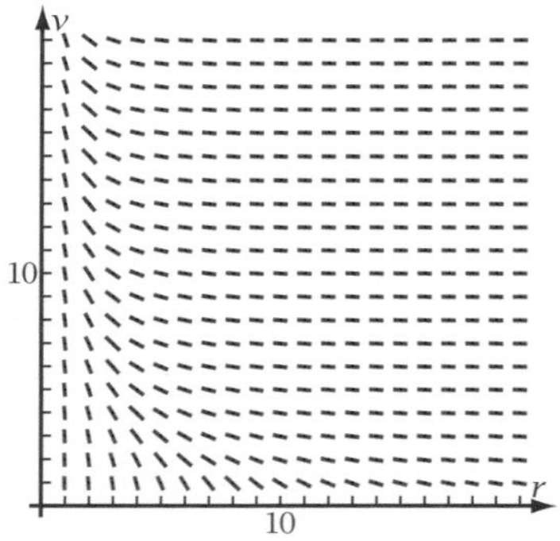


Figure 7-4o

c. If the spaceship starts at earth's surface ($r = 1$) with an initial velocity of $v = 10$ km/sec, it will not escape earth's gravity. On a photocopy of Figure 7-4o, sketch this particular solution. About how far from earth's surface does the ship stop and start falling back?

d. Show on your photocopied figure that if the spaceship starts from the earth's surface with an initial velocity of 12 km/sec, it will escape the earth's gravity. About how fast will it be going when it is far from earth?

e. If the spaceship starts from earth's surface with an initial velocity of 18 km/sec, what will its velocity approach far from earth? Does it lose as much speed starting at 18 km/sec as it does starting at 12 km/sec? How do you explain this observation?

f. Show that the spaceship will escape from earth's gravity if it starts with an initial velocity of 10 km/sec from a space platform in orbit that is 1 earth-radius above the earth's surface (that is, $r = 2$).

10. *Slope Fields on the Grapher:* Generate on your grapher the slope field for

$$\frac{dy}{dx} = 0.5y(1 - 0.15y),$$

as shown in Figure 7-4p. If your grapher does not have a built-in program to generate slope fields, obtain one or write one. Save this program to use in Section 7-5.

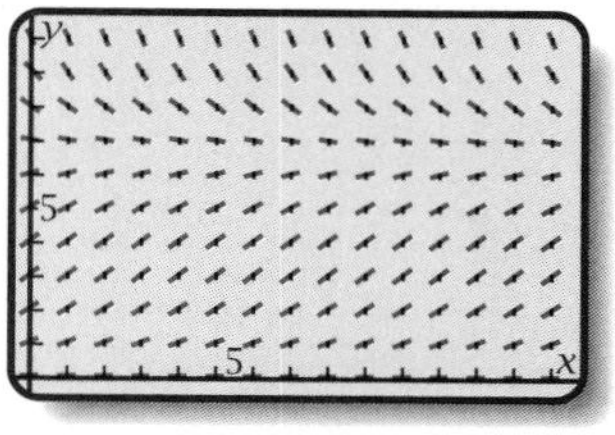


Figure 7-4p

# 7-5 Numerical Solution of Differential Equations by Using Euler's Method

In Section 7-4, you sketched approximate solutions of differential equations, using their slope fields. In this section you will learn a numerical method for calculating approximate $y$-values for a particular solution, and you'll plot the points either by hand or on the grapher. This method is called Euler's method, after Swiss mathematician Leonhard Euler (1707–1783). (Euler is pronounced "oi′-ler.")

**OBJECTIVE**

Given a differential equation and its slope field, calculate points on the graph iteratively by starting at one point and finding the next point by following the slope for a given $x$-distance.

Euler's method for solving a differential equation numerically is based on the fact that a differentiable function has local linearity at any given point. For instance, if $dy/dx = \cos xy$, you can calculate the slope at any point $(x, y)$ and follow the linear function to another point $\Delta x$ units away. If $\Delta x$ is small, the new point will be close to the actual point on the graph. Figure 7-5a illustrates the procedure.

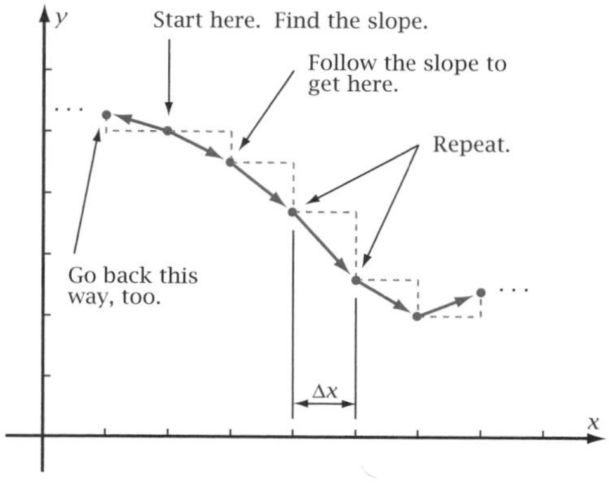


Figure 7-5a

- Start at a given point $(x, y)$ on the graph.
- Calculate the slope at this point by using the differential equation.
- For a given value of $\Delta x$, calculate the value of $dy$, specifically $(dy/dx)(\Delta x)$, which is the change in $y$ along the linear graph.
- Add $\Delta x$ and $dy$ to the previous values of $x$ and $y$ to get a new point, $(x, y)$.
- Repeat the process, starting at the new point $(x, y)$.

As the figure shows, you can go in both directions from the starting point, as long as it makes sense in the context of the problem to do so.

In the following problem set you will work on your own or with your study group to learn the details of how to use Euler's method.

## Problem Set 7-5

### *Do These Quickly*

The following problems are intended to refresh your skills. You should be able to do all ten problems in less than five minutes.

**Q1.** If $dy/dx$ is directly proportional to $y$, then $dy/dx$ = -?-.

**Q2.** If $dy/dx = 3y$, then the general solution for $y$ is -?-.

**Q3.** If $dy/dx = 0.1\,xy$, what is the slope of the slope-field line at the point (6, 8)?

**Q4.** If $y = Ce^{0.2x}$ and $y = 100$ when $x = 0$, then $C$ = -?-.

**Q5.** $\int dv/(1 - v)$ = -?-

**Q6.** $(d/dx)(\sec x)$ = -?-

**Q7.** Find $f'(x)$ if $f(x) = \int_1^x (3t + 5)^4\,dt$.

**Q8.** Sketch the graph of $y'$ for Figure 7-5b.

**Q9.** Differentiate implicitly: $x^3y^5 = x + y$.

**Q10.** If $\lim_{x\to 4} f(x) = f(4)$, then $f$ is -?- at $x = 4$.

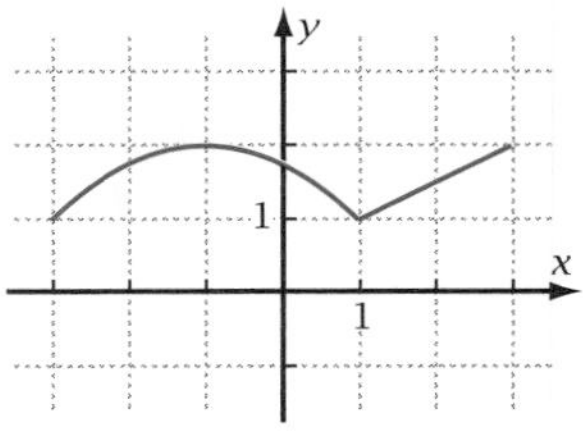


Figure 7-5b

1. *How Euler's Method Works:* Figure 7-5c shows the slope field for the differential equation

$$\frac{dy}{dx} = -\frac{x}{2y}.$$

a. Start at the point (0, 3), calculate the slope at that point, then assume that the graph is linear between $x = 0$ and $x = 0.5$. What will the value of $y$ be at $x = 0.5$?

b. Find the slope at the point $(0.5, y)$, in Problem 1a, and use it to find an approximate value of $y$ at $x = 1$, assuming that the graph is linear between $x = 0.5$ and $x = 1$.

c. Repeat the computations you did for 1a and b to make a table of values, as shown on the next page.

d. On a photocopy of Figure 7-5c, plot the $y$-values you calculated in 1c by using Euler's method. For which values of $x$ do the Euler's method $y$-values seem to follow the slope field? For which values of $x$ is this numerical solution clearly incorrect?

| $x$ | $y$ | slope | $dy$ |
|---|---|---|---|
| 0 | 3 | 0 | 0 |
| 0.5 | 3 | −0.0833... | −0.0416... |
| 1 | 2.9583... | ______ | ______ |
| 1.5 | ______ | ______ | ______ |
| 2 | ______ | ______ | ______ |
| 2.5 | ______ | ______ | ______ |
| 3 | ______ | ______ | ______ |
| 3.5 | ______ | ______ | ______ |
| 4 | ______ | ______ | ______ |
| 4.5 | ______ | ______ | ______ |
| 5 | ______ | ______ | ______ |
| 5.5 | ______ | ______ | ______ |
| 6 | ______ | ______ | ______ |
| 6.5 | ______ | ______ | ______ |
| 7 | ______ | ______ | ______ |

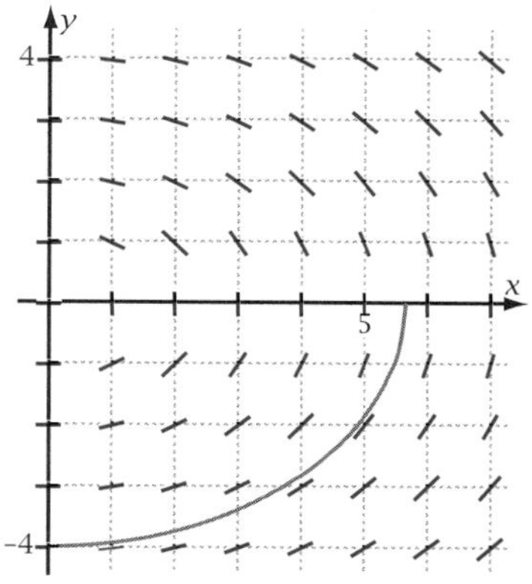

Figure 7-5c

2. *Numerical Program for Euler's Method:* Obtain or write a program for computing $y$-values by Euler's method. The program should allow you to enter the differential equation, say as $y_1$, in terms of both $x$ and $y$. Then you should be able to input the initial condition $(x, y)$ and the value of $\Delta x$, such as the point (0, 3) and the number 0.5 in Problem 1, respectively. Test your program by using it to calculate the values in the table given in Problem 1c.

3. *Accuracy of Euler's Method:* In this problem you will use your program from Problem 2 to solve the differential equation

$$\frac{dy}{dx} = -\frac{x}{2y},$$

from Problem 1, with different values of $\Delta x$, and you'll compare your results with the exact solution.

   a. The curve in Quadrant IV of Figure 7-5c shows the exact particular solution of the differential equation that contains the point (0, −4). Solve the differential equation algebraically. Use your result to calculate $y$ when $x = 5$ and show that this point is on the graph.

   b. Use your program from Problem 2 to calculate values of $y$ by Euler's method, starting at the point (0, −4), using $\Delta x = 0.5$. Record in a table the $y$-values for $x = 0, 1, 2, 3, 4, 5, 6$, and 7.

   c. On a photocopy of Figure 7-5c, plot the values from the table you made in 3b. Write some comments on how well Euler's method fits the exact solution.

   d. Repeat 3b and c, using $\Delta x = 0.1$. Again, record only the calculated $y$-values for $x = 0, 1, 2, 3, 4, 5, 6$, and 7. Comment on the relative accuracy of Euler's method as smaller values of $\Delta x$ are used.

   e. Figure out a time-efficient way to calculate $y$ when $x = 5$, using Euler's method with $\Delta x = 0.01$. How closely does this value match the exact value you calculated in 3a?

4. *Graphical Program for Euler's Method:* Obtain or write a grapher program for plotting a particular solution of a differential equation by Euler's method. You can adapt your program from Problem 2 if you like. The differential equation can be entered as

$y_1$. The input should include the initial point and the value of $\Delta x$. As each point is calculated the grapher should draw a line segment to it from the previous point. The program should allow the graph to be plotted to the right or to the left of the initial point, depending on the sign of $\Delta x$. The program should work in conjunction with the slope-field program of Section 7-4 so that the solution can be superimposed on the corresponding slope field. Test the program by using the information in Problem 3c, and show that the graph resembles that in Figure 7-5c.

5. Figure 7-5d shows the slope field for the differential equation

$$\frac{dy}{dx} = -0.2xy.$$

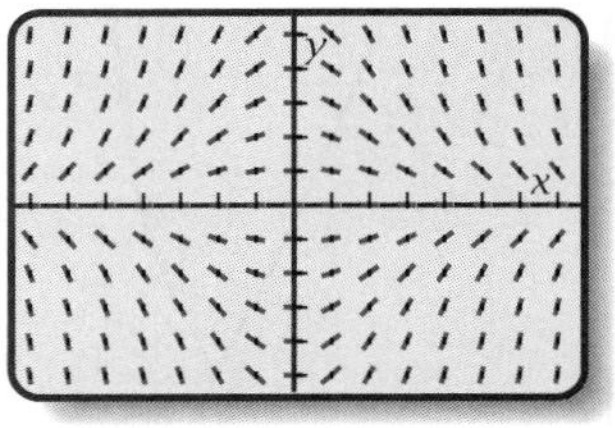

Figure 7-5d

   a. Use your grapher programs to plot the slope field and the particular solution that contains the point (3, 2). Sketch the solution on a photocopy of Figure 7-5d.
   b. Plot the particular solution that contains the point (1, −2). Sketch the solution on the photocopy.

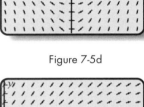

6. Figure 7-5e shows the slope field for the differential equation

$$\frac{dy}{dx} = -0.1x + 0.2y.$$

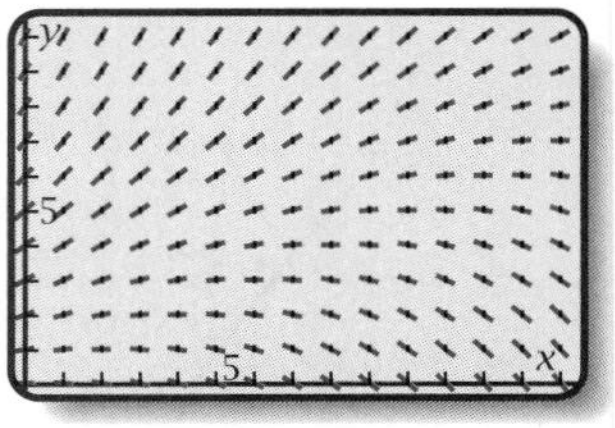

Figure 7-5e

   a. Use your grapher programs to plot the slope field and the particular solution that contains the point (0, 2). Sketch the solution on a photocopy of Figure 7-5e.
   b. Plot the particular solution that contains the point (0, 4). Sketch the solution on the photocopy.
   c. The solution you plotted in 6a curves downward, and that in 6b curves upward. It seems reasonable that somewhere between these two solutions there is one that has a straight-line graph. By experimenting on your grapher, find this particular solution. Record the initial point you used and sketch the solution on the photocopy.

7. *U.S. Population Project:* The following table shows the U.S. population (in millions) from 1940 through 1990. In this problem you will use this data to make a mathematical model for predicting the population in future years and for seeing how far back the model fits for previous years.
   a. For the years 1950, 1960, 1970, and 1980, find symmetric difference quotients, $\Delta P/\Delta t$, where $P$ is population in millions and $t$ is time in years since 1940. (Why can't you do this for 1940 and 1990?)

| year | population |
|---|---|
| 1940 | 131.7 |
| 1950 | 151.4 |
| 1960 | 179.3 |
| 1970 | 203.2 |
| 1980 | 226.5 |
| 1990 | 248.7 |

   b. For each year given in 7a, find $\Delta P/\Delta t$ as a fraction of $P$. That is, find $(\Delta P/\Delta t)/P$.
   c. It is reasonable to assume that the rate of growth of a population in a fixed region such as the United States (as a fraction of the size of that population) is some

function of the population. For instance, when the population gets too large, its growth rate slows because of overcrowding. Find the function (linear, logarithmic, exponential, or power) that best fits the values of $(\Delta P/\Delta t)/P$ as a function of $P$. Justify your answer.

d. Assume that $dP/dt$ obeys the same equation as $\Delta P/\Delta t$. Write a differential equation based on your answer to 7c. Transform the equation so that $dP/dt$ is by itself on one side. The result is called the **logistic equation**. The word *logistics* usually refers to the art of planning and coordinating the details of an operation, such as a military campaign, but originates from the Greek word logistikos, meaning "reckoning" or "reason."

e. Plot a slope field. Use $-50 \le t \le 100$ and $0 \le P \le 500$. Print the slope field or sketch it on a photocopy of Figure 7-5f.

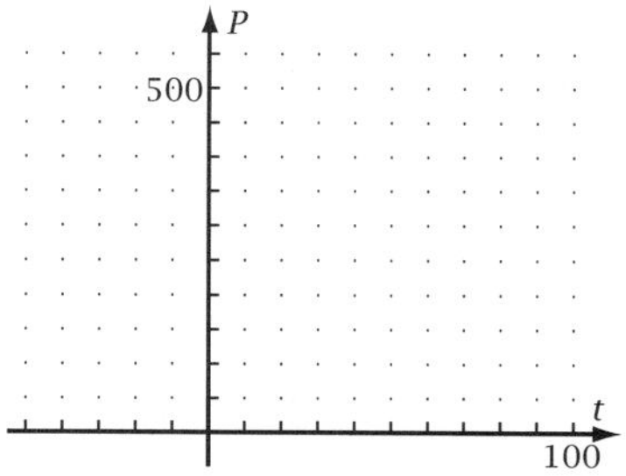

Figure 7-5f

f. Make a table of population predicted by Euler's method for each 10 yr from $t = -50$ through $t = 100$. Use as an initial condition the population in 1940 ($t = 0$). Use steps of $\Delta t = 1$ yr. Plot the points on the graph you drew in 7e and connect them with a smooth curve.

g. According to this mathematical model, what will be the ultimate population of the United States? How does this number appear in the differential equation and on the slope field?

h. Plot the populations for the six given years on the graph you drew in 7e. Does the population really seem to follow the solution by Euler's method?

i. Write a paragraph describing how well the predicted populations in 7f agree with the actual populations from 1940 through 1990.

j. Consult some reference material to find the results of censuses dating back through 1900. How well do your predicted values compare with the actual ones? How can you explain any large discrepancies between predicted and actual values?

k. Suppose that in the year 2010, 200 million people immigrate to the United States. Predict the population for the next 40 yr. What does the logistic-equation model say about the population growth under this condition?

8. *Algebraic Solution of the Logistic Equation:* It is possible to solve the logistic differential equation like that in Problem 7 algebraically. Suppose that

$$\frac{dy}{dx} = 3y(10 - y).$$

Separating the variables and integrating gives

$$\int \frac{1}{y(10 - y)}\, dy = 3\int dx.$$

In this problem you will learn how to do the integration on the left side. Then you will apply what you have learned so that you can algebraically solve the logistic equation in Problem 7.

a. The fraction in the integral on the left can be split into **partial fractions** like this:

$$\frac{1}{y(10 - y)} = \frac{A}{y} + \frac{B}{10 - y},$$

where $A$ and $B$ stand for constants. Using suitable algebra, find the values of $A$ and $B$.

b. Integrate the differential equation. Show that the integrated equation can be transformed into

$$y = \frac{10}{1 + ke^{-30x}},$$

where $k$ is a constant related to the constant of integration.

c. Solve the logistic equation from Problem 7d algebraically. Transform the answer so that population is in terms of time. Use the initial condition that $P = 131.7$ in 1940 (when $t = 0$) to evaluate $k$.

d. Use the algebraic solution you found in 8c to predict the population in 1950, 1960, 1970, 1980, and 1990. How well do the approximate solutions found by Euler's method in Problem 7f compare with these exact solutions? How well do the exact solutions compare with the actual population in these years? Write a paragraph that describes your observations about how well different mathematical models agree with each other and about how well they fit data from the real world.

9. *Journal Problem:* Update your journal with what you've learned since the last entry. Include such things as those listed here.
   - The one most important thing you have learned since your last journal entry
   - How slope fields and numerical methods can be used to solve differential equations without finding an algebraic solution
   - How much faith you would put into a computer-generated prediction of the U.S. population for the year 2050
   - What you now better understand about differential equations
   - Any technique or idea about differential equations that you're still unclear about

# 7-6 Predator-Prey Population Problems

If a population, such as animals or people, has plenty of food and plenty of room, the population tends to grow exponentially with time. You have seen that such exponential growth is a result of the fact that the rate of growth is proportional to the size of the population. The more people there are, the more babies are born per year. In Section 7-5, you used the logistic equation to model population growth in an environment where overcrowding limits the ultimate size of the population.

In this section you will explore the effects on the populations of two species in an environment where one of the species eats the other as its food supply. If the predator population is small, the prey population grows. Then, as a result of the increased food supply, the predator population starts to grow and can eventually become so large that it reduces the prey population. Then the predator population will decrease because there is less food, and so it goes! The models you will use for foxes and rabbits in the following problem set also apply to such populations as bats and mosquitoes, cattle and grass, and sharks and other fish.

**OBJECTIVE**

Use slope fields to solve problems of population growth in an environment where one population relies on another population for its food supply.

# Problem Set 7-6

## *Do These Quickly*

The following problems are intended to refresh your skills. You should be able to do all ten problems in less than five minutes.

**Q1.** $\int_a^b f(x)\,dx = \lim_{n\to\infty} \sum f(c)\Delta x$ is a (brief) statement of the —?—.

**Q2.** $\int_a^b f(x)\,dx = g(b) - g(a)$ is a (brief) statement of the —?—.

**Q3.** $\int f(x)dx = g(x)$ if and only if $f(x) = g'(x)$ is a statement of the —?—.

**Q4.** ". . . then there is a point $c$ in $(a, b)$ such that $f(c) = k$" is the conclusion of —?—.

**Q5.** ". . . then there is a point $c$ in $(a, b)$ such that $f'(c) = 0$" is the conclusion of —?—.

**Q6.** ". . . then there is a point $c$ in $(a, b)$ such that $f'(c) = \dfrac{f(b) - f(a)}{b - a}$" is the conclusion of —?—.

**Q7.** ". . . then $f'(x) = g'(h(x)) \cdot h'(x)$" is the conclusion of —?—.

**Q8.** $f(x) = \cos x + C$ is the —?— solution of a differential equation.

**Q9.** $f(x) = \cos x + 5$ is a(n) —?— solution of a differential equation.

**Q10.** $f(0) = 6$ is a(n) —?— condition for the differential equation in Q9.

Ona Nyland moves to an uninhabited island. Being lonely for company, she imports some pet rabbits. The rabbits multiply and become a nuisance! So she imports some foxes to control the rabbit population. In Problems 1–15, you will investigate the populations of foxes and rabbits, based upon assumptions about the way the animals grow and interact with one another.

1. Let $R$ be the number of hundreds of rabbits and let $F$ be the number of foxes at any given time, $t$. If there were no foxes, the rabbit population would grow at a rate proportional to the population. That is, $dR/dt$ would equal $k_1R$, where $k_1$ is a positive constant. Show that the rabbit population would grow exponentially with time under this condition.

2. If there were no rabbits for the foxes to eat, the fox population would decrease at a rate proportional to the population. That is, $dF/dt$ would equal $-k_2F$, where $k_2$ is a positive constant. Show that the fox population would decrease exponentially under this condition.

3. Assume that foxes eat rabbits at a rate proportional to the number of encounters between foxes and rabbits. This rate is proportional to the product of the number of rabbits and foxes. (If there are twice as many rabbits, there are twice as many encounters and vice versa.) Thus the rabbit population decreases at a rate $k_3RF$ in addition to increasing at $k_1R$. The fox population increases at a rate $k_4RF$ as well as decreasing at $k_2F$. Write differential equations for $dR/dt$ and for $dF/dt$ under these conditions.

4. Use the chain rule to write a differential equation for $dF/dR$. What happens to $t$?

5. Assume that the four constants in the differential equation are such that

$$\frac{dF}{dR} = \frac{-F + 0.025RF}{R - 0.04RF}.$$

If $R = 70$ and $F = 15$, calculate $dF/dR$.

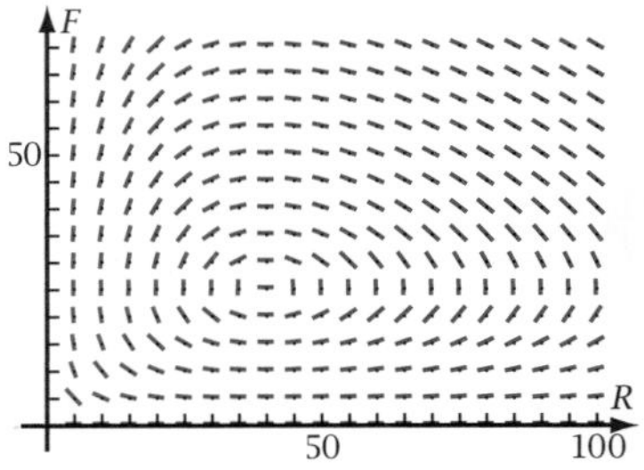

Figure 7-6a

6. Figure 7-6a shows the slope field for this differential equation. Show the initial condition given in Problem 5. Then show the relative populations of rabbits and foxes as time progresses. How do you tell from the differential equations you wrote for Problem 3 whether to start going to the right or to the left?

7. How would you describe the behavior of the rabbit and fox populations?

8. Is there a fixed point at which both the rabbit and the fox populations do not change? Explain.

9. The logistic equation of Section 7-5 shows that, because of overcrowding, the rate of change of population is decreased by an amount proportional to the square of the population. Assume that

$$\frac{dR}{dt} = R - 0.04RF - 0.01R^2.$$

Calculate $dF/dR$ (not $dR/dt$!) at $R = 70$ and $F = 15$ under this condition.

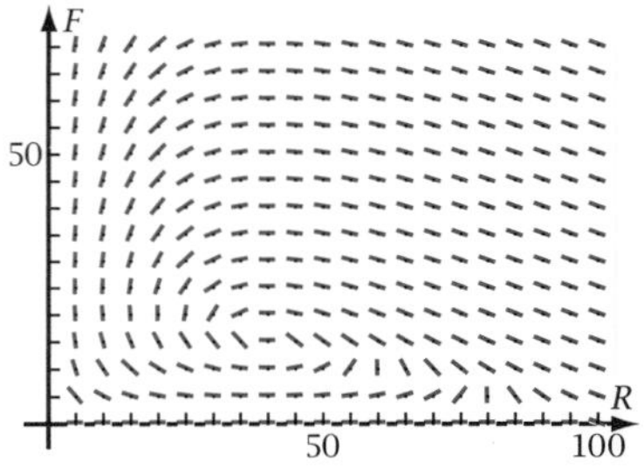

Figure 7-6b

10. The slope field in Figure 7-6b is for $dF/dR$, which you calculated in Problem 9. Use the initial condition in Problem 9 to sketch the predicted populations.

11. How does the graph in Problem 10 differ from that in Problem 6? How does overcrowding by rabbits affect the ultimate rabbit population? The ultimate fox population?

12. Ona seeks to reduce the rabbit population by allowing hunters to come to the island. She allows the hunters to take 1000 rabbits per unit of time, so $dR/dt$ is decreased by an additional 10. Calculate $dF/dR$ at the point $(R, F) = (70, 15)$ under these conditions.

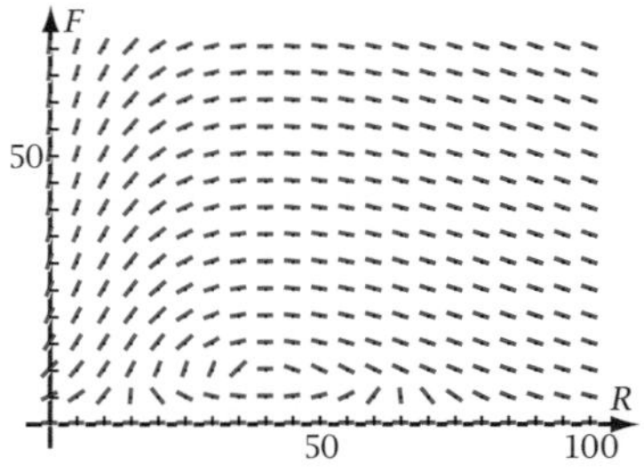

Figure 7-6c

13. The slope field in Figure 7-6c is for the differential equation

$$\frac{dF}{dR} = \frac{-F + 0.025RF}{R - 0.04RF - 0.01R^2 - 10}.$$

Trace the predicted populations under these conditions, starting at the point (70, 15).

14. Describe what happens to the populations of rabbits and foxes under these conditions.

15. Worried about the fate of the foxes in Problem 13, Ona imports 15 more of them. Starting at the point (70, 30), trace the populations. According to this mathematical model, what is the effect of importing more foxes? Surprising?!

# 7-7 Chapter Review and Test

In this chapter you have seen that by knowing the rate at which a population changes, you can write an equation for the derivative of the population. This differential equation can be solved numerically by Euler's method, graphically by slope field, or exactly by algebraic integration.

The Review Problems below are numbered according to the sections of this chapter. The Concepts Problems allow you to apply your knowledge to new situations. The Chapter Test is more like a typical classroom test your instructor might give you.

## Review Problems

R0. Update your journal with what you've learned since the last entry. Include such things as those listed here.

- The one most important thing you have learned in studying Chapter 7
- Which boxes you have been working on in the "define, understand, do, apply" table
- The proportion property of exponential functions and their derivatives, and this property's converse
- The fact that a function equation can be found from the rate of change of the function
- How differential equations can be solved graphically and numerically
- Any ideas about calculus that you're still unclear about

R1. *Punctured Tire Problem:* You run over a nail! The pressure, $P(t)$ pounds per square inch (psi), of the air remaining in your tire is given by

$$P(t) = 35(0.98^t),$$

where $t$ is the number of seconds since the tire was punctured. Calculate $P(0)$, $P(10)$, and $P(20)$. Show by example that although $P'(t)$ decreases as $t$ increases, the ratio $P'(t)/P(t)$ stays constant. Prove in general that $P'(t)/P(t)$ is constant.

R2. *Ramjet Problem:* A ramjet (Figure 7-7a) is a relatively simple jet engine. The faster the plane goes, the more air is "rammed" into the engine, and thus the more power the engine generates. Assume that the rate at which the plane's speed changes is directly proportional to the speed.

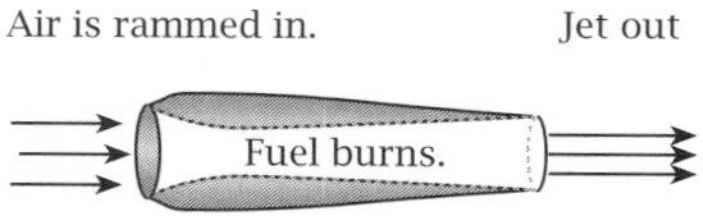
Air is rammed in.
Jet out
Fuel burns.

Figure 7-7a

a. Write a differential equation that expresses the assumption above.

b. Solve the differential equation. Show the integration step and describe what happens to the absolute value sign.

c. Evaluate the constants in the equation if the plane is going 400 mi/hr at time $t = 0$ sec and 500 mi/hr at time $t = 40$ sec.

d. When will the plane reach the speed of sound, 750 mi/hr?

R3. a. Find the general solution of the differential equation $dy/dx = 6y^{1/2}$.

b. Find the particular solution of the equation in R3a that contains the point (3, 25).

c. Plot the graph of the particular solution you found in R3b. Sketch the result.

d. Find $dy/dx$ for this differential equation when $x = 2$. Show on your graph that your answer is reasonable.

e. *Memory Retention Problem:* Paula Tickle starts her campaign for election to the senate. She meets people at a rate of about 100 per day, and she tries to remember as many names as possible. She finds that after seven full days, she remembers names of 600 of the 700 people she met. Assume that the rate of change of the number of names she remembers, $dN/dt$, equals 100 minus an amount that is directly proportional to $N$.

   i. Write a differential equation that expresses the assumption above, and solve the equation subject to the initial condition that she knew no names when $t = 0$.

   ii. How many names should Miss Tickle remember after 30 days?

   iii. Does your mathematical model predict that her brain will "saturate" after a long time, or does it predict that she can remember unlimited numbers of names?

   iv. After how many days of campaigning will Paula be able to remember the names of only 30 of the people she meets that day?

R4. Figure 7-7b shows the slope field for

$$\frac{dy}{dx} = -\frac{20}{xy} + 0.05y.$$

a. Calculate the slope at the points (2, 5) and (10, 16). Show that these slopes agree with the graph.

b. On a photocopy of Figure 7-7b, draw the particular solutions that contain (1, 8) and (1, 12). Describe the major difference in the behavior of the two graphs.

c. Does the particular solution that contains (1, 10) behave like that containing (1, 12) or that containing (1, 8)? Justify your answer.

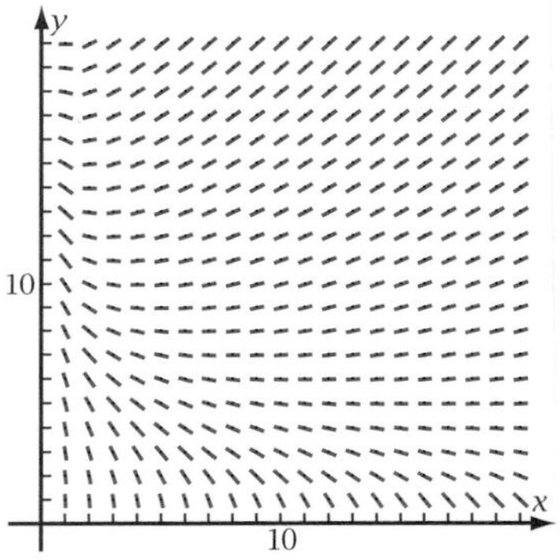


Figure 7-7b

R5. a. For the differential equation given in Problem R4, use Euler's method to calculate values of $y$ for the particular solution that contains (1, 9). Use $\Delta x = 1$. Where does the graph seem to cross the $x$-axis? On a photocopy of Figure 7-7b, plot the points you calculated.

b. Use Euler's method, as you did in R5a, but with an increment of $\Delta x = 0.1$. Record the $y$-value for each integer value of $x$ that shows in Figure 7-7b. Plot these points on the photocopy you used in R5a.

c. Write a few sentences commenting on the accuracy of Euler's method far away from the initial point when you use a relatively large value of $\Delta x$.

d. At what value of $x$ would the graph described in R5c cross the $x$-axis?

R6. *Predator-Prey Problem:* Space explorers visiting a planet in a nearby star system discover a population of 600 humanlike beings called Xaltos living by preying on a herd of 7000 creatures that bear a remarkable resemblance to yaks. They figure the differential equation that relates the two populations is

$$\frac{dy}{dx} = \frac{-0.5(x - 6)}{(y - 7)},$$

where $x$ is the number of hundreds of Xaltos and $y$ is the number of thousands of yaks. Figure 7-7c shows the slope field for this differential equation.

a. The numerator of the fraction in the differential equation is $dy/dt$ and the denominator is $dx/dt$. Explain why the two populations presently seem to be in equilibrium with each other.

b. Suppose that 300 more Xaltos move into the community. Starting at the point (9, 7), draw the particular solution of the differential equation on a photocopy of Figure 7-7c. Explain why the graph goes clockwise from this initial point. Describe what happens to the two populations as time goes on.

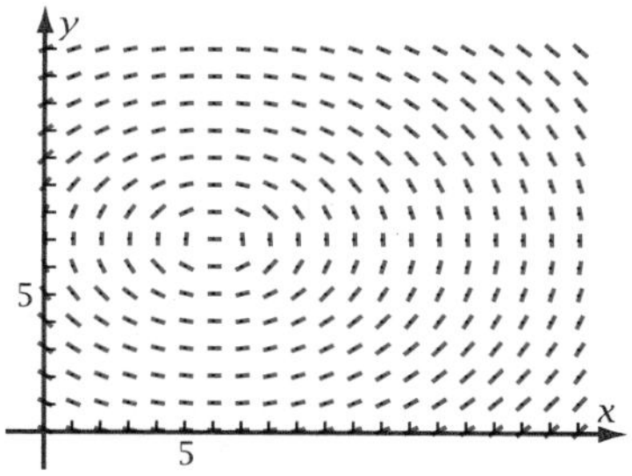

Figure 7-7c

c. Suppose that instead of 300, 1300 more Xaltos move into the community. Draw the particular solution, using this initial condition. What dire circumstance befalls the populations under this condition? Surprising?!

d. What if only 900 more Xaltos move in instead of the 1300 described in R6c? Would the same fate befall the populations? Justify your answer.

## Concepts Problems

C1. *Differential Equations Leading to Polynomial Functions:* You have shown that if $dy/dx$ is directly proportional to $y$, then $y$ is an exponential function of $x$. In this problem you will investigate similar differential equations that lead to other kinds of functions.

a. If $dy/dx$ is directly proportional to $y^{1/2}$, show that $y$ is a quadratic function of $x$.

b. Make a conjecture about what differential equation would make $y$ a cubic function of $x$.

c. Verify or refute your conjecture by solving the differential equation. If your conjecture was wrong, make other conjectures until you find the one that is right.

d. Once you succeed with C1c, you should be able to write a differential equation whose solution is any specified degree. Demonstrate that you have seen the pattern by writing and solving a differential equation whose solution is an eighth-degree function.

*C2. *Film Festival Problem:* In this chapter you have assumed a certain behavior for the derivative of a function. Then you have integrated to find an equation for the function. In this problem you will reverse the procedure. You will use measured values of a function, then find the derivative to make use of the mathematical model.

In order to make money for trips to contests, the math club at Wyden High plans to rent some video cassettes and present an all-night Halloween film festival in the school gym. The club members want to predict how much money they could make from such a project and to set the admission price so that they make the greatest amount of money.

---

* Adapted from data by Landy Godbold, as cited by Dan Teague.

The club conducts a survey of the entire student body, concluding with the question "What is the most you would pay to attend the festival?" Here are the results.

| maximum dollars | number of people |
|---|---|
| 2.00 | 100 |
| 2.50 | 40 |
| 3.00 | 60 |
| 4.00 | 120 |
| 4.50 | 20 |
| 5.50 | 40 |
| 6.00 | 80 |

a. Make a chart that shows the total number of people likely to attend as a function of the admission price.

b. Plot the data you charted in C2a. What kind of function might be a reasonable mathematical model for people in terms of dollars? Fit an equation of this kind to the data.

c. The amount of money club members expect to make is the product of price and number of people. Write an equation that expresses amount of money as a function of price.

d. What price should club members charge to make the greatest amount of money? Justify your answer.

e. Why would club members expect to make less money if they charged more than the price you determined in C2d? Why would they expect to make less money if they charged less than the price in C2d?

C3. *Gompertz Growth Curve Problem:* Another function with a sigmoid (S-shaped) graph sometimes used for population growth is the Gompertz function, whose general equation is

$$g(t) = ae^{-ce^{-kt}},$$

where $g(t)$ is the population at time $t$, and $a, c$, and $k$ are positive constants. The graphs of these functions look somewhat like Figure 7-7d. In this problem you will investigate effects of the constants, maximum growth rates, and limiting population values.

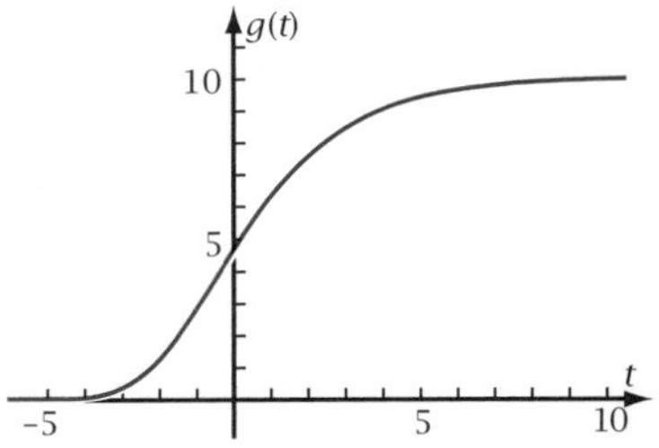

Figure 7-7d

a. Let $a = 10$, $c = 0.8$, and $k = 0.5$ so that the equation is

$$g(t) = 10e^{-0.8e^{-0.5t}}$$

Plot the graph of this particular Gompertz function. Confirm that it looks like the graph in Figure 7-7d. What does the limit of $g(t)$ appear to be as $t$ approaches infinity? Confirm your answer by taking the limit in the equation. If $g(t)$ represents population, what is the significance of this limit in the real world?

b. Find the equation of the particular Gompertz function that fits the United States population figures for 1960, 1970, and 1980.

| year | population (millions) |
|---|---|
| 1960 | 179 |
| 1970 | 203 |
| 1980 | 226 |

You may let time be zero in 1970. To get the exponential constants down to where you can deal with them, you may take the ln of both sides of the equation twice. By clever use of algebra, you can get two equations involving only the constant $a$. Then you can use your grapher to calculate the value of $a$. Plot the graph of the function. At what value does the population seem to level off?

c. Suppose that the 1980 data point had been 227 million instead of 226 million. How would this change affect the predicted ultimate population of the United States? Does the Gompertz equation seem to be fairly sensitive to slight changes in initial conditions?

C4. *Hot Tub Problem, Continued:* In Problem 5 of Problem Set 7-3, you wrote a differential equation for the volume of water remaining in a hot tub as it drained. That equation is

$$\frac{dV}{dt} = -2V^{1/2},$$

where $V$ is the volume of water that remains $t$ minutes after the drain is opened. By solving the differential equation, you found that the 196 $ft^3$ of water initially in the tub drained in 14 min. Suppose that while the drain is open, water flows in at the rate $F$ $ft^3$/min. Explore the effect of such an inflow on the remaining amount as a function of time.

## Chapter Test

T1. *Phoebe's Space Leak Problem:* Phoebe is returning to earth in her spaceship when she detects an oxygen tank leak. She knows that the rate of change of pressure is directly proportional to the pressure of the remaining oxygen.

a. Write a differential equation that expresses this fact and solve it subject to the initial condition that pressure is 3000 psi (pounds per square inch) at time $t = 0$ when Phoebe discovers the leak.

b. Five hours after she discovers the leak, the pressure has dropped to 2300 psi. At that time, Phoebe is still 20 hr away from earth. Will she make it home before the pressure drops to 800 psi? Justify your answer.

T2. *Swimming Pool Chlorination Problem:* Suppose that a pool is filled with chlorine-free water. The chlorinator is turned on, dissolving chlorine in the pool at a rate of 30 g/hr. But chlorine also escapes to the atmosphere at a rate proportional to the amount dissolved in the water. For this particular pool, the escape rate is 13 g/hr when the amount dissolved is 100 g.

a. Write a differential equation that expresses this information and solve it to express number of grams of chlorine in the pool as a function of the number of hours the chlorinator has been running. Be clever to find an initial condition!

b. How long will it take for the chlorine content to build up to the desired 200 g?

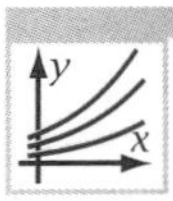

T3. The slope field in Figure 7-7e is for the differential equation

$$\frac{dy}{dx} = -0.36\frac{x}{y}.$$

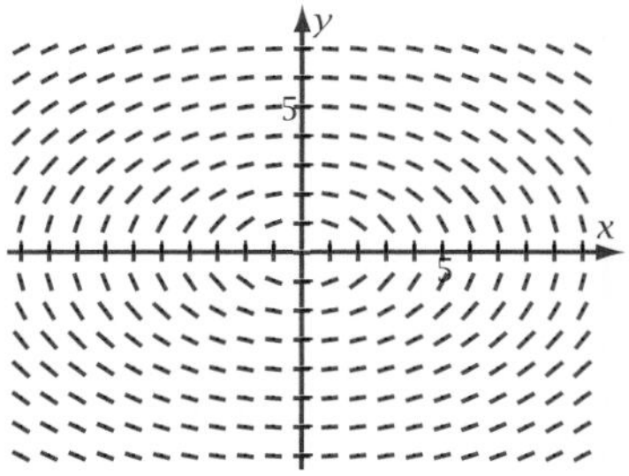

Figure 7-7e

a. On a photocopy of Figure 7-7e, sketch the particular solution that contains the point (0, 4).

b. Use Euler's method for the particular solution you sketched in T3a to find $y$ at $x = 6$. Use $\Delta x = 0.1$.

c. Separate the variables and solve the differential equation algebraically. Transform the solution so that $y$ is expressed explicitly in terms of $x$.

d. Evaluate $y$ when $x = 6$ for the algebraic solution you found in T3c. How close does the solution by Euler's method you found in T3b come to this exact solution? How close did the graphical solution you found in T3a come to the exact solution at $x = 6$?

T4. Write a paragraph telling the most important thing you learned as a result of studying this chapter.

# 7-8 Cumulative Review: Chapters 1-7

In your study of calculus so far, you have learned that calculus involves four major concepts, studied by four techniques. You should be able to do four major things with the concepts.

| concepts | techniques | be able to do |
|---|---|---|
| Limits | Graphical | Define them. |
| Derivatives | Numerical | Understand them. |
| Indefinite integrals | Algebraic | Do them. |
| Definite integrals | Verbal | Apply them. |

Two of these concepts, derivatives and definite integrals, are used to work problems involving, respectively, the rate of change of a function, or the product of $x$ and $y$ for a function in which $y$ depends on $x$. Both derivatives and definite integrals are founded on the concept of limit. Indefinite integrals, which are simply antiderivatives, provide an amazing link between derivatives and definite integrals via the fundamental theorem of calculus.

The following problems constitute a "semester exam" in which you are to demonstrate your mastery of these concepts as you have studied them so far.

## Problem Set 7-8

*Rocket Problems:* Ella Vader (Darth's daughter) is driving in her rocket ship. At time $t = 0$ min she fires her rocket engine. The ship speeds up for a while, then slows down as the planet Alderaan's gravity takes its effect. The graph of her velocity, $v(t)$ miles per minute, is shown in Figure 7-8a. In Problems 1–16, you will analyze Ella's motion.

1. On a sketch of Figure 7-8a, draw a narrow vertical strip of width $dt$. Show a sample point $(t, v(t))$ on the graph within the strip. What physical quantity does $v(t)\,dt$ represent?

2. If you take the sum $\sum v(t)\,dt$ from $t = 0$ to $t = 8$, what calculus concept equals the limit of this sum as $dt$ approaches zero?

3. Ella figures that her velocity is given by

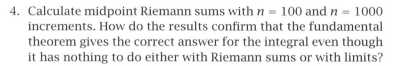

$$v(t) = t^3 - 21t^2 + 100t + 80.$$

Use the fundamental theorem of calculus to find the distance she goes from $t = 0$ to $t = 8$.

4. Calculate midpoint Riemann sums with $n = 100$ and $n = 1000$ increments. How do the results confirm that the fundamental theorem gives the correct answer for the integral even though it has nothing to do either with Riemann sums or with limits?

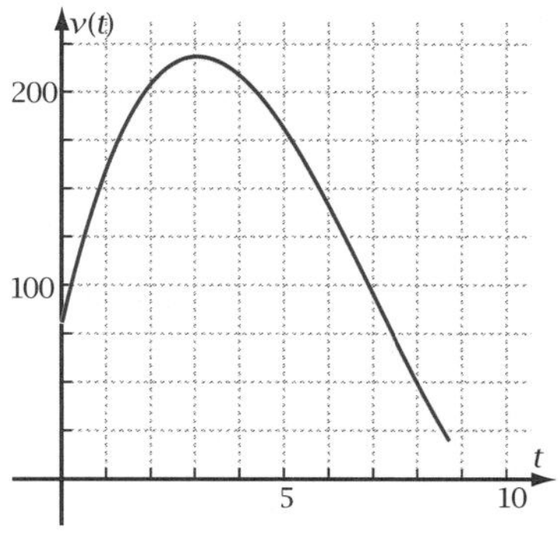


Figure 7-8a

5. On a sketch of Figure 7-8a, draw a representation of an upper sum with $n = 8$ increments.

6. Explain why, for an integrable function, any Riemann sum is squeezed to the same limit as the upper and lower sums as the widths of the increments approach zero.

7. Write the definition of definite integral. Write a statement of the fundamental theorem of calculus. Be sure to tell which is which.

8. Calculate the integral in Problem 3 numerically by using your grapher's integrate feature. Calculate the integral again graphically by counting squares. Compare the answers with the exact value.

9. Use symmetric difference quotients with $\Delta t = 0.1$ min and $\Delta t = 0.01$ min to estimate the rate of change of Ella's velocity when $t = 4$ min.

10. Write the definition of derivative.

11. For most kinds of functions there is a way to find the derivative algebraically. Use the appropriate method to find the exact rate of change of Ella's velocity when $t = 4$.

12. At $t = 4$, was Ella speeding up or slowing down? Justify your answer.

13. On a photocopy of Figure 7-8a, draw a line at the point $(4, v(4))$, having slope $v'(4)$. Clearly show how you construct the line. How is the line related to the graph?

14. What is the physical name of the instantaneous rate of change of velocity?

15. Ella's maximum velocity seems to occur at $t = 3$. Use derivatives appropriately to find out whether the maximum occurs when $t$ is exactly 3 sec.

16. Find an equation for $v''(t)$, the second derivative of $v(t)$ with respect to $t$.

*Compound Interest Problems:* When money is left in a savings account for which the interest is compounded continuously, the instantaneous rate at which the money increases, $dm/dt$, is directly proportional to $m$, the amount in the account at that instant.

17. Write a differential equation that expresses the property above.
18. Show the steps in solving the differential equation in Problem 17 for $m$ as a function of $t$.
19. In one word, how does $m$ vary with $t$?
20. The solution in Problem 18 is called the —?— solution of the differential equation. What word goes in the blank?
21. Find the particular solution in Problem 18 if $m$ is \$10,000 at $t = 0$ and \$10,900 at $t = 1$.
22. In Problem 21, the amount of money in the account grew by \$900 in one year. True or false: The amount of money will grow by \$9,000 in 10 yr. Justify your answer.

*Discrete Data Problems:* The techniques of calculus were invented for dealing with continuous functions. The concepts can also be applied to functions specified by a table of data. The following table gives values of $y$ for various values of $x$.

| $x$ | $y$ |
|---|---|
| 30 | 74 |
| 32 | 77 |
| 34 | 83 |
| 36 | 88 |
| 38 | 90 |
| 40 | 91 |
| 42 | 89 |

23. Use Simpson's rule to estimate $\int_{30}^{42} y\,dx$.
24. Estimate $dy/dx$ if $x = 36$. Show how you get your answer.

*Mean Value Theorem Problems:* The proof of the fundamental theorem is based on the mean value theorem. This theorem is a corollary of Rolle's theorem.

25. State Rolle's theorem.
26. Sketch a graph that illustrates the conclusion of the mean value theorem.

*Graphing Problems:* Calculus is useful for analyzing the behavior of graphs of functions.

27. Figure 7-8b shows the graph of function $f$. On a photocopy of this figure, sketch the derivative graph, $f'$.
28. The function

$$f(x) = 2^x - \frac{|x-1|}{x-1}$$

has a discontinuity at $x = 1$. Sketch the graph. What kind of discontinuity is it?

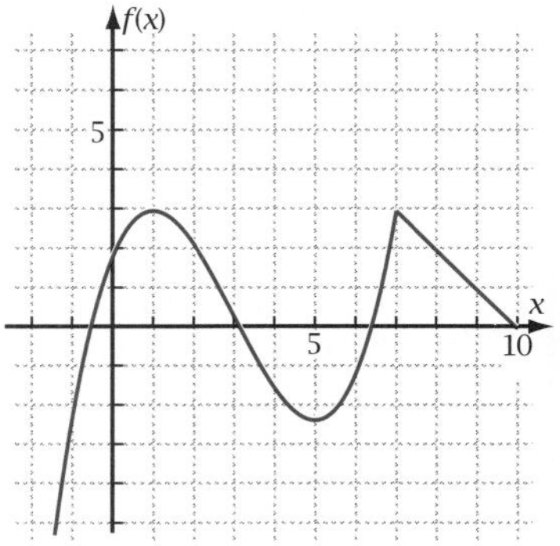

Figure 7-8b

29. The function $g(x) = x^{1/3}(x - 1)$ has $g(0) = 0$. Show that $g'(0)$ is undefined. Show what the graph of $g$ looks like in a neighborhood of $x = 0$. You may use your grapher's cube root.

*Differential Equation Problems:* Figure 7-8c shows the slope field for the differential equation

$$\frac{dy}{dx} = 0.25\frac{x}{y}.$$

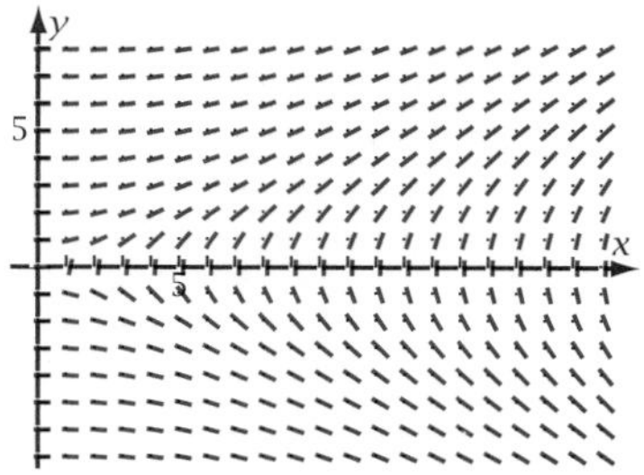

Figure 7-8c

30. On a photocopy of the graph, sketch the particular solutions that contain the points (0, 3) and (10, 4).

31. The two solutions in Problem 30 share a common asymptote. Sketch the asymptote. State an initial condition that would give the asymptote as the graph of the solution.

32. Solve the differential equation by separating the variables and integrating. Find the equation of the particular solution that contains the point (10, 4).

33. Use the function in Problem 32 to calculate the exact value of $y$ when $x = 10.5$.

34. Demonstrate that you understand the idea behind Euler's method by calculating the first point to the right of the point (10, 4) in Problem 32, with $\Delta x = 0.5$. How does this value compare with the exact value in Problem 33?

*Algebraic Techniques Problems:* You have learned algebraic techniques for differentiating, antidifferentiating, and calculating limits.

35. Find $\frac{d}{dx}(\sin^{-1}x^3)$.

36. Find $\frac{dy}{dx}$ if $x = \ln(\cos t)$ and $y = \sec t$.

37. Find $\int \frac{dx}{4 - 3x}$.

38. Find $h'(x)$ if $h(x) = 5^x$.

39. Find $\lim_{x \to 0} \frac{\sin 5x + \cos 3x - 5x - 1}{x^2}$.

40. Plot the graph of the fraction given in Problem 39. Sketch the result. Show how the graph confirms your answer to Problem 39.

*Journal Problems:* You have kept a calculus journal in which you record what you've learned and what you're still unsure about.

41. Write what you think is the one most important thing you have learned so far as a result of taking calculus.

42. Write one thing in calculus about which you are still unsure.

CHAPTER

# 8 The Calculus of Plane and Solid Figures

A cable hanging under its own weight forms a curve called a catenary. A cable supporting a uniform horizontal load, such as the cables in the Golden Gate Bridge, forms a parabola. By slicing such graphs into short segments the differential of arc length can be found. Integrating this differential allows computation of the exact length of hanging cables and chains, important information for construction of bridges.

# Mathematical Overview

In Chapter 8 you will learn how definite integrals let you find exact area, volume, and length by slicing an object into small pieces, then adding and taking the limit. You will also use derivatives to find where geometric figures have maxima, minima, and other interesting features. You will explore the geometrical figures in four ways.

***Graphically*** The logo at the top of each even-numbered page of this chapter shows an object for which you can find length, area, volume, and points of inflection.

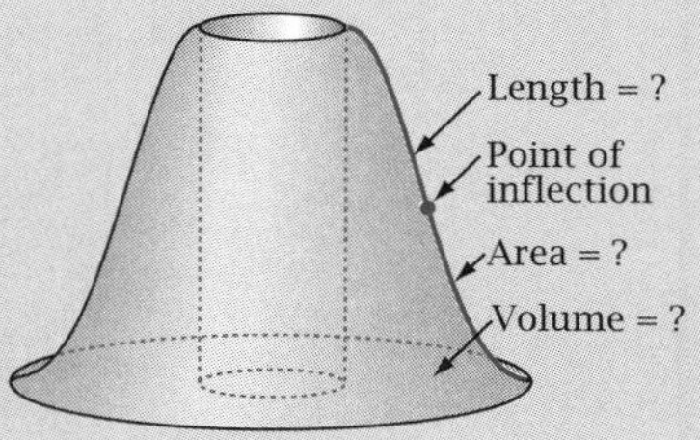


***Numerically***

| $x$ | $f'(x)$ | $f(x)$ |
|---|---|---|
| 1.8 | 0.72 | 13.931 |
| 1.9 | 0.33 | 13.984 |
| 2.0 | 0 | 14 ← Max. |
| 2.1 | -0.27 | 13.987 |
| 2.2 | -0.48 | 13.949 |
| ... | ... | ... |

***Algebraically*** $V = \pi \int_a^b (x_2^2 - x_1^2)\, dy$, volume by slicing into washers.

***Verbally*** *I think the most important thing I learned is that when you find area, volume, length, and so forth, you use the same technique. Draw a picture showing a representative slice of the object, pick a sample point within the slice, find the differential of the quantity I'm trying to find, then add up the differentials and take the limit, which means integrate.*

# 8-1 Cubic Functions and Their Derivatives

Recall that the graph of a quadratic function, $f(x) = ax^2 + bx + c$, is always a parabola. The graph of a cubic function, $f(x) = ax^3 + bx^2 + cx + d$, is called a **cubic parabola**. To begin your application of calculus to geometric figures, you will learn about the second derivative, which tells the rate at which the (first) derivative changes. From the second derivative you can learn something about the curvature of a graph and whether the graph curves upward or downward.

***OBJECTIVE*** Work alone or with your study group to explore the graphs of various cubic functions and to make connections between the function's graph and its derivatives.

Figure 8-1a shows the graphs of three cubic parabolas. They have different shapes depending on the relative sizes of the coefficients $a$, $b$, and $c$. (The constant $d$ affects only the vertical placement of the graph, not its shape.) Sometimes they have two distinct vertices, sometimes none at all. In Exploratory Problem Set 8-1, you will accomplish the objective of this section.

## Exploratory Problem Set 8-1

1. In Figure 8-1a,

$$f(x) = x^3 - 6x^2 + 9x + 3,$$
$$g(x) = x^3 - 6x^2 + 15x - 9, \text{ and}$$
$$h(x) = x^3 - 6x^2 + 12x - 3.$$

For each function, find an equation for the derivative. Plot the function and its derivative on the same screen. Then list as many connections as you can find between the function graph and the derivative graph. Sketches will help.

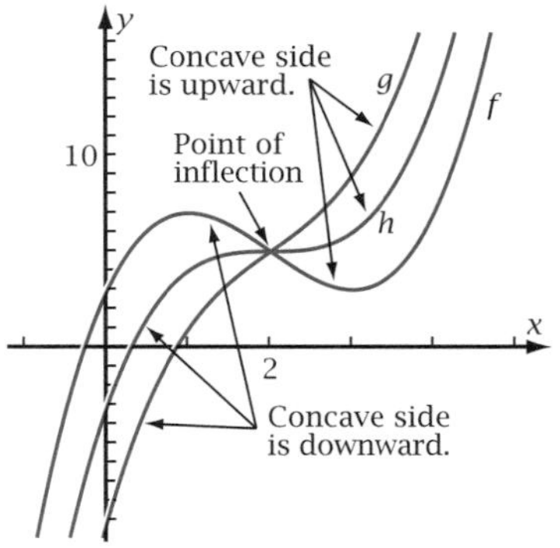

Figure 8-1a

2. What connection can you see between the graph of the derivative of a function and whether or not the function has two distinct vertex points (high or low points)?
3. The **second derivative** of a function is the derivative of the (first) derivative. For instance, $f''(x)$ (pronounced "$f$ double prime of $x$") is equal to $6x - 12$. Find equations for the second derivatives $g''(x)$ and $h''(x)$. What do you notice?
4. Figure 8-1a illustrates what it means for a curve to be **concave upward** at a given point, or **concave downward**. What connection do you notice between the second derivative and the direction of the concave side of the graph?
5. A graph has a *point of inflection* where it changes from concave downward to concave upward. Tell two ways you could locate a point of inflection using derivatives.

# 8-2 Critical Points and Points of Inflection

If a moving object comes to a stop, several things could happen. It could remain stopped, start off again in the same direction, or start off again in some different direction. When a car stops or reverses direction, its velocity goes through zero (hopefully!). When a baseball is hit by a bat, its velocity changes abruptly and is undefined at the instant of contact. Figure 8-2a shows how displacement, $d$, and velocity, $v$ (derivative), could vary with time, $x$.

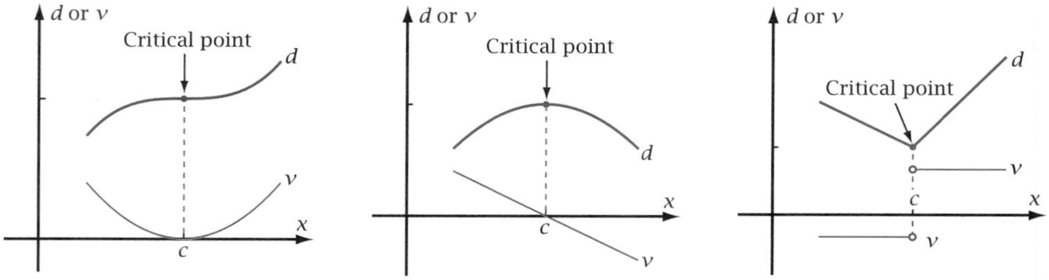


Car pauses, then starts again. Derivative is zero but does not change sign. "Plateau" point for *d*.

Car stops and backs up. Derivative is zero and does change sign. Local maximum point for *d*.

Baseball is hit. Derivative is undefined and changes sign. Local minimum point for *d*.

Figure 8-2a

A point where the derivative is zero or undefined is called a **critical point**. The word comes from "crisis." (When one reaches a crisis, things stop and can go in different directions.) "Critical point" is sometimes used for the point on the $x$-axis and sometimes for the point on the graph itself. You must decide which is meant from the context.

The $y$-value at a critical point can be a **local maximum** or a **local minimum** (Figure 8-2a, center and right). The word "local" is used to indicate that $f(c)$ is the maximum or minimum of $f(x)$ when $x$ is kept in a neighborhood (locality) of $c$. The **global maximum** and **global minimum** are the largest and smallest of the local maxima and minima, respectively. (Maxima and minima are the plural forms.) A critical point with zero derivative but no maximum or minimum (Figure 8-2a, left) is called a **plateau point**.

There are connections between the derivative of a function and the behavior of its graph at a critical point. For instance, if the derivative changes from positive to negative (Figure 8-2a, center), there is a maximum point in the function graph. As you saw in Section 8-1, the second derivative of a function tells which way the concave side of the graph points. A **point of inflection** occurs where the concavity changes direction.

***OBJECTIVE***

From information about the first and second derivatives of a function, tell whether the $y$-value is a local maximum or minimum at a critical point, tell whether the graph has a point of inflection, and use this information to sketch the graph or find the equation of the function.

**■ Example 1** For the function graphed in Figure 8-2b, sketch a number-line graph for $f'$ and a number-line graph for $f''$ showing the sign of each derivative in a neighborhood of the critical point at $x = 2$. Indicate on the number lines whether $f(2)$ is a local maximum or a local minimum, or whether the graph has a point of inflection at $x = 2$.

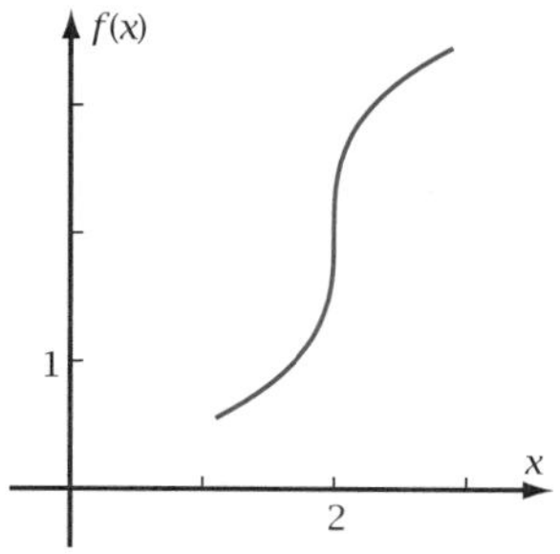


Figure 8-2b

**Solutions** Sketch a number line for $f'$ and another one for $f''$. Each one needs three regions: one for x, one for the derivative, and one for $f(x)$. Figure 8-2c shows a convenient way to sketch them.

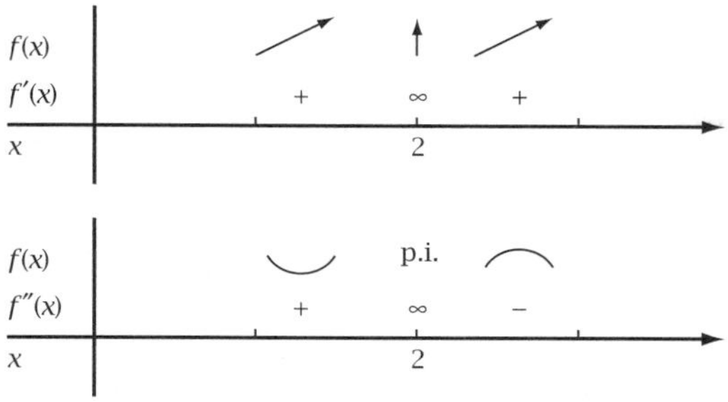


Figure 8-2c

The graph is vertical at $x = 2$, so $f'(2)$ is infinite. Insert the symbol $\infty$ in the $f'(x)$ region above $x = 2$, and sketch a vertical arrow above it in the $f(x)$ region.

The graph of $f$ slopes up on both sides of $x = 2$. Since the derivative is positive when the function is increasing, put a plus sign in the $f'(x)$ region on both sides of $x = 2$. Show upward sloping arrows in the $f(x)$ region above the plus signs. Since there is not a maximum or minimum value of $f(x)$ at $x = 2$, you don't need to write any words in that region.

The graph is concave up for $x < 2$ and concave down for $x > 2$. Since a positive second derivative indicates concave up and vice versa, put a plus sign in the $f''(x)$ region to the left of $x = 2$ and a minus sign to the right. Draw arcs in the $f(x)$ region to indicate the direction of concavity of the $f$ graph. Since the concavity changes (from up to down) at $x = 2$, the graph has a point of inflection there. Write "p.i." in the $f(x)$ region above $x = 2$. ■

### *A Note on Concavity and Curvature*

The word *concave* comes from the Latin cavus, meaning "hollow." So do "cave" and "cavity." If the second derivative is positive, the first derivative is increasing. Figure 8-2d shows why the concave side is upward in this case and vice versa. As shown in Figure 8-2e, the larger the absolute value of $f''(x)$, the more sharply the graph curves. However, as you will learn in Section 10-7, the curvature also depends on the slope of the graph. For a given value of $f''(x)$, the steeper the slope, the less the curvature.

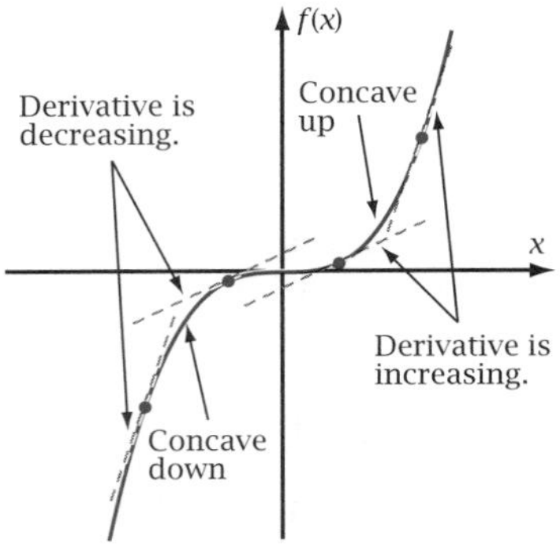


Figure 8-2d

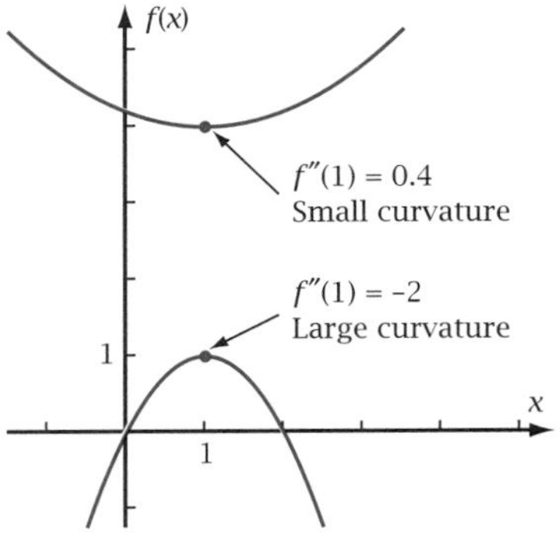


Figure 8-2e

In Example 2, you will reverse the procedure of Example 1 and construct the graph of a function from the number lines for its first and second derivatives.

■ ***Example 2*** Figure 8-2f shows number-line graphs for the first and second derivatives of a continuous function $f$. Use this information to sketch the graph of $f$ if $f(4) = 0$. The abbreviation "e.p." signifies an endpoint of the domain. Describe the behavior of the function at critical points.

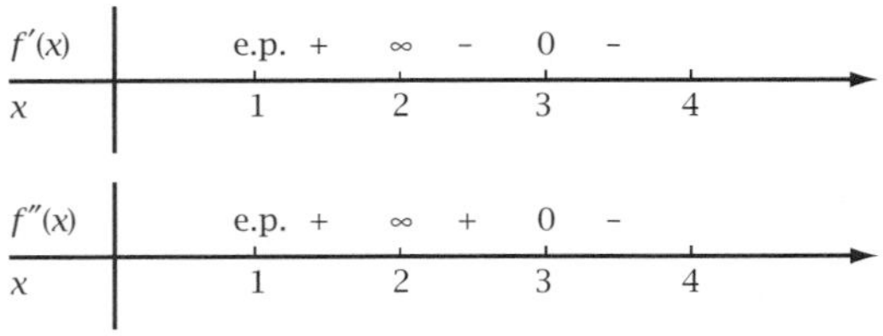


Figure 8-2f

***Solution*** Sketch the number lines. Add arrows and arcs in the $f(x)$ region to show the slope and concavity in the intervals between critical points (Figure 8-2g). Add words to describe what features the graph will have at the critical points of $f$ and $f'$. Sketch a continuous function (no asymptotes) having the prescribed features, crossing the $x$-axis at $x = 4$ (Figure 8-2h). The graph you draw could be somewhat different, but it must have the features shown on the number lines in Figure 8-2g.

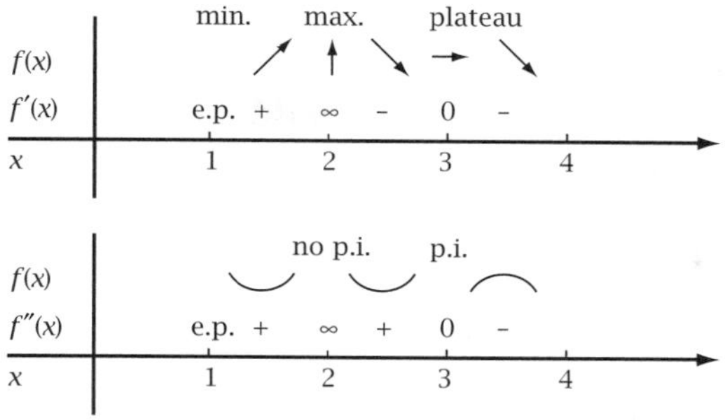


Figure 8-2g

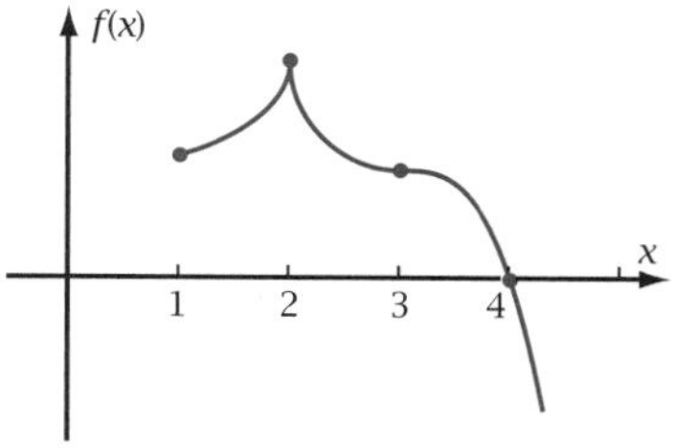


Figure 8-2h

In Example 3, you are given both the equation for the function and an accurate graph. You will be asked to find critical features algebraically, some of which may be hard to see.

**Example 3** Figure 8-2i shows the graph of $f(x) = x^{4/3} + 4x^{1/3}$.

a. Sketch number lines for $f'$ and $f''$ showing features that appear clearly on the graph.

b. Find equations for $f'(x)$ and $f''(x)$. Show algebraically that the critical points you drew in part a are correct. Fix any errors.

c. Write $x$– and $y$–coordinates of all maxima, minima, and points of inflection.

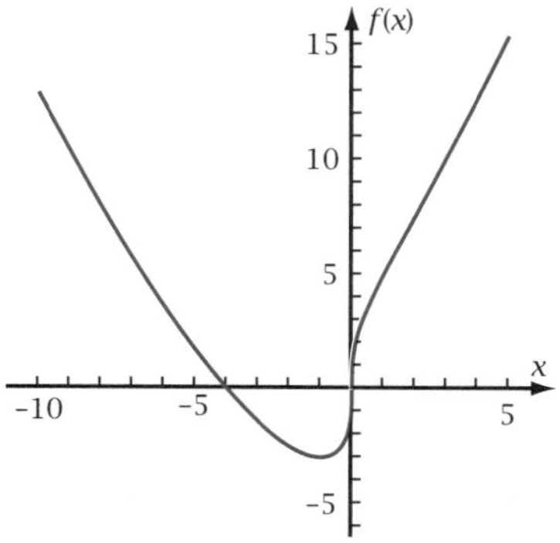


Figure 8-2i

**Solutions**

a. Figure 8-2j shows the two number lines. $f'(x)$ is zero at $x = -1$, and infinite at $x = 0$. The graph is concave up for $x < 0$, and appears to be concave down for $x > 0$.

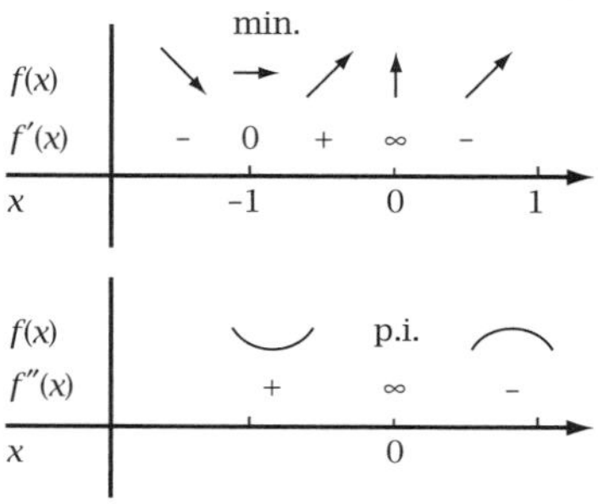


Figure 8-2j

b. $f'(x) = \frac{4}{3}x^{1/3} + \frac{4}{3}x^{-2/3} = \frac{4}{3}x^{-2/3}(x+1)$

$f''(x) = \frac{4}{9}x^{-2/3} - \frac{8}{9}x^{-5/3} = \frac{4}{9}x^{-5/3}(x-2)$

Factor out the power of $x$ with the smaller exponent.

Critical points occur where either $f'(x) = 0$ or $f'(x)$ is undefined.

$f'(x) = 0 \Longleftrightarrow \frac{4}{3}x^{-2/3}(x+1) = 0$

$x^{-2/3} = 0$ or $x + 1 = 0$ — A product is zero if and only if one of its factors is zero.

$\therefore x = -1$ — $x^{-2/3} = 1/x^{2/3}$, which cannot equal zero. So the other factor must be zero.

$f'(x)$ is undefined $\Leftrightarrow x = 0$ — $0^{-2/3} = 1/0^{2/3} = 1/0$, which is infinite.

$\therefore$ critical points occur at $x = 0$ and $x = -1$, as observed in part a.

Inflection points occur where $f'$ has critical points; that is, $f''(x)$ is zero or undefined.

$f''(x) = 0 \Longleftrightarrow \frac{4}{9}x^{-5/3}(x-2) = 0$

$x^{-5/3} = 0$ or $x - 2 = 0$

$\therefore x = 2$ — Why?

$f''(x)$ is undefined $\Leftrightarrow x = 0$ — Why?

In order for there to be a point of inflection, $f''(x)$ must change sign.
At $x = 2$, the factor $(x - 2)$ in $f''(x)$ changes sign.
At $x = 0$, the factor $(4/9)x^{-5/3}$ changes sign.
Inflection points are at $x = 0$ and $x = 2$.

Any power of a positive number is positive. If $x$ is negative, then $x^{-5/3}$ is negative. The cube root of a negative number is negative, the fifth power of that answer is also negative, and the reciprocal (negative exponent) of that negative answer is still negative.

Since the point at $x = 2$ did not show up in the original number line for $f''$ in part a, add this feature to your sketch, as shown in Figure 8-2k.

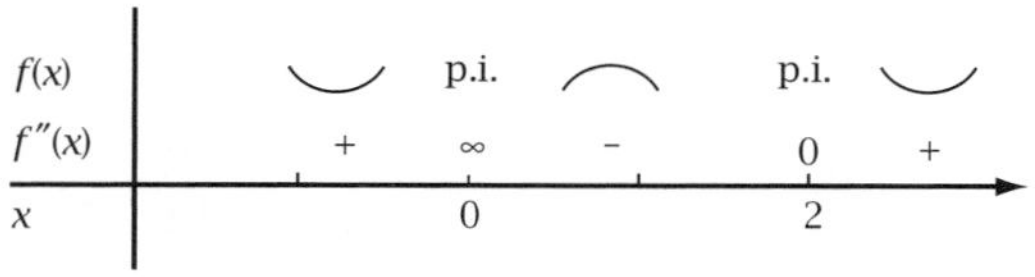


Figure 8-2k

c. To find the $y$-coordinates of the maxima and minima, substitute the $x$ values from part b into the $f(x)$ equation.

$f(-1) = (-1)^{4/3} + 4(-1)^{1/3} = 1 - 4 = -3$

$f(0) = 0$

$f(2) = (2)^{4/3} + 4(2)^{1/3} = 7.559\ldots$

The local and global minima of $f(x)$ are both $-3$ at $x = -1$.
Points of inflection are at $(0, 0)$ and at $(2, 7.559\ldots)$.
There are no local or global maxima. — $f(x)$ approaches infinity as $x$ approaches $\pm\infty$.

■

### *A Note on Powers with Negative Bases*

Noninteger powers with negative bases are awkward. For instance, $(-1)^{1/3}$ has a real value, $-1$; $(-1)^{1/6}$ has no real values; and $(-1)^{\pi}$ has infinitely many distinct, complex values. As a result, calculators usually require you to enter noninteger powers such as $x^{4/3}$ in the form $(x^{1/3})^4$ or $(x^4)^{1/3}$, with an exponent having 1 as its numerator and an integer denominator. That way the calculator can tell what kind of number the answer will be, real or imaginary.

### *A Note on Infinite Slope and Infinite Curvature*

If $f(x)$ is defined but $f'(x)$ is infinite, such as at $x = 0$ in Example 3, then the graph will have a vertical tangent at that point. If $f(x)$ and $f'(x)$ are defined but $f''(x)$ is infinite, then the graph will have infinite curvature at that point. Infinite curvature may be hard to imagine, as you will see in Problem 40 of Problem Set 8-2.

### *A Note on Undefined versus Infinite*

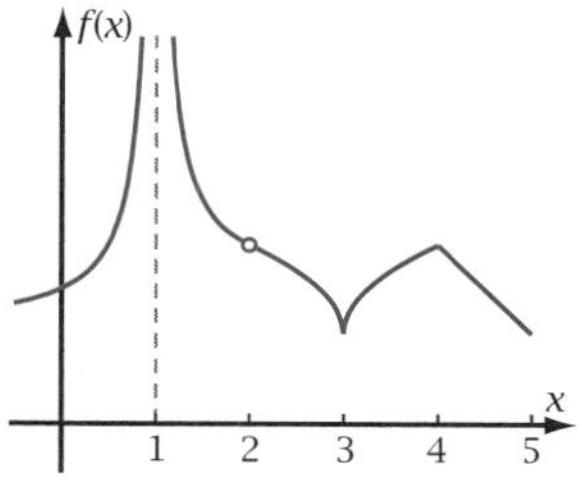

Figure 8-2l

There are several reasons a function or its derivative may be undefined. Figure 8-2l shows five possibilities.

- $f(1)$ is undefined because it is infinite. That is, the limit of $f(x) = \infty$ as $x$ approaches 1. (Do not say, "$f(1) = \infty$." This is bad form.)
- $f(2)$ is undefined but is not infinite. There is a finite limit for $f(x)$ as $x$ approaches 2.
- $f'(2)$ is undefined because $f(2)$ is undefined.
- $f'(3)$ is undefined because it is infinite. That is, the limit of $f'(x) = \pm\infty$ as $x$ approaches 3.
- $f'(4)$ is undefined but is not infinite. The left and right limits of $f'(x)$ are both real numbers, but they are not equal to each other.

Sometimes you will find critical points from just an equation for a function. Example 4 shows how to do this graphically and numerically and how to confirm the results algebraically.

**Example 4** Let $f(x) = -x^3 + 4x^2 + 5x + 20$, with domain $x \in [-2.5,\ 5]$.

a. Plot the graph. Estimate the $x$- and $y$-coordinates of all local maxima or minima and of all points of inflection. Tell the global maximum and minimum.

b. Write equations for $f'(x)$ and $f''(x)$. Use them to find, either numerically or algebraically, the precise values of the $x$-coordinates in part a.

c. Tell why there are no other critical points or points of inflection.

***Solutions***

a. Figure 8-2m shows the graph in the given domain. By tracing, you find the following:
Local minima of 20 at the endpoint $x = 5$, and about 18.625 at $x \approx -0.5$.
Global minimum is about 18.625.
Local maxima of 48.125 at the endpoint $x = -2.5$, and about 44.192 at $x \approx 3.2$.
Global maximum is about 48.125.
Point of inflection is at approximately (1.3, 31).

b. $f'(x) = -3x^2 + 8x + 5$
$f''(x) = -6x + 8$

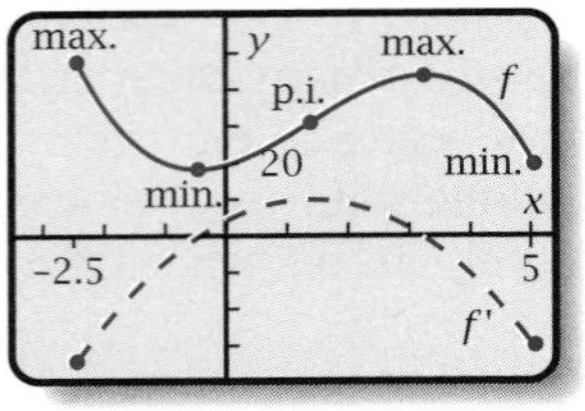


Figure 8-2m

The graph of $f'$ is shown on the same screen as $f$ in Figure 8-2m. To locate the critical points precisely, either use your graphers solve feature to find numerically where $f'(x) = 0$, or use the quadratic formula. Thus,

$$x = \frac{-8 \pm \sqrt{64 - 4(-3)(5)}}{2(-3)}$$

$$x = -0.5225\ldots \text{ or } 3.1892\ldots,$$

both of which confirm the estimates in part a.

To find the point of inflection precisely, set $f''(x) = 0$ and solve. Thus,

$$-6x + 8 = 0 \Leftrightarrow x = \tfrac{4}{3},$$

which confirms the estimate of $x \approx 1.3$ in part a.

c. Since $f'(x)$ is quadratic, there can be at most two zeros, both of which were found in part b. Since $f''(x)$ is linear, there is exactly one zero, which was found in part b. Therefore, there are no more critical points or points of inflection. ■

Figure 8-2n and the accompanying boxes present the definitions and properties of this section.

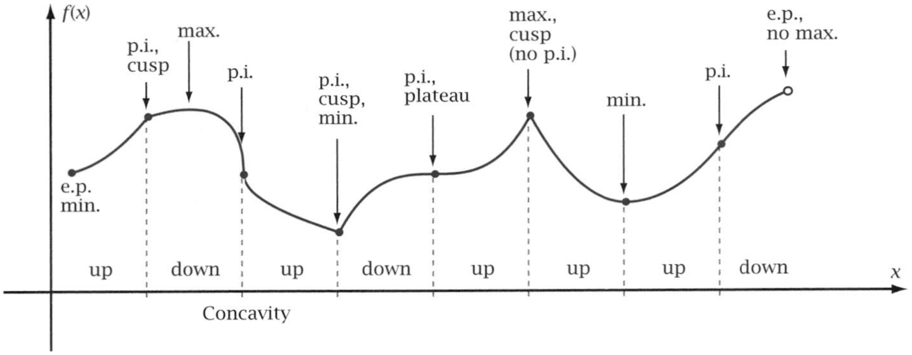


Figure 8-2n

### *Definitions: Critical Points and Related Features*

- A **critical point** on a graph occurs at $x = c$ if $f(c)$ is defined, and if and only if $f'(c)$ either is zero or is undefined.
- $f(c)$ is a **local maximum** (or relative maximum) of $f(x)$ if and only if $f(c) \geq f(x)$ for all $x$ in a neighborhood of $c$ (that is, in an open interval containing $c$).
- $f(c)$ is a **local minimum** (or relative minimum) of $f(x)$ if and only if $f(c) \leq f(x)$ for all $x$ in a neighborhood of $c$.
- $f(c)$ is the **global maximum** (or absolute maximum) of $f(x)$ if and only if $f(c) \geq f(x)$ for all $x$ in the domain of $f$.
- $f(c)$ is the **global minimum** (or absolute minimum) of $f(x)$ if and only if $f(c) \leq f(x)$ for all $x$ in the domain of $f$.
- The value of $f''(c)$ is called the **concavity** of the graph of $f$ at $x = c$.
- The point $(c, f(c))$ is a **point of inflection** if and only if $f''(x)$ changes sign at $x = c$. (Old spelling: inflexion, meaning "not bent.")
- The point $(c, f(c))$ is a **cusp** if and only if $f'$ is discontinuous at $x = c$.
- The point $(c, f(c))$ is a plateau point if and only if $f'(c) = 0$, but $f'(x)$ does not change sign at $x = c$.

### *Properties: Maximum, Minimum, and Point of Inflection*

- If $f'(x)$ goes from positive to negative at $x = c$ and $f$ is continuous at $x = c$, then $f(c)$ is a local maximum.
- If $f'(x)$ goes from negative to positive at $x = c$, and $f$ is continuous at $x = c$, then $f(c)$ is a local minimum.
- If $f''(c)$ is positive, then the graph of $f$ is concave upwards at $x = c$.
- If $f''(c)$ is negative, then the graph of $f$ is concave downwards at $x = c$.
- If $f''(x)$ changes sign at $x = c$ and $f$ is continuous at $x = c$, then $(c, f(c))$ is a point of inflection (by definition).
- A maximum or minimum point (but not a point of inflection) can occur at an endpoint of the domain of a function.

### *Symbols for Derivatives*

The following table lists different symbols for first and second derivatives. Each one is convenient for a specific purpose. Make sure you are comfortable with any of them.

| function value | first derivative | second derivative |
|---|---|---|
| $f(x)$ | $f'(x)$ | $f''(x)$ |
| $y$ | $y'$ | $y''$ |
| $y$ | $\dfrac{dy}{dx}$ | $\dfrac{d^2y}{dx^2}$ |

The symbol $d^2y/dx^2$ is read "the second derivative of $y$ with respect to $x$," or more briefly, "$d$ squared $y$, $dx$ squared." The symbol comes from thinking of $d/dx$ as an operator that acts on $dy/dx$ and then doing "algebra" on $d/dx(dy/dx)$.

$$\frac{d}{dx}\left(\frac{dy}{dx}\right) \to \frac{d}{dx}\left(\frac{d}{dx}(y)\right) \to \left(\frac{d}{dx}\right)^2(y) \to \frac{d^2}{dx^2}(y) \to \frac{d^2y}{dx^2}$$

# Problem Set 8-2

### *Do These Quickly*

The following problems are intended to refresh your skills. You should be able to do all ten problems in less than five minutes.

***Q1.*** Sketch: $y = x^2$

***Q2.*** Sketch: $y = x^3$

***Q3.*** Sketch: $y = \cos x$

***Q4.*** Sketch: $y = \sin^{-1} x$

***Q5.*** Sketch: $y = e^{-x}$

***Q6.*** Sketch: $y = \ln x$

***Q7.*** Sketch: $y = \tan x$

***Q8.*** Sketch: $y = x$

***Q9.*** Sketch: $y = 1/x$

***Q10.*** Sketch: $x = 2$

For Problems 1-12, sketch number-line graphs for $f'$ and for $f''$ showing what happens to the value and to the sign of each derivative in a neighborhood of $x = 2$.

1.

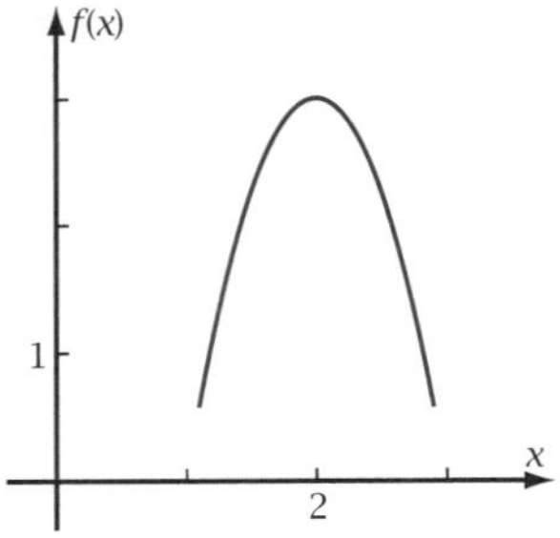


2.

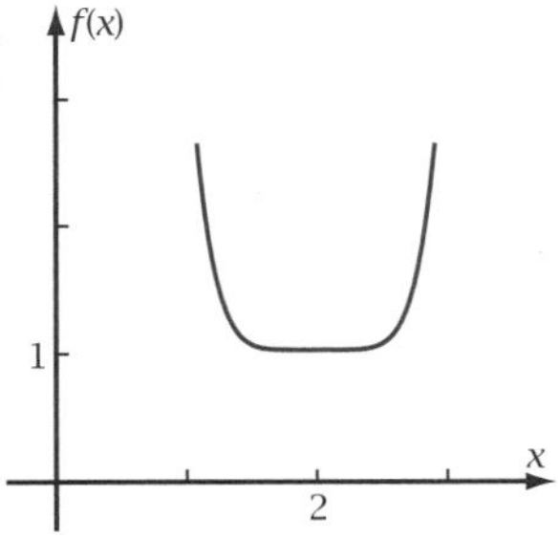


3.

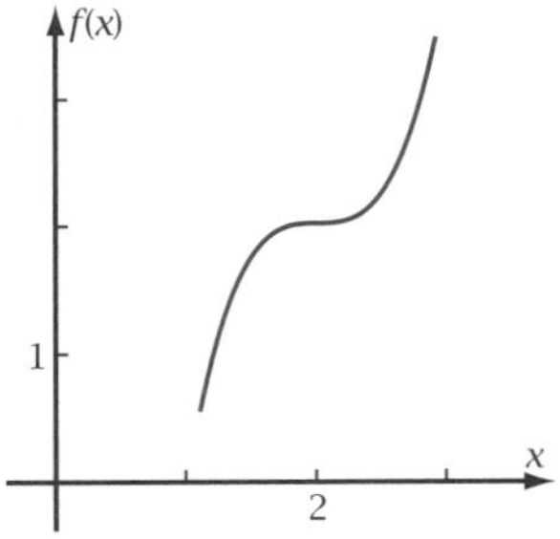


4.

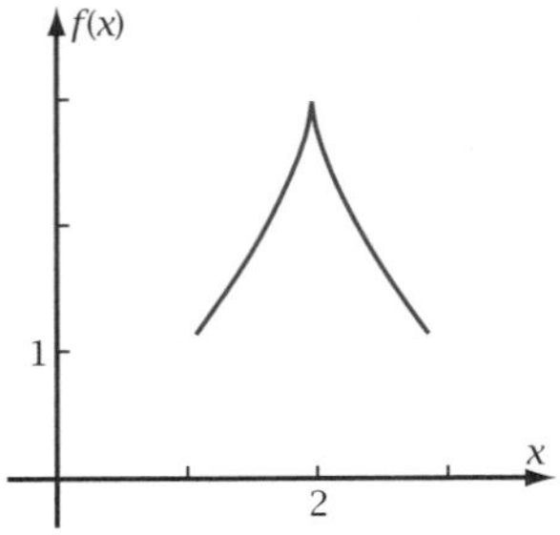


5.

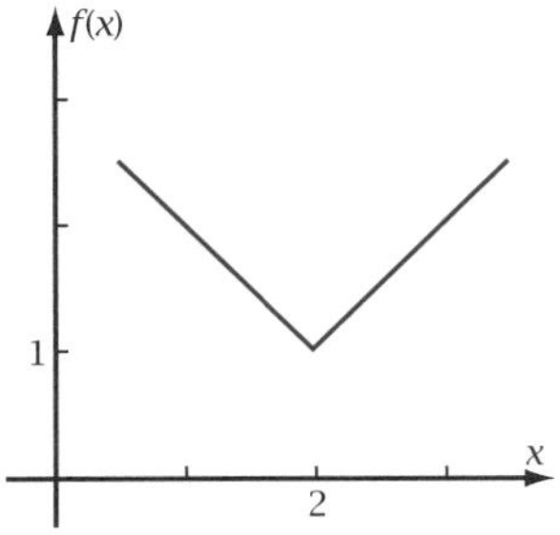


6.

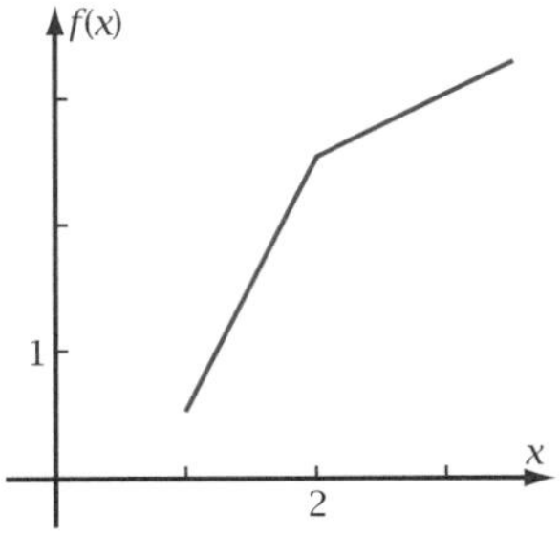

7.

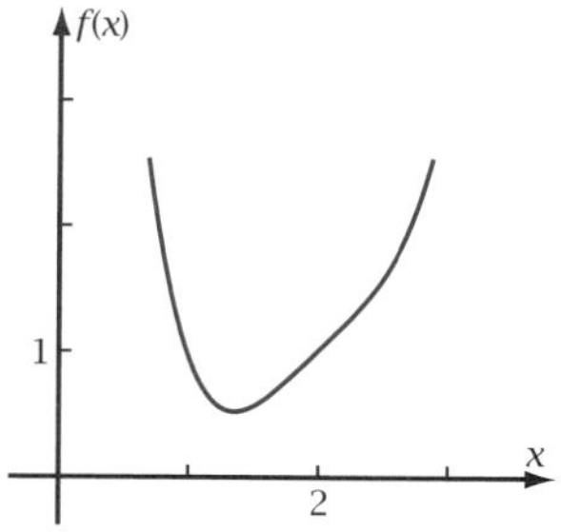


8.

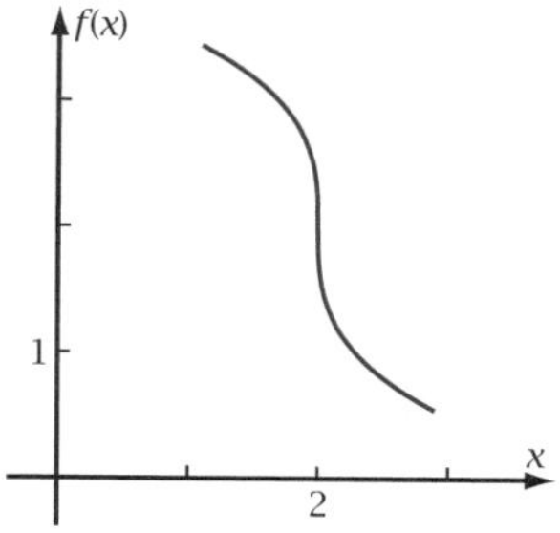


9.

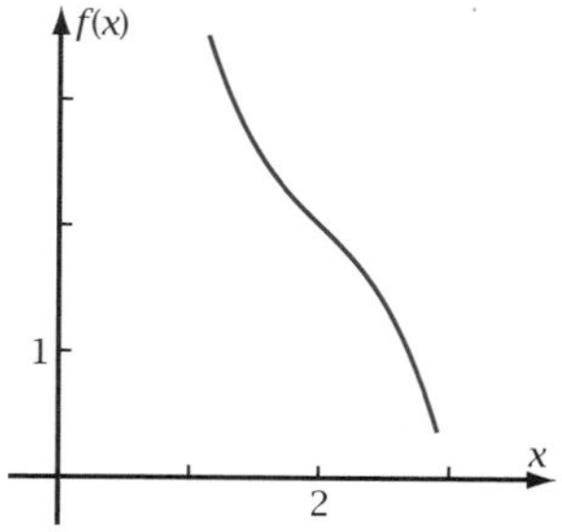


10.

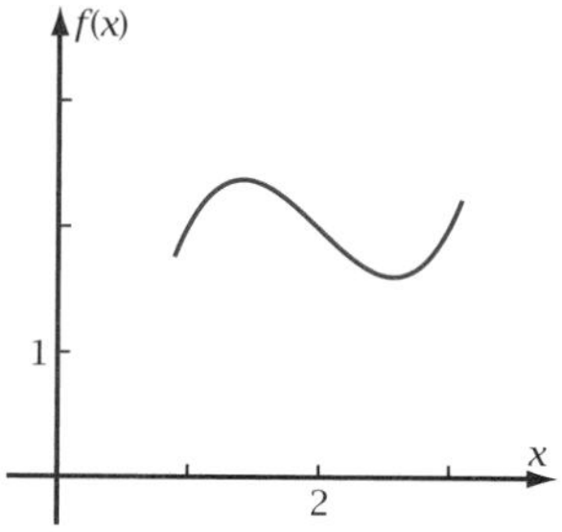


11.

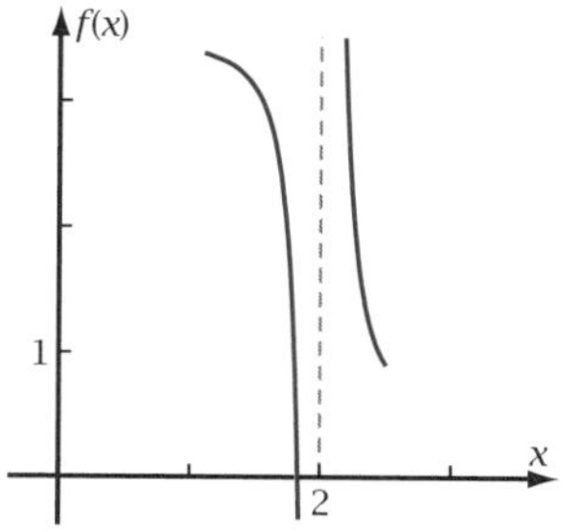


12.

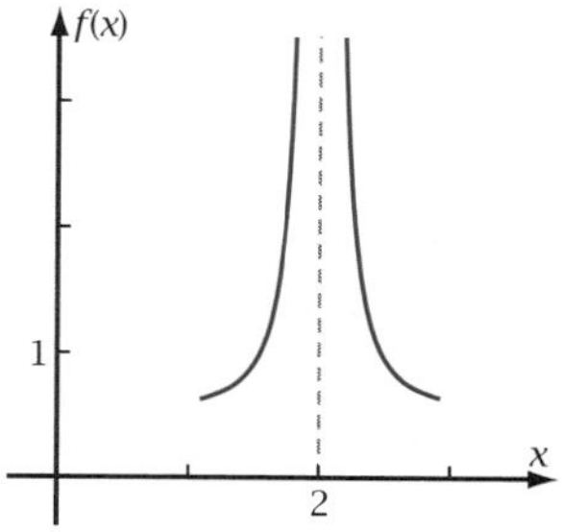


For Problems 13–18, mark the number lines with information about the behavior of the graph. Sketch a graph of a continuous function $f$ consistent with the information about the derivatives.

13.

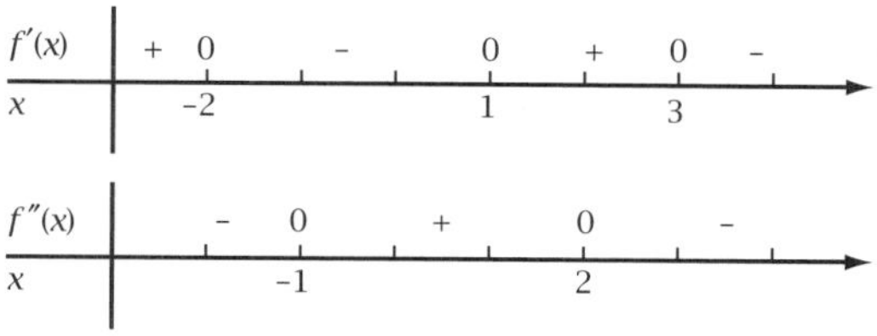


14.

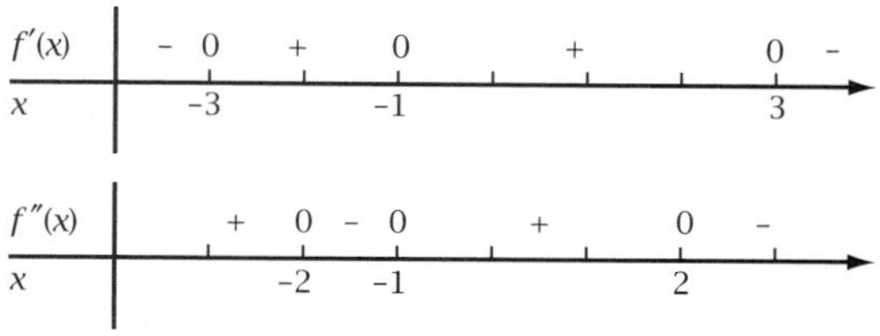


15.

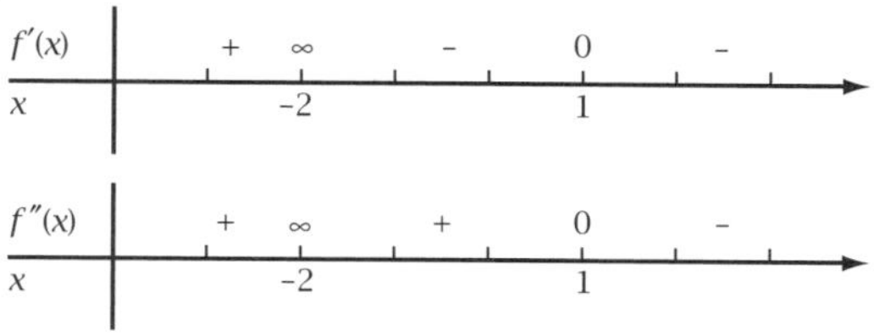


16.

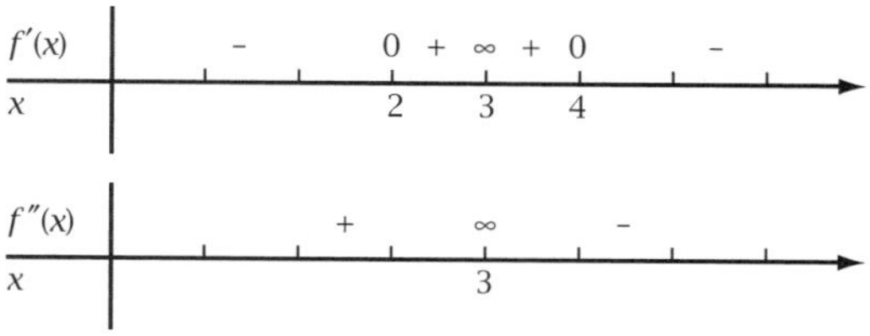


17.

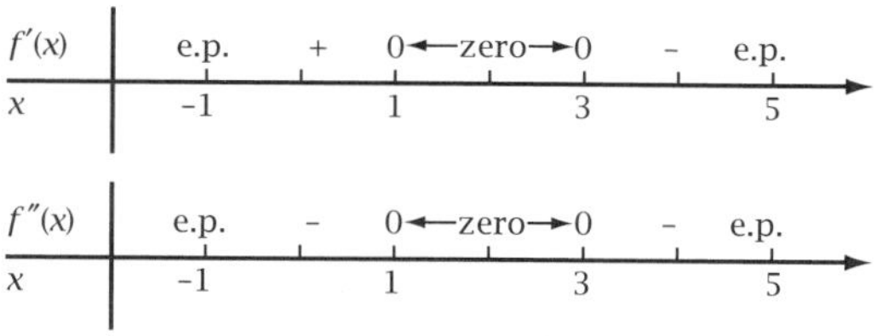


18.

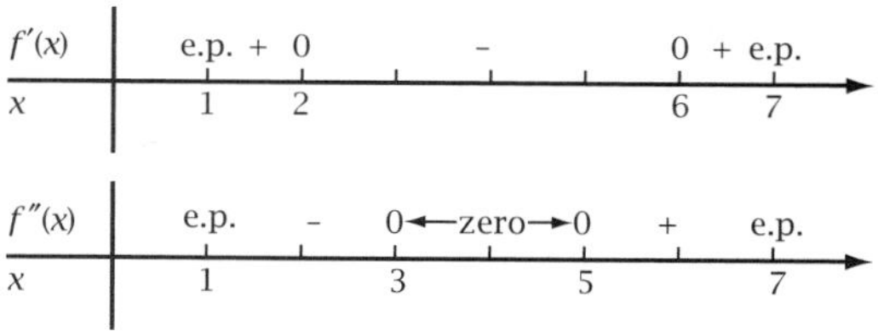

19. Let $f(x) = 6x^5 - 10x^3$ (Figure 8-2o).

a. Use derivatives to find the $x$-coordinates for all critical points of $f$ and $f'$.

b. Explain why there are critical points in part a that do not show up on this graph.

c. Explain why there is no maximum or minimum point at $x = 0$, even though $f'(0)$ equals zero.

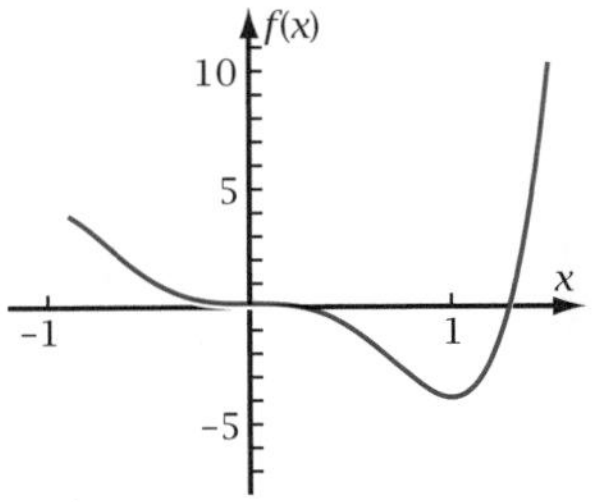


Figure 8-2o

20. Let $f(x) = 0.1x^4 - 3.2x + 7$ (Figure 8-2p).

a. Use derivatives to find the $x$-coordinates of all critical points of $f$ and $f'$.

b. Explain why there is no point of inflection at $x = 0$, even though $f''(0)$ equals zero.

c. Under what conditions for $f'(x)$ and $f''(x)$ can a graph be "straight" without being horizontal?

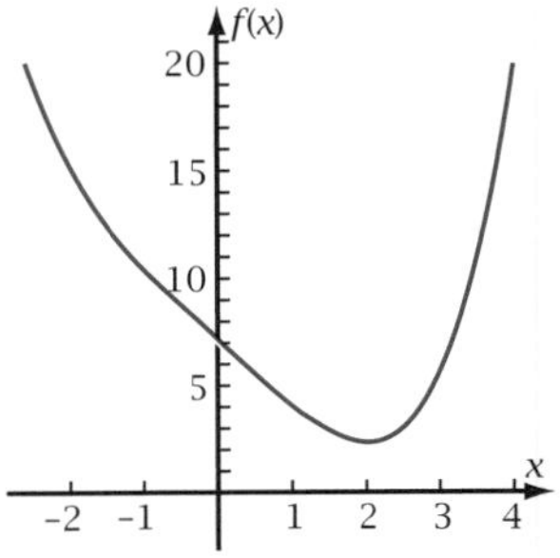


Figure 8-2p

21. Let $f(x) = xe^{-x}$ (Figure 8-2q).

a. Use derivatives to find the $x$-coordinates of all critical points of $f$ and $f'$.

b. How can you tell that there is a point of inflection even though it does not show up on the graph?

c. Does the graph cross the $x$-axis at any point other than (0, 0)? Justify your answer.

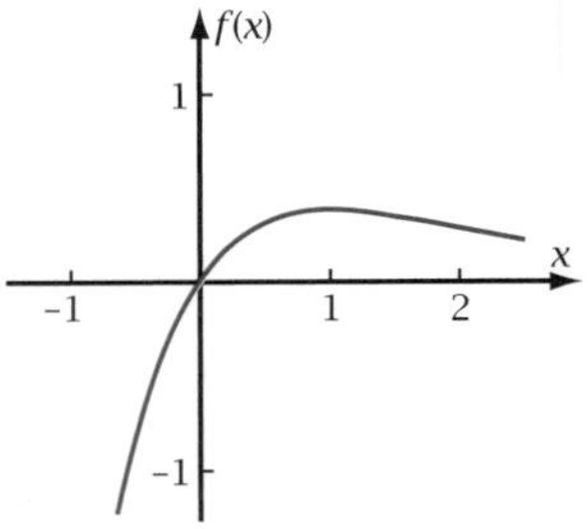


Figure 8-2q

22. Let $f(x) = x^2 \ln x$ (Figure 8-2r).

a. Use derivatives to find the $x$-coordinates of all critical points of $f$ and $f'$.

b. Show that the limit of $f(x)$ is zero as $x$ approaches zero from the right, but not from the left. L'Hospital's rule will help.

c. Are there any critical points that do not show up on the graph? If so, where, and what kind? If not, explain how you know.

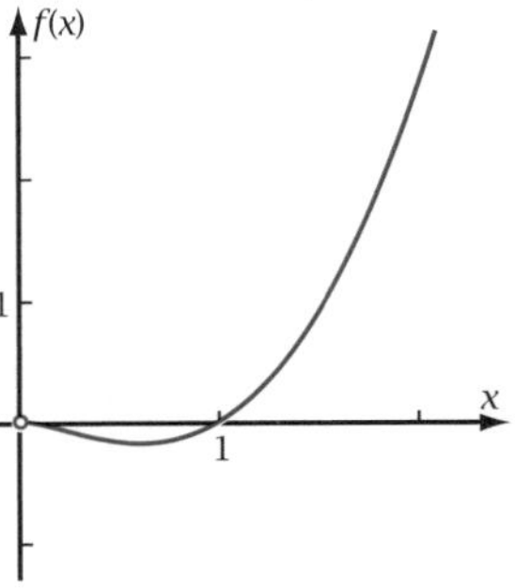


Figure 8-2r

23. Let $f(x) = x^{5/3} + 5x^{2/3}$ (Figure 8-2s).

a. Use derivatives to find the $x$-coordinates of all critical points of $f$ and $f'$.

b. Explain why there is a tangent line at the cusp, even though $f'(x)$ is undefined there.

c. Is there a point of inflection at the cusp? Is there a point of inflection anywhere else?

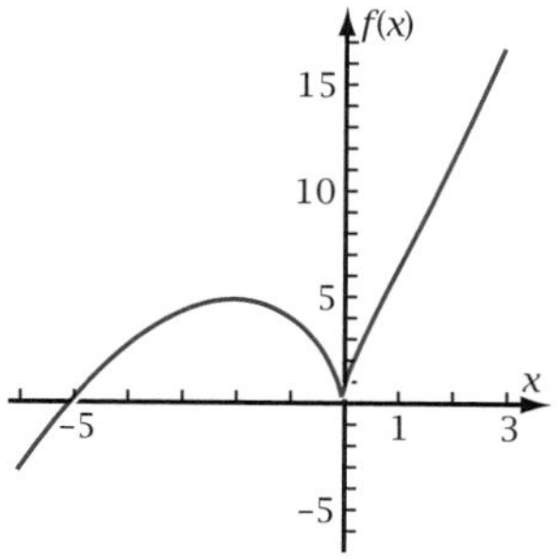

Figure 8-2s

24. Let $f(x) = x^{1.2} - 3x^{0.2}$ (Figure 8-2t).

a. Use derivatives to find the $x$-coordinates of all critical points of $f$ and $f'$.

b. The tangent is vertical at $x = 0$. How do you know that there aren't several different values of $y$ at $x = 0$?

c. Is the graph straight or curved when $x$ is less than $-2$? If it is curved, which way is the concave side directed?

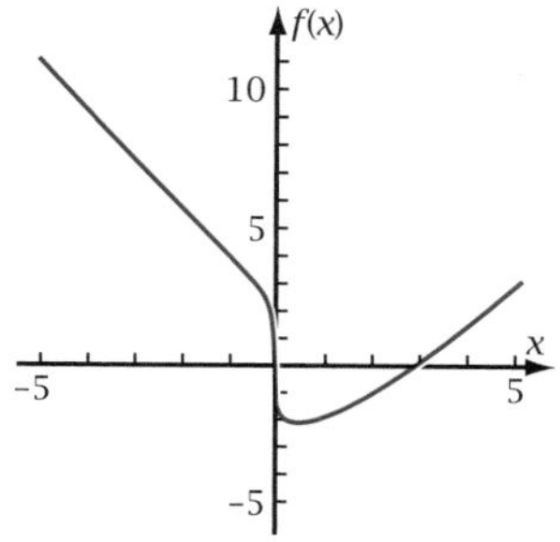

Figure 8-2t

25. Let $f(x) = \dfrac{x^2}{x^2 - 1}$ (Figure 8-2u).

a. Use derivatives to find the $x$-coordinates of all critical points of $f$ and $f'$.

b. Why are the discontinuities at $x = \pm 1$ not removable?

c. As $x$ gets very large, does the graph cross the $x$-axis, approach it without crossing, or level off somewhere above the $x$-axis? Justify your answer.

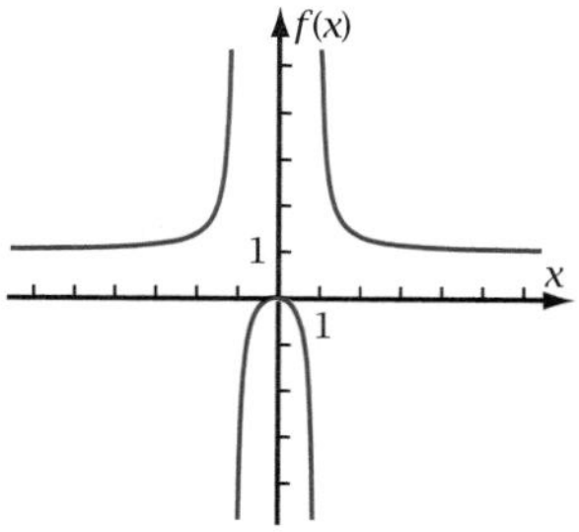

Figure 8-2u

26. Let $f(x) = x + \dfrac{x - 1}{x^2 - 1}$, (Figure 8-2v).

a. Use derivatives to find the $x$-coordinates of all critical points of $f$ and $f'$.

b. Explain why the discontinuity at $x = 1$ is removable, but the discontinuity at $x = -1$ is not removable.

c. By appropriate algebra, find an equation for the diagonal asymptote the graph approaches as $|x|$ becomes infinitely large.

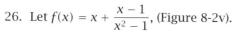

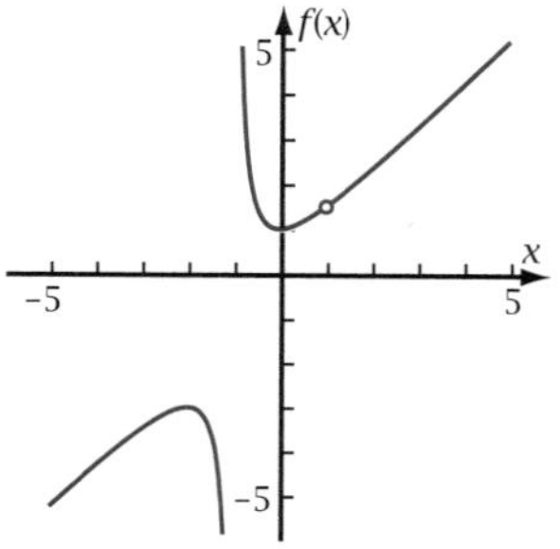

Figure 8-2v

For Problems 27–32,

a. Plot the graph. Estimate the $x$- and $y$-coordinates of all local maxima or minima and all points of inflection. Tell the global maximum and minimum.

b. Write equations for $f'(x)$ and $f''(x)$. Use them to find numerically or algebraically the precise values of the $x$-coordinates in part a.

c. Explain why there are no other critical points or points of inflection.

27. $f(x) = -x^3 + 5x^2 - 6x + 7$

28. $f(x) = x^3 - 7x^2 + 9x + 10$

29. $f(x) = 0.1x^3 + 1.5x^2 + 7.6x - 3$

30. $f(x) = -x^3 + 9x^2 - 28x + 20$

31. $f(x) = 3x^4 + 8x^3 - 6x^2 - 24x + 37$, for $x \in [-3, 2]$

32. $f(x) = (x - 1)^5 + 4$, for $x \in [-1, 3]$

33. *Point of Inflection of a Cubic Function:* The general equation of a quadratic function is

$$y = ax^2 + bx + c, \text{ where } a \neq 0.$$

You recall from algebra that the "middle" of a quadratic function graph (that is, the vertex) is at $x = -b/(2a)$. The "middle" of a cubic function graph is at its point of inflection. Prove that if $f(x) = ax^3 + bx^2 + cx + d$, where $a \neq 0$, then the point of inflection is located at $x = -b/(3a)$.

34. *Maximum and Minimum Points of a Cubic Function:* The maximum and minimum points of a cubic function are located symmetrically on either side of the point of inflection. Prove that this is true in general for the cubic function $f(x) = ax^3 + bx^2 + cx + d$. In terms of the coefficients $a$, $b$, $c$, and $d$, how far on either side of the point of inflection do the maximum and minimum points occur?

35. *Equation from Critical Points:* Find the particular equation of the cubic function with a local maximum at (5, 10) and its point of inflection at (3, 2). Use your grapher to confirm your equation.

36. *Can You Generate This Figure?* Figure 8-2w shows the graph of a piecewise-defined function in four different parts of its domain, as follows:

$$(1, 2] : f(x) = a + \frac{b}{x - 1}$$

$$[2, 3] : f(x) = c + \sqrt{3 - x}$$

$$[3, 4] : f(x) = c + \sqrt{x - 3}$$

$$[4, 5] : f(x) = mx + d$$

If $f(3) = 1$, $f$ is continuous for all $x$ in (1, 5], and is differentiable at $x = 2$, find the values of the constants in the equations. Confirm that your answers are correct by plotting the graph.

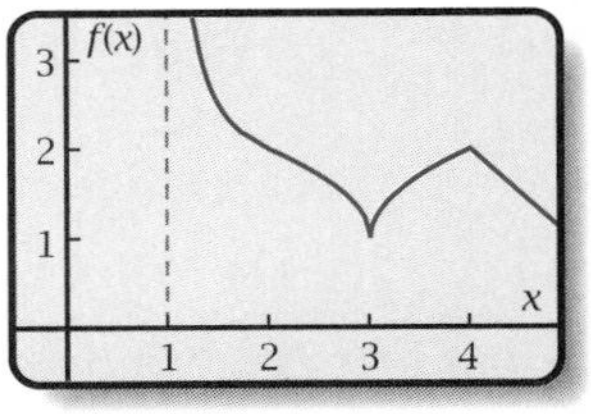

Figure 8-2w

37. *Concavity Concept Problem:* Figure 8-2x shows the graph of $f(x) = x^3$. Tangent lines are drawn where $x = -0.8, -0.5, 0.5$, and 0.8.

   a. Calculate the slope for each given tangent point.

   b. What is happening to the slope as $x$ increases from $-0.8$ to $-0.5$? As $x$ increases from 0.5 to 0.8? How do the values of the second derivative confirm these findings?

   c. On which side of the tangent line does the graph of a function lie if the graph is concave up at the point of tangency?

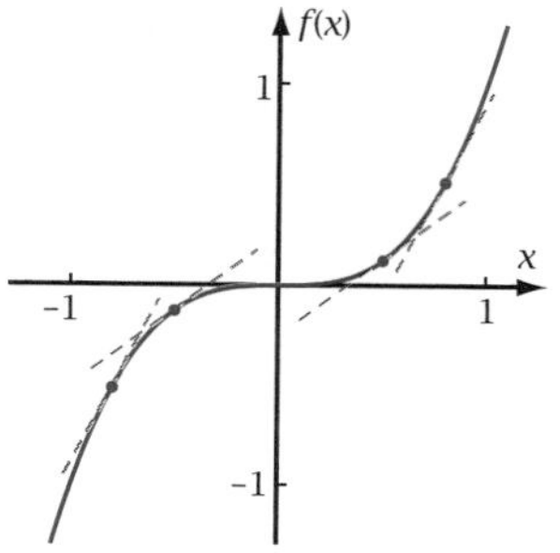


Figure 8-2x

38. *Naive Graphing Problem:* Ima Evian plots the graph of $y = x^3$, using $x = -1$, 0, and 1 (Figure 8-2y). From these three points she concludes that the graph is a straight line. Explain to Ima how she could use derivatives to avoid making this false conclusion.

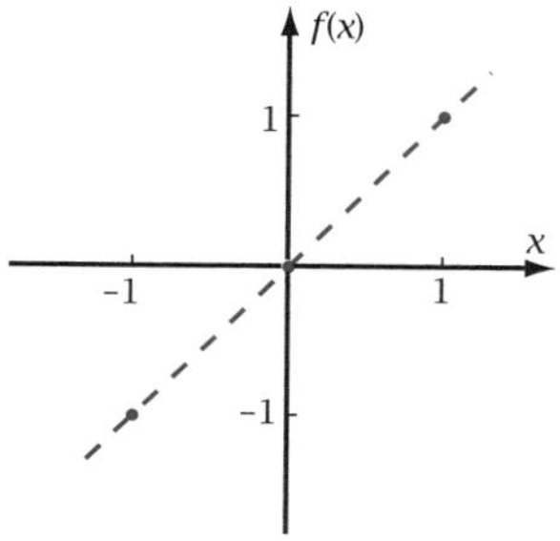


Figure 8-2y

39. *Connections Between a Zero First Derivative and the Graph:* If $f'(c) = 0$, the only thing you know for sure about the graph of $f$ is that it is horizontal at $x = c$. At least five things may be true about the graph of $f$ as $x$ increases through $c$.

   - The graph stops increasing and starts decreasing (Figure 8-2z).
   - The graph stops decreasing and starts increasing (Figure 8-2aa).
   - The graph stops increasing but starts increasing again (Figure 8-2bb).
   - The graph stops decreasing but starts decreasing again (Figure 8-2cc).
   - The graph is locally constant at $x = c$ (Figure 8-2dd).

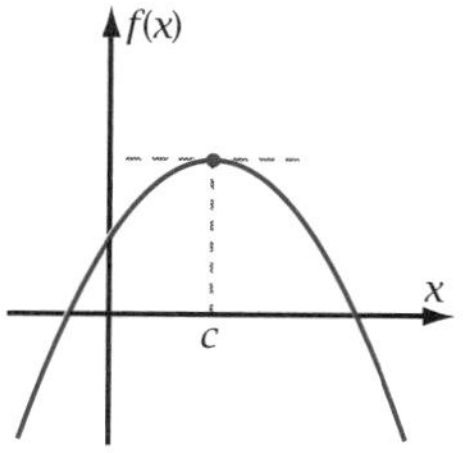


Figure 8-2z

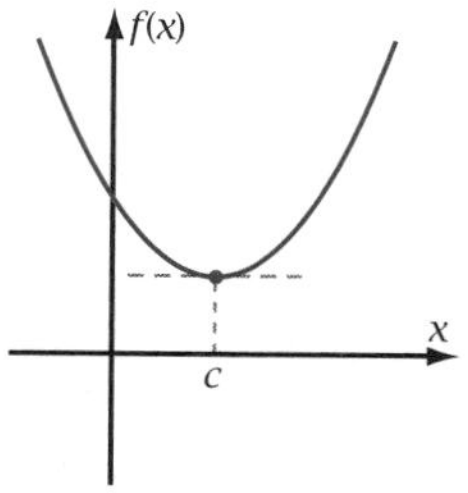


Figure 8-2aa

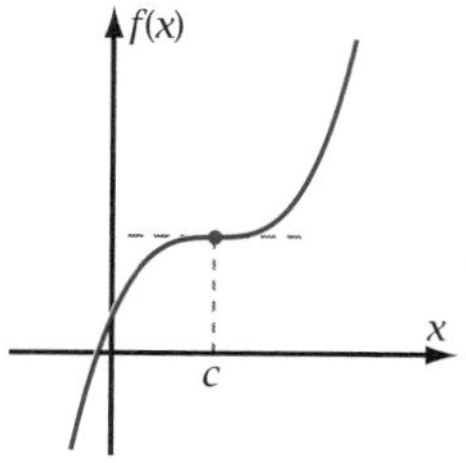


Figure 8-2bb

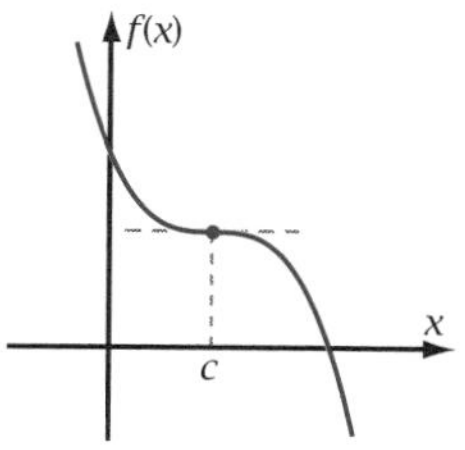


Figure 8-2cc

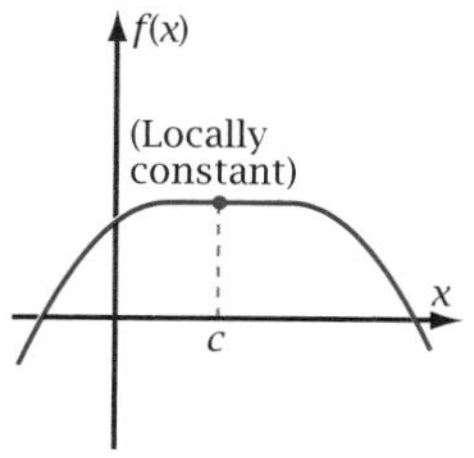


Figure 8-2dd

   a. If you find that the first derivative of a function is zero at $x = c$, why can't you conclude that there is a maximum point in the graph of $f(x)$ at $x = c$?

b. Write the particular equation for a function that has a maximum at (1, 4), as in Figure 8-2z.

c. Write the particular equation for a function that has a minimum at (1, 2), as in Figure 8-2aa.

d. Write the particular equation for a function that has a horizontal tangent at (1, 3), as in Figure 8-2bb or 8-2cc, but has no maximum or minimum point there.

e. Write the particular equation for a function that is locally constant in a neighborhood of the point (1, 2), as in Figure 8-2dd.

40. *Infinite Curvature Problem:* Show that the graph of

$$f(x) = 10(x - 1)^{4/3} + 2$$

is defined and differentiable at $x = 1$, but that the second derivative is infinite there. Explore the behavior of $f(x)$ close to $x = 1$ by zooming in on that point on the graph or by constructing a table of values. Describe what you discover.

41. *Historical Problem—The Second Derivative Test:* In the days before graphers, one way to find critical points was to use algebra to solve the equation $f'(x) = 0$. Once you found a critical point, you had to find out whether the point was a local maximum, a local minimum, or neither. This could be done by examining the sign of the second derivative at each critical point. In this problem you will see how this *second derivative test* was done. Suppose that

$$f(x) = \tfrac{1}{5}x^5 - x^4 + \tfrac{2}{3}x^3 + 2x^2 - 3x + 7.$$

a. Find an equation for $f'(x)$. You should find that the resulting polynomial can be factored into linear factors.

b. For what values of $x$ is $f'(x)$ equal to zero? What does $f''(x)$ equal at each of these values?

c. Based on your answers to 41b, which way is the graph concave at each critical point? Without actually plotting the graph, how can you tell from the concavity whether the graph has a local maximum or a local minimum at these critical points? Confirm your answers by plotting the graph of $f$.

d. The following box gives a statement of the second derivative test. For each of the three parts, make a sketch showing why that part is true.

**Procedure: The Second Derivative Test for Maxima and Minima**

If $f'(c) = 0$ and $f''(c)$ is positive, then there is a local minimum at $x = c$.
If $f'(c) = 0$ and $f''(c)$ is negative, then there is a local maximum at $x = c$.
If $f'(c) = 0$ and $f''(c)$ is zero, then no conclusion can be made about local maxima or minima at $x = c$.

42. *Exponential and Polynomial Look-Alike Problem:* The graphs of the functions

$$f(x) = e^{0.06x} \text{ and } g(x) = 1 + 0.06x + 0.0018x^2 + 0.000036x^3$$

are shown in Figure 8-2ee. The graphs look remarkably alike! Are they really the same function? Examine the function values and the derivative values. For example, do both $f$ and $g$ have the same derivative at $x = 0$? Do they have the same derivative at other places? Show that function $g$ has an $x$-intercept but function $f$ does not.

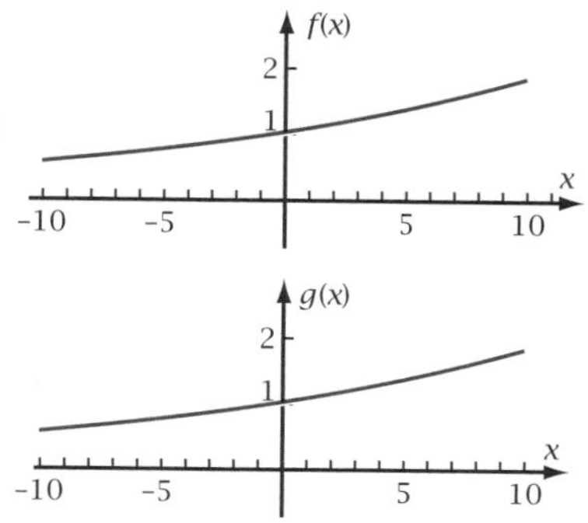

Figure 8-2ee

43. *A Pathological Function:* Consider the function defined by

$$f(x) = \begin{cases} (x-1)^3 \sin \dfrac{1}{x-1} + 2, & \text{if } x \neq 1, \\ 2, & \text{if } x = 1. \end{cases}$$

a. Plot the graph of the trigonometric branch of $f$. Use a friendly window of about [0, 2] for $x$ and a $y$-window of [1.99, 2.01].

b. As defined, is $f$ continuous at $x = 1$? Justify your answer.

c. Use the definition of derivative to prove that $f'(1) = 0$.

d. Zoom in on the point (1, 2). Does the graph appear to be locally linear at (1, 2) if you use $f(1) = 2$? How do you reconcile your answer with the fact that $\sin[1/(x - 1)]$ makes an infinite number of cycles between 1 and any value of $x$ close to 1? Why do you suppose that $f$ is said to be a "pathological" function?

e. In the reading material for this section it was stated that at least five things could be true about $f$ if $f'(c) = 0$. Tell a sixth thing that could be true.

44. *Journal Problem:* Update your journal with things you've learned since the last entry. You should include such things as those listed here.
- The one most important thing you have learned since the last journal entry
- The relationships between the signs of the first and second derivatives and the behavior of the graph of the function itself.
- The way the first and second derivative can be used to locate the maxima, minima, and points of inflection algebraically
- How your understanding of derivative has improved
- Any techniques or ideas about the behavior of graphs that are still unclear to you

# 8-3 Maxima and Minima in Plane and Solid Figures

In Section 8-2, you found maximum and minimum values of a function where the equation was already given. The problems of this section require you first to find an equation for the area, volume, or perimeter of a geometric figure, then to use the now-familiar techniques to find extreme values. As a result you will be able to investigate such things as how the canning industry saves money by packaging the maximum volume of product with the minimum amount of metal.

## OBJECTIVE

Given a plane or solid figure, find the maximum or minimum perimeter, area, or volume.

**■ Example 1** Barb Dwyer must build a rectangular corral along the river bank. Three sides of the corral will be fenced with barbed wire. The river forms the fourth side of the corral (Figure 8-3a). The total length of fencing available is 1000 ft. What is the maximum area the corral could have? How should the fence be built to enclose this maximum area? Justify your answers.

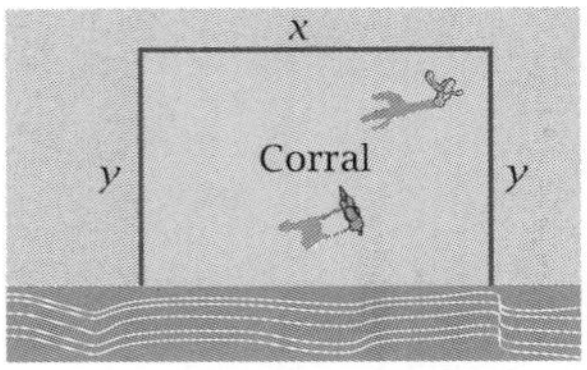


Figure 8-3a

**Solution** The first thing to realize is that the area is to be maximized. So you need an equation for area as a function of one or more variables. Letting $A$ stand for area and $x$ and $y$ stand for the length of fence parallel to and perpendicular to the river, respectively, you can write

$$A = xy.$$

Next you must find A in terms of one variable. Since there is a total of 1000 ft of fencing, you can write an equation relating $x$ and $y$.

$$x + 2y = 1000 \implies x = 1000 - 2y, \text{ where } y \in [0, 500]$$ Why this domain for $y$?

$$\therefore A = (1000 - 2y)(y) = 1000y - 2y^2$$

Figure 8-3b shows the graph of $A$ versus $y$. It is a parabola opening downward, with its maximum point halfway between the two $y$-intercepts. Since these intercepts are $y = 0$ and $y = 500$, and these points are the ends of the domain, the maximum point is at

$$y = 250.$$

Confirming this fact by derivatives,

$$A' = 1000 - 4y$$

$A' = 0$ if and only if

$$1000 - 4y = 0 \Leftrightarrow y = 250.$$

$$\therefore x = 1000 - 2(250) = 500$$

$$\therefore A = (500)(250) = 125{,}000$$

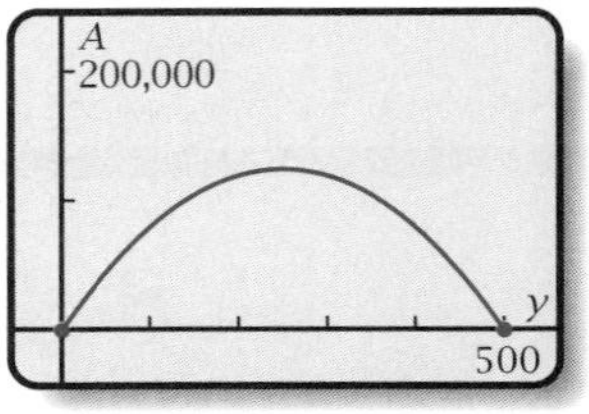


Figure 8-3b

Barb should make the corral 250 ft perpendicular to the river, and 500 ft parallel to the river. The maximum area the corral can have is 125,000 square feet. ■

**■ *Example 2*** The part of the parabola $y = 4 - x^2$ from $x = 0$ to $x = 2$ is rotated about the $y$-axis to form a surface. A cone is inscribed in the resulting paraboloid with its vertex at the origin and its base touching the parabola (Figure 8-3c). At what radius and altitude does the maximum volume occur? What is this maximum volume? Justify your answer.

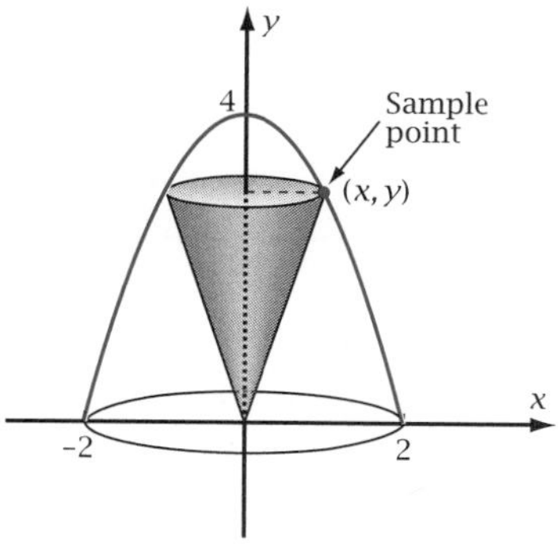


Figure 8-3c

***Solution*** Pick sample point $(x, y)$ on the parabola in the first quadrant where the cone touches it. Since it is volume you are to maximize, find an equation for volume $V$ in terms of $x$ and $y$.

$V = \frac{1}{3}\pi x^2 y$ — Pick sample point $(x, y)$. Use $V = (\frac{1}{3})$(base area)(height) to get $V$ in terms of $x$ and $y$.

$V = \frac{1}{3}\pi x^2(4 - x^2), x \in [0, 2]$ — Get $V$ in terms of one variable, and specify a domain.

$= \frac{\pi}{3}(4x^2 - x^4)$ — Sums are easier to differentiate than products.

$V' = \frac{\pi}{3}(8x - 4x^3)$

$V' = \frac{4\pi}{3}(x)(2 - x^2)$ — Products are easier to equate to zero than sums.

$V' = 0 \Leftrightarrow x = 0 \text{ or } 2 - x^2 = 0 \Leftrightarrow x = 0 \text{ or } x = \pm\sqrt{2}$ — The $-\sqrt{2}$ is out of the domain.

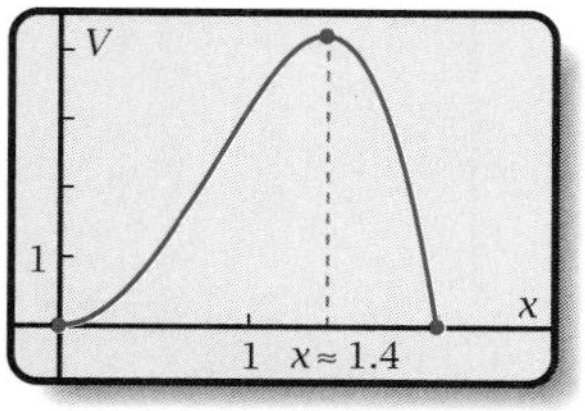


Figure 8-3d

Figure 8-3d shows that the maximum comes at $x \approx 1.4$. At the critical point $x = 0$, the volume is a minimum. At the other endpoint, $x = 2$, the volume is also minimum.

The maximum volume is at $x = \sqrt{2}$. The volume at this point is

$$V = \frac{\pi}{3}(2)(4 - 2)$$
$$= 4\pi/3 = 4.18879....$$

■

There are some key steps in Examples 1 and 2 that will lead you to success in max-min problems. These steps are listed in the following box.

**Technique: Analysis of Maximum-Minimum Problems**

1. Make a sketch if one isn't already drawn.
2. Write an equation for the variable you are trying to maximize or minimize.
3. Get the equation in terms of one variable and specify a domain.
4. Find an approximate maximum or minimum by grapher.
5. Find the exact maximum or minimum by seeing where the derivative is zero or infinite. Check any endpoints of the domain.
6. Answer the question by writing what was asked for in the problem statement.

## Problem Set 8-3

### *Do These Quickly*

The following problems are intended to refresh your skills. You should be able to do all ten problems in less than five minutes.

**Q1.** Differentiate: $y = (3x + 5)^{-1}$

**Q2.** Integrate: $\int (x + 6)^{-1}\,dx$

**Q3.** Differentiate: $y = x^{-2/3}$

**Q4.** Integrate: $\int x^{-2/3}\,dx$

**Q5.** Integrate: $\int x^{-2}\,dx$

**Q6.** Integrate: $\int x^{0}\,dx$

**Q7.** $(d/dx)(\cos^{-1}x) =$ -?-

**Q8.** $\int \cot x\,dx =$ -?-

**Q9.** Sketch the graph of $y = x^{1/3}$.

**Q10.** Sketch the graph of $y''$ for the cubic function in Figure 8-3e.

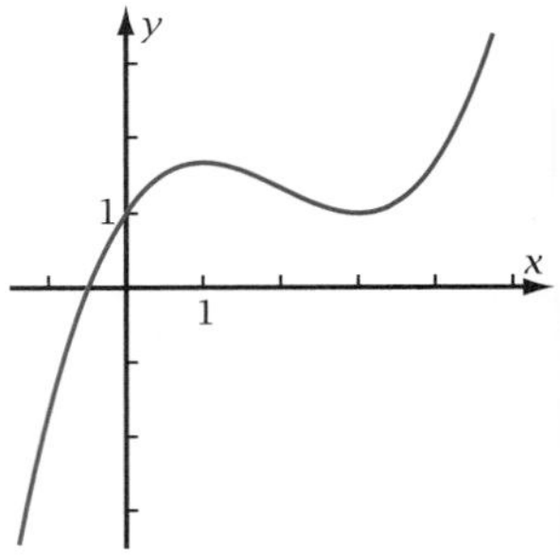

Figure 8-3e

1. *Divided Stock Pen Problem:* A rectangular stock pen (Figure 8-3f) is to be built using a total of 600 ft of fencing. Part of this fencing will be used to build a fence across the middle of the rectangle (see diagram). Find the length and width of the rectangle that give the maximum total area. Justify your answer.

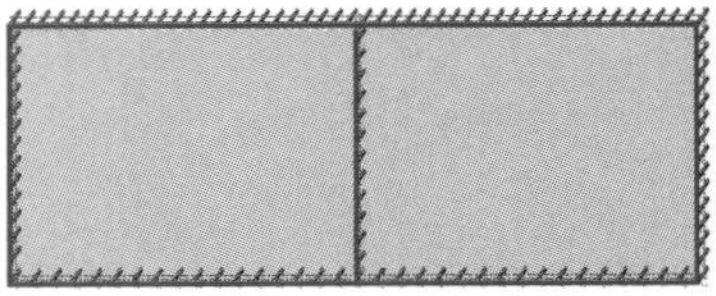
Figure 8-3f

2. *Motel Problem:* A six-room motel is to be built with the floor plan shown in Figure 8-3g. Each room is to have 350 ft$^2$ of floor space.
   a. What dimensions should the rooms be in order to have the minimum total length of walls to build? Justify your answer.
   b. How would your answer to 1a change if the motel had ten rooms? Just three rooms?

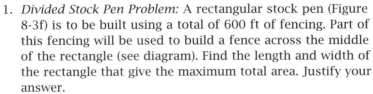

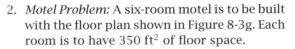

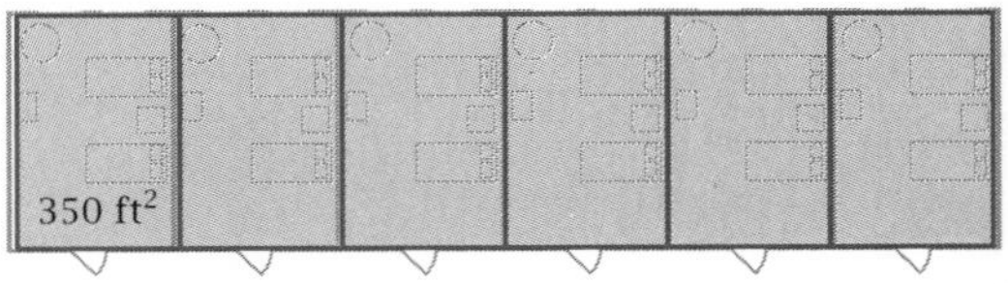

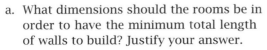

Figure 8-3g

3. *Two-Field Problem:* Ella Mental has 600 ft of fencing to enclose two fields. One is to be a rectangle twice as long as it is wide, and the other is to be a square (Figure 8-3h). The square field must contain at least 100 ft$^2$. The rectangular one must contain at least 800 ft$^2$.
   a. If $x$ is the width of the rectangular field, what is the domain of $x$?
   b. Plot the graph of the total area contained in the two fields as a function of $x$.
   c. What is the greatest area that can be contained in the two fields? Justify your answer.

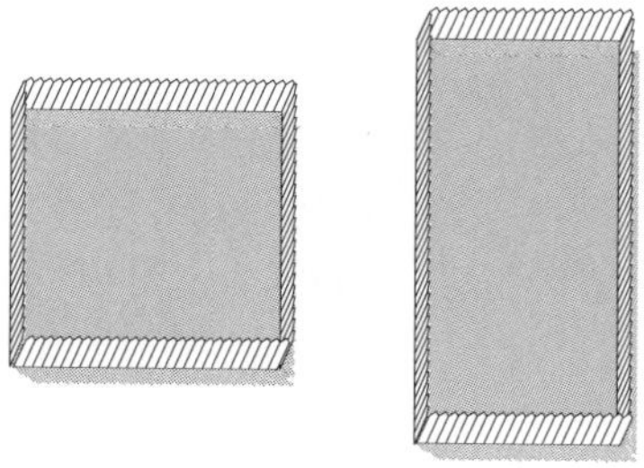

Figure 8-3h

4. *Two-Corral Problem:* Suppose that you work on Big Bill Spender's Ranch. Big Bill tells you to build a circular fence around the lake and to use the remainder of your 1000 yd of fencing to build a square corral (Figure 8-3i). To keep the fence out of the water, the diameter of the circular enclosure must be at least 50 yd.
   a. If you must use all of 1000 yd of fencing, how would you build the fences so as to enclose the minimum total area? Justify your answer.
   b. What would you tell Big Bill if he asked you to build the fences so as to enclose the maximum total area?

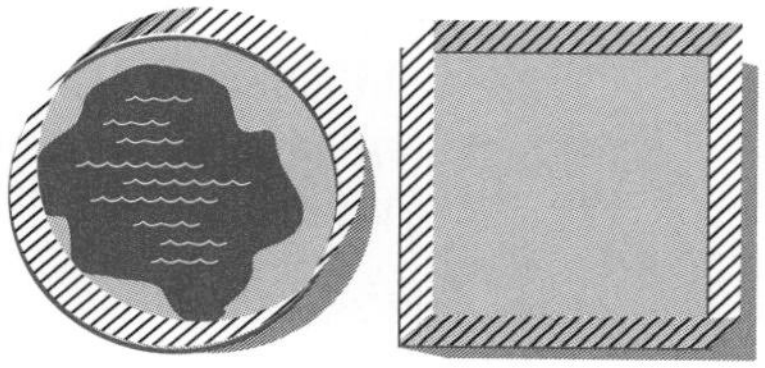

Figure 8-3i

5. *Open Box I:* A rectangular box with a square base and no top (Figure 8-3j) is to be made of a total of 120 cm$^2$ of cardboard.
   a. Find the dimensions of the box of maximum volume.
   b. Make a conjecture about the depth of the maximum-volume box in relation to the base length if the box has a fixed surface area.

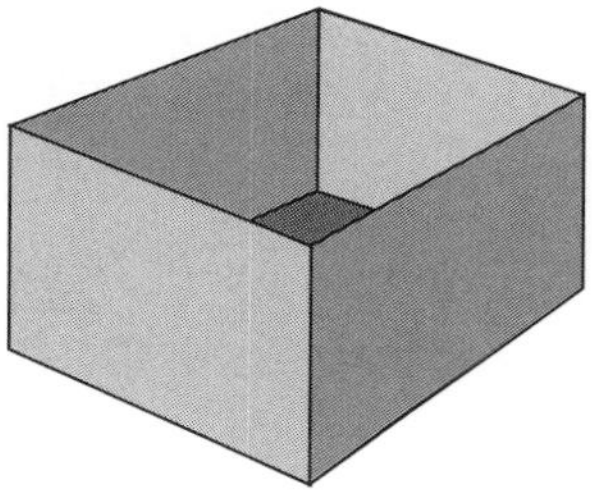

Figure 8-3j

6. *Open Box II (Project):* For this project you are to investigate the volume of the box formed by cutting out squares from the four corners of a 20 by 12 unit piece of graph paper (Figure 8-3k) and folding up the edges to form a box without a top.
   a. Each group should pick a different value of $x$, such as 1, 2, 3, 4, ..., cut out the squares from the graph paper, then fold and tape it to form a box. What is the largest possible value of $x$?
   b. Calculate the volume of each box. Which integer value of $x$ gives the largest volume?
   c. Find the value of $x$ that gives the maximum volume. What is this volume?
   d. Construct a box of maximum volume.

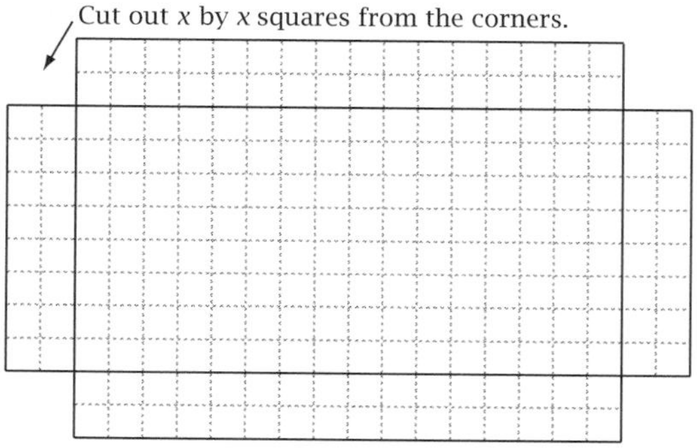
Cut out $x$ by $x$ squares from the corners.

Figure 8-3k

7. *Open Box III:* A glass fish tank is to be constructed to hold 72 $\text{ft}^3$ of water. Its base and sides are to be rectangular. The top, of course, is to be open. It is to be constructed so that its width will be 5 ft but the length and depth are variable. Building the tank costs \$10 per square foot for the base and \$5 per square foot for the sides. What is the cost of the least expensive tank? Justify your answer.

8. *Open Box IV (Project):* The diagram shows an open-top box with rectangular base $x$ by $y$ units and rectangular sides. The depth of the box is $z$ units (Figure 8-3l).

   a. Hold the depth constant. Show that the maximum volume of the box for a given amount of material occurs when $x = y$.

   b. Set $y = x$, but let both vary as the depth varies. Find the values of $x$ and $z$ that give the maximum volume for a given amount of material.

   c. In what ratio are the values of $x$ and $z$ for the maximum-volume box in 8b? Is the maximum-volume box tall and skinny or short and fat? Based on geometry, why is your answer reasonable?

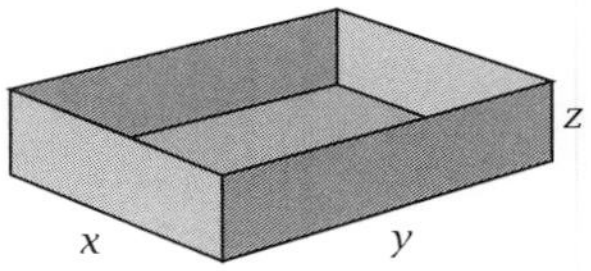

Figure 8-3l

9. *Shortest-Distance Problem:* What point on the graph of $y = e^x$ is closest to the origin (Figure 8-3m)? Justify your answer.

10. *Track and Field Problem:* A track 400 m in periphery is to be laid out on the practice field (Figure 8-3n). Each semicircular end must have a radius of at least 20 m, and each straight section must be at least 100 m. How should the track be laid out so that it encompasses the least area? Justify your answer.

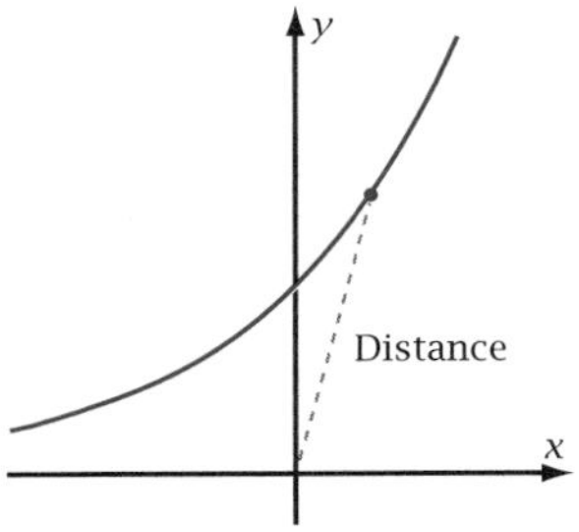

Figure 8-3m

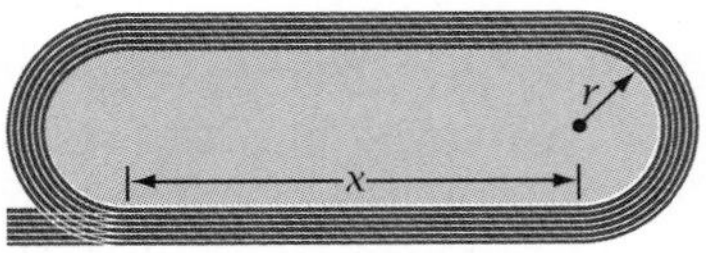

Figure 8-3n

11. *Ladder Problem:* A ladder is to reach over a fence 8 ft high to a wall that is 1 ft behind the fence (Figure 8-3o). What is the length of the shortest ladder that can be used? Justify your answer.

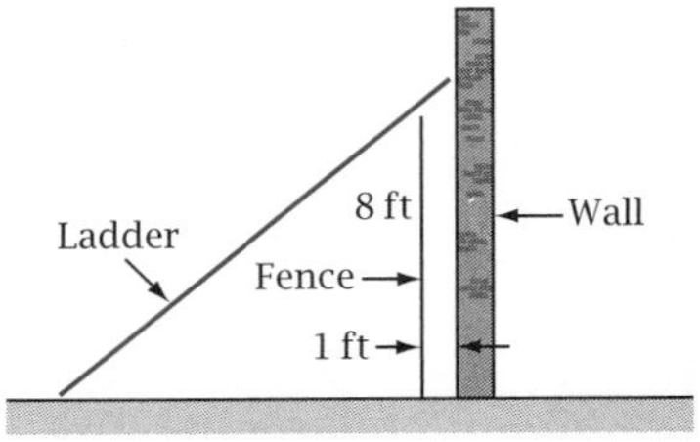

Figure 8-3o

12. *Ladder in the Hall Problem:* A nonfolding ladder is to be taken around a corner where two hallways intersect at right angles (Figure 8-3p). One hall is 7 ft wide, and the other is 5 ft wide. What is the maximum length the ladder can be so that it will pass around such a corner, given that the ladder must be carried parallel to the floor?

13. *Rotated Rectangle Problem:* A rectangle of perimeter 1200 mm is rotated in space using one of its legs as the axis (Figure 8-3q). The volume enclosed by the resulting cylinder depends on the proportions of the rectangle. Find the dimensions of the rectangle that maximize the cylinder's volume.

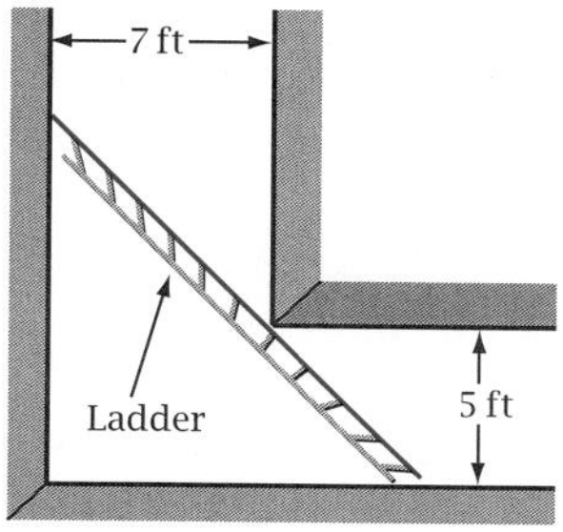


Figure 8-3p

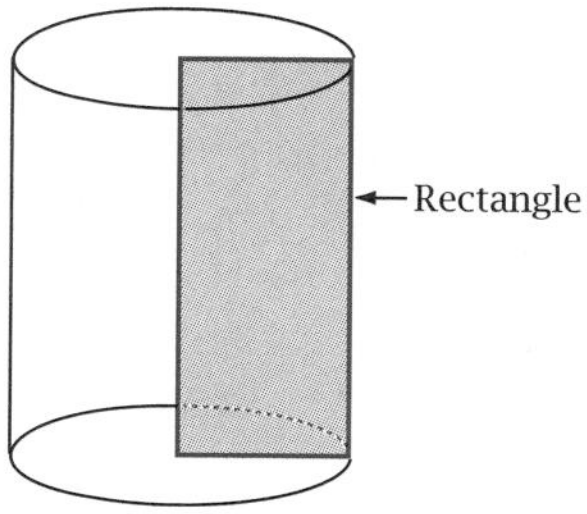


Figure 8-3q

14. *Rotated Rectangle Generalization Problem:* The rectangle of maximum area for a given perimeter $P$ is a square. Does rotating a square about one of its sides (as in Problem 13) produce the maximum-volume cylinder? If so, prove it. If not, what proportions do produce the maximum-volume cylinder?

15. *Tin Can Problem:* A popular size of tin can with "normal" proportions has a diameter of 7.3 cm and an altitude of 10.6 cm (Figure 8-3r).

    a. What is its volume?

    b. The volume is to be kept the same, but the proportions are to be changed. Write an equation expressing total surface of the can (lateral surface plus two ends) as a function of radius and altitude. Transform the equation so that the volume is in terms of radius alone.

    c. Find the radius and altitude of the can such that it has minimum surface area. Is the can tall and skinny or short and fat? What is the ratio of diameter to altitude? Justify your answers.

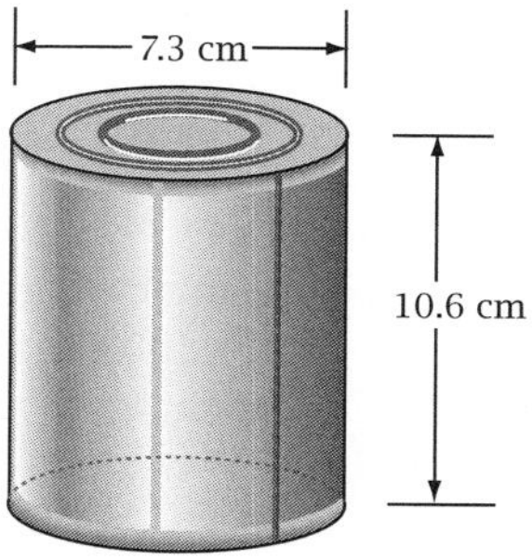


Figure 8-3r

    d. Does the normal can use close to the minimum amount of metal? What percent of the metal in the normal can could be saved by using cans with the minimum dimensions?

    e. If the United States uses 20 million of these cans a day and the metal in a normal can is worth \$0.06, how much money could be saved a year by using minimum-area cans?

16. *Tin Can Generalization Project:* The tin can of minimum cost in Problem 15 is not necessarily the one with minimum surface area. In this problem you will investigate the effects of wasted metal in the manufacturing process and of overlapping metal in the seams.

a. Assume that the metal for the ends of the can in Problem 15 costs $k$ times as much per square centimeter as the metal for the cylindrical walls. Find the value of $k$ that makes the minimum-cost can have the proportions of the actual can. Is it reasonable in the real world for the ends to cost this much more (or less) per square centimeter than the walls? Explain.

b. Assume that the ends of the tin can in Problem 15 are cut from squares and that the rest of the metal from the squares is wasted. What value of $k$ in 16a would make the actual can have minimum cost under this assumption? Is the can that uses the minimum amount of metal under this assumption closer to the proportions of the actual can or farther away?

c. Assume that the ends of the can are made from metal disks that overhang by 0.6 cm all the way around. They are made this way in order to have enough overlap to fabricate the joints at the top and bottom of the can. Assume also that there must be an extra 0.5 cm of metal in the circumference of the can in order to have an overlap for the vertical seam. How do these assumptions affect the dimensions of the minimum-area can in Problem 15?

17. *Cup Problem:* Suppose you have been hired by the Yankee Cup Company. They currently make a cylindrical paper cup of diameter 5 cm and altitude 7 cm. Your job is to see whether paper can be saved by making cups that hold the same amount of liquid but have different proportions.

a. Find the dimensions of a same-volume cup that uses a minimum amount of paper.

b. What is the ratio of diameter to altitude for the minimum-area cup?

c. Paper costs \$2.00 per square meter. Yankee makes 300 million of this kind of cup per year. Write a proposal to your boss telling her whether or not you think it would be worthwhile to change the dimensions of Yankee's cup to those of the minimum cup. Be sure to show that the area of the proposed cup really is a minimum.

d. Show that in general if a cup of given volume $V$ has minimum total surface area, then the radius is equal to the altitude.

18. *Duct Problem:* A duct made of sheet metal connects one rectangular opening in an air-conditioning system to another rectangular opening (Figure 8-3s). The rectangle on the left is at $x = 0$ in. and the one on the right is at $x = 100$ in. Cross sections perpendicular to the $x$-axis are rectangles of width $z = 30 + 0.2x$ and $y = 40 - 0.2x$.

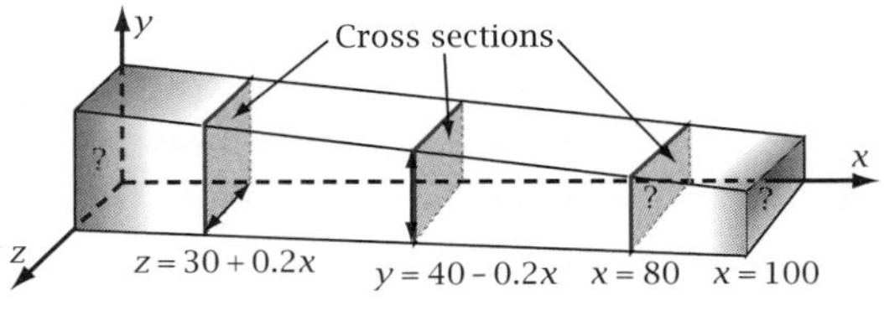


Figure 8-3s

a. Find the areas of the two end rectangles.

b. What is the cross-sectional area of the duct at $x = 80$?

c. What $x$-values give the maximum and the minimum cross-sectional areas?

19. *Rectangle in Sinusoid Problem:* A rectangle is inscribed in the region bounded by one arch of the graph of $y = \cos x$ and the $x$-axis (Figure 8-3t). What value of $x$ gives the maximum area? What is the maximum area?

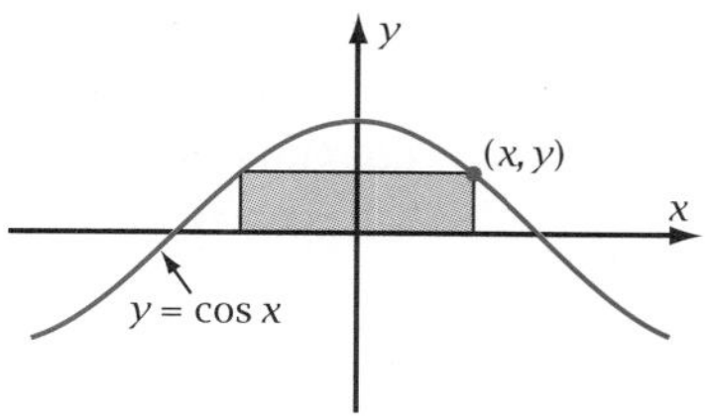


Figure 8-3t

20. *Building Problem:* Bill Ding plans to build a new hardware store. He buys a rectangular lot that is 50 ft by 200 ft, the 50-ft dimension being along the street. The store is to have 4000 $ft^2$ of floor space. Construction costs \$100 per linear foot for the part of the store along the street and only \$80 per linear foot for the parts along the sides and back. To what dimensions should Bill build the store to minimize construction costs? Justify your answer.

21. *Triangle under Cotangent Problem:* A right triangle has a vertex at the origin and a leg along the $x$-axis. Its other vertex touches the graph of $y = \cot x$, as shown in Figure 8-3u.

    a. As the right angle approaches the origin, the altitude of the triangle approaches infinity, and the base length approaches zero. Find the limit of the area as the right angle approaches the origin.

    b. What is the maximum area the triangle can have if the domain is the half-open interval $(0, \pi/2]$? Justify your answer.

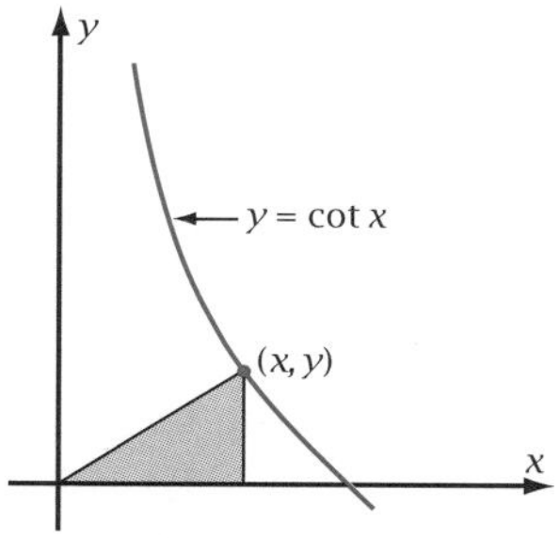


Figure 8-3u

22. *Triangle under Exponential Curve Problem:* A right triangle has one leg on the $x$-axis. The vertex at the right end of that leg is at the point (3, 0). The other vertex touches the graph of $y = e^x$. The entire triangle is to lie in the first quadrant. Find the maximum area of this triangle. Justify your answer.

23. *Rectangle in Parabola Problem:* A rectangle is inscribed in the region bounded by the $x$-axis and the parabola $y = 9 - x^2$ (Figure 8-3v).

    a. Find the length and width of the rectangle of greatest area. Justify your answer.

    b. Find the length and width of the rectangle of greatest perimeter. Justify your answer.

    c. Does the rectangle of greatest area have the greatest perimeter?

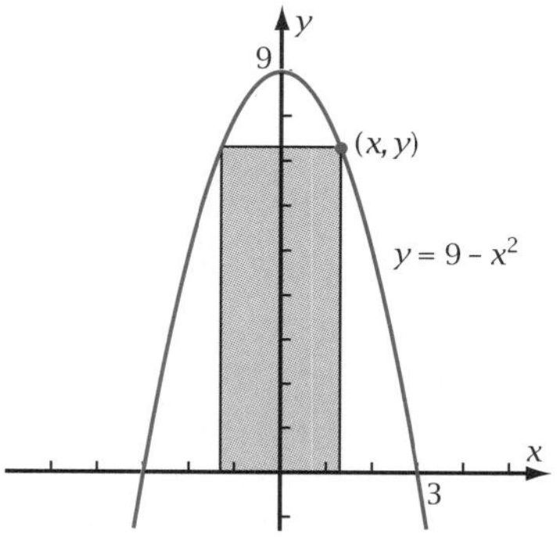


Figure 8-3v

24. *Cylinder in Paraboloid Problem:* The parabola $y = 9 - x^2$ is rotated about the $y$-axis to form a paraboloid. A cylinder is coaxially inscribed in the paraboloid (Figure 8-3w).

a. Find the radius and altitude of the cylinder of maximum volume. Justify your answer.

b. Find the radius and altitude of the cylinder of maximum lateral area.

c. Find the radius and altitude of the cylinder of maximum total area (including the ends). Justify your answer.

d. Does the maximum-volume cylinder have the same dimensions as either of the maximum-area cylinders in 24b or c?

e. Does rotating the maximum area rectangle in Problem 23a produce the maximum volume cylinder in this problem?

f. If the cylinder of maximum volume is inscribed in the paraboloid formed by rotating the parabola $y = a^2 - x^2$ about the $y$-axis, does the ratio (cylinder radius):(paraboloid radius) depend in any way on how long the paraboloid is? (That is, does it depend on the value of the constant $a$?) Justify your answer.

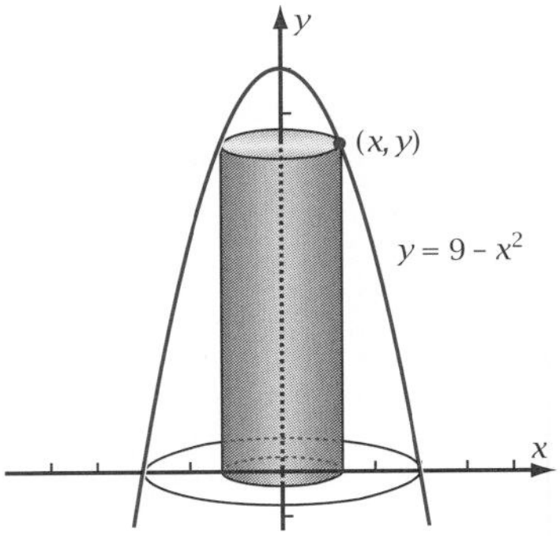

Figure 8-3w

25. *Cylinder in Sphere Problem:* A cylinder is to be inscribed in a sphere of radius 10 cm (Figure 8-3x). The bottom and top bases of the cylinder are to touch the surface of the sphere. The volume of the cylinder will depend on whether it is tall and skinny or short and fat.

a. Let $(x, y)$ be the coordinates of a point on the circle, as shown. Write an equation for the volume of the cylinder in terms of $x$ and $y$.

b. What radius and altitude of the cylinder will give it the maximum volume? What is this volume? Justify your answer.

c. How are the radius and altitude of the maximum-volume cylinder related to each other? How is the maximum cylinder volume related to the volume of the sphere?

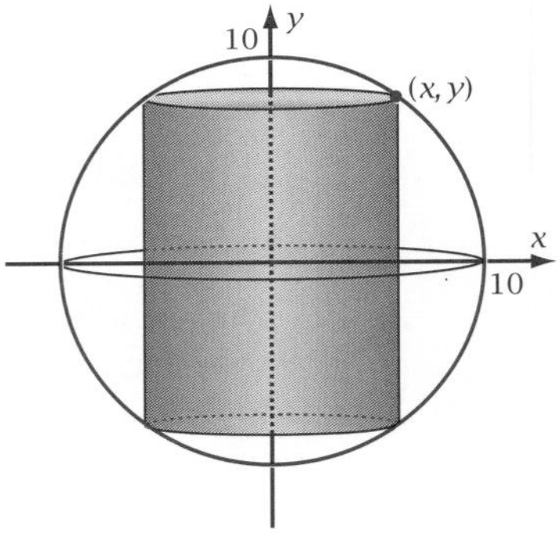

Figure 8-3x

26. *Conical Nose Cone Problem:* In the design of a missile nose cone, it is important to minimize the surface area exposed to the atmosphere. For aerodynamic reasons, it is important that the cone be long and slender. Suppose that a right circular nose cone is to contain a volume of $5\pi$ ft$^3$. Find the radius and height of the nose cone of minimum lateral surface area, subject to the restriction that the height must be at least twice the radius of the base. (The differentiation may be easier if you minimize the square of the area.)

27. *Cylinder in Cone Problem:* A cone of altitude 7 cm and base radius 5 cm has a cylinder inscribed in it, with the base of the cylinder contained in the base of the cone (Figure 8-3y).

a. Find the radius of the cylinder of maximum lateral area (sides only).

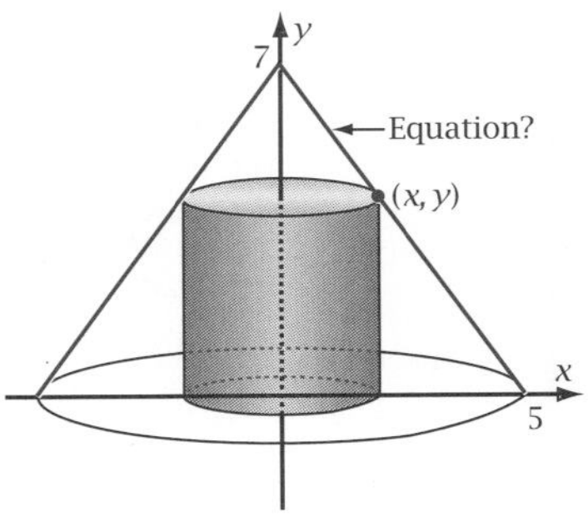

Figure 8-3y

b. Find the radius of the cylinder of maximum total area (including the top and bottom bases). Justify your answer.

28. *General Cylinder in Cone Problem:* A given cone has a cylinder inscribed in it, with its base contained in the base of the cone.

a. How should the radius of the cone and cylinder be related for the lateral surface of the cylinder to have a maximum area? Justify your answer.

b. Find the radius of the cylinder that gives the maximum total area.

c. If the cone is short and fat, the maximum total area occurs where the altitude of the cylinder drops to zero and all the material is used in the top and bottom bases. How must the radius and altitude of the cone be related for this phenomenon to happen?

29. *Elliptical Nose Cone Problem:* The nose of a new cargo plane is to be a half-ellipsoid of diameter 8 m and length 9 m (Figure 8-3z). The nose swings open so that a cylindrical cargo container can be placed inside. What is the greatest volume this container could hold? What are the radius and altitude of this largest container? Justify your answer.

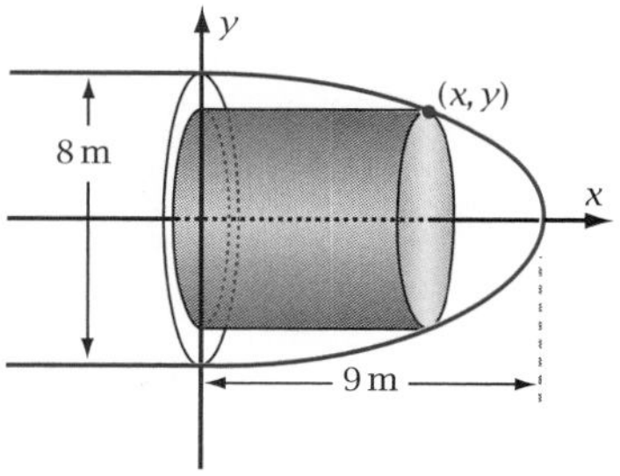

Figure 8-3z

30. *Submarine Pressure Hull Project:* According to a new design, the forward end of a submarine hull is to be the shape of a paraboloid 16 m long and 8 m in diameter (Figure 8-3aa). Since this is a doubly curved surface, it is hard to bend thick steel plates into this shape. So the paraboloid is to be made of relatively thin steel, and the pressure hull built inside as a cylinder (a singly curved surface). A frustum of a cone is also a singly curved surface, which would be about as easy to make and which might be able to contain more volume (Figure 8-3bb). How much more volume could be contained in the maximum-volume frustum than in the maximum-volume cylinder? Some things you will need to find are the equation of this particular parabola and the equation for the volume of a frustum of a cone.

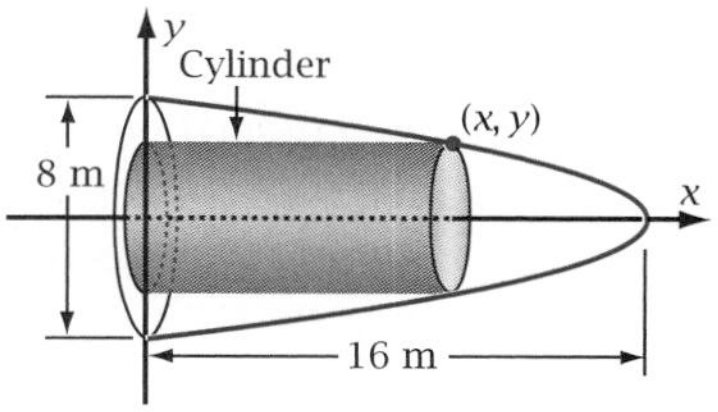

Figure 8-3aa

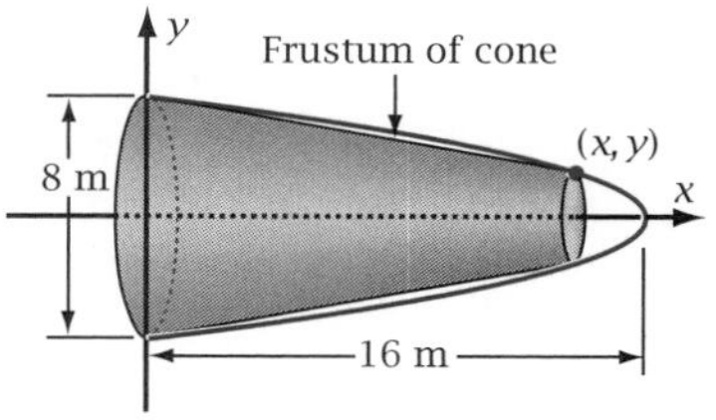

Figure 8-3bb

31. *Local Maximum Property Problem:* The definition of local maximum is as follows: $f(c)$ is a local maximum of $f$ on the interval $(a, b)$ if and only if $f(c) \geq f(x)$ for all values of $x$ in $(a, b)$. Figure 8-3cc illustrates this definition.

a. Prove that if $f(c)$ is a local maximum of $f$ on $(a, b)$ and $f$ is differentiable at $x = c$ in $(a, b)$, then $f'(c) = 0$. To do this, you can consider the sign of the difference quotient when $x$ is to the left and to the right of $c$, then take left and right limits.

b. Explain why the property in 31a would be false without the hypothesis that $f$ is differentiable at $x = c$.

c. Explain why the converse of the property in 31a is false.

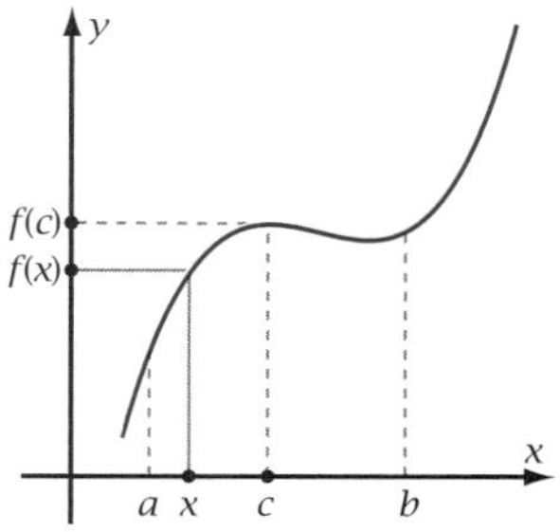

Figure 8-3cc

32. *Corral with Short Wall Project:* Millie Watt needs to use an electric fence to build a rectangular corral along a wall. Part or all of the wall forms all or part of one side of the corral. The total length of fence (excluding the wall) is to be 1000 ft. Find the maximum area that can be enclosed if the following is true.
    a. The wall is 600 ft long (Figure 8-3dd, left).
    b. The wall is 400 ft long (Figure 8-3dd, center).
    c. The wall is 200 ft long (Figure 8-3dd, right).

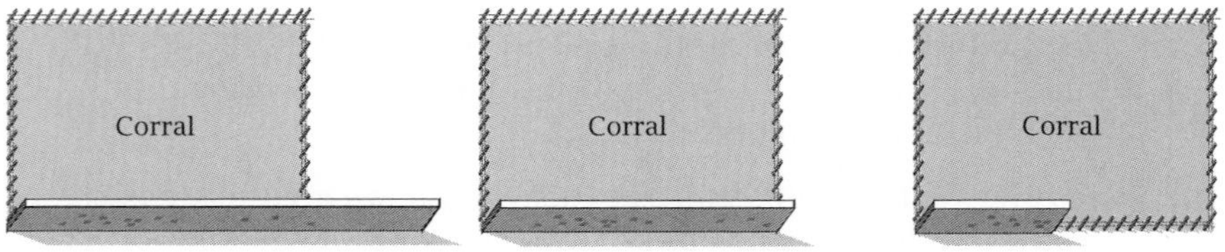


Figure 8-3dd

33. *Journal Problem:* Update your journal with things you've learned since the last entry. You should include such things as those listed here.
    - The one most important thing you have learned since the last journal entry
    - The critical features you can tell about the graph of a function from its two derivatives
    - The way you solve a real-world problem involving a maximum or minimum value
    - Any techniques or ideas about extreme-value problems that are still unclear to you.

# 8-4 Area of a Plane Region

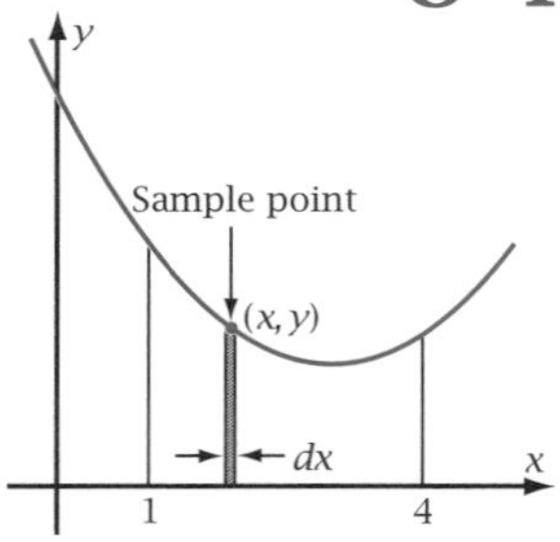


Figure 8-4a

In Section 5-10, you learned the following procedure for setting up a definite integral.

- Slice the region under a graph into narrow vertical strips of width $dx$.
- Show a representative strip and a sample point $(x, y)$ on the graph within the strip.
- Write the differential $y\,dx$ for the product of $x$ and $y$ corresponding to that strip.
- Add up the $y\,dx$'s and take the limit (that is, integrate).

Figure 8-4a illustrates the process. In this section you will apply this technique to find the areas of regions bounded by two curves or by curves for which slicing is best done horizontally.

**OBJECTIVE**

Given a plane region bounded by the graphs of one or more relations, write a definite integral representing the area of the region, and evaluate the integral numerically or algebraically (using the fundamental theorem of calculus) to find the area.

**Example 1** Find algebraically (by the fundamental theorem of calculus) the area of the "triangular" region in Quadrant I that is bounded by the graphs of $y = 4 - x^2$ and $y = 4x - x^2$ and the $y$-axis.

**Solution** Sketch the graph as shown in Figure 8-4b. Be careful to select the proper "triangular" region, in this case the one bounded by the $y$-axis. Then draw a representative slice. Choose sample points, one on each graph, for the same value of $x$. Finding $dA$ involves geometry and algebra.

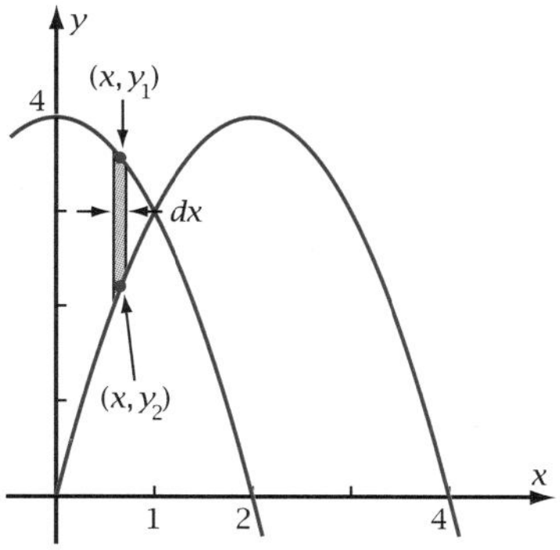

Figure 8-4b

$$\begin{aligned} dA &= (y_1 - y_2)\,dx \\ &= (4 - x^2 - 4x + x^2)\,dx \\ &= (4 - 4x)\,dx \end{aligned}$$

Be sure you subtract (larger $y$-value) − (smaller $y$-value) so that the height of the rectangle will be positive. Before you can integrate, you must find the limits of integration. The first strip is at the $y$-axis, so the lower limit of integration is $x = 0$. The last strip is at the point where the two graphs cross. If you cannot tell this point by inspection ($x = 1$, in this case), you can set the two $y$-values equal to each other and solve for $x$. The answer is the upper limit of integration.

$$4 - x^2 = 4x - x^2 \Rightarrow 4 = 4x \Rightarrow x = 1$$

$$A \approx \sum dA = \sum (4 - 4x)\,dx$$ Total area is approximately the sum of the $dA$'s.

$$A = \int_0^1 (4 - 4x)\,dx$$ A definite integral is a limit of a Riemann sum.

$$= 4x - 2x^2 \Big|_0^1$$ Use the fundamental theorem.

$$= 4 - 2 - 0 + 0 = 2$$ ■

Sometimes vertical slicing makes the problem hard to analyze. Figure 8-4c shows the region bounded by the graphs of $x = 3 + 2y - y^2$ and $x + y = -1$.

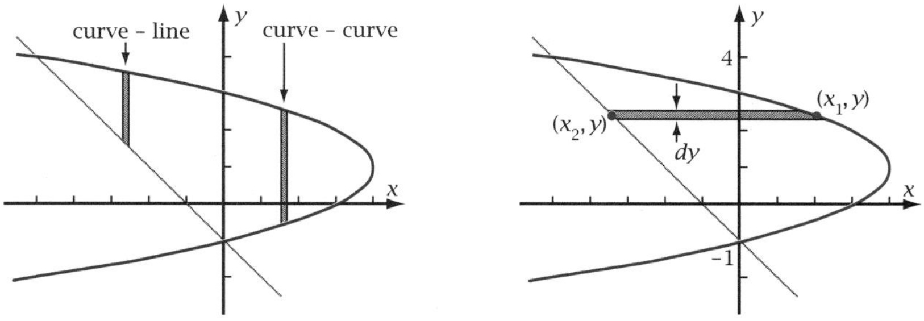

Figure 8-4c

The length of the vertical strip is given by different rules for different parts of the domain. If $x$ is negative the length of the strip is given by

curve − line.

For positive values of $x$, the length is given by

curve − curve.

This difficulty is circumvented by slicing horizontally, as shown in Example 2.

**■ Example 2** For the region in Figure 8-4c bounded by the graphs of $x = 3 + 2y - y^2$ and $x + y = -1$, write an integral for the area and evaluate it numerically. Evaluate the integral exactly by the fundamental theorem and compare your answers.

**Solution** See the right-hand graph in Figure 8-4c. Pick sample points $(x_1, y)$ and $(x_2, y)$. Then

$$dA = (\text{curve} - \text{line})\,dy = (x_1 - x_2)\,dy$$
$$= [3 + 2y - y^2 - (-y - 1)]\,dy = (4 + 3y - y^2)\,dy.$$

The graphs intersect where the two $x$-values are equal.

$$3 + 2y - y^2 = -y - 1$$
$$0 = y^2 - 3y - 4 \Rightarrow (y + 1)(y - 4) = 0 \Rightarrow y = -1 \text{ or } y = 4$$

The total area is found by adding the $dA$'s and taking the limit (that is, integrating).

$$A = \int_{-1}^{4} (4 + 3y - y^2)\,dy \qquad \text{Write an integral equal to the area.}$$
$$= 20.83333\ldots \qquad \text{Use numerical integration.}$$

The answer can also be found using the fundamental theorem.

$$A = 4y + \tfrac{3}{2}y^2 - \tfrac{1}{3}y^3 \Big|_{-1}^{4}$$
$$= 16 + 24 - \tfrac{64}{3} - (-4) - \tfrac{3}{2} + \tfrac{-1}{3}$$
$$= 20\tfrac{5}{6}, \text{ which equals } 20.8333\ldots.$$

■

# Problem Set 8-4

### *Do These Quickly*

The following problems are intended to refresh your skills. You should be able to do all ten problems in less than five minutes.

**Q1.** Integrate: $\int x^{-2}\,dx$

**Q2.** Integrate: $\int u^{-1}\,du$

**Q3.** Integrate: $\int u^n\,du$

**Q4.** Integrate: $\int (\ln x)^7 (dx/x)$

**Q5.** Integrate: $\int \ln 3\,dx$

**Q6.** Integrate: $\int 4^x\,dx$

**Q7.** Integrate: $\int \sec x \tan x\,dx$

**Q8.** Sketch the graph of $y' : y = |x - 2| + 3$.

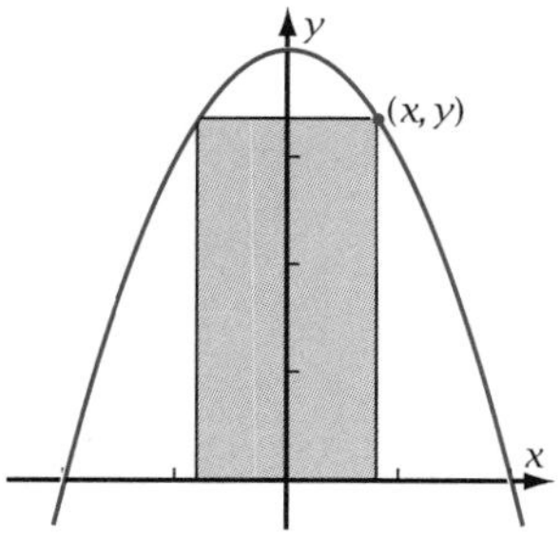


Figure 8-4d

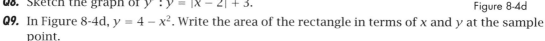

**Q9.** In Figure 8-4d, $y = 4 - x^2$. Write the area of the rectangle in terms of $x$ and $y$ at the sample point.

**Q10.** Find the maximum area of the rectangle in Figure 8-4d.

For Problems 1–14, sketch the region, write an integral for the area, and calculate the area either approximately by numerical integration, or exactly by the fundamental theorem.

1. Bounded by the graph of $y = -x^2 + 6x - 5$ and the $x$-axis
2. Bounded by the graph of $y = x^2 - x - 6$ and the $x$-axis
3. Bounded by the graph of $x = (y - 1)(y - 4)$ and the $y$-axis
4. Bounded by the graph of $x = 5 + 4y - y^2$ and the $y$-axis
5. Bounded by the graphs of $y = x^2 - 2x - 2$ and $y = x + 2$
6. Bounded by the graphs of $y = -2x + 7$ and $y = x^2 - 4x - 1$
7. Bounded by the graphs of $y = 0.5x^2 + 2x$ and $y = -x^2 + 2x + 6$
8. Bounded by the graphs of $y = 0.2x^2 + 3$ and $y = x^2 - 4x + 3$
9. Bounded by the graphs of $y = 2e^{0.2x}$ and $y = \cos x$, between $x = 0$ and $x = 5$
10. Bounded by the graphs of $y = \sec^2 x$ and $y = e^{2x}$, in Quadrant I, for $x \le 1$
11. Bounded by the graphs of $y = x + 3$ and $x = -y^2 + 6y - 7$
12. Bounded by the graphs of $y = -2x + 11$ and $x = 0.25y^2 - 0.5y - 0.75$
13. Bounded by the graphs of $y = x^3 - 4x$ and $y = 3x^2 - 4x - 4$ (The grapher will help you find the region.)
14. Bounded by the graphs of $y = x^{2/3}$ and $y = (x + 1)^{1/2} + 1$ (The grapher will help you find the region and locate the intersection points.)

15. Wanda Wye needs to find $dA$ for the region bounded by $y = x^2$ and $y = x$ (Figure 8-4e). She wants to know whether to use

(line − curve) or (curve − line).

Explain to Wanda how she can always choose the correct way. Also, tell her what her answer will be if she chooses the wrong one.

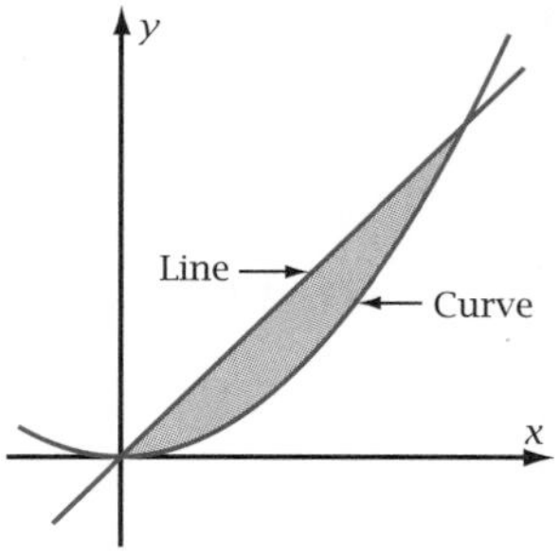

Figure 8-4e

16. Peter Doubt must find the area of the region shown in Figure 8-4f.

a. Explain to Peter why horizontal slicing is not appropriate for this problem.

b. Peter is worried because some of the region is below the $x$-axis. Explain why, with proper slicing, each value of $dA$ will be positive and that he thus need not worry.

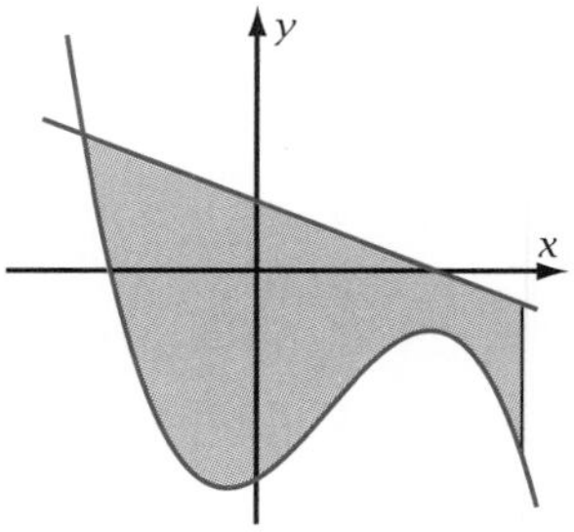

Figure 8-4f

17. *Parabolic Region Problem:* Prove that the area of a parabolic region as shown in Figure 8-4g is always 2/3 of the area of the circumscribed rectangle. Show the significance of what you have proved by using the result to find quickly the area of the parabolic region bounded by the graph of $y = 67 - 0.6x^2$ and the horizontal line $y = 7$.

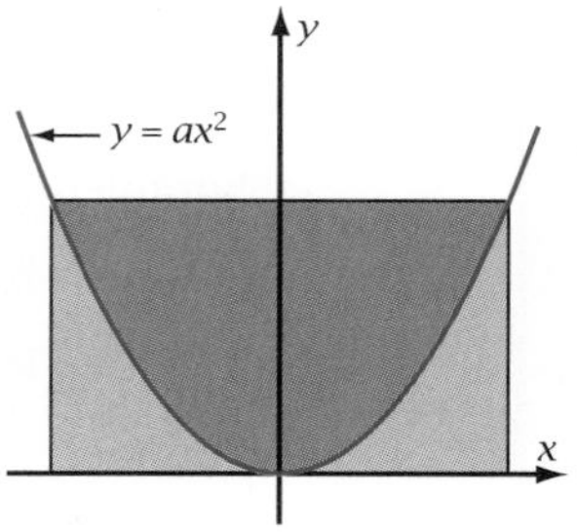

Figure 8-4g

18. *Sinusoidal Region Problem:* Show that the area under one arch of the sinusoid $y = \sin x$ (Figure 8-4h) is a rational number by finding this number. Demonstrate the significance of this fact by finding quickly the area under one arch of $y = 7\cos 5x$.

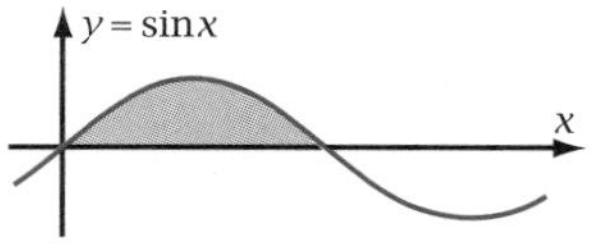

Figure 8-4h

19. *Ellipse Area Problem:* Figure 8-4i shows the ellipse

$$9x^2 + 25y^2 = 225.$$

Write an integral equal to the area of the region. Evaluate the integral numerically. This answer can also be found without calculus, using the $x$-radius and the $y$-radius of the ellipse. Make a conjecture about a formula for the area of an ellipse. How does your conjectured formula compare with that for the area of a circle?

20. *Area of a Region Parametrically Problem:* The ellipse in Figure 8-4i has parametric equations

$$x = 5\cos t$$
$$y = 3\sin t.$$

The area of a representative vertical strip is $dA = 2y\,dx$. Find the area by expressing both $y$ and $dx$ in terms of $t$. You must also find out what the limits of integration are for $t$, corresponding to the $x$-limits in Problem 19.

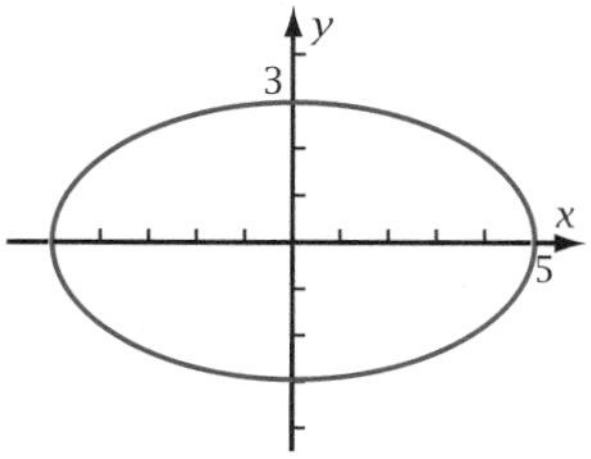

Figure 8-4i

21. *Golf Course Problem:* Figure 8-4j shows a small putting green to be constructed on a new golf course. The dimensions $x$ and $y$ are in yards. Find, approximately, the area of the putting green. Tell how you arrived at your answer.

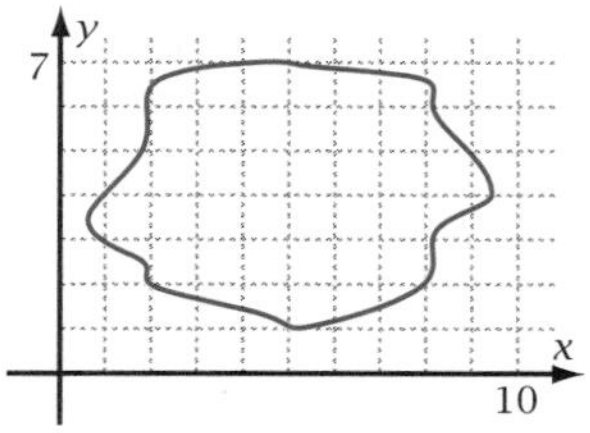

Figure 8-4j

22. *Area Check Problem:* Find the area of the region bounded by the graph of $y = x^2$ and the line $y = x + 6$ exactly, using the fundamental theorem. Then calculate midpoint Riemann sums with $n = 10$, $n = 100$, and $n = 1000$ increments. Show that the Riemann sums are approaching the exact answer as the number of increments becomes large.

23. *Curve Sketching Review Problem:* Given $t(x) = x + \sin x$, plot the graph of $t$ using an $x$-window of about $0 \le x \le 4\pi$. Sketch the result. Then calculate the $x$-coordinates of all points at which the tangent to the graph is horizontal. Does $t'(x)$ change signs at any of these points? Show any such points on your graph.

24. *Maximum-Minimum Review Problem:* A rectangle is to be inscribed in the ellipse of Problem 19. The sides of the rectangle are to be parallel to the $x$-, and $y$-axes, with the corners touching the ellipse. Find the maximum area such a rectangle could have.

# 8-5 Volume of a Solid by Plane Slicing

In Section 8-4, you refreshed your memory about setting up definite integrals by slicing a region into narrow strips. In this section you will extend the technique to find volumes of solids that have curved boundaries. The idea is to slice the solid into thin, flat *slabs*, find the volume of a representative slab by multiplying its area by its thickness, then add the volumes and take the limit as the thickness approaches zero.

**OBJECTIVE**

Given a solid whose cross-sectional area varies along its length, find its volume by slicing into slabs and performing the appropriate calculus, and show that your answer is reasonable.

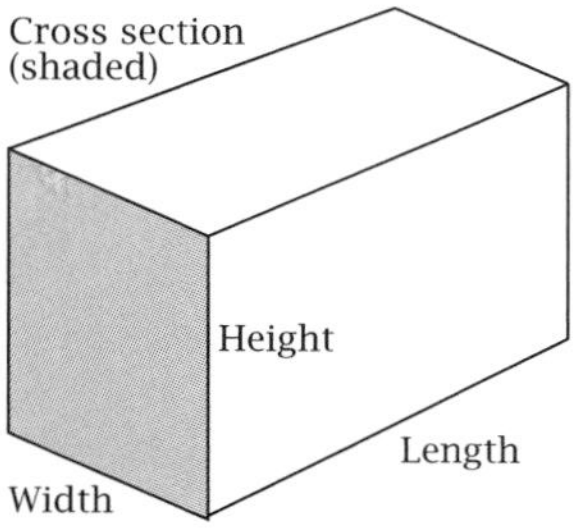

Figure 8-5a

Figure 8-5a shows a rectangular solid. Its volume is (length)(width)(height). The area of a cross section is (width)(height). So volume of this solid is

Volume = (area)(length).

If a solid has some other shape, its volume is still (area)(length). But the area may vary for different cross sections. Example 1 shows you how to find the volume.

**Example 1** (Rotate a region around the $x$-axis.) The region under the graph of $y = x^{1/3}$ from $x = 0$ to $x = 8$ is rotated about the $x$-axis to form a solid. Write an integral equal to the volume of the solid and evaluate it to find the volume. Assume that $x$ and $y$ are in centimeters. Show that your answer is reasonable.

**Solution**

First, draw a picture of the region (Figure 8-5b, left). Next, slice the region into strips as though you planned to find the area. The idea is to slice perpendicular to the axis around which the region will rotate. Show a representative strip as in Figure 8-5b. Pick a sample point $(x, y)$ that is on the graph of $y = x^{1/3}$.

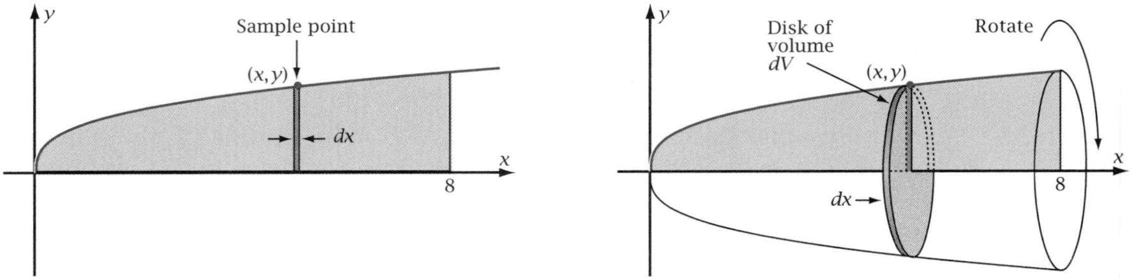


Draw the region.
Slice a strip perpendicular to the axis of rotation.
Pick a sample point $(x, y)$.

Rotate the region and the strip to form a solid. The rotating strip forms a flat disk of volume $dV$.

Figure 8-5b

Then draw what the solid looks like as the region rotates around the $x$-axis (Figure 8-5b, right). As the region turns, the rotating strip generates a **disk.** This disk can be thought of as a short, fat cylinder whose "altitude" is $dx$ and whose cross section at any value of $x$ is close to what it is at the sample point $(x, y)$. The volume of the disk, $dV$, is

$$dV = \text{(cross-sectional area at the sample point)(altitude, } dx\text{)}.$$

Since the radius of the disk is $y$, its volume will be

$$dV = \pi y^2\, dx = \pi (x^{1/3})^2\, dx = \pi x^{2/3}\, dx.$$

The solid itself can be considered to be made up of a stack of these disks. So the approximate volume of the solid is equal to the sum of the disk volumes.

$$V \approx \sum dV = \sum \pi x^{2/3}\, dx$$

The exact volume is the limit of this Riemann sum—that is, the definite integral.

$$V = \int_0^8 x^{2/3}\, dx$$ Definite integral equal to the volume.

$$= \pi \cdot \tfrac{3}{5}x^{5/3}\Big|_0^8 = \tfrac{3}{5}(32)\pi - \tfrac{3}{5}(0)\pi = 19.2\pi$$ Evaluate using the fundamental theorem.

$$= 60.318\ldots \approx 60.3 cm^3$$ Write a real-world answer, suitably rounded, with units.

*Checks:*
Volume of circumscribed cylinder would be $\pi(2^2)(8) = 32\pi > 19.2\pi$. ✓
Volume of inscribed cone would be $(\frac{1}{3})\pi(2^2)(8) = 10.66\ldots\pi < 19.2\pi$. ✓
Numerical integration: $V \approx 19.20000037\pi \approx 19.2\pi$ ✓ ■

■ **Example 2** (*Rotate a region around the y-axis.*) The region in Quadrant I bounded by the parabola $y = 4 - x^2$ is rotated about the $y$-axis to form a solid paraboloid. Find the volume of the paraboloid if $x$ and $y$ are in inches. Show that your answer is reasonable.

**Solution** First sketch the region as shown in the left-hand diagram of Figure 8-5c. Slice the region into strips perpendicular to the axis of rotation (the $y$-axis, this time). Show one representative strip with a sample point $(x, y)$ on the graph. Then sketch the solid that would result if this region is rotated about the $y$-axis (right diagram). As in Example 1, the strip generates a flat disk as it rotates. Let $dV$ be the volume of the disk and proceed as follows.

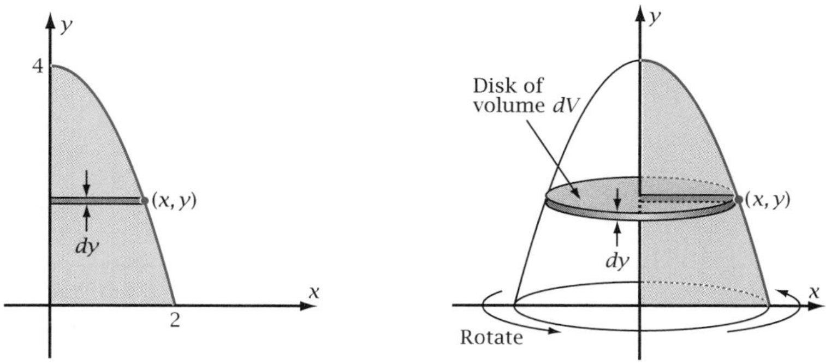

y
4
(x, y)
dy
x
2
Draw the region.
Slice a strip perpendicular
to the axis of rotation.
y
Disk of
volume dV
(x, y)
dy
x
Rotate
Rotate the region and the strip
to form a solid. The rotating
strip forms a flat disk.

Figure 8-5c

$dV = \pi x^2\, dy$ — Volume = (area)(length); the radius is $x$ this time.

$= \pi(4 - y)\, dy$ — Get $dV$ in terms of one variable.

$\therefore V = \int_0^4 \pi(4 - y)\, dy = \pi(4y - \frac{1}{2}y^2)\Big|_0^4$ — Add volumes of slices and take the limit (integrate).

$= \pi(16 - 8) - \pi(0 - 0) = \underline{8\pi} = 25.132\ldots \approx 25.1 \text{ in}^3$

*Checks:* Volume of circumscribed cylinder would be $\pi(2^2)(4) = 16\pi > 8\pi$. ✓
Volume of inscribed cone would be $(1/3)\pi(2^2)(4) = 5.33\ldots\pi < 8\pi$. ✓
Numerical integration: $V = 8\pi = 8\pi$ ✓ ■

■ **Example 3** (*Rotate a region bounded by two curves.*) Let $R$ be the region that is bounded by the graphs of $y_1 = 6e^{-0.2x}$ and $y_2 = \sqrt{x}$, and by the vertical lines $x = 1$ and $x = 4$. Find the volume of the solid generated when $R$ is rotated about the $x$-axis. Assume that $x$ and $y$ are in feet. Show that your answer is reasonable.

**Solution** Sketch region $R$ and slice it into strips perpendicular to the axis of rotation ($x$-axis). Show a representative strip with two sample points, one on each graph (Figure 8-5d, left). As $R$ rotates, the strip will trace out a disk with a hole in the middle (a **washer**, for those of you who are familiar with nuts and bolts). The volume $dV$ of the washer will be the volume of the outer disk minus the volume of the inner disk.

$dV = \pi y_1^2 dx - \pi y_2^2\, dx$ — Volume of outer disk minus volume of inner disk.

$dV = \pi(y_1^2 - y_2^2)\, dx$ — Start here if you're brave enough!

$dV = \pi(36e^{-0.4x} - x)\, dx$ — Substitute for $y_1$ and $y_2$ and do the squaring.

$$\therefore V = \pi \int_1^4 (36e^{-0.4x} - x)\, dx$$

Add the volumes of the strips and find the limit.

$$= 34.65811\ldots\pi$$

Use numerical integration since an "exact" answer was not called for.

$$= 108.881\ldots \approx 108.9 \text{ ft}^3$$

The $\pi$ could have been included in the numerical integration.

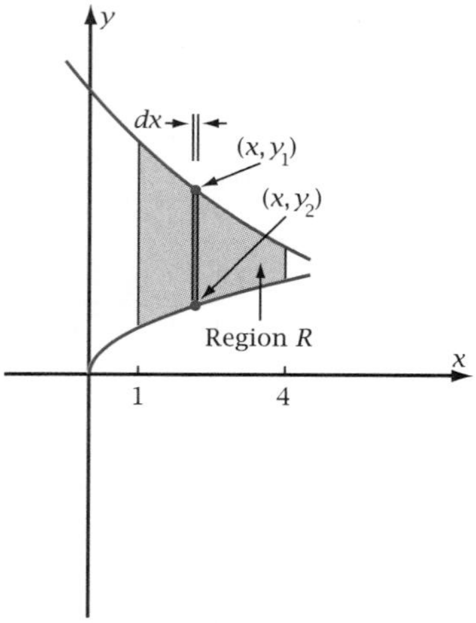


Draw the region. Slice a strip perpendicular to the axis of rotation. Pick *two* sample points, $(x, y_1)$ and $(x, y_2)$.

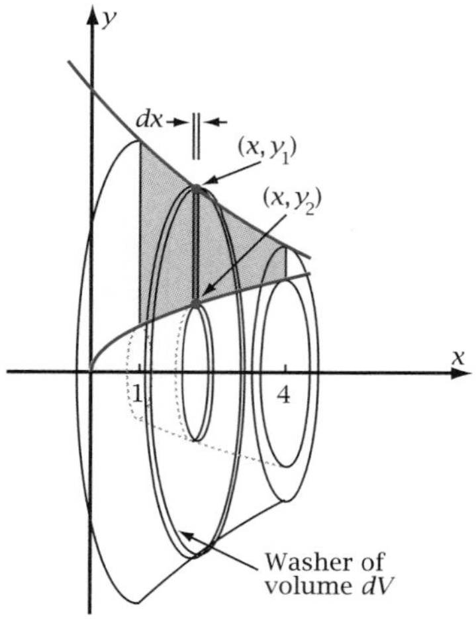


Rotate the region and the strip to form a solid. The rotating strip forms a flat washer of volume $dV$.

Figure 8-5d

*Checks:* Volume of outer cylinder would be $\pi(6e^{-0.2})^2(4-1) = 72.39\ldots\pi$. ✓
Volume of inner cylinder would be $\pi(1)^2(4-1) = 3\pi$. ✓
$\therefore$ volume of solid is bounded above by $69.39\ldots\pi \geq 34.658\ldots\pi$. ✓ ■

In Examples 1–3, the figure has been generated by rotating a region. Such a figure is given the (obvious!) name **solid of revolution**. As the strip rotated, it generated a disk or washer. The same disk or washer would be generated if the solid were generated first, then sliced with planes perpendicular to the axis of rotation. As a result, the technique you have been using is called finding **volumes by plane slices**.

Once you realize this fact, you can find volumes of solids that are *not* generated by rotation. All you have to do is find the cross-sectional area in terms of the displacement perpendicular to the cross section. Example 4 shows how.

**■ Example 4** (*Plane slices of a noncircular solid*) A 2 in. by 2 in. by 4 in. wooden block is carved into the shape shown in Figure 8-5e. The graph of $y = \sqrt{4-x}$ is drawn on the back face of the block. Then wood is shaved off the front and top faces in such a way that the remaining solid has square cross sections perpendicular to the $x$-axis. Find the volume of the solid. Show that your answer is reasonable.

**Solution** The right-hand diagram in Figure 8-5e shows a **slab** formed by slicing the solid with planes perpendicular to the $x$-axis. Each such slab has a length

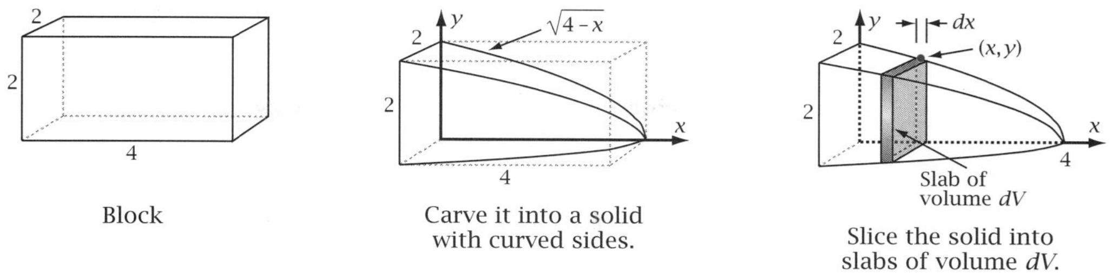


Figure 8-5e

approximately equal to the $y$-value at the sample point shown. Thus the cross-sectional area of the slice is about equal to $y^2$ since the cross section is a square. Using the fact that volume equals cross-sectional area times length (or thickness, in this case), you can write the following.

$dV = y^2\,dx = (4 - x)\,dx$ — Do the geometry and algebra.

$\therefore V = \int_0^4 (4 - x)\,dx = 4x - \frac{1}{2}x^2 \Big|_0^4 = 16 - 8 - 0 + 0 = 8\text{in}^3$ — Do the calculus.

*Checks:*
Volume of block is $(2)(2)(4) = 16 > 8$. ✓
Volume of inscribed pyramid would be $(1/3)(2)(2)(4) = 5.33\ldots < 8$. ✓
Numerical integration: $V = 8 = 8$ ✓ ■

All of the examples above involve the same basic reasoning, as summarized here.

### Technique: Volume of a Solid by Plane Slicing

- Cut the solid into flat slices, formed either by strips in a rotated region or by planes passed through the solid. Get disks, washers, or slabs whose volumes can be found in terms of the solid's cross section at sample point(s) $(x, y)$.
- Do geometry to get $dV$ in terms of the sample point(s).
- Do algebra to get $dV$ in terms of one variable.
- Do calculus to add up all the $dV$'s and take the limit (that is, integrate).
- Check your answer to make sure it's reasonable.

## Problem Set 8-5

### Do These Quickly

The following problems are intended to refresh your skills. You should be able to do all ten problems in less than five minutes.

**Q1.** Integrate: $\int (x^2 + x + 1)\,dx$

**Q2.** Integrate: $\int x^{3/4}\,dx$

**Q3.** Differentiate: $y = x^{2/3}$

**Q4.** Integrate: $\int e^{-3x}\,dx$

**Q5.** Integrate: $\int \csc x \cot x\,dx$

**Q6.** Differentiate: $y = \ln 5x$

**Q7.** Write the definition of definite integral.

**Q8.** The conclusion, ". . . then there is a value of $x = c$ in $(a, b)$ such that $f'(c) = [f(b) - f(a)]/(b - a)$" is for the —?— theorem.

**Q9.** Sketch the graph of a function that is continuous at $x = 4$, but not differentiable there.

**Q10.** Sketch the graph of $y = 2^{-x}$.

1. *Paraboloid Problem:* The region in the first quadrant under the graph of $y = 9 - x^2$ is rotated about the $y$-axis to form a solid paraboloid (Figure 8-5f). Assume that $x$ and $y$ are in feet.
   a. Find the exact volume of the paraboloid using the fundamental theorem of calculus.
   b. Find the approximate volume by integrating numerically.
   c. Show that your answers are reasonable by doing a quick geometrical check.

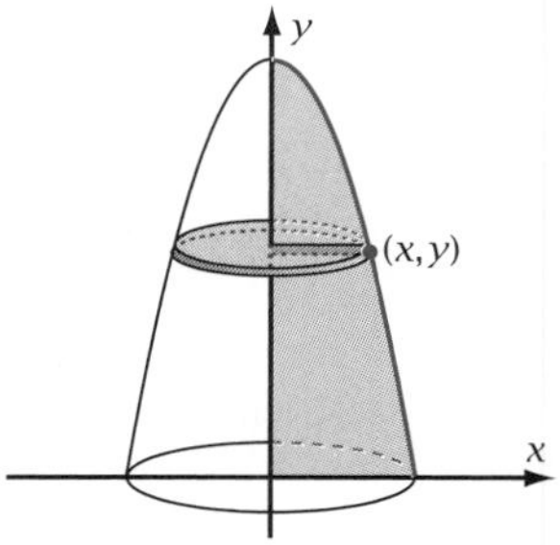


Figure 8-5f

2. *Cone Problem:* A solid cone is formed by rotating about the $y$-axis the first-quadrant triangle bounded by the line $y = 10 - 2x$ and the two axes (Figure 8-5g). Assume that $x$ and $y$ are in centimeters.
   a. Find the exact volume of the cone using the fundamental theorem of calculus.
   b. Show that the volume in 2a agrees with the formula from geometry.
   c. How does the volume of the cone compare to the volume of the cylinder that can be circumscribed about it?

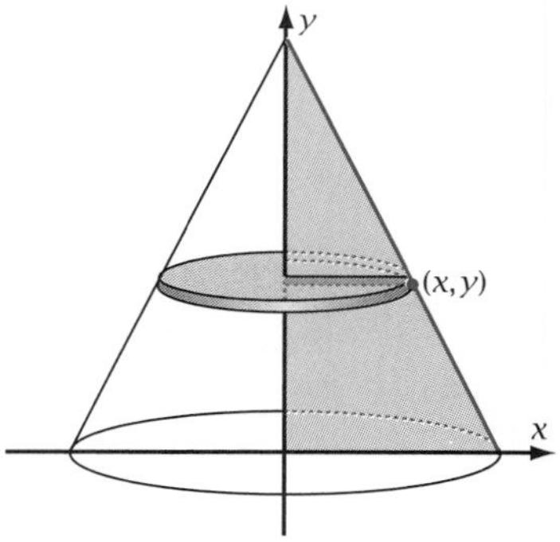


Figure 8-5g

3. Let $R$ be the region under the graph of $y = 4x - x^2$ from $x = 1$ to $x = 4$. Find the exact volume of the solid generated by rotating $R$ about the $x$-axis.
4. Let $R$ be the region under the graph of $y = x^{1.5}$ from $x = 1$ to $x = 9$. Find the exact volume of the solid generated by rotating $R$ about the $x$-axis.
5. Let $R$ be the region in Quadrant I bounded by the graphs of $y = \ln x$ and $y = 1$. Find the exact volume of the solid generated by rotating $R$ about the $y$-axis.
6. Let $R$ be the region bounded by the $y$-axis, the lines $y = 1$ and $y = 8$, and the curve $y = x^{3/4}$. Find the exact volume of the solid generated by rotating $R$ about the $y$-axis.

7. *Washer Slices Problem:* Figure 8-5h shows the solid formed by rotating around the $y$-axis the region that is bounded by the graphs of $y = x^4$ and $y = 8x$. Find the exact volume of the solid using the fundamental theorem of calculus. Assume that $x$ and $y$ are in inches. Show that your answer is reasonable by a quick geometrical check and by numerical integration.

8. *Exponential Horn Problem:* A horn for a public address system is to be made with the inside cross sections increasing exponentially with distance from the speaker. The horn will have the shape of the solid formed when the region bounded by $y = e^{0.4x}$ and $y = x + 1$ from $x = 0$ to $x = 3$ is rotated about the $x$-axis (Figure 8-5i). Find the volume of the material used to make this speaker. Assume that $x$ and $y$ are in feet. Show that the exact answer by the fundamental theorem agrees with the answer obtained by numerical integration.

9. The region between $x = 0$, $x = 8$ and bounded by the graphs of $y = x^{1/3}$ and $y = 10e^{-0.1x}$ is rotated around the $x$-axis to form a solid. Find its exact volume.

10. The region bounded by the graphs of $y = 4 - x$ and $y = 4 - x^2$ is rotated around the $y$-axis to form a solid. Find its exact volume.

11. *Paraboloid Volume Formula Problem:* Prove that the volume of a paraboloid is always one-half the volume of the circumscribed cylinder. To do this, realize that any paraboloid is congruent to a paraboloid generated by rotating a parabola of general equation $y = ax^2$ about the $y$-axis.

12. *Riemann Sum Limit Problem:* The region in Quadrant I bounded by $y = 0.3x^{1.5}$, $x = 4$, and the $x$-axis is rotated about the $x$-axis to form a solid.

    a. Find the volume of the solid by performing the appropriate calculus.

    b. Find three midpoint Riemann sums, $M_{10}$, $M_{100}$, and $M_{1000}$, for the volume of the solid. Show that these sums are getting closer to the exact value as the number of increments increases.

13. *Different Axis Problem I:* The region in Quadrant I under the graph of $y = 4 - x^2$ is rotated around the line $x = 3$ to form a solid (Figure 8-5j). Sketch the washer formed as the horizontal slice shown rotates. What are the inner and outer radii of the washer? Find the volume of the solid.

14. *Different Axis Problem II:* The region in Quadrant I under the graph of $y = 4 - x^2$ shown in Figure 8-5j is rotated around the line $y = -5$ to form another solid. Find its volume.

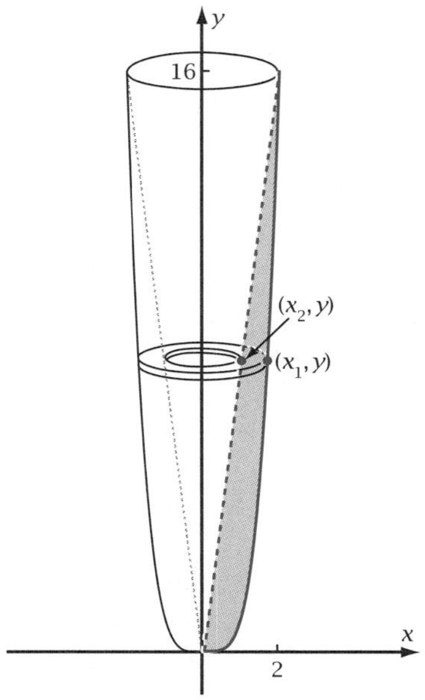


Figure 8-5h

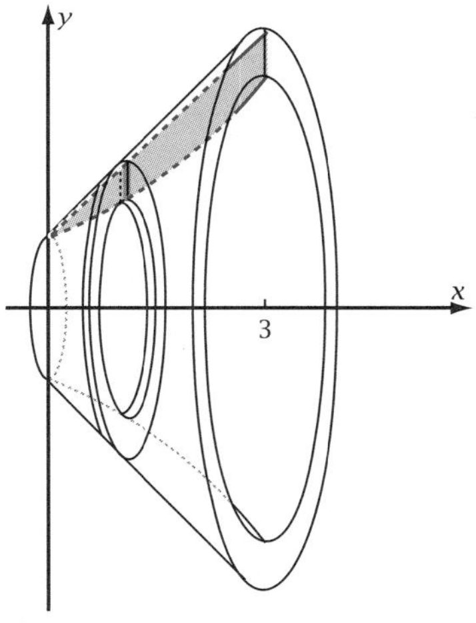


Figure 8-5i

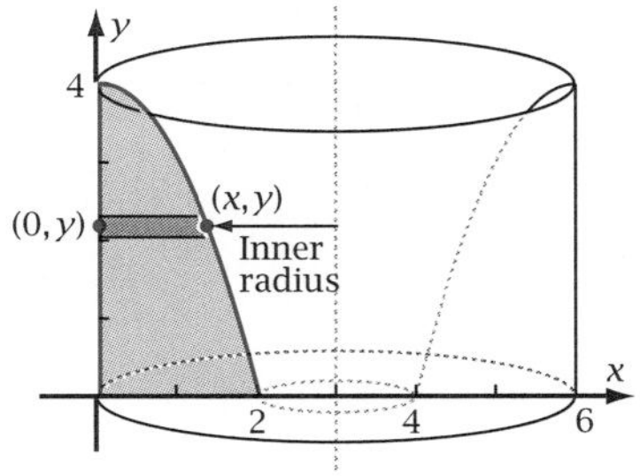


Figure 8-5j

15. *New Integral Problem I:* The region under the graph of $y = \sin x$ from $x = 0$ to $x = 1.2$ is rotated about the $x$-axis to form a solid.

   a. Write an integral for the volume of this solid.

   b. Evaluate the integral approximately by numerical integration.

   c. Transform the integrand using a clever application of the double-argument properties from trigonometry so that it is linear in sine or cosine of a multiple of $x$. Then find the exact volume by evaluating the integral using the fundamental theorem. Show that the answer you got in 15b is close to this exact value.

16. *New Integral Problem II:* The region bounded by the graph of $y = \tan x$, the line $y = 1$, and the $y$-axis is rotated about the $x$-axis to form a solid.

   a. Write an integral for the volume of this solid.

   b. Evaluate the integral approximately by numerical integration.

   c. See whether you can get the indefinite integral and thus find the exact value of the volume.

17. *Pyramid Problem:* A pyramid has a square base 8 cm by 8 cm and altitude 15 cm (Figure 8-5k). Each cross section perpendicular to the $y$-axis is a square. Find the volume of the pyramid. Show that it is equal to one-third the volume of the circumscribed rectangular solid with the same base and altitude.

18. *Horn Problem:* Figure 8-5l shows a horn-shaped solid formed in such a way that a plane perpendicular to the $x$-axis cuts a circular cross section. Each circle has its center on the graph of $y = 0.2x^2$ and a radius ending on the graph of $y = 0.16x^2 + 1$. Find the volume of the solid if $x$ and $y$ are in centimeters.

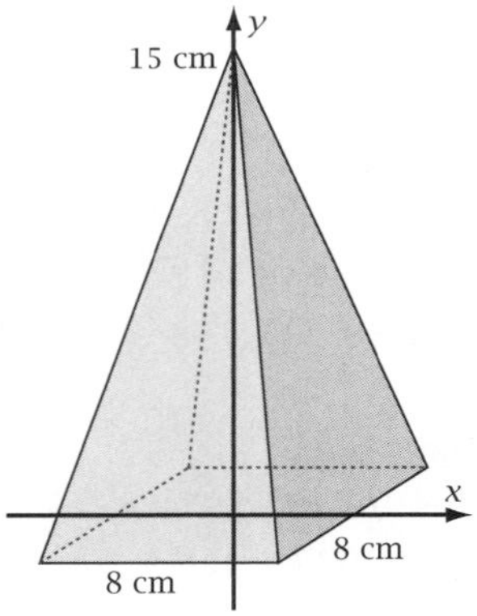


Figure 8-5k

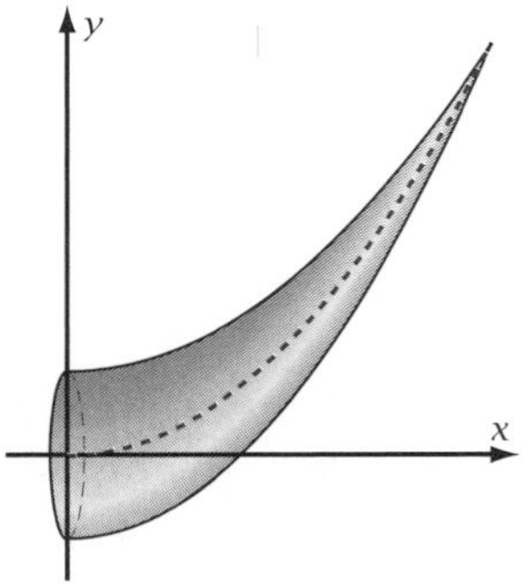


Figure 8-5l

19. *Triangular Cross-Section Problem:* Region $R$ under the graph of $y = x^{0.6}$ from $x = 0$ to $x = 4$ forms the back side of a solid (Figure 8-5m). Cross sections of the solid perpendicular to the $x$-axis are isosceles right triangles with their right angle on the $x$-axis.

   a. Find the volume of the solid.

   b. Quick! Tell what the volume of the solid would be if the cross sections were squares instead of right triangles.

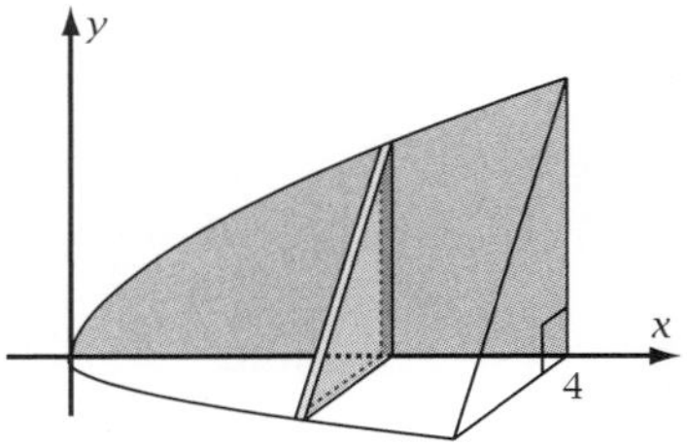


Figure 8-5m

20. *Wedge Problem:* Figure 8-5n shows a cylindrical log of radius 6 in. A wedge is cut from the log by sawing halfway through it perpendicular to its central axis, then sawing diagonally from a point 3 in. above the first cut. Your job is to find the volume of the wedge.

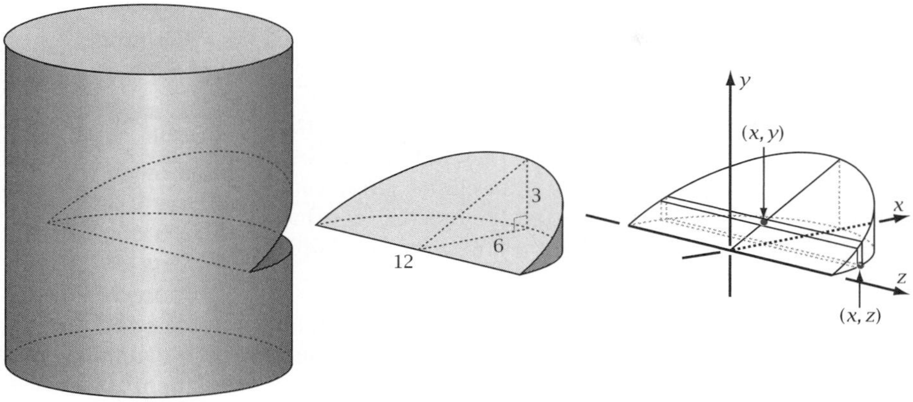


Figure 8-5n

a. Write the equation of the line that runs up the top surface of the wedge (in the $xy$-plane).

b. Write the equation of the circle in the $xz$-plane that forms the boundary for the bottom surface of the wedge.

c. Slice the wedge into slabs using planes perpendicular to the $x$-axis. Find an equation for the volume $dV$ of a representative slab. Use the result to find the volume of the wedge.

21. *Generalized Wedge Problem:* Find a formula for the volume of a wedge of altitude $h$ cut to the central axis of a log of radius $r$, as in Figure 8-5n, where one cut is perpendicular to the axis of the log.

22. *Cone Volume Formula Proof Problem:* Prove that the volume of a right circular cone of base radius $r$ and altitude $h$ is given by

$$V = \frac{1}{3}\pi r^2 h.$$

You may find it helpful to draw the cone in a Cartesian coordinate system. If you put either the vertex of the cone or the center of its base at the origin, a slanted element of the cone will be a line segment whose equation you can find in terms of $x$ and $y$.

23. *Sphere Problem:* Figure 8-5o shows a sphere of radius 10 cm.

a. Find the volume of the sphere by calculus.

b. Show that the answer you got in 23a agrees with the formula that you learned in geometry.

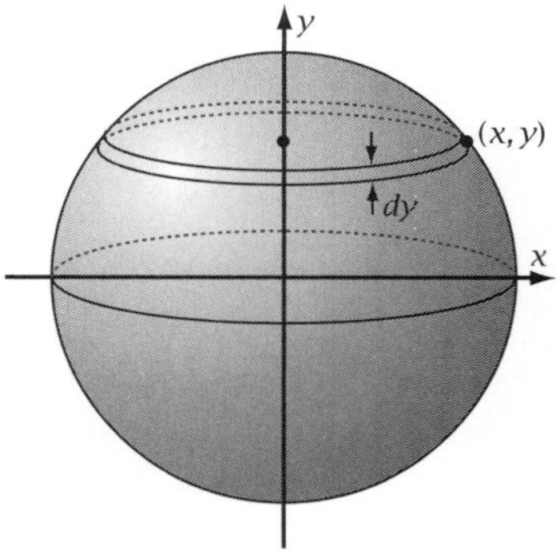


Figure 8-5o

24. *General Volume of a Sphere Problem:* By calculus, derive the formula

$$V = \frac{4}{3}\pi r^3$$

for the volume of a sphere of radius $r$.

25. *Volume of an Ellipsoid Problem:* Figure 8-5p shows the ellipsoid

$$\left(\frac{x}{a}\right)^2 + \left(\frac{y}{b}\right)^2 + \left(\frac{z}{c}\right)^2 = 1.$$

Find the volume of the ellipsoid in terms of $a$, $b$, and $c$, the radii along the three axes. To get $dV$, show that every cross section perpendicular to the $x$-axis is an ellipse similar in proportions to the ellipse in the $yz$-plane. Use the fact that the area of an ellipse is $\pi uv$, where $u$ and $v$ are the radii along the major and minor axes.

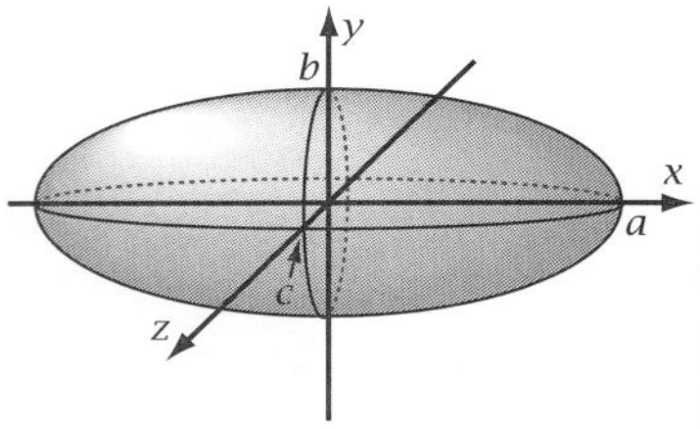

Figure 8-5p

26. *Highway Cut Problem:* Figure 8-5q shows a cut through a hill that is to be made for a new highway. Each vertical cross section of the cut perpendicular to the roadway is an isosceles trapezoid whose sides make angles of 52° with the horizontal. The roadway at the bottom of the trapezoid is 50 yd wide. The cut is 600 yd long from its beginning to its end.

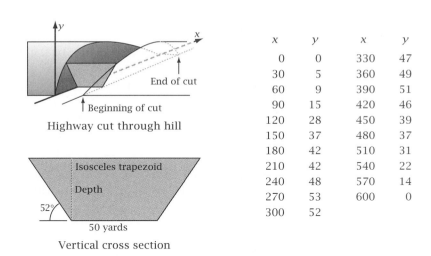

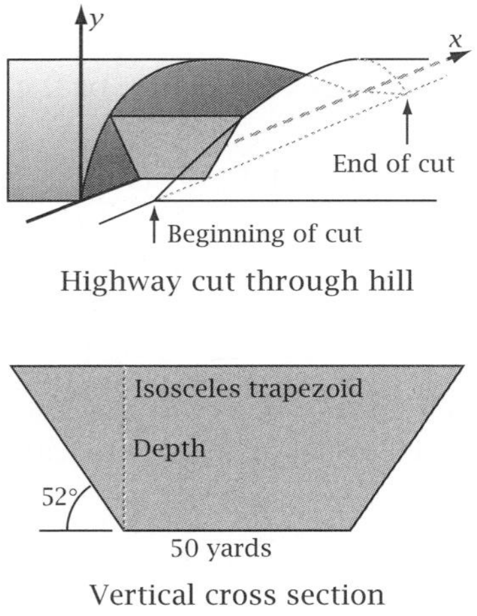

Figure 8-5q

| $x$ | $y$ | $x$ | $y$ |
|---|---|---|---|
| 0 | 0 | 330 | 47 |
| 30 | 5 | 360 | 49 |
| 60 | 9 | 390 | 51 |
| 90 | 15 | 420 | 46 |
| 120 | 28 | 450 | 39 |
| 150 | 37 | 480 | 37 |
| 180 | 42 | 510 | 31 |
| 210 | 42 | 540 | 22 |
| 240 | 48 | 570 | 14 |
| 270 | 53 | 600 | 0 |
| 300 | 52 | | |

You are to find how many cubic yards of earth must be removed in order to construct the cut. To estimate this volume, survey crews have measured the depth, $y$, of the cut at various distances, $x$, from the beginning. The table above shows these depths. Write an integral involving $y$ and $dx$ that represents the volume of earth to be removed. Then evaluate the integral by a suitable numerical technique. If earth removal costs \$12.00 per cubic yard, about how much will it cost to make the cut?

27. *Submarine Problem:* The countries of Parra and Noya are spying on each other. The Noyaks find that the Parrians are designing a new submarine, the *Black November.*

The cross sections perpendicular to the horizontal axis of the sub will be circles with centers on that axis. The only quantitative piece of information the Noyaks have found is that the radius $y$ at any distance $x$ from the bow of the sub is given by

$$y = 2x^{0.5} - 0.02x^{1.5},$$

where $x$ and $y$ are in meters. Your mission is to find out as much about the submarine as possible from this information.

a. Plot the graph of the radius as a function of distance from the bow. Sketch the result.

b. The sub will end where the equation indicates that the radius becomes negative. How long will the *Black November* be? How does this compare to the length of a football field?

c. What is the beam (the maximum diameter) of the sub? How far from the bow is this maximum diameter?

d. Fast submarines have a length-to-beam ratio of 7 or more. Do you expect the *Black November* to be fast or slow?

e. What will be the volume of the submarine?

f. The displacement of a ship is the number of tons the ship weighs. [The term *displacement* is used because a (floating) ship weighing $T$ tons will displace $T$ tons of water.] Given that a cubic meter of seawater is about 1042 kg, how many metric tons will the *Black November* displace? (A metric ton is 1000 kg.)

*28. *Preview Problem:* Figure 8-5r shows the solid formed by rotating a region in Quadrant I about the $y$-axis. The region has been sliced into strips parallel to the axis of rotation, rather than perpendicular to it. Sketch the geometrical figure formed by the strip shown in the figure. What name could be given to this figure? See whether you can find an expression for $dV$, the volume of the figure formed by rotating the strip, in terms of the sample point $(x, y)$.

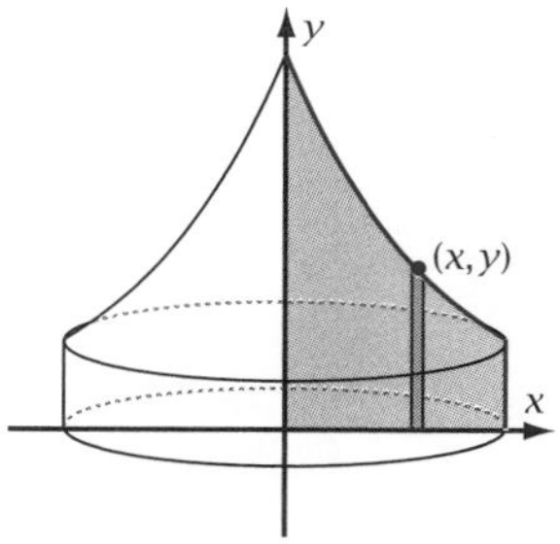

Figure 8-5r

*This problem prepares you for Section 8-6.

# 8-6 Volume of a Solid of Revolution by Cylindrical Shells

Figure 8-6a shows the region under the graph of $y = 4x - x^2$ from $x = 0$ to $x = 3$. Suppose that this region is to be rotated about the $y$-axis to form a solid. Slicing the region perpendicular to the $y$-axis as you did in Section 8-5 would be awkward. As shown on the left in Figure 8-6a, the lengths of the strips are not given by a single rule for all values of $y$. As a result, you have to consider two parts of the solid, one from the $x$-axis up to the cusp and the other from the cusp up to the vertex of the parabola.

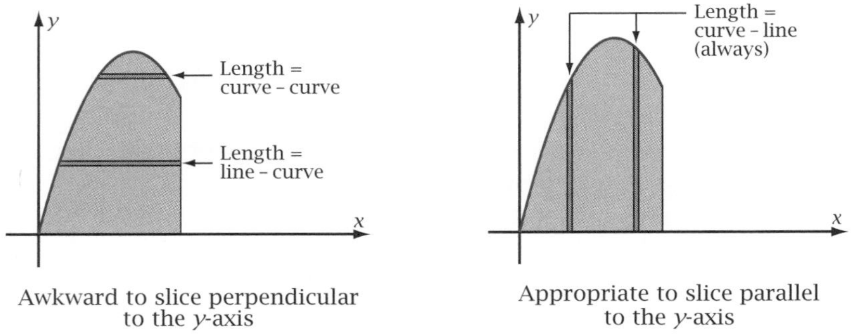


Figure 8-6a

If you slice the region into strips parallel to the $y$-axis, the length of the strip is always equal to (curve−line). As shown in Figure 8-6b, these parallel strips will generate **cylindrical shells** as the region rotates.

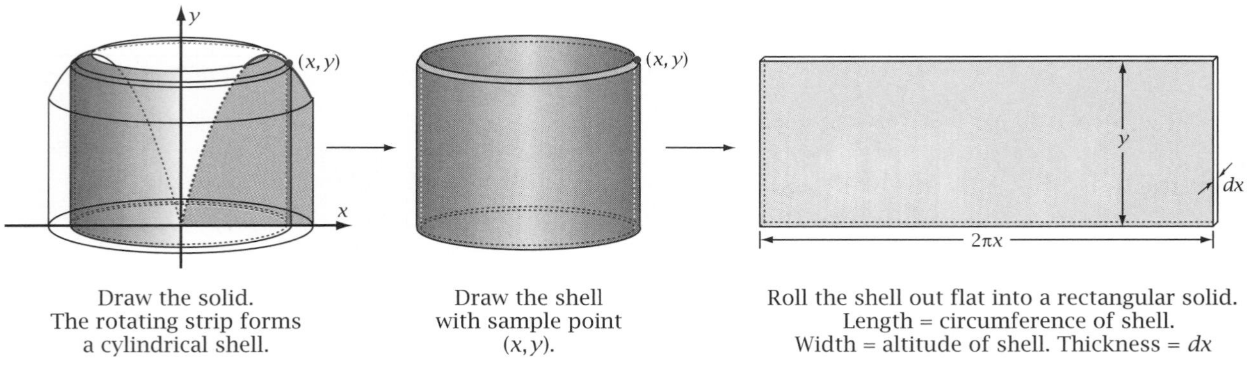

y
(x, y)
x
Draw the solid.
The rotating strip forms
a cylindrical shell.
(x, y)
Draw the shell
with sample point
(x, y).
y
dx
2πx
Roll the shell out flat into a rectangular solid.
Length = circumference of shell.
Width = altitude of shell. Thickness = dx


Figure 8-6b

***OBJECTIVE***

Find the volume of a solid of revolution by slicing it into cylindrical shells.

The shells in Figure 8-6b are like tin cans without ends. Since a shell is thin, its volume $dV$ can be found by cutting down its side and rolling it out flat (Figure 8-6b, right). The resulting rectangular solid will have the following approximate dimensions.

| | |
|---|---|
| Length: | Circumference of the shell at the sample point ($2\pi x$, in this case) |
| Width: | Altitude of the shell at the sample point ($y$, in this case) |
| Thickness: | Width of the strip ($dx$, in this case) |

Consequently, the volume of the shell is given by the following property.

**Property: Differential of Volume for Cylindrical Shells**

$$dV = \text{(circumference) (altitude) (thickness)}$$

The volume of the solid will be approximately equal to the sum of the volumes of the shells (Figure 8-6c). The exact volume will be the limit of this sum—that is, the definite integral. The innermost shell is at $x = 0$, and the outermost is at $x = 3$. Thus the limits of integration will be from 0 to 3. (The part of the solid from $x = -3$ to $x = 0$ is just the image of the region being rotated, not the region itself.) Example 1 shows the details of calculating the volume of this solid.

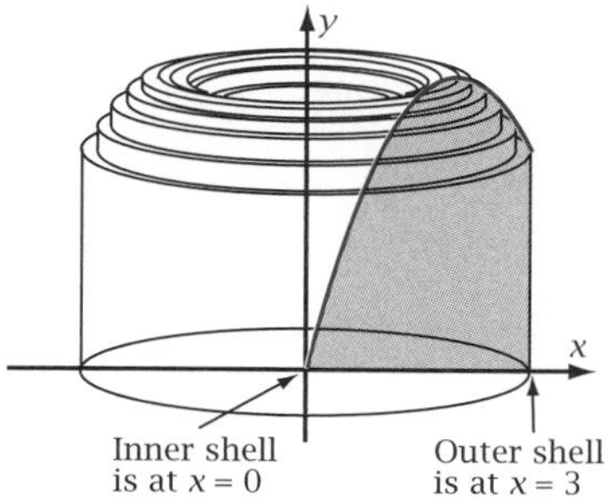


Figure 8-6c

**■ Example 1** The region under the graph of $y = 4x - x^2$ from $x = 0$ to $x = 3$ is rotated about the $y$-axis to form a solid. Find the volume of the solid by slicing into cylindrical shells. Use the fundamental theorem to obtain the exact answer. Show that your answer is reasonable.

**Solution** The volume of a representative cylindrical shell is

$$dV = \text{(circumference) (altitude) (thickness)}$$
$$= (2\pi x)(y)(dx).$$

Recall the rolled-out shell in Figure 8-6b.

Substituting $4x - x^2$ for $y$ gives

$$dV = 2\pi x(4x - x^2)\,dx = 2\pi(4x^2 - x^3)\,dx.$$

The volume is found by adding all the $dV$'s and taking the limit.

$$V = \int_0^3 2\pi(4x^2 - x^3)\,dx$$
$$= 2\pi\left(\tfrac{4}{3}x^3 - \tfrac{1}{4}x^4\right)\Big|_0^3$$
$$= 2\pi\left(36 - \tfrac{81}{4} - 0 + 0\right)$$
$$= 31.5\pi = 98.96\ldots.$$

*Checks:*
Volume of circumscribed cylinder is $\pi(3^2)(4) = 36\pi > 31.5\pi$. ✓
Numerical integration: Integral= $31.5\pi$ ✓ ■

In case you are wondering whether the distortion of the shell as you roll it out flat causes the final answer, $31.5\pi$, to be inaccurate, the answer is, No. As $\Delta x$ approaches zero, so do the inaccuracies in the shell approximation. In Section 11-7, you will learn that if the approximate value of $dV$ differs from the exact value by nothing more than *infinitesimals of higher order*, for instance $(dx)(dy)$, then the integral will give the exact volume.

Cylindrical shells can be used to find volumes when these conditions are encountered.

- The rotation is not around the $y$-axis.
- The axis of rotation is not a bound of integration.
- Both ends of the shell's altitude are variable.

Example 2 shows how this can be done.

**■ Example 2** Let $R$ be the region bounded below by the graph of $y = x^{1/2}$, above by the graph of $y = 2$, and on the left by the graph of $y = x$. Find the volume of the solid generated when R is rotated about the line $y = -1$. Assume that $x$ and $y$ are in feet. Show that your answer is reasonable.

**Solution** First draw the region, as in the left-hand diagram of Figure 8-6d. Find the points of intersection of the graphs. Slice parallel to the axis of rotation. Mark the two resulting sample points as $(x_1, y)$ and $(x_2, y)$. Then rotate the region about the line $y = -1$. As shown in the center diagram of Figure 8-6d, it helps to draw only the back half of the solid. Otherwise the diagram becomes so cluttered it is hard to tell which lines are which. Roll out the shell and find $dV$.

$$dV = \text{(circumference) (altitude) (thickness)}$$
$$= 2\pi(y+1)(x_1 - x_2)\,dy$$

Altitude is always larger value minus smaller value. Radius is the difference between the $y$-values, $y - (-1) = y + 1$.

For the curve $y = x^{1/2}$, solve to get $x_1 = y^2$.
For the line $y = x$, "solve" to get $x_2 = y$.

$$\therefore dV = 2\pi(y+1)(y^2 - y)\,dy$$
$$\therefore V = \pi\int_1^2 2(y+1)(y^2 - y)\,dy$$

Innermost shell is at $y = 1$; outermost shell is at $y = 2$.

$$= 4.5\pi$$

Integrate numerically or algebraically.

$$= 14.1371\ldots \approx 14.1\text{ft}^3$$

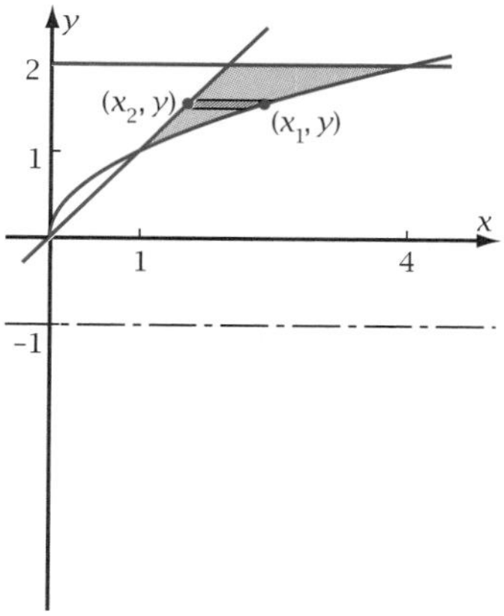


Draw the region. Slice parallel to axis of rotation. Show two sample points.

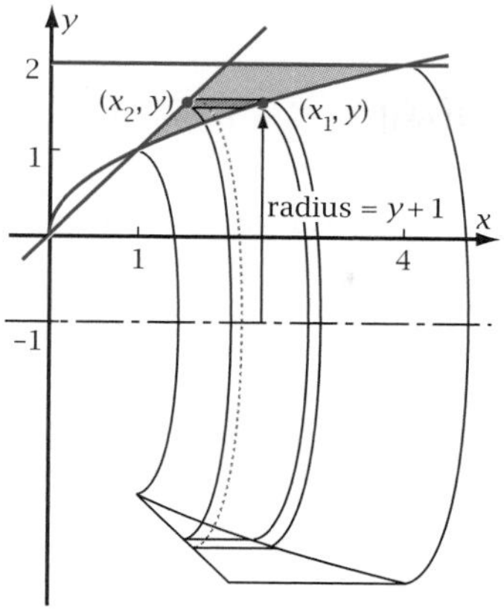


Rotate about the *x*-axis. Show only the back half of the solid. The rotating strip generates the cylindrical shell.

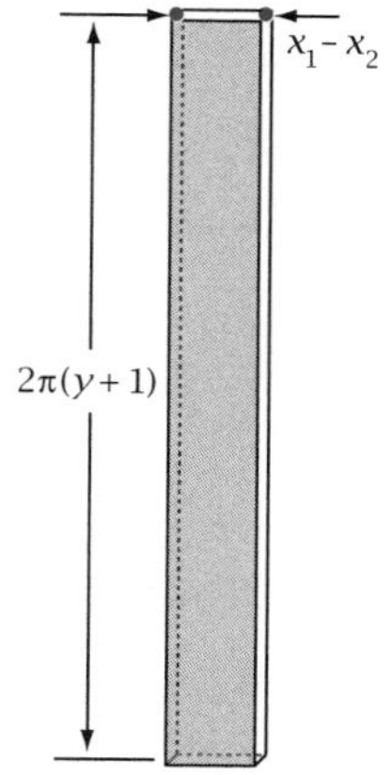


Roll out the (whole) shell into a flat rectangular solid.

Figure 8-6d

*Check:*

Outer cylinder – inner cylinder $= \pi(3^2)(3) - \pi(2^2)(3) = 15\pi > 4.5\pi$ ✓ ■

# Problem Set 8-6

## *Do These Quickly*

The following problems are intended to refresh your skills. You should be able to do all ten problems in less than five minutes.

**Q1.** Sketch the graph: $y = x^2$

**Q2.** Sketch the graph: $y = -x^2$

**Q3.** Sketch the graph: $y = x^{-2}$

**Q4.** Sketch the graph: $y = 2^x$

**Q5.** Sketch the graph: $y = 2^{-x}$

**Q6.** Sketch the graph: $y = 2x$

**Q7.** Sketch the graph: $y = \ln x$

**Q8.** Sketch the graph of a continuous function whose derivative is shown in Figure 8-6e.

**Q9.** $y = x^3 - 3x$ has a local minimum at $x =$ -?-.

**Q10.** $\int \sec^2 x \, dx =$ -?-.

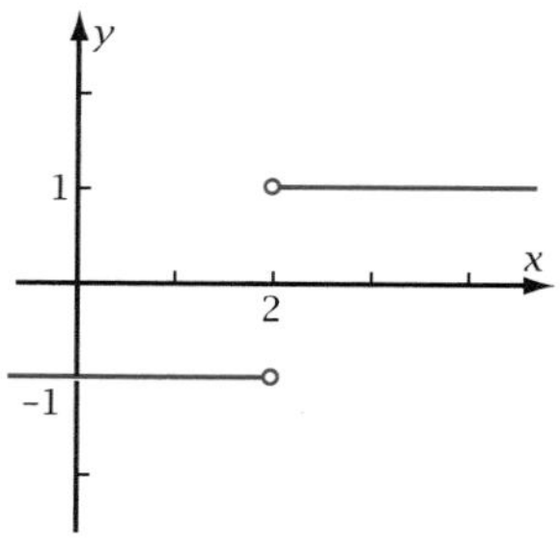


Figure 8-6e

1. Figure 8-6f shows the solid formed by rotating about the $y$-axis the region in Quadrant I under the graph of $y = 4 - x^2$.
   a. Find the volume $dV$ of a cylindrical shell. Transform $dV$ so that it is in terms of one variable.
   b. Find the exact volume of the solid by using the fundamental theorem.
   c. Find the volume again by plane slicing. Use planes perpendicular to the $y$-axis to form slabs of thickness $dy$. Show that you get the same answer as in 1b.

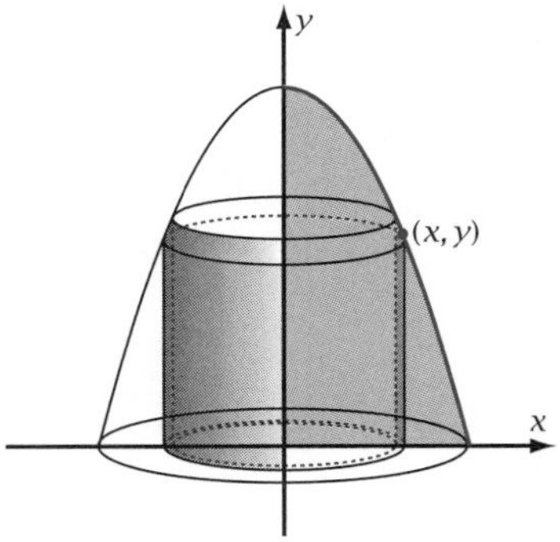


Figure 8-6f

2. Figure 8-6g shows the solid formed by rotating around the $x$-axis the region under the graph of $y = x^{2/3}$ from $x = 0$ to $x = 8$.
   a. What is the altitude of the cylindrical shell in terms of the sample point $(x, y)$?
   b. Find the volume $dV$ of a cylindrical shell. Transform $dV$ so that it is in terms of one variable.
   c. Find the exact volume of the solid using the fundamental theorem.
   d. Find the volume again, by plane slicing. Is the answer the same as in 2c?

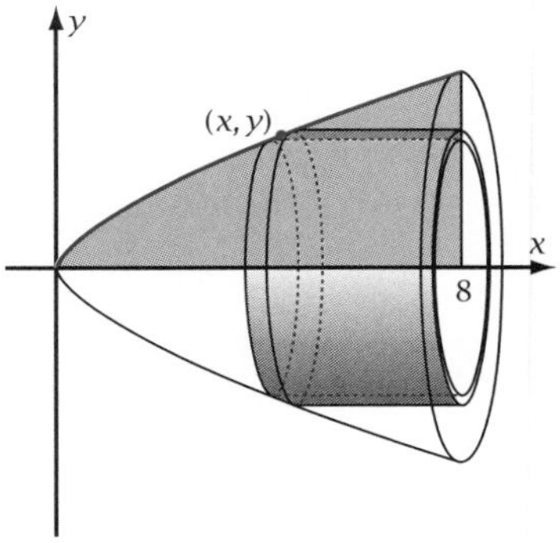


Figure 8-6g

For Problems 3–18, find the volume of the solid by slicing into cylindrical shells. You may use numerical integration. Use familiar geometric relationships to show geometrically that your answer is reasonable.

3. Rotate around the $y$-axis the region under the graph of $y = -x^2 + 4x + 3$ from $x = 1$ to $x = 4$.
4. Rotate around the $y$-axis the region under the graph of $y = x^2 - 8x + 17$ from $x = 2$ to $x = 5$.
5. Rotate about the $x$-axis the region bounded by the $y$-axis and the graph of $x = -y^2 + 6y - 5$.
6. Rotate about the $x$-axis the region bounded by the $y$-axis and the graph of $x = y^2 - 10y + 24$.
7. Rotate around the $y$-axis the region above the graph of $y = x^3$ that is bounded by the lines $x = 1$ and $y = 8$ (Figure 8-6h).

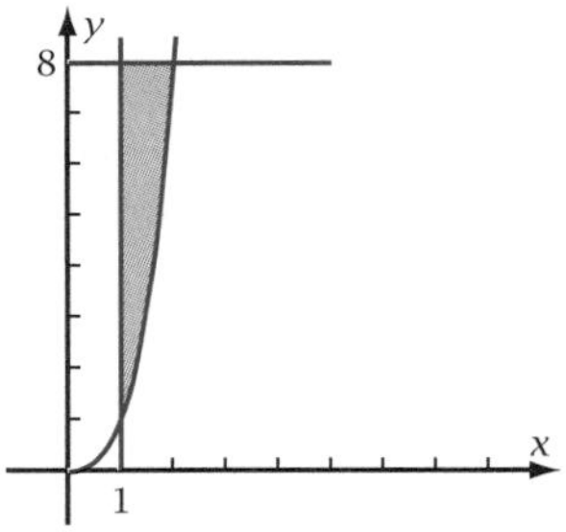


Figure 8-6h

8. Rotate around the $y$-axis the region in Quadrant I above the graph of $y = 1/x$ that is bounded by the lines $y = 4$ and $x = 3$.

9. Rotate around the $x$-axis the region in Quadrant I above the graph of $y = 1/x^2$ that is bounded by the lines $x = 5$ and $y = 4$ (Figure 8-6i).

10. Rotate around the $x$-axis the region in Quadrant I below the graph of $y = x^{2/3}$, above the line $y = 1$ and bounded by the line $x = 8$.

11. Rotate around the $y$-axis the region bounded by the graph of $y = x^2 - 6x + 7$ and the line $x - y = -1$ (Figure 8-6j).

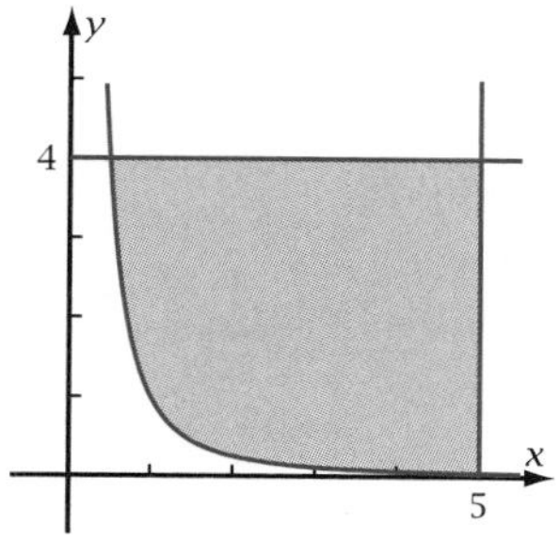


Figure 8-6i

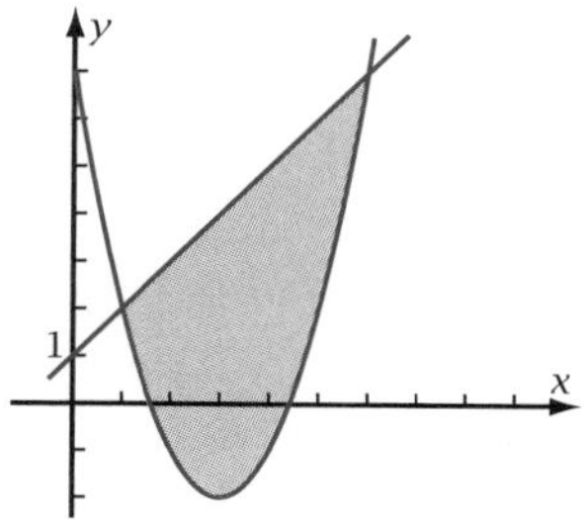


Figure 8-6j

12. Rotate around the $x$-axis the region in Quadrant I bounded by the graph of $y = x^{1/3}$ and the line $y = 0.5x - 2$.

13. Rotate around the line $x = 5$ the region under the graph of $y = x^{3/2}$ from $x = 1$ to $x = 4$ (Figure 8-6k).

14. Rotate around the line $x = 3$ the region under the graph of $y = x^{-2}$ from $x = 1$ to $x = 2$.

15. Rotate around the line $x = 4$ the region bounded by the graph of $y = x^4$ and the line $y = 5x + 6$.

16. Rotate around the line $x = -1$ the region bounded by the graph of $y = \sqrt{x}$ and the lines $x + y = 6$ and $x = 1$.

17. Rotate around the line $x = -2$ the region bounded by the graphs of $y = -x^2 + 4x + 1$ and $y = 1.4^x$ (Figure 8-6l). You will need to find one of the intersections numerically.

18. Rotate about the line $y = -1$ the region in Figure 8-6l from Problem 17. Tell why it would not be appropriate to find the volume of this figure by cylindrical shells.

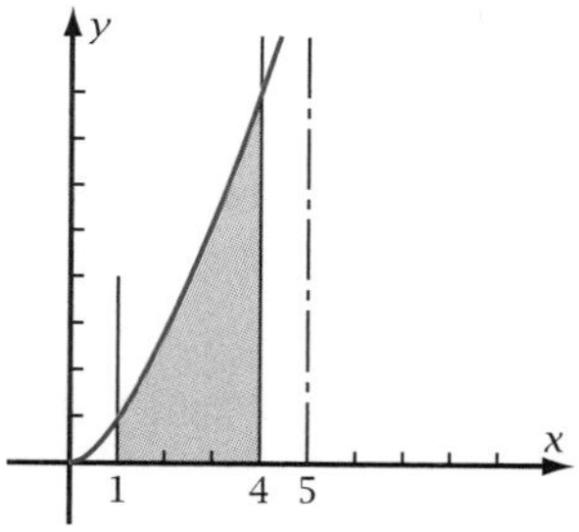


Figure 8-6k

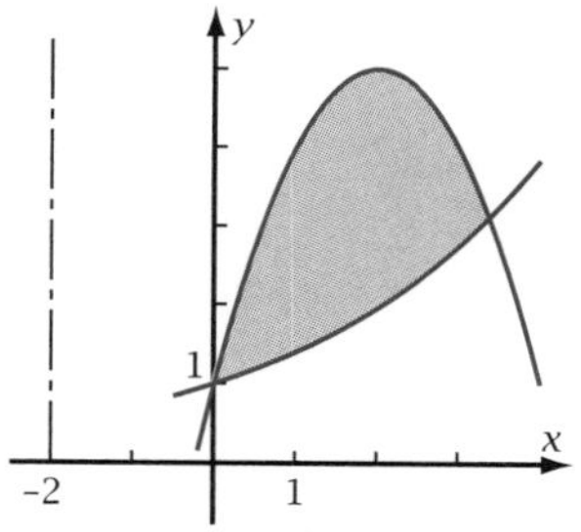


Figure 8-6l

For Problems 19 and 20, find the volume of the solid by slicing into plane slabs, thus verifying the answer obtained by cylindrical shells.

19. Use the solid given in Problem 7.

20. Use the solid given in Problem 8.

21. *Limit of Riemann Sum Problem:* The region under the graph of $y = x^{1/3}$ from $x = 0$ to $x = 8$ is rotated around the $x$-axis to form a solid. Find the volume exactly by slicing into cylindrical shells and using the fundamental theorem. Then find three midpoint Riemann sums for the integral, using $n = 8$, $n = 100$, and $n = 1000$ increments. Show that the Riemann sums approach the exact answer as $n$ increases.

22. *Unknown Integral Problem:* Figure 8-6m shows the region under $y = \sin x$ from $x = 0$ to $x = 2$, rotated about the $y$-axis to form a solid.

    a. Write an integral for the volume of this solid using cylindrical shells. Evaluate the integral numerically.

    b. Explain why the integral cannot be evaluated by the fundamental theorem using the techniques you have learned so far.

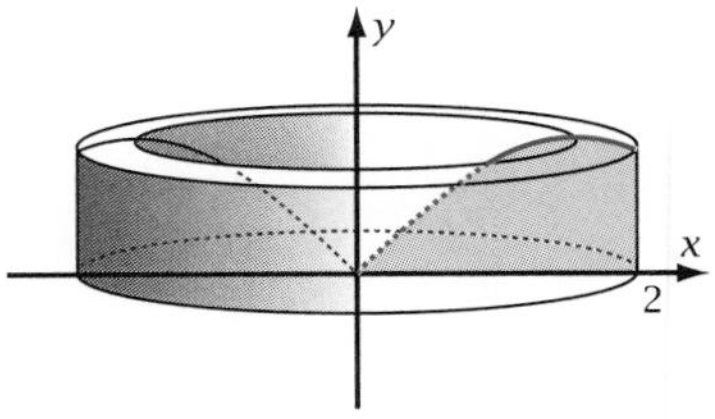

Figure 8-6m

23. *Parametric Curve Problem:* Figure 8-6n shows the ellipse with parametric equations

$$x = 5\cos t$$
$$y = 3\sin t.$$

    a. Slice the region horizontally, then rotate it about the $x$-axis to form an ellipsoid. Find the volume of the ellipsoid by first writing $dV$ in terms of the parameter $t$.

    b. Slice the region vertically, then rotate it about the $x$-axis to form the same ellipsoid. Show that you get the same volume.

    c. Find the volume of the solid generated by rotating the ellipse around the line $x = 7$.

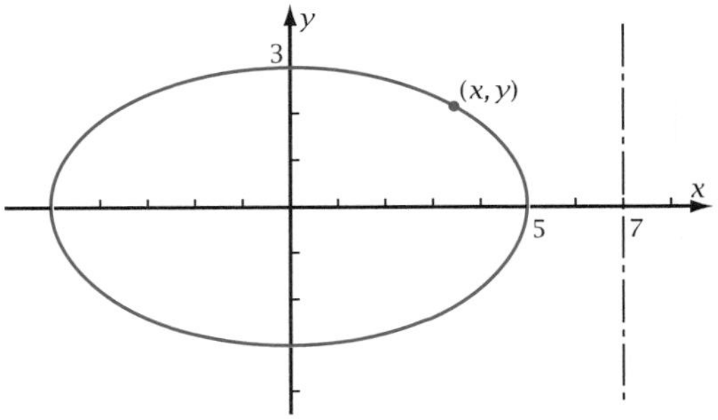

Figure 8-6n

24. *Journal Problem:* Update your journal with things you've learned since the last entry. You should include such things as those listed here.
    - The one most important thing you have learned since the last journal entry
    - The basic concept from geometry that is used to find volumes by calculus
    - The similarities of slicing into disks, washers, and other plane slices
    - The difference between plane slicing and cylindrical shells
    - Any techniques or ideas about finding volumes that are still unclear to you.

# 8-7 Length of a Plane Curve—Arc Length

At the beginning of this chapter you were introduced to the geometry of plane and solid figures, such as the bell-shaped solid shown in Figure 8-7a. You can now find the volume of a solid by plane slices or cylindrical shells and the area of a plane region. In the next two sections you will find the length of a curved line and the area of a curved surface in space.

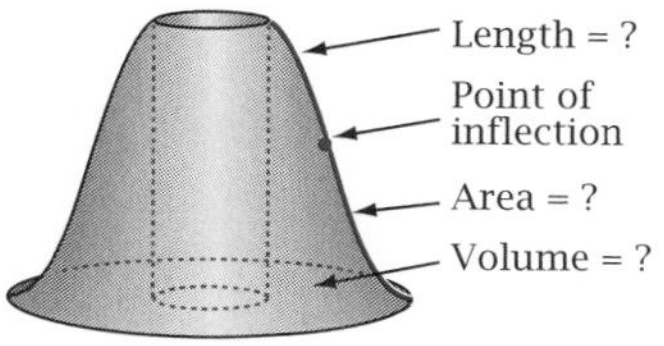


Figure 8-7a

**OBJECTIVE**

Give the equation for a plane curve, find its length approximately by calculating and summing the lengths of the chords, or exactly by calculus.

**■ Example 1** Find approximately the length of the parabola $y = x^2$ from $x = -1$ to $x = 2$ (Figure 8-7b, left).

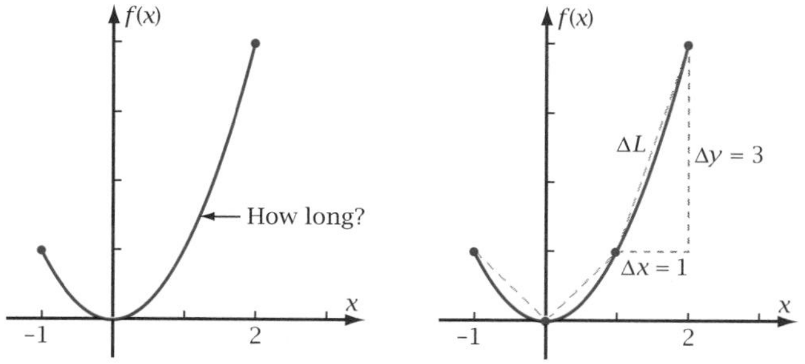


Figure 8-7b

**Solution** The right-hand diagram in Figure 8-7b shows three chords drawn to the graph. The sum of the lengths of the chords is approximately the length of the graph. By the Pythagorean theorem,

$$L \approx \sqrt{2} + \sqrt{2} + \sqrt{10} = 5.990704\ldots \approx 5.99 \text{ units.}$$ Explain why.

■

In general, the length of any one chord will be

$$\Delta L = \sqrt{\Delta x^2 + \Delta y^2}.$$ $\sqrt{\Delta x^2 + \Delta y^2}$ means $\sqrt{(\Delta x)^2 + (\Delta y)^2}$.

Using smaller values of $\Delta x$ (that is, a greater number $n$ of chords), the following is true.

$n = 30:$ $\quad L \approx 6.12417269\ldots$ By the program of Problem 33 in Problem Set 8-7.

$n = 100:$ $\quad L \approx 6.12558677\ldots$

$n = 1000:$ $\quad L \approx 6.12572522\ldots$ The values are approaching a limit!

The limit of the sums of the chord lengths equals the exact length of the curve.

### *Property: Length of a Plane Curve (Arc Length)*

A curve between two points in the $xy$-plane has length

$$L = \lim_{\Delta x \to 0, \Delta y \to 0} \sum \sqrt{\Delta x^2 + \Delta y^2},$$

provided that this limit exists.

The limit of a chord length sum can be found exactly by transforming it to a Riemann sum,

$$\sum g(c)\Delta x.$$

The first thing to do is make the factor $\Delta x$ appear. Although $\Delta x^2$ is not a factor of both terms in the expression $\Delta x^2 + \Delta y^2$, it can still be factored out.

$$\Delta x^2 + \Delta y^2 = \left[1 + \frac{\Delta y^2}{\Delta x^2}\right]\Delta x^2 = \left[1 + \left(\frac{\Delta y}{\Delta x}\right)^2\right]\Delta x^2$$

So a chord length sum can be written

$$\sum \sqrt{\left[1 + \left(\frac{\Delta y}{\Delta x}\right)^2\right]\Delta x^2} = \sum \sqrt{1 + \left(\frac{\Delta y}{\Delta x}\right)^2}\,\Delta x.$$

The remaining radicand contains $\Delta y/\Delta x$, which you should recognize as the difference quotient that approaches $f'(x)$ as $\Delta x$ approaches zero. In fact, if $f$ is a differentiable function, the mean value theorem tells you that there is a number $x = c$ within the interval where $f'(c)$ is exactly equal to $\Delta y/\Delta x$ (Figure 8-7c). So a chord length sum can be written

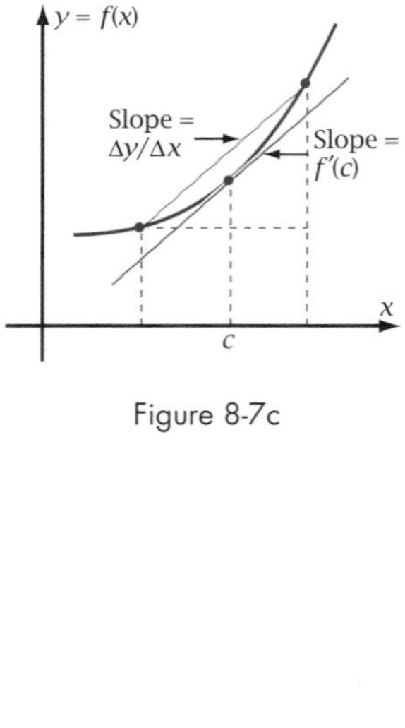


Figure 8-7c

$$\sum \sqrt{1 + f'(c)^2}\,\Delta x,$$

where the sample points, $x = c$, are chosen at a point in each subinterval where the conclusion of the mean value theorem is true. The length $L$ of the curve is thus the limit of a Riemann sum and hence a definite integral.

$$L = \int_a^b \sqrt{1 + f'(x)^2}\,dx$$ The *exact* length of the curve!

The quantity $dL = \sqrt{1 + f'(x)^2}\,dx$, the differential of curve length (often called "arc length"), can be written in a form that is easier to remember and use. Recalling that $f'(x) = dy/dx$, and that the differentials $dy$ and $dx$ can be written as separate quantities, you can write

$$dL = \sqrt{1 + \left(\frac{dy}{dx}\right)^2}\, dx, \text{ or, more simply,}$$

$$dL = \sqrt{dx^2 + dy^2}.$$

Differential of arc length.

It is easy to remember $dL$ in the last form above because it looks like the Pythagorean theorem. There are also some algebraic advantages of this form, as you will see in later examples.

**Example 2** Write an integral to find the exact length of the curve in Example 1 and evaluate it.

**Solution**

$$y = x^2 \Rightarrow dy = 2x\,dx$$

$$\therefore dL = \sqrt{dx^2 + (2x\,dx)^2} = \sqrt{1 + 4x^2}\,dx$$

$$\therefore L = \int_{-1}^{2} \sqrt{1 + 4x^2}\,dx$$

When you study trigonometric substitution in Chapter 9, you will be able to evaluate integrals like this using the fundamental theorem. Numerical integration gives

6.1257266....

Equations for more complex curves can be written in parametric form. Example 3 shows how this can be done.

**Example 3** The ellipse in Figure 8-7d has parametric equations

$$x = 6 + 5\cos t$$

$$y = 4 + 3\sin t.$$

Write an integral equal to the length of the graph and evaluate it numerically. Check your answer for reasonability.

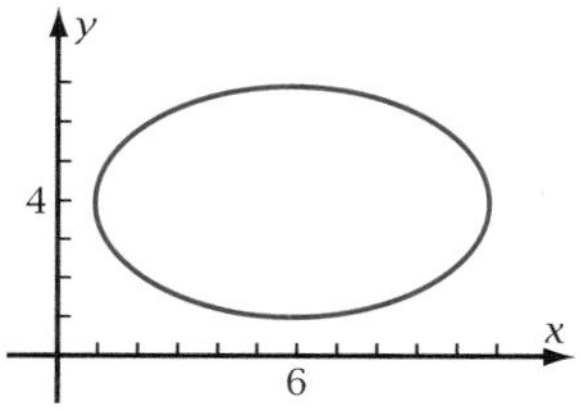


Figure 8-7d

**Solution**

$$x = 6 + 5\cos t \Rightarrow dx = -5\sin t\,dt$$

$$y = 4 + 3\sin t \Rightarrow dy = 3\cos t\,dt$$

$$dL = \sqrt{dx^2 + dy^2}$$

$$= \sqrt{(-5\sin t\,dt)^2 + (3\cos t\,dt)^2}$$

$$= \sqrt{25\sin^2 t + 9\cos^2 t}\,dt$$

Explain the "$dt$."

$$L = \int_0^{2\pi} \sqrt{25\sin^2 t + 9\cos^2 t}\,dt$$

$$\approx \underline{25.52699...}$$

*Check:* A circle of radius 4 has length $2\pi \cdot 4 = 25.13274....$ ✓

The indefinite integral in Example 3 cannot be evaluated using any of the elementary functions. It is called an *elliptic integral*, which you may study in later courses.

Occasionally a curve length problem will involve an integral that can be evaluated by the fundamental theorem. Example 4 shows one instance.

**Example 4** Plot the graph of $y = \frac{2}{3}x^{3/2}$. Find exactly the length from $x = 0$ to $x = 9$.

**Solution** The graph is shown in Figure 8-7e. It starts at the origin and rises gently to the point (9, 18).

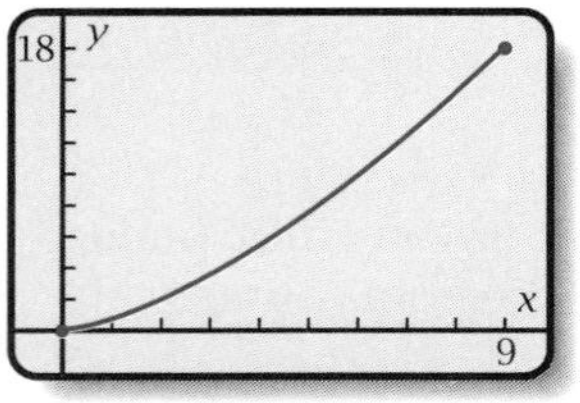


Figure 8-7e

$$dy = x^{1/2}\,dx$$
$$dL = \sqrt{dx^2 + dy^2}$$
$$= \sqrt{dx^2 + (x^{1/2}\,dx)^2}$$
$$= \sqrt{1+x}\,dx$$
$$L = \int_0^9 \sqrt{1+x}\,dx = \int_0^9 (1+x)^{1/2}\,dx$$
$$= \tfrac{2}{3}(1+x)^{3/2}\Big|_0^9 = \tfrac{2}{3}(10^{3/2}) - \tfrac{2}{3}(1^{3/2})$$
$$= \tfrac{2}{3}(10^{3/2} - 1) \quad \text{Exact length.}$$
$$= 20.41518\ldots \quad \text{Approximation for exact length.}$$

## Problem Set 8-7

### *Do These Quickly*

The following problems are intended to refresh your skills. You should be able to do all ten problems in less than five minutes.

**Q1.** Sketch: $y = x^2$

**Q2.** Show the region under $y = x^2$ from $x = 1$ to $x = 4$.

**Q3.** Write an integral for the area of the region in Problem Q2.

**Q4.** Do the integration in Problem Q3.

**Q5.** Evaluate the integral in Problem Q4.

**Q6.** Sketch the solid generated by rotating the region in Problem Q2 about the $y$-axis.

**Q7.** Write an integral for the volume of the solid in Problem Q6.

**Q8.** Do the integration indicated in Problem Q7.

**Q9.** Evaluate the integral in Problem Q8.

**Q10.** Figure 8-7f illustrates the —?— theorem.

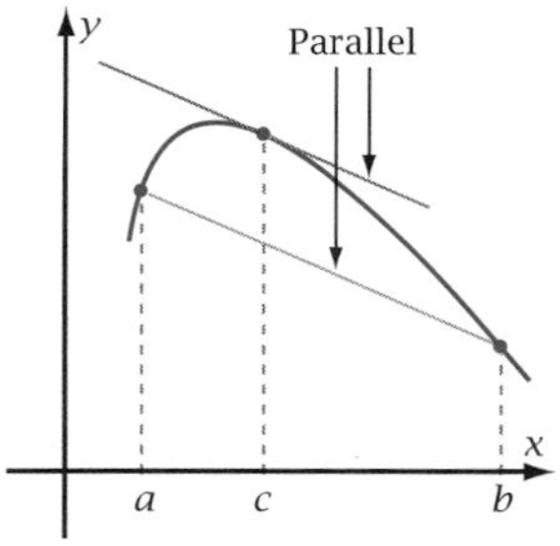


Figure 8-7f

For Problems 1–4,

a. Sketch the graph for $x$ in the given interval.

b. Find its approximate length using five chords with equal values of $\Delta x$.

c. Find its length more precisely using a definite integral evaluated numerically.

1. $y = e^x \quad x \in [0,\ 2]$

2. $y = 2^x \quad x \in [0,\ 3]$

3. $y = \tan x \quad x \in [0,\ 1.5]$

4. $y = \sec x \quad x \in [0,\ 1.5]$

For Problems 5–16,

a. Plot the graph for $x$ in the given interval. Sketch the result.

b. Find the approximate length using a definite integral evaluated numerically.

c. Show that your answer is reasonable.

5. $y = x^2 - 5x + 3 \quad x \in [1,\ 6]$

6. $y = 4x - x^2 \quad x \in [0,\ 4]$

7. $y = 16 - x^4 \quad x \in [-1,\ 2]$

8. $y = x^3 - 9x^2 + 5x + 50 \quad x \in [-1,\ 9]$

9. $y = (\ln x)^2 \quad x \in [0.1,\ e]$

10. $y = x \sin x \quad x \in [0,\ 4\pi]$

11. $y = \tan x \quad x \in [0,\ 1.5]$

12. $y = \sec x \quad x \in [0,\ 1.5]$

13. Astroid: $t \in [0,\ 2\pi]$
$x = 5\cos^3 t$
$y = 5\sin^3 t$

14. Cardioid: $t \in [0, 2\pi]$
$x = 5(2\cos t - \cos 2t)$
$y = 5(2\sin t - \sin 2t)$

15. Epicycloid: $t \in [0, 2\pi]$
$x = 5\cos t - \cos 5t$
$y = 5\sin t - \sin 5t$

16. Involute of a circle: $t \in [0,\ 4\pi]$
$x = \cos t + t\sin t$
$y = \sin t - t\cos t$

For Problems 17–20,

a. Plot the graph for $x$ in the given interval. Sketch the result.

b. Find the exact length using a definite integral evaluated by the fundamental theorem.

c. Show that your answer is reasonable. (For Problem 19, find a common denominator under the radical sign.)

17. $y = 4x^{3/2} \quad x \in [0,\ 4]$

18. $y = \dfrac{x^3}{12} + \dfrac{1}{x} \quad x \in [1,\ 2]$

19. $y = 3x^{2/3} + 5 \quad x \in [1,\ 8]$

20. $\frac{1}{3}(x^2 + 2)^{3/2} \quad x \in [0,\ 3]$

21. *Golden Gate Bridge Problem:* The photograph shows the Golden Gate Bridge across San Francisco Bay in California. The center span of the bridge is about 4200 ft long. The suspension cables hang in parabolic arcs from towers about 750 ft above the water's surface. These cables come as close as 220 ft to the water at the center of the span. Use this information to write an equation of the particular quadratic function expressing the distance of the cables from the water as a function of the horizontal displacement from center span. Use the equation to calculate the length of the parabolic cable.

22. *Chain Problem:* When a chain hangs under its own weight, its shape is a **catenary** (which comes from the Latin word for "chain"). Figure 8-7g shows a catenary with its vertex on the $y$-axis. Its equation is

$$y = 0.2(e^x + e^{-x}),$$

where $x$ and $y$ are in feet. Find the length of this chain from $x = -4$ to $x = 4$. How does this length compare with that of a parabola,

$$y = ax^2 + c,$$

which has the same vertex and endpoints?

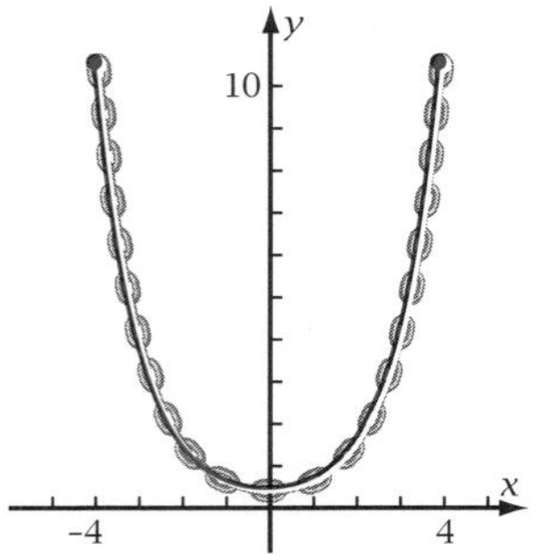

Figure 8-7g

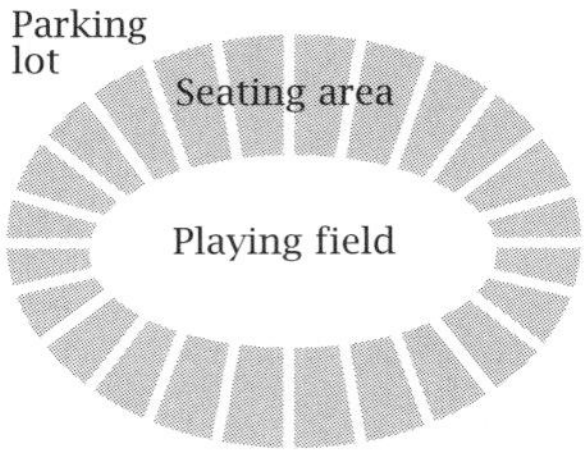

Figure 8-7h

23. *Stadium Problem:* Figure 8-7h shows the seating area for a sports stadium. The ellipses have the following parametric equations.

| Outer Ellipse: | Inner Ellipse: |
|---|---|
| $x = 120\cos t$ | $x = 100\cos t$ |
| $y = 100\sin t$ | $y = 50\sin t$ |

Both $x$ and $y$ are in meters. Find the lengths of the boundaries between the outer ellipse and the parking lot, and between the inner ellipse and the playing field.

24. *Parabola Surprise Problem!* A parabola has parametric equations

$$x = 8\cos 2t$$
$$y = 5\sin t.$$

Find the length from $t = 0$ to $t = 2\pi$. Why does the answer seem unreasonably high?

25. *Implicit Relation Problem I:* Use the fundamental theorem to find exactly the length of the graph of $9x^2 = 4y^3$ between the points $(0, 0)$ and $(2\sqrt{3}, 3)$. Consider $y$ to be the independent variable.

26. *Implicit Relation Problem II:* Use the fundamental theorem to find exactly the length of the semicubical parabola $x^2 = y^3$ between the points $(-1, 1)$ and $(8, 4)$. Consider $y$ to be the independent variable. You will have to break the graph into two branches (sketch a graph).

27. *Spiral Problem:* Figure 8-7i shows the spiral whose parametric equations are

$$x = \frac{t}{\pi}\cos t$$
$$y = \frac{t}{\pi}\sin t.$$

What range of $t$ generates the part of the spiral shown in the figure? Find the length of the spiral by the fundamental theorem if you can, or by numerical methods.

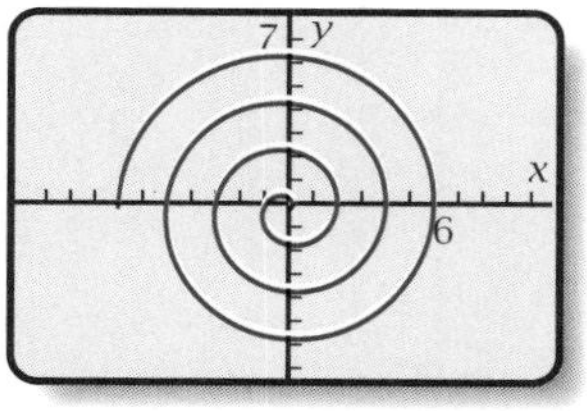

Figure 8-7i

28. *Length of a Circle Problem:* Write parametric equations for a circle of radius $r$ centered at the origin. Then use appropriate algebra, trigonometry, and calculus to prove the familiar circumference formula $C = 2\pi r$.

29. *Sinusoid Length Investigation Problem:* Write an integral for the length of one cycle of the sinusoid of constant amplitude $A$,

$$y = A \sin x.$$

Find lengths of the sinusoid for various values of $A$. From the results of your work, try to reach a conclusion about how the length varies with $A$. For instance, does doubling $A$ double the length?

30. *Ellipse Length Investigation Problem:* Write an integral for the length of the ellipse

$$x = \cos t$$
$$y = A \sin t.$$

Find lengths of the ellipse for various values of $A$. From the results of your work, try to reach a conclusion about how the length varies with $A$. For instance, does doubling $A$ double the length?

31. *Fatal Error Problem:* Mae Danerror wants to find the length of $y = (x - 2)^{-1}$ from $x = 1$ to $x = 3$. She partitions [1, 3] into five equal subintervals, and gets 18.2774 ... for the length. Explain to Mae why she has made a fatal error in her approach to the problem.

32. *Mistake Problem:* Amos Take finds the length of the curve $y = \sin 2\pi x$ from $x = 0$ to $x = 10$ by dividing the interval [0, 10] into 5 subintervals of equal length. He gets an answer of exactly 10. Feeling he may have made a mistake, he tries again with 20 subintervals, and gets the same answer, 10. Show Amos that he did make a mistake. Show him how he can get a quite accurate answer using only 5 subintervals.

33. *Program for Arc Length by Brute Force:* Write a program to calculate the approximate length of a curve by summing the lengths of the chords. The equation for the function can be stored in the $y=$ menu. The program should allow you to input the lower and upper bounds of the domain and the number of increments to be used. The output should be the approximate length of the curve. To make the program more entertaining to run, you might have it display the increment number and the current sum of the lengths at each pass through the loop. You may assume that your program is working correctly if it gives 6.12417269 ... for the length of $y = x^2$ from $x = -1$ to $x = 2$ (Example 1) with $n = 30$ increments.

# 8-8 Area of a Surface of Revolution

Suppose that the graph of a function $y = f(x)$ is rotated around the $x$-axis. The result will be a surface in space (Figure 8-8a, left). You are to find the area of the surface.

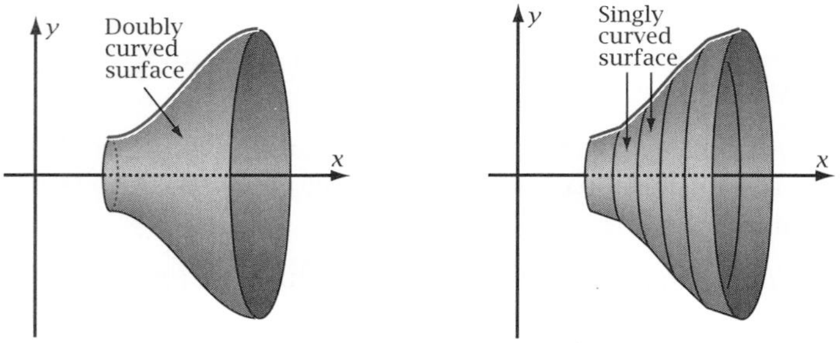


Rotate a curved graph, get a doubly curved surface.

Rotate (straight) chords, get singly curved surfaces.

Figure 8-8a

A graph curved in one direction that rotates in another direction forms a **doubly curved** surface. Like a map of the Earth, a doubly curved surface cannot be flattened out. But if you draw chords on the graph as you did for finding arc length, the rotating chords generate singly curved **frustums of cones**, as shown in the right-hand diagram in Figure 8-8a. The frustums can be flattened (Figure 8-8b), allowing you to find their areas by geometry.

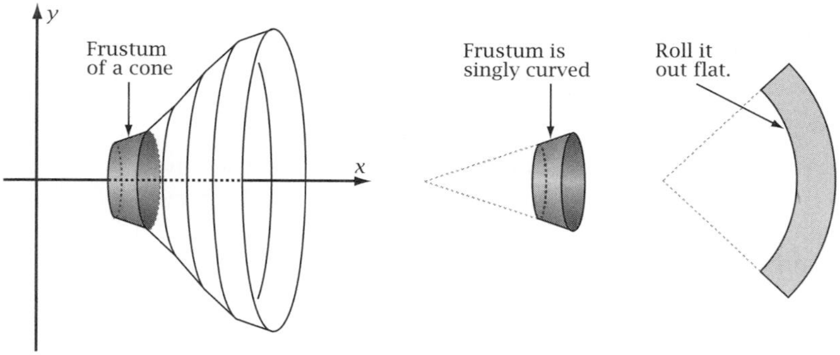


Rotated chords form frustums of cones.

One of the frustums.

A singly curved surface can be rolled out flat.

Figure 8-8b

**OBJECTIVE**

Find the area of a surface of revolution by slicing the surface into frustums of cones.

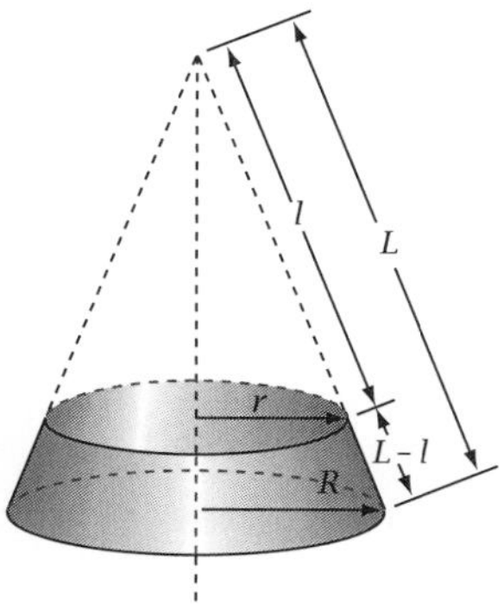


Figure 8-8c

The surface area of a cone is $S = \pi RL$, where $R$ is the base radius, and $L$ is the slant height (Figure 8-8c). The area of a frustum is the area of the big cone minus the area of the small one; that is,

$$S = \pi RL - \pi rl,$$

where $R$ and $L$ are for the large cone and $r$ and $l$ are for the small one. By clever algebra (which you will be asked to do in Problem 26), this equation can be transformed to

$$S = 2\pi\left(\frac{R+r}{2}\right)(L - l).$$

The quantity $(R + r)/2$ is the average of the two radii. The quantity $(L - l)$ is the slant height of the frustum. It is the same as $Dl$ in the arc length problems of Section 8-8. So the differential of surface area, $dS$, is

$$dS = 2\pi \text{ (average radius)(slant height)} = 2\pi \text{ (average radius) } dL.$$

Note that $2\pi$(average radius) equals the distance traveled by the midpoint of the chord as the chord rotates around.

**Property: Area of a Surface of Revolution**

If $y$ is a differentiable function of $x$, then the area of the surface formed by rotating the graph of the function around an axis is

$$S = \int_a^b \text{(circumference)}\, dL = 2\pi \int_a^b \text{(radius)}\, dL,$$

where $dL = \sqrt{dx^2 + dy^2}$ and $a$ and $b$ are the $x$- or $y$-coordinates of the endpoints of the graph.

The radius must be found from information about the surface.

**Example 1** The graph of $y = \sin x$ from $x = 1$ to $x = 3$ is rotated around various axes to form surfaces. Find the area of the surface if the graph is rotated about

a. the $y$-axis

b. the line $y = 2$

Show that your answers are reasonable.

**Solution**

a. Figure 8-8d shows the surface for the graph rotated around the $y$-axis.

$$dy = \cos x\, dx$$

$$\sqrt{dx^2 + \cos^2 x\, dx^2} = \sqrt{1 + \cos^2 x}\, dx$$

Radius $= x$, so

$$dS = 2\pi x\sqrt{1 + \cos^2 x}\, dx.$$

$$\therefore S = 2\pi \int_1^3 x\sqrt{1 + \cos^2 x}\, dx.$$

By numerical integration,

$$S \approx 9.5111282\ldots\pi = 29.88009\ldots.$$

As a check on this answer, consider the area of a flat washer of radii 1 and 3 (Figure 8-8e). Its area is

$$\pi(3^2 - 1^2) = 25.132\ldots.$$

So the 29.88 ... answer is reasonable.

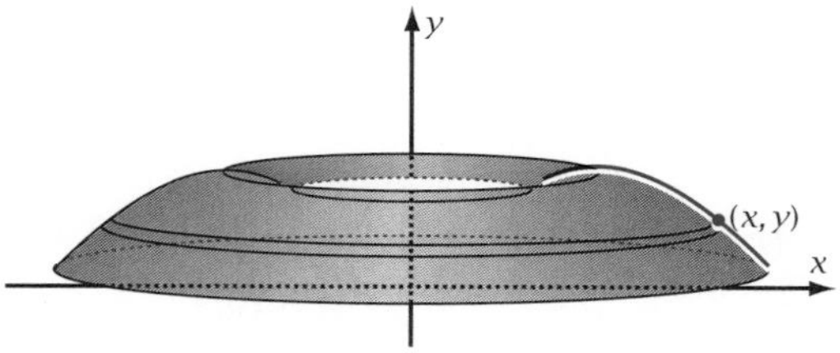

Figure 8-8d

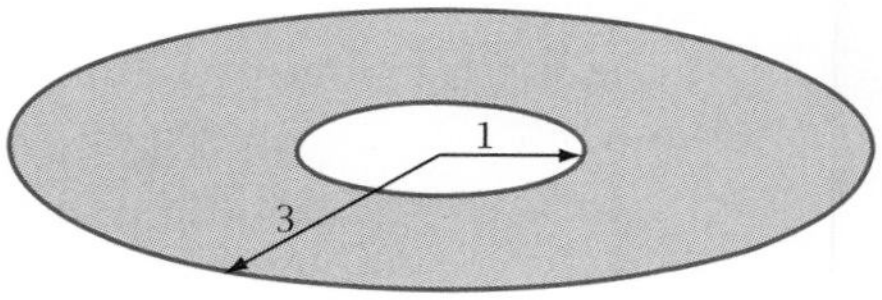

Figure 8-8e

b. Figure 8-8f shows the surface for rotation around $y = 2$. Note that $dL$ is the same as in part a. Only the radius is different.

$$\text{radius} = 2 - y = 2 - \sin x$$

So the surface area is

$$S = 2\pi \int_1^3 (2 - \sin x)\sqrt{1 + \cos^2 x}\, dx.$$

By numerical integration,

$$S \approx 5.836945\ldots\pi = 18.337304\ldots.$$

As a reasonability check, the answer should be a bit more than a cylinder of altitude 2 and radius 1 (Figure 8-8g). That area is

$$2\pi(1^2)(2) = 12.566\ldots,$$

which is in the ballpark.

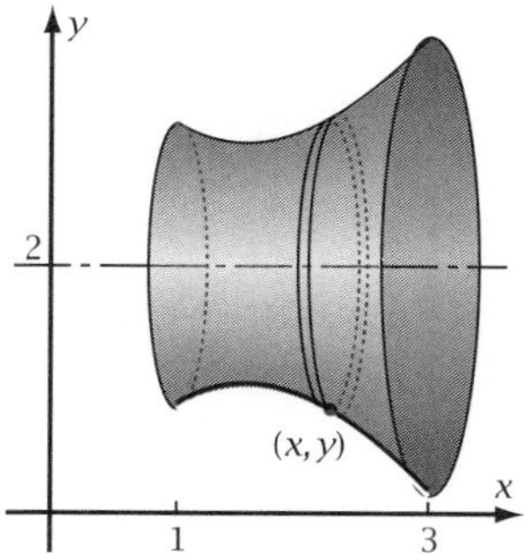

Figure 8-8f

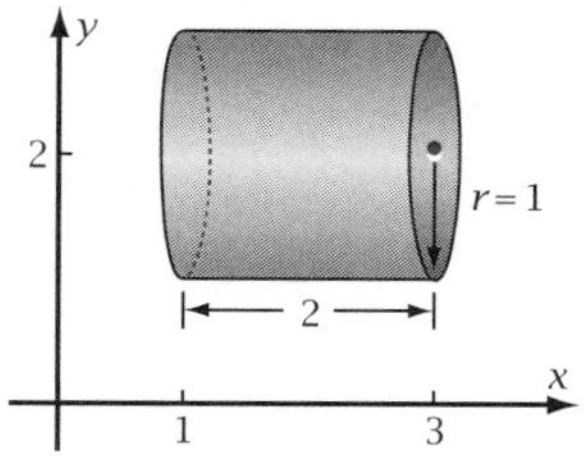

Figure 8-8g

## Problem Set 8-8

### *Do These Quickly*

The following problems are intended to refresh your skills. You should be able to do all ten problems in less than five minutes.

**Q1.** If $y = x^3$, then $dL$ (arc length) = -?-.

**Q2.** If $y = \tan x$, then $dL$ = -?-.

**Q3.** $\int \sin^5 x \cos x \, dx$ = -?-.

**Q4.** $\int_1^5 x^3 \, dx$ = -?-.

**Q5.** If $y = x e^x$, then $y'$ = -?-.

**Q6.** The maximum of $y = x^2 - 8x + 14$ on the interval [1, 6] is -?-.

**Q7.** If $\lim U_n = \lim L_n$ for function $f$, then $f$ is -?-.

**Q8.** Write the definition of derivative.

**Q9.** Write the physical meaning of derivative.

**Q10.** $\int \sec 2x \, dx$ = -?-.

1. *Paraboloid Problem:* A paraboloid is formed by rotating around the $y$-axis the graph of $y = 0.5x^2$ from $x = 0$ to $x = 3$.
   a. Write an integral for the area of the paraboloid. Evaluate it numerically.
   b. Show that your answer is reasonable by comparing it with suitable geometric figures.
   c. The indefinite integral in 1a is relatively easy to evaluate. Do so, and thus find the exact area. Show that your answer in 1a is close to the exact answer.

2. *Rotated Sinusoid Problem:* One arch of the graph of $y = \sin x$ is rotated around the $x$-axis to form a football-shaped surface.
   a. Sketch the surface.
   b. Write an integral equal to the area of the surface. Evaluate it numerically.
   c. Show that your answer is reasonable by comparing it with suitable geometric figures.

3. *Ln-Curved Surface, Problem I:* The graph of $y = \ln x$ from $x = 1$ to $x = 3$ is rotated around the $x$-axis to form a surface. Find the area of the surface.

4. *Ln-Curved Surface, Problem II:* The graph of $y = \ln x$ from $x = 1$ to $x = 3$ is rotated around the $y$-axis to form a surface. Find the area of the surface.

5. *Reciprocal Curved Surface Problem I:* The graph of $y = 1/x$ from $x = 0.5$ to $x = 2$ is rotated around the $y$-axis to form a surface. Find its area.

6. *Reciprocal Curved Surface Problem II:* The graph of $y = 1/x$ from $x = 0.5$ to $x = 2$ is rotated around the $x$-axis to form a surface. Find its area. How does this answer compare with that in Problem 5?

7. *Cubic Paraboloid Problem I:* The cubic paraboloid $y = x^3$ from $x = 0$ to $x = 2$ is rotated around the $y$-axis to form a cuplike surface. Find the area of the surface.

8. *Cubic Paraboloid Problem II:* The part of the cubic parabola

$$y = -x^3 + 5x^2 - 8x + 6$$

in Quadrant I is rotated about the $y$-axis to form a surface. Find the area of the surface.

For Problems 9–16, write an integral equal to the area of the surface. Evaluate it exactly, using the fundamental theorem. Find a decimal approximation for the exact area.

9. $y = \sqrt{x}$, from $x = 0$ to $x = 1$, around the $x$-axis
10. $y = x^3$, from $x = 1$ to $x = 2$, around the $x$-axis
11. $y = \dfrac{x^4}{8} + \dfrac{x^{-2}}{4}$, from $x = 1$ to $x = 2$, around the $x$-axis
12. $y = x^2$, from $x = 0$ to $x = 2$, around the $y$-axis
13. $y = \frac{1}{3}(x^2 + 2)^{3/2}$, from $x = 0$ to $x = 3$, around the $y$-axis
14. $y = 2x^{1/3}$, from $x = 1$ to $x = 8$, around the $y$-axis
15. $y = \dfrac{x^3}{3} + \dfrac{1}{4x}$, from $x = 1$ to $x = 3$, around the line $y = -1$
16. $y = \dfrac{x^3}{3} + \dfrac{1}{4x}$, from $x = 1$ to $x = 3$, around the line $x = 4$
17. *Sphere Zone Problem:* The circle with equation $x^2 + y^2 = 25$ is rotated around the $x$-axis to form a sphere (Figure 8-8h).

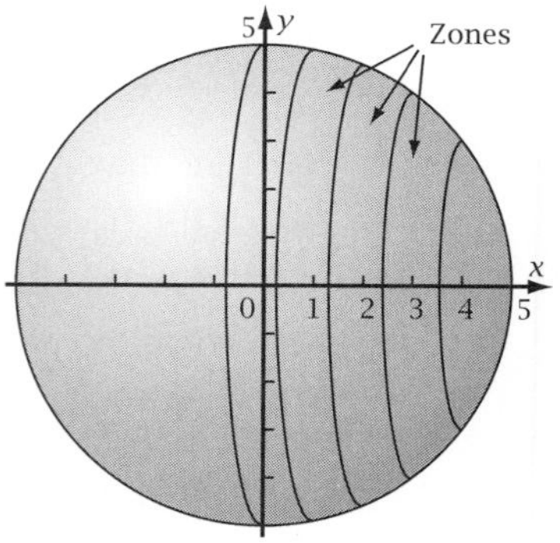


Figure 8-8h

   a. Slice the sphere with planes perpendicular to the $x$-axis. Write the differential of surface area, $dS$, in terms of $x$.
   b. Find the area of the zone between
      i. $x = 0$ and $x = 1$
      ii. $x = 1$ and $x = 2$
      iii. $x = 2$ and $x = 3$
      iv. $x = 3$ and $x = 4$
      v. $x = 4$ and $x = 5$
   c. As you progress from the center of a sphere toward a pole, you would expect the areas of zones of equal altitude to decrease because their radii are decreasing, but also to increase because their arc lengths are increasing (Figure 8-8i). From the results of 17b, which of these two opposing features seems to predominate in the case of a sphere?

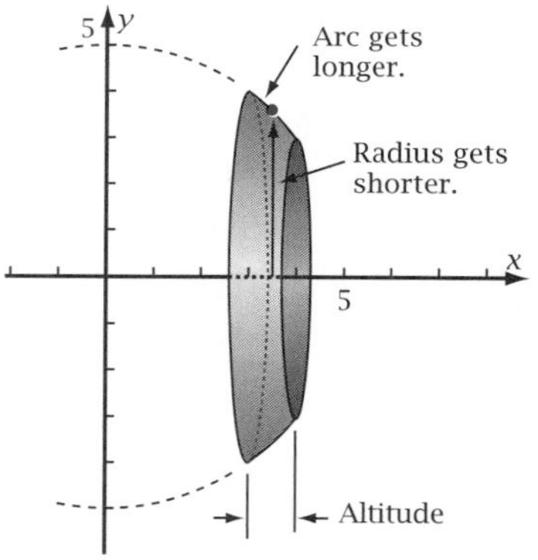


Figure 8-8i

18. *Sphere Total Area Formula Problem:* Prove that the surface area of a sphere of radius $r$ is given by $S = 4\pi r^2$.
19. *Sphere Volume and Surface Problem:* The volume of a sphere may be found by slicing it into **spherical shells** (Figure 8-8j). If the shell is thin, its volume is approximately equal to its surface area times its thickness. The approximation becomes exact as the thickness of the shell approaches zero. Use the area formula in Problem 18 to derive the volume formula for a sphere,

$$V = \tfrac{4}{3}\pi r^3.$$

20. *Sphere Rate of Change of Volume Problem:* Prove that the instantaneous rate of change of the volume of a sphere with respect to its radius is equal to the sphere's surface area.

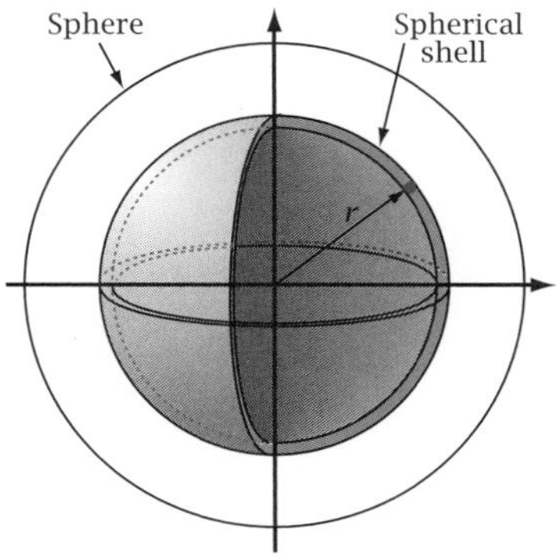


Figure 8-8j

21. *Paraboloid Surface Area Problem:* Figure 8-8k shows the paraboloid formed by rotating around the $y$-axis the graph of a parabola $y = ax^2$. Derive a formula for the surface area of a paraboloid in terms of its base radius $r$ and the constant $a$ in the equation.

22. *Zone of a Paraboloid Problem:* Zones of equal altitude on a sphere have equal areas (Problem 17). Is this property also true for a paraboloid (Figure 8-8k)? If so, support your conclusion with appropriate evidence. If not, does the area increase or decrease as you move away from the vertex?

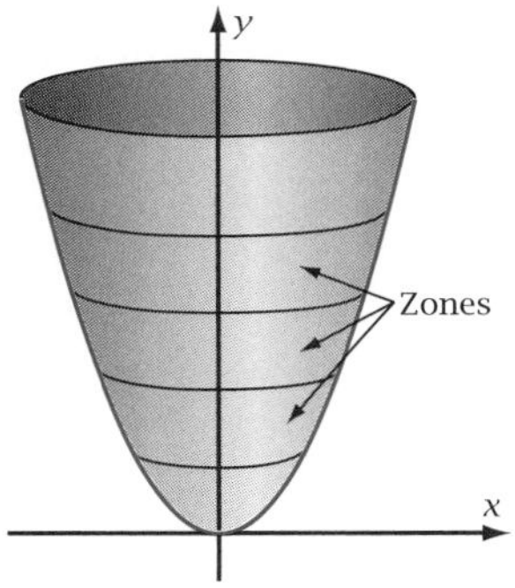


Figure 8-8k

23. *Ellipsoid Problem:* The ellipse, with $x$-radius 5 and $y$-radius 3 and parametric equations

$$x = 5\cos t$$
$$y = 3\sin t,$$

is rotated around the $x$-axis to form an ellipsoid (a football-shaped surface). Write an integral for the surface area of the ellipsoid and evaluate it numerically. Show why the Cartesian equation $(x/5)^2 + (y/3)^2 = 1$ for the same ellipsoid would be difficult to use because of what happens to $dL$ at the end of the ellipsoid, at $x = 5$.

24. *Cooling Tower Problem:* Cooling towers for some power plants are made in the shape of hyperboloids of one sheet (see photograph). This shape is picked because it can be made using all straight reinforcing rods. A framework is made, then concrete is applied to form a relatively thin shell that is quite strong, yet has no structure inside to get in the way. In this problem you will find the area of such a cooling tower.

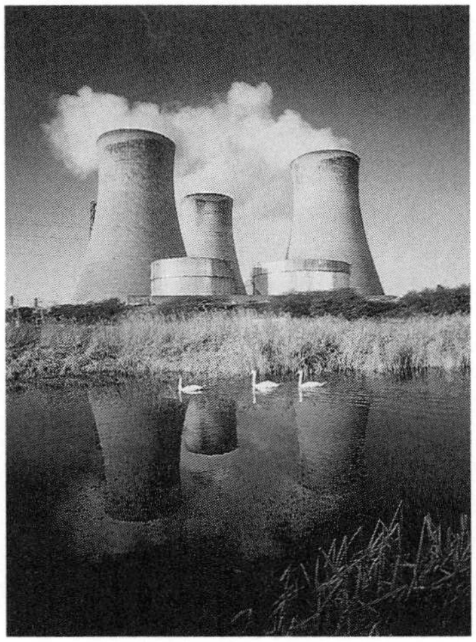

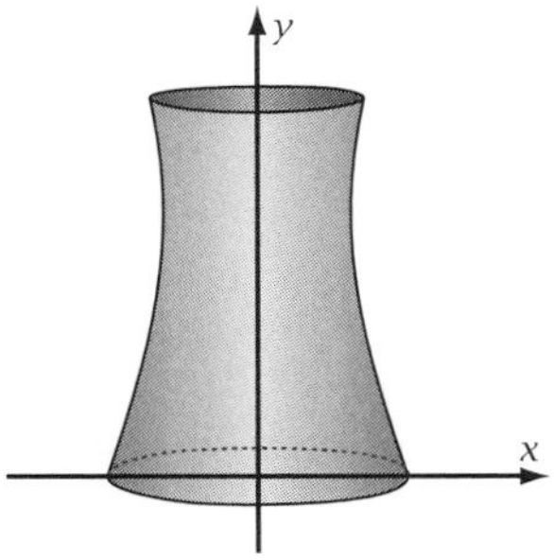


Figure 8-8l

The cooling tower depicted in Figure 8-8l is formed by rotating about the $y$-axis the hyperbola with the parametric equations

$$x = 35\sec t$$
$$y = 100 + 80\tan t,$$

where $x$ and $y$ are in feet.

a. The hyperbola starts at $y = 0$. What is the radius of the hyperboloid at its bottom?

b. The hyperbola stops where $t = 0.5$. What is the radius at the top of the hyperboloid? How tall is the cooling tower?

c. What is the radius of the cooling tower at its narrowest? How high up does this narrowest point come?

d. Find the surface area of the hyperboloid.

e. The walls of the cooling tower are to be 4 in. thick. Approximately how many cubic yards of concrete will be needed to build the tower?

25. *Lateral Area of a Cone Problem:* Figure 8-8m shows a cone of radius $R$ and slant height $L$. The cone is a singly curved surface, so it can be cut and rolled out into a plane surface that is a sector of a circle. Show that the area of the lateral surface of a cone is

$$S = \pi RL.$$

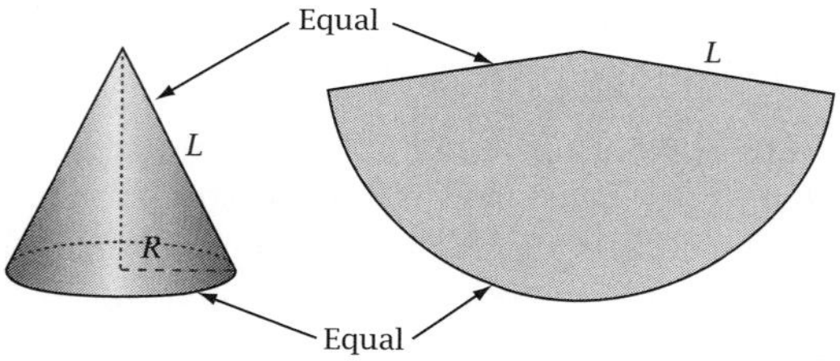

Figure 8-8m

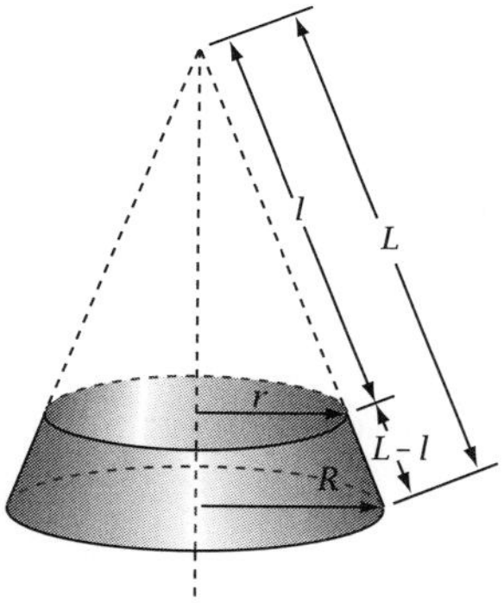

Figure 8-8n

26. *Lateral Area of a Frustum Problem:* Figure 8-8n shows that a frustum of a cone is a difference between two similar cones, one of radius and slant height $R$ and $L$; the other, $r$ and $l$. By the properties of similar triangles,

$$\frac{R}{L} = \frac{r}{l}.$$

Use this fact and clever algebra to transform the area of the frustum so that it is in terms of the average radius and the frustum slant height,

$$S = \pi RL - \pi rl = 2\pi\left(\frac{R + r}{2}\right)(L - l).$$

# 8-9 Lengths and Areas for Polar Coordinates

You have seen how to find lengths of curves specified by parametric equations and by regular Cartesian equations. In this section you will find lengths and areas when the curve is specified by polar coordinates. In polar coordinates, the position of a point is given by the displacement from the origin (the **pole**) and the angle with the positive $x$-axis (the **polar axis**).

Suppose that an object is located at point $(x, y)$ in the Cartesian plane (Figure 8-9a). Let $r$ (for "radius") be the directed distance from the pole to the object. Let $\theta$ be the directed angle from the polar axis to a ray from the pole through the point $(x, y)$. Then the ordered pair $(r, \theta)$ contains polar coordinates of $(x, y)$. Note that in $(r, \theta)$ the variable $r$ is the dependent variable, not the independent one. Figure 8-9a also shows how $(r, \theta)$ can be plotted if $r$ is negative. In this case, $\theta$ is an angle to the ray opposite the ray through $(x, y)$.

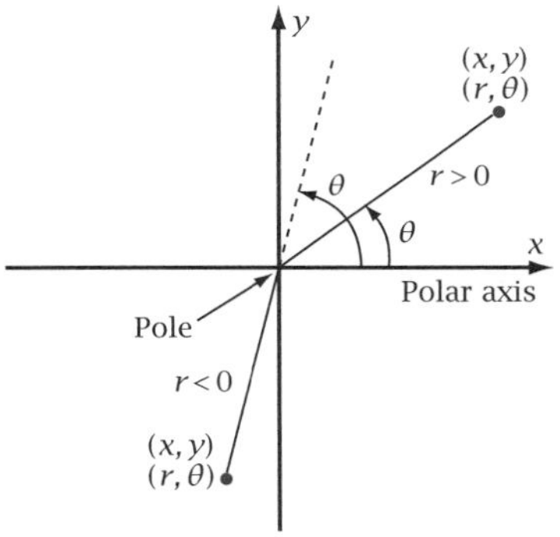

Figure 8-9a

Suppose that the polar coordinates of a moving object are given by

$$r = 5 + 4\cos\theta.$$

By picking values of $\theta$, you or your grapher can calculate and plot the corresponding values of $r$. The polar graph in this case (Figure 8-9b) is a **limaçon**, a French word for "snail." (The cedilla under the c makes its pronunciation "s.")

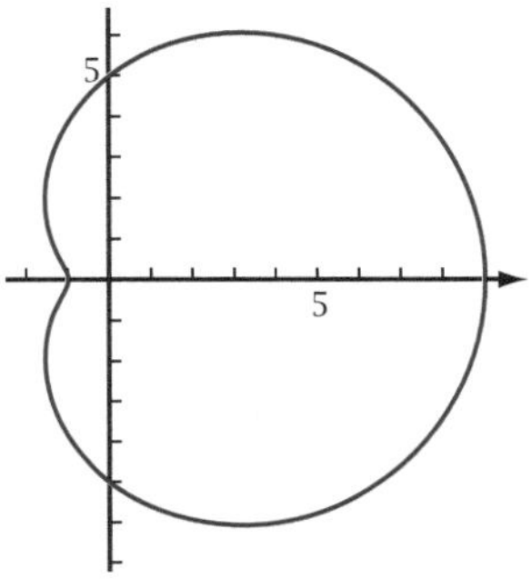

Figure 8-9b

**OBJECTIVE**

Given the equation of a polar function, find the area of a region bounded by the graph and the length of the graph.

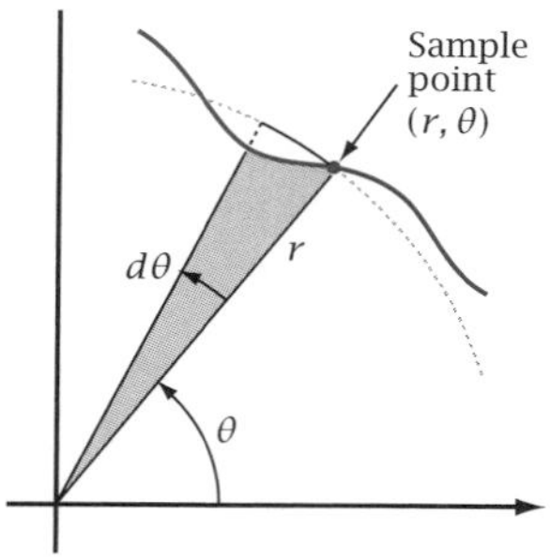


Figure 8-9c

### Area

Figure 8-9c shows a wedge-shaped region between a polar curve and the pole, swept out as $\theta$ increases by a small amount $d\theta$. The point $(r, \theta)$ on the graph can be used as a sample point for a Riemann sum. The area of the region is approximately the area of a circular sector of radius $r$ and central angle $d\theta$. The sector has area $d\theta/(2\pi)$ of a whole circle. Let $dA$ be the sector's area.

$$\therefore dA = \pi r^2 \cdot \frac{d\theta}{2\pi} = \frac{1}{2}r^2 d\theta$$

The area of an entire region swept out as $\theta$ increases from $a$ to $b$ is found by summing the areas of the sectors between $a$ and $b$ and taking the limit as $d\theta$ approaches zero (that is, integrating).

### Area of a Region in Polar Coordinates

The area $A$ of the region swept out between the graph of $r = f(\theta)$ and the pole as $\theta$ increases from $a$ to $b$ is given by

$$A = \lim_{\Delta\theta \to 0} \sum \tfrac{1}{2}r^2\Delta\theta = \int_a^b \tfrac{1}{2}r^2 d\theta.$$

**■ Example 1** Find the area of the region enclosed by the limaçon $r = 5 + 4\cos\theta$.

**Solution** The graph is shown in Figure 8-9b. You can plot it with your grapher in polar mode. If you start at $\theta = 0$, the graph makes a complete cycle and closes at $\theta = 2\pi$.

$dA = \tfrac{1}{2}(5 + 4\cos\theta)^2\, d\theta$ — Find the area of a sector, $dA$.

The entire limaçon is generated as $\theta$ increases from 0 to $2\pi$.

$\therefore A = \tfrac{1}{2}\int_0^{2\pi}(5 + 4\cos\theta)^2 d\theta$ — Add the sector areas and take the limit (that is, integrate).

$= 103.672\ldots$ square units — By numerical integration.

As a rough check, the limaçon is somewhat larger than a circle of diameter 10 units. The area of the circle is $25\pi = 78.5\ldots$. So $103.6\ldots$ is reasonable for the limaçon. (Since the limaçon is symmetrical, you could integrate from 0 to $\pi$ and double the answer.) ■

The integral of a power property cannot be used in Example 1 because $d\theta$ cannot be made the differential of the inside function. In Section 9-5, you will learn a technique for evaluating this integral algebraically using the fundamental theorem. You will find that the exact answer is $33\pi$. If you divide the unrounded numerical answer, $103.672\ldots$, by $\pi$ you should get 33.

Example 2 shows you how to find the area swept out as a polar curve is generated if $r$ becomes negative somewhere, or if part of the region overlaps another part.

**■ Example 2** Figure 8-9d shows the limaçon $r = 1 + 3\sin\theta$.

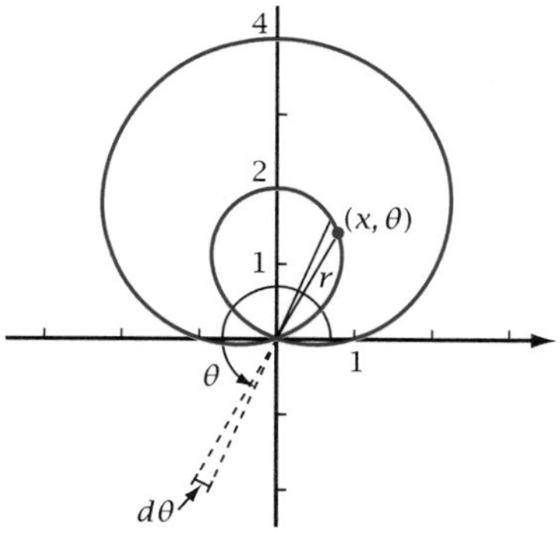


Figure 8-9d

a. Find the area of the region inside the inner loop.

b. Find the area of the region between the outer loop and the inner loop.

***Solution***

a. Figure 8-9d shows a wedge-shaped slice of the region and a sample point $(r, \theta)$ on the inner loop of the graph.

$$dA = \tfrac{1}{2}r^2\,d\theta = \tfrac{1}{2}(1 + 3\sin\theta)^2$$

By plotting and tracing, you will find that the inner loop corresponds to values of $\theta$ roughly between $\pi$ and $2\pi$. You will also find that $r$ is negative, as shown in Figure 8-9d. However, $dA$ will be positive for positive values of $d\theta$ because the $r$ is squared. To find the limits of integration precisely, set $r$ equal to zero.

$$1 + 3\sin\theta = 0 \Rightarrow \sin\theta = -\tfrac{1}{3}$$

$$\Rightarrow \theta = -0.3398\ldots + 2\pi n \text{ or } \pi - (-0.3398\ldots) + 2\pi n$$

By using $n = 1$ in the first equation and $n = 0$ in the second equation, you can find values of $\theta$ in the desired range.

$$\theta = 3.4814\ldots \text{ or } 5.9433\ldots$$

For convenience, store these values as $a$ and $b$ in your grapher.

$$A = \int_a^b \tfrac{1}{2}(1 + 3\sin\theta)^2 d\theta \approx 2.527636\ldots \qquad \text{By numerical integration.}$$

As a rough check, the inner loop has an area slightly smaller than that of a circle of diameter 2. See Figure 8-9d. That area is $\pi \cdot 1^2 = 3.141\ldots$.

b. The outer loop begins and ends where the inner loop ends and begins. The appropriate values of the limits of integration as found in part a are $a = -0.3398\ldots$ and $b = 3.4814\ldots$. Store these values in your grapher and repeat the numerical integration.

$$A = \int_a^b \tfrac{1}{2}(1 + 3\sin\theta)^2\,d\theta \approx 14.751123\ldots$$

It is important for you to realize that this is the area of the entire outer loop, between the graph and the pole, swept out as $\theta$ increases from $-0.33\ldots$ to $3.48\ldots$. The area of the region between the two loops is the difference between this and the area of the inner loop.

$$A \approx 14.751123\ldots - 2.527636\ldots = 12.223487\ldots$$ ■

### Arc Length

Figure 8-9e shows a part of a polar curve traced out as $\theta$ increases by $d\theta$. An arc of a circle drawn at $(r, \theta)$ would have length $r\,d\theta$ since $\theta$ is measured in radians. The length $dL$ is close to that of the hypotenuse of a right triangle of legs $r\,d\theta$ and $dr$. By the Pythagorean theorem,

$$dL = \sqrt{dr^2 + (r\,d\theta)^2}.$$

Factoring out $d\theta^2$ and taking its square root,

$$dL = \sqrt{\left(\frac{dr}{d\theta}\right)^2 + r^2}\,d\theta.$$

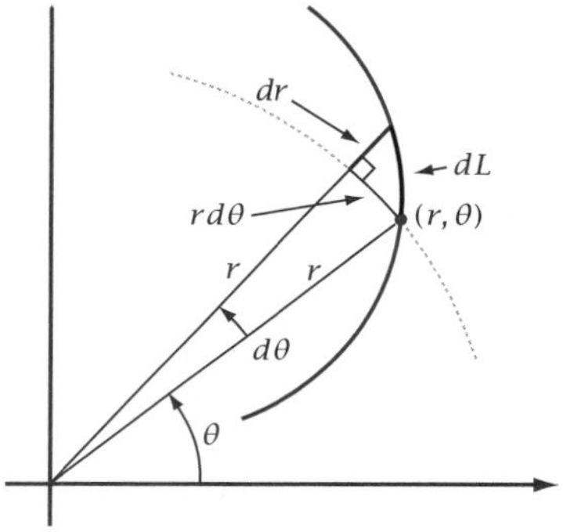


Figure 8-9e

The length of the entire path traced as $\theta$ increases from $a$ to $b$ is found by summing the $dL$'s and finding the limit (that is, integrating).

> **Length of a Curve in Polar Coordinates**
>
> The length $L$ traced out along the polar curve $r = f(\theta)$ as $\theta$ increases from $a$ to $b$ is given by
>
> $$L = \lim_{\Delta\theta \to 0} = \sum dL = \int_a^b \sqrt{dr^2 + (r\,d\theta)^2} = \int_a^b \sqrt{(dr/d\theta)^2 + r^2}\,d\theta.$$

**■ Example 3** Find the length of the limaçon $r = 1 + 3\sin\theta$ in Example 2 (Figure 8-9d).

**Solution**

$$\frac{dr}{d\theta} = 3\cos\theta$$

$$\therefore\ dL = \sqrt{(3\cos\theta)^2 + (1 + 3\sin\theta)^2}\,d\theta$$

By plotting the graph and tracing, you will find that the graph starts repeating itself after $\theta$ has increased by $2\pi$ radians. So convenient limits of integration are 0 to $2\pi$. A smaller interval would not generate the entire graph. A larger interval would count parts of the graph more than once.

$$L = \int_0^{2\pi} \sqrt{(3\cos\theta)^2 + (1 + 3\sin\theta)^2}\, d\theta$$

$$L \approx 19.3768\ldots \text{ units} \qquad \text{By numerical integration.}$$

The inner and outer loops of the limaçon are close to circles of diameters 2 and 4, respectively. The circumferences of these circles add up to $2\pi \cdot 1 + 2\pi \cdot 2 = 18.84\ldots$. So $19.3\ldots$ is reasonable for the length of the limaçon. ■

# Problem Set 8-9

### *Do These Quickly*

The following problems are intended to refresh your skills. You should be able to do all ten problems in less than five minutes.

**Q1.** Differentiate: $f(x) = 5x^3 - 7x^2 + 4x - 11$

**Q2.** Differentiate: $g(x) = (4x - 9)^3$

**Q3.** Differentiate: $h(x) = \sin^3 x$

**Q4.** Differentiate: $u(x) = \sec 3x$

**Q5.** Differentiate: $v(x) = e^{-x}$

**Q6.** Differentiate: $r(x) = 1/x$

**Q7.** Integrate: $\int (1/x)\, dx$

**Q8.** Integrate: $\int x\, dx$

**Q9.** Integrate: $\int 3\, dx$

**Q10.** Integrate: $\int dx$

1. Figure 8-9f shows the polar graph of the circle $r = 10\sin\theta$, with diameter 10.
   a. Find the area of the region swept out between the graph and the pole in one revolution as $\theta$ increases from 0 to $2\pi$.
   b. Why is the answer in 1a twice the area of the region inside the circle? Why don't you get a negative value for the area integral as $\theta$ increases from $\pi$ to $2\pi$, even though $r$ is negative for these values of $\theta$?

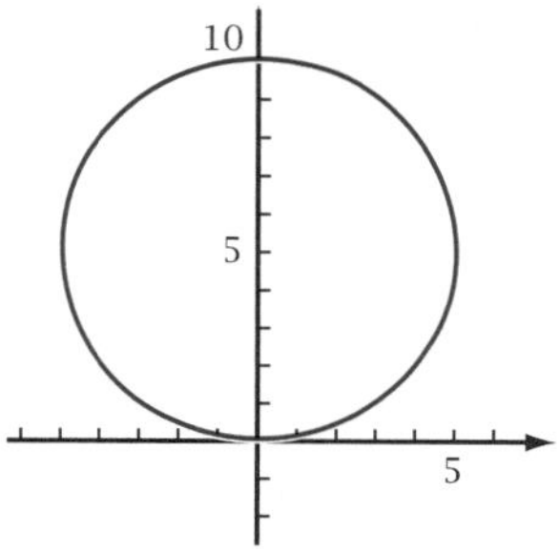

Figure 8-9f

2. Find the length of the circle $r = 10\sin\theta$ in Figure 8-9f that is traced out as $\theta$ makes one revolution, increasing from 0 to $2\pi$ radians. Why is the answer twice the circumference of the circle? Why do you suppose the polar coordinate length formula is phrased dynamically, in terms of the length "traced out," rather than statically in terms of the length "of" the curve?

For Problems 3–10,

a. Plot the graph, thus confirming the one shown here.

b. Find the area of the region enclosed by the graph.

c. Find the length of the graph.

3. The limaçon $r = 4 + 3\sin\theta$

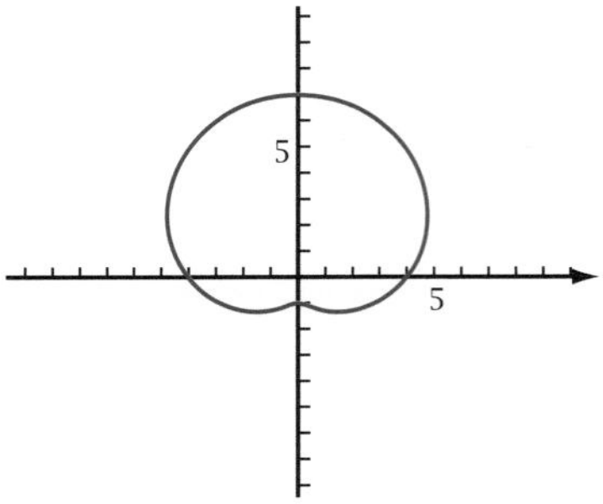


4. The limaçon $r = 5 - 3\cos\theta$

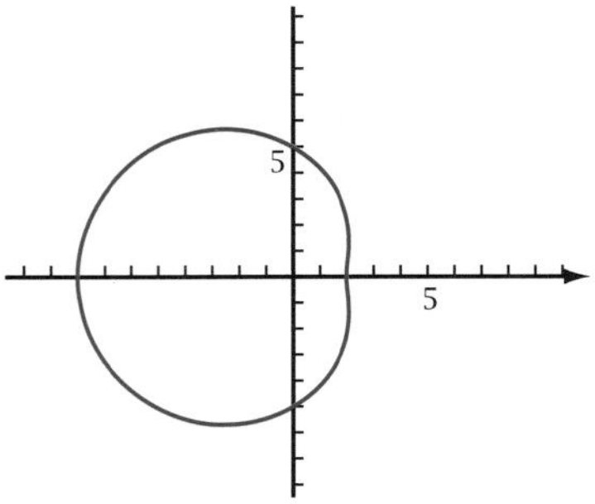


5. The curve $r = 7 + 3\cos 2\theta$

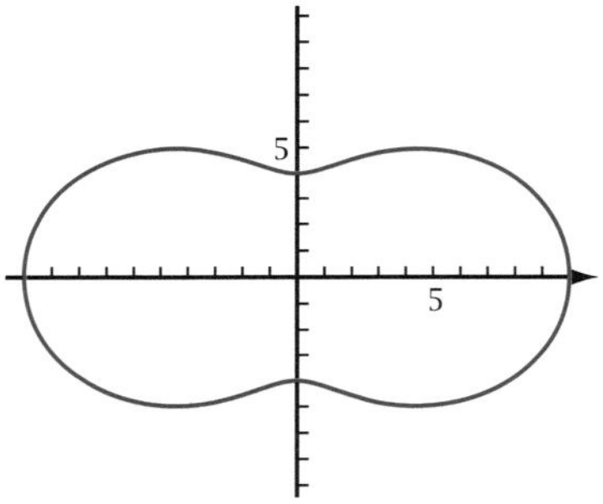


6. The four-leaved rose $r = 8\cos 2\theta$

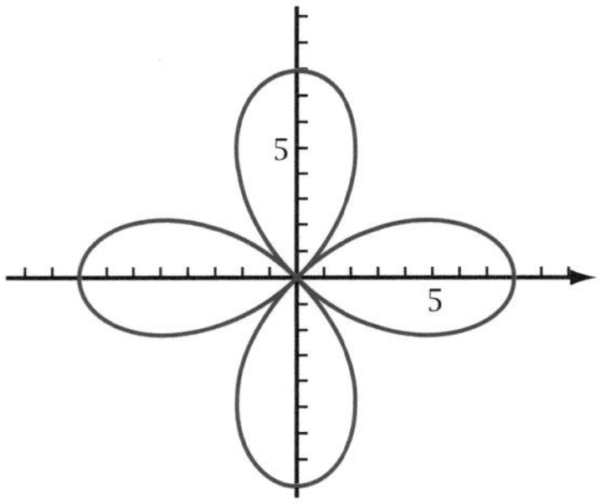


7. The cardioid $r = 5 + 5\cos\theta$

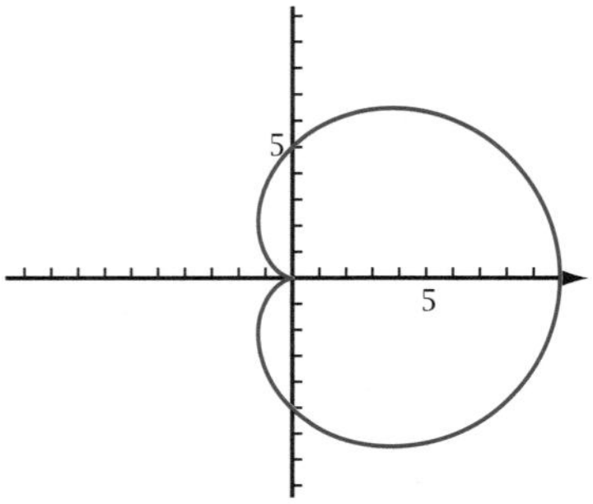


8. The ellipse $r = \dfrac{10}{3 - 2\cos\theta}$

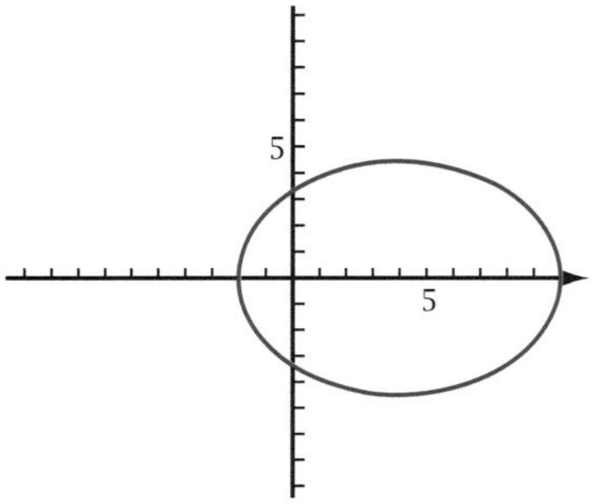


9. The *three-leaved rose* $r = \sin 3\theta$ (Be careful of the range of $\theta$-values!)

10. The *cissoid of Diocles* $r = 4\sec\theta - 4\cos\theta$, and the lines $\theta = -1$ and $\theta = 1$

11. Figure 8-9g shows the *lemniscate of Bernoulli* with polar equation

$$r = \sqrt{49 \cos 2\theta}.$$

What range of values of $\theta$ causes the right-hand loop to be generated? What is the total area of the region enclosed by both loops?

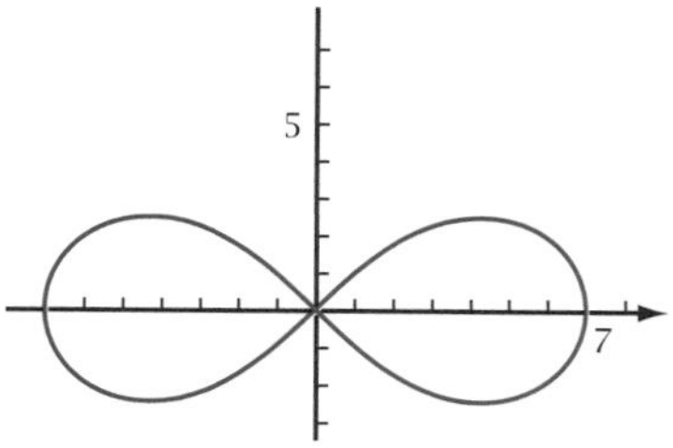

Figure 8-9g

12. The polar graph of $r = \csc \theta + 4$ is a *conchoid of Nicomedes.* The graph is unbounded but contains a closed loop. Find the area of the region inside the loop.

13. Figure 8-9h shows these polar graphs.

$$\text{Cardioid: } r = 4 + 4 \cos \theta$$
$$\text{Circle: } r = 10 \cos \theta.$$

Where do the graphs intersect? What is the area of the region outside the cardioid and inside the circle?

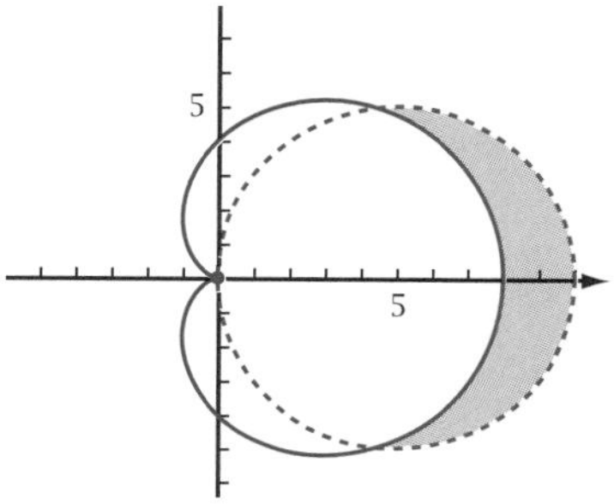

Figure 8-9h

14. Find the area of the region that is inside the circle $r = 5$ and outside the cardioid $r = 5 - 5 \cos \theta$.

15. Figure 8-9i shows the Archemedian spiral $r = 0.5\theta$.
    a. Find the length of the part of the spiral shown.
    b. Find the area of the region in Quadrant I that lies between the outermost branch of the spiral and the next branch in toward the pole.

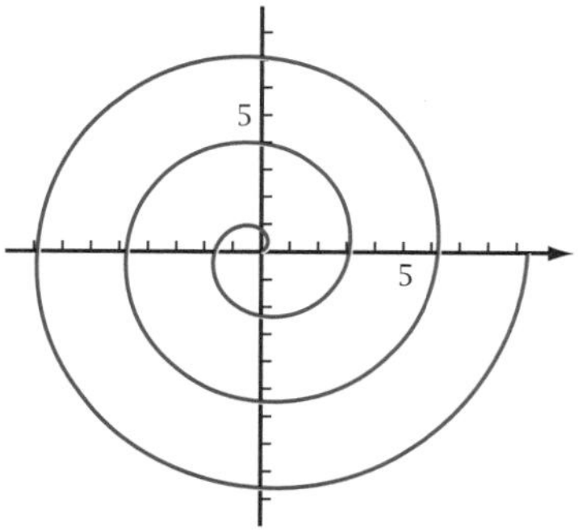

Figure 8-9i

16. For the limaçon $r = 4 + 6 \cos \theta$, find the area of the region that lies between the inner and outer loops.

17. *Column Scroll Problem:* The spiral design at the top of Ionic columns in ancient Greek architecture is an example of a *lituus* (pronounced "lit′-you-us"). Plot the lituus

$$r = 5\theta^{-1/2}$$

traced out as $\theta$ increases from 0 to $6\pi$.
    a. Find the length from $\theta = \pi/2$ to $\theta = 6\pi$.
    b. Let $\theta = 1$ radian. Sketch an arc of a circle centered at the pole, from the polar axis to the point $(r, 1)$ on the lituus. Find the area of the sector of the circle corresponding to this arc. Repeat the calculation for $\theta = 2$ and $\theta = 3$. What seems to be true about these areas?

18. *Line Problem:* Show that the graph of $r = \sec \theta$ is a line. Find the length of the segment from $\theta = 0$ to $\theta = 1.5$ using the calculus of polar coordinates. Then confirm that your answer is correct by appropriate geometry.

19. *LP Record Project:* In this project you are to calculate the length of the groove on an old $33\frac{1}{3}$ rpm record. Obtain such a record. Figure out a way to measure the number of grooves per centimeter in the radial direction. Then figure out a polar equation for the spiral formed by the grooves. By integrating, calculate the length of the groove from the outer one to the inner one. Perform a quick calculation to show that your answer is reasonable.

20. *Kepler's Law Project:* Figure 8-9j shows the path of a spaceship in an elliptical orbit. The earth is at the pole (one focus of the ellipse). The polar equation of the ellipse is

$$r = \frac{100}{3 - 2\cos\theta},$$

where $\theta$ is in radians and $r$ is in thousands of miles. In this problem you will investigate the speed of the spaceship at various places.

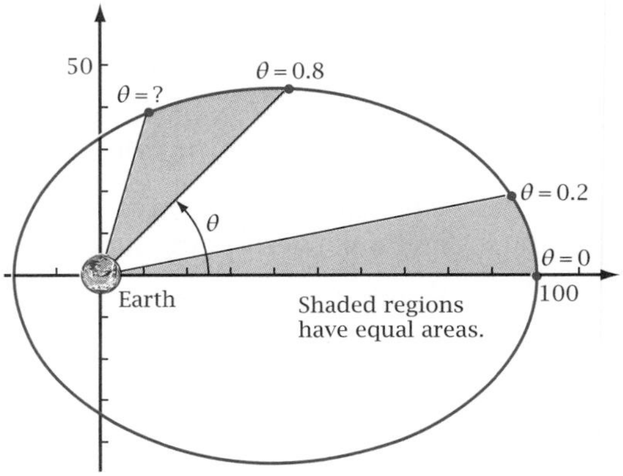

Figure 8-9j

a. Find the area of the elliptical sector from $\theta = 0$ to $\theta = 0.2$.

b. German astonomer Johannes Kepler (1571–1630) observed that an object in orbit sweeps out sectors of equal area in equal times. This fact is known as **Kepler's second law** of planetary motion. (His first law states that the orbit is an ellipse where the object being orbited is located at one focus.) If the sector in Figure 8-9j starting at $\theta = 0.8$ has area equal to the one in 20a, at what value of $\theta$ does the sector end?

c. **Kepler's third law** states that the period of an orbiting object is related to its distance from the object being orbited. If $a$ is half the major axis of the orbit, then the period $P$ is

$$P = ka^{1.5}.$$

Find the value of the constant $k$ using data for the moon. The moon is about $a = 240{,}000$ mi from earth and has a period of about 655 hr (27.3 d · 24 hr).

d. What is the period of the spaceship in Figure 8-9j?

e. How many hours does it take the spaceship to travel from $\theta = 0$ to $\theta = 0.2$? How many hours does it take to travel from $\theta = 0.8$ to the value of $\theta$ in 20b?

f. How many miles does the spaceship travel on its elliptical path between $\theta = 0$ and $\theta = 0.2$? How many miles does it travel between $\theta = 0.8$ and the value of $\theta$ in 20b?

g. Find the average speed (distance/time) of the spaceship for each of the two arcs in 20f.

h. See whether you can explain physically why a spaceship would move faster when it is closer to the earth than it does when it is farther away.

21. *The Derivative dy/dx for Polar Coordinates Problem:* Figure 8-9k shows the polar graph of the spiral

$$r = \theta$$

superimposed on a Cartesian $xy$-plane. A tangent line is plotted at the point $(r, 7)$.

a. Estimate the slope of the tangent line.

b. Polar and Cartesian coordinates are related by the parametric equations

$$x = r\cos\theta$$
$$y = r\sin\theta.$$

By appropriate use of the parametric chain rule, find an equation for $dy/dx$ and use it to show algebraically that the slope you found in 21a is correct.

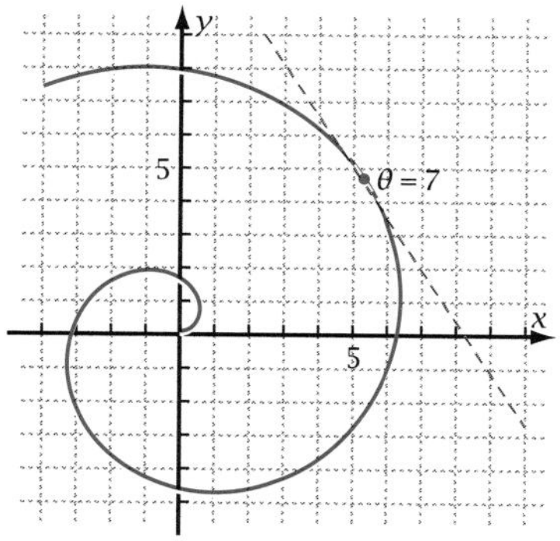

Figure 8-9k

22. *Project—The Angle Between the Radius and the Tangent Line:* A remarkably simple relationship exists between $dr/d\theta$ in polar coordinates and the angle $\psi$ (Greek letter psi, pronounced the same as "sigh") measured counterclockwise from the radius to the tangent line (Figure 8-9l). In this project you will derive and apply this relationship.

a. Explain why $\tan\theta = y/x$.

b. Let $\phi$ (Greek letter phi, "fee" or "fye") be the angle from the positive horizontal direction to the tangent line (Figure 8-9l). The slope of the tangent line is $dy/dx$. Explain why

$$\tan\phi = \frac{dy/d\theta}{dx/d\theta}.$$

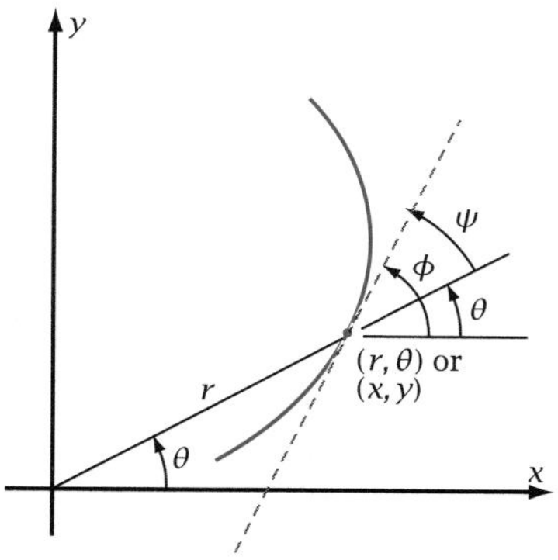

Figure 8-9l

c. You recall from trigonometry that $\tan(A - B) = \dfrac{\tan A - \tan B}{1 + \tan A \tan B}$. Use this property, the results of 22a and b, and appropriate algebra to show that

$$\tan\psi = \frac{x(dy/d\theta) - y(dx/d\theta)}{x(dx/d\theta) + y(dy/d\theta)}.$$

d. Use the fact that $x = r\cos\theta$ and $y = r\sin\theta$ to show that the numerator in 22c equals $r^2$.

e. Use the fact that $r^2 = x^2 + y^2$ to show that $r\dfrac{dr}{d\theta}$ equals the denominator in 22c, and thus the following property holds.

**Property: The Angle Psi in Polar Coordinates**

If $\psi$ is the angle measured counterclockwise from the radius to the tangent line of a polar graph, then

$$\tan\psi = \frac{r}{dr/d\theta} = \frac{r}{r'}.$$

f. Figure 8-9m shows the cardioid

$$r = a - a\cos\theta,$$

where $a$ stands for a nonzero constant. Prove that for this cardioid the angle $\psi$ is always equal to one-half of $\theta$. You will find that the half-argument properties for tangent, which you may recall from trigonometry, are helpful.

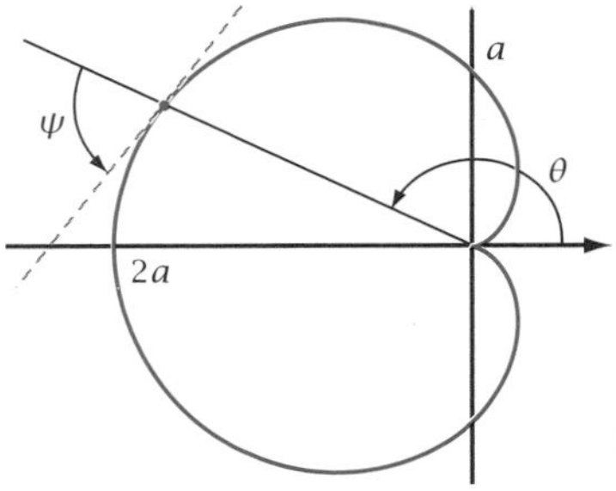


Figure 8-9m

g. Figure 8-9n shows a cross section through a chambered nautilus shell. The spiral has the property that the angle $\psi$ is a constant. Use this fact and the property in 22e to find the general equation of this **equiangular spiral**. Choose two values of $\theta$ on the photograph and measure the corresponding values of $r$. Use these values as initial conditions to find the particular equation for the outer spiral. Confirm that your equation is correct by plotting it, tracing to another value of $\theta$, and showing that the point is actually on the photographed spiral. Use the constants in your equation to calculate the value of $\psi$. Measure a photocopy of the shell to show that your calculated value of $\psi$ is correct.

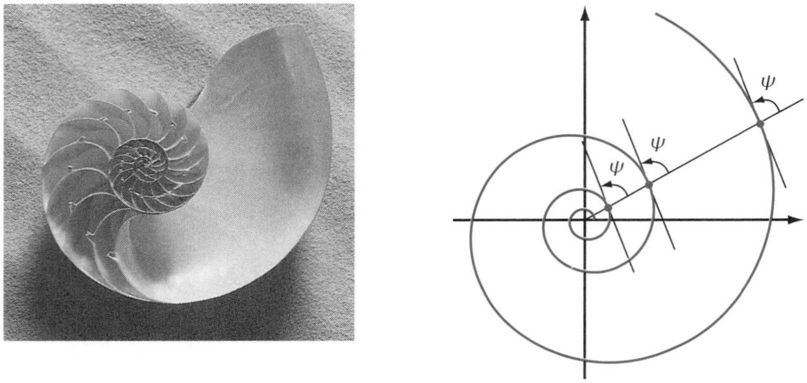


Equiangular spiral. $\psi$ is constant.

Figure 8-9n

# 8-10 Chapter Review and Test

In this chapter you have seen a major application of derivatives and integrals to geometrical problems. The rate of change of the area or volume of a figure describes how fast these quantities change as a given dimension changes. Maximum or minimum areas or volumes occur where the rate of change equals zero. Areas, volumes, and curved lengths can be calculated by slicing a figure into small pieces, adding the pieces, and taking the limit. The resulting limits of Riemann sums are equal to definite integrals. You evaluated these integrals numerically or by the fundamental theorem if you were able to find the indefinite integral.

The Review Problems are numbered according to the sections of this chapter. The Concepts Problems allow you to apply your knowledge to new situations. The Chapter Test is typical of a classroom test.

## Review Problems

R0. Update your journal with things you've learned since the last entry. You should include such things as those listed here.

- The one most important thing you have learned in studying Chapter 8
- How the volume, length, and surface area of a geometric figure are found
- How volume, length, and surface area are found in polar coordinates or with parametric functions
- Which boxes you have been working on in the "define, understand, do, apply" table

R1. Three cubic functions have equations

$$f(x) = x^3 - 9x^2 + 30x - 10,$$
$$g(x) = x^3 - 9x^2 + 27x - 10, \text{ and}$$
$$h(x) = x^3 - 9x^2 + 24x - 10.$$

a. Plot the graphs on the same screen. Sketch the results.

b. Write equations for the first and second derivative of each function.

c. Which function has two distinct values of $x$ at which the first derivative is zero? What are these values of $x$? What features occur at these points?

d. Which function has a horizontal tangent line somewhere but no local maximum or minimum points?

e. Each function has a point of inflection. Show that the second derivative is zero at each of the points of inflection.

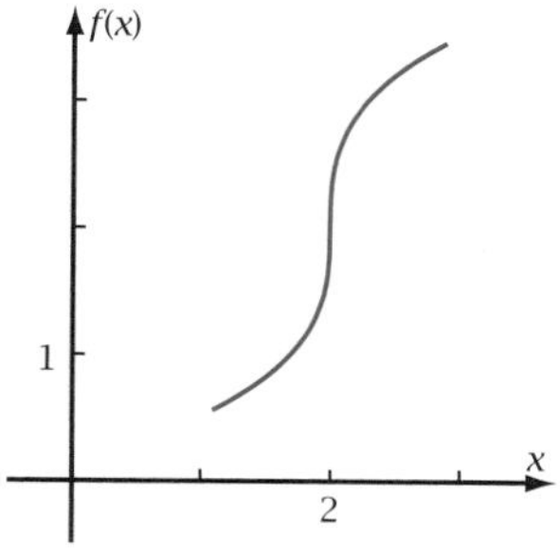

Figure 8-10a

R2. a. For the function in Figure 8-10a, sketch a number-line graph for $f'$ and for $f''$ showing the sign of each derivative in a neighborhood of the critical point at $x = 2$. Indicate on the number lines whether there is a local maximum, a local minimum, or a point of inflection at $x = 2$.

b. Sketch the graph of a function whose derivatives have the features given in Figure 8-10b.

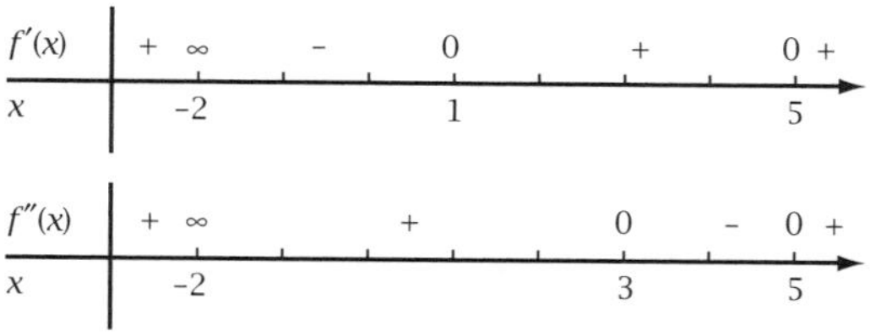

Figure 8-10b

c. Figure 8-10c shows the graph of

$$f(x) = x^{2/3} - x.$$

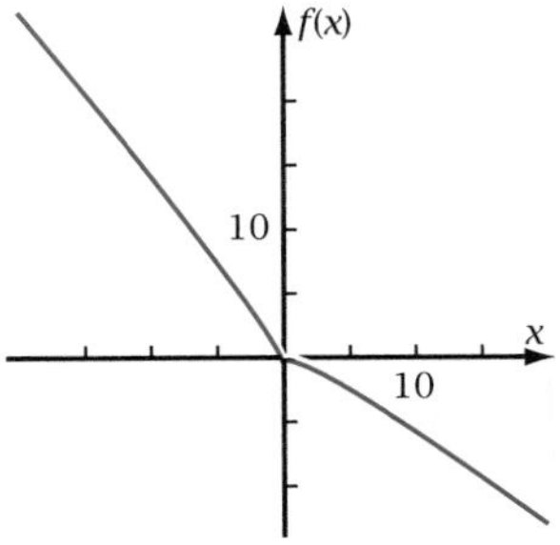

Figure 8-10c

i. Write equations for $f'(x)$ and $f''(x)$.

ii. The graph appears to slope downward for all $x$. Does $f(x)$ have any local maxima or minima? If so, where? If not, explain how you can tell.

iii. The graph appears to be concave downward for all $x$. Are there any points of inflection? If so, where? If not, explain how you can tell.

iv. Write the global maximum and minimum values of $f(x)$ for $x$ in the closed interval [0, 5].

d. For $f(x) = x^2e^{-x}$, find the maxima, minima, and points of inflection and sketch the graph.

R3. a. *Storage Battery Problem:* A normal automobile battery has six cells divided by walls (Figure 8-10d). For a particular battery, each cell must have an area of 10 $\text{in}^2$, looking down from the top. What dimensions of the battery will give the minimum total wall length (including outsides)? A typical battery is 9 in. by 6.7 in. (that is, 1.5-in. cell width). Does minimum wall length seem to be a consideration in battery design?

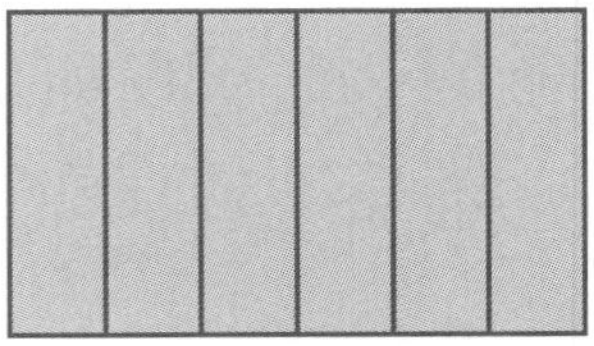
Figure 8-10d

b. *Cylinder in Cubic Paraboloid Problem:* A rectangle is inscribed in the region in Quadrant I under the cubic parabola $y = 8 - x^3$. Two sides of the rectangle are on the $x$- and $y$-axes, and the opposite corner of the rectangle touches the graph. The figure is rotated about the $y$-axis. The curve generates a cubic paraboloid, and the rectangle generates a cylinder. What rectangle dimensions give the largest-volume cylinder?

R4. a. Find the area of the region bounded by the graph of $y = \ln x$, the $y$-axis, and the lines $y = 1$ and $y = 2$. Use the fundamental theorem. Verify your answer numerically.

b. Find the area of the region bounded by the graphs of $y = x^{1/3}$ and $y = x/3 - 2/3$.

c. *Mystery Problem:* Mr. Rhee must find the area of the region bounded by the graphs of $y = x^3$ and $y = x$. He finds, correctly, that the graphs intersect at $x = -1$ and $x = 1$. So he integrates

$$\int_{-1}^{1} (x^3 - x)\,dx = \tfrac{1}{4}x^4 - \tfrac{1}{2}x^2 \Big|_{-1}^{1} = \tfrac{1}{4} - \tfrac{1}{2} - \tfrac{1}{4} + \tfrac{1}{2} = 0. \qquad \text{(Surprise!)}$$

Explain to Mr. Rhee what went wrong.

R5. a. The region under the graph of $y = e^{0.2x}$ from $x = 0$ to $x = 4$ is rotated around the $x$-axis to form a solid. Find its volume.

b. The region in Quadrant I bounded by the graphs of $y = x^{0.25}$ and $y = x$ rotates around the $y$-axis to form a solid. Find its volume.

c. *Oblique Cone Problem:* Figure 8-10e shows an oblique circular cone with base at $y = 0$. Each cross section perpendicular to the $y$-axis is a circle, with diameter extending from the graph of $y = x + 2$ to $y = 3x - 6$. Find the volume of the cone. Is its volume larger or smaller than that of a right circular cone of the same altitude, 6, and base radius, 2?

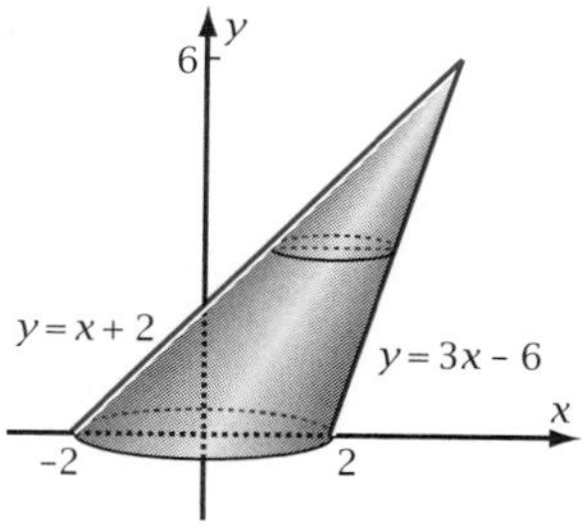

Figure 8-10e

R6. a. The region in Quadrant I bounded by the graphs of $y = x^{1/3}$ and $y = x^2$ is rotated about the $x$-axis to form a solid. Find the volume of the solid by cylindrical shells.

b. Find the volume of the solid in R6a by plane slices. Show that the answer is the same.

c. *Various Axes Problem:* The region bounded by the parabola $y = x^2$ and the line $y = 4$ is rotated to form various solids. Find the volume of the solid for the following axes of rotation:

i. $y$-axis | ii. $x$-axis

iii. Line $y = 5$ | iv. Line $x = 3$

R7. a. Write an integral equal to the length of the parabola $y = x^2$ between $x = -1$ and $x = 2$. Evaluate the integral numerically.

b. Find exactly the length of the graph of $y = x^{3/2}$ from $x = 0$ to $x = 9$ using the fundamental theorem. Find a decimal approximation for the answer. Check your answer by employing suitable geometry.

c. Find the length of the following spiral from $t = 0$ to $t = 4$.

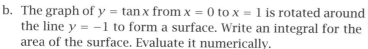

$$x = t\cos \pi t$$
$$y = t\sin \pi t$$

R8. a. Find, exactly by the fundamental theorem, the area of the surface formed by rotating around the $y$-axis the graph of $y = x^{1/3}$ from $x = 0$ to $x = 8$. Find a decimal approximation for the answer. Check your answer by employing suitable geometry.

b. The graph of $y = \tan x$ from $x = 0$ to $x = 1$ is rotated around the line $y = -1$ to form a surface. Write an integral for the area of the surface. Evaluate it numerically.

c. The spiral in Problem R7c is rotated about the $y$-axis to form a "sea shell." Find its surface area.

R9. Figure 8-10f shows the spiral

$$r = \theta$$

from $\theta = 0$ to $\theta = 5\pi/2$.

a. Find the length of this part of the spiral.

b. Find the area of the region in Quadrant I that is outside the first cycle and inside the second cycle of the spiral.

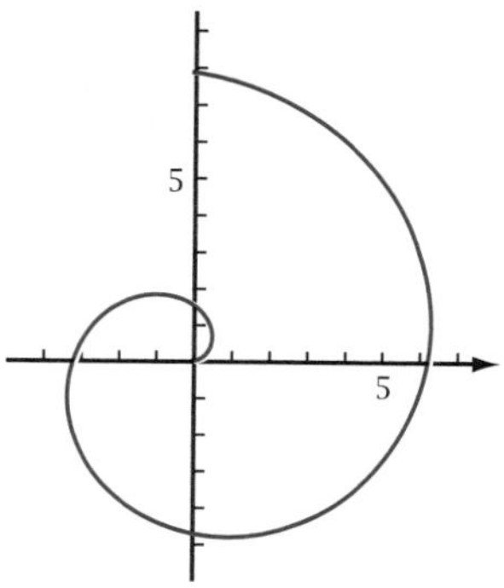

Figure 8-10f

## Concepts Problems

C1. *Oil Viscosity Problem:* The viscosity (resistance to flow) of normal motor oil decreases as the oil warms up. "All-weather" motor oils retain about the same viscosity throughout the range of operating temperatures. Suppose that the viscosity of 10W-40 oil is given by

$$\mu = 130 - 12T + 15T^2 - 4T^3, \text{ for } 0 \le T \le 3,$$

where $\mu$ (Greek letter *mu*, pronounced "mew" or "moo") is the viscosity in centipoise and $T$ is the temperature in hundreds of degrees.

a. At what temperature in this domain will the maximum viscosity occur?

b. What is the minimum viscosity in this domain? Justify your answer.

C2. *"Straight Point" Problem:* Show that the graph of $f(x) = (x - 1)^4 + x$ has a zero second derivative at $x = 1$ but does not have a point of inflection there. Sketch what the graph will look like in the vicinity of $x = 1$. Describe what is true about the graph at $x = 1$.

C3. *Infinite Derivative Problem:* The functions $f(x) = x^{2/3}$ and $g(x) = x^{-2/3}$ both have infinite first derivatives at $x = 0$, but the behavior of each is quite different there. Sketch a graph showing the difference.

C4. *Chapter Logo Problem:* The logo on each even-numbered page of this chapter shows a solid formed by rotating about the line $x = 4$ the part of the graph

$$y = 3 + 5\left[0.5 + 0.5\cos\left(\tfrac{\pi}{3}(x - 5)\right)\right]^2$$

from $x = 5$ to $x = 7.5$. A cylindrical hole 1 unit in radius is coaxial with the solid. Figure 8-10g shows the coordinate system in which this diagram was drawn.

a. Find the length of the segment of graph that was rotated.

b. Find the $x$-coordinate of the point of inflection.

c. Find the area of the doubly curved surface of the solid.

d. Find the volume of the solid.

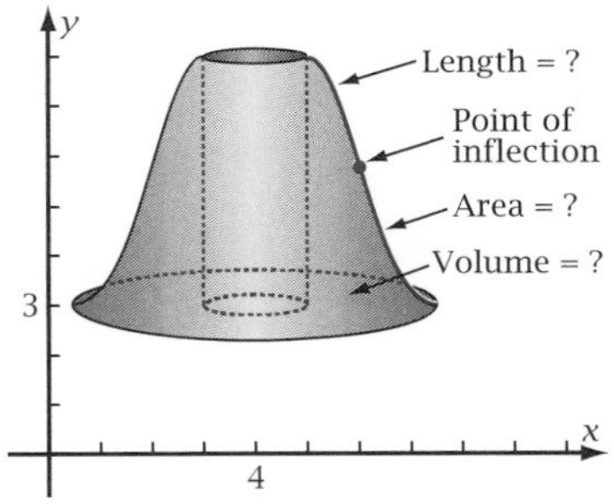


Figure 8-10g

C5. *Area by Planimeter Project:* You have learned how to calculate the area of a region algebraically using the fundamental theorem and also numerically. There is a mechanical device called a planimeter (compensating polar planimeter) that finds the area geometrically from a drawing of the region. In this problem you are to borrow a planimeter and use it to find the area of Texas from a map.

a. Photocopy the map of Texas in Figure 8-10h. Be sure that the scale is photocopied, too, because some copy machines shrink the picture.

b. Set up the planimeter with the tracer point at a convenient starting point on the map. Set the dial to zero. Then trace around the boundary until you return to the starting point.

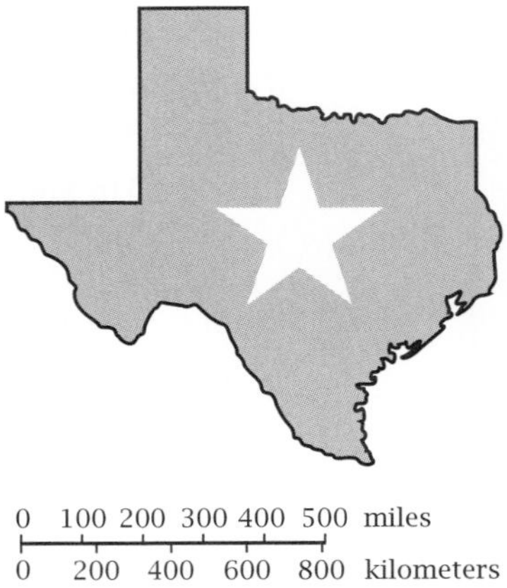


Figure 8-10h

c. Read the final setting on the dial. The planimeter may have a vernier scale for reading tenths of a unit.

d. Measure the scale on the map to find out how many miles correspond to 1 cm. Be clever! Then find out how many square miles correspond to 1 $cm^2$. Finally, calculate the area of Texas to as many significant digits as the data justify.

e. Find out from the planimeter's instruction manual the theoretical basis on which the instrument works. Write a paragraph or two describing what you learned.

f. Check an almanac or encyclopedia to see how accurate your measurement is.

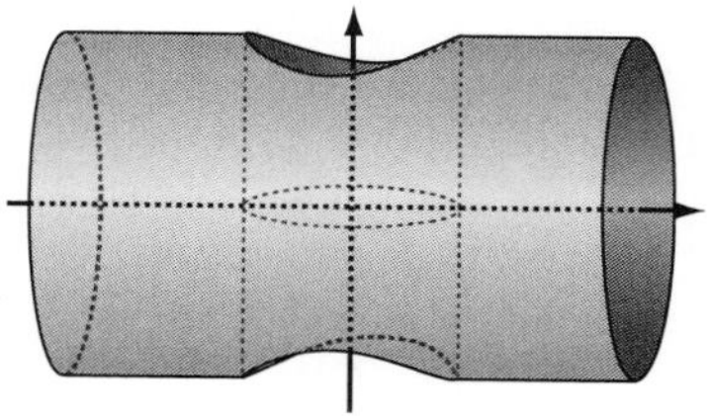
Figure 8-10i

C6. *Hole in the Cylinder Project:* A cylinder of uranium 10 cm in diameter has a hole 6 cm in diameter drilled through it. (Figure 8-10i) The axis of the hole intersects the axis of the cylinder at right angles. Find the volume of the uranium drilled out. Find the value of the uranium drilled out. You may assume that uranium is worth \$200 a gram. Be resourceful to find out the density of uranium.

C7. *Three-Hole Project:* A cube 2 cm on each edge has three mutually perpendicular holes drilled through its faces (Figure 8-10j). Each hole has a diameter of 2 cm, so it comes right to the cube faces which it parallels. Find the volume of the solid remaining after the three holes are drilled.

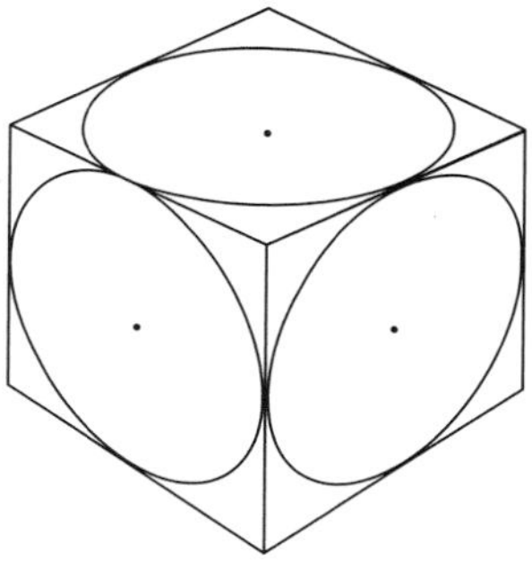
Figure 8-10j

## Chapter Test

T1. Figure 8-10k shows the graph of

$$f(x) = x^3 - 7.8x^2 + 20.25x - 13.$$

Ascertain whether the graph has a relative maximum and a relative minimum, a horizontal tangent at the point of inflection, or just a point of inflection with no horizontal tangent. Justify your answer.

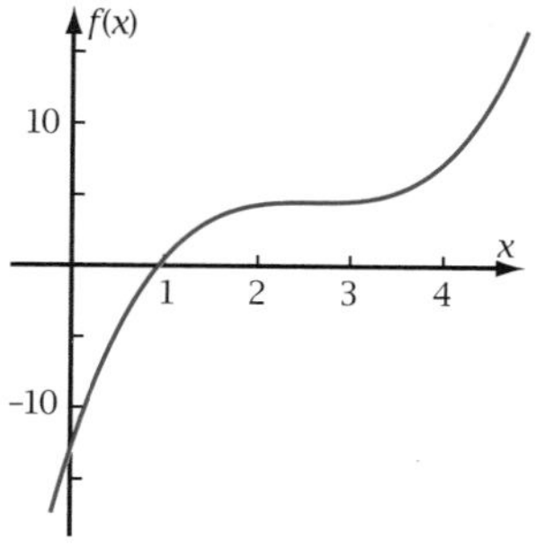

Figure 8-10k

T2. Figure 8-10l shows critical values of $f'(x)$ and $f''(x)$ for a continuous function $f$, as well as the signs of the derivatives in the intervals between these points. Sketch a possible graph of $f$ using the initial condition that $f(0) = 3$.

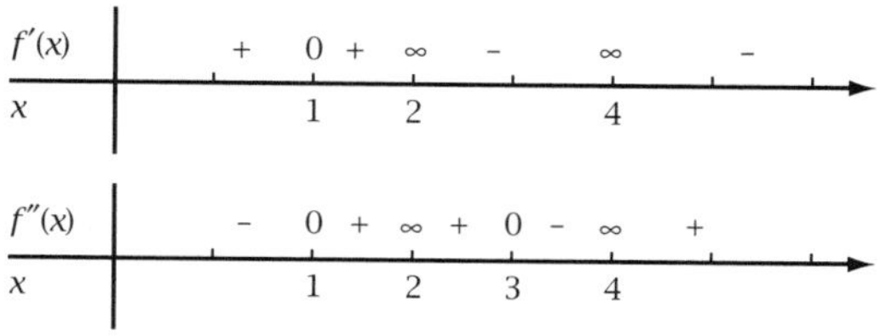

Figure 8-10l

Problems T3–T8 are concerned with the region $R$ shown in Figure 8-10m. Region $R$ is bounded by the graph of $y = x^3$ from $x = 0$ to $x = 2$, the $y$-axis, and the line $y = 8$.

T3. Write a definite integral to find the length of the graph of $y = x^3$ from $x = 0$ to $x = 2$. Evaluate the integral to find the length.

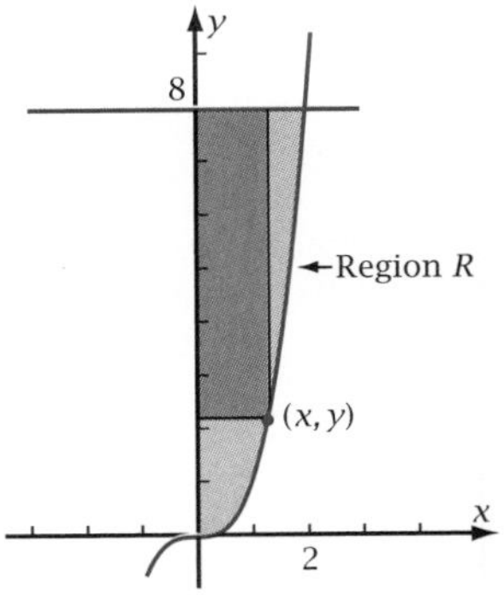

Figure 8-10m

T4. Write a definite integral equal to the area of the surface generated by rotating the segment of graph in Problem T3 about the $y$-axis. Evaluate the integral.

T5. A rectangular region is inscribed in region $R$ as shown in Figure 8-10m. As $R$ rotates about the $y$-axis, the rectangular region generates a cylinder. Find exactly the maximum volume the cylinder could have. Justify your answer.

T6. Using slices of $R$ perpendicular to the $y$-axis, write an integral equal to the volume of the solid formed by rotating $R$ around the $y$-axis. Evaluate the integral algebraically using the fundamental theorem.

T7. Using slices of $R$ parallel to the $y$-axis, write another integral equal to the volume in Problem T6. Show that the volume determined this way is exactly the same as that in Problem T6.

T8. Suppose that a cylinder is circumscribed about the solid in Problem T6. What fraction of the volume of this cylinder is the volume of the solid?

T9. For the ellipse with parametric functions

$$x = 5\cos t$$
$$y = 2\sin t$$

a. Plot the graph and sketch it.

b. Find the length of the ellipse.

c. Show that the volume of the ellipsoid formed by rotating the ellipse about the $x$-axis is

$$V = \frac{4}{3}\pi\,(x\text{-radius})\,(y\text{-radius})^2.$$

For Problems T10 and T11, use the spiral $r = 5e^{0.1\theta}$ shown in Figure 8-10n.

T10. Find the length of the part of the spiral shown.

T11. Find the area of the region in Quadrant I that is outside the second revolution of the spiral and inside the third revolution.

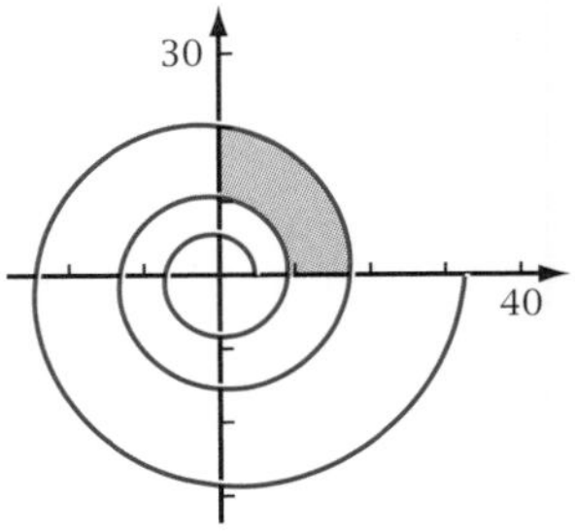

Figure 8-10n

CHAPTER

# 9 Algebraic Calculus Techniques for the Elementary Functions

The Gateway Arch in St. Louis is built in the form of a catenary, the same shape a chain forms when it hangs under its own weight. In this shape the stresses act along the length of the arch and cause no bending. The equation of a catenary involves the hyperbolic functions, which have properties similar to the circular functions of trigonometry.

# Mathematical Overview

In Chapter 9 you will learn ways to integrate each of the elementary functions and their inverses. These are

- algebraic
- trigonometric
- logarithmic
- hyperbolic

You will do this in four ways.

***Graphically***

The logo at the top of each even-numbered page of this chapter shows the graphical meaning of the integration by parts formula, used to integrate products.

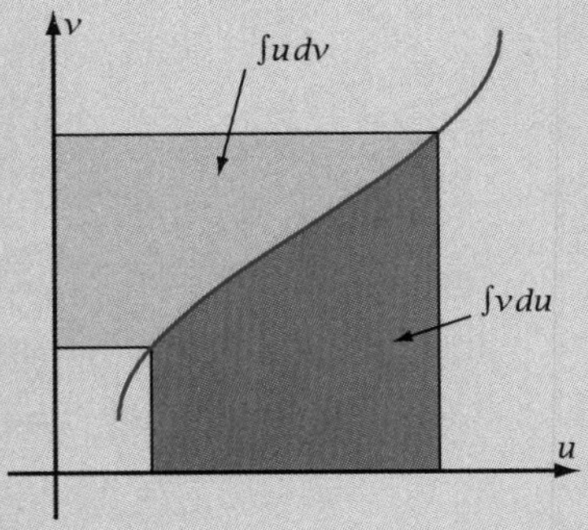


***Numerically***

| $x$ | $\ln x$ | $\int_1^x \ln t\, dt$ |
|---|---|---|
| 1 | 0 | 0 |
| 2 | 0.693 ... | 0.386 ... |
| 3 | 1.098 ... | 1.295 ... |
| 4 | 1.386 ... | 2.545 ... |
| 5 | 1.609 ... | 4.047 ... |
| ... | ... | ... |

***Algebraically***

$\int u\, dv = uv - \int v\, du$, the integration by parts formula.

***Verbally***

*The most fundamental method of integration seems to be integration by parts. With it I can integrate products of functions. I can also use it to find algebraic integrals for the inverse trigonometric functions.*

# 9-1 Introduction to the Integral of a Product of Two Functions

Suppose you are to find the volume of the solid formed by rotating the region under $y = \cos x$ around the $y$-axis (Figure 9-1a). The value of $dV$, the differential of volume, is

$$dV = 2\pi x \cdot y \cdot dx = 2\pi x \cos x \, dx.$$

Thus the volume is

$$V = 2\pi \int_0^{\pi/2} x \cos x \, dx.$$

The integrand, $x \cos x$, involves a **product** of two functions. So far you have been able to evaluate such integrals only by approximate numerical methods because you usually could not find the antiderivative of a product.

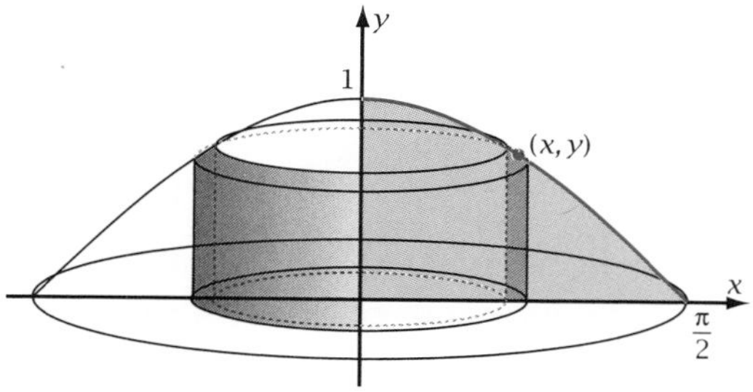


Figure 9-1a

In this chapter you will learn algebraic techniques for integrating the so-called **elementary functions**. These are the **algebraic functions**, involving no operations other than addition, subtraction, multiplication, division, and roots (rational exponential powers); and the elementary *transcendental functions*, which are the trigonometric and inverse trigonometric functions, logarithmic and exponential functions, and *hyperbolic* functions. The hyperbolic functions are defined in terms of exponential functions but have properties similar to those of the trigonometric functions.

Some of the techniques you will learn were essential before the advent of the computer made numerical integration easily available. They are now interesting mostly for historical reasons and because they give you insight into how to approach a problem. Your instructor will guide you to the ones that are important for your course. You will see how algebraically "brave" one had to be to learn calculus in the days "BC" ("before calculators"). But for each technique you learn you will get the thrill of knowing, "I can do it on my own, without a calculator!"

**OBJECTIVE**

On your own or with your study group, find the indefinite integral $\int x \cos x \, dx$, and use the result to find exactly the volume of the solid in Figure 9-1a using the fundamental theorem.

## Exploratory Problem Set 9-1

1. Find the volume of the solid in Figure 9-1a approximately by numerical integration.
2. Let $f(x) = x \sin x$. Use the derivative of a product formula to find an equation for $f'(x)$. You should find that $x \cos x$, the integrand in Problem 1, is one of the terms.
3. Multiply both sides of the equation for $f'(x)$ in Problem 2 by $dx$. Then integrate both sides. (That's easy! You just write an integral sign ("$\int$") in front of each term!)
4. The integral $\int x \cos x \, dx$ should be one term in the equation of Problem 3. Use suitable algebra to isolate this integral. Then do the integrating on the other side of the equation. Recall what $\int f'(x)\, dx$ equals!
5. Use the result of Problem 4 to find the exact volume of the solid in Figure 9-1a.
6. Find a decimal approximation for the exact volume in Problem 5. How close did the approximation in Problem 1 come to this exact volume?
7. The technique of this exercise is called *integration by parts*. Why do you suppose this name is used? How do you suppose the function $f(x) = x \sin x$ was chosen in Problem 2?

# 9-2 Integration by Parts—A Way to Integrate Products

Figure 9-2a shows the solid generated by rotating about the $y$-axis the region under the graph of $y = \cos x$. The volume of this solid is given by

$$V = 2\pi \int_0^{\pi/2} x \cos x \, dx.$$

In Section 9-1, you saw that this product of functions can be integrated algebraically. In this section you will learn why the integration by parts technique works.

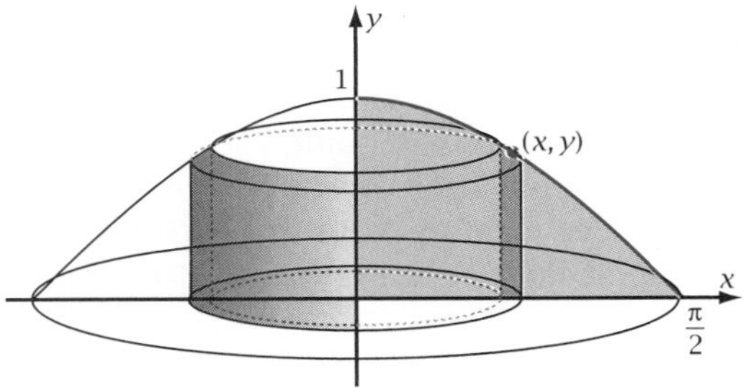


Figure 9-2a

**OBJECTIVE**

Given an integral involving a product, evaluate it algebraically using integration by parts.

To see how to integrate a product of two functions, it helps to start with the formula for the differential of a product. If $y = uv$, where $u$ and $v$ are differentiable functions of $x$, then

$$dy = du \cdot v + u \cdot dv$$

Commuting the $du$ and $v$ in the right-hand side of the equation and integrating both sides gives

$$\int dy = \int v\,du + \int u\,dv$$

Either integral on the right-hand side can be isolated and written in terms of the remaining quantities. For instance,

$$\int u\,dv = \int dy - \int v\,du.$$

Since $\int dy = y$ (ignoring, for the time being, "+$C$") and $y = uv$, you can write

$$\int u\,dv = uv - \int v\,du.$$

For $\int x \cos x\,dx$, let $u = x$ and let $dv = \cos x\,dx$. Then the following holds.

$du = dx$ and $v = \int \cos x\,dx = \sin x + C$ — Differentiate $u$ and integrate $dv$.

$\therefore \int x \cos x\,dx = x(\sin x + C) - \int (\sin x + C)\,dx$ — Substitute for $u$, $v$, and $du$ in the equation $\int u\,dv = uv - \int v\,du$.

$= x \sin x + Cx + \cos x - Cx + C_1$ — A new constant of integration comes from the second integral.

$= x \sin x + \cos x + C_1$ — The old constant of integration cancels out!

The integral of a product of two functions can always be written as

$$\int \text{(one function)(differential of another function)}.$$

Associating the integrand into two factors leads to the name "integration by parts." It succeeds if the new integral, $\int v\,du$, is simpler to integrate than the original one, $\int u\,dv$.

### Technique: Integration by Parts

A way to integrate a product is to write it in the form

$$\int \text{(one function)(differential of another function)}.$$

If $u$ and $v$ are differentiable functions of $x$, then

$$\int u\,dv = uv - \int v\,du.$$

It's a good idea to memorize the integration by parts formula as you will use it often. Example 1 shows a way to use this formula.

■ **Example 1** Do the integrating: $\int 5xe^{3x}\,dx$

**Solution**

$$\int 5xe^{3x}\,dx \qquad \text{Let } u = 5x, \quad dv = e^{3x}\,dx.$$

$$\therefore du = 5\,dx, \quad v = \int e^{3x}\,dx = \tfrac{1}{3}e^{3x} + C.$$

Write $u$ and $dv$ to the right, out of the way, as shown.
Differentiate $u$ and integrate $dv$ to find $du$ and $v$.

$$= 5x(\tfrac{1}{3}e^{3x} + C) - \int (\tfrac{1}{3}e^{3x} + C)5\,dx$$

Use the integration by parts formula, $\int u\,dv = uv - \int v\,du$.

$$= \tfrac{5}{3}xe^{3x} + 5Cx - \int \tfrac{5}{3}e^{3x}\,dx - \int 5C\,dx$$

$$= \tfrac{5}{3}xe^{3x} + 5Cx - \tfrac{5}{9}e^{3x} - 5Cx + C_1$$

$$= \tfrac{5}{3}xe^{3x} - \tfrac{5}{9}e^{3x} + C_1$$

■

Again, the original constant $C$ in integrating $\int dv$ conveniently "drops out." The $C_1$ comes from the last integral. In Problem 46 of Problem Set 9-3, you will prove that this is always the case. So you don't need to worry about putting in the $+C$ until the last integral disappears. Example 2 shows that you may have to integrate by parts more than once.

■ **Example 2** Do the integrating: $\int x^2 \cos 4x\,dx$

**Solution**

$$\int x^2 \cos 4x\,dx \qquad u = x^2 \qquad dv = \cos 4x\,dx$$

$$du = 2x\,dx \qquad v = \tfrac{1}{4}\sin 4x$$

$$= x^2 \cdot \tfrac{1}{4}\sin 4x - \int (\tfrac{1}{4}\sin 4x)(2x\,dx)$$

Use $\int u\,dv = uv - \int v\,du$.

Note that the integral still involves a product of two functions.

$$= \tfrac{1}{4}x^2 \sin 4x - \int (2x)(\tfrac{1}{4}\sin 4x\,dx)$$

Associate the $dx$ with the sine factor, as it was originally.

$$u = 2x \qquad dv = \tfrac{1}{4}\sin 4x\,dx$$

$$du = 2dx \qquad v = -\tfrac{1}{16}\cos 4x$$

$$= \tfrac{1}{4}x^2 \sin 4x - [-\tfrac{1}{8}x\cos 4x - \int (-\tfrac{1}{16}\cos 4x)(2)\,dx]$$

Use integration by parts again.

$$= \tfrac{1}{4}x^2 \sin 4x + \tfrac{1}{8}x\cos 4x - \tfrac{1}{32}\sin 4x + C$$

■

Integration by parts is successful in this example because at both steps the second integral, $\int v\,du$, is less complex than $\int u\,dv$ at the start of the step. You could also have chosen these terms.

$$u = \cos 4x \qquad dv = x^2\,dx$$

$$du = -4\sin 4x dx \qquad v = \tfrac{1}{3}x^3$$

However, the new integral, $-\tfrac{4}{3}\int x^3 \sin 4x\,dx$, would have been more complicated than the original one. The following conclusions will help you decide how to split up an integral of a product into appropriate parts.

**Technique: Choosing the Parts in Integration by Parts**

To evaluate $\int u\,dv$, the following criteria should be met.

**Primary criterion:** $dv$ must be something you can integrate.

**Secondary criterion:** $u$ should, if possible, be something that gets simpler (or at least not much more complicated) when it is differentiated.

# Problem Set 9-2

### *Do These Quickly*

The following problems are intended to refresh your skills. You should be able to do all ten problems in less than five minutes.

**Q1.** Differentiate: $y = x \tan x$

**Q2.** Integrate: $\int x^{10}\,dx$

**Q3.** Sketch: $y = e^{-x}$

**Q4.** Integrate: $\int \cos 3x\,dx$

**Q5.** Differentiate: $y = \cos 5x \sin 5x$

**Q6.** Sketch: $y = 2/x$

**Q7.** $r(x) = \int t(x)\,dx$ if and only if -?-.

**Q8.** Definition: $f'(x) =$ -?-.

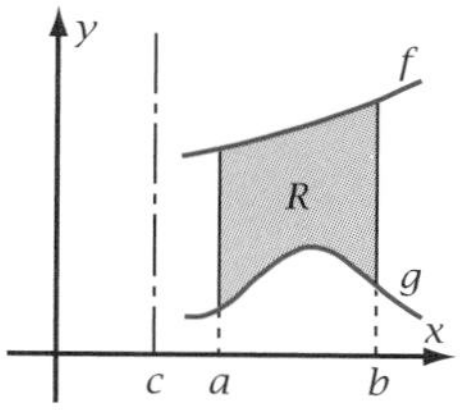


Figure 9-2b

**Q9.** If region $R$ (Figure 9-2b) is rotated around the line $x = c$, the volume of the solid is -?-.

**Q10.** If $f(6.2) = 13$, $f(6.5) = 19$, and $f(6.8) = 24$, then $f'(6.5) \approx$ -?-.

For Problems 1–10 integrate by parts.

1. $\int x \sin x\,dx$
2. $\int x \cos 3x\,dx$
3. $\int xe^{4x}\,dx$
4. $\int 6x\,e^{-3x}\,dx$
5. $\int (x+4)e^{-5x}\,dx$
6. $\int (x+7)e^{2x}\,dx$
7. $\int x^3 \ln x\,dx$
8. $\int x^5 \ln 3x\,dx$
9. $\int x^2 e^x\,dx$
10. $\int x^2 \sin x\,dx$
11. *Integral of the Natural Logarithm Problem:* The integral $\int \ln x\,dx$ can be evaluated by parts, but you must be clever to make the "obvious" choice of parts! Find $\int \ln x\,dx$.

# 9-3 Rapid Repeated Integration by Parts

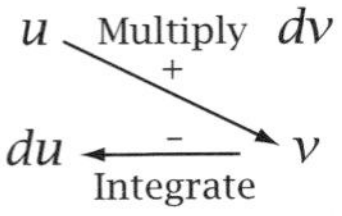

Figure 9-3a

There is a pattern that helps you remember the integration by parts formula. Write $u$ and $dv$ on one line. Below them write $du$ and $v$. The pattern is, "Multiply diagonally down, then integrate across the bottom." The arrows in Figure 9-3a remind you of this pattern. The plus and minus signs on the arrows say to add $uv$ and subtract $\int v\,du$.

This pattern is particularly useful when you must integrate by parts several times.

**OBJECTIVE**

Use the pattern of Figure 9-3a to simplify repeated integration by parts.

Here's the way Example 2 of Section 9-2 was done.

$$\int x^2 \cos 4x\,dx \qquad u = x^2 \quad dv = \cos 4x\,dx$$
$$du = 2x\,dx \quad v = \tfrac{1}{4}\sin 4x$$
$$= x^2 \cdot \tfrac{1}{4}\sin 4x - \int (\tfrac{1}{4}\sin 4x)(2x\,dx)$$
$$= \tfrac{1}{4}x^2 \sin 4x - \int (2x)(\tfrac{1}{4}\sin 4x\,dx) \qquad u = 2x \quad dv = \tfrac{1}{4}\sin 4x\,dx$$
$$du = 2\,dx \quad v = -\tfrac{1}{16}\cos 4x$$
$$= \tfrac{1}{4}x^2 \sin 4x - \left[-\tfrac{1}{8}x\cos 4x - \int (\tfrac{1}{16}\cos 4x)(2)\,dx\right]$$
$$= \tfrac{1}{4}x^2 \sin 4x + \tfrac{1}{8}x\cos 4x - \tfrac{1}{32}\sin 4x + C$$

Note that the function to be differentiated appears in the left-hand column and the function to be integrated appears in the right-hand one. For instance, $2x$ appears as part of $du$ in the first step and again as $u$ in the next step. If you head the left column "$u$" and the right column "$dv$," and leave out $dx$ and other redundant information, the work can be shortened as follows.

$$\int x^2 \cos 4x\,dx$$

$$= \tfrac{1}{4}x^2 \sin 4x + \tfrac{1}{8}x\cos 4x - \tfrac{1}{32}\sin 4x + C$$

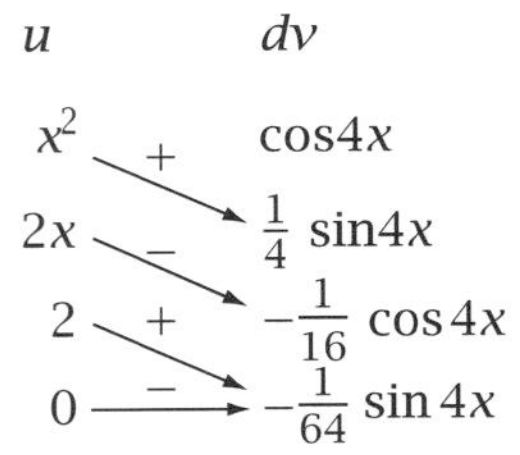


The second diagonal arrow has a minus sign because the minus sign from the first $\int v\,du$ carries over. The third diagonal arrow has a plus sign since $(-)(-)$ from the step before gives a plus. If you put in the third step (fourth line), the last integral is $\int 0\,dx$, which equals $C$, the constant of integration.

### *Technique: Rapid Repeated Integration by Parts*

- Choose parts $u$ and $dv$. Differentiate the $u$'s and integrate the $dv$'s.
- Multiply down each diagonal.
- Integrate once across the bottom.
- Use alternating signs shown on the arrows.

If you get 0 in the $u$-column, the one integral will be $\int 0\,dx$, which equals $C$.

Examples 1–4 show some special cases and how to handle them.

### *Make the Original Integral Reappear*

When you do repeated integration by parts, the original integral may reappear.

**Example 1** Do the integrating: $\int e^{6x}\cos 4x\,dx$

| $u$ | | $dv$ |
|---|---|---|
| $e^{6x}$ | $+$ | $\cos 4x$ |
| $6e^{6x}$ | $-$ | $\frac{1}{4}\sin 4x$ |
| $36e^{6x}$ | $+$ | $-\frac{1}{16}\cos 4x$ |

**Solution**

$$\int e^{6x}\cos 4x\,dx$$

$$= \tfrac{1}{4}e^{6x}\sin 4x + \tfrac{6}{16}e^{6x}\cos 4x - \tfrac{36}{16}\int e^{6x}\cos 4x\,dx$$

Why + and −, not − and +?

The integral on the right is the same as the original one on the left but has a different coefficient. Adding $\frac{36}{16}\int e^{6x}\cos 4x\,dx$ to both sides of the equation gives

$$\tfrac{52}{16}\int e^{6x}\cos 4x\,dx = \tfrac{1}{4}e^{6x}\sin 4x + \tfrac{6}{16}e^{6x}\cos 4x + C$$

The "$+C$" must be displayed on the right-hand side of the equation because no indefinite integral remains there. Multiplying both sides by $\frac{16}{52}$ and simplifying gives

$$\int e^{6x}\cos 4x\,dx = \tfrac{1}{13}e^{6x}\sin 4x + \tfrac{3}{26}e^{6x}\cos 4x + C_1. \qquad C_1 = \tfrac{16}{52}C$$

∎

In case you have doubts about the validity of what has been done, the answer can be checked by differentiation.

$$y = \tfrac{1}{13}e^{6x}\sin 4x + \tfrac{3}{26}e^{6x}\cos 4x + C_1$$

$$y' = \tfrac{6}{13}e^{6x}\sin 4x + \tfrac{4}{13}e^{6x}\cos 4x + \tfrac{9}{13}e^{6x}\cos 4x - \tfrac{6}{13}e^{6x}\sin 4x$$

$$y' = e^{6x}\cos 4x$$

The original integrand.

### *Use Trigonometric Properties to Make the Original Integral Reappear*

In Example 1, you found that the original integral reappeared on the right-hand side of the equation. Sometimes you can use properties of the trigonometric functions to make this happen. Example 2 shows how this can be done. Note the clever choice of $u$ and $dv$!

**Example 2** Do the integrating: $\int \sin^2 x\,dx$

| $u$ | | $dv$ |
|---|---|---|
| $\sin x$ | $+$ | $\sin x$ |
| $\cos x$ | $-$ | $-\cos x$ |

**Solution**

$$\int \sin^2 x\,dx$$

$$= -\sin x\cos x + \int \cos^2 x\,dx$$

$$= -\sin x\cos x + \int (1 - \sin^2 x)\,dx \qquad \text{By the Pythagorean properties.}$$

$$= -\sin x\cos x + \int 1\,dx - \int \sin^2 x\,dx \qquad \int \sin^2 x\,dx \text{ reappears!}$$

$$\therefore 2\int \sin^2 x\,dx = -\sin x\cos x + x + C \qquad \text{Do the indicated algebra.}$$

$$\int \sin^2 x\,dx = -\tfrac{1}{2}\sin x\cos x + \tfrac{1}{2}x + C_1$$

∎

It would have been possible to make $\int \sin^2 x\,dx$ reappear by carrying the integration by parts one more step. Something unfortunate happens in this case, as shown here.

$$\int \sin^2 x\,dx$$
$$= -\sin x \cos x + \cos x \sin x + \int \sin^2 x\,dx$$

| $u$ | | $dv$ |
|---|---|---|
| $\sin x$ | $+$ ↘ | $\sin x$ |
| $\cos x$ | $-$ ↘ | $-\cos x$ |
| $-\sin x$ | ← $+$ | $-\sin x$ |

This time the original integral appears on the right-hand side but with 1 as its coefficient. When you subtract $\int \sin^2 x\,dx$ from both sides and simplify, you wind up with

$$0 = 0,$$

which is true, but not very helpful! Stopping one step earlier as in Example 2 avoids this difficulty.

### *Reassociate Factors Between Steps*

The table form of repeated integration by parts relies on the fact that the $u$ and $dv$ stay separate at each step. Sometimes it is necessary to reassociate some of the factors of $u$ with $dv$, or vice versa, before taking the next step. The table format can still be used. Example 3 shows how.

**Example 3** Do the integrating: $\int x^3 e^{x^2}\,dx$

**Solution** The quantity $x\,e^{x^2}\,dx$ can be integrated like this:

$$\int x\,e^{x^2}\,dx = \tfrac{1}{2}\int e^{x^2}(2x\,dx) = \tfrac{1}{2}e^{x^2} + C$$

The technique is to make $xe^{x^2}\,dx$ show up in the $dv$ column.

| $u$ | | $dv$ | |
|---|---|---|---|
| $x^2$ | $+$ ↘ | $xe^{x^2}$ | |
| $2x$ | | $\frac{1}{2}e^{x^2}$ | Choose the parts this way. |
| - - - - - - | | - - - - - - | Draw a dashed line. |
| $2$ | $-$ ↘ | $\frac{1}{2}xe^{x^2}$ | |
| $0$ | ← $+$ | $\frac{1}{4}e^{x^2}$ | Associate the $x$ with the other factor. |

$$\therefore \int x^3 e^{x^2}\,dx = \tfrac{1}{2}x^2 e^{x^2} - \tfrac{1}{2}e^{x^2} + C$$ ■

The dashed line across the two columns indicates that the factors above the line have been reassociated to the form shown below the line. The arrows indicate which of the terms are actually multiplied together to give the answer.

### *Integral of the Natural Logarithm Function*

In Problem 11 of Problem Set 9-2, you were asked to integrate $\ln x$. To do this, you must be clever in selecting the "parts." Example 4 shows you how.

■ ***Example 4*** Do the integrating: $\int \ln x\, dx$

***Solution***

$$\int \ln x\, dx$$
$$= x\ln x - \int \frac{1}{x}(x)\, dx$$
$$= x\ln x - x + C.$$

| $u$ | | $dv$ |
|---|---|---|
| $\ln x$ | $+$ | $1$ |
| $1/x$ | $-$ | $x$ |

*dv* can be integrated! ■

**Property: Integral of the Natural Logarithm Function**

$$\int \ln x\, dx = x\ln x - x + C$$

In Problem Set 9-3, you will practice rapid repeated integration by parts. You will justify the fact that the "$+C$" can be left out in the integration of $dv$. You will also practice integrating other familiar functions.

# Problem Set 9-3

### Do These Quickly

The following problems are intended to refresh your skills. You should be able to do all 10 in less than 5 minutes.

**Q1.** Differentiate: $f(t) = te^t$

**Q2.** Integrate: $\int r^5\, dr$

**Q3.** Differentiate: $g(m) = m \sin 2m$

**Q4.** Integrate: $\int \sec^2 x\, dx$

**Q5.** Integrate: $\int (x^3 + 11)^5 (x^2\, dx)$

**Q6.** Integrate: $\int (x^3 + 11)\, dx$

**Q7.** Find $\lim_{x\to 0} \left(\frac{\sin x}{x}\right)$.

**Q8.** Find $\lim_{x\to 0} \left(\frac{\sin x}{2x}\right)$.

**Q9.** If region $R$ (Figure 9-3b) is rotated about the $x$-axis, the volume of the solid is -?-.

**Q10.** Sketch the paraboloid formed by rotating $y = x^2$ from $x = 0$ to 2 around the $y$-axis.

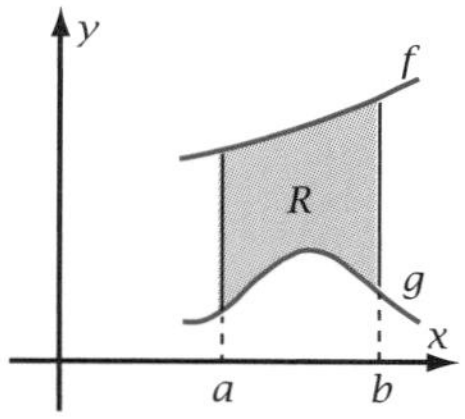


Figure 9-3b

For Problems 1–20, do the integrating.

1. $\int x^3 e^{2x}\, dx$

2. $\int x^5 e^{-x}\, dx$

3. $\int x^4 \sin x\, dx$

4. $\int x^2 \cos x\, dx$

5. $\int x^5 \cos 2x\, dx$

6. $\int x^3 \sin 5x\, dx$

7. $\int e^x \sin x\, dx$

8. $\int e^x \cos x\, dx$

9. $\int e^{3x} \cos 5x\, dx$

10. $\int e^{4x} \sin 2x\, dx$

11. $\int x^7 \ln 3x \, dx$

12. $\int x^5 \ln 6x \, dx$

13. $\int x^4 \ln 7 \, dx$

14. $\int e^{7x} \cos 5 \, dx$

15. $\int \sin^5 x \cos x \, dx$

16. $\int x(3 - x^2)^{2/3} \, dx$

17. $\int x^3 (x + 5)^{1/2} \, dx$

18. $\int x^2 \sqrt{2 - x} \, dx$

19. $\int \ln x^5 \, dx$

20. $\int e^{\ln 7x} \, dx$

For Problems 21–32, do the integrating. You may reassociate factors between steps or use the trigonometric functions or logarithm properties in the integration by parts.

21. $\int x^5 e^{x^2} \, dx$

22. $\int x^5 e^{x^3} \, dx$

23. $\int x(\ln x)^3 \, dx$

24. $\int x^3 (\ln x)^2 \, dx$

25. $\int x^3 (x^2 + 1)^4 \, dx$

26. $\int x^3 \sqrt{x^2 - 3} \, dx$

27. $\int \cos^2 x \, dx$

28. $\int \sin^2 0.4x \, dx$

29. $\int \sec^3 x \, dx$

30. $\int \sec^2 x \tan x \, dx$ (Be clever!)

31. $\int \log_3 x \, dx$

32. $\int \log_{10} x \, dx$

For Problems 31–38, write the antiderivative.

33. $\int \sin x \, dx$

34. $\int \cos x \, dx$

35. $\int \csc x \, dx$

36. $\int \sec x \, dx$

37. $\int \tan x \, dx$

38. $\int \cot x \, dx$

39. Wanda Y. Knott evaluates $\int x^2 \cos x \, dx$, letting $u = x^2$ and $dv = \cos x \, dx$. She gets

$$x^2 \sin x - \int 2x \sin x \, dx.$$

For the second integral, she lets $u = \sin x$ and $dv = 2x \, dx$. Show Wanda why her second choice of $u$ and $dv$ is inappropriate.

40. Amos Take evaluates $\int x^2 \cos x \, dx$ by parts, letting $u = \cos x$ and $dv = x^2 \, dx$. Show Amos that although his choice for $dv$ can be integrated, it is a mistake to choose the parts as he did.

41. If you evaluate $\int e^x \sin x \, dx$, the original integral reappears after two integrations by parts. It will also reappear after four integrations by parts. Show why it would be unproductive to evaluate the integral this way.

42. The integral $\int \cos^2 x \, dx$ can be integrated by clever use of trigonometric properties, as well as by parts. Substitute $\frac{1}{2}(1 + \cos 2x)$ for $\cos^2 x$ and integrate. Compare this answer with that which you obtain using integration by parts, and show that the two answers are equivalent.

43. *Area Problem:* Sketch the graph of $y = xe^{-x}$ from $x = 0$ to $x = 3$. Where does the function have its high point in the interval [0, 3]? Find algebraically, with the fundamental theorem, the area of the region under the graph from $x = 0$ to $x = 3$.

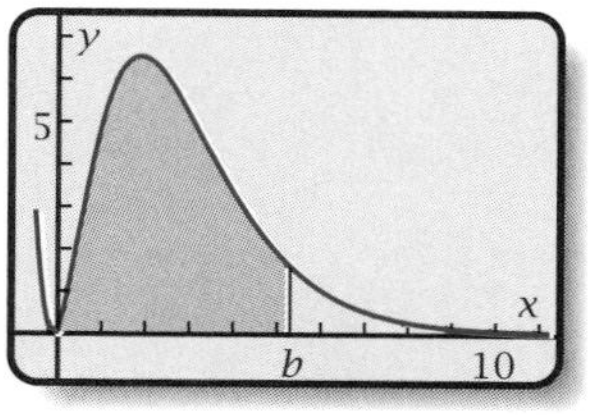

Figure 9-3c

44. *Unbounded Region Area Problem:* Figure 9-3c shows the region under the graph of $y = 12x^2e^{-x}$ from $x = 0$ to $x = b$. Find an equation for this area in terms of $b$. Then find the limit of the area as $b$ approaches infinity. Does the area approach a finite number, or does it increase without bound as $b$ increases? Justify your answer.

45. *Volume Problem:* The region under the graph of $y = \ln x$ from $x = 1$ to $x = 5$ is rotated around the $x$-axis to form a solid. Find its volume exactly, using the fundamental theorem.

46. *Proof Problem:* In setting up an integration by parts problem, you select $dv$ to equal something useful, and integrate to find $v$. Prove that whatever number you pick for the constant of integration at this point, it will cancel out later in the integration by parts process.

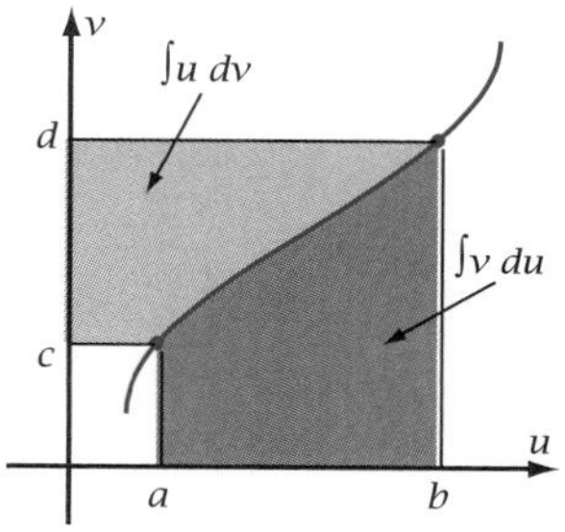

Figure 9-3d

47. *Areas and Integration by Parts:* Figure 9-3d shows the graph of function $v$ plotted against function $u$. As $u$ goes from $a$ to $b$, $v$ goes from $c$ to $d$. Show that the integration by parts formula can be interpreted in terms of areas on this diagram. (This diagram is the same as the logo at the top of each even page in this chapter.)

48. *Integral of ln Generalization Problem:* Derive a formula for $\int \ln ax\,dx$, where $a$ stands for a non-zero constant.

*49. *Introduction to Reduction Formulas Problem:* For $\int \sin^7 x\,dx$, integrate once by parts. Use the Pythagorean properties in an appropriate manner to write the remaining integral as two integrals, one involving $\sin^5 x$ and the other involving $\sin^7 x$. Then use algebra to combine the two integrals involving $\sin^7 x$, and thus express $\int \sin^7 x\,dx$ in terms of $\int \sin^5 x\,dx$. Use the resulting pattern repeatedly to finish evaluating $\int \sin^7 x\,dx$. The pattern leads to a reduction formula, as you will learn in the next section.

50. *Journal Problem:* Update your journal with techniques and concepts you have learned since the last entry. In particular, tell about integration by parts, the kind of integral it is used for, and the rapid way in which it can be accomplished.

*This problem prepares you for the next section.

# 9-4 Reduction Formulas and Computer Software

In this section you will develop formulas that allow you to integrate algebraically powers of the trigonometric functions. Repeated integration by parts can be used for integrals such as

$$\int \sin^6 x\, dx.$$

The choice for $dv$ is $\sin x\, dx$ because it can be integrated and the result is no more complicated. But the other part, $u = \sin^5 x$, gets more complex when you differentiate it.

| $u$ | | $dv$ |
|---|---|---|
| $\sin^5 x$ | $+$ | $\sin x$ |
| $5\sin^4 x \cos x$ | $-$ | $-\cos x$ |

So you just put the integral back together and hope for the best!

$$\int \sin^6 x\, dx$$
$$= -\sin^5 x \cos x + 5\int \sin^4 x \cos^2 x\, dx$$
$$= -\sin^5 x \cos x + 5\int \sin^4 x(1 - \sin^2 x)\, dx$$

Use the Pythagorean property to return to sines.

$$= -\sin^5 x \cos x + 5\int \sin^4 x\, dx - 5\int \sin^6 x\, dx$$

The original integral appears on the right-hand side with a coefficient of $-5$. Adding $5\int \sin^6 x\, dx$ to the first and last members of the above equation (and using the transitive property to ignore the two members in the middle) gives

$$6\int \sin^6 x\, dx = -\sin^5 x \cos x + 5\int \sin^4 x\, dx.$$

Dividing by 6 gives

$$\int \sin^6 x\, dx = -\tfrac{1}{6}\sin^5 x \cos x + \tfrac{5}{6}\int \sin^4 x\, dx.$$

The integral $\int \sin^6 x\, dx$ has been replaced by an expression in terms of $\int \sin^4 x\, dx$. The new integral has the same form as the original but is "reduced" in complexity. By repeating the above integration with $n$ instead of 6 as the exponent, you can find an equation expressing this integral with any nonzero exponent in terms of an integral with that exponent reduced by 2.

$$\int \sin^n x\, dx = -\frac{1}{n}\sin^{n-1} x \cos x + \frac{n-1}{n}\int \sin^{n-2} x\, dx$$

An equation such as this one is called a **reduction formula**. It can be used again on the new integral. For the above example, the work would look like this.

$$\int \sin^6 x\, dx$$
$$= -\tfrac{1}{6}\sin^5 x \cos x + \tfrac{5}{6}\int \sin^4 x\, dx$$
$$= \text{ " } + \tfrac{5}{6}\left(-\tfrac{1}{4}\sin^3 x \cos x + \tfrac{3}{4}\int \sin^2 x\, dx\right)$$
$$= \text{ " } - \tfrac{5}{24}\sin^3 x \cos x + \tfrac{5}{8}\int \sin^2 x\, dx$$
$$= \text{ " } - \text{ " } + \tfrac{5}{8}\left(-\tfrac{1}{2}\sin^1 x \cos x + \tfrac{1}{2}\int \sin^0 x\, dx\right)$$
$$= \text{ " } - \text{ " } - \tfrac{5}{16}\sin x \cos x + \tfrac{5}{16}\int dx.$$

The last integral equals $x + C$.

$$= -\tfrac{1}{6}\sin^5 x \cos x - \tfrac{5}{24}\sin^3 x \cos x - \tfrac{5}{16}\sin x \cos x + \tfrac{5}{16}x + C.$$

Answer.

You can use ditto marks, as shown, to avoid having to rewrite the first terms so many times.

### Definition: Reduction Formula

A reduction formula is an equation expressing an integral of a particular kind in terms of an integral of exactly the same kind, but of reduced complexity.

**OBJECTIVE**

Given an integral involving powers of functions, derive a reduction formula, and given a reduction formula, use it to evaluate an indefinite integral either by pencil and paper or by computer software.

The following formulas for integration of the six trigonometric functions (recall from Section 6-9) are repeated here to refresh your memory.

### Properties: Integrals of the Trigonometric Functions

$$\int \sin x\,dx = -\cos x + C \qquad \int \cos x\,dx = \sin x + C$$

$$\int \tan x\,dx = \ln|\sec x| + C = -\ln|\cos x| + C \qquad \int \cot x\,dx = -\ln|\csc x| + C = \ln|\sin x| + C$$

$$\int \sec x\,dx = \ln|\sec x + \tan x| + C = -\ln|\sec x - \tan x| + C \qquad \int \csc x\,dx = -\ln|\csc x + \cot x| + C = \ln|\csc x - \cot x| + C$$

The work at the beginning of this section shows that a reduction formula can be derived by choosing a particular case, integrating, and looking for a pattern in the answer. However, to be perfectly sure the result is correct, start with a general integral of the type in question, using a letter such as $n$ to stand for the (constant) exponent. Example 1 shows you how the derivation can be done for the integral of $\sec^n x\,dx$.

**Example 1**

a. Derive a reduction formula for $\int \sec^n x\,dx$ that can be used if $n \ge 2$.

b. Use the reduction formula to evaluate $\int \sec^5 x\,dx$.

c. Check your answer to part b by computer software.

**Solutions**

a. The best choice for $dv$ is $\sec^2 x\,dx$, because it can be integrated easily and its integral, $\tan x$, is simpler than the original integrand. The work looks like this.

| $u$ | | $dv$ |
|---|---|---|
| $\sec^{n-2} x$ | $+$ | $\sec^2 x$ |
| $(n-2)\sec^{n-3} x \sec x \tan x$ | $-$ | $\tan x$ |

$$\int \sec^n x\,dx$$

$$= \sec^{n-2}x \tan x - (n-2)\int \sec^{n-2}x \tan^2 x\,dx$$

$$= \sec^{n-2}x \tan x - (n-2)\int \sec^{n-2}x(\sec^2 x - 1)\,dx$$

$$= \sec^{n-2}x \tan x - (n-2)\int (\sec^n x - \sec^{n-2}x)\,dx$$

$$= \sec^{n-2}x \tan x - (n-2)\int \sec^n x\,dx + (n-2)\int \sec^{n-2}x\,dx$$

The desired integral now appears in the last member of the equation, with $-(n-2)$ as its coefficient. Adding $(n-2)\int \sec^n x\,dx$ to the first and last members (and eliminating the middle members by transitivity) gives

$$(n-1)\int \sec^n x\,dx = \sec^{n-2}x\tan x + (n-2)\int \sec^{n-2}x\,dx.$$

Dividing both members by $(n-1)$ produces the desired reduction formula.

$$\int \sec^n x\,dx = \frac{1}{n-1}\sec^{n-2}x\tan x + \frac{n-2}{n-1}\int \sec^{n-2}x\,dx$$

b.
$$\begin{aligned}&\int \sec^5 x\,dx\\ &= \tfrac{1}{4}\sec^3 x\tan x + \tfrac{3}{4}\int \sec^3 x\,dx\\ &= \tfrac{1}{4}\sec^3 x\tan x + \tfrac{3}{4}(\tfrac{1}{2}\sec x\tan x + \tfrac{1}{2}\int \sec x\,dx)\\ &= \tfrac{1}{4}\sec^3 x\tan x + \tfrac{3}{8}\sec x\tan x + \tfrac{3}{8}\int \sec x\,dx\\ &= \tfrac{1}{4}\sec^3 x\tan x + \tfrac{3}{8}\sec x\tan x + \tfrac{3}{8}\ln|\sec x + \tan x| + C\end{aligned}$$

c. Symbol-manipulating software may present the answer in a slightly different form. For instance, the Mathematics Exploration Toolkit gives

$$\frac{12\ln(|\sec(x)+\tan(x)|)\cos^6(x) + 12\cos^4(x)\sin(x) + 8\cos^2(x)\sin(x)}{32\cos^6(x)} + C$$

By converting $\sin x/\cos x$ to $\tan x$, and $\cos x$ to $1/\sec x$, you get an answer equivalent to that in part b. ■

Sometimes a reduction formula can be derived without integrating by parts as Example 2 shows.

**■ Example 2** Derive a reduction formula for $\int \cot^n x\,dx$ that can be used if $n \ge 2$.

**Solution**

$$\begin{aligned}&\int \cot^n x\,dx\\ &= \int \cot^{n-2}x(\cot^2 x\,dx)\\ &= \int \cot^{n-2}x(\csc^2 x - 1)\,dx && \text{Use the Pythagorean properties to transform to cosecant.}\\ &= \int \cot^{n-2}x\csc^2 x\,dx - \int \cot^{n-2}x\,dx\\ &= -\frac{1}{n-1}\cot^{n-1}x - \int \cot^{n-2}x\,dx && \text{Integral of a power function.}\end{aligned}$$

The last expression has the integral of cotangent with an exponent 2 less than the original integral and is thus a reduction formula. ■

**■ Example 3** Use the reduction formula in Example 2 to evaluate $\int \cot^5 x\,dx$.

**Solution**

$$\begin{aligned}&\int \cot^5 x\,dx\\ &= -\tfrac{1}{4}\cot^4 x - \int \cot^3 x\,dx\\ &= -\tfrac{1}{4}\cot^4 x - (-\tfrac{1}{2}\cot^2 x - \int \cot x\,dx)\\ &= -\tfrac{1}{4}\cot^4 x + \tfrac{1}{2}\cot^2 x + \ln|\sin x| + C\end{aligned}$$ ■

You will derive the following reduction formulas in Problem Set 9-4.

**Reduction Formulas: Integrals of Powers of Trigonometric Functions**

(For reference only. Do not try to memorize these!)

$$\int \sin^n x\,dx = -\frac{1}{n}\sin^{n-1}x\cos x + \frac{n-1}{n}\int \sin^{n-2}x\,dx, \text{ for } n \ge 2$$

$$\int \cos^n x\,dx = \frac{1}{n}\cos^{n-1}x\sin x + \frac{n-1}{n}\int \cos^{n-2}x\,dx, \text{ for } n \ge 2$$

$$\int \tan^n x\,dx = \frac{1}{n-1}\tan^{n-1}x - \int \tan^{n-2}x\,dx, \text{ for } n \ge 2$$

$$\int \cot^n x\,dx = -\frac{1}{n-1}\cot^{n-1}x - \int \cot^{n-2}x\,dx, \text{ for } n \ge 2$$

$$\int \sec^n x\,dx = \frac{1}{n-1}\sec^{n-2}x\tan x + \frac{n-2}{n-1}\int \sec^{n-2}x\,dx, \text{ for } n \ge 2$$

$$\int \csc^n x\,dx = -\frac{1}{n-1}\csc^{n-2}x\cot x + \frac{n-2}{n-1}\int \csc^{n-2}x\,dx, \text{ for } n \ge 2$$

Don't try to memorize the reduction formulas! You are almost bound to make a mistake, and there is nothing quite as useless as a wrong formula. Fortunately you will not have to make a career out of evaluating reduction formulas. Your purpose here is to see how the computer comes up with an answer as in Example 1 when it integrates a power of a trigonometric function.

## Problem Set 9-4

### *Do These Quickly*

The following problems are intended to refresh your skills. You should be able to do all ten problems in less than five minutes.

**Q1.** In integration by parts, $\int u\,dv =$ -?-.

**Q2.** Sketch: $y = 3\cos x$

**Q3.** Sketch: $y = \cos 2x$

**Q4.** Differentiate: $y = x\ln 5x$

**Q5.** Integrate: $\int \sin^5 x\cos x\,dx$

**Q6.** Integrate: $\int dx/x$

**Q7.** Integrate: $\int_1^3 e^{2x}\,dx$

**Q8.** Sketch the graph of a function that is continuous at (3, 1) but not differentiable there.

**Q9.** Find: $(d/dx)(\tan^{-1}x)$

**Q10.** Integrate: $\int \sec x\,dx$

For Problems 1–6, take the first step in integration by parts or use appropriate trigonometry to write the given integral in terms of an integral with a reduced power of the same function.

1. $\int \sin^9 x\,dx$

2. $\int \cos^{10} x\,dx$

3. $\int \cot^{12} x\,dx$

4. $\int \tan^{20} x\,dx$

5. $\int \sec^{13} x\,dx$

6. $\int \csc^{100} x\,dx$

For Problems 7–12, derive the reduction formula in the table on page 449 directly, using $n$ as the exponent, rather than using a particular constant as in Problems 1–6.

7. $\int \cos^n x\,dx, \quad n = 0$

8. $\int \sin^n x\,dx, \quad n = 0$

9. $\int \tan^n x\,dx, \quad n = 0$

10. $\int \cot^n x\,dx, \quad n = 0$

11. $\int \csc^n x\,dx, \quad n = 0$

12. $\int \sec^n x\,dx, \quad n = 0$

For Problems 13–18, integrate by one of these methods.

a. Use pencil and paper, and the appropriate reduction formula.
b. Use computer software.

13. $\int \sin^5 x\,dx$

14. $\int \cos^5 x\,dx$

15. $\int \cot^6 x\,dx$

16. $\int \tan^7 x\,dx$

17. $\int \sec^4 x\,dx$

18. $\int \csc^4 x\,dx$

19. *Cosine Area Problem:* Figure 9-4a shows the graphs of

$y = \cos x,$
$y = \cos^3 x,$ and
$y = \cos^5 x.$

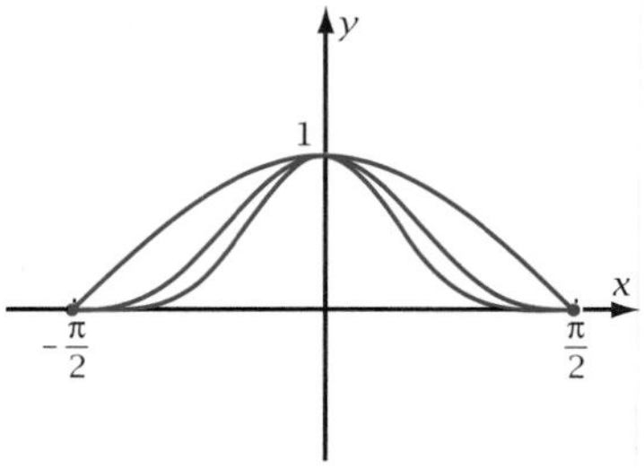

Figure 9-4a

a. Which graph goes with which function?
b. By numerical integration find the approximate area of the region under each graph from $x = -\pi/2$ to $\pi/2$.
c. Find exactly each area in 19b by the fundamental theorem. Use the reduction formulas.
d. Based on the graphs, explain why the areas you calculated are reasonable.
e. Plot the graph of $y = \cos^{100} x$. Sketch the result.
f. As the exponent $n$ gets larger, the graph of $y = \cos^n x$ gets "narrower." Does the limit of the area as $n$ approaches infinity seem to be zero? Explain.

*20. *Integral of* $\cos^5 x$ *Another Way:* The integral $\int \cos^5 x\,dx$ can be written

$$\int \cos^5 x\,dx = \int (\cos^4 x)\cos x\,dx.$$

The factor $\cos^4 x$ can be converted to powers of sine by appropriate use of the Pythagorean properties from trigonometry. The result will be three integrals that you will be able to evaluate by the fundamental theorem. Find the area of the region under the graph of $y = \cos^5 x$ from $x = -\pi/2$ to $\pi/2$ using this technique for integration. Compare your answer with that in Problem 19c.

*This problem prepares you for the next section.

21. *Integral of Secant Cubed Problem:* The integral $\int \sec^3 x\,dx$ seems to appear often, as you will see in the next few sections. Use an appropriate technique to do the integration. Then see whether you can figure out a way to remember the answer.

22. *Reduction Formula for* $\int \sin^n ax\,dx$*:* Derive a reduction formula for

$$\int \sin^n ax\,dx,\ n \geq 2,\ a \neq 0.$$

Then use the reduction formula to evaluate $\int \sin^5 3x\,dx$.

23. Prove that $\int \sin^3 ax\,dx = -\dfrac{1}{3a}(\cos ax)(\sin^2 ax + 2) + C\ (a \neq 0)$.

24. Prove that $\int \cos^3 ax\,dx = \dfrac{1}{3a}(\sin ax)(\cos^2 ax + 2) + C\ (a \neq 0)$.

# 9-5 Integrating Special Powers of Trigonometric Functions

In Section 9-4, you found algebraically the indefinite integrals of any positive integer power of any trigonometric function. In this section you will see how to integrate some special powers of these functions without having to resort to reduction formulas.

**OBJECTIVE**

Be able to integrate odd powers of sine or cosine, even powers of secant or cosecant, and squares of sine or cosine without having to use the reduction formulas.

### Odd Powers of Sine and Cosine

**Example 1** Do the integrating: $\int \sin^7 x\,dx$

**Solution** The key to the technique is associating one $\sin x$ factor with $dx$, then transforming the remaining (even) number of sines into cosines using the Pythagorean properties.

$$\begin{aligned}
&\int \sin^7 x\,dx\\
&= \int \sin^6 x(\sin x\,dx)\\
&= \int (\sin^2 x)^3(\sin x\,dx)\\
&= \int (1-\cos^2 x)^3(\sin x\,dx)\\
&= \int (1-3\cos^2 x+3\cos^4 x-\cos^6 x)(\sin x\,dx)\\
&= \int \sin x\,dx - 3\int \cos^2 x\sin x\,dx + 3\int \cos^4 x\sin x\,dx - \int \cos^6 x\sin x\,dx\\
&= -\cos x + \cos^3 x - \tfrac{3}{5}\cos^5 x + \tfrac{1}{7}\cos^7 x + C
\end{aligned}$$

■

Each integral in the next-to-last line of Example 1 has the form of the integral of a power, $\int u^n\,du$. So you wind up integrating power functions rather than trigonometric functions. This technique will work for odd powers of sine or cosine because associating one of the factors with $dx$ leaves an even number of sines or cosines to be transformed into the cofunction.

### Squares of Sine and Cosine

In Section 8-9, you found the area inside the limaçon $r = 5 + 4\cos\theta$ (Figure 9-5a) is

$$A = \frac{1}{2}\int_0^{2\pi} (5 + 4\cos\theta)^2\,d\theta.$$

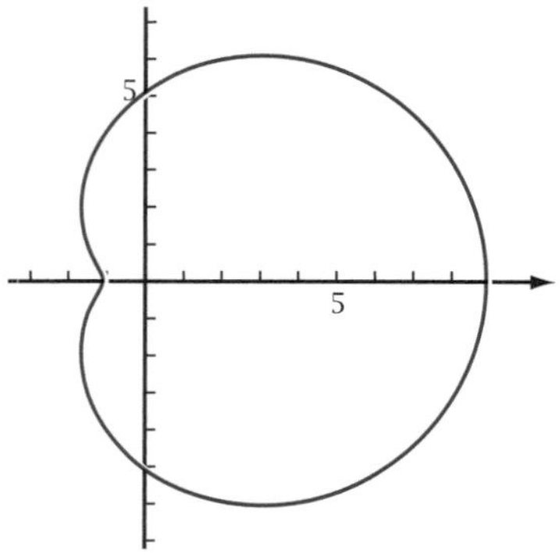


Figure 9-5a

Expanding the binomial power gives

$$A = \frac{1}{2}\int_0^{2\pi} (25 + 40\cos\theta + 16\cos^2\theta)\,d\theta.$$

The last term in the integral has $\cos^2\theta$. The integrals $\int \sin^2 x\,dx$ and $\int \cos^2 x\,dx$ occur frequently enough to make it worthwhile to learn an algebraic shortcut. The double argument property for cosine is

$$\cos 2x = \cos^2 x - \sin^2 x.$$

The right-hand side can be written either entirely in terms of cosine or entirely in terms of sine.

$$\cos 2x = 2\cos^2 x - 1$$
$$\cos 2x = 1 - 2\sin^2 x$$

Performing algebra on these two equations gives the following.

**Property: Double Argument Properties for Sine and Cosine, Transformed**

$$\cos^2 x = \frac{1}{2}(1 + \cos 2x)$$
$$\sin^2 x = \frac{1}{2}(1 - \cos 2x)$$

These two equations allow $\int \sin^2 x\,dx$ and $\int \cos^2 x\,dx$ to be transformed so that the integrand is linear in $\cos 2x$.

$$\int \cos^2 x\,dx = \tfrac{1}{2}\int (1 + \cos 2x)\,dx = \tfrac{1}{2}x + \tfrac{1}{4}\sin 2x + C$$
$$\int \sin^2 x\,dx = \tfrac{1}{2}\int (1 - \cos 2x)\,dx = \tfrac{1}{2}x - \tfrac{1}{4}\sin 2x + C$$

**■ Example 2** Do the integrating: $\int \sin^2 8x\,dx$

***Solution***

$$\int \sin^2 8x\,dx$$
$$= \tfrac{1}{2}\int (1 - \cos 16x)\,dx$$
$$= \tfrac{1}{2}x - \tfrac{1}{32}\sin 16x + C.$$ ■

### Even Powers of Secant and Cosecant

The technique for integrating odd powers of sine and cosine can be adapted to even powers of secant and cosecant. Example 3 shows how.

**■ Example 3** Do the integrating: $\int \sec^8 5x\,dx$

***Solution***

$$\int \sec^8 5x\,dx$$
$$= \int \sec^6 5x(\sec^2 5x\,dx)$$
$$= \int (\sec^2 5x)^3(\sec^2 5x\,dx)$$
$$= \int (\tan^2 5x + 1)^3(\sec^2 5x\,dx)$$
$$= \int (\tan^6 5x + 3\tan^4 5x + 3\tan^2 5x + 1)(\sec^2 5x\,dx)$$
$$= \int \tan^6 5x\sec^2 5x\,dx + 3\int \tan^4 5x\sec^2 5x\,dx + 3\int \tan^2 5x\sec^2 5x\,dx + \int \sec^2 5x\,dx$$
$$= \tfrac{1}{35}\tan^7 5x + \tfrac{3}{25}\tan^5 5x + \tfrac{1}{5}\tan^3 5x + \tfrac{1}{5}\tan 5x + C$$ ■

The advantage of the techniques in Examples 2 and 3 is that you don't have to remember the reduction formulas. The disadvantages are that you must remember certain trigonometric properties, the binomial formula for expanding powers of binomials, and just which powers of which functions can be integrated this way. Problem Set 9-5 gives you some opportunities for practice. You will also find the exact area of the limaçon in Figure 9-5a.

## Problem Set 9-5

### Do These Quickly

The following problems are intended to refresh your skills. You should be able to do all ten problems in less than five minutes.

**Q1.** Find $f'(1): f(x) = x^3 - 7x$

**Q2.** Find $g'(2): g(x) = \ln x$

**Q3.** Find $h'(3): h(x) = (2x - 7)^6$

**Q4.** Find $t'(4): t(x) = \sin(\pi/12)x$

**Q5.** Find $p'(5): p(x) = xe^x$

**Q6.** Solve: $x^{1/3} = 8$

**Q7.** Sketch the graph: $(x/3)^2 + (y/5)^2 = 1$

**Q8.** $\int u\,dv = uv - \int v\,du$ is the —?— formula.

**Q9.** For Figure 9-5b, sketch the (continuous) antiderivative, $f(x)$, that contains point (2, 1).

**Q10.** $\int [f(x)]^n\,dx = g(x) + \int [f(x)]^{n-1}\,dx$ is called a —?— formula.

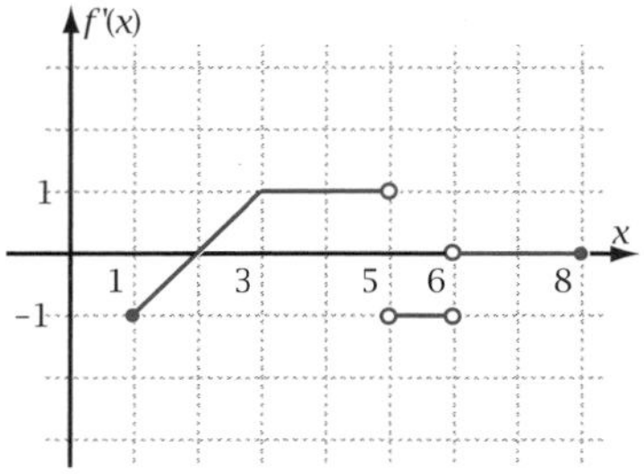

Figure 9-5b

For Problems 1–30, do the integration.

1. $\int \sin^5 x\,dx$
2. $\int \cos^7 x\,dx$
3. $\int \cos^7 9x\,dx$
4. $\int \sin^3 10x\,dx$
5. $\int \sin^4 3x \cos 3x\,dx$
6. $\int \cos^8 7x \sin 7x\,dx$
7. $\int \cos^6 8x \sin^3 8x\,dx$
8. $\int \sin^4 2x \cos^3 2x\,dx$
9. $\int \sin^5 x \cos^2 x\,dx$
10. $\int \cos^3 x \sin^2 x\,dx$
11. $\int \cos^2 x\,dx$
12. $\int \sin^2 x\,dx$
13. $\int \sin^2 5x\,dx$
14. $\int \cos^2 6x\,dx$
15. $\int \sec^4 x\,dx$
16. $\int \csc^6 x\,dx$
17. $\int \csc^8 6x\,dx$
18. $\int \sec^4 100x\,dx$
19. $\int \tan^{10} x \sec^2 x\,dx$
20. $\int \cot^8 x \csc^2 x\,dx$
21. $\int \sec^{10} x \tan x\,dx$
22. $\int \csc^8 x \cot x\,dx$
23. $\int \sec^{10} 20\,dx$
24. $\int \csc^8 12\,dx$
25. $\int (\cos^2 x - \sin^2 x)\,dx$
26. $\int (\cos^2 x + \sin^2 x)\,dx$
27. $\int (\sin x)^{-2}\,dx$
28. $\int (\cos 3x)^{-2}\,dx$
29. $\int \sec^3 x\,dx$
30. $\int \csc^3 x\,dx$

31. *Area Problem I:* Figure 9-5c shows the region bounded by the graph of

$$y = \cos 5x \sin 3x$$

from $x = 0$ to $x = 2\pi$.

a. Using integration by parts, find the indefinite integral $\int \cos 5x \sin 3x\,dx$.

b. Show that the region has just as much area below the $x$-axis as it has above.

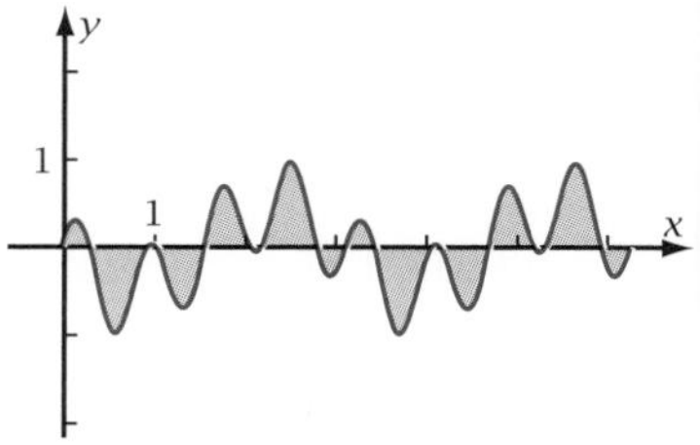

Figure 9-5c

32. *Area Problem II:* Let $f(x) = \sin^3 x$.

   a. Plot the graph from $x = 0$ to $x = \pi$. Sketch the result.

   b. Find the area of the region under the graph of $f$ from $x = 0$ to $x = \pi$ exactly, using the fundamental theorem and the integration techniques of this section.

   c. Verify your answer to 32b by integrating numerically.

   d. Quick! Find the integral of $f(x)$ from $x = -\pi$ to $x = \pi$. State what property allows you to answer this question so quickly.

33. *Volume Problem I:* One arch of the graph of $y = \sin x$ is rotated about the $x$-axis to form a football-shaped solid (Figure 9-5d). Find its volume. Use the fundamental theorem.

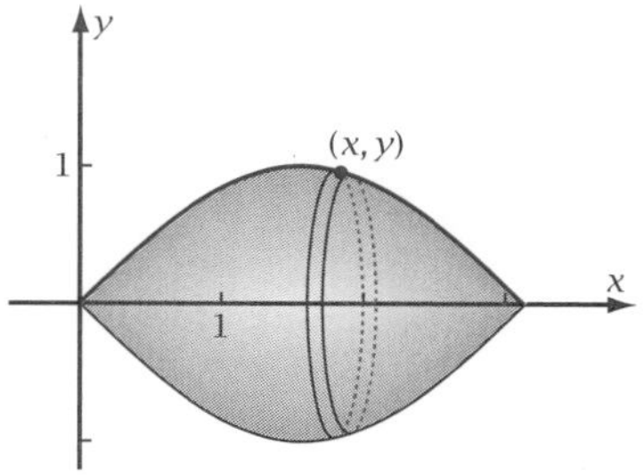

Figure 9-5d

34. *Volume Problem II:* The region under the graph of $y = \sec^2 x$ from $x = 0$ to $x = 1$ is rotated about the line $y = -3$ to form a solid.

   a. Find the exact volume of the solid.

   b. Find the exact volume of the solid if the region is rotated about the line $x = -3$.

35. *Limaçon Area Problem:* Figure 9-5e shows the limaçon

$$r = 5 + 4\cos\theta,$$

which appears at the beginning of this section. By numerical integration the area of the region from $\theta = 0$ to $\theta = \pi/4$ is 29.101205 ... square units. Find this area exactly, using the fundamental theorem. Write the answer using radicals and $\pi$, if necessary. Show that this exact answer, when evaluated, gives the same answer as obtained numerically.

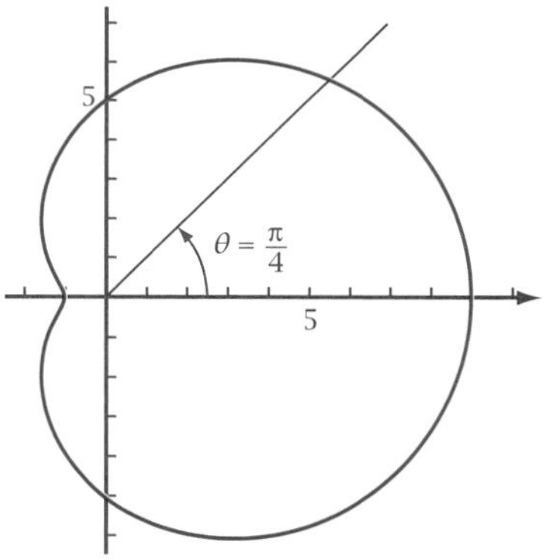

Figure 9-5e

36. *Cardioid Area Problem:* Figure 9-5f shows the general cardioid

$$r = a(1 + \cos\theta),$$

where $a$ is a constant. A circle of radius $a$ is inscribed in the cardioid. By the fundamental theorem, find the exact area inside the cardioid in terms of $a$. Explain how this area corresponds to the area of the circle.

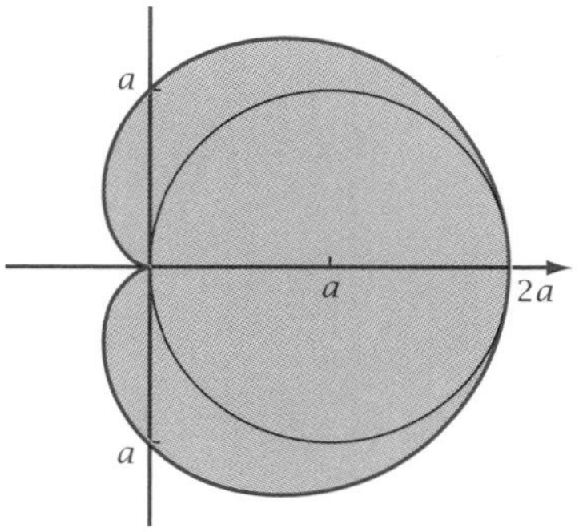

Figure 9-5f

37. *Journal Problem:* Update your journal with things you've learned since the last entry. You should include such things as those listed here.
   - The one most important thing you have learned since the last journal entry
   - The basis behind integration by parts, and what kind of function can be integrated that way
   - The reason one might want to go to the trouble of using the fundamental theorem to integrate, rather that simply using a Riemann sum or the trapezoidal rule
   - Any techniques or ideas about derivatives that are still unclear to you

# 9-6 Integration by Trigonometric Substitution

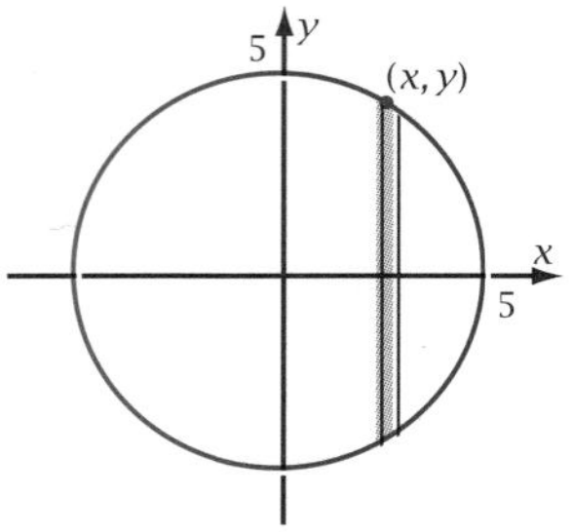


Figure 9-6a

Recall from geometry that the area of a circle is $A = \pi r^2$, where $r$ is the radius. This formula can be derived by calculus if you know how to integrate certain square root functions.

The circle in Figure 9-6a has equation

$$x^2 + y^2 = 25.$$

Draw a vertical strip. Pick a sample point in the strip on the upper half of the circle. The area of any one strip is $2y\,dx$. The upper half of the circle has equation

$$y = \sqrt{25 - x^2}.$$

So the area of the entire circle is

$$A = 2\int_{-5}^{5} \sqrt{25 - x^2}\,dx.$$

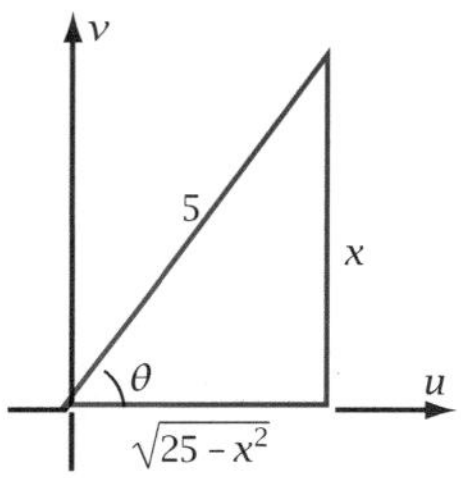


Figure 9-6b

The indefinite integral $\int \sqrt{25 - x^2}\,dx$ cannot be done as a power because $dx$ is not the differential of the inside function, $25 - x^2$. But there is an algebraic way to do the integration.

Here's your suggested thought process:

- Hmm . . . This looks Pythagorean. Like somebody was trying to find the third side of a right triangle.
- Draw a right triangle as in Figure 9-6b, placing the angle $\theta$ in standard position in a $uv$-coordinate system.
- The radicand is $25 - x^2$. So the hypotenuse must be 5 and one leg must be $x$.
- Put $x$ on the vertical leg (to avoid a minus sign in $dx$ later) and $\sqrt{25 - x^2}$ on the other leg.

$\therefore \dfrac{x}{5} = \sin\theta \Rightarrow x = 5\sin\theta \Rightarrow dx = 5\cos\theta\,d\theta$ — Use trigonometric ratios.

and $\dfrac{\sqrt{25 - x^2}}{5} = \cos\theta \Rightarrow \sqrt{25 - x^2} = 5\cos\theta$ — Use trigonometric ratios.

$\therefore \int \sqrt{25 - x^2}\,dx$

$= \int (5\cos\theta)(5\cos\theta\,d\theta)$ — Do the trigonometric substitution.

$= 25\int \cos^2\theta\,d\theta$

$= \frac{25}{2}\int (1 + \cos 2\theta)\,d\theta$ — Double-argument properties.

$= \frac{25}{2}\theta + \frac{25}{4}\sin 2\theta + C$ — Do the integrating.

$= \frac{25}{2}\theta + \frac{25}{2}\sin\theta\cos\theta + C$ — Double-argument properties.

$= \dfrac{25}{2}\sin^{-1}\dfrac{x}{5} + \dfrac{25}{2}\cdot\dfrac{x}{5}\cdot\dfrac{\sqrt{25 - x^2}}{5} + C$ — Do the reverse substitution. See triangle in Figure 9-6b.

$= \dfrac{25}{2}\sin^{-1}\dfrac{x}{5} + \dfrac{x}{2}\sqrt{25 - x^2} + C$ — Answer.

Multiplying by 2 from the original integral and evaluating from $x = -5$ to $x = 5$ gives

$$A = 2\int_{-5}^{5} \sqrt{25 - x^2}\, dx = 25 \sin^{-1}\tfrac{x}{5} + x\sqrt{25 - x^2}\,\Big|_{-5}^{5}$$

$$= 25 \sin^{-1}1 + 5\sqrt{25 - 25} - 25 \sin^{-1}(-1) - 5\sqrt{25 - 25}$$

$$= 25 \cdot \frac{\pi}{2} + 0 - 25 \cdot \frac{-\pi}{2} = 25\pi,$$

which agrees with the answer from the area formula, $A = \pi \cdot 5^2$.

The substitution above rationalizes the integrand by taking advantage of the Pythagorean properties of trigonometric functions. The technique works for square roots of quadratics. Your success in using this **trigonometric substitution** depends on drawing the triangle, then deciding what to call the legs and hypotenuse. After the substitution has been made, you must also be able to integrate the trigonometric functions that appear.

**OBJECTIVE**

Be able to rationalize an integrand containing the square root of a quadratic binomal by using trigonometric substitution, then do the integration.

In the preceding work the radical contained $(\text{constant})^2 - x^2$. The situation is different if the radical contains $x^2-(\text{constant})^2$. Example 1 shows you what happens.

**■ Example 1** Do the integrating: $\displaystyle\int \frac{dx}{\sqrt{x^2 - 9}}$

**Solution** Draw the triangle. This time $x$ is the hypotenuse and 3 is a leg. Putting 3 on the horizontal leg allows you to use secant instead of cosecant (Figure 9-6c), thus avoiding a minus sign when you find $dx$.

$$\tfrac{x}{3} = \sec\theta \Rightarrow x = 3\sec\theta \Rightarrow$$

$$dx = 3\sec\theta\tan\theta\, d\theta, \text{ and } \frac{\sqrt{x^2 - 9}}{3} = \tan\theta \Rightarrow \sqrt{x^2 - 9} = 3\tan\theta$$

$$\therefore \int \frac{dx}{\sqrt{x^2 - 9}}$$

$$= \int \frac{3\sec\theta\tan\theta\, d\theta}{3\tan\theta}$$ Do the substitution.

$$= \int \sec\theta\, d\theta$$

$$= \ln|\sec\theta + \tan\theta| + C$$

$$= \ln\left|\frac{x}{3} + \frac{\sqrt{x^2 - 9}}{3}\right| + C$$ Do the reverse substitution.

$$= \ln|x + \sqrt{x^2 - 9}| - \ln 3 + C$$ Log of a quotient.

$$= \ln|x + \sqrt{x^2 - 9}| + C_1$$ ln 3 is constant. ■

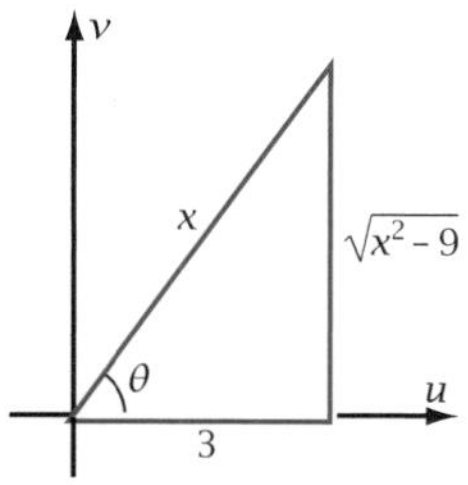

Figure 9-6c

Example 2 shows what to do if the sign in the quadratic is a plus instead of a minus. It also shows that trigonometric substitution can be used even if there is no radical and if the constant is not a square.

**■ Example 2** Do the integrating: $\int \dfrac{dx}{x^2 + 37}$

***Solution*** Draw a triangle (Figure 9-6d). Since the sign between terms is a plus sign, both $x$ and $\sqrt{37}$ are legs. By putting $x$ on the vertical leg, you can use $\tan\theta$ instead of $\cot\theta$. The hypotenuse is $\sqrt{x^2 + 37}$.

$$\frac{x}{\sqrt{37}} = \tan\theta \Rightarrow x = \sqrt{37}\tan\theta \Rightarrow$$

$$dx = \sqrt{37}\sec^2\theta\, d\theta, \text{ and}$$

$$\frac{\sqrt{x^2 + 37}}{\sqrt{37}} = \sec\theta \Rightarrow \sqrt{x^2 + 37} = \sqrt{37}\sec\theta$$

$$\therefore \int \frac{dx}{x^2 + 37} = \int \frac{\sqrt{37}\sec^2\theta\, d\theta}{37\sec^2\theta}$$

$$= \frac{1}{\sqrt{37}}\int d\theta = \frac{1}{\sqrt{37}}\theta + C$$

$$= \frac{1}{\sqrt{37}}\tan^{-1}\frac{x}{\sqrt{37}} + C$$

Since $x/\sqrt{37} = \tan\theta$, $\theta = \tan^{-1}(x/\sqrt{37})$. ■

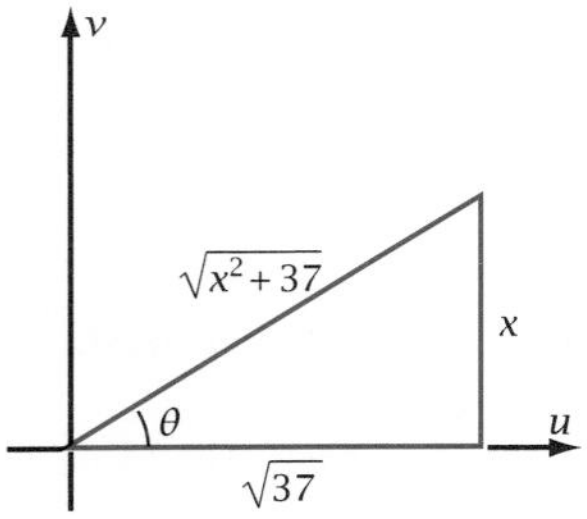

Figure 9-6d

### *Definite Integrals by Trigonometric Substitution*

The reverse substitution in the preceding examples is done to revert to $x$, as in the original integral. For a definte integral, you can avoid the reverse substitution if you change the limits of integration to $\theta$ instead of $x$. Example 3 shows you this can be done with the integral for the area of a circle at the beginning of this section.

**■ Example 3** Find the area of the zone of the circle

$$x^2 + y^2 = 25$$

between $x = -2$ and $x = 3$ (Figure 9-6e).

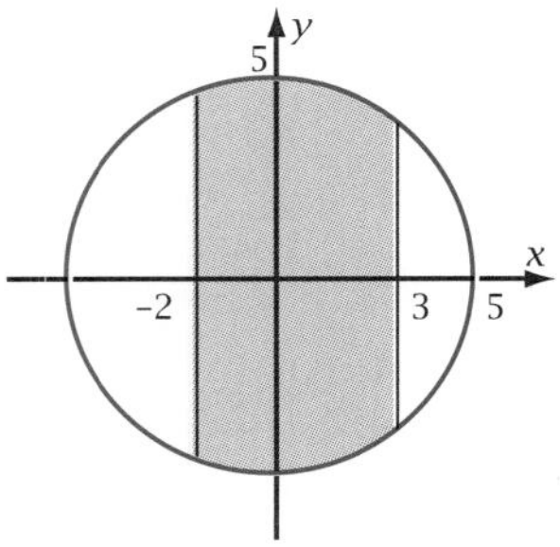

Figure 9-6e

**Solution** This problem is the same as at the beginning of this section except for the limits of integration. The area is

$$A = 2\int_{-2}^{3} \sqrt{25 - x^2}\, dx.$$

Let $x = 5\sin\theta$. Then $dx = 5\cos\theta\, d\theta$, $\sqrt{25 - x^2} = 5\cos\theta$, and $\theta = \sin^{-1}\frac{x}{5}$.
If $x = 3$, then $\theta = \sin^{-1}\frac{3}{5} = \sin^{-1} 0.6$. If $x = -2$, then $\theta = \sin^{-1}\frac{-2}{5} = \sin^{-1}(-0.4)$.

$$\therefore A = 2\int_{\sin^{-1}(-0.4)}^{\sin^{-1}0.6} (5\cos\theta)(5\cos\theta\, d\theta) \qquad \text{Substitute } \theta \text{ limits.}$$

$$= 25\,\theta + \frac{25}{2}\sin 2\theta \Big|_{\sin^{-1}(-0.4)}^{\sin^{-1}0.6} \qquad \text{See the problem at the beginning of this section.}$$

$$= 25\sin^{-1}0.6 + \frac{25}{2}\sin(2\sin^{-1}0.6) - 25\sin^{-1}(-0.4) - \frac{25}{2}\sin[2\sin^{-1}(-0.4)]$$

$$= 47.5406002\ldots$$

By numerical integration, $A \approx 47.5406\ldots$, which is close to $47.5406002\ldots$. ■

In Problem 35 of Problem Set 9-6, you will see what happens in trigonometric substitution if $x$ is negative, and thus $\theta$ is not in Quadrant I.

# Problem Set 9-6

### *Do These Quickly*

The following problems are intended to refresh your skills. You should be able to do all ten problems in less than five minutes.

**Q1.** Integrate: $\int \cos 3x\, dx$

**Q2.** Integrate: $\int \sin 4x\, dx$

**Q3.** Integrate: $\int \tan 5x\, dx$

**Q4.** Integrate: $\int \cot 6x\, dx$

**Q5.** Integrate: $\int \sec 7x\, dx$

**Q6.** Find: $(d/dx)(\tan 5x)$

**Q7.** Find $y'$: $y = \sin 4x$

**Q8.** For Figure 9-6f, the maximum acceleration on $[a, b]$ is at $t =$ -?-.

**Q9.** State the fundamental theorem of calculus.

**Q10.** Write the definition of indefinite integral.

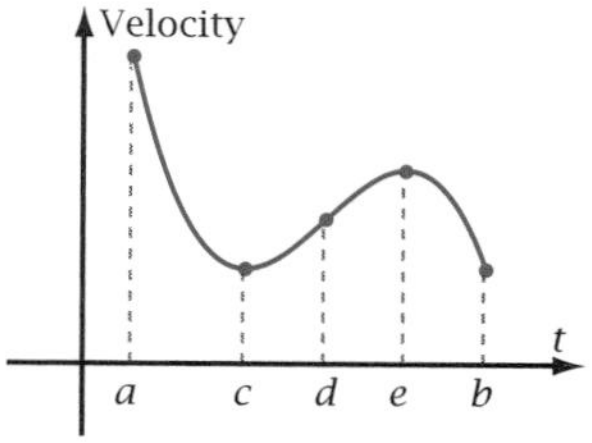

Figure 9-6f

For Problems 1–16, do the integration.

1. $\int \sqrt{49 - x^2}\, dx$
2. $\int \sqrt{100 - x^2}\, dx$
3. $\int \sqrt{x^2 + 16}\, dx$
4. $\int \sqrt{81 + x^2}\, dx$
5. $\int \sqrt{9x^2 - 1}\, dx$
6. $\int \sqrt{16x^2 - 1}\, dx$
7. $\int \frac{dx}{\sqrt{17 - x^2}}$
8. $\int \frac{dx}{\sqrt{13 - x^2}}$

9. $\int \frac{1}{\sqrt{x^2+1}}\,dx$

10. $\int \frac{1}{\sqrt{x^2-121}}\,dx$

11. $\int x^2\sqrt{x^2-9}\,dx$

12. $\int x^2\sqrt{9-x^2}\,dx$

13. $\int (1-x^2)^{3/2}\,dx$

14. $\int (x^2-81)^{3/2}\,dx$

15. $\int \frac{dx}{81+x^2}$

16. $\int \frac{dx}{25x^2+1}$

Some integrals that can be done by trigonometric substitution can also be done other ways.

a. For Problems 17 and 18, evaluate the integral by trigonometric substitution.

b. Evaluate the integral again as a power. Show that the two answers are equivalent.

17. $\int \frac{x\,dx}{\sqrt{x^2+25}}$

18. $\int \frac{x\,dx}{\sqrt{x^2-49}}$

Integrals such as in Problems 19 and 20 can be evaluated by trigonometric substitution. For instance, in Problem 19, the hypotenuse would be 3 and one leg would be $(x-5)$. Do the integration.

19. $\int \frac{dx}{\sqrt{9-(x-5)^2}}$

20. $\int \frac{dx}{\sqrt{36-(x+2)^2}}$

Integrals such as in Problems 21 and 22 can be transformed into ones like Problems 19 and 20 by first completing the square. In Problem 21, $x^2+8x-20=(x^2+8x+16)-36$, which equals $(x+4)^2-36$. Do the integration.

21. $\int \frac{dx}{\sqrt{x^2+8x-20}}$

22. $\int \frac{dx}{\sqrt{x^2-14x+50}}$

For Problems 23 and 24, evaluate the integral exactly using the fundamental theorem. Compare the answer with the one you get by numerical integration.

23. $\int_{-3}^{8} \sqrt{100-x^2}\,dx$

24. $\int_{-1}^{4} \sqrt{x^2+25}\,dx$

25. *Arc Length of a Parabola Problem:* Use the fundamental theorem to find exactly the length of a parabola $y=3x^2$ from $x=0$ to $x=5$. Find a decimal approximation for the answer. Compare the decimal approximation with the answer by numerical integration.

26. *Area of an Ellipse Problem:*

a. Use the fundamental theorem to find exactly the area of the region bounded by the ellipse $9x^2+25y^2=225$ between $x=-3$ and $x=4$ (Figure 9-6g). Compare a decimal approximation of this answer with the answer by numerical integration.

b. Find the exact area of the entire ellipse. How is this area related to the 5 and 3, which are the $x$- and $y$-radii of the ellipse?

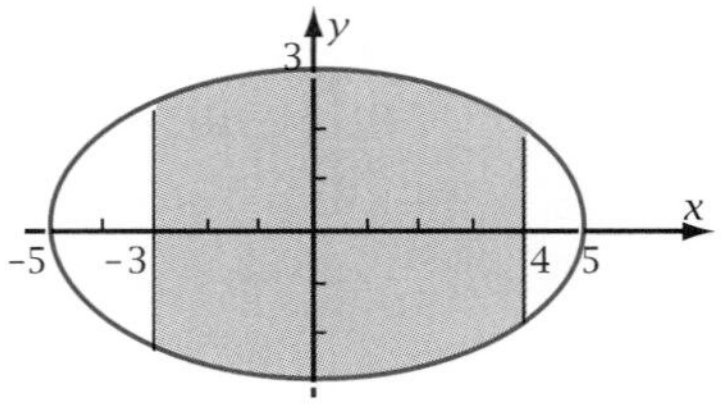

Figure 9-6g

27. *Circle Area Formula Problem:* Derive by calculus the area formula, $A=\pi r^2$, for the circle

$$x^2+y^2=r^2.$$

28. *Ellipse Area Formula Problem:* Derive by calculus the area formula for an ellipse. You may start with the general equation for an ellipse with semiaxes $a$ and $b$,

$$\left(\frac{x}{a}\right)^2 + \left(\frac{y}{b}\right)^2 = 1$$

(Figure 9-6h). Show that the formula reduces to the area of a circle if $a = b$.

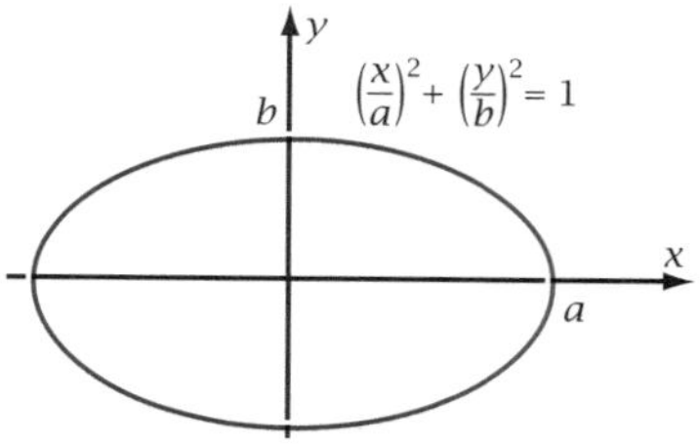


Figure 9-6h

29. *Ellipsoid Problem:* The ellipse in Problem 28 is rotated about the $y$-axis to form an ellipsoid. Find the volume inside the ellipsoid in terms of the constants $a$ and $b$. What difference would there be in the answer if the ellipse had been rotated about the $x$-axis?

30. *Hyperbola Area Problem:* Use the fundamental theorem to find exactly the area of the region bounded above and below by the hyperbola

$$x^2 - y^2 = 9$$

from $x = 3$ to $x = 5$ (Figure 9-6i). Find an approximation for this answer, and compare it with the answer obtained by integrating numerically.

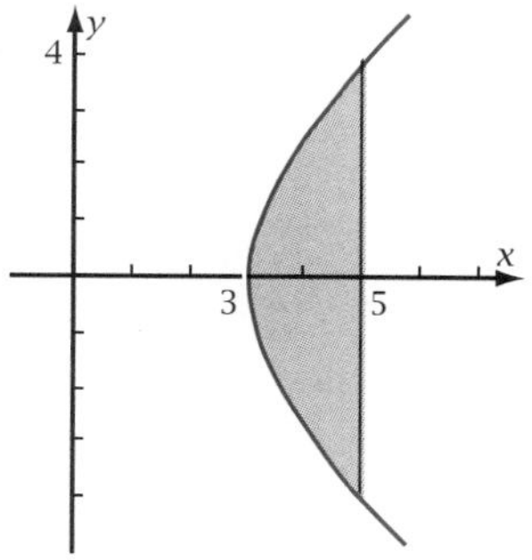


Figure 9-6i

31. *Hyperboloid Problem:* The region in Problem 30 is rotated about the $y$-axis to form a hollow solid. (The inside surface of the solid is a *hyperboloid of one sheet.*) Find the volume of the solid.

32. *Average Radius Problem:* The **average radius** of a solid of rotation may be defined to be the distance $\bar{x}$ for which

$$\text{Volume} = 2\pi\bar{x} \cdot A,$$

where $a$ is the area of the region being rotated. Find the average radius of the hyperboloidal solid in Problem 31. Is the average radius more than, less than or exactly halfway through the region in the $x$ direction as you progress outward from the $y$-axis?

33. *Area of an Ellipse, Parametrically:* The ellipse in Figure 9-6h has parametric equations

$$x = a\cos t$$
$$y = b\sin t.$$

Find the area of the ellipse directly from the parametric equations. Show that the answer is the same as in Problem 28. How does the integration technique used in this case compare with the trigonometric substitution method used in Problem 28?

34. *Length of a Spiral in Polar Coordinates:* In Problem 15 of Problem Set 8-9, you found the length of the spiral with polar equation

$$r = 0.5\theta.$$

The spiral is shown in Figure 9-6j. Now that you know how to integrate by trigonometric substitution, you can find the exact length. Find the length of the part of the spiral shown using the fundamental theorem. Compare this answer with the value you get by numerical integration.

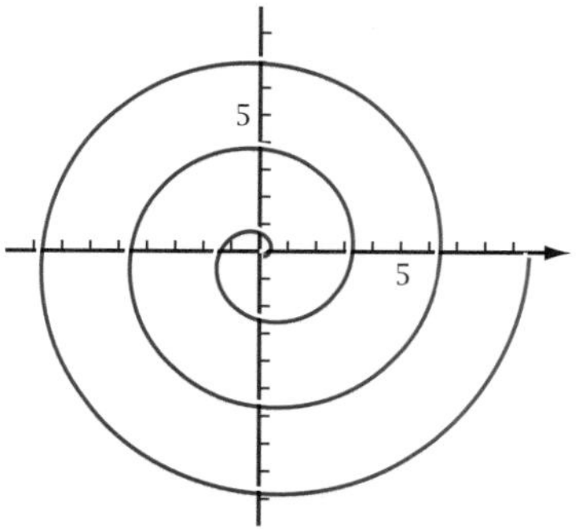


Figure 9-6j

35. *Trigonometric Substitution for Negative Values of x:* In trigonometric substitutions you let $x/a$ equal $\sin\theta$, $\tan\theta$, or $\sec\theta$. If $x$ is negative, then $\theta$ is not in Quadrant I. Thus

$$\theta = \sin^{-1}\frac{x}{a}, \qquad \theta = \tan^{-1}\frac{x}{a}, \qquad \text{or} \qquad \theta = \sec^{-1}\frac{x}{a}.$$

If you restrict $\theta$ to the other quadrant in the range of the inverse trigonometric function, you find the same indefinite integral as if you naively assumed that $\theta$ is always in Quadrant I. Show that this is the case for each of these three trigonometric substitutions.

# 9-7 Integration of Rational Functions by Partial Fractions

In unrestrained population growth the rate of change of the population is proportional to the number of people. This happens because the more people there are, the more babies are born each year. In restrained population growth there is a maximum population a region can sustain. In this case, the rate of population growth is also proportional to how close the number of people is to that maximum. For instance, if the region can sustain 10.5 million people, then a differential equation for population growth could be

$$\frac{dP}{dt} = 0.038P(10.5 - P),$$

where $P$ is population in millions, and 0.038 is the proportionality constant. You may already have seen this differential equation in connection with the *logistic equation* in Section 7-4. Separating the variables and integrating gives

$$\int \frac{1}{P(10.5 - P)}\,dP = 0.038\int dt.$$

The integral on the left-hand side contains a **rational algebraic function** of $P$. That is, the integrand can be written as (polynomial)/(polynomial). In this section you will learn an algebraic method to find the antiderivative on the left-hand side of the equation. The method involves breaking the rational expression into a sum of relatively simple **partial fractions**, each of which is easy to integrate. In theory, at least, many ratios of polynomials that have a numerator of degree lower than the denominator degree can be written as

$$\frac{\text{Polynomial}}{\text{Polynomial}} = \frac{\text{constant}}{\text{linear}} + \frac{\text{constant}}{\text{linear}} + \cdots + \frac{\text{constant}}{\text{linear}}.$$

**OBJECTIVE**

Find the integral of a rational algebraic function by first resolving the integrand into partial fractions.

**■ Example 1** (Heaviside Method) Evaluate the indefinite integral: $\int \frac{4x + 41}{x^2 + 3x - 10}\,dx$.

**Solution** The first step is factoring the denominator. The rational expression thus becomes

$$\frac{4x + 41}{(x + 5)(x - 2)}.$$

Your thought process goes something like this: "Hmmm . . . It looks like someone has been adding fractions, where $(x + 5)(x - 2)$ is the common denominator!" So you write

$$\frac{4x + 41}{(x + 5)(x - 2)} = \frac{A}{x + 5} + \frac{B}{x - 2}.$$

A clever way to isolate the constant $A$ is to multiply both sides of the equation by $(x + 5)$.

$$(x + 5)\frac{4x + 41}{(x + 5)(x - 2)} = (x + 5)\frac{A}{x + 5} + (x + 5)\frac{B}{x - 2}$$

$$\frac{4x + 41}{x - 2} = A + (x + 5)\frac{B}{x - 2}$$

Substituting $-5$ for $x$ in the transformed equation gives

$$\frac{4(-5) + 41}{-5 - 2} = A + (-5 + 5)\frac{B}{-5 - 2} = A + 0.$$

$$\therefore\ -3 = A$$

Similarly, multiplying both sides by $(x - 2)$ isolates the constant $B$.

$$(x - 2)\frac{4x + 41}{(x + 5)(x - 2)} = (x - 2)\frac{A}{x + 5} + (x - 2)\frac{B}{x - 2}$$

$$\frac{4x + 41}{x + 5} = (x - 2)\frac{A}{x + 5} + B$$

Substituting 2 for $x$ eliminates the $A$ term and gives

$$\frac{4(2) + 41}{2 + 5} = (2 - 2)\frac{A}{2 + 5} + B = 0 + B.$$

$$\therefore 7 = B$$

Substituting $-3$ for $A$ and 7 for $B$, and putting the integral back together gives

$$\int \frac{4x + 41}{x^2 + 3x - 10}\,dx = \int \left(\frac{-3}{x + 5} + \frac{7}{x - 2}\right) dx$$

$$= -3\ln|x + 5| + 7\ln|x - 2| + C.$$

■

Transforming into partial fractions as shown in Example 1 is called the **Heaviside method** after Oliver Heaviside (1850–1925). The method can be shortened enough to be done in one step in your head! Here's how.

**■ Example 2** (Heaviside Shortcut) Integrate by resolving into partial fractions: $\int \frac{x-2}{(x-5)(x-1)}\,dx$

***Solution*** Thought process:

- Write the integral and the denominators of the partial fractions.

$$\int \frac{x-2}{(x-5)(x-1)}\,dx = \int \left(\frac{\quad}{x-5} + \frac{\quad}{x-1}\right) dx$$

Tell yourself, "If $x$ is 5, then $(x-5)$ equals zero." Cover up the $(x-5)$ with your finger, and substitute 5 into what is left.

$$\int \frac{x-2}{\quad (x-1)}\,dx \qquad \text{Do arithmetic: } \frac{5-2}{5-1} = \frac{3}{4}.$$

Finger

- The answer, 3/4, is the numerator for $(x-5)$. To find the numerator for $(x-1)$, repeat the process, but cover up the $(x-1)$ and substitute 1, the number that makes $(x-1)$ zero.

$$\int \frac{x-2}{(x-5)\quad}\,dx \qquad \text{Do arithmetic: } \frac{1-2}{1-5} = \frac{1}{4}.$$

Finger

- Fill in the 3/4 and 1/4 where they belong. The entire process is just one step, like this.

$$\int \frac{x-2}{(x-5)(x-1)}\,dx = \int \left(\frac{\frac{3}{4}}{x-5} + \frac{\frac{1}{4}}{x-1}\right) dx$$
$$= \tfrac{3}{4}\ln|x-5| + \tfrac{1}{4}\ln|x-1| + C \qquad ■$$

In Problem Set 9-7, you will practice integrating by partial fractions. You will also find out what to do if the denominator has

- Unfactorable quadratic factors
- Repeated linear factors

# Problem Set 9-7

***Do These Quickly***

The following problems are intended to refresh your skills. You should be able to do all ten problems in less than five minutes.

***Q1.*** Factor: $x^2 - 25$

***Q2.*** Multiply: $(x-3)(x+5)$

***Q3.*** Factor: $x^2 - 4x - 12$

***Q4.*** Multiply: $(x+7)^2$

***Q5.*** Factor: $x^2 + 8x + 16$

***Q6.*** Multiply: $(x-8)(x+8)$

***Q7.*** If $f(x) = \ln x$, then $f^{-1}(x) =$ -?-.

**Q8.** For the data in the table, use Simpson's rule to find $\int_1^9 g(x)\,dx$.

| $x$ | $g(x)$ |
|---|---|
| 1 | 10 |
| 3 | 15 |
| 5 | 16 |
| 7 | 14 |
| 9 | 13 |

**Q9.** Show that $x^2 + 50x + 1000$ cannot be factored using real numbers only.

**Q10.** Show that $x^2 + 36$ cannot be factored using real numbers only.

For Problems 1–10, integrate by first resolving the integrand into partial fractions.

1. $\displaystyle\int \frac{11x - 15}{x^2 - 3x + 2}\,dx$
2. $\displaystyle\int \frac{7x + 25}{x^2 - 7x - 8}\,dx$
3. $\displaystyle\int \frac{(5x - 11)\,dx}{x^2 - 2x - 8}$
4. $\displaystyle\int \frac{(3x - 12)\,dx}{x^2 - 5x - 50}$
5. $\displaystyle\int \frac{21\,dx}{x^2 + 7x + 10}$
6. $\displaystyle\int \frac{10x\,dx}{x^2 - 9x - 36}$
7. $\displaystyle\int \frac{9x^2 - 25x - 50}{(x + 1)(x - 7)(x + 2)}\,dx$
8. $\displaystyle\int \frac{7x^2 + 22x - 54}{(x - 2)(x + 4)(x - 1)}\,dx$
9. $\displaystyle\int \frac{4x^2 + 15x - 1}{x^3 + 2x^2 - 5x - 6}\,dx$
10. $\displaystyle\int \frac{-3x^2 + 22x - 31}{x^3 - 8x^2 + 19x - 12}\,dx$

### *Improper Algebraic Fractions*

If the numerator is of higher degree than the denominator, long division will reduce the integrand to a polynomial plus a "proper" fraction. For instance,

$$\frac{x^3 - 9x^2 + 24x - 17}{x^2 - 6x + 5} = x - 3 + \frac{x - 2}{x^2 - 6x + 5}.$$

For Problems 11 and 12, perform the integration by first dividing.

11. $\displaystyle\int \frac{3x^3 + 2x^2 - 12x + 9}{x - 1}\,dx$
12. $\displaystyle\int \frac{x^3 - 7x^2 + 5x + 40}{x^2 - 2x - 8}\,dx$

### *Unfactorable Quadratics*

Heaviside's method does not work for integrals such as

$$\int \frac{7x^2 - 4x}{(x^2 + 1)(x - 2)}\,dx$$

that have an unfactorable quadratic in the denominator (unless you are willing to use imaginary numbers!). However, the quadratic term can have a linear numerator. In this case you can write

$$\frac{7x^2 - 4x}{(x^2+1)(x-2)} = \frac{Ax+B}{x^2+1} + \frac{C}{x-2}$$

$$= \frac{(Ax+B)(x-2) + C(x^2+1)}{(x^2+1)(x-2)}$$

$$= \frac{Ax^2 - 2Ax + Bx - 2B + Cx^2 + C}{(x^2+1)(x-2)}.$$

So $Ax^2 + Cx^2 = 7x^2$, $-2Ax + Bx = -4x$, and $-2B + C = 0$. Solving the system

$$\begin{aligned} A + \phantom{B} + C &= 7 \\ -2A + B \phantom{+C} &= -4 \\ -2B + C &= 0 \end{aligned}$$

gives $A = 3$, $B = 2$, and $C = 4$. Therefore,

$$\frac{7x^2 - 4x}{(x^2+1)(x-2)} = \frac{3x+2}{x^2+1} + \frac{4}{x-2}.$$

For Problems 13 and 14, integrate by first resolving into partial fractions.

13. $\displaystyle\int \frac{4x^2 + 6x + 11}{(x^2+1)(x+4)}\,dx$

14. $\displaystyle\int \frac{4x^2 - 15x - 1}{x^3 - 5x^2 + 3x + 1}\,dx$

### *Repeated Linear Factors*

If a power of a linear factor appears in the denominator, the fraction could have come from adding partial fractions with that power or any lower power. For instance, the integral

$$\int \frac{x^2 - 4x + 18}{(x+4)(x-1)^2}\,dx \text{ can be written } \int \left[\frac{A}{x+4} + \frac{B}{x-1} + \frac{C + Dx}{(x-1)^2}\right] dx.$$

However, the numerator of the original fraction has only three coefficients, and the right-hand side of the equation has four unknown constants. So one of the constants is arbitrary and can take on any value you decide. The smart move is to let $D = 0$ so that there will be three partial fractions that are as easy to integrate as possible.

For Problems 15 and 16, integrate by resolving the integrand into partial fractions.

15. $\displaystyle\int \frac{4x^2 + 18x + 6}{(x+5)(x+1)^2}\,dx$

16. $\displaystyle\int \frac{3x^2 - 53x + 245}{x^3 - 14x^2 + 49x}\,dx$

*"Old Problem" New Problems:* Sometimes a problem that seems to fit the pattern of a new problem actually reduces to an old problem. For Problems 17 and 18, evaluate the integral with this idea in mind.

17. $\displaystyle\int \frac{dx}{x^3 - 6x^2 + 12x - 8}$

18. $\displaystyle\int \frac{1}{x^4 + 4x^3 + 6x^2 + 4x + 1}\,dx$

19. *Rumor Problem:* There are 1000 students attending Lowe High. One day 10 students arrive at school bearing the rumor that final exams will be canceled! On the average, each student talks to other students at a rate of 2 students/hour, passing on the rumor to students, some of whom have already heard it and some of whom have

not. Thus the rate at which students hear the rumor for the first time is 2 times the number who have already heard it, times the fraction of the students who have not yet heard it. If $y$ is the number of students who have heard the rumor at time $t$ hours since school started, then

$$\frac{dy}{dt} = 2y\frac{1000 - y}{1000}.$$

a. Solve this differential equation algebraically, subject to the initial condition that $y = 10$ when school started at $t = 0$.

b. How many students had heard the rumor after the first hour? At lunch time ($t = 4$)? At the end of the school day ($t = 8$)?

c. How many students had heard the rumor at the time it was spreading the fastest? At what time was this?

d. Figure 9-7a shows the slope field for the differential equation. Plot the solution in 19a on a photocopy of the figure. How does the curve relate to the slope field?

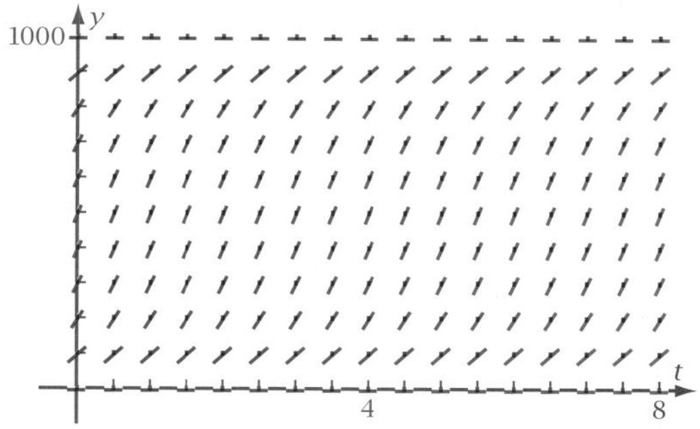

Figure 9-7a

20. *Epidemic Problem:* A new disease arrives at the town of Scorpion Gulch. When a person with the disease contacts a person who has not yet had the disease, the uninfected person may or may not catch the disease. The disease is not fatal, but it persists with the infected person forever after. Of the $N$ people who live there, let $P$ be the number of them who have the disease after $t$ days.

a. Suppose that each person contacts an average of 3 people per day. In terms of $P$ and $N$, how many contacts will there be between infected and uninfected people per day?

b. Suppose that the probability of passing on the disease to an uninfected person is only 10% at each contact. Explain why

$$\frac{dP}{dt} = 0.3P\frac{N - P}{N}.$$

c. Solve the differential equation in 20b for $P$ in terms of $t$. Use the initial condition that $P = P_0$ at time $t = 0$.

d. If 1000 people live in Scorpion Gulch and 10 people are infected at time $t = 0$, how many will be infected after 1 week?

e. For the conditions in 20d, how long will it be until 99% of the population is infected?

21. *Area Problem:* Find an equation for the area of the region under the graph of

$$y = \frac{25}{x^2 + 3x - 4}$$

from $x = 2$ to $x = b$, where $b$ is a constant greater than 2 (Figure 9-7b). Let $b = 7$ and check your answer by numerical integration. Does the area approach a finite limit as $b$ approaches infinity? Justify your answer.

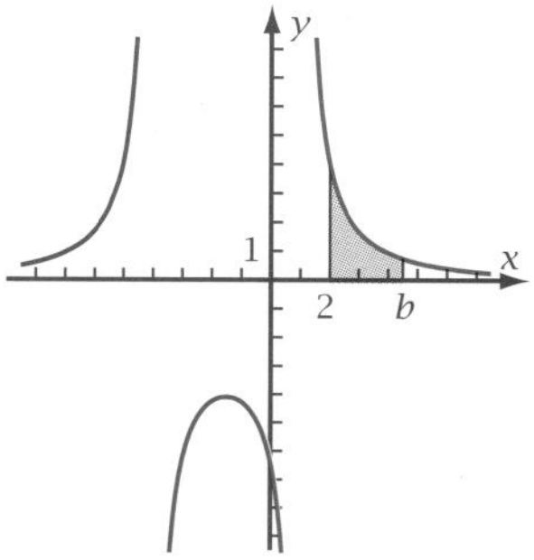

Figure 9-7b

22. *Volume Problem:* The region in Problem 21 is rotated about the $y$-axis to form a solid. Find an equation in terms of the constant $b$ for the volume of the solid. Check your answer by numerical integration using $b = 7$. Does the volume approach a finite limit as $b$ approaches infinity? Justify your answer.

23. *Equivalent Answers Problem:* Evaluate this integral three ways.

$$\int \frac{x-3}{x^2-6x+8}\,dx$$

a. By first resolving into partial fractions.

b. By completing the square, followed by trigonometric substitution.

c. Directly, as the integral of the reciprocal function.

d. Show that the three answers are equivalent.

24. *Logistic Curve Problem, Algebraically:* For unrestrained population growth, the rate of change of population is directly proportional to the population. That is, $dp/dt = kp$, where $p$ is population, $t$ is time, and $k$ is a constant. One assumption for restrained growth is that there is a certain maximum size $m$ for the population, and the rate goes to zero as the population approaches that size. Use this information to answer the following questions.

a. Show that the differential equation $dp/dt = kp(m - p)$ has the properties mentioned.

b. At what value of $p$ is the growth rate the greatest?

c. Separate the variables, then solve the equation by integrating. If you have worked correctly, the integral on one side of the equation can be evaluated by partial fractions.

d. Transform your answer so that $p$ is explicitly in terms of $t$. Show that it can be expressed in the form of the logistic equation,

$$p = p_0\frac{1+b}{1+be^{-kt}},$$

where $p_0$ is the population at time $t = 0$ and $b$ is a constant.

e. Census figures for the United States are as follows.

1960: 179.3 million
1970: 203.2 million
1980: 226.5 million

Let $t$ be the number of years that have elapsed since 1960. Use these as initial conditions to evaluate $p_0$, $b$, and $k$. Write the particular solution.

f. Predict the outcome of the 1990 census. How close does your answer come to the actual 1990 population, 248.7 million?

g. Based on the logistic model what will be the ultimate U.S. population?

h. Is this mathematical model very sensitive to the initial conditions? For instance, suppose that the 1970 population had really been 204.2 million instead of 203.2 million. How much would this affect the predicted ultimate population?

# 9-8 Integrals of the Inverse Trigonometric Functions

At the beginning of this chapter it was mentioned that there are three types of functions that, along with their inverses, come under the category **elementary transcendental functions**. They are as follows:

| | |
|---|---|
| Trigonometric | Inverse trigonometric |
| Logarithmic | Inverse logarithmic (exponential) |
| Hyperbolic | Inverse hyperbolic |

The name *transcendental* implies that the operations needed to calculate values of the functions "transcend," or go beyond, the operations of algebra (addition, subtraction, multiplication, division, and root extraction). You have already learned algebraic calculus techniques for the first four types of functions, except for integrating the inverse trigonometric functions. In this section you will learn how to integrate the inverse trigonometric functions algebraically. In Section 9-9, you will explore the hyperbolic functions, which are related both to exponential and trigonometric functions.

**OBJECTIVE**

Be able to integrate (antidifferentiate) each of the six inverse trigonometric functions.

### *Background: Definition and Derivatives of the Inverse Trigonometric Functions*

In Section 4-5, you learned definitions of the inverse trigonometric functions, and how to find algebraic formulas for their derivatives. These definitions and derivative formulas are repeated here for easy reference.

**Definitions: Inverse Trigonometric Functions (Principal Branches)**

$y = \sin^{-1}x$ if and only if $\sin y = x$ and $y \in \left[-\frac{\pi}{2}, \frac{\pi}{2}\right]$

$y = \cos^{-1}x$ if and only if $\cos y = x$ and $y \in [0, \pi]$

$y = \tan^{-1}x$ if and only if $\tan y = x$ and $y \in \left(-\frac{\pi}{2}, \frac{\pi}{2}\right)$

$y = \cot^{-1}x$ if and only if $\cot y = x$ and $y \in (0, \pi)$

$y = \sec^{-1}x$ if and only if $\sec y = x$ and $y \in [0, \pi]$, but $y \neq \frac{\pi}{2}$

$y = \csc^{-1}x$ if and only if $\csc y = x$ and $y \in \left[-\frac{\pi}{2}, \frac{\pi}{2}\right]$, but $y \neq 0$

*Note:* The names *arcsin, arccos, arctan, arccot, arcsec,* and *arccsc* can be used to help distinguish, for instance, $\tan^{-1}x$ from $1/\tan x$.

**Properties: Derivatives of the Six Inverse Trigonometric Functions**

$$\frac{d}{dx}(\sin^{-1}x) = \frac{1}{\sqrt{1-x^2}} \qquad \frac{d}{dx}(\cos^{-1}x) = -\frac{1}{\sqrt{1-x^2}}$$

$$\frac{d}{dx}(\tan^{-1}x) = \frac{1}{1+x^2} \qquad \frac{d}{dx}(\cot^{-1}x) = -\frac{1}{1+x^2}$$

$$\frac{d}{dx}(\sec^{-1}x) = \frac{1}{|x|\sqrt{x^2-1}} \qquad \frac{d}{dx}(\csc^{-1}x) = -\frac{1}{|x|\sqrt{x^2-1}}$$

*Note:* Your grapher must be in the radian mode.

Memory Aid: The derivative of each "co-" inverse function is the opposite of the derivative of the corresponding inverse function because each co-inverse function is decreasing as $x$ starts increasing from zero.

### Integrals

The technique for integrating inverse trigonometric functions is (surprisingly!) integration by parts. Example 1 shows you how this is done.

**■ Example 1** Integrate: $\int \tan^{-1}x\,dx$

**Solution**

$$\int \tan^{-1}x\,dx$$

$$= x\tan^{-1}x - \int \frac{x\,dx}{x^2+1}$$

$$= x\tan^{-1}x - \tfrac{1}{2}\ln|x^2+1| + C$$

| $u$ | | $dv$ |
|---|---|---|
| $\tan^{-1}x$ | $+$ | $1$ |
| $\frac{1}{x^2+1}$ | $-$ | $x$ |

The last integral can be transformed to the integral of the reciprocal function. The absolute value in the argument of ln is optional since $x^2 + 1$ is always positive. ■

In Problem Set 9-8, you will derive algebraic formulas for the integrals of the other five inverse trigonometric functions. These formulas are listed in the following box. They were more important in the first 300 years of calculus, before such technology as your grapher made numerical integration quick and easily accessible. Like climbing Mount Everest, they are interesting more from the standpoint that they can be done, rather than because they are of great practical use.

**Properties: Algebraic Integrals of the Inverse Trigonometric Functions**

$$\int \sin^{-1}x\,dx = x\sin^{-1}x + \sqrt{1-x^2} + C$$

$$\int \cos^{-1}x\,dx = x\cos^{-1}x - \sqrt{1-x^2} + C$$

$$\int \tan^{-1}x\,dx = x\tan^{-1}x - \tfrac{1}{2}\ln|x^2+1| + C = x\tan^{-1}x - \ln\sqrt{x^2+1} + C$$

$$\int \cot^{-1}x\,dx = x\cot^{-1}x + \tfrac{1}{2}\ln|x^2+1| + C = x\cot^{-1}x + \ln\sqrt{x^2+1} + C$$

$$\int \sec^{-1}x\,dx = x\sec^{-1}x - \operatorname{sgn}x\ln|x + \sqrt{x^2-1}| + C$$

$$\int \csc^{-1}x\,dx = x\csc^{-1}x + \operatorname{sgn}x\ln|x + \sqrt{x^2-1}| + C$$

## Problem Set 9-8

### *Do These Quickly*

The following problems are intended to refresh your skills. You should be able to do all ten problems in less than five minutes.

**Q1.** To integrate a product, use —?—.

**Q2.** To integrate a rational function, use —?—.

**Q3.** To integrate $\int \sqrt{x^2+1}\,dx$, use the —?— trigonometric substitution.

**Q4.** To integrate $\int \sqrt{x^2-1}\,dx$, use the —?— trigonometric substitution.

**Q5.** To integrate $\int \sqrt{1-x^2}\,dx$, use the —?— trigonometric substitution.

**Q6.** Integrate: $\int (x^2+1)^7(x\,dx)$

**Q7.** If $f(x) = 3 + |x-5|$, then the maximum of $f(x)$ on $[1, 6]$ is -?-.

**Q8.** If $f(x) = 3 + |x-5|$, then the minimum of $f(x)$ on $[1, 6]$ is -?-.

**Q9.** If $f(x) = 3 + |x-5|$, then $f'(5)$ is -?-.

**Q10.** If $h(x) = x^3 + x$, then the graph of $h$ has a point of inflection at $x =$ -?-.

For Problems 1–6, find the indefinite integral. Check your answer against those in the preceding box.

1. $\int \tan^{-1}x\,dx$
2. $\int \cot^{-1}x\,dx$
3. $\int \cos^{-1}x\,dx$
4. $\int \sin^{-1}x\,dx$
5. $\int \sec^{-1}x\,dx$
6. $\int \csc^{-1}x\,dx$

7. *Answer Verification Problem:* Evaluate the integral $\int_1^4 \tan^{-1}x\,dx$ algebraically. Find a decimal approximation for the answer. Then evaluate the integral numerically. How close does the numerical answer come to the exact, algebraic answer?

8. *Simpson's Rule Review Problem:* Plot the graph of $y = \sec^{-1}x$ from $x = 1$ to $x = 3$. You may do this in parametric mode, with $x = 1/\cos t$ and $y = t$. Sketch the graph. Use Simpson's rule with $n = 10$ increments to find a numerical approximation for the area of the region under this graph from $x = 1$ to $x = 3$. Then find the exact area by integrating algebraically. How close does the answer using Simpson's rule come to the exact answer?

9. *Area Problem:* Figure 9-8a shows the region above the graph of $y = \sin^{-1}x$, below $y = \pi/2$, and to the right of the $y$-axis. Find the area of this region by vertical slices. Find the area again, this time using horizontal slices. Show that the two answers are equivalent.

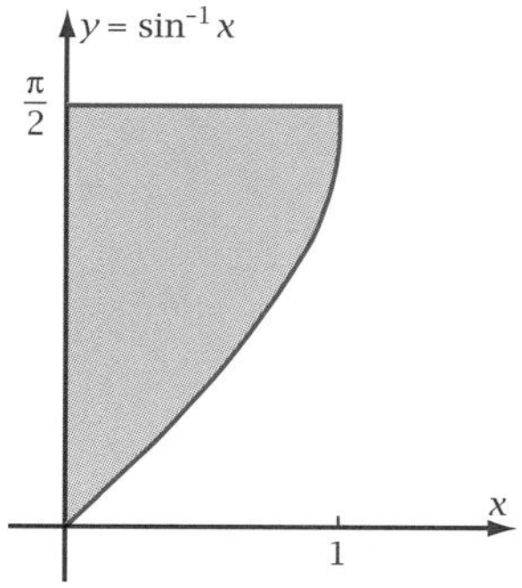

Figure 9-8a

10. *Volume Problem:* Figure 9-8b shows the region under the graph of $y = \tan^{-1}x$ from $x = 0$ to $x = 1$, rotated about the $y$-axis to form a solid. Find the exact volume of the solid using the fundamental theorem. Show that your answer is reasonable by numerical integration and by comparing it with a suitable geometric figure.

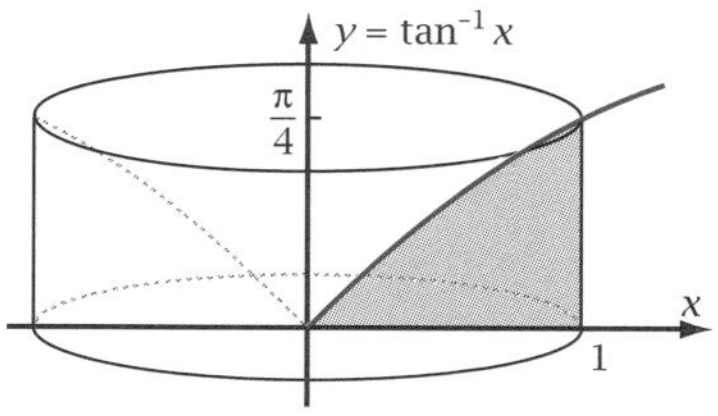

Figure 9-8b

# 9-9 Calculus of the Hyperbolic and Inverse Hyperbolic Functions

Figure 9-9a shows what a chain might look like if suspended between two nails driven into the frame of a chalkboard. Although the shape resembles a parabola, it is actually a **catenary** from the Latin *catena*, meaning "chain." Its graph is the **hyperbolic cosine** function,

$$y = a + b\cosh cx$$

(pronounced "kosh," with a short "o"). As shown in Figure 9-9b, a parabola is more sharply curved at the vertex than a catenary is.

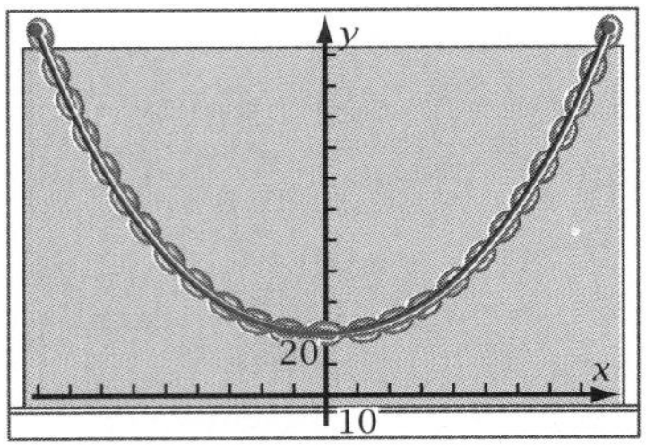

Figure 9-9a

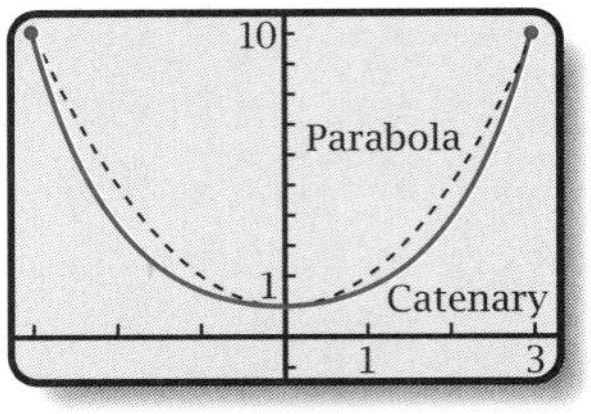

Figure 9-9b

Cosh and the related hyperbolic sine and tangent are important enough to be on most graphers. In this section you will see that the hyperbolic functions are related both to the natural exponential function and to the circular sine and cosine functions. You will see why a chain hangs in the shape of a hyperbolic cosine and why the functions are called hyperbolic.

### *Definitions of the Six Hyperbolic Functions*

"Out of a clear, blue sky," define two functions, $u$ and $v$:

$$u = \tfrac{1}{2}(e^x + e^{-x}) \qquad \text{and} \qquad v = \tfrac{1}{2}(e^x - e^{-x}).$$

The $u$ graph is identical to $y = \cosh x$, as you could see by plotting $y = u$ and $y = \cosh x$ on the same screen (Figure 9-9c, left). The $v$ graph is identical to $y = \sinh x$ (pronounced "sinch of $x$," although the letter "c" does not appear in writing). The right-hand diagram in Figure 9-9c shows $y = \sinh x$ and $y = v$. The dashed graphs are $y = 0.5e^x$ and $y = \pm 0.5e^{-x}$.

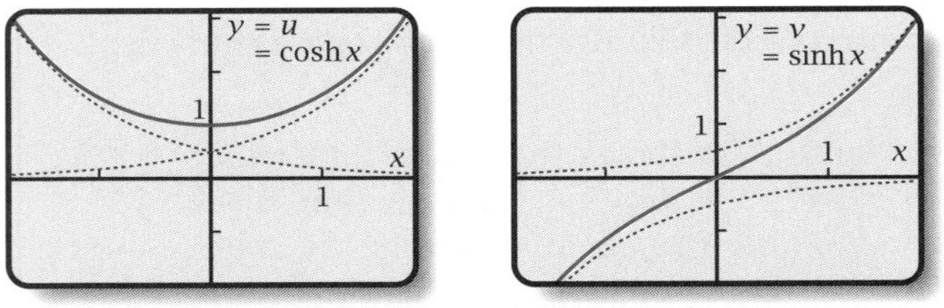

Figure 9-9c

The reason these functions are called "hyperbolic" shows up if you eliminate $x$ and get an equation with $u$ and $v$ alone. Squaring $u$ and $v$, then subtracting gives the following.

$$u^2 = \frac{1}{4}(e^{2x} + 2 + e^{-2x})$$ Why just 2 for the middle term?

$$v^2 = \frac{1}{4}(e^{2x} - 2 + e^{-2x})$$

$$u^2 - v^2 = 1$$ A unit equilateral hyperbola in the $uv$-coordinate system.

This is the equation of a hyperbola in a $uv$-coordinate system. Function $u$ is the horizontal coordinate of a point on the hyperbola, and function $v$ is the vertical coordinate. These coordinates have the same relationship to the unit equilateral hyperbola $u^2 - v^2 = 1$ as the "circular" functions cosine and sine have to the unit circle, $u^2 + v^2 = 1$ (Figure 9-9d).

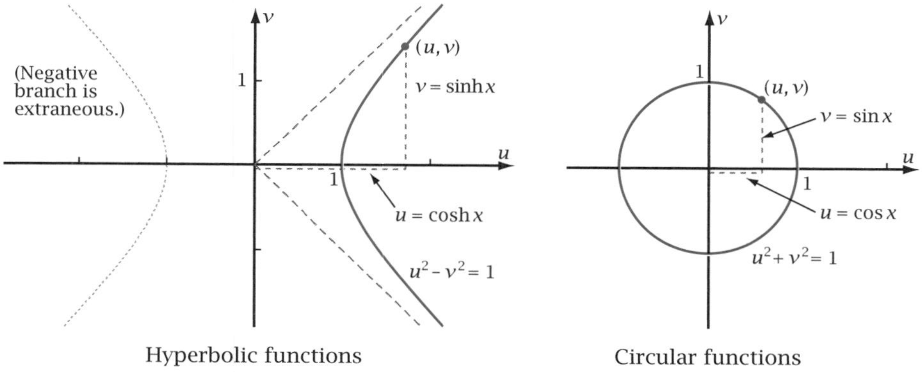


Figure 9-9d

The other four hyperbolic functions are defined in the same way as the other four circular (trigonometric) functions, namely, as reciprocals and quotients of the first two. The symbols come from adding an "h" to the corresponding circular function symbol. There are no widely accepted pronunciations for symbols such as tanh $x$ and csch $x$ other than "hyperbolic tangent of $x$," and so on.

### Definitions: The Hyperbolic Functions

$\sinh x = \frac{1}{2}(e^x - e^{-x})$ $\qquad$ $\cosh x = \frac{1}{2}(e^x + e^{-x})$

$\tanh x = \dfrac{\sinh x}{\cosh x}$ $\qquad$ $\coth x = \dfrac{\cosh x}{\sinh x}$

$\operatorname{sech} x = \dfrac{1}{\cosh x}$ $\qquad$ $\operatorname{csch} x = \dfrac{1}{\sinh x}$

From the fact that $u^2 - v^2 = 1$ and the above definitions, the Pythagorean properties follow.

### Pythagorean Properties of the Hyperbolic Functions

$$\cosh^2 x - \sinh^2 x = 1$$
$$1 - \tanh^2 x = \operatorname{sech}^2 x$$
$$\coth^2 x - 1 = \operatorname{csch}^2 x$$

**OBJECTIVE**

Be able to differentiate and integrate any of the six hyperbolic functions and their inverses, and use the hyperbolic cosine function as a mathematical model.

### Derivatives of the Hyperbolic Functions

The derivatives of cosh and sinh have an interesting relationship.

$$\frac{d}{dx}\cosh x = \tfrac{1}{2}(e^x - e^{-x}) = \sinh x \quad \text{and} \quad \frac{d}{dx}\sinh x = \tfrac{1}{2}(e^x + e^{-x}) = \cosh x$$

This "cyclical" property of the derivatives is similar to that of the circular sine and cosine.

$$\sin' x = \cos x, \quad \text{and} \quad \cos' x = -\sin x.$$

The derivatives of the other four hyperbolic functions can be found by first transforming to $\sinh x$ and $\cosh x$. Example 1 shows you how.

**■ Example 1** Find the derivative: $y = \coth x$

**Solution** By definition of coth,

$$y = \frac{\cosh x}{\sinh x}.$$

Applying the derivative of a quotient property gives the following.

$$y' = \frac{(\sinh x)(\sinh x) - (\cosh x)(\cosh x)}{\sinh^2 x}$$
$$= \frac{\sinh^2 x - \cosh^2 x}{\sinh^2 x}$$
$$= \frac{-1}{\sinh^2 x} \qquad \text{By the Pythagorean properties.}$$
$$y' = -\operatorname{csch}^2 x$$

■

The derivatives of all the hyperbolic functions are summarized in the following box. In Problems 37 and 38 of Problem Set 9-9, you will be asked to derive some of these.

### Properties: Derivatives of Hyperbolic Functions

$\sinh' x = \cosh x$ $\qquad \cosh' x = \sinh x$
$\tanh' x = \operatorname{sech}^2 x$ $\qquad \coth' x = -\operatorname{csch}^2 x$
$\operatorname{sech}' x = -\operatorname{sech} x \tanh x$ $\qquad \operatorname{csch}' x = -\operatorname{csch} x \coth x$

### *Integrals of Hyperbolic Functions*

The integrals of cosh and sinh come directly from the derivative formulas. The integrals of tanh and coth are found in much the same way you integrated tan and cot. Example 2 shows how coth is integrated. The integrals of sech and csch require clever substitutions you have not yet learned. In Problems C1 and C2 of Problem Set 9-13, you will see how to do this.

**■ Example 2** Integrate: $\int \coth x\,dx$

**Solution** The technique is to use the definition of coth. The resulting quotient has a numerator that is the derivative of the denominator. You wind up integrating the reciprocal function.

$$\int \coth x\,dx$$
$$= \int \frac{\cosh x}{\sinh x}\,dx$$
$$= \int \frac{1}{\sinh x}\cosh x\,dx$$
$$= \ln|\sinh x| + C$$ ■

The integrals of the six hyperbolic functions are listed in the following box. In Problem Set 9-9, you will be asked to derive some of these.

**Properties: Integrals of the Hyperbolic Functions**

$\int \sinh x\,dx = \cosh x + C$ $\int \cosh x\,dx = \sinh x + C$

$\int \tanh x\,dx = \ln(\cosh x) + C$ $\int \coth x\,dx = \ln|\sinh x| + C$

$\int \operatorname{sech} x\,dx = \sin^{-1}(\tanh x) + C$ $\int \operatorname{csch} x\,dx = \ln|\tanh(x/2)| + C$

### *Inverse Hyperbolic Functions*

Recall that the inverse of a function is the relation you obtain by interchanging the two variables. For instance, if $y = \sinh x$, then the inverse relation has the equation

$$x = \sinh y.$$

The dependent variable $y$ is called the **inverse hyperbolic sine of** $x$. The symbol often used is similar to that for inverse circular functions,

$$y = \sinh^{-1} x.$$

This is read, "Inverse hyperbolic sine of $x$," or simply "sinch inverse of $x$." The term $\boldsymbol{y} =$ **argsinh** $\boldsymbol{x}$ is also used, in honor of the fact that $y$ is the "argument whose sinh is $x$." This symbol parallels $y = \arcsin x$ for the inverse circular functions.

The graphs of $y = \sinh x$ and $y = \sinh^{-1} x$ are shown in Figure 9-9e. As is true with any function and its inverse, the two graphs are reflections of each other in the line $y = x$.

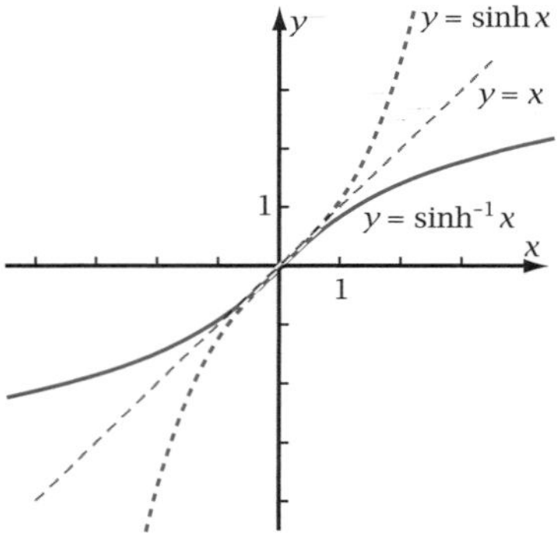

Figure 9-9e

### *Derivatives of the Inverse Hyperbolic Functions*

To differentiate an inverse hyperbolic function, just use the definition to transform back to the natural function. Then differentiate implicitly.

**Example 3** Find the derivative: $y = \cosh^{-1} x$, for $x > 1$.

**Solution**

$$y = \cosh^{-1} x$$

$$\cosh y = x$$

$$\sinh y \frac{dy}{dx} = 1 \qquad dy/dx \text{ comes from the chain rule.}$$

$$\frac{dy}{dx} = \frac{1}{\sinh y} \qquad \text{Divide each member by } \sinh y.$$

$$\frac{dy}{dx} = \frac{1}{\sqrt{\cosh^2 y - 1}} \qquad \cosh^2 y - \sinh^2 y = 1, \text{ so } \sinh^2 y = \cosh^2 y - 1.$$

$$\frac{dy}{dx} = \frac{1}{\sqrt{x^2 - 1}} \qquad \cosh y = x$$

Differentiation formulas for the other five inverse hyperbolic functions can be derived in a similar way, as you will do in Problem 39 of Problem Set 9-9. The six derivatives are summarized in the following box.

**Properties: Inverse Hyperbolic Function Derivatives**

$$\frac{d}{dx}(\sinh^{-1} x) = \frac{1}{\sqrt{x^2+1}} \qquad \frac{d}{dx}(\cosh^{-1} x) = \frac{1}{\sqrt{x^2-1}}, \quad x > 1$$

$$\frac{d}{dx}(\tanh^{-1} x) = \frac{1}{1-x^2}, \quad |x| < 1 \qquad \frac{d}{dx}(\coth^{-1} x) = \frac{1}{1-x^2}, \quad |x| > 1$$

$$\frac{d}{dx}(\operatorname{sech}^{-1} x) = -\frac{1}{x\sqrt{1-x^2}}, \quad x \text{ in}(0,1) \qquad \frac{d}{dx}(\operatorname{csch}^{-1} x) = -\frac{1}{|x|\sqrt{1+x^2}}, \quad x \neq 0$$

### *Integrals of Inverse Hyperbolic Functions*

The integrals of the inverse hyperbolic functions can be found by straightforward integration by parts. Example 4 shows you how.

**■ *Example 4*** Integrate: $\int \sinh^{-1}x\,dx$

***Solution***

$$\int \sinh^{-1}x\,dx$$
$$= x\sinh^{-1}x - \int \frac{1}{\sqrt{x^2+1}}\,x\,dx$$
$$= x\sinh^{-1}x - \tfrac{1}{2}\int (x^2+1)^{-1/2}(2x\,dx)$$
$$= x\sinh^{-1}x - \tfrac{1}{2}\cdot\tfrac{2}{1}(x^2+1)^{1/2} + C$$
$$= x\sinh^{-1}x - (x^2+1)^{1/2} + C$$

| $u$ | | $dv$ |
|---|---|---|
| $\sinh^{-1}x$ | $+$ | $1$ |
| $\dfrac{1}{\sqrt{x^2+1}}$ | $-$ | $x$ |

Can you give a reason?

■

The following box lists the indefinite integrals of the inverse hyperbolic functions. You should understand that these properties exist, and should know how to derive them if you are called upon to do so. However, unless you plan to make a career out of integrating inverse hyperbolic functions, there is no need to memorize them!

**Properties: Inverse Hyperbolic Function Integrals**

$$\int \sinh^{-1}x\,dx = x\sinh^{-1}x - (x^2+1)^{1/2} + C$$
$$\int \cosh^{-1}x\,dx = x\cosh^{-1}x - (x^2+1)^{1/2} + C, \quad x > 1$$
$$\int \tanh^{-1}x\,dx = x\tanh^{-1}x + \tfrac{1}{2}\ln|1-x^2| + C, \quad |x| < 1$$
$$\int \coth^{-1}x\,dx = x\coth^{-1}x + \tfrac{1}{2}\ln|1-x^2| + C, \quad |x| > 1$$
$$\int \operatorname{sech}^{-1}x\,dx = x\operatorname{sech}^{-1}x + \sin^{-1}x + C, \quad x \text{ in } (0,1)$$
$$\int \operatorname{csch}^{-1}x\,dx = x\operatorname{csch}^{-1}x + \operatorname{sgn}x\sinh^{-1}x + C, \quad x \neq 0$$

### *Hyperbolic Cosine as a Mathematical Model*

A chain hangs in the shape of the catenary

$$y = k\cosh\tfrac{1}{k}x + C,$$

where $k$ and $C$ stand for constants. In Problem 25 of Problem Set 9-9, you will learn why this is true. Example 5 shows you how to derive the particular equation.

**■ *Example 5*** A chain hangs from above a chalkboard (Figure 9-9f). Its ends are at $(\pm 90, 120)$, and its vertex is at (0, 20), where $x$ and $y$ are in centimeters along and above the chalk tray, respectively.

a. Find the particular equation of the catenary.

b. How high is the chain above the chalk tray when $x = 50$?

c. At what values of $x$ is the chain 110 cm above the chalk tray?

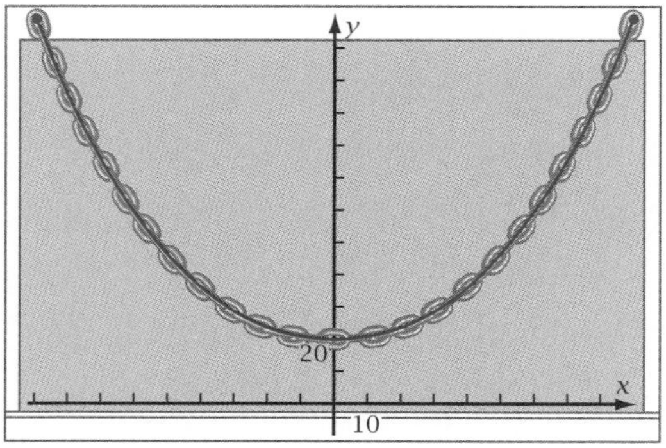


Figure 9-9f

***Solutions***

a. $y = k\cosh \frac{1}{k}x + C$ — Write the general equation of the catenary.

$20 = k\cosh \frac{1}{k}(0) + C = k + C$ — Substitute (0, 20); cosh 0 = 1.

$120 = k\cosh \frac{1}{k}(90) + C$ — Substitute (90, 120).

$100 = k\cosh \frac{90}{k} - k$ — Eliminate $C$ by subtracting equations.

$0 = k\cosh \frac{90}{k} - k - 100 \Rightarrow k = 51.780122\ldots$ — Use your grapher's solve feature.

$20 = 51.78\ldots + C \Rightarrow C = -31.78\ldots$

$\therefore y = 51.78\ldots \cosh \frac{1}{51.78\ldots} x - 31.78\ldots$

b. $y = 51.78\ldots \cosh \frac{50}{51.78\ldots} - 31.78\ldots = 46.0755\ldots$

The chain is about 46.1 cm above the chalk tray when $x = 50$.

c. $110 = 51.78\ldots \cosh \frac{1}{51.78\ldots} x - 31.78$

$\cosh \frac{1}{51.78\ldots} x = 2.7381\ldots$

$\frac{1}{51.78\ldots} x = \pm\cosh^{-1} 2.7381\ldots = \pm 1.66526\ldots$

$x = \pm 86.2278\ldots$

The chain is about 110 cm above the chalk tray when $x \approx \pm 86.2$ cm ■

# Problem Set 9-9

## *Do These Quickly*

The following problems are intended to refresh your skills. You should be able to do all ten problems in less than five minutes.

**Q1.** What trigonometric substitution should be used for $\int (x^2 + 5)^{3/2}\,dx$?

**Q2.** Integrate: $\int xe^x\,dx$

**Q3.** Integrate: $\int \sec^2 3x\,dx$

**Q4.** Integrate: $\int x^{-1/2}\,dx$

**Q5.** Integrate: $\int x^{-1}\,dx$

**Q6.** $\int \sin^n x\,dx = \frac{1}{n}\sin^{n-1}x\cos x + \frac{n-1}{n}\int \sin^{n-2}x\,dx$ is called $a(n)$ —?—.

**Q7.** True or false: $\sec' x = \ln|\sec x + \tan x| + C$

**Q8.** Write the formula for $dL$, the differential of arc length.

**Q9.** Name the appropriate integration method for $\int (x+5)/[(x-3)(x+2)]\,dx$.

**Q10.** If $f(x) = \sin^{-1}x$, then $f'(x) =$ —?—.

1. *Hyperbolic Function Graphing Problem:* Sketch the graphs of each of the six hyperbolic functions. You may plot these on your grapher first to see what they look like. The graphs of coth, sech, and csch may be plotted by taking advantage of their definitions to write the equations for these functions in terms of functions that appear on your grapher.

2. *Inverse Hyperbolic Function Graphing Problem:* Sketch the graphs of the inverses of the six hyperbolic functions. This is most easily done in parametric mode on your grapher, letting $x = \cosh t$ and $y = t$, for example. For each one that is not a function, darken what you think would be the principal branch (just one value of $y$ for each value of $x$), and write an inequality that restricts the range to specify this branch.

For Problems 3–22, do the integration or differentiation.

3. $f(x) = \tanh^3 x$
4. $f(x) = 5\,\mathrm{sech}\,3x$
5. $\int \cosh^5 x \sinh x\,dx$
6. $\int (\sinh x)^{-3}\cosh x\,dx$
7. $g(x) = \mathrm{csch}\,x \sin x$
8. $g(x) = \tan x \tanh x$
9. $\int \mathrm{sech}^2 4x\,dx$
10. $\int \mathrm{sech}\,7x \tanh 7x\,dx$
11. $h(x) = x^2 \coth x$
12. $h(x) = x^{2.5}\mathrm{csch}\,4x$
13. $\int_1^3 \tanh x\,dx$
14. $\int_{-4}^4 \sinh x\,dx$
15. $q(x) = \dfrac{\sinh 5x}{\ln 3x}$
16. $r(x) = \dfrac{\cosh 6x}{\cos 3x}$
17. $\int_0^1 x\sinh x\,dx$
18. $\int_a^b x^2\cosh x\,dx$
19. $y = 3\sinh^{-1}4x$
20. $y = 5\tanh^{-1}(x^3)$
21. $\int \tanh^{-1} 5x\,dx$
22. $\int 4\cosh^{-1}6x\,dx$

*Hyperbolic Substitution Problems:* For Problems 23 and 24, integrate by hyperbolic substitution, using the fact that $\cosh^2 t = \sinh^2 t + 1$, and $\sinh^2 t = \cosh^2 t - 1$.

23. $\int \sqrt{x^2+9}\,dx$
24. $\int \sqrt{x^2-25}\,dx$

25. *Hanging Chain or Cable Problem:* If a chain (or a flexible cable that doesn't stretch) is hung between two supports, it takes the shape of a hyperbolic cosine curve,

$$y = \frac{h}{w}\cosh\frac{w}{h}x + C,$$

where $x$ and $y$ are horizontal and vertical distances to a point on the chain, $h$ is the horizontal tensile force exerted on the chain, and $w$ is the weight of the chain per unit length. In this problem you will show why this is true. Figure 9-9g shows the graph of the chain in an $xy$-coordinate system. Any point on the chain experiences horizontal and vertical forces of $h$ and $v$, respectively. Force $h$ is constant, and depends on how tightly the chain is pulled at its ends. Force $v$ varies and equals the weight of the part of the chain below point $(x, y)$. The resultant tension vector points along the graph.

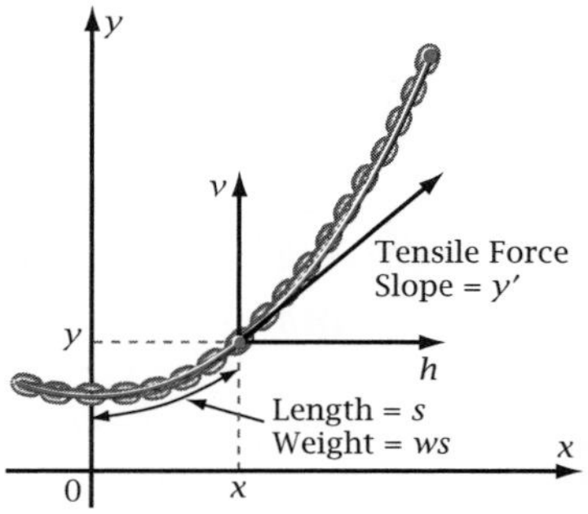

Figure 9-9g

a. Explain why the slope, $y' = dy/dx$, of the graph at point $(x, y)$ is equal to $v/h$.

b. The weight of the chain from 0 to $x$ equals the length, $s$, times the weight per unit length, $w$. Explain why this equation is true.

$$y' = \frac{w}{h}s$$

c. If you differentiate both sides of the equation in 23b, you get the differential equation

$$d(y') = \frac{w}{h}\,ds$$

Using what you know about arc length, show that this differential equation can be written

$$d(y') = \frac{w}{h}\left(1 + (y')^2\right)^{1/2}dx$$

d. Separating the variables in the equation in 23c and integrating gives

$$\int [1 + (y')^2]^{-1/2}\,d(y') = \int \frac{w}{h}\,dx.$$

Perform a hyperbolic substitution on the left, letting $y' = \sinh t$, and integrate to find

$$\sinh^{-1} y' = \frac{w}{h}x + C.$$

e. Use the fact that $y' = 0$ at the vertex, $x = 0$, to evaluate the constant of integration, $C$.

f. Based on the above work, show that

$$y' = \sinh\frac{w}{h}x.$$

g. From 25f, show that the equation of the hanging chain is as shown in the following box.

**Property: Equation of Hanging Chain or Cable**

$$y = \frac{h}{w}\cosh\frac{w}{h}x + C$$

where $w$ is the weight of chain per unit length,
$h$ is the horizontal tensile force on chain (in units consistent with $w$),
$x$ is the distance from the axis of symmetry to point $(x, y)$ on the chain,
$y$ is the vertical distance from the $x$-axis to point $(x, y)$, and
$C$ is a vertical distance determined by the position of the chain.

26. *Can You Duplicate This Graph?* Figure 9-9h shows the graph of a hyperbolic cosine function with general equation

$$y = k\cosh\frac{1}{k}x + C.$$

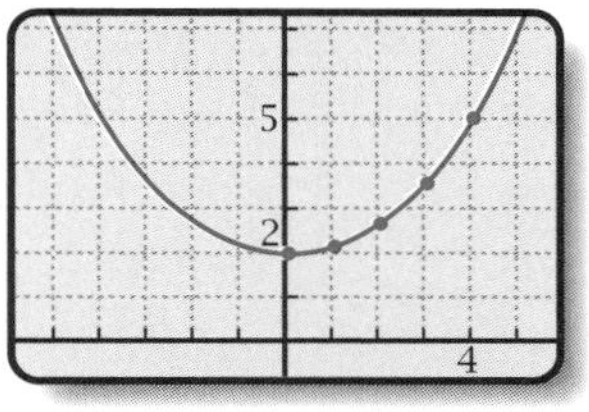

Figure 9-9h

a. Find the particular equation. Check your equation by showing that its graph agrees with points in the figure.

b. Calculate $y$ if $x$ is 20.

c. Calculate $x$ if $y$ is 4. Show that your answer is consistent with the graph.

d. Find the slope of the graph if $x$ is 3. Show that a line of this slope through the point on the graph where $x = 3$ is tangent to the graph.

e. Find the area of the region under the graph from $x = -1$ to $x = 3$.

f. Find the length of the graph from $x = -1$ to $x = 3$.

27. *Power Line Problem:* An electrical power line is to be suspended between pylons 300 ft apart (Figure 9-9i). The cable weighs 0.8 lb/ft, and will be connected to the pylons 110 ft above ground.

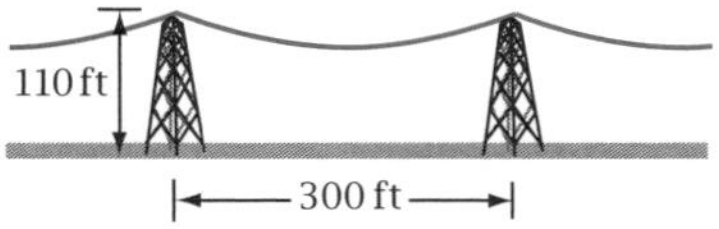

Figure 9-9i

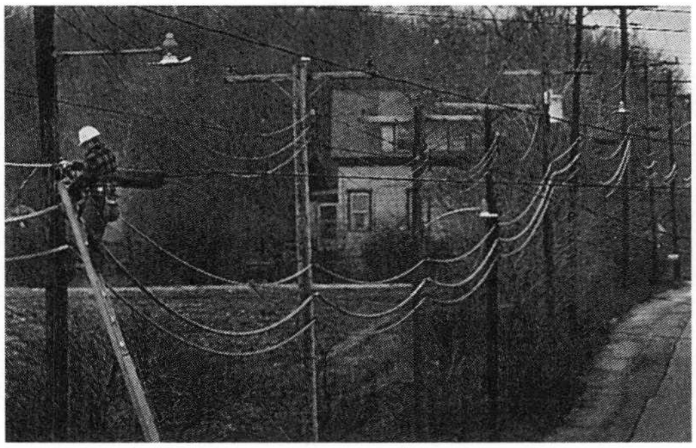

a. It is planned to use a horizontal tensile force of $h = 400$ lb to hold the cable. Write the particular equation of the resulting catenary. Use the equation to calculate how close to the ground the cable will come.

b. How long will the cable in 27a be? How much will it weigh?

c. For the cable in 27a, where will the maximum total tensile force be, at the middle or at the ends? What will this maximum tension be equal to?

d. The power company decides that the cable must come no closer than 100 ft from the ground. How high a horizontal force would be needed to achieve this clearance if the cables are still connected on 110 ft pylons?

28. *Hanging Chain Experiment:* Obtain a length of chain; about 6–10 feet is reasonable. Hang the chain between two convenient supports such as nails driven into the upper frame of a chalkboard. Let the chain hang down fairly far, as shown in Figure 9-9f (page 479). Set up a coordinate system with the $y$-axis halfway between the two supports. The $x$-axis can be some convenient horizontal line like the chalk tray. In this experiment you are to derive an equation for the vertical distance from the $x$-axis to the chain and to check it by actual measurement.

   a. Measure the $x$- and $y$-coordinates of the two supports and the vertex. Use centimeters.

   b. Find the particular equation of the particular catenary that fits the three data points.

   c. Make a table of values of $y$ versus $x$ for each 10 cm, going both ways from $x = 0$ and ending at the two supports.

   d. Mark the chain links at the supports then take down the chain. Plot the points you calculated in 28c on the chalkboard. Find some way to make sure the $y$-distances are truly vertical. Then hang back the chain to see how well it fits the catenary.

   e. Find the particular equation of the parabola (quadratic function) that fits the three measured data points. Make a table of $y$-values as in 28c and plot these values on the chalkboard. How does the parabola differ from the catenary?

   f. Use your equation from 28b to calculate the length of the chain between the two supports. Then stretch out the chain on the floor and measure it. How close does the calculated value come to the measured value?

29. *Bowl Problem:* The graph of $y = \sinh x$ from $x = 0$ to $x = 1$ is rotated about the $y$-axis to form a bowl (Figure 9-9j). Assume that $x$ and $y$ are in feet.

   a. Find the surface area of the bowl.

   b. The bowl is to be silver-plated inside and out. The cost of plating is \$57 per square foot. How much will plating cost?

   c. How much liquid could be held inside the bowl if it were filled to within a half-inch of the top?

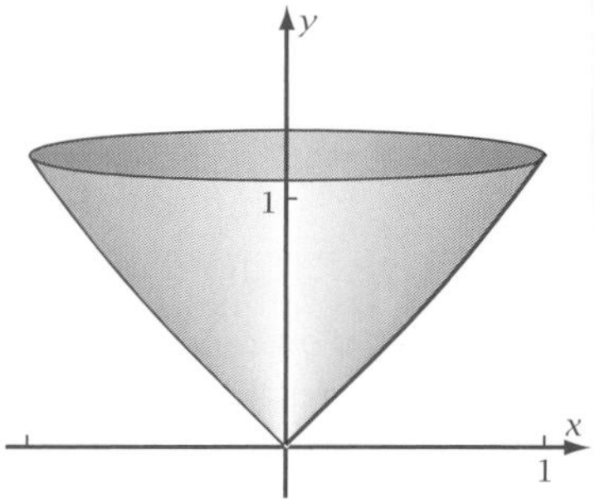

Figure 9-9j

30. *Gateway Arch Problem:* The Gateway to the West Arch in St. Louis is built in the shape of an inverted catenary (Figure 9-9k). This shape was used since compression forces act tangentially to the structure, as do the tensile forces on a chain, thus avoiding bending of the stainless steel from which the arch is constructed. The outside of the arch is 630 ft wide at the base and 630 ft high. The inside of the arch is 520 ft wide and 612 ft high.

   a. Find particular equations of the inner and outer catenaries.

   b. Verify that your equations are correct by plotting them on your grapher.

   c. The stress created by wind blowing against the arch depends on the area of the region between the two graphs. Find this area.

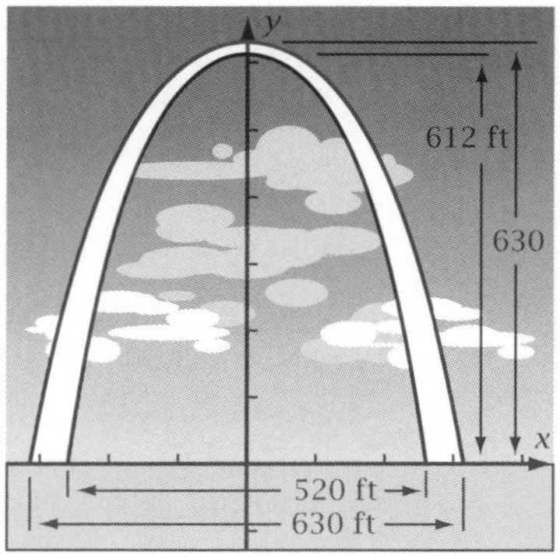

Figure 9-9k

d. A spider starts at the point where the left end of the outside of the arch meets the ground and crawls all the way up, then down the other side to the ground. As she crawls she leaves one strand of web. How long is the strand she leaves?

e. How steeply must the spider climb when she first starts up?

f. A. V. Ator wants to fly a plane underneath the arch. The plane has a (total) wingspan of 120 ft. Below what height, $y$, can A. V. fly to ensure that each wing misses the inside of the arch by at least 50 ft horizontally?

31. *Derivative Verification Problem:* For $H(x) = \operatorname{csch} x$,

a. Find $H'(1)$ exactly, using the differentiation formula.

b. Find $H'(1)$ approximately, using the symmetric difference quotient with $\Delta x = 0.01$. By what percentage does the approximate answer differ from the exact answer?

32. *Integral Verification Problem:* Evaluate $\int_1^2 \operatorname{sech} x\, dx$ by the fundamental theorem, using the antiderivative formula for the hyperbolic secant. Then evaluate the integral approximately using numerical integration. How does the numerical answer compare to the exact answer?

33. *Integration by Parts Problem:* Evaluate $\int e^x \sinh 2x\, dx$ by parts. Then integrate again by first using the definition of sinh to transform to exponential form. Show that the two answers are equivalent. Which technique is easier?

34. *Integration Surprise Problem!* Try to integrate by parts.

$$\int e^x \sinh x\, dx$$

What causes integration by parts to fail? Recalling the definition of sinh, figure another way to do the integrations, and do it.

35. *Derivations of the Pythagorean Properties of Hyperbolic Functions:*

a. Starting with the definition of $\cosh x$ and $\sinh x$, prove that $\cosh^2 x - \sinh^2 x = 1$.

b. Divide both members of the equation in 37a by $\cosh^2 x$, and thus derive the property $1 - \tanh^2 x = \operatorname{sech}^2 x$.

c. Derive the property $\coth^2 x - 1 = \operatorname{csch}^2 x$.

36. *Double-Argument Properties of Hyperbolic Functions:*

a. Explain why $\sinh 2x = \frac{1}{2}(e^{2x} - e^{-2x})$.

b. Derive the double-argument property $\sinh 2x = 2 \sinh x \cosh x$.

c. Derive the double-argument property $\cosh 2x = \cosh^2 x + \sinh^2 x$.

d. Derive the other form of the double-argument property, $\cosh 2x = 1 + 2\sinh^2 x$.

e. Derive the property $\sinh^2 x = \frac{1}{2}(\cosh 2x - 1)$.

37. *Hyperbolic Radian Problem:* In trigonometry you learn that the argument, $x$ radians, in the circular functions $\sin x$ or $\cos x$ equals an arc length on the unit circle (Figure 9-9l, left). In this problem you will show that the same is not true for $x$ "hyperbolic" radians in $\sinh x$ and $\cosh x$. You will show that the arguments both in circular and hyperbolic radians equal the area of a sector of the circular or hyperbolic region shown in Figure 9-9l.

a. Show that the unit circle $u^2 + v^2 = 1$ between $u = \cos 2$ and $u = 1$ is 2 units long, but the hyperbola $u^2 - v^2 = 1$ between $u = 1$ and $u = \cosh 2$ is greater than 2 units long.

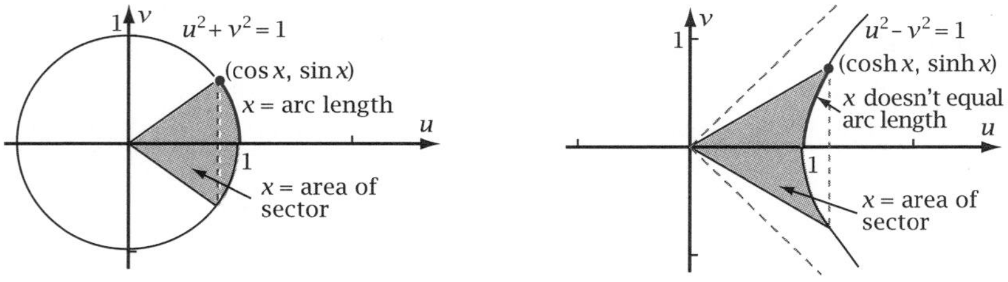


Figure 9-9l

b. Show that 2 is the area of the hyperbolic sector in Figure 9-9l with the point $(u, v) = (\cosh 2, \sinh 2)$ as its upper boundary.

c. Show that $x$ is the area of the circular sector with the point $(u, v) = (\cos x, \sin x)$ as its upper boundary.

d. Show in general that $x$ is the area of the hyperbolic sector with the point $(u, v) = (\cosh x, \sinh x)$ as its upper boundary.

38. *Algebraic Derivatives of the Other Five Inverse Hyperbolic Functions:* Derive the differential formulas given in this section for the following expressions.

a. $\dfrac{d}{dx}(\sinh^{-1} x)$

b. $\dfrac{d}{dx}(\tanh^{-1} x)$

c. $\dfrac{d}{dx}(\coth^{-1} x)$

d. $\dfrac{d}{dx}(\operatorname{sech}^{-1} x)$

e. $\dfrac{d}{dx}(\operatorname{csch}^{-1} x)$

# 9-10 Improper Integrals

Suppose that you are driving along the highway at 80 ft/sec (about 55 mi/hr). At time $t = 0$ sec you take your foot off the accelerator and let the car start slowing down. Assume that your velocity is given by

$$v(t) = 80e^{-0.1t},$$

where $v(t)$ is in feet per second. According to this mathematical model the velocity approaches zero as time increases but is never equal to zero. So you are never quite stopped. Would the distance you go approach a limiting value, or would it increase without bound? In this section you will learn how to answer such questions by evaluating *improper integrals*.

**OBJECTIVE**

Given an improper integral, tell whether or not it **converges** (that is, approaches a finite number as a limit). If it does, find the number to which it converges.

Figure 9-10a shows the velocity function mentioned above. The distance the car goes between $t = 0$ and $t = b$ is equal to the area of the region under the graph. Thus

$$\begin{aligned}\text{Distance} &= \int_0^b 80e^{-0.1t}\,dt \\ &= -800e^{-0.1t}\Big|_0^b \\ &= -800e^{-0.2b} + 800.\end{aligned}$$

If $b = 10$ sec, the distance is 505.6 ... ft. As $b$ approaches infinity, the $-800e^{-0.2b}$ term approaches zero. Thus the distance approaches 800 ft. The mathematical model tells you that the car never passes a point 800 ft from where you started slowing. The integral

$$\int_0^\infty 80e^{-0.1t}\,dt$$

is called an improper integral because one of its limits of integration is not finite. The integral *converges* to 800 because the integral from 0 to $b$ approaches 800 as $b$ approaches infinity. Suppose the velocity function had been $v(t) = 320(t + 4)^{-1}$. The graph (Figure 9-10b) looks almost the same. The velocity still approaches zero as time increases. The distance would be

$$\begin{aligned}\text{Distance} &= \int_0^b 320(t+4)^{-1}\,dt \\ &= 320\ln|t+4|\Big|_0^b \\ &= 320\ln|b+4| - 320\ln 4.\end{aligned}$$

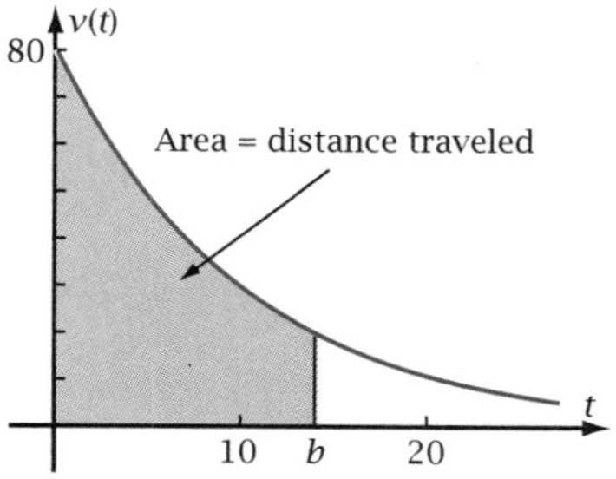

Figure 9-10a

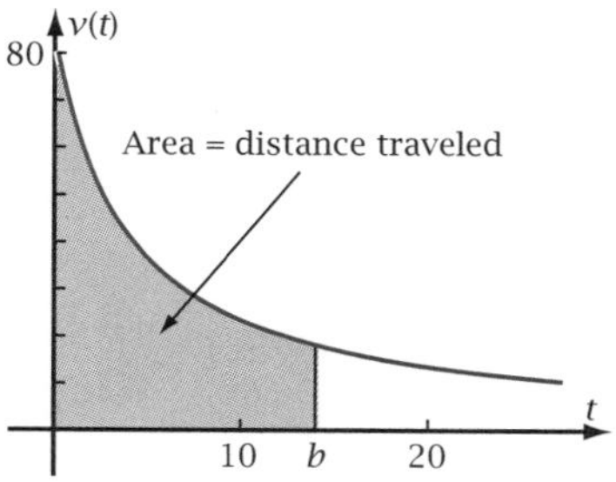

Figure 9-10b

As $b$ approaches infinity, so does $\ln|b + 4|$. The integral *diverges*. Unlike the first mathematical model, this one tells you the car would go arbitrarily far from the starting point if you waited long enough!

A definite integral is improper if the following hold.

- The upper or lower limit of integration is infinite.
- The integrand is discontinuous for at least one value of $x$ at or between the limits of integration.

**Definition: Improper Integrals**

$$\int_a^{\infty} f(x)\,dx = \lim_{b\to\infty}\int_a^b f(x)\,dx$$

$$\int_{-\infty}^{b} f(x)\,dx = \lim_{a\to-\infty}\int_a^b f(x)\,dx$$

$$\int_a^{b} f(x)\,dx = \lim_{k\to c^+}\int_k^b f(x)\,dx + \lim_{k\to c^-}\int_a^k f(x)\,dx,\ f \text{ is discontinuous at } x = c \text{ in } [a, b]$$

An improper integral **converges** to a certain number if each applicable limit shown above is finite. Otherwise, the integral **diverges**.

Note that an improper integral with an infinite limit of integration always diverges if the integrand has a limit other than zero as the variable of integration approaches infinity.

■ ***Example 1*** For the improper integral $\int_0^{\infty} x^2e^{-x}\,dx$,

a. Graph the integrand and tell whether or not the integral might converge.

b. If the integral might converge, find out whether or not it does, and if so, to what limit it converges.

***Solution***

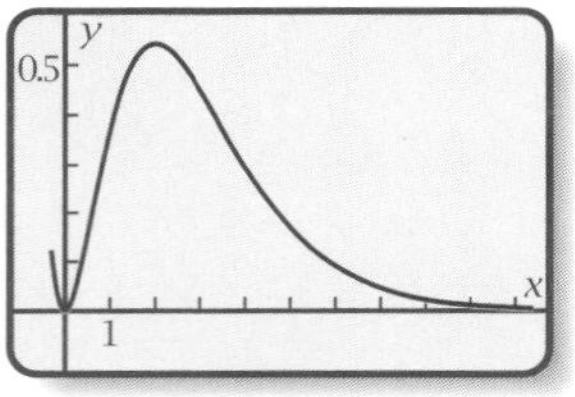


Figure 9-10c

a. Figure 9-10c shows that the integral might converge because the integrand seems to approach zero as $x$ gets very large.

b. Replace $\infty$ with $b$ and let $b$ approach infinity.

$$\int_0^{\infty} x^2e^{-x}\,dx = \lim_{b\to\infty}\int_0^b x^2e^{-x}\,dx$$

Integrating by parts twice gives

$$\lim_{b\to\infty}(-x^2e^{-x} - 2xe^{-x} - 2e^{-x})\Big|_0^b = \lim_{b\to\infty}(-b^2e^{-b} - 2be^{-b} - 2e^{-b} + 0 + 0 + 2).$$

The limit of $b^2e^{-b}$ can be found by two applications of l'Hospital's rule.

$$\lim_{b\to\infty} b^2e^{-b} = \lim_{b\to\infty}\frac{b^2}{e^b} \to \frac{\infty}{\infty}$$ Write the expression as a quotient.

$$= \lim_{b\to\infty}\frac{2b}{e^b} \to \frac{\infty}{\infty}$$ Use l'Hospital's rule. (Take the derivative of numerator and denominator.)

$$= \lim_{b\to\infty}\frac{2}{e^b} \to \frac{2}{\infty}$$ Use l'Hospital's rule again.

$$= 0$$ Limit of the form (finite/infinite) is zero.

Similarly, the second and third terms in the limit each go to zero. Therefore, $\lim_{b\to\infty}(-b^2e^{-b} - 2be^{-b} - 2e^{-b} + 0 + 0 + 2) = 2$. ■

■ ***Example 2*** For the improper integral $\int_0^{\infty} x^{0.2}\,dx$,

a. Graph the integrand and tell whether or not the integral might converge.

b. If the integral might converge, find out whether or not it does, and if so, to what limit it converges.

**Solution**

a. The graph in Figure 9-10d indicates that the integral does not converge. Since the limit of the integrand, $x^{0.2}$, is not 0 as $x$ approaches infinity, the integral diverges.

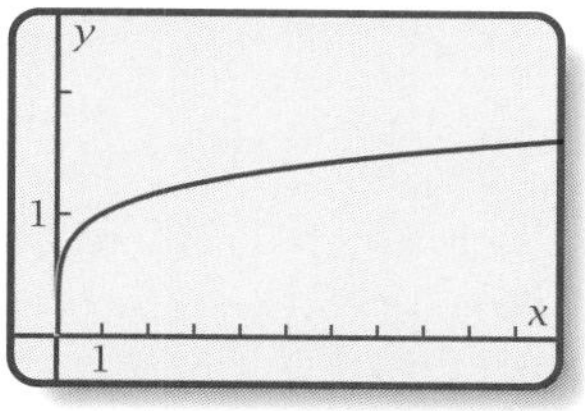


Figure 9-10d

b. Nothing remains to be done because the integral diverges. ■

■ **Example 3** For the improper integral $\int_{-2}^{2} \frac{1}{x}\,dx$,

a. Graph the integrand and tell whether or not the integral might converge.

b. If the integral might converge, find out whether or not it does, and if so, to what limit it converges.

**Solution**

a. Figure 9-10e shows the graph of the function. Since there is a discontinuity at $x = 0$, you must evaluate two integrals, one from $-2$ to $b$ and the other from $a$ to 2. You write

$$\int_{-2}^{2} \frac{1}{x}\,dx = \lim_{b \to 0^-} \int_{-2}^{b} \frac{1}{x}\,dx + \lim_{a \to 0^+} \int_{a}^{2} \frac{1}{x}\,dx.$$

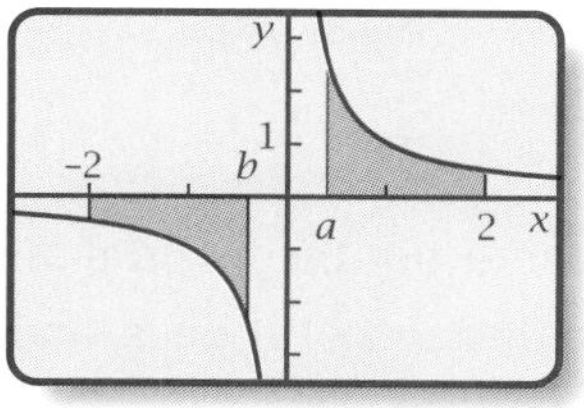


Figure 9-10e

At first glance, you might think that the integral converges to zero. If $a$ and $b$ are the same distance from the origin, then there is just as much negative "area" below the $x$-axis as there is area above. In order for the integral to converge, however, both of the integrals shown above must converge. Checking the first one,

$$\lim_{b \to 0^-} \int_{-2}^{b} \frac{1}{x}\,dx = \lim_{b \to 0^-} \ln|x| \Big|_{-2}^{b} = \lim_{b \to 0^-} (\ln|b| - \ln|-2|).$$

Since $\ln 0$ is infinite, this integral diverges. Thus, the original integral also diverges.

b. There is nothing to be done for part b because the integral diverges. ■

# Problem Set 9-10

### *Do These Quickly*

The following problems are intended to refresh your skills. You should be able to do all ten problems in less than five minutes.

**Q1.** Sketch: $y = e^{-x}$

**Q2.** What function has a graph like Figure 9-10f?

**Q3.** What function has a graph like Figure 9-10g?

**Q4.** What function has a graph like Figure 9-10h?

**Q5.** What function has a graph like Figure 9-10i?

**Q6.** $\int \cosh x\, dx =$ —?—

**Q7.** $y = \cosh x \Rightarrow y' =$ —?—

**Q8.** $y = \cos x \Rightarrow y' =$ —?—

**Q9.** $\int \cos x\, dx =$ —?—

**Q10.** What is the maximum value of $y$ if $y = -x^2 + 10x + 7$?

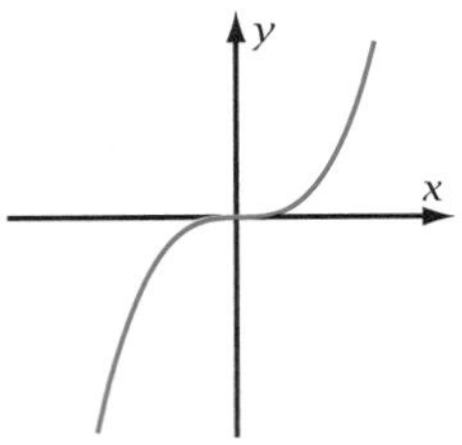

Figure 9-10f

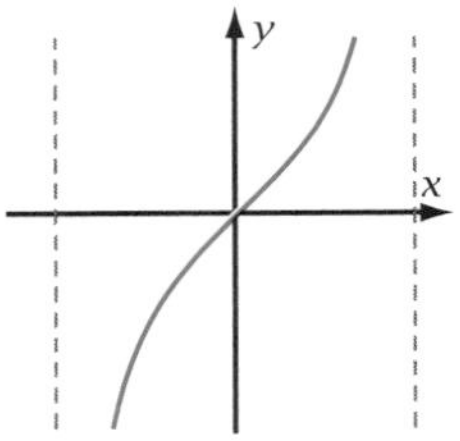

Figure 9-10g

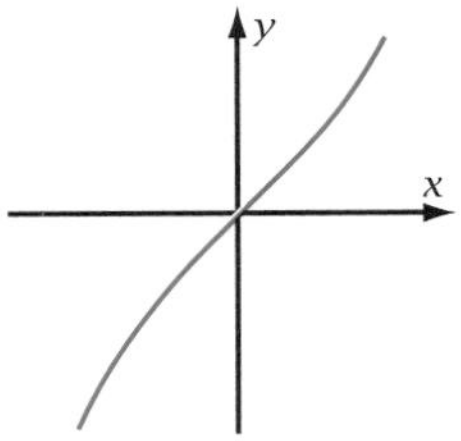

Figure 9-10h

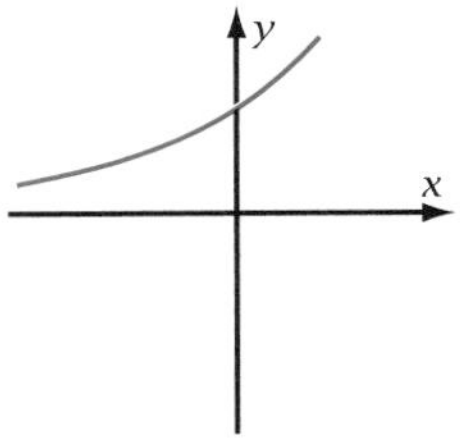

Figure 9-10i

For Problems 1–20,

a. Tell from the graph of the integrand whether or not the integral might converge.

b. If the integral might converge, find out whether or not it does, and if so, the limit to which it converges.

1. $\displaystyle\int_2^\infty \frac{1}{x^2}\,dx$
2. $\displaystyle\int_3^\infty \frac{1}{x^4}\,dx$
3. $\displaystyle\int_1^\infty \frac{1}{x}\,dx$
4. $\displaystyle\int_0^1 \frac{1}{x}\,dx$
5. $\displaystyle\int_1^\infty \frac{1}{x^{0.2}}\,dx$
6. $\displaystyle\int_1^\infty \frac{1}{x^{1.2}}\,dx$
7. $\displaystyle\int_0^1 \frac{1}{x^{0.2}}\,dx$
8. $\displaystyle\int_0^1 \frac{1}{x^{1.2}}\,dx$
9. $\displaystyle\int_0^\infty \frac{dx}{1+x^2}$
10. $\displaystyle\int_0^\infty \frac{dx}{1+x}$
11. $\displaystyle\int_0^1 \frac{dx}{x\ln x}$
12. $\displaystyle\int_3^\infty \frac{dx}{x(\ln x)^2}$
13. $\displaystyle\int_2^\infty e^{-0.4x}\,dx$
14. $\displaystyle\int_0^\infty e^{0.02x}\,dx$
15. $\displaystyle\int_{-1}^2 \sqrt{x}\,dx$
16. $\displaystyle\int_1^7 (x-3)^{-2/3}\,dx$
17. $\displaystyle\int_0^\infty xe^{-x}\,dx$
18. $\displaystyle\int_0^3 (x-1)^{-2}\,dx$
19. $\displaystyle\int_0^\infty \cos x\,dx$
20. $\displaystyle\int_0^\infty \sin x\,dx$

21. *Divergence by Oscillation Problem:* The improper integrals in Problems 19 and 20 are said to diverge by oscillation. Explain why these words make sense. A graph may help.

22. *p-Integral Problem:* An integral of the form

$$I_p = \int_1^{\infty} \frac{1}{x^p}\,dx,$$

where $p$ stands for a constant, is called a ***p*-integral**. For some values of the exponent $p$, the integral converges and for others it doesn't. Figure 9-10j shows an example for which the two graphs look practically identical, but only one of the integrals converges. In this problem your objective is to find the values of $p$ for which the $p$-integral converges and those for which it diverges.

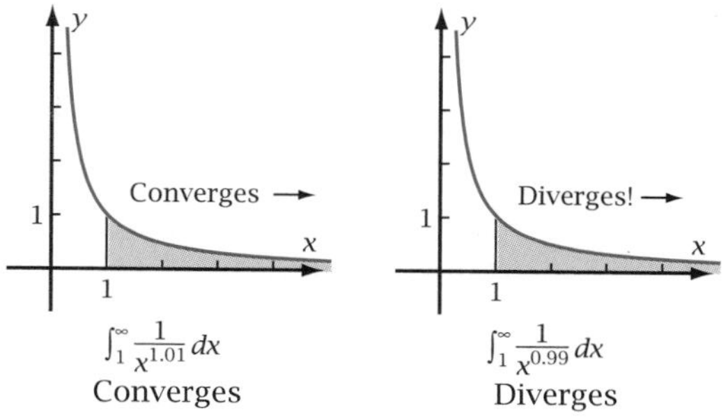

Figure 9-10j

a. Show that $I_p$ converges if $p = 1.001$, but not if $p = 0.999$.

b. Does $I_p$ converge if $p = 1$? Justify your answer.

c. Complete the statement, "$I_p$ converges if $p$ —?—, and diverges if $p$ —?—."

23. *Volume of an Unbounded Solid Problem:* Figure 9-10k shows the region under the graph of $y = 1/x$ from $x = 1$ to $x = b$.

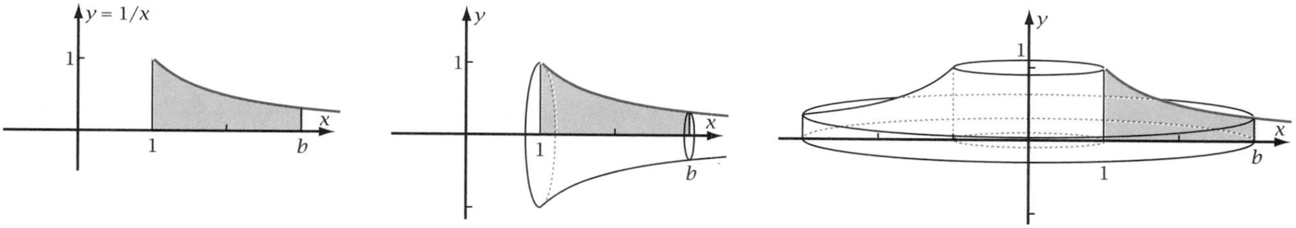

Figure 9-10k

a. Does the region's area approach a finite limit as $b$ approaches infinity? Explain.

b. The region is rotated about the $x$-axis to form a solid. Does the volume of the solid approach a finite limit as $b \to \infty$? If so, what is the limit? If not, explain why not.

c. The region is rotated about the $y$-axis to form a different solid. Does this volume approach a finite limit as $b \to \infty$? If so, what is the limit? If not, explain why not.

d. True or false: "If a region has infinite area, then the solid formed by rotating that region about an axis has infinite volume."

24. *Infinite Paint Bucket Problem:* The graph of $y = -1/x$ from $x = 0$ to $x = 1$ is rotated about the $y$-axis to form an infinitely deep paint bucket (Figure 9-10l). Explain why a vertical cross section along the $y$-axis will have an infinite area and thus why the surface area of the bucket itself is infinite. Then show that the bucket could be completely filled with a finite volume of paint, thus coating the infinite surface area. Surprising??!

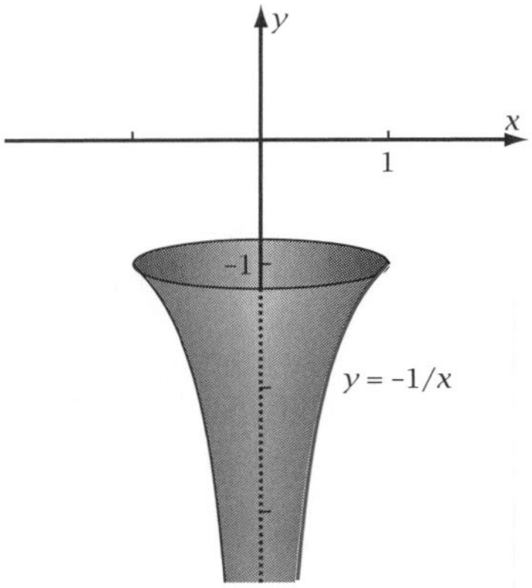

Figure 9-10l

25. *The Gamma Function and Factorial Function:* In this problem you will explore

$$f(x) = \int_0^\infty t^x e^{-t}\,dt,$$

where $x$ is a constant with respect to the integration. Figure 9-10m shows the integrand for $x = 1$, $x = 2$, and $x = 3$.

a. Find $f(1)$, $f(2)$, and $f(3)$ by evaluating the improper integral. Along the way you will have to show, for instance, that

$$\lim_{b \to \infty} b^3 e^{-b} = 0.$$

b. From the pattern you see in the answers to 25a, make a conjecture about what $f(4)$, $f(5)$, and $f(6)$ are equal to.

c. Integrate by parts once and thus show that

$$f(x) = x \cdot f(x-1).$$

Use the answer to confirm your conjecture in part (b).

d. The result of the above work forms a basis for the definition of the factorial function. Explain why this definition is consistent with the definition $x! = (x)(x-1)(x-2)\ldots(2)(1)$.

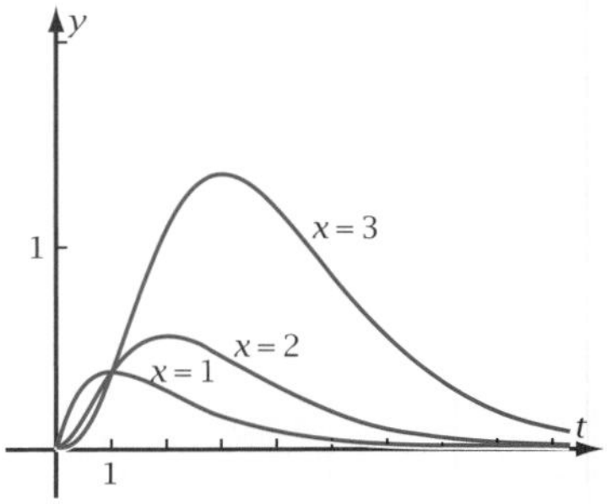

Figure 9-10m

**Definition: The Factorial Function (and the Gamma Function)**

| | |
|---|---|
| $x! = \int_0^\infty t^x e^{-t}\,dt$ | The factorial function. |
| $\Gamma(x) = (x-1)!$ | The gamma function. ($\Gamma$ is the uppercase Greek letter gamma.) |

e. Confirm that the integral for 3! approaches 6 by integrating numerically from $t = 0$ to $t = b$ for some fairly large value of $b$. How large a value of $b$ makes the integral come within 0.000,001 of 6?

f. The improper integral can be used to define factorials for noninteger values of $x$. Write an integral equal to 0.5!. Evaluate it numerically, using the value of $b$ from 25e. How can you tell from the graphs in Figure 9-10m that your answer will be closer than 0.000,001 to the correct answer? How does your answer compare with the value in the National Bureau of Standards Handbook of Mathematical Functions, namely, $0.5! = 0.8862269255$?

g. Quick! Without further integration, calculate 1.5!, 2.5!, and 3.5!. (Remember 25c.)

h. Show that $0! = 1$, as you probably learned in algebra.

i. Show that $(-1)!$, $(-2)!$, $(-3)!$, . . . , are infinite but $(-0.5)!$, $(-1.5)!$, and $(-2.5)!$ are finite.

j. Show that the value of 0.5! in 25f can be expressed rather simply in terms of $\pi$.

26. *Spaceship Work Problem:* A 1000-lb spaceship is to be sent to a distant location. The work required to get the spaceship away from the earth's gravity equals the force times the distance the spaceship is moved. But the force $F$, which is 1000 lb at the earth's surface, decreases with the square of the distance from the earth's center,

$$F = \frac{1000}{r^2},$$

where $r$ is the number of earth-radii. Since there is always some force no matter how far you travel from earth, additional work is always being done. Does the amount of work increase without bound as $r$ goes to infinity? Show how you arrive at your answer.

27. *Piecewise Continuity Problem:* Figure 9-10n shows the graph of

$$y = 2^x - \frac{|x-2|}{x-2}$$

Suppose that you are to evaluate

$$\int_1^3 \left(2^x - \frac{|x-2|}{x-2}\right) dx.$$

Although the integrand is discontinuous on the closed interval [1, 3], there is only a step discontinuity at $x = 2$. The integrand is continuous everywhere else in [1, 3]. Such a function is said to be *piecewise-continuous* on the given interval. In this problem you will show that a piecewise-continuous function is integrable on the given interval.

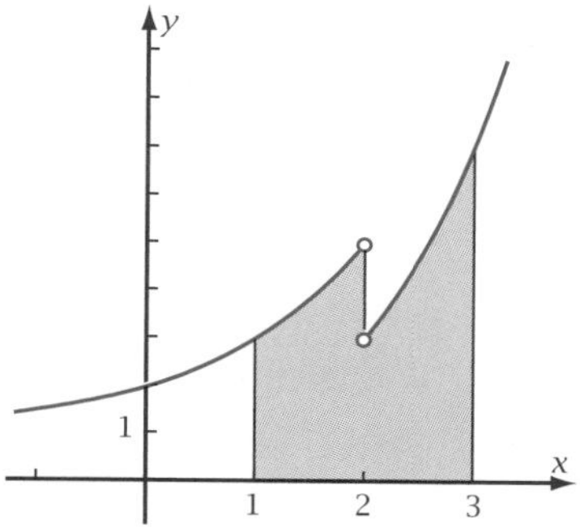

Figure 9-10n

**Definition: Piecewise Continuity**

Function $f$ is piecewise-continuous on the interval $[a, b]$ if and only if there is a finite number of values of $x$ in $[a, b]$ at which $f(x)$ is discontinuous, the discontinuities are either removable or step discontinuities, and $f$ is continuous elsewhere on $[a, b]$.

a. Write the integral above as the sum of two integrals, one from $x = 1$ to $x = 2$ and the other from $x = 2$ to $x = 3$.

b. Both integrals in 27a are improper. Write each one using the correct limit terminology.

c. Show that both integrals in 27b converge. Observe that the expression $|x-2|/(x-2)$ equals one constant to the left of $x = 2$, and a different constant to the right. Find the value to which the original integral converges.

d. Explain why the following property is true.

**Property: Integrability of Piecewise-Continuous Functions**

If function $f$ is piecewise-continuous on the interval $[a, b]$, then $f$ is integrable on $[a, b]$.

e. True or false: "A function is integrable on the interval $[a, b]$ if and only if it is continuous on $[a, b]$." Justify your answer.

28. *Journal Problem:* Update your journal with things you've learned since the last entry. You should include such things as those listed here.
    - The one most important thing you have learned since the last journal entry
    - The big integration technique that allows you to integrate a product of two functions
    - Other integration techniques that involve substitutions and algebraic transformations
    - Hyperbolic functions
    - Improper integrals
    - Why the fundamental theorem, not numerical integration, is needed for improper integrals
    - Any techniques or ideas about the calculus of transcendental functions that are still unclear to you

# 9-11 Miscellaneous Integrals and Derivatives

By the time you finish this section you will have seen all of the classical algebraic techniques for performing calculus. These techniques were the only way calculus could be done before the advent of the computer made numerical methods easily implementable.

**OBJECTIVE** Algebraically integrate or differentiate expressions containing the elementary functions.

### *Techniques: Differentiation*

- Sum: $(u + v)' = u' + v'$
- Product: $(uv)' = u'v + uv'$ Or, use logarithmic differentiation technique.
- Quotient: $(u/v)' = (u'v - uv')/v^2$ Or, use logarithmic differentiation technique.
- Composite: $(f(u))' = f'(u)u'$ (chain rule)
- Implicit: $f(y) = g(x) \Rightarrow f'(y)y' = g'(x)$ (Use the chain rule, where $y$ is the inside function.)
- Power function: $(x^n)' = nx^{n-1}$
- Exponential function: $(n^x)' = (n^x)\ln n$ (Use the logarithmic differentiation technique.)
- Logarithmic function: $(\log_b x)' = (1/x)(1/\ln b)$
- Logarithmic differentiation technique:

$$y = f(x) \Rightarrow \ln y = \ln f(x) \Rightarrow (1/y)y' = [\ln f(x)]' \Rightarrow y' = y[\ln f(x)]'$$

- Trigonometric function: $\sin' x = \cos x$, $\cos' x = -\sin x$
- Inverse trigonometric function: Differentiate implicitly.
- Hyperbolic function: $\sinh' x = \cosh x$, $\cosh' x = \sinh x$
- Inverse hyperbolic function: Differentiate implicitly.

### Techniques: Indefinite Integration

- Known derivative: $\int f'(x)\,dx = f(x) + C$
- Sum: $\int (u + v)dx = \int u\,dx + \int v\,dx$
- Product: $\int u\,dv = uv - \int v\,du$ — Integrate by parts.
- Reciprocal Function: $\int u^{-1}\,du = \ln|u| + C$
- Power Function: $\int u^n\,du = u^{n+1}/(n+1) + C,\ n \neq -1$ — ("$u$-substitution" method).
- Power of a Function: $\int f^n(x)\,dx$ — Use a reduction formula.
- Square root of a quadratic: Integrate by trigonometric substitution; complete the square first, if necessary.
- Rational algebraic function: Convert to a sum by long division and by resolving into partial fractions.
- Inverse function [exponential (logarithmic), trigonometric, or hyperbolic]: Integrate by parts.

## Problem Set 9-11

For Problems 1–100, differentiate the given function, or evaluate the given integral.

1. $y = \sec 3x \tan 3x$
2. $y = \sinh 5x \tanh 5x$
3. $\int x \cosh 4x\,dx$
4. $\int x \cos x\,dx$
5. $f(x) = (3x + 5)^{-1}$
6. $f(x) = (5 - 2x)^{-1}$
7. $\int (3x + 5)^{-1}\,dx$
8. $\int (5 - 2x)^{-1}\,dx$
9. $t(x) = \tan^5 4x$
10. $h(x) = \operatorname{sech}^3 7x$
11. $\int \sin^2 x\,dx$
12. $\int \cos^2 x\,dx$
13. $y = \dfrac{6x - 11}{x + 2}$
14. $y = \dfrac{5x + 9}{x - 4}$
15. $\int \dfrac{6x - 11}{x + 2}\,dx$
16. $\int \dfrac{5x + 9}{x - 4}\,dx$
17. $f(t) = \sqrt{1 + t^2}$
18. $g(t) = \sqrt{t^2 - 1}$
19. $\int \sqrt{1 + t^2}\,dt$
20. $\int \sqrt{t^2 - 1}\,dt$
21. $y = x^3 e^x$
22. $y = x^4 e^{-x}$
23. $\int x^3 e^x\,dx$
24. $\int x^4 e^{-x}\,dx$
25. $f(x) = \sin^{-1} x$
26. $g(x) = \tan^{-1} x$
27. $\int \sin^{-1} x\,dx$
28. $\int \tan^{-1} x\,dx$
29. $\int \dfrac{1}{x^2 + 4x - 5}\,dx$
30. $\int \dfrac{1}{x^2 - 6x - 7}\,dx$
31. $\int \dfrac{1}{\sqrt{x^2 + 4x - 5}}\,dx$
32. $\int \dfrac{1}{\sqrt{x^2 - 6x - 7}}\,dx$

33. $f(x) = \tanh x$

34. $f(x) = \coth x$

35. $\int \tanh x\, dx$

36. $\int \coth x\, dx$

37. $y = e^{2x}\cos 3x$

38. $y = e^{-3x}\cos 4x$

39. $\int e^{2x}\cos 3x\, dx$

40. $\int e^{-3x}\cos 4x\, dx$

41. $g(x) = x^3 \ln 5x$

42. $h(x) = x^2 \ln 8x$

43. $\int x^3 \ln 5x\, dx$

44. $\int x^2 \ln 8x\, dx$

45. $y = \dfrac{x}{(x+2)(x+3)(x+4)}$

46. $y = \dfrac{x}{(x-1)(x-2)(x-3)}$

47. $\int \dfrac{x}{(x+2)(x+3)(x+4)}\, dx$

48. $\int \dfrac{x}{(x-1)(x-2)(x-3)}\, dx$

49. $y = \cos^3 x \sin x$

50. $y = \sin^5 x \cos x$

51. $\int \cos^3 x \sin x\, dx$

52. $\int \sin^5 x \cos x\, dx$

53. $\int \cos^3 x\, dx$

54. $\int \sin^5 x\, dx$

55. $\int \cos^4 x\, dx$

56. $\int \sin^6 x\, dx$

57. $g(x) = (x^4 + 3)^3$

58. $f(x) = (x^3 - 1)^4$

59. $\int (x^4 + 3)^3\, dx$

60. $\int (x^3 - 1)^4\, dx$

61. $\int (x^4 + 3)^3 x^3\, dx$

62. $\int (x^3 - 1)^4 x^2\, dx$

63. $\int (x^4 + 3)\, dx$

64. $\int (x^3 - 1)\, dx$

65. $f(x) = \int_1^x (t^4 + 3)^3\, dt$

66. $h(x) = \int_5^x (t^3 - 1)^4\, dt$

67. $\int_1^2 xe^x\, dx$

68. $\int_0^2 xe^{-x}\, dx$

69. $r(x) = xe^x$

70. $s(x) = xe^{-x}$

71. $q(x) = \dfrac{\ln x + 2}{x}$

72. $r(x) = \dfrac{(\ln x)^3 + 4}{x}$

73. $\int \dfrac{\ln x + 2}{x}\, dx$

74. $\int \dfrac{(\ln x)^3 + 4}{x}\, dx$

75. $f(x) = e^{x^2}$

76. $f(x) = e^{x^3}$

77. $\int xe^{x^2}\, dx$

78. $\int x^2 e^{x^3}\, dx$

79. $\int x^3 e^{x^2}\, dx$

80. $\int x^5 e^{x^3}\, dx$

In Problems 81–100, $a$, $b$, $c$, $d$, and $n$ stand for constants.

81. $\int e^{ax}\cos bx\, dx$

82. $\int e^{ax}\sin bx\, dx$

83. $\int \sin^2 cx\, dx$

84. $\int \cos^2 cx\, dx$

85. $f(x) = \dfrac{ax + b}{cx + d}$

86. $f(x) = (ax + b)^n$

87. $\displaystyle\int \frac{ax + b}{cx + d}\,dx$

88. $\displaystyle\int (ax + b)^n\,dx$

89. $\displaystyle\int (x^2 + a^2)^{-1/2}x\,dx$

90. $\displaystyle\int (a^2 - x^2)^{-1/2}x\,dx$

91. $\displaystyle\int (x^2 + a^2)^{-1/2}\,dx$

92. $\displaystyle\int (a^2 - x^2)^{-1/2}\,dx$

93. $f(x) = x^2 \sin ax$

94. $f(x) = x^2 \cos ax$

95. $\displaystyle\int x^2 \sin ax\,dx$

96. $\displaystyle\int x^2 \cos ax\,dx$

97. $\displaystyle\int \sinh ax\,dx$

98. $\displaystyle\int \cosh ax\,dx$

99. $\displaystyle\int \cos^{-1} ax\,dx$

100. $\displaystyle\int \sin^{-1} ax\,dx$

### *Historical Topic #1—Rationalizing Algebraic Substitutions*

Before calculators and computers were readily available to perform numerical integration, it was important to be able to find algebraic formulas for as many integrals as possible. Much time was spent by users of mathematics searching for clever integration techniques, and by students of mathematics in learning these techniques. Two such techniques are shown here and in Problem 107. An integral such as

$$I = \int \frac{1}{1 + \sqrt[3]{x}}\,dx$$

that has a radical in the denominator can be transformed to a rational integrand by substituting a variable either for the radical or for the entire denominator. Here's how you would go about it. Let $u = 1 + \sqrt[3]{x}$. Then $(u - 1)^3 = x$, from which $dx = 3(u - 1)^2\,du$. Substituting $u$ for the denominator and $3(u - 1)^2\,du$ for $dx$ gives

$$\begin{aligned} I &= 3\int \frac{(u-1)^2}{u}\,du = 3\int \left(u - 2 + \tfrac{1}{u}\right)du = \tfrac{3}{2}u^2 - 6u + 3\ln|u| + C \\ &= \tfrac{3}{2}(1 + \sqrt[3]{x})^2 - 6(1 + \sqrt[3]{x}) + 3\ln|1 + \sqrt[3]{x}| + C. \end{aligned}$$

For Problems 101–106, evaluate the integrals by algebraic substitution.

101. $\displaystyle\int \frac{1}{1 + \sqrt{x}}\,dx$

102. $\displaystyle\int \frac{1}{1 - \sqrt{x}}\,dx$

103. $\displaystyle\int \frac{1}{1 + \sqrt[4]{x}}\,dx$

104. $\displaystyle\int \frac{1}{\sqrt{x} + \sqrt[3]{x}}\,dx$

105. $\displaystyle\int \frac{1}{\sqrt{e^x + 1}}\,dx$

106. $\displaystyle\int \frac{1}{\sqrt{e^x - 1}}\,dx$

### *Historical Topic #2—Rational Functions of sin x and cos x by u = tan (x/2)*

107. From trigonometry, you recall the double-argument properties for cosine and sine,

$$\cos 2t = 2\cos^2 t - 1, \quad \text{and} \quad \sin 2t = 2\sin t \cos t.$$

a. Explain how these properties justify the following equations.

$$\cos x = 2\cos^2 \tfrac{x}{2} - 1, \quad \text{and} \quad \sin x = 2\sin \tfrac{x}{2} \cos \tfrac{x}{2}$$

b. Show that the equations in 107a can be transformed to

$$\cos x = \frac{1 - \tan^2 \frac{x}{2}}{1 + \tan^2 \frac{x}{2}}, \quad \text{and} \quad \sin x = \frac{2 \tan \frac{x}{2}}{1 + \tan^2 \frac{x}{2}}$$

c. Let $u = \tan(x/2)$. Show that $x = 2\tan^{-1} u$, and thus that the following properties are true.

**Property: u = tan (x/2) Substitution**

$$\cos x = \frac{1 - u^2}{1 + u^2}, \qquad \sin x = \frac{2u}{1 + u^2}, \qquad \text{and} \qquad dx = \frac{2}{1 + u^2}\, du$$

d. Let $u = \tan(x/2)$. Use the results of 107c to show that this integral reduces to $\int du$:

$$\int \frac{1}{1 + \cos x}\, dx$$

e. Do the integration in 107d and then do the reverse substitution to show that the integral equals $\tan(x/2) + C$.

108. *Another Indefinite Integral of Secant:*

a. Transform the integral

$$\int \sec x\, dx,$$

using the substitution $u = \tan(x/2)$ from Problem 107 to get

$$\int \frac{2}{1 - u^2}\, du.$$

b. Perform the integration in 108a. Show that the result is

$$\ln \left| \frac{1 + \tan \frac{x}{2}}{1 - \tan \frac{x}{2}} \right| + C.$$

c. Recall from trigonometry the following.

i. $\tan(A + B) = \dfrac{\tan A + \tan B}{1 - \tan A \tan B}$

ii. $\tan \frac{\pi}{4} = 1$

Use this information to show that

$$\int \sec x\, dx = \ln \left| \tan\left(\tfrac{\pi}{4} + \tfrac{x}{2}\right) \right| + C.$$

d. Evaluate $\int_0^1 \sec x\, dx$ two ways: (i) using the result of 108c and (ii) using the more familiar integral formula. Show that the answers are equivalent.

For Problems 109–111, use the substitution $u = \tan(x/2)$ to evaluate the integral.

109. $\displaystyle\int \frac{1}{1 - \cos x}\, dx$

110. $\displaystyle\int \frac{1}{1 + \sin x}\, dx$

111. $\displaystyle\int \frac{\cos x}{1 - \cos x}\, dx$

# 9-12 Integrals in Journal

In this chapter you have learned algebraic techniques by which the elementary transcendental functions can be integrated and differentiated. The integration techniques include:

- Recognition of the integrand as the derivative of a familiar function
- Integral of the power function, $\int u^n\,du,\ n \neq -1$
- Integral of the reciprocal function, $\int u^{-1}\,du$
- Integration by parts
- Reduction formulas
- Trigonometric substitution
- Partial fractions
- Other substitutions

These techniques let you find the equation of a function whose derivative is given. They also allow you to use the fundamental theorem to find the exact value of a definite integral.

Although differentiating a function is relatively easy, the reverse process, integrating, can be like unscrambling eggs! Integrals that look almost the same, such as

$$\int (x^2+1)^{10} x\,dx \qquad \text{and} \qquad \int (x^2+1)^{10}\,dx,$$

may require completely different techniques. An integrand, such as $e^{-x^2}$ in

$$\int e^{-x^2}\,dx,$$

may be an elementary function but not the derivative of any other elementary function. [This integral gives the area under the bell curve in statistics (Figure 9-12a).]

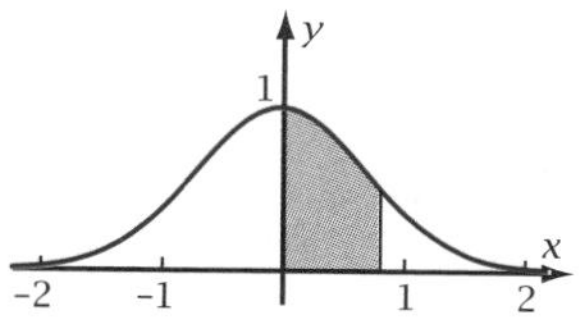

Figure 9-12a

In this section you will record a short table of integrals in your journal. Constructing the table will bring together the various techniques of integration. The end product will give you a reference guide that you can use to recall various integrals and how you derived them. As a result, you will better be able to use publications such as CRC Tables, and to understand the output from symbol-manipulating computers.

## Problem Set 9-12

1. *Table of Integrals Problem:* Record a short table of integrals in your journal. The table should be arranged by the nature of the integrand, rather than by the technique used. The table should include integrals of the algebraic functions and each one of the elementary transcendental functions:
   - Power and reciprocal
   - Exponential and Logarithmic
   - Circular and reverse circular
   - Hyperbolic and inverse hyperbolic

   You should include examples of other frequently occurring forms such as rational function, square root of a quadratic, and power of a trigonometric function (especially $\int \sin^2 x\,dx$, $\int \sec^3 x\,dx$, and so on). For each entry, you should state or show how the formula is derived.

# 9-13 Chapter Review and Test

In this chapter you have learned to do algebraically the calculus of elementary transcendental functions—exponential and logarithmic, circular (trigonometric), hyperbolic, and their inverses. The Review Problems are numbered according to the sections of this chapter. The Concepts Problems allow you to apply your knowledge to new situations. The Chapter Test is typical of a classroom test.

## Review Problems

R0. Update your journal with things you've learned since the last entry. You should include such things as those listed here.

- The one most important thing you have learned in studying Chapter 9
- Which boxes you have been working on in the "define, understand, do, apply" table.
- Any techniques or ideas about calculus that are still unclear to you

R1. Let $f(x) = x\cos x$. Find $f'(x)$, observing the derivative of a product property. From the results, figure out an equation for the indefinite integral $\int x\sin x\,dx$. Check your work by using the equation to evaluate the definite integral

$$\int_1^4 x\sin x\,dx$$

and comparing it with the approximate answer you get by numerical integration.

R2. Integrate: $\int 5x\sin 2x\,dx$

R3. a. Integrate: $\int x^3\cos 2x\,dx$

b. Integrate: $\int e^{4x}\sin 3x\,dx$

c. Integrate: $\int x(\ln x)^2\,dx$

d. The region under the graph of $y = x\ln x$ from $x = 1$ to $x = 2$ is rotated about the $y$-axis to form a solid. Find the volume of the solid.

R4. a. Integrate by parts once to express $\int \cos^{30}x\,dx$ in terms of an integral of a reduced power of $\cos x$.

b. Use the appropriate reduction formula to evaluate $\int \sec^6 x\,dx$.

c. Derive the reduction formula for $\int \tan^n x\,dx$.

R5. a. Integrate without reduction formula: $\int \cos^5 x\,dx$

b. Integrate without reduction formula: $\int \sec^6 x\,dx$

c. Integrate without reduction formula: $\int \sin^2 7x\,dx$

d. Integrate without reduction formula: $\int \sec^3 x\,dx$

e. Integrate without reduction formula: $\int \tan^9 32\,dx$

f. Find exactly the area of the region inside the limaçon with polar equation $r = 9 + 8\sin\theta$ from $\theta = 0$ to $\theta = \pi/4$.

R6. a. Integrate: $\int \sqrt{x^2 - 49}\,dx$

b. Integrate: $\int \sqrt{x^2 - 10x + 34}\,dx$

c. Integrate: $\int \sqrt{1 - 0.25x^2}\,dx$

d. Find exactly, using the fundamental theorem, the area of the zone of a circle of radius 5 between the lines 3 units and 4 units from the center (Figure 9-13a).

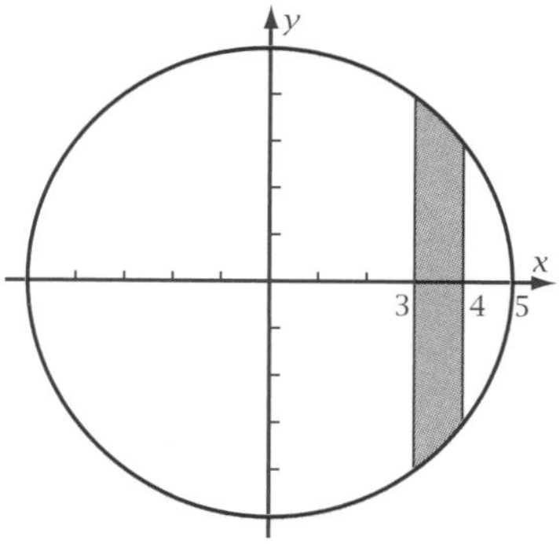


Figure 9-13a

R7. Integrate:

a. $\int \dfrac{(6x+1)\,dx}{x^2-3x-4}$

b. $\int \dfrac{5x^2-21x-2}{(x-1)(x+2)(x-3)}\,dx$

c. $\int \dfrac{5x^2+3x+45}{x^3+9x}\,dx$

d. $\int \dfrac{5x^2+27x+32}{x(x+4)^2}\,dx$

e. *Differential Equation Problem:* Figure 9-13b shows the slope field for the differential equation

$$\frac{dy}{dx} = 0.1(y-3)(y-8).$$

Solve this differential equation subject to the initial condition that $y = 7$ when $x = 0$. On a photocopy of the slope field, plot the graph of your solution, thus showing that it is reasonable.

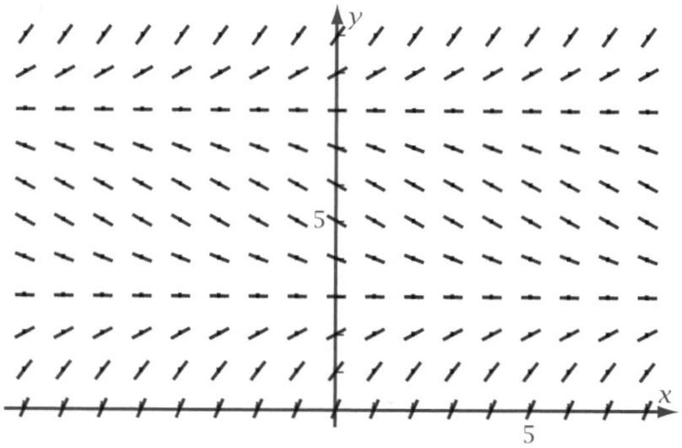


Figure 9-13b

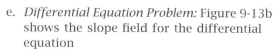

R8. a. Sketch the graph: $y = \cos^{-1}x$

b. Differentiate: $f(x) = \sec^{-1}3x$

c. Integrate: $\int \tan^{-1}5x\,dx$

d. Find the area of the region in Quadrant I bounded by the graph of $y = \cos^{-1}x$.

R9. a. Sketch the graph: $f(x) = \sinh x$

b. Sketch the graph: $g(x) = \cosh^{-1}x$

c. Differentiate: $h(x) = x^2\operatorname{sech}x$

d. Differentiate: $f(x) = \sinh^{-1}5x$

e. Integrate: $\int \tanh 3x\,dx$

f. Integrate: $\int \cosh^{-1}7x\,dx$

g. Using the definitions of $\cosh x$ and $\sinh x$, prove that $\cosh^2x - \sinh^2x = 1$.

h. Find a particular equation of the catenary with vertex at (0, 5) and point (3, 7). Use the equation to predict the value of $y$ if $x = 10$. Find the values of $x$ if $y = 20$.

R10. a. Evaluate: $\int_3^{\infty} (x-2)^{-1.2}\,dx$

b. Evaluate: $\int_{\pi/2}^{0} \tan x\,dx$

c. Evaluate: $\int_{-1}^{1} x^{-2/3}\,dx$

d. Evaluate: $\int_0^4 \left(\sqrt{x} - \dfrac{|x-1|}{x-1}\right)dx$

e. For what values of $p$ does the $p$-integral $\int_1^{\infty} x^{-p}\,dx$ converge?

R11. a. Differentiate: $f(x) = x\sin^{-1}x$

b. Integrate: $\int x\sin^{-1}x\,dx$

c. Differentiate: $\tanh(e^x)$

d. Integrate: $\int (x^3 - x)^{-1}\,dx$

e. Differentiate: $f(x) = (1 - x^2)^{1/2}$

f. Integrate: $\int (1 - x^2)^{1/2}\,dx$

g. Differentiate: $g(x) = (\ln x)^2$

h. Integrate: $\int x\ln x\,dx$

R12. Explain why $\int (9 - x^2)^{-1/2}\,dx$ has an inverse sine in the answer but $\int (9 - x^2)^{-1/2}x\,dx$ does not.

# Concepts Problems

C1. *Integral of* sech $x$ *Problem:* Derive the formula

$$\int \operatorname{sech} x\,dx = \sin^{-1}(\tanh x) + C.$$

The integrand can be transformed to a square root involving tanh $x$ by use of the Pythagorean property relating sech $x$ and tanh $x$. Then a very clever trigonometric substitution can be used to rationalize the radical. Confirm that the formula works by evaluating the integral on the interval $[0, 1]$, then checking by numerical integration.

C2. *Integral of* csch $x$ *Problem:* Derive the formula

$$\int \operatorname{csch} x\,dx = \ln|\tanh \tfrac{x}{2}| + C.$$

The integrand can be transformed to functions of tanh $(x/2)$ by first observing that

$$\sinh 2A = 2\sinh A\cosh A,$$

from which

$$\operatorname{csch} x = \frac{1}{2\sinh\frac{x}{2}\cosh\frac{x}{2}}.$$

Clever algebra, followed by an application of the Pythagorean properties, produces the desired result. Then substitute $u$ for tanh $(x/2)$. You will have to be clever again to figure out what to substitute for $dx$ in terms of $du$. The resulting integral is remarkably simple! Confirm that the formula works by evaluating the integral on the interval $[1, 2]$, then checking by numerical integration.

C3. *Another Integral of* csc $x$*:* Derive the formula

$$\int \csc x\,dx = \ln|\tan\tfrac{x}{2}| + C.$$

Confirm that the formula works by evaluating the integral on the interval $[0.5, 1]$, then checking by numerical integration.

C4. *Another Definition of π Problem:* Figure 9-13c shows the region under the graph of $y = (x^2 + 1)^{-1}$, extending to infinity in both directions. Show that the area of this infinitely long region is exactly equal to $\pi$. This fact is remarkable because the integrand has nothing to do with circles, yet the answer is the most fundamental number concerned with circles!

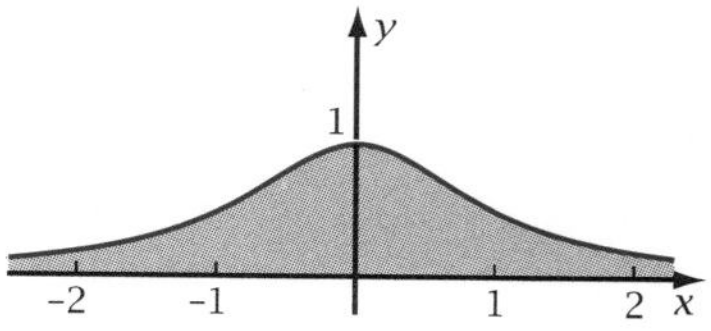

Figure 9-13c

C5. *Upper Bound Problem:* Figure 9-13d shows the graphs of $f(x) = \ln x$ and $g(x) = \tan^{-1}x$. As $x$ gets large, both graphs are increasing, but concave down. The inverse tangent graph approaches $\pi/2$. Prove that the graph of $f(x) = \ln x$ is unbounded above. You can do this by assuming that it is bounded above by some number $M$, then finding a contradiction by finding a value of $x$ in terms of $M$ for which $\ln x > M$.

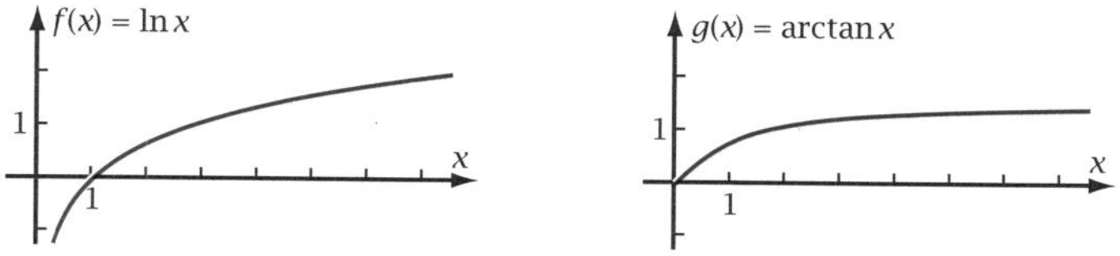

Figure 9-13d

## Chapter Test

[Author's Note: This test is longer than a normal 60-minute classroom test.]

For Problems T1–T6, evaluate the indefinite integral.

T1. $\int \sin^5 x \cos x\, dx$

T2. $\int x^3 \sinh 6x\, dx$

T3. $\int \cos^{-1} x\, dx$

T4. $\int \sec^3 x\, dx$

T5. $\int e^{2x} \cos 5x\, dx$

T6. $\int \ln 3x\, dx$

For Problems T7 and T8, differentiate.

T7. $f(x) = \text{sech}^3(e^{5x})$

T8. $g(x) = \sin^{-1} x$

T9. Given $f(x) = \tanh^{-1} x$, find a formula for $f'(x)$ in terms of $x$ by appropriate implicit differentiation. Demonstrate that the formula is correct by approximating $f'(0.6)$ using numerical differentiation.

T10. Find the particular equation of the form $y = k\cosh(1/k)x + C$ for the catenary containing vertex (0, 1) and point (5, 3).

T11. Integrate $\int \frac{x-3}{x^2 - 6x + 5}\, dx$ three ways:

a. By trigonometric substitution, after completing the square.

b. By partial fractions.

c. As the integral of the reciprocal function.

d. Show that all three answers are equivalent.

T12. Evaluate $\int \cos^2 x\, dx$ by appropriate use of the double-argument properties.

T13. Evaluate $\int \cos^5 x\, dx$ two ways:

a. By transforming four of the cosines to sines, and integrating as powers of sine.

b. By using the reduction formula,

$$\int \cos^n x\, dx = \frac{1}{n}\cos^{n-1} x \sin x + \frac{n-1}{n}\int \cos n^{-2} x\, dx.$$

c. Show that the two answers are equivalent.

T14. Evaluate the improper integral: $\int_0^\infty xe^{-0.1x}\, dx$

CHAPTER

# 10 The Calculus of Motion—Averages, Extremes, and Vectors

The distance a spaceship has gone equals velocity multiplied by time. But the velocity varies. Displacement is the integral of velocity, and velocity is the integral of acceleration. By measuring acceleration of the spaceship at frequent time intervals, the displacement can be calculated by numerical calculus methods.

# Mathematical Overview

Chapter 10 extends your study of objects in motion. You will distinguish between such things as

- distance vs. displacement
- acceleration vs. velocity
- maximum vs. minimum
- linear vs. plane motion

You will do this in four ways.

***Graphically*** The logo at the top of each even-numbered page of this chapter shows the position vector, velocity vector, and acceleration vector for an object moving in a curved, plane path.

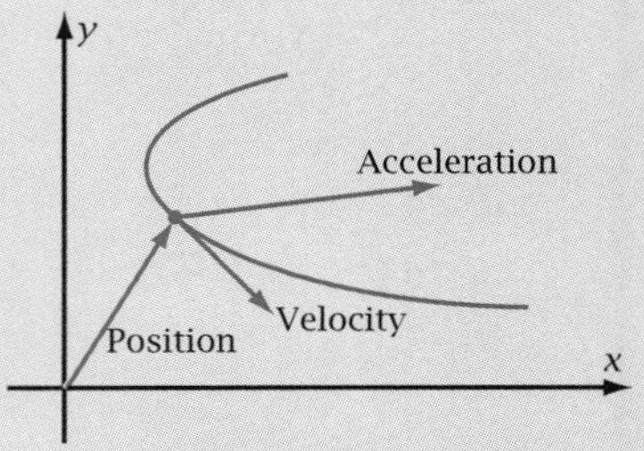


***Numerically***

| time | accel. | vel. |
|---|---|---|
| 0 | 1.3 | 20.0 |
| 2 | 1.7 | 23.0 |
| 4 | 2.2 | 26.9 |
| 6 | 2.1 | 31.2 |
| 8 | 1.5 | 34.8 |
| … | … | … |

***Algebraically*** Distance $= \int_a^b |v(t)|\, dt.$ Displacement $= \int_a^b v(t)\, dt.$

***Verbally*** *Now I know the precise definition of the average value of a function. It is the integral of the function between two limits divided by the difference between those limits.*

# 10-1 Introduction to Distance and Displacement for Motion along a Line

You have learned that velocity is the rate of change of position with respect to time. In this chapter you will concentrate on the distinction between distance (how far) and displacement (how far, and in what direction). You will sharpen your understanding of the difference between speed (how fast) and velocity (how fast and which direction). Once you have made these distinctions for motion in one dimension (along a line), you will use vectors to analyze motion in two dimensions (in a plane). Along the way you will find maximum, minimum, and average values of velocity and position functions.

**OBJECTIVE**

Given an equation for the velocity of a moving object, find the distance traveled and the displacement from the starting point for a specified time interval.

Suppose that you drive 100 mi and then return 70 of those miles (Figure 10-1a). Although you have gone a **distance** of 170 mi, your **displacement**, which is measured from the starting point, is only 30 mi. Problem Set 10-1 will clarify the distinction between these two quantities. You may work on your own or with your study group.

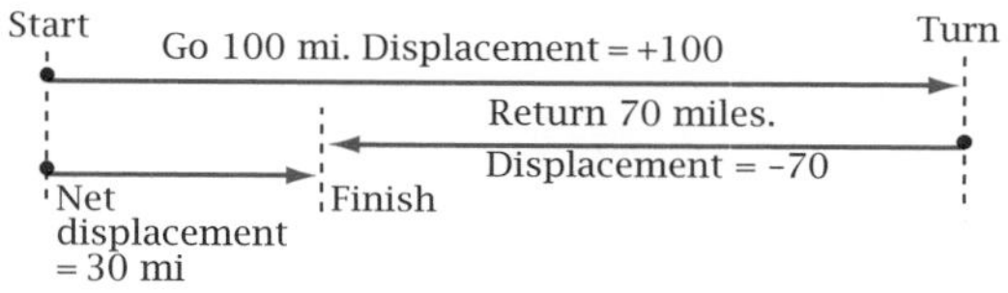


Figure 10-1a

## Exploratory Problem Set 10-1

*Calvin's Swimming Problem:* Calvin enters an endurance swimming contest. The objective is to swim upstream in the river for a period of 10 min. The river flows at 30 ft/min. Calvin jumps in and starts swimming upstream at 100 ft/min. Phoebe ascertains that as he tires his speed through the water decreases exponentially with time according to the equation $v_c = 100(0.8)^t$. Thus Calvin's net velocity (Figure 10-1b) is only

$$v = 100(0.8)^t - 30.$$

1. At what time will Calvin's velocity become negative?
2. How far will Calvin go upstream—that is, while his velocity is positive? How far will he go back downstream (while his velocity is negative) until $t = 10$? What is the total distance he will have gone in the 10 min?
3. What will Calvin's displacement from the starting point be at the end of the 10 min? Will he be upstream or downstream of his starting point?

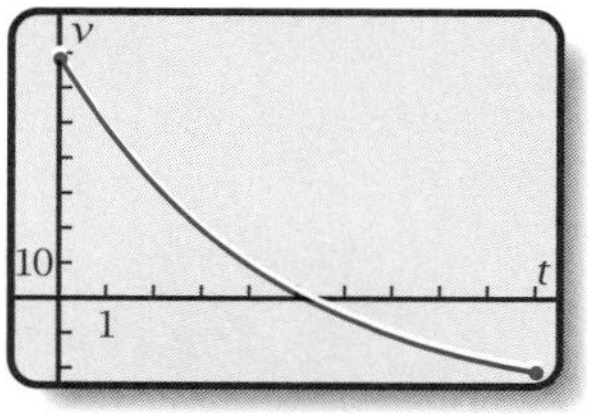


Figure 10-1b

4. Write a definite integral that can be used to find the displacement after 10 min in one computation. Check it by doing the integration and comparing with Problem 3.

5. Write one definite integral that represents the total distance Calvin goes in the 10 min. A clever application of absolute value will help. Integrate numerically.

# 10-2 Distance, Displacement, and Acceleration for Linear Motion

Most real objects such as cars and birds travel in two or three dimensions. In Section 10-7, you will see how to use vectors to analyze such motion. For the time being, consider only objects moving in a straight line. In Section 10-1, you saw the distinction between the distance a moving object travels and its displacement from the starting point. If the velocity is positive, the displacement is positive. If the velocity is negative, then the displacement is negative. In the latter case the distance traveled is the opposite of the displacement. The two ideas can be combined with the aid of the absolute value function, as follows.

**Property: Distance and Displacement**

Displacement $= \int_a^b \text{(velocity)}\ dt$

Distance $= \int_a^b |\text{velocity}|\ dt$

**OBJECTIVE**

Given velocity or acceleration as a function of time for an object in linear motion, find the displacement at a given time and the distance traveled in a given time interval.

**■ Example 1** A moving object has velocity $v(t) = t^2 - 7t + 10$ ft/sec in the time interval $[1, 4]$.

a. Find the time subintervals in which the velocity is positive and those in which it is negative.

b. Find the distance the object travels in each of these subintervals.

c. Use a single integral to find the displacement in the time interval $[1, 4]$ and use a single integral to find the distance traveled in this interval.

d. Show how the answers to part c can be found from the answers to parts a and b.

**Solutions**

a. The graph of $v$ versus $t$ (Figure 10-2a) shows that the velocity changes from positive to negative at $t = 2$. This fact can be confirmed algebraically by solving

$$t^2 - 7t + 10 = 0 \Rightarrow t = 2 \text{ or } t = 5.$$

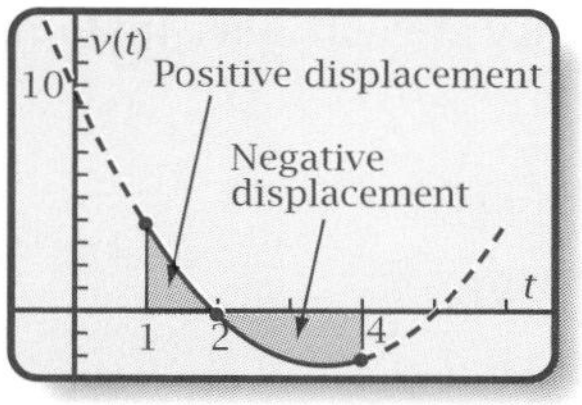

Figure 10-2a

Positive velocity: [1, 2)
Negative velocity: (2, 4]

b. For [1, 2],

$$\text{Displacement} = \int_1^2 (t^2 - 7t + 10)\,dt = 1.8333\ldots = 1\tfrac{5}{6}.$$

Numerically, or by fundamental theorem.

$$\therefore \text{distance} = 1\tfrac{5}{6}\text{ft}$$

For [2, 4],

$$\text{Displacement} = \int_2^4 (t^2 - 7t + 10)\,dt = -3.3333\ldots = -3\tfrac{1}{3}.$$

$$\therefore \text{distance} = 3\tfrac{1}{3}\text{ft}$$

c. For [1, 4],

$$\text{Displacement} = \int_1^4 (t^2 - 7t + 10)\,dt = -1.5$$

$$\text{Distance} = \int_1^4 |t^2 - 7t + 10|\,dt$$

Use the absolute value function on your grapher.

$$= 5.1666\ldots = 5\tfrac{1}{6}\text{ft}$$

Use numerical integration (see note.)

d. For displacement, $1\frac{5}{6} + (-3\frac{1}{3}) = -1.5$ (checks).

For distance, $1\frac{5}{6} + 3\frac{1}{3} = 5\frac{1}{6}$ (checks). ■

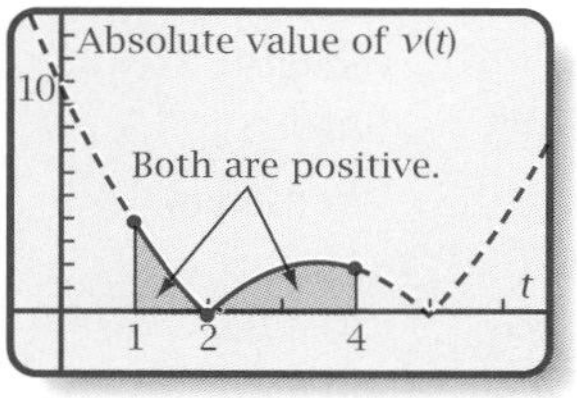

Figure 10-2b

*Note:* If you want to evaluate the integral in part c algebraically using the fundamental theorem, divide the interval [1, 4] as in part b. The integrand has a cusp at $t = 2$ (Figure 10-2b) at which the absolute-value function changes from $+(t^2 - 7t + 10)$ to $-(t^2 - 7t + 10)$. (Recall from algebra that the absolute value of a negative number is the opposite of that number.) The final answer is still the sum,

$$1\tfrac{5}{6} + (+3\tfrac{1}{3}) = 5\tfrac{1}{6}\text{ ft.}$$

Figure 10-2b also shows that the integrand for distance is always positive (or zero), meaning that the distance traveled is positive. This is true even though the object in Example 1 is displaced a negative amount from its starting point.

**■ *Example 2*** A car accelerates for 24 sec. Its acceleration in (mi/hr)/sec is measured each 3 sec and is listed in the table.

| time (sec) | acceleration [(mi/hr)/sec] |
|---|---|
| 0 | 1.3 |
| 3 | 1.7 |
| 6 | 2.2 |
| 9 | 2.1 |
| 12 | 1.5 |
| 15 | 0.3 |
| 18 | −0.4 |
| 21 | −1.1 |
| 24 | −1.4 |

a. Plot the graph of acceleration versus time.

b. At time $t = 0$, the car was going 20 mi/hr. Predict its velocity at each 3 sec instant from 0 through 24.

c. Plot the graph of velocity versus time.

d. Approximately how far did the car go in this 24-sec interval?

***Solutions***

a. The graph is shown in Figure 10-2c.

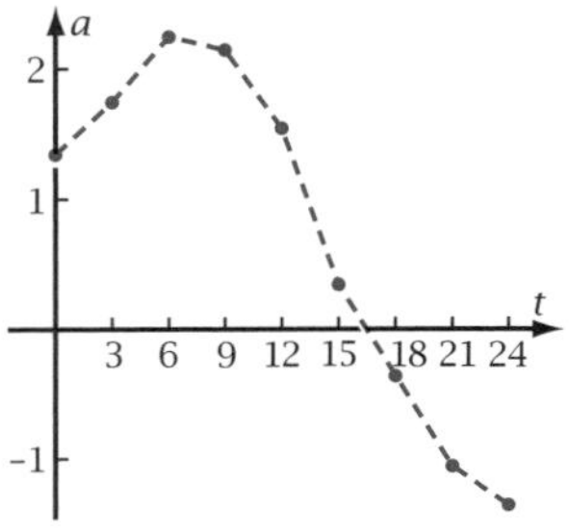


Figure 10-2c

b. Since acceleration is the derivative of velocity with respect to time, the velocity is the integral of acceleration.

$$v = \int a\,dt$$

You can estimate the average acceleration for each 3-sec interval. For interval 1,

$$\text{Average acceleration} = \tfrac{1}{2}(1.3 + 1.7) = 1.50.$$

The change in velocity is thus $(1.50)(3) = 4.50$. Since the initial velocity was given to be 20, the velocity at the end of the interval is about $20 + 4.50 = 24.50$.

The process is equivalent to integrating by the trapezoidal rule. The calculations can be done by extending the given table using a computer spreadsheet or at least a spreadsheet format.

| time (sec) | acceleration [(mi/hr)/sec] | average acceleration [(mi/hr)/sec] | $\Delta v$ (mi/hr) | velocity (mi/hr) |
|---|---|---|---|---|
| 0 | 1.3 | — | — | 20 (Given) |
| 3 | 1.7 | 1.50 | 4.50 | 24.5 |
| 6 | 2.2 | 1.95 | 5.85 | 30.35 |
| 9 | 2.1 | 2.15 | 6.45 | 36.8 |
| 12 | 1.5 | 1.80 | 5.40 | 42.2 |
| 15 | 0.3 | 0.90 | 2.70 | 44.9 |
| 18 | −0.4 | −0.05 | −0.15 | 44.75 |
| 21 | −1.1 | −0.75 | −2.25 | 42.5 |
| 24 | −1.4 | −1.25 | −3.75 | 38.75 |

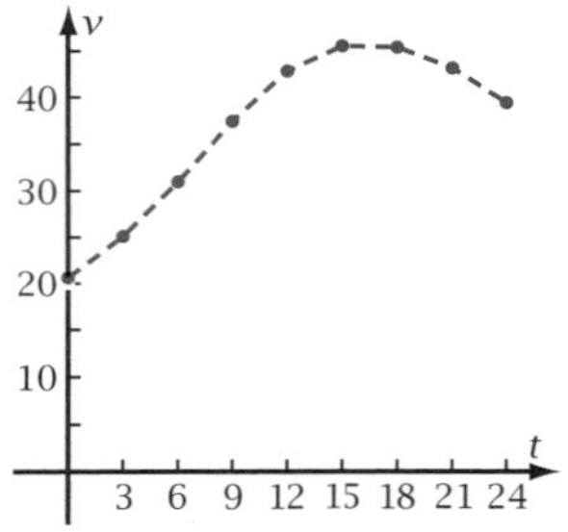


Figure 10-2d

c. The graph is shown in Figure 10-2d.

d. Finding the displacement at the end of each 3-sec interval can be done the same way you found the velocity. Find an average velocity for the interval, multiply by $\Delta t$, and add the result to the displacement at the beginning of the interval. The displacement at $t = 0$ is zero because you are finding the displacement from the starting point. The only catch is that you must use 3/3600 hr for $\Delta t$ since $v$ is in miles per hour. The calculations can be done by extending the table from part b, putting appropriate instructions into the spreadsheet.

| time (sec) | acceleration [(mi/hr)/sec] | average acceleration [(mi/hr)/sec] | $\Delta v$ (mi/hr) | velocity (mi/hr) | average velocity (mi/hr) | displacement (mi) |
|---|---|---|---|---|---|---|
| 0 | 1.3 | — | — | 20 | — | 0.000 |
| 3 | 1.7 | 1.50 | 4.50 | 24.5 | 22.25 | 0.018 . . . |
| 6 | 2.2 | 1.95 | 5.85 | 30.35 | 27.425 | 0.041 . . . |
| 9 | 2.1 | 2.15 | 6.45 | 36.8 | 33.575 | 0.069 . . . |
| 12 | 1.5 | 1.80 | 5.40 | 42.2 | 39.5 | 0.102 . . . |
| 15 | 0.3 | 0.90 | 2.70 | 44.9 | 43.55 | 0.138 . . . |
| 18 | −0.4 | −0.05 | −0.15 | 44.75 | 44.825 | 0.175 . . . |
| 21 | −1.1 | −0.75 | −2.25 | 42.5 | 43.625 | 0.212 . . . |
| 24 | −1.4 | −1.25 | −3.75 | 38.75 | 40.625 | 0.246 . . . |

The last column shows the total displacement from $t = 0$ to the end of the time interval. For the 24 sec the total displacement was about 0.246 mi, or about 1300 ft. ■

## Problem Set 10-2

### *Do These Quickly*

The following problems are intended to refresh your skills. You should be able to do all ten problems in less than five minutes.

**Q1.** You traveled 30 mi/hr for 4 hr. How far did you go?

**Q2.** You traveled 75 mi in 3 hr. How fast did you go?

**Q3.** You traveled 50 mi at 40 mi/hr . How long did it take?

**Q4.** Differentiate: $f(x) = \ln x$

**Q5.** Integrate: $\int \ln x\, dx$

**Q6.** Differentiate: $f(t) = \tan t$

**Q7.** Differentiate: $g(t) = \tanh t$

**Q8.** Integrate: $\int x^2\, dx$

**Q9.** Integrate: $\int 2^x\, dx$

**Q10.** Differentiate: $h(x) = 2^x$

For Problems 1–4, an object moving in a straight line has velocity $v(t)$ in the given time interval.

a. Find the time subintervals in which the velocity is positive, and those in which it is negative.

b. Find the distance the object travels in each of these subintervals.

c. Use a single integral to find the displacement in the given time interval and use a single integral to find the distance traveled in this interval.

d. Show how the answers to part c can be found from the answers to parts a and b.

e. Find the acceleration of the object at the midpoint of the time interval.

1. $v(t) = t^2 - 10t + 16$ ft/sec from $t = 0$ to $t = 6$ sec
2. $v(t) = \tan 0.2t$ cm/sec from $t = 10$ sec to $t = 20$ sec
3. $v(t) = \sec \frac{\pi}{24} t - 2$ km/hr, from $t = 1$ sec to $t = 11$ hr
4. $v(t) = t^3 - 5t^2 + 8t - 6$ mi/min, from $t = 0$ to $t = 5$ min

For Problems 5–8, first find an equation for the velocity of a moving object from the equation for acceleration. Recall that acceleration is the derivative of velocity. Then find the displacement and distance traveled by the moving object in the given time interval.

5. $a(t) = t^{1/2}$ (ft/sec)/sec, $v(0) = -18$ ft/sec, from $t = 0$ to $t = 16$ sec
6. $a(t) = t^{-1}$ (cm/sec)/sec, $v(1) = 0$ cm/sec, from $t = 0.4$ sec to $t = 1.6$ sec
7. $a(t) = 6 \sin t$ (km/hr)/hr, $v(0) = -9$ km/h, from $t = 0$ to $t = \pi$ hr
8. $a(t) = \sinh t$ (mi/hr)/hr, $v(0) = -2$ mi/hr, from $t = 0$ to $t = 5$ hr
9. *Meg's Velocity Problem:* Meg floorboards her car, giving it a velocity of $v = t^{1/2} - 2$ ft/sec at time $t$ seconds after she started accelerating.
   a. Find the time(s) at which $v = 0$.
   b. Find her net displacement for the time interval [1, 9].
   c. Find the total distance she travels for the time interval [1, 9].
10. *Periodic Motion Problem:* The velocity of a moving object is given by $v = \sin 2t$ cm/sec.
    a. Find the distance the object travels from the time it starts ($t = 0$) to the first time it stops.
    b. Find the displacement of the object from its starting point and the total distance it travels from $t = 0$ to $t = 4.5\pi$. Be clever!
11. *Car on the Hill Problem:* Faye Ling's car runs out of gas as she is driving up a long hill. She lets the car roll without putting on the brakes. As it slows down, stops, and starts rolling backwards, its velocity up the hill is given by

    $$v = 60 - 2t,$$

    where $v$ is in feet per second and $t$ is the number of seconds since the car ran out of gas.
    a. What is the car's net displacement between $t = 10$ and $t = 40$?
    b. What is the total distance the car rolls between $t = 10$ and $t = 40$?
12. *Rocket Problem:* If a rocket is fired straight up from earth, it experiences acceleration from two sources:
    - Upward, $a_u$ in (meters per second) per second, due to the rocket engine
    - Downward, $a_d$ in (meters per second) per second, due to gravity

    The net acceleration is $a = a_u + a_d$. However, the upward acceleration has a discontinuity at the time the rocket engine stops. Suppose that the accelerations are given by

    $$a_u = \begin{cases} 40 \cos 0.015t, & 0 \le t \le 100 \\ 0, & t > 100 \end{cases}$$
    $$a_d = -9.8 \text{ for all } t.$$

a. Plot graphs of $a$ and $v$ versus $t$ for the first 300 sec.

b. At what value of $t$ does $a$ become negative? At what value of $t$ does $v$ become negative?

c. Find the displacement of the rocket at time $t = 300$ and the distance the rocket traveled between $t = 0$ and $t = 300$. What does the relationship between these two numbers tell you about what is happening in the real world at $t = 100$?

d. How fast, and in what direction is the rocket traveling at $t = 300$?

13. *Subway Problem:* A train accelerates as it leaves one subway station, then decelerates as it comes into the next one. Three calculus students take an accelerometer aboard the train. They measure the accelerations, $a$, given in the table in (miles per hour) per second, at the given values of $t$ seconds.

| time, $t$ (sec) | acceleration, $a$ [(mi/hr)/sec] |
|---|---|
| 0 | 1.2 |
| 5 | 4.7 |
| 10 | 2.9 |
| 15 | 0.6 |
| 20 | 0 |
| 25 | 0 |
| 30 | 0 |
| 35 | 0 |
| 40 | −0.4 |
| 45 | −1.4 |
| 50 | −3.8 |
| 55 | −3.2 |
| 60 | 0 |

a. Calculate the velocity and displacement at the end of each time interval. Assume that the velocity was zero at time zero. You may use a computer spreadsheet.

b. Show that the train has stopped at $t = 60$.

c. How can the velocity be zero at $t = 0$ but the acceleration be positive at that time?

d. How can acceleration be zero from $t = 20$ to $t = 35$, while the velocity is not zero?

e. How far is it between the two stations?

14. *Spaceship Problem:* A spaceship is to be sent into orbit around the earth. You must find out whether the proposed design of the last stage booster rocket will get the spaceship going fast enough and far enough so that it can orbit. Based on the way the fuel burns, the acceleration of the spaceship is predicted to be as in the table on the next page, where time is in seconds and acceleration is in (miles per hour) per second.

a. Initially the spaceship is 400 mi from the launch pad, going 6000 mi/hr. Calculate the velocity and acceleration at the end of each time interval. You may use a spreadsheet.

| time (sec) | acceleration [(mi/hr)/sec] | |
|---|---|---|
| 0 | 3 | |
| 10 | 14 | |
| 20 | 30 | |
| 30 | 36 | |
| 40 | 43 | |
| 50 | 42 | |
| 60 | 64 | |
| 70 | 78 | |
| 80 | 89 | |
| 90 | 6 | |
| 100 | 0 | (Rocket burns out) |

b. Consulting the specifications, you find that when the last stage finishes firing (100 sec, in this case) the spaceship must
   - Be at least 1000 mi away from the launch pad
   - Be moving at least 17,500 mi/hr

   Based on your work, conclude whether each of these specifications will be
   - Definitely met
   - Definitely not met
   - Too close to say without more information

15. *Physics Formula Problem:* Elementary physics courses usually deal only with motion under a constant acceleration, such as motion under the influence of gravity. Under this condition, certain formulas relate acceleration, velocity, and displacement. These formulas are easily derived by calculus. Let $a$ be the acceleration (a constant). Let $v_0$ be the initial velocity (when time $t = 0$). Let $s_0$ be the initial displacement (again, when time $t = 0$). Derive the following formulas.

    a. $v = v_0 + at$

    b. $s = v_0t + \frac{1}{2}at^2 + s_0$

16. *Elevator Project:* When a normal elevator starts going up, you feel a jerk until it gets up to speed. This is because the acceleration changes almost instantly from zero to some positive value. In this problem you will explore another way for an elevator's acceleration to be arranged such that the jerk is minimized.

    a. Suppose an elevator starts from rest ($v = 0$) at the bottom floor ($s = 0$ ft) and is given a constant acceleration of 2 ft/sec$^2$ for 6 sec. Thereafter, the elevator rises with constant velocity. Find the velocity and displacement of the elevator as functions of time. Sketch three graphs: acceleration, velocity, displacement, for times $t = 0$ to $t = 10$ sec.

    b. How does the acceleration graph show that passengers on the elevator get a jerk at $t = 0$ and another jerk at $t = 6$?

    c. If the acceleration increases gradually to a maximum value, then decreases gradually to zero, the jerks will be eliminated. Show that if the acceleration is given by

    $$a = 2 - 2\cos(\pi/3)t$$

    for the first 6 sec, then the elevator's acceleration has this property.

    d. Using the acceleration function in 16c, find the velocity as a function of time.

e. Sketch the graph of velocity as a function of time, if the velocity remains at its value at $t = 6$ seconds as the elevator goes up. How does this velocity graph differ from that in 16a?

f. How far does the elevator go while it is getting up to top speed?

g. The elevator is to be slowed down the same way it was speeded up, over a 6 second time period. If the elevator is to go all the way to the 50th story, 600 ft above the bottom floor, where should it start slowing down?

h. How long does it take for the elevator to make the complete trip?

i. If the elevator were to go up just one floor (12 ft), would the new acceleration and deceleration functions in 16c and f still provide a smooth ride? If so, how do you tell? If not, what functions could be used to smooth out the ride?

# 10-3 Average Value Problems in Motion and Elsewhere

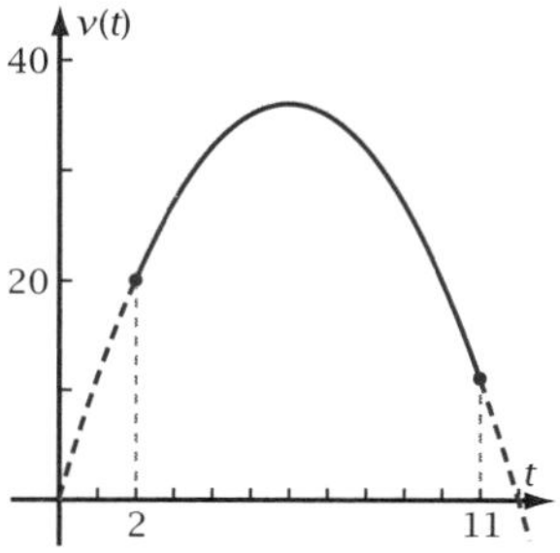

Figure 10-3a

Suppose that the velocity of a moving object is given by

$$v(t) = 12t - t^2,$$

where $t$ is in seconds and $v(t)$ is in feet per second. What would be meant by the average velocity in a time interval such as from $t = 2$ to $t = 11$? The equation "distance = (rate)(time)" is the basis for the answer. Dividing both sides by time gives rate = (distance)/(time). This concept is extended to velocity by using displacement instead of distance.

$$\text{average velocity} = \frac{\text{displacement}}{\text{time}}$$

Figure 10-3a shows the graph of $v(t)$. The total displacement in feet, $s$, is the integral of the velocity from 2 to 11.

$$\begin{aligned} s &= \int_2^{11} (12t - t^2)\,dt \\ &= 6t^2 - \tfrac{1}{3}t^3 \Big|_2^{11} \\ &= 261 \end{aligned}$$

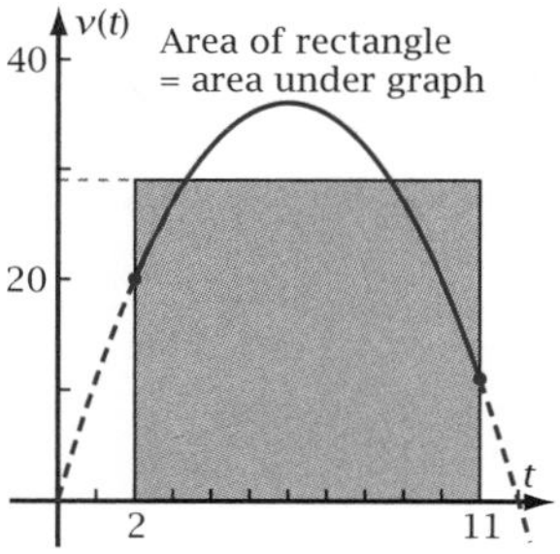

Figure 10-3b

The time to travel the 261 ft is $(11 - 2)$, or 9 sec. So the average velocity is

$$v_{av} = \frac{261}{9} = 29.$$

Plotting the average velocity on the $v(t)$ graph (Figure 10-3b) reveals several conclusions.

- The area of the rectangle with altitude equal to $v_{av}$ and base 9 is also equal to the total displacement. So the area of the rectangle equals the area under the $v(t)$ graph.
- Because the area of the rectangle equals the area of the region, there is just as much of the region above the $v_{av}$ line as there is "empty" space in the rectangle

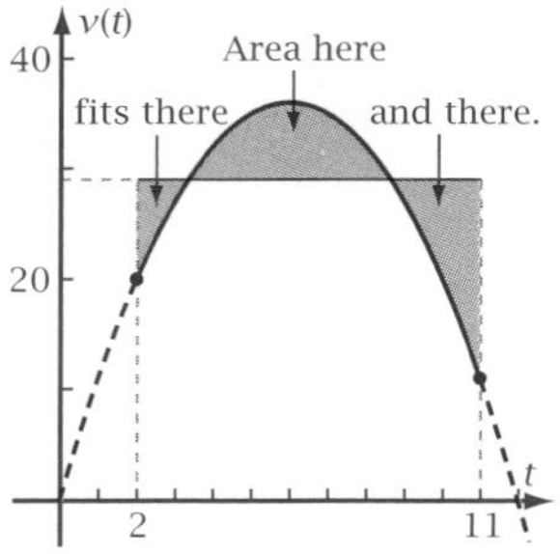


Figure 10-3c

below the line. If you could "pour" the region above the line into the spaces below the line, it would just fit (Figure 10-3c).

- The average velocity $v_{av}$ is not equal to the average of the initial and final velocities. From the equation, $v(2) = 20$ and $v(11) = 11$. The average, 29 (which equals displacement/time), is higher than either one and is thus not equal to their average.
- Another object, starting at the same time and place, but moving with a constant velocity equal to the average velocity, would finish at the same time and place as the first object.

The facts that average velocity equals (displacement)/(time), and that displacement is found by integrating the velocity lead to the following general definition of average velocity.

### *Definition: Average Velocity*

If $v(t)$ is the velocity of a moving object as a function of time then the average velocity from time $t = a$ to $t = b$ is

$$v_{av} = \frac{\int_a^b v(t)\,dt}{b-a}.$$

That is, average velocity $= \dfrac{\text{total displacement}}{\text{total time}}$.

The reasoning used to define average velocity can be extended to define average value for any function. The following is the definition of average value of a function.

### *Definition: Average Value of a Function*

If function $f$ is integrable on $[a, b]$, then the average value of $y = f(x)$ on the interval $x = a$ to $x = b$ is

$$y_{av} = \frac{\int_a^b f(x)\,dx}{b-a}.$$

***OBJECTIVE*** Calculate the average value for a function given its equation.

# Problem Set 10-3

### *Do These Quickly*

The following problems are intended to refresh your skills. You should be able to do all ten problems in less than five minutes.

***Q1.*** What is your average speed if you go 40 mi in 0.8 hr?

***Q2.*** How far do you go in 3 min if your average speed is 600 mi/hr?

***Q3.*** How long does it take to go 10 mi at an average speed of 30 mi/hr?

**Q4.** The first positive value of $x$ at which $y = \cos x$ has a local maximum is -?-.

**Q5.** $y = e^x$ has a local maximum at what value of $x$?

**Q6.** $y = x^2 - 3x + 11$ has a local minimum at $x =$ -?-.

**Q7.** For $f(x) = (x - 5)^2$, the global maximum for $x \in [1, 3]$ is -?-.

**Q8.** If $f(x) = x^{0.8}$, then $f'(0) =$ -?-.

**Q9.** Name the theorem that states that under suitable conditions, a function's graph has a tangent line parallel to a given secant line.

**Q10.** The graph of $\left(\frac{x}{3}\right)^2 + \left(\frac{y}{5}\right)^2 = 1$ is a(n) -?-.

For Problems 1–6,

a. Find the average value of the function on the given interval.

b. Sketch a graph showing the geometrical interpretation of the average value.

1. $f(x) = x^3 - x + 5,\ x \in [1, 5]$
2. $f(x) = x^{1/2} - x + 7,\ x \in [1, 9]$
3. $g(x) = 3 \sin 0.2x,\ x \in [1, 7]$
4. $h(x) = \tan x,\ x \in [0.5, 1.5]$
5. $v(t) = \sqrt{t},\ t \in [1, 9]$
6. $v(t) = 100(1 - e^{-t}),\ t \in [0, 3]$

For Problems 7–10, find a formula in terms of $k$ for the average value of the given function on the interval $[0, k]$, where $k$ is a positive constant ($a$ stands for a constant).

7. $f(x) = ax^2$
8. $f(x) = ax^3$
9. $f(x) = ae^x$
10. $f(x) = \tan x,\ k < \frac{\pi}{2}$
11. *Average Velocity from Acceleration Problem:* Suppose you are driving 60 ft/sec (about 40 mi/hr) behind a truck. When you get the opportunity to pass, you step on the accelerator, giving the car an acceleration $a = 6/\sqrt{t}$, where $a$ is in (feet per second) per second and $t$ is in seconds. How fast are you going 25 sec later when you have passed the truck? How far did you travel in that time? What was your average velocity for the 25-sec interval?
12. *Ida's Speeding Ticket Problem:* Ida Livermore is rushing to take pizzas to her customers when she is stopped for speeding. Her ticket states that she was clocked at speeds up to 50 mi/hr during a 4-min period, and that her fine will be \$140 (\$7 for each mile per hour over the 30-mi/hr speed limit). Ida is good at calculus. She figures that her speed was a quadratic function of time over the 4-min period, being 30 mi/hr at the beginning and end, and peaking at 50 mi/hr (Figure 10-3d). She argues she should be charged only for her average speed above 30 mi/hr. How much less will her fine be if she wins her appeal?

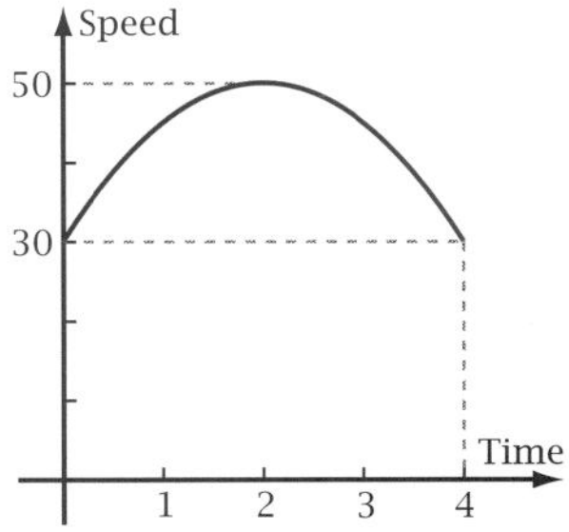

Figure 10-3d

13. *Average Velocity for Constant Acceleration Problem:* Prove that if an object moves with constant acceleration $a$, such as it does in ideal free fall, then its average velocity over a time interval is the average of the velocities at the beginning and end of the interval. (This result leads to one of the physics formulas you may have learned, and which may have led you to a false conclusion about average velocity when the acceleration is not constant.)

14. *Average Velocity for Other Accelerations Problem:* Show by counterexample that if the acceleration of an object varies over a time interval, then the average velocity over that interval might not equal the average of the velocities at the beginning and end of the interval.

15. *Average Voltage Problem:* For the normal alternating current supplied to houses, the voltage varies sinusoidally with time (Figure 10-3e), making 60 complete cycles each second. Thus

$$v = A \sin 120\pi t,$$

where $v$ is in volts, $t$ is in seconds, and $A$ is the maximum voltage during a cycle. The nominal "110 volts" is the average of the absolute value of the voltage. Use the fundamental theorem to find the average value of $y = |A \sin 120\pi t|$ from $t = 0$ to $t = 1/60$. Use the result to calculate the maximum voltage $A$ if the average is 110 v. Show how this number can be found more easily using $y = \sin x$ and an appropriate interval of integration.

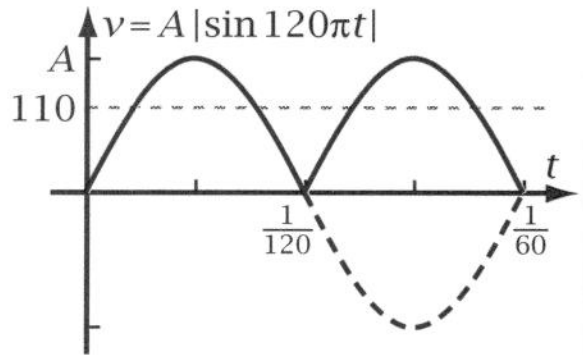


Figure 10-3e

16. *Root Mean Square Deviation Problem:* To measure how hilly a landscape is or how rough a machined surface is, people ask the question, "On average, how far do points on the surface deviate from the mean level?" If you simply average the deviations, you will get zero. As shown in Figure 10-3f, there is just as much area above the mean as there is below. One way used to overcome this difficulty is

- Square the deviations.
- Find the average of the squares.
- Take the square root of the average to get an answer with the same dimensions as the original deviations.

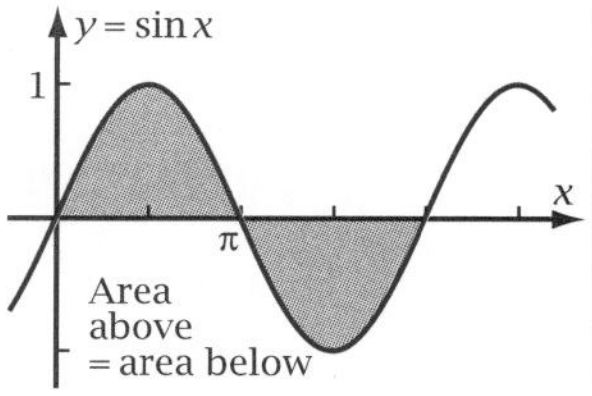


Figure 10-3f

The result is called the **root mean square deviation.** For instance, the roughness of a machined surface might be reported as, "0.1 microinches, rms," where rms stands for root mean square, and a microinch is one-millionth of an inch.

a. Suppose that the deviations from average are sinusoidal, as in Figure 10-3f. That is, $d = k \sin x$, where $d$ is deviation, $x$ is displacement along the surface, and $k$ is a constant amplitude. Find the average of $d^2$ for one complete cycle. Use the result to calculate the rms deviation.

b. Plot the graph of $y = \sin^2 x$. Sketch the result. Show that the resulting graph is itself a sinusoid and find its equation.

c. Show that the answer to 16a can be determined graphically from 16b, without having to use calculus.

d. Suppose a surface is "lumpy," as in Figure 10-3g, and has the shape of the graph of $y = |\sin x|$. Find the average value of $y$, $y_{av}$. Then find the rms deviation, using the fact that

$$\text{Deviation} = y - y_{av}.$$

Based on your answer, would this surface be rougher or smoother than a sinusoidal surface with the same maximum distance between high points and low points as in Figure 10-3g?

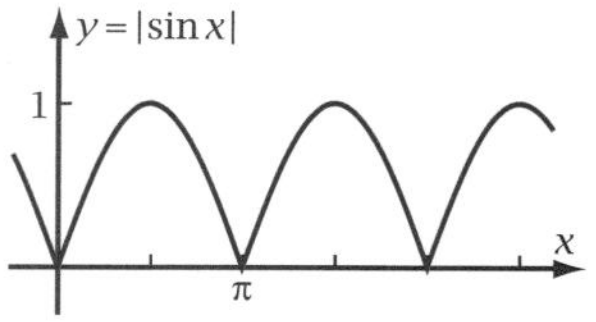


Figure 10-3g

# 10-4 Related Rates

Thus far in this chapter you have considered only motion along a line. Now you will investigate situations in which more than one distance is varying. You will find relationships between the rates at which the distances or other variables change.

***OBJECTIVE***

Given a situation in which several quantities vary, predict the rate at which one of them is changing when you know other related rates.

■ ***Example 1*** An airplane is flying 600 mi/hr on a horizontal path that will take it directly over an observer. The airplane is 7 mi high (Figure 10-4a).

a. Write an equation for the rate of change of the line-of-sight distance, $z$, between the observer and the airplane in terms of the horizontal displacement, $x$, from observer to airplane.

b. Plot $dz/dt$ as a function of $x$. Sketch the result.

c. How fast is $z$ changing when $x$ is 10 mi? When $x$ is $-5$ mi (that is, 5 mi beyond the observer)? Interpret the answers.

d. Interpret the graph in part b when $x = 0$ and when $|x|$ is very large.

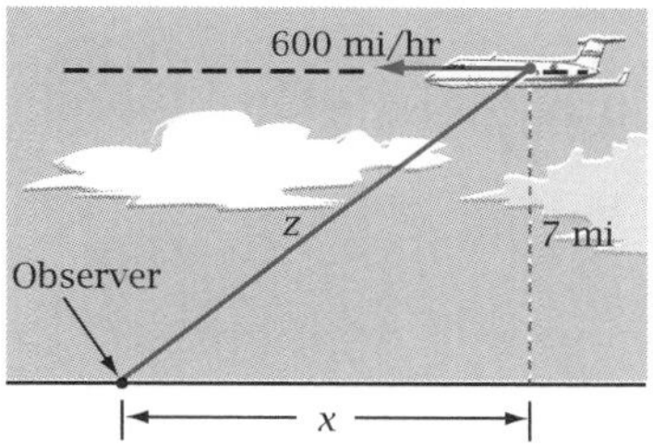


Figure 10-4a

***Solutions***

a. You know the rate of change of $x$ with respect to time $t$, and you want the rate of change of $z$. So the key to the problem is establishing a relationship between $z$ and $x$. Here's how.

Know: $\dfrac{dx}{dt} = -600$ — Why is it negative?

Want: $\dfrac{dz}{dt}$

$z^2 = x^2 + 7^2$ — Find a relationship between $x$ and $z$ (Pythagorean theorem).

$2z\dfrac{dz}{dt} = 2x\dfrac{dx}{dt}$ — Differentiate implicitly with respect to $t$. Remember the chain rule!

$\dfrac{dz}{dt} = \dfrac{x}{z}\dfrac{dx}{dt} = -600\dfrac{x}{z} = \dfrac{-600x}{\sqrt{x^2 + 49}}$ — By algebra and the Pythagorean theorem.

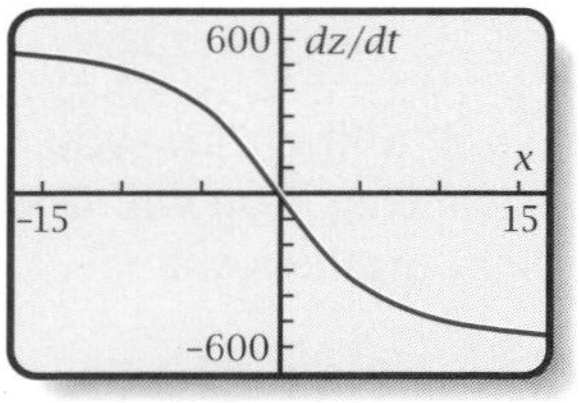


Figure 10-4b

b. Figure 10-4b shows the graph.

c. When $x = 10$, $dz/dt = -491.539\ldots$, meaning that the distance is decreasing at about 492 mi/hr as the airplane approaches. When $x = -5$, $dz/dt = 348.74\ldots$, meaning that the distance is increasing at about 349 mi/hr as the airplane flies away.

d. At $x = 0$, the airplane is directly overhead. Although it is still moving at 600 mi/hr, the distance between the airplane and the observer is not changing at that instant. Thus, $dz/dt = 0$, as shown by the graph. For large values of $|x|$ the rate approaches $\pm 600$ mi/hr, the speed of the airplane. This happens because $z$ and $x$ are very nearly equal when the plane is far away. ■

**■ *Example 2*** Suppose you are drinking root beer from a conical paper cup. The cup has a diameter of 8 cm and a depth of 10 cm. As you suck on the straw, root beer leaves the cup at the rate of 7 $\text{cm}^3$/sec. At what rate is the level of the liquid in the cup changing

a. When the liquid is 6 cm deep?

b. At the instant when the last drop leaves the cup?

***Solutions***

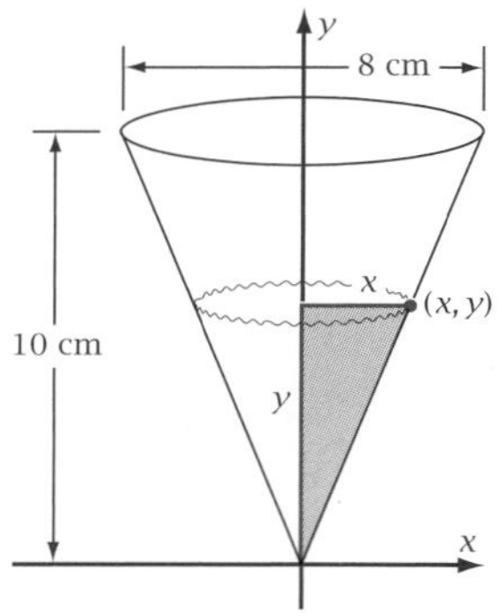


Figure 10-4c

a. The secret to getting started is drawing an appropriate diagram, then identifying the known rate and the wanted rate. Figure 10-4c shows a cross section through the cup. Since the level of the liquid varies, you should label the depth with a variable, even though you are looking for the rate when the depth is 6.
Let $y$ = no. of cm deep.
Let $x$ = no. of cm radius of liquid surface.

Know: $\dfrac{dV}{dt} = -7\text{cm}^3/\text{sec}$  Want: $\dfrac{dy}{dt}$

$V = \frac{1}{3}\pi x^2 y$  Volume of a cone.

By the properties of similar triangles, $x$ can be expressed in terms of $y$, thus reducing the problem to just the two variables whose rates you know or want.

$$\frac{x}{4} = \frac{y}{10} \Rightarrow x = 0.4y$$

$$\therefore V = \frac{1}{3}\pi(0.4y)^2(y) = \frac{4}{75}\pi y^3$$

$$\frac{dV}{dt} = \frac{4}{25}\pi y^2 \frac{dy}{dt}$$

$$\frac{dy}{dt} = \frac{25}{4\pi y^2} \cdot \frac{dV}{dt}$$ Get a general formula before you substitute particular values.

$$\frac{dy}{dt} = \frac{25}{4\pi \cdot 6^2}(-7) = \frac{-175}{144\pi} = -0.3868\ldots \approx -0.39\text{cm/sec}$$

b. At the instant the last drop leaves, $y = 0$. Substituting $y = 0$ into the general formula of part a leads to division by zero. So the liquid level is changing infinitely fast!! ■

## Problem Set 10-4

### *Do These Quickly*

The following problems are intended to refresh your skills. You should be able to do all ten problems in less than five minutes.

**Q1.** The number of feet from the starting point is called —?—.

**Q2.** The total feet traveled is called —?—.

**Q3.** $\int |v|\, dt$ is used to find the —?—.

**Q4.** $\int v\, dt$ is used to find the —?—.

**Q5.** If velocity and acceleration are both negative, is the object speeding up or slowing down?

**Q6.** If $dy/dx$ is negative, then $y$ is getting —?—.

**Q7.** $\int xe^x\, dx =$ —?—.

**Q8.** If $y = x \cos x$, then $y' =$ —?—.

**Q9.** If $y = \ln x$, then $dy/dt =$ —?—.

**Q10.** The only point of inflection in the graph of $y = xe^x$ is at $x =$ —?—.

1. *Bacteria Spreading Problem:* Bacteria are growing in a circular colony one bacterium thick. The bacteria are growing at a constant rate, thus making the area of the colony increase at a constant rate of 12 $\text{mm}^2$/hr. Find an equation expressing the rate of change of area as a function of the radius, $r$, of the colony. Plot $dr/dt$ as a function of $r$. How fast is $r$ changing when it equals 3 mm? Describe the way $dr/dt$ changes with the radius of the circle.

2. *Balloon Problem:* Phil LaRupp blows up a spherical balloon. He recalls that the volume is $(4/3)\pi r^3$. Find $dV/dt$ as a function of $r$ and $dr/dt$. In order for the radius to increase at 2 cm/sec, how fast must Phil blow air into the balloon when $r = 3$? When $r = 6$? Plot the graph of $dV/dt$ under these conditions. Sketch the result and interpret the graph.

3. *Ellipse Problem:* You recall that the area of an ellipse is $A = \pi ab$, where $a$ and $b$ are the lengths of the semiaxes (Figure 10-4d). Suppose that an ellipse is changing size but always keeps the same proportions, $a = 2b$. At what rate is the length of the major axis changing when $b = 12$ cm and the area is decreasing at 144 $\text{cm}^2$/sec?

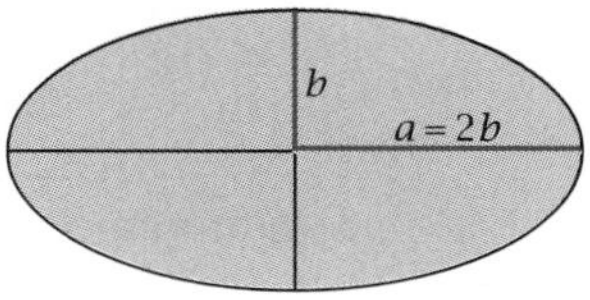

Figure 10-4d

4. *Bathtub Problem:* A tub has cross sections the shape of the quartic parabola $y = x^4$, where both $x$ and $y$ are in feet. The tub is 5 ft long, has vertical ends (which make it uncomfortable for bathing, but convenient for calculus!), and sits as flat as possible on the floor (Figure 10-4e). When you pull the plug, water flows out at a rate proportional to the depth of the water remaining, $dV/dt = ky$.

   a. Find $dV$, the differential of volume for a horizontal slice, in terms of $x$ and $dy$. Then get an equation for $dV/dt$ involving $dy/dt$. In terms of the constant $k$, figure out how fast the depth is changing when the water is 6 in. deep.

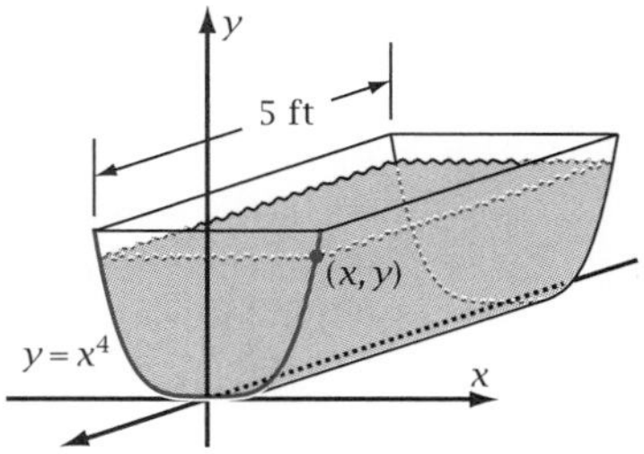

Figure 10-4e

b. Would the rate be faster, slower, or the same if you are sitting in the tub when the water is 6 in. deep?

5. *Base Runner Problem:* Milt Famey hits a line drive to center field. As he rounds second base, he heads directly for third, running at 20 ft/sec (Figure 10-4f). Write an equation expressing the rate of change of his distance from home plate as a function of his displacement from third base. Plot the graph in a suitable domain. How fast is this distance changing when he is halfway to third? At third? Is the latter answer reasonable? Explain.

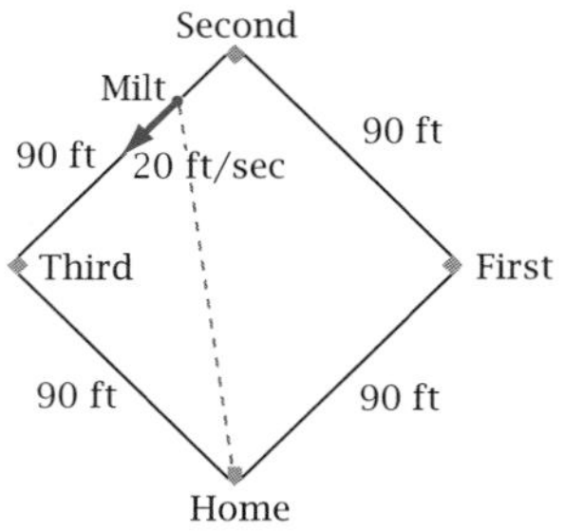


Figure 10-4f

6. *Tugboat Problem:* A tugboat moves a ship up to the dock by pushing its stern at a rate of 3 m/sec (Figure 10-4g). The ship is 200 m long. Its bow remains in contact with the dock and its stern remains in contact with the pier. At what rate is the bow moving along the dock when the stern is 120 m from the dock? Plot the graph of this rate as a function of the distance between the stern and the dock.

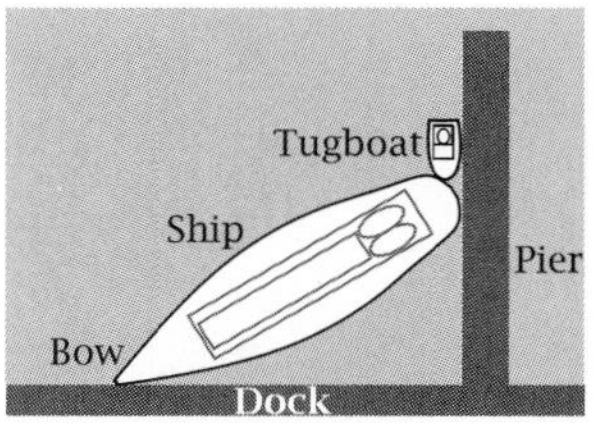


Figure 10-4g

7. *Rectangle Problem I:* The length of a rectangle is increasing at 3 ft/min, and the width is decreasing at 2 ft/min. When the length is 50 ft and the width is 20 ft, is the area of the rectangle increasing or decreasing? At what rate?

8. *Rectangle Problem II:* A rectangle of length $L$ and width $W$ has a constant area of 1200 in$^2$. The length changes at a rate of $dL/dt$ inches per minute.

   a. Find $dW/dt$ in terms of $W$ and $dL/dt$.

   b. At a particular instant the length is increasing at 6 in./min and the width is decreasing at 2 in./min. Find the dimensions of the rectangle at this instant.

   c. At the instant in 8b, is the length of the diagonal of the rectangle increasing or decreasing? At what rate?

9. *Luke and Leia's Trash Compactor Problem:* Luke and Leia are trapped inside a trash compactor on the Death Star (Figure 10-4h). The side walls are moving apart at 0.1 m/sec, but the end walls are moving together at 0.3 m/sec. The volume of liquid inside the compactor is 20 cubic meters, a constant.

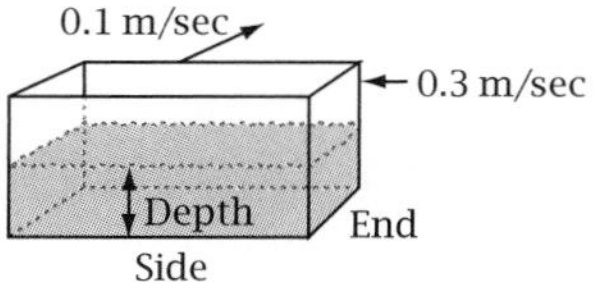


Figure 10-4h

   a. Write an equation expressing the rate of change of depth of the liquid in terms of the width and length of the region inside the compactor.

   b. When the side walls are 5 m long and the end walls are 2 m long, is the depth of liquid increasing or decreasing? At what rate?

10. *Darth Vader's Problem:* Darth Vader's spaceship is approaching the origin along the positive $y$-axis at 50 km/sec. Meanwhile, his daughter Ella's spaceship is moving away from the origin along the positive $x$-axis at 80 km/sec. When Darth is at $y = 1200$ km and Ella is at $x = 500$ km, is the distance between them increasing or decreasing? At what rate?

11. *Point on a Parabola Problem:* A point moves along the parabola $y = x^2$ (Figure 10-4i) in such a way that the rate of change of $x$ with respect to time $t$ is directly proportional to the value of $x$. That is, $dx/dt = kx$, where $k$ stands for a constant.

 a. Find a general equation for $dy/dt$ as a function of $x$.

 b. Find the constant of proportionality, $k$, if $dx/dt = 10$ when $x = 5$.

 c. Find the value of $dy/dt$ when $x = 7$.

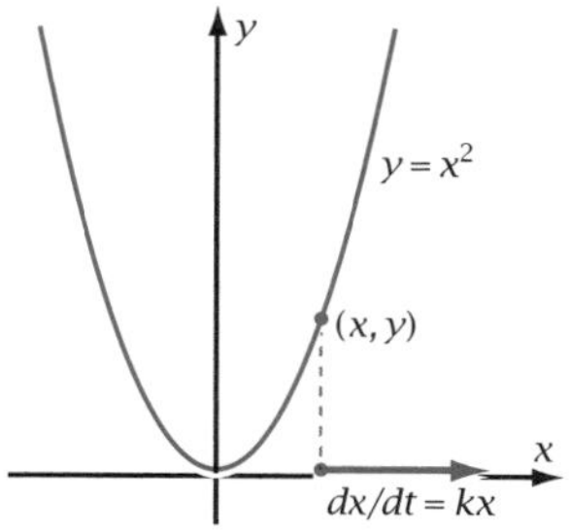

Figure 10-4i

12. *Point on a Tangent Graph Problem:* A particle moves along the graph of $y = \tan x$. Its velocity in the $x$-direction is 5 units per minute. When $x = 1$, what is its velocity in the $y$-direction?

13. *Barn Ladder Problem:* A ladder to the loft in a barn is arranged so that it can be pushed up against the wall when it is not in use. The top of the ladder slides in a track on the wall, and the bottom is free to roll across the floor on wheels (Figure 10-4j). To make the ladder easier to move, a counterweight is attached to the top of the ladder by a rope over a pulley. As the ladder goes away from the wall, the counterweight goes up and vice versa.

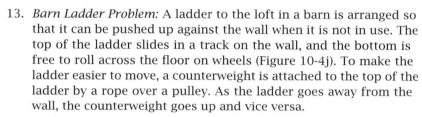

 a. The ladder is 20 ft long. Write an equation expressing the velocity the counterweight moves as a function of the distance the bottom of the ladder is from the wall and the velocity the bottom of the ladder moves away from the wall.

 b. Find the velocity of the counterweight when the bottom is 4 ft from the wall, and is being pushed toward the wall at 3 ft/sec.

 c. If the ladder is allowed to drop all the way to the floor with the bottom moving at 2 ft/sec and the top remains in contact with the wall, how fast is the counterweight moving when the top just hits the floor? Surprising?!

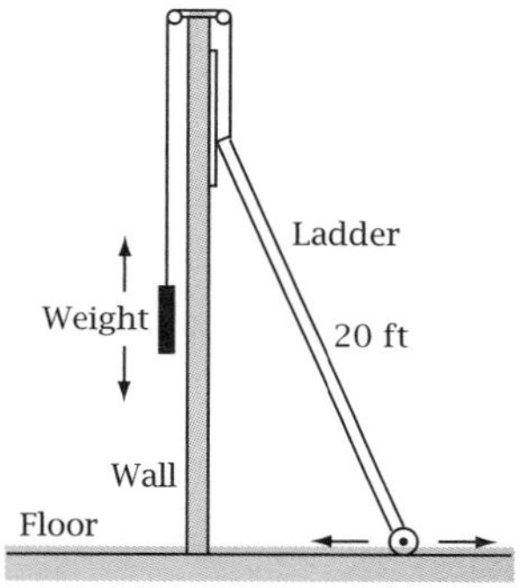

Figure 10-4j

14. *Kinetic Energy Problem:* The kinetic energy of a moving object equals half the product of the mass and the square of the velocity.

$$K = \tfrac{1}{2}mV^2$$

As a spaceship is being fired into orbit, all three of these quantities vary. Suppose that the kinetic energy of a particular spaceship is increasing at a constant rate of 100,000 units per second and that mass is decreasing at 20 kg/sec because fuel is being consumed. At what rate is the velocity changing when the spaceship's mass is 5000 kg and it is traveling at 10 km/sec?

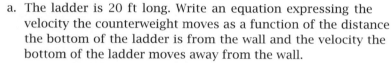

15. *Conical Water Tank Problem:* The water tank shown in Figure 10-4k has diameter 6 m and depth 5 m.

 a. If the water is 3 m deep, and is rising at 5 m/hr, at what rate is the volume changing?

 b. If the water is being pumped out at 2 $m^3$/hr, at what rate is the depth changing

  i. When the water is 4 m deep?

  ii. When the last drop is pumped out?

 c. If water flows out under the action of gravity, the rate of change of volume is directly proportional to the square root of the water's

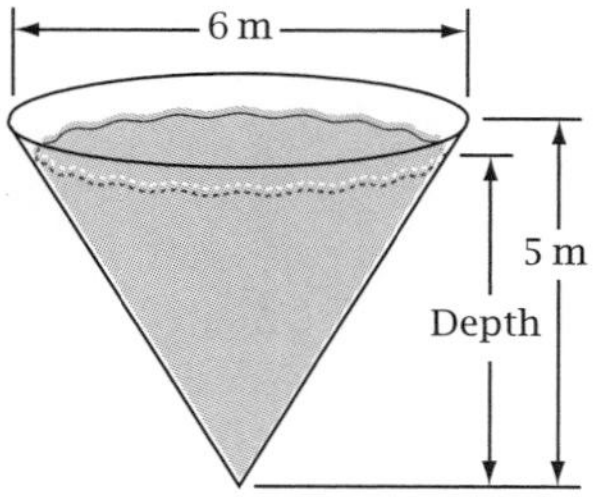

Figure 10-4k

depth. Suppose that the volume $V$ is decreasing at 0.5 $m^3$/hr when the depth is 4 m.

i. Find $dV/dt$ in terms of the depth of the water.

ii. Find $dV/dt$ when the water is 0.64 m deep.

iii. Find the rate of change of depth when the water is 0.64 m deep.

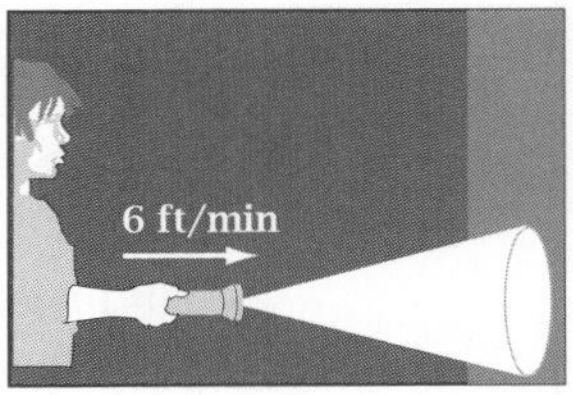

Figure 10-4l

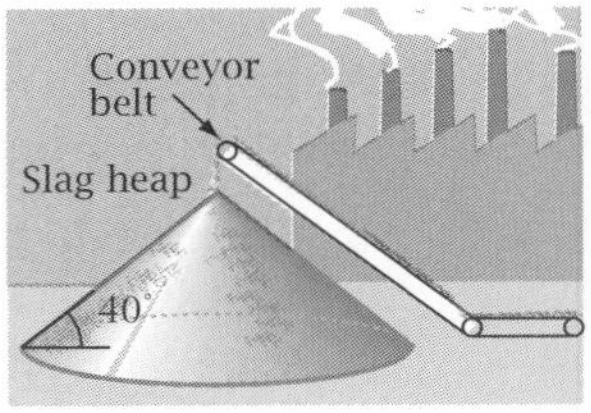

Figure 10-4m

16. *Conical Tank Generalization Problem:* Suppose that a conical tank as in Figure 10-4k has a radius of a units and a depth of $b$ units. Water enters or leaves the tank at $dV/dt$ cubic units per unit time, where $dV/dt$ is not necessarily a constant. Write an equation expressing the rate of change of depth of the water in the tank as a function of depth and $dV/dt$.

17. *Cone of Light Problem:* A spotlight shines on the wall, forming a cone of light in the air (Figure 10-4l). The light is being moved closer to the wall, making the cone's altitude decrease at 6 ft/min. At the same time, the light is being refocused, making the radius increase at 7 ft/min. At the instant when the altitude is 3 ft and the radius is 8 ft, is the volume of the cone increasing or decreasing? How fast?

18. *Slag Heap Problem:* Slag left over from the manufacture of cement is being piled outside the cement plant. The resulting slag heap is a cone whose elements make an angle of 40° with the horizontal (Figure 10-4m). Environmentalists measure the circumference of the heap one day, finding it to be 3000 ft, and increasing at 7 ft/day. About how fast is the cement plant generating slag?

19. *Cone in Hemisphere Problem:* A right circular cone is inscribed in a hemisphere (Figure 10-4n). The figure is expanding in such a way that the combined surface area of the hemisphere and its base is increasing at a constant rate of 18 $in^2$/sec. At what rate is the volume of the cone changing when the radius of the common base is 4 in.?

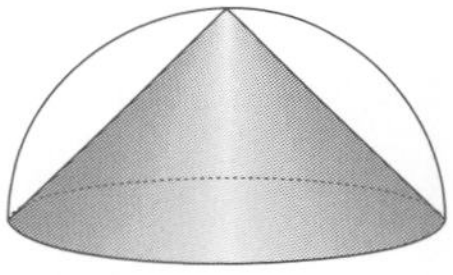
Figure 10-4n

20. *Planetary Motion Problem:* On October 10, 1988, Mars was at its closest position to earth. It then receded at an increasing rate (Figure 10-4o). In this problem you will analyze the rate at which the distance between the two planets changes. Assume that the orbits of the two planets are both circular and are both in the ecliptic plane. The radius of earth's orbit is 93 million mi and the radius of Mars' orbit is 141 million mi. Assume also that the speed each planet moves along its path is constant. (This would be exactly true if the orbits were circular.) Mars orbits the sun once each 687 earth-days. The earth, of course, orbits once each 365 earth-days. Answer the following questions.

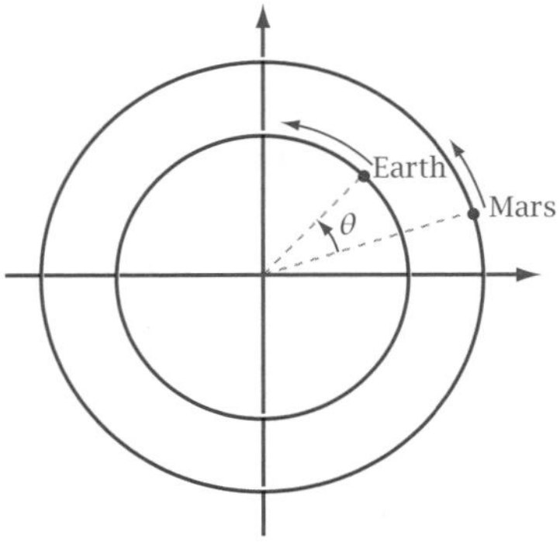

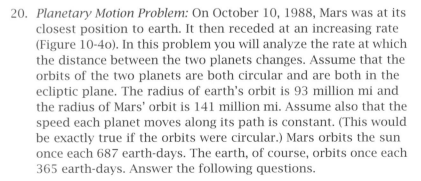

Figure 10-4o

a. What are the angular velocities of earth and Mars about the sun in radians per day? What is their relative angular velocity? That is, what is $d\theta/dt$?

b. What is the period of the planets' relative motion? On what day and date were the two planets next at their closest?

c. Write an equation expressing the distance $D$ between the planets as a function of $\theta$.

d. At what rate is $D$ changing today? Transform your answer to miles per hour.

e. Will $D$ be changing its fastest when the planets are 90° apart? If so, prove it. If not, find the angle $\theta$ at which $D$ is changing fastest. Transform the answer to degrees.

f. Plot the graph of $D$ versus time for at least one period of the planets' relative motion. Is the graph a sinusoid?

21. *Speeding Piston Project:* The engine in a car is going 3000 revolutions per minute (rpm). As the crankshaft turns in the $xy$-plane, the piston goes up and down inside the cylinder (Figure 10-4p). The radius of the crankshaft is 6 cm. The connecting rod is 20 cm long and fastens to a point 8 cm below the top of the piston. Let $y$ be the distance from the top of the piston to the center of the crankshaft. Let $\theta$ be an angle in standard position measured from the positive $x$-axis and increasing as the crankshaft rotates counterclockwise.

    a. Write an equation expressing $y$ in terms of $\theta$. You should find that the law of cosines is helpful.

    b. Find an equation for the rate of change of $y$ with respect to $t$ in terms of $\theta$ and $d\theta/dt$.

    c. Find an equation for the acceleration of the point on top of the piston. Remember that $d\theta/dt$ is a constant since the engine is going at a constant 3000 rpm.

    d. Between what two values of $\theta$ is the top of the piston going down with an acceleration greater than that of gravity (980 cm/sec²)?

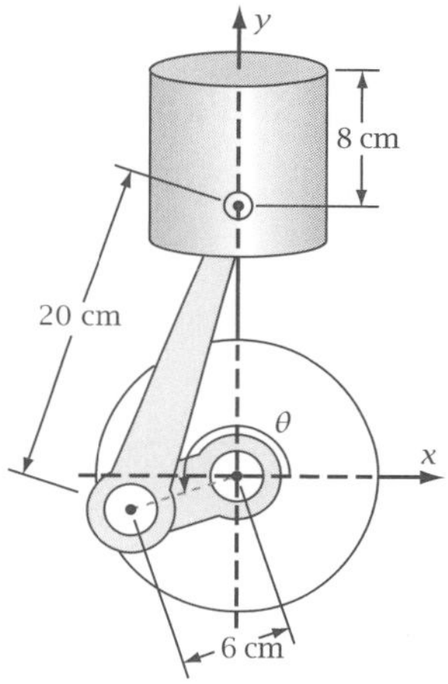


Figure 10-4p

# 10-5 Minimal Path Problems

Suppose you are swimming in the ocean. When you finish, you could swim straight to the place on the shoreline where you left your towel, or you could swim straight to the shoreline, then walk to the towel (Figure 10-5a). Swimming straight to the

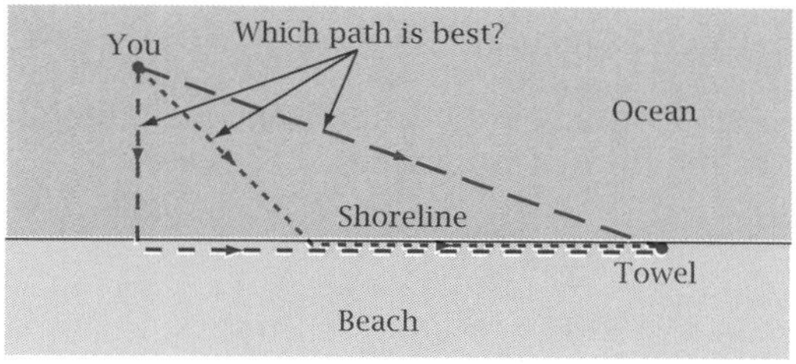


Figure 10-5a

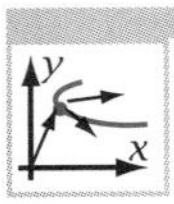

towel minimizes the distance you must go. Heading for the closest point on the shoreline minimizes your time in the water. But your total time might be minimized if you head for a point between the towel and the closest point because you can walk faster than you can swim.

A third alternative is to swim to some point between the towel and the closest point on the shoreline, shortening the walk while increasing the swim by just a little. Your objective in this section will be to analyze such problems to find the **minimal path**, which takes the least total time.

**OBJECTIVE**

Given a situation in which something goes from one place to another through two different media at different rates, find the path that minimizes a total time or cost.

**Example 1**

Suppose you are 200 yd from the beach and want to get to the place where you left your towel in the minimum possible time. You can walk on the beach at 110 yd/min but can swim only 70 yd/min. Let $x$ be the distance from the foot of your perpendicular to the beach to the point where you will make landfall (Figure 10-5b). What value of $x$ minimizes your total time if your towel is

a. 600 yd from the foot of the perpendicular?

b. 100 yd from the foot of the perpendicular?

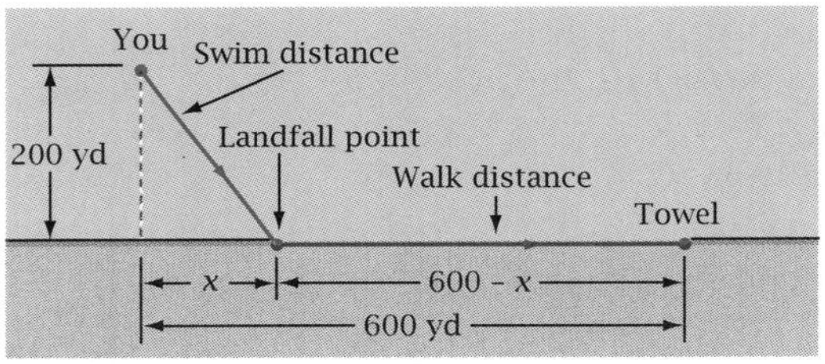


Figure 10-5b

**Solutions**

a. Distance to swim is $\sqrt{x^2 + 200^2}$.
Distance to walk is $(600 - x)$, where $x \le 600$.
$\therefore$ total time will be

$$t = \tfrac{1}{70}\sqrt{x^2 + 200^2} + \tfrac{1}{110}(600 - x).$$

To find the minimum total time, find the distance, $x$, at which $t$ stops decreasing and starts increasing. This can be done graphically by plotting $t$ as a function of $x$ and tracing (Figure 10-5c). The minimum is somewhere between $x = 160$ and 170.

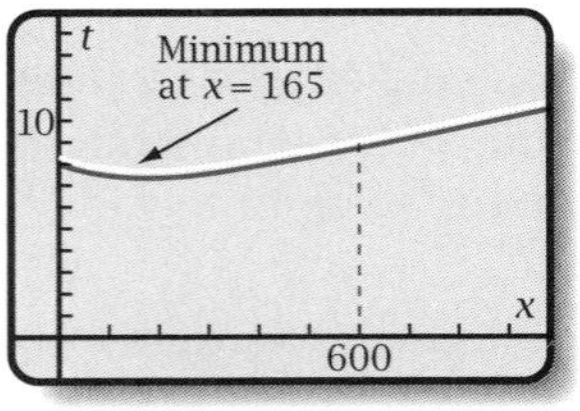


Figure 10-5c

The exact value can be found algebraically by finding the value of $x$ that makes the derivative of $t$ equal to zero.

$$\frac{dt}{dx} = \tfrac{1}{140}(x^2 + 200^2)^{-1/2}(2x) - \tfrac{1}{110}$$

$$= \tfrac{x}{70}(x^2 + 200^2)^{-1/2} - \tfrac{1}{110}$$

$$\frac{dt}{dx} = 0 \qquad \text{if and only if}$$

$$\frac{x}{70}(x^2 + 200^2)^{-1/2} = \frac{1}{110}$$

$$70(x^2 + 200^2)^{1/2} = 110x$$ Take the reciprocal of both sides, then multiply by $x$.

$$4900(x^2 + 200^2) = 12100x^2$$

$$4900(200^2) = 7200x^2$$

$$x = \pm 164.9915\ldots$$ $+164.9\ldots$ is in the desired range, thus confirming the graphical solution.

Head for a point about 165 yd from the foot of the perpendicular.

b. If the towel is only 100 yd from the foot of the perpendicular, the domain of $x$ is $[0, 100]$, and the equation for $t$ is

$$t = \frac{1}{70}\sqrt{x^2 + 200^2} + \frac{1}{110}(100 - x).$$

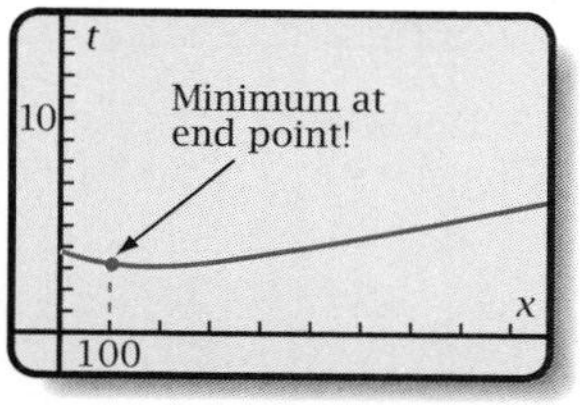


Figure 10-5d

The graph of this equation is shown in Figure 10-5d. Surprisingly, the minimum is at the same value, $x \approx 165$, as in part a. The 600 or 100 disappears when you differentiate, so the zero of the derivative is not affected by this number. However, the 165 is out of the domain. It is beyond the towel! By the graph in Figure 10-5d, you can see that the minimum time comes at the endpoint, $x = 100$.

Head straight for the towel. ■

These problems are sometimes called "drowning swimmer" problems, because they are often phrased in such a way that a person on the beach must rescue a drowning swimmer and wants to take the path that reaches the swimmer in a minimum length of time. (The swimmer might drown if one were to take all that time to do the calculations!)

In Problem Set 10-5, you will work more minimum path problems. Then you will show that there is a remarkably simple way to find the minimum path if you will do calculus algebraically on the general case instead of "brute-force" plotting on a particular case.

## Problem Set 10-5

### *Do These Quickly*

The following problems are intended to refresh your skills. You should be able to do all ten problems in less than five minutes.

**Q1.** Solve: $\sqrt{x} = 9$

**Q2.** Differentiate: $y = \sqrt{100 - x^2}$

**Q3.** Integrate: $\int x\sqrt{100 - x^2}\,dx$

**Q4.** Differentiate: $y = \sin^{-1} 3x$

**Q5.** Integrate: $\int xe^{2x}\,dx$

**Q6.** Differentiate: $y = \tanh x$

**Q7.** Going 60 cm at 40 cm/hr takes -?- hr.

For Problems Q8–Q10, use the velocity-time function in Figure 10-5e:

***Q8.*** At what time(s) is the moving object at rest?

***Q9.*** At what time(s) does the moving object change directions?

***Q10.*** At what time(s) does the acceleration function have a local maximum?

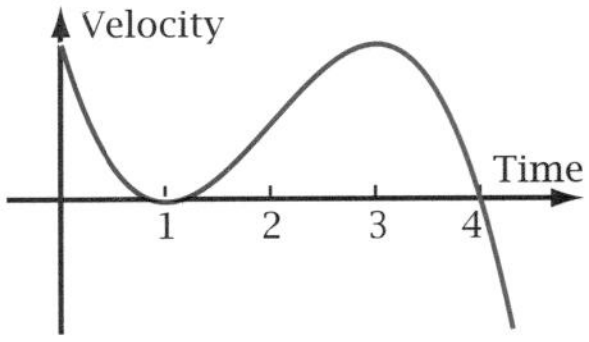


Figure 10-5e

1. *Swim and Run Problem:* In a swim-and-run biathlon, Ann Athlete must get to a point on the other side of a 50-m-wide river, 100 m downstream from her starting point (Figure 10-5f). Ann can swim 2 m/sec and run 5 m/sec. Toward what point on the opposite side of the river should Ann swim in order to minimize her total time?

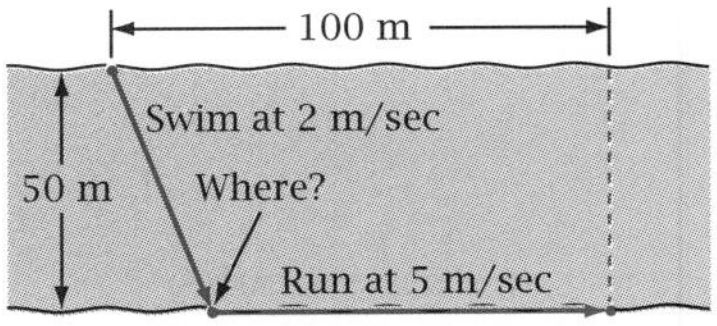


Figure 10-5f

2. *Scuba Diver Problem:* A scuba diver heads for a point on the bottom that is 30 m below the surface and 100 m horizontally from the point where she entered the water. She can move 13 m/min on the surface but only 12 m/min as she is descending. How far from her entry point should she start descending to reach her destination in minimum time?

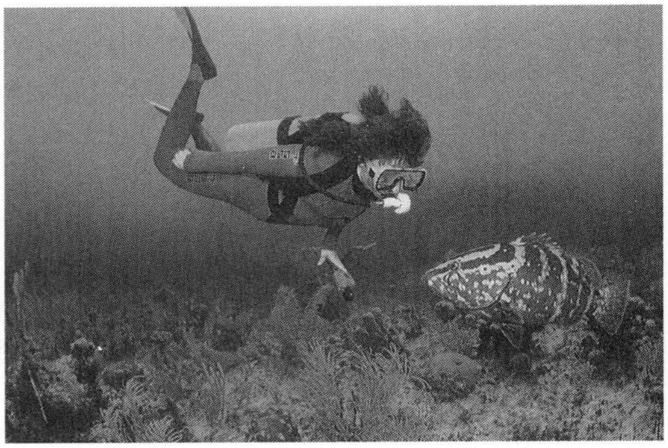

3. *Pipeline Problem:* Earl Wells owns an oil lease. A new well 300 m from the road is to be connected to storage tanks 1000 m down the road from the well (Figure 10-5g). Building pipeline across the field costs \$50 per meter, while building it along the road costs only \$40 per meter. How should the pipeline be laid out in order to minimize its total cost?

4. *Elevated Walkway Problem:* A walkway is to be built from the corner of one building to the corner of another building across the street and 400 ft down the block. It is 120 ft across the street (Figure 10-5h). Engineering studies show that the walkway will weigh 3000 lb/ft where it parallels the street, and 4000 lb/ft where it crosses the street. How should the walkway be laid out in order to minimize its total weight?

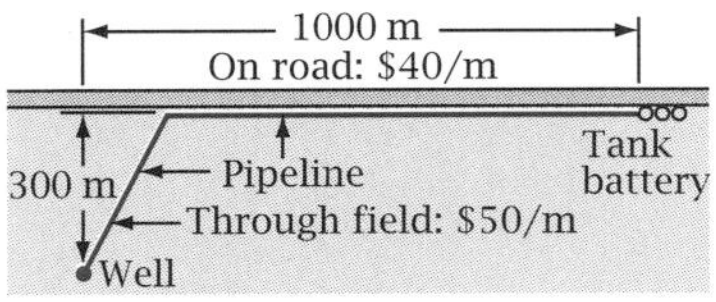


Figure 10-5g

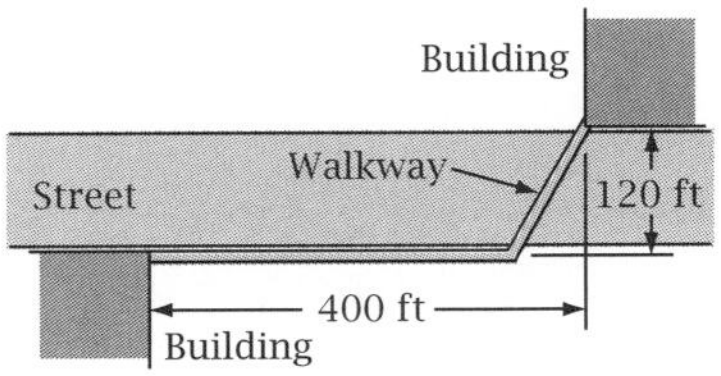


Figure 10-5h

5. *Minimum Path Discovery Problem:* In this problem you will explore a relationship between the minimum path and the two speeds or costs per meter.

   a. In the Swim and Run Problem, let $\theta$ be the (acute) angle between the slant path and a perpendicular to the river (Figure 10-5i, top diagram). Show that the sine of this angle equals the ratio of the two speeds. That is, show that $\sin\theta = 2/5$.

   b. In the *Pipeline Problem,* let $\theta$ be the acute angle between the slant path and a perpendicular to the road (Figure 10-5i, bottom diagram). Show that the sine of this angle equals the ratio of the two costs per meter. That is, show that $\sin\theta = 40/50$.

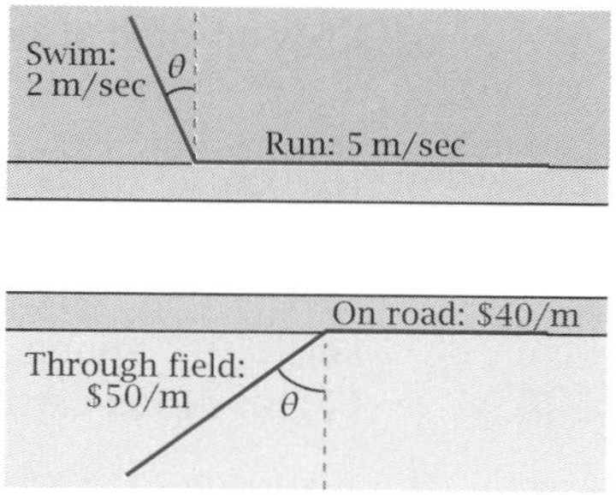

Figure 10-5i

6. *Minimum Path Generalization Problem:* A swimmer is at a distance of $p$ ft from the beach. His towel is at the water's edge, $k$ ft along the beach (Figure 10-5j). He swims at an angle $\theta$ to a line perpendicular to the beach and makes landfall at a point $x$ ft from the point on the beach that was originally closest to him. He can swim $s$ ft/min and walk $w$ ft/min, where $s < w$. Prove that his total time is a minimum if *the sine of the angle the slant path makes with the perpendicular equals the ratio of the two speeds.* That is, prove the following property.

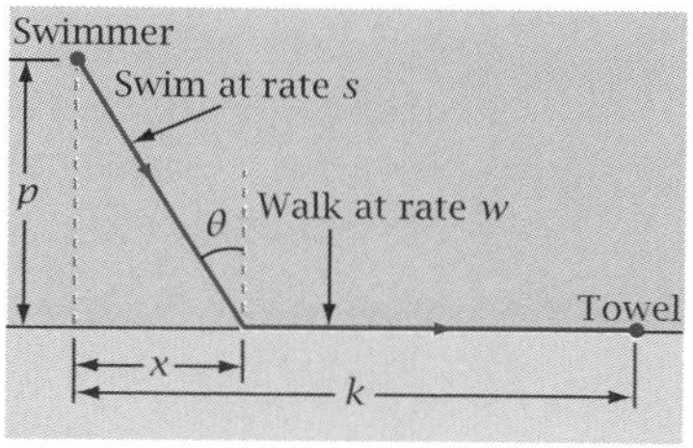

Figure 10-5j

**Property: Minimum Path**

For the path shown in Figure 10-5j, if $\sin\theta = s/w$, then the total time taken is a minimum.

7. *Scuba Diver Problem Revisited:* Work Problem 2 again, using the minimum path property of Problem 6. Which way is it easier to work the problem? Tell one reason why mathematicians find general solutions to typical problems.

8. *Elevated Walkway Problem Revisited:* Work Problem 4 again, using the minimum path property of Problem 6. Since weight equals distance multiplied by cost per foot (rather than distance divided by velocity), you will have to adapt the property appropriately. Which is the easier way to work the problem? Tell one reason why mathematicians find general solutions to typical problems.

9. *Pipeline Problem, Near Miss:* Suppose you present your boss with a solution to the *Pipeline Problem* (Problem 3), but in order to save some trees, the value of $x$ must be a few meters away from the optimum value. Will this fact make much difference in the total cost of the pipeline? Tell how you reach your conclusion.

10. *Calvin and Phoebe's Commuting Problem:* Calvin lives at the corner of Alamo and Heights Streets (Figure 10-5k). Phoebe lives on High Street, 500 ft from its intersection with Heights Street. Since they have been going steady, Calvin finds that he is spending a lot of of time walking between the two houses. He seeks to minimize the time by cutting across the field to a point that is $x$ ft from the Heights-High intersection. He finds that he can walk 5 ft/sec along the streets but only 3 ft/sec across the rough, grassy field. What value of $x$ minimizes Calvin's time getting to Phoebe's?

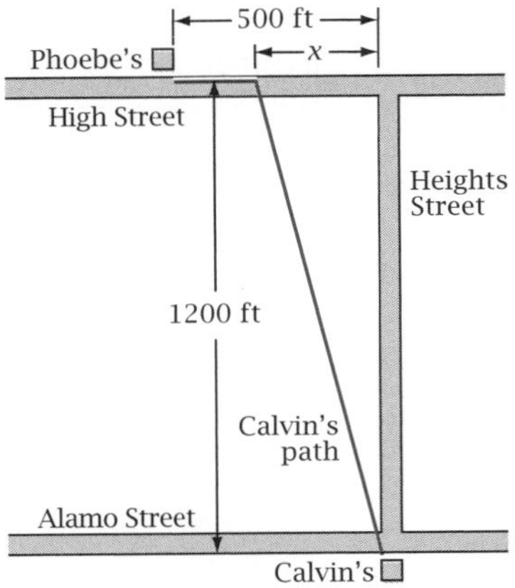


Figure 10-5k

11. *Robinson Crusoe Problem:* Robinson Crusoe is shipwrecked on a desert island. He builds a hut 70 yd from the shore. His wrecked ship is 120 yd from the shore, 300 yd down from the hut (Figure 10-5l). Crusoe makes many trips between the hut and the ship and wants to minimize the time each trip takes. He can walk 130 yd/min and pole his raft 50 yd/min. Where on the shoreline should he moor his raft so that the trips can be made in minimum time?

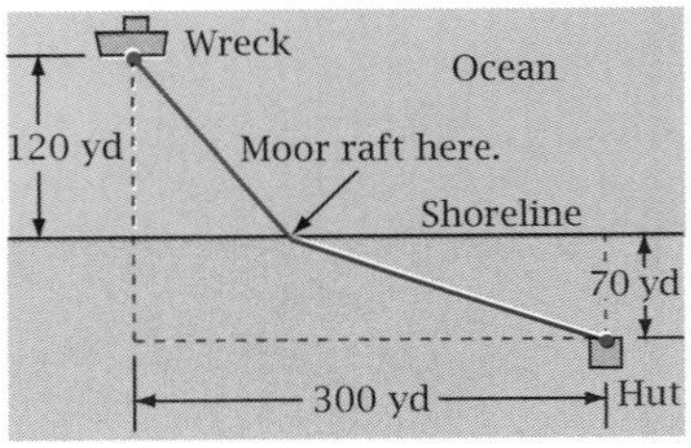


Figure 10-5l

12. *Robinson Crusoe Follow-Up Problem:* Let $\theta_1$ and $\theta_2$ be the angles between the two paths and a line perpendicular to the beach (Figure 10-5m) in the *Robinson Crusoe Problem.* Use the answer to the problem to calculate the measures of these angles. Then show that the ratio of the sines of the angles equals the ratio of the two speeds. That is, show

$$\frac{\sin\theta_1}{\sin\theta_2} = \frac{50}{130}.$$

13. *Robinson Crusoe Generalization Problem:* Figure 10-5n shows the general case of the Robinson Crusoe Problem, where the wreck, $A$, and the hut, $B$, are $a$ and $b$ units from the shore, respectively, and $k$ units apart parallel to the shore. The velocities through the water and on land are $v_1$ and $v_2$, respectively. Prove that the minimum time from wreck to hut is where

$$\frac{\sin\theta_1}{\sin\theta_2} = \frac{v_1}{v_2}.$$

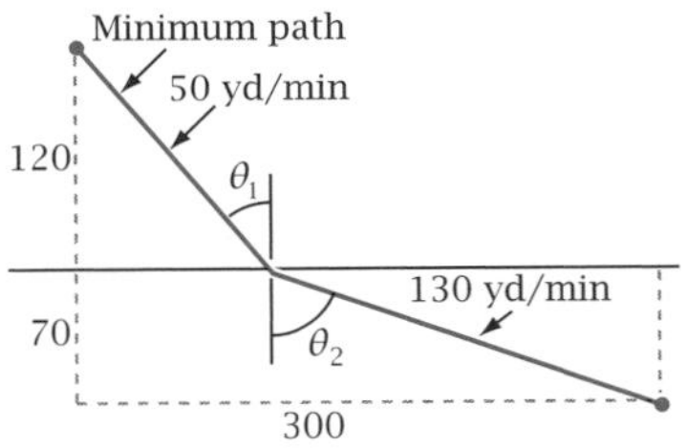


Figure 10-5m

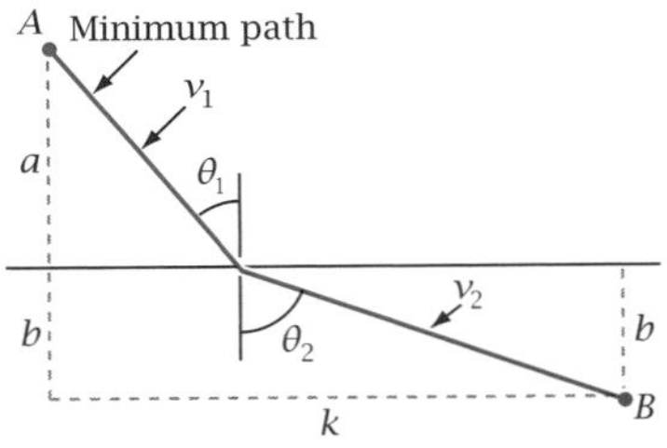


Figure 10-5n

14. *Snell's Law of Refraction Problem:* About 350 years ago the Dutch physicist Willebrod Snellius observed that when light passes from one substance into another, such as from air to water, the rays bend at the interface (Figure 10-5o). He found that the angles $\theta_1$ and $\theta_2$ that the incoming and outgoing rays make with a perpendicular to the interface obey the following rule:

$$\frac{\sin\theta_1}{\sin\theta_2} = \frac{v_1}{v_2},$$

where $v_1$ and $v_2$ are the speeds of light in the two substances.

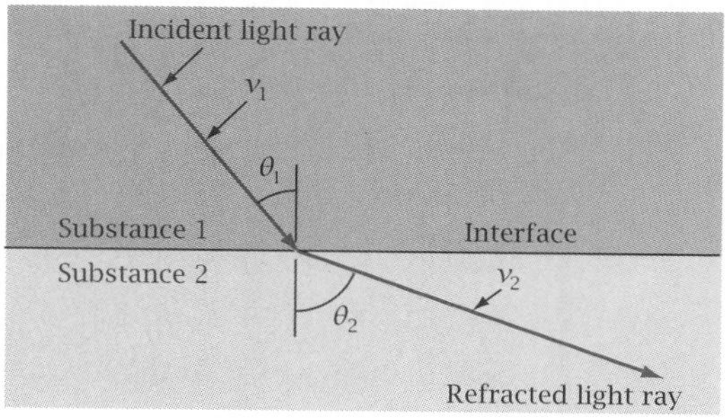

Figure 10-5o

a. In what ways does this real-world situation correspond to the *Robinson Crusoe Problems*?

b. What can you conclude about the time light takes to get from one point to another when it passes through different substances?

c. When you are above the surface of the water in a swimming pool, objects on the bottom always appear closer to the surface than they actually are. Explain how this can be true, and what this fact tells you about the relative speeds of light in air and in water.

15. *Journal Problem:* Update your journal with things you have learned since the last entry. You should include such things as those listed here.
    - The one most important thing you have learned since the last journal entry
    - The big difference between displacement and distance
    - The meaning of average value of a function
    - How one solves a typical related rates problem
    - The main idea behind minimum path problems
    - Any techniques or ideas about objects in motion that are still unclear

# 10-6 Maximum and Minimum Problems in Motion and Elsewhere

In Section 10-5, you found minimum paths, whereby one could travel between points in the least time or build structures between points for the least cost. In this section you will find maximum and minimum values in other phenomena.

**OBJECTIVE**

Given a situation in the real or mathematical world where a function is to be maximized or minimized, write an equation for the function and find the maximum or minimum values.

The technique is similar to that in the previous section and in the analysis of plane and solid figures from Section 8-3. Therefore, no specific examples are given in this section.

## Problem Set 10-6

### *Do These Quickly*

The following problems are intended to refresh your skills. You should be able to do all ten problems in less than five minutes.

**Q1.** If $f(x) = x \sin x$, find $f'(x)$.

**Q2.** If $g(x) = x \ln x$, find $g''(x)$.

**Q3.** If $h(x) = xe^x$, find $\int h(x)\, dx$.

**Q4.** The minimum path problems of Section 10-5 are equivalent to what law from physics?

**Q5.** $\ln(\exp x) = $ —?—

**Q6.** Sketch a paraboloid.

**Q7.** Sketch $y = x^{1/3}$.

**Q8.** $\int_a^b |\text{velocity}|\, d(\text{time}) =$ total distance or net displacement?

**Q9.** Who is credited with inventing calculus?

**Q10.** Find the sum: $1 + 2 + 3 + \cdots + 98 + 99 + 100$

1. *Rocket Problem:* Jeff is out Sunday driving in his spaceship. As he approaches Mars, he fires his retro rockets. Starting 30 seconds later, his distance from Mars is given by

$$D = t + \frac{1}{t},$$

where $D$ is in thousands of miles and $t$ is in minutes. Plot the graphs of $D$ and $D'$ versus $t$. Sketch them on your paper. What are his maximum and minimum distances from Mars in the time interval $[0.5, 3]$? Justify your answers.

2. *Truck Problem:* Les Moore owns a truck. His driver, Ouida Liver, regularly makes the 100-mile trip between Tedium and Ennui. Since Les must pay Ouida \$10 per hour to drive the truck, it is to his advantage for her to make the trip as quickly as possible. However, the cost of fuel varies directly with the square of the speed, and is \$.10 per mile at a speed of 30 mph. The truck can go as fast as 85 mph. Plot cost and derivative of cost versus speed. Sketch the graphs. What speed gives the minimum total cost for the 100-mile trip? (Ignore the cost of tickets, and so on, for going over the speed limit.) Justify your answer.

3. *Number Problem I:* Find the number which exceeds its square by the greatest amount. That is, find $x$ if $x - x^2$ is to be as large as possible.

4. *Number Problem II:* Find the number greater than or equal to 2 which exceeds its square by the greatest amount.

5. *Fran's Optimal Study Time Problem:* Fran Tick forgot to study for her calculus test until late Sunday night. She knows she will score zero if she doesn't study at all, and that her potential score will be

$$S = \frac{100t}{t + 1}$$

if she studies for $t$ hours. She also realizes that the longer she studies, the more fatigued she will become. So her actual score will be less than the potential score. Her "fatigue factor" is

$$F = \frac{9}{t+9}$$

This is the number she must multiply by the potential score to find her actual grade, $G$. That is, $G = S \cdot F$.

a. Sketch the graphs of $S$, $F$, and $G$ versus time, $t$.

b. What is the optimum number of hours for Fran to study? That is, how long should she study to maximize her estimated grade, $G$?

c. How many points less than the optimum will Fran make if she studies
   i. 1 hour more than the optimum?
   ii. 1 hour less than the optimum?

6. *Motor Oil Viscosity Problem:* The viscosity (resistance to flow) of normal motor oil decreases as temperature goes up. All-temperature oils have roughly the same viscosity throughout their range of operating temperatures. Suppose that 10W-30 motor oil has viscosity

$$\mu = 130 - 12T + 15T^2 - 4T^3,$$

where $\mu$ (Greek letter "mu") is the viscosity in centipoise, $T$ is the temperature in hundreds of degrees, and the equation applies for temperatures from 0° through 300°C.

a. Find the temperature in the domain at which the maximum viscosity occurs.

b. Find the minimum viscosity in the domain.

c. Suppose that the oil is being heated in such a way that $T = \sqrt{t}$, where $t$ is time in minutes. At what rate is the viscosity changing when the temperature is 100°C?

7. *Cylinder-in-the-Cone Problem I:* A right circular cone has an altitude of 6 inches and a base of radius 10 inches. A right circular cylinder is inscribed in the cone, coaxial with it.

a. Plot the graphs of volume and total surface area of the cylinder as a function of its radius. Sketch the graphs.

b. What are the radius and altitude of the cylinder which give it the maximum volume? The maximum total surface area? Do the two maxima occur at the same radius?

8. *Cylinder-in-the-Cone Problem II:* A cone of radius 6 in. and altitude 18 in. has a cylinder inscribed in it. The cylinder's altitude starts at 0 in. and increases at 2 in./min.

a. When the altitude of the cylinder is 12 in., will its volume be increasing or decreasing? At what rate?

b. What will be the maximum volume of the cylinder in the time interval [0, 9]? Justify your answer.

c. What will be the maximum volume of the cylinder in the time interval [4, 6]?

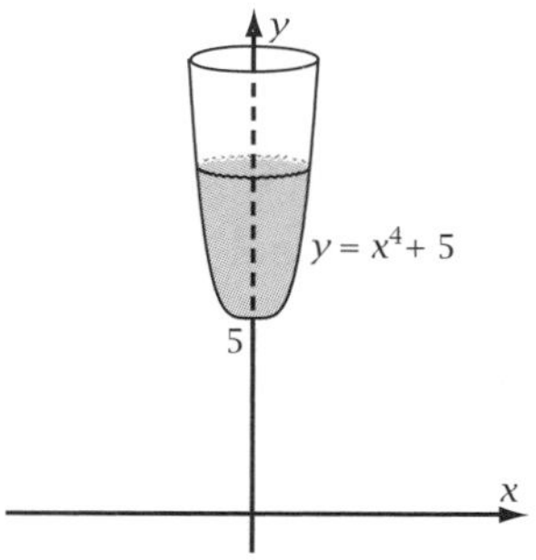

Figure 10-6a

9. *Quartic Parabola Tank Problem:* A water storage tank has the shape of the surface formed by rotating about the $y$-axis the graph of $y = x^4 + 5$, where $x$ and $y$ are in meters (Figure 10-6a). At what rate is the depth of the water changing when the water is 3m deep in the tank and is being drained at $0.7\text{m}^3$ per minute?

10. *Cylinder in Paraboloid Problem:* A paraboloid is formed by rotating the graph of $y = 4 - x^2$ around the $y$-axis. A cylinder is inscribed in the paraboloid (Figure 10-6b).

   a. If the radius of the cylinder is 1.5 units, and is increasing at 0.3 units per second, is the volume of the cylinder increasing or decreasing? At what rate?

   b. What is the maximum volume the cylinder could have? Justify your answer.

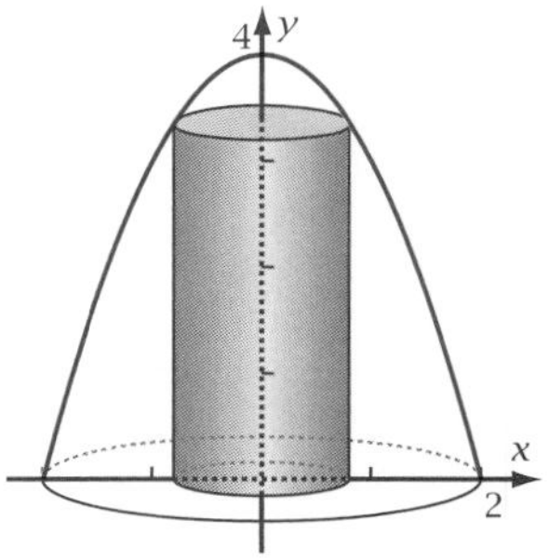

Figure 10-6b

11. *Pig Sale Problem:* Ann Aggie's pig weighs 1000 lb, and is gaining 15 lb/day. She could sell it for \$900 at today's price of 90 cents per pound, or wait till it gains some more weight and hope to get more than \$900. Unfortunately, the price per pound is dropping at 1 cent per pound each day. So she must decide when is the best time to sell.

   a. Write functions for weight and for price per pound in terms of the number of days after today. Then write a function for the total amount Ann will get for the pig.

   b. Find the time when the derivative of total amount will be zero. Convince Ann that at this time the total amount is a maximum, not a minimum.

   c. If Ann sells at the time in 11b, how much will she get for the pig?

12. *Bridge Problem:* Suppose that you work for a construction company that has a contract to build a new bridge across Scorpion Gulch, downstream from the present bridge (Figure 10-6c). You collect information from various sources in order to decide just where to build the bridge. From the surveyors you find that the width of the gulch is

   $$\text{Width} = 10(x^2 - 8x + 22)\text{ ft},$$

   where $x$ is the number of miles downstream from the old bridge. The depth of the water is

   $$\text{Depth} = 20x + 10\text{ft}.$$

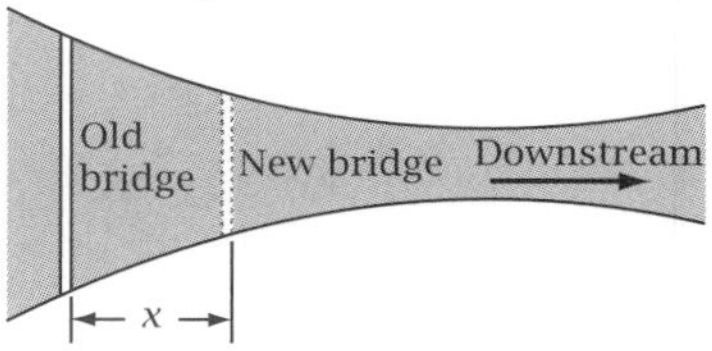

Figure 10-6c

   a. The Structural Department specifies that the bridge can be built in water as much as 130 ft deep, but that it can be no more than 310 ft long. The City Traffic Department specifies that the bridge must be at least 1 mi downstream from the present bridge. What is the domain of $x$ ?

   b. What are the shortest and longest lengths the bridge could be?

   c. The cost of building the bridge is proportional to the product of the length of the bridge and the depth of the water. Where should the bridge be built to minimize the cost? Justify your answer.

   d. Is the shortest bridge also the cheapest bridge? Explain.

# 10-7 Vector Functions for Motion in a Plane

Until now you have considered velocity and acceleration of an object moving back and forth in a line. The displacement, $x$, from some fixed point depends on time, $t$.

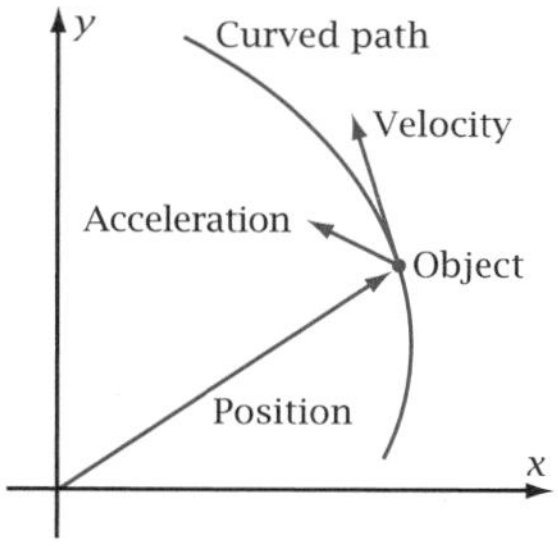


Figure 10-7a

In this section you will consider objects moving along a path in a plane. Both $x$ and $y$ will depend on $t$. For such motion the velocity and acceleration may act at an angle to each other. Therefore, it is convenient to use vectors to represent the objects' position, velocity, and acceleration.

Figure 10-7a shows the path a moving object might take in a plane. Its **velocity vector** points in the direction of motion and has magnitude (length) equal to the speed of the object. Its **acceleration vector**, acting at an angle to the path, changes both the object's speed and direction, thus pulling it into a curved path. The position of the object can be represented by a **position vector**, which tells the direction and distance from the origin to the object at any given time, $t$.

Parametric equations can be used to write the position vector as a function of time. The resulting **vector function** can be differentiated to find velocity and acceleration vectors.

**OBJECTIVE**

Given the equation of a vector function for the position of a moving object, find the first and second derivatives of position with respect to time, and interpret the way these vectors influence the motion of the object.

### Background: Vectors

A **vector quantity** is a quantity that has both magnitude and direction. Quantities that have only magnitude are called **scalar quantities**. Volume, mass, time, distance (not displacement!), and money are scalar quantities. They can be represented by points on a "scale" such as a number line. (The word "scalar" comes from the Latin *scalaris*, meaning "like a ladder.")

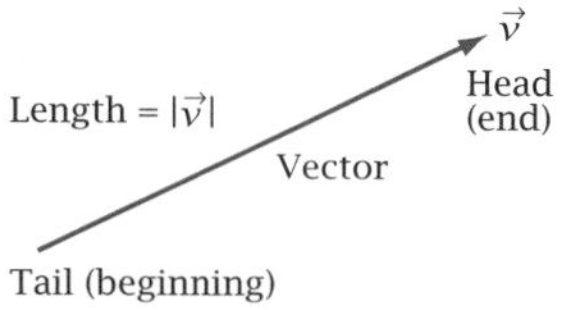


Figure 10-7b

Vector quantities can be represented mathematically by directed line segments, called simply **vectors**. An overhead arrow such as $\vec{v}$ denotes a variable used for a vector (Figure 10-7b). The length of the line segment represents the **magnitude** of the vector quantity, also called its **absolute value** or its **norm**. The direction the segment points represents the direction in which the vector quantity acts.

Two vectors are **equal** if and only if they have the same magnitude and the same direction (Figure 10-7c, left). You are free to move vectors around from place to place, as long as you keep them pointing the same way and don't change their lengths. The **opposite** of a vector, written $-\vec{v}$, is a vector of the same magnitude as $\vec{v}$ but pointing in the opposite direction (Figure 10-7c, middle). The **zero vector** is a vector of magnitude zero. It can be pointing in any direction!

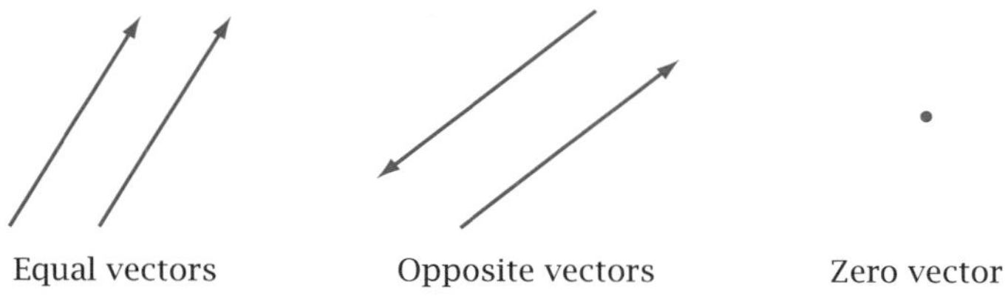


Figure 10-7c

Vectors are **added** by moving one of them so that its tail is at the head of the other (Figure 10-7d). The sum is the vector from the beginning of the first vector to the end of the second. Vectors are **subtracted** by adding the opposite of the second vector to the first one.

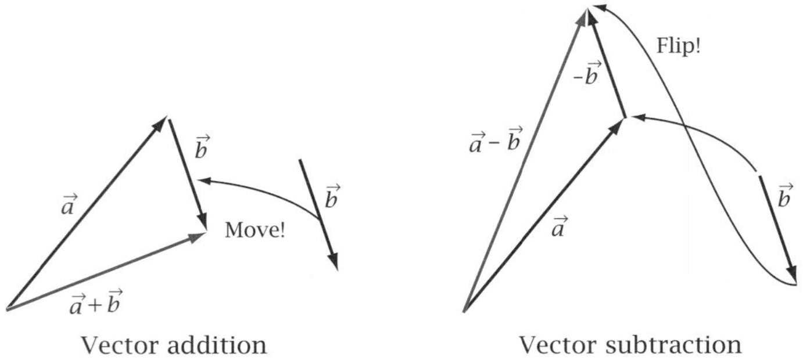


Figure 10-7d

Vectors are most easily worked with in a coordinate system (Figure 10-7e). Any vector $\vec{v}$ is a sum of a vector in the $x$-direction and one in the $y$-direction (called **components** of the vector). If $\vec{i}$ and $\vec{j}$ are **unit vectors** in the $x$- and $y$-directions, respectively, then

$$\vec{v} = x\vec{i} + y\vec{j}.$$

The **dot product** (*inner* product or *scalar* product) of two vectors is the number you get by placing the vectors tail-to-tail (Figure 10-7f), then multiplying their magnitudes and the cosine of the angle between the vectors; that is,

$$\vec{v}_1 \cdot \vec{v}_2 = |\vec{v}_1||\vec{v}_2|\cos\theta.$$

In Problem 14 of Problem Set 10-7, you will show that the dot product is also equal to

$$\vec{v}_1 \cdot \vec{v}_2 = x_1x_2 + y_1y_2,$$

where $\vec{v}_1 = x_1\vec{i} + y_1\vec{j}$ and $\vec{v}_2 = x_2\vec{i} + y_2\vec{j}$. The dot product is useful for finding the length of a "shadow" that one vector would cast on another. This **scalar projection**, $P$, of $\vec{v}_1$ on $\vec{v}_2$ is given by

$$P = |\vec{v}_1|\cos\theta,$$

as shown in Figure 10-7g. Multiplying by a clever form of 1 makes a dot product appear on the right-hand side of the equation.

$$P = \frac{|\vec{v}_1||\vec{v}_2|\cos\theta}{|\vec{v}_2|} = \frac{\vec{v}_1 \cdot \vec{v}_2}{|\vec{v}_2|}$$

The **vector projection** of $\vec{v}_1$ on $\vec{v}_2$ is a vector in the direction of $\vec{v}_2$, with magnitude $P$.

### *Derivatives of a Position Vector Function—Velocity and Acceleration*

The derivative of a scalar-valued function is the limit of $\Delta y/\Delta x$ as $\Delta x$ approaches zero. Similarly the derivative of a vector function, $\vec{r}$, is

$$\frac{d\vec{r}}{dt} = \lim_{\Delta t \to 0} \frac{\Delta \vec{r}}{\Delta t}.$$

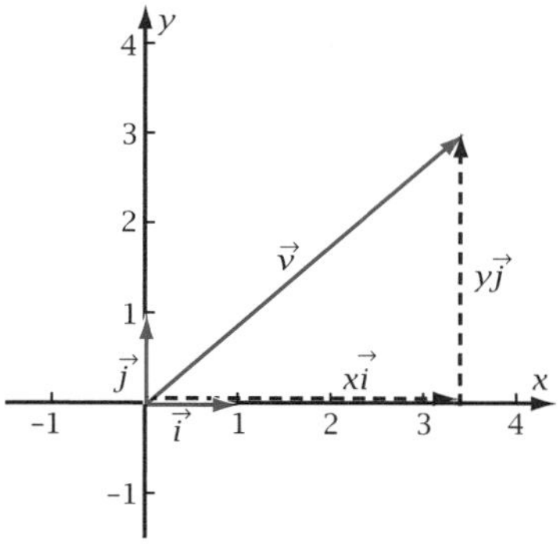


Figure 10-7e

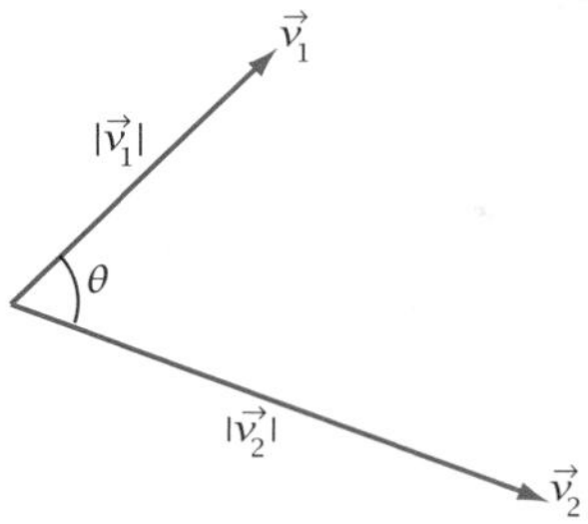


Figure 10-7f

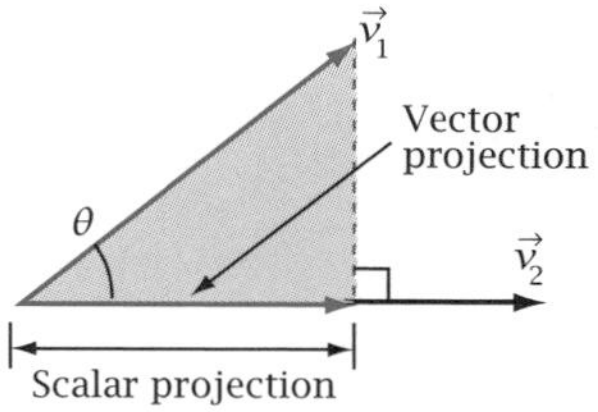


Figure 10-7g

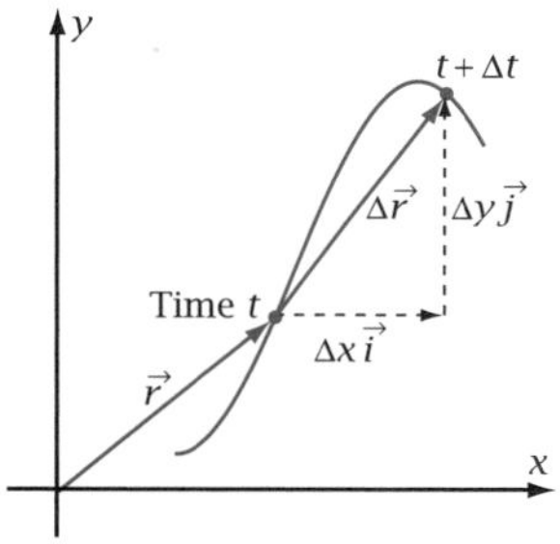


Figure 10-7h

Figure 10-7h shows vector $\vec{r}$ to the position of a moving object at time $t$. Vector $\Delta\vec{r}$ is the vector from this position to a new position at time $t + \Delta t$. Vector $\Delta\vec{r}$ can be resolved into horizontal and vertical components, $\Delta x\vec{i}$ and $\Delta y\vec{j}$. So,

$$\frac{d\vec{r}}{dt} = \lim_{\Delta t \to 0} \frac{\Delta x\vec{i} + \Delta y\vec{j}}{\Delta t}$$

$$= \lim_{\Delta t \to 0} \left(\frac{\Delta x}{\Delta t}\vec{i} + \frac{\Delta y}{\Delta t}\vec{j}\right)$$ $\Delta t$ distributes, and can be associated with $\Delta x$ and $\Delta y$.

$$= \lim_{\Delta t \to 0} \frac{\Delta x}{\Delta t}\vec{i} + \lim_{\Delta t \to 0} \frac{\Delta y}{\Delta t}\vec{j}$$ The limit of a sum property applies to vectors.

$$= \frac{dx}{dt}\vec{i} + \frac{dy}{dt}\vec{j}.$$ Definition of derivative. (The unit vectors are constant.)

Thus, if the components of a *position vector* are specified by functions of $t$, you can find $d\vec{r}/dt$ simply by differentiating each function and multiplying the answers by $\vec{i}$ and $\vec{j}$. As you will see in Example 1, the resulting vector is *tangent* to the path of the moving object. By the Pythagorean theorem, its length is

$$\left|\frac{d\vec{r}}{dt}\right| = \sqrt{\left(\frac{dx}{dt}\right)^2 + \left(\frac{dy}{dt}\right)^2} = \frac{\sqrt{dx^2 + dy^2}}{dt} = \frac{dL}{dt}.$$

But $dL/dt$ is the *speed* of the object along its curved path. Thus $d\vec{r}/dt$ is the *velocity vector* for the moving object. The *acceleration vector* is found by differentiating the velocity vector's components, the same way the velocity is found from the displacement.

### Properties: Velocity and Acceleration Vectors

If $\vec{r}(t) = x(t)\vec{i} + y(t)\vec{j}$ is the **position vector** for a moving object,
then $\vec{v}(t) = \vec{r}\,'(t) = x'(t)\vec{i} + y'(t)\vec{j}$ is the **velocity vector**,
and $\vec{a}(t) = \vec{v}\,'(t) = \vec{r}\,''(t) = x''(t)\vec{i} + y''(t)\vec{j}$ is the **acceleration vector**.
The **speed** of the moving object equals $|\vec{v}(t)| = \sqrt{(dx/dt)^2 + (dy/dt)^2}$.

**Example 1** Given the vector equation

$$\vec{r}(t) = (5\sin t)\vec{i} + (5\cos^2 t)\vec{j}$$

for the position, $\vec{r}(t)$, of a moving object, where distances are in feet and time $t$ is in seconds,

a. Plot the path of the object. Sketch the result. Then show the position vectors $\vec{r}(0)$, $\vec{r}(0.5)$, $\vec{r}(1)$, $\vec{r}(1.5)$, and $\vec{r}(2)$. Interpret the location of $\vec{r}(2)$.

b. Calculate the difference vector $\Delta\vec{r} = \vec{r}(1) - \vec{r}(0.5)$ by subtracting the respective components. Sketch $\Delta\vec{r}$ with its tail at the head of $\vec{r}(0.5)$. Where is the head of $\Delta\vec{r}$?

c. The **average velocity** vector of the object for interval $[0.5, t]$ is the difference quotient

$$\vec{v}_{\text{av}} = \frac{\vec{r}(t) - \vec{r}(0.5)}{t - 0.5}.$$

Find the average velocities for $[0.5, 1]$ and $[0.5, 0.6]$. Sketch these vectors starting at the head of the position vector $\vec{r}(0.5)$.

d. Find the (instantaneous) velocity vector, $\vec{v}(0.5)$. Plot it starting at the end of $\vec{r}(0.5)$, thus showing that it is tangent to the path. How do the average velocity vectors in part c relate to the $\vec{v}(0.5)$?

e. Find the speed of the object at time $t = 0.5$.

**Solutions**

a. Plot with your grapher in parametric mode

$$x = 5\sin t$$
$$y = 5\cos^2 t.$$

If you use the grid on option it will be easier to sketch the graph on dot paper (Figure 10-7i). The position vectors are as follows.

$$\vec{r}(0) = 0\vec{i} + \vec{j}$$
$$\vec{r}(0.5) = 2.39\ldots\vec{i} + 3.85\ldots\vec{j}$$
$$\vec{r}(1) = 4.20\ldots\vec{i} + 1.45\ldots\vec{j}$$
$$\vec{r}(1.5) = 4.98\ldots\vec{i} + 0.02\ldots\vec{j}$$
$$\vec{r}(2) = 4.54\ldots\vec{i} + 0.86\ldots\vec{j}$$

The heads of the vectors lie on the path. (That's why they are called position vectors!) They progress clockwise from the vertical. At time $t = 2$ the object has started back in the counterclockwise direction, as you can see by tracing.

b.
$$\Delta\vec{r} = \vec{r}(1) - \vec{r}(0.5)$$
$$= (5\sin 1 - 5\sin 0.5)\vec{i} + (5\cos^2 1 - 5\cos^2 0.5)\vec{j}$$
$$= 1.81\ldots\vec{i} - 2.39\ldots\vec{j}$$

Figure 10-7j shows this difference vector. If you start it at the head of $\vec{r}(0.5)$, then $\Delta\vec{r}$ ends at the head of $\vec{r}(1)$, as you can see by counting spaces on the dot paper.

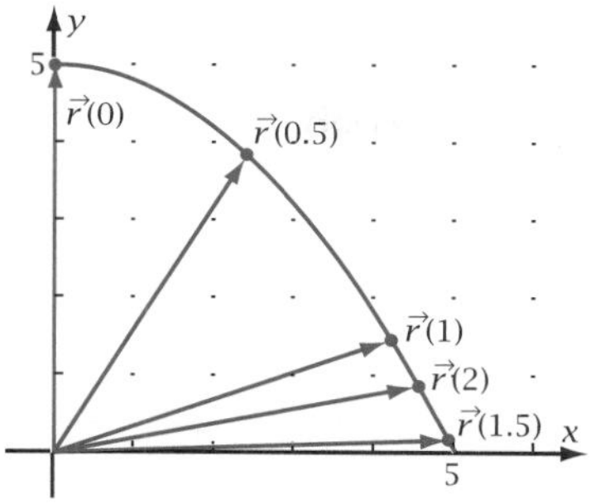


Figure 10-7i

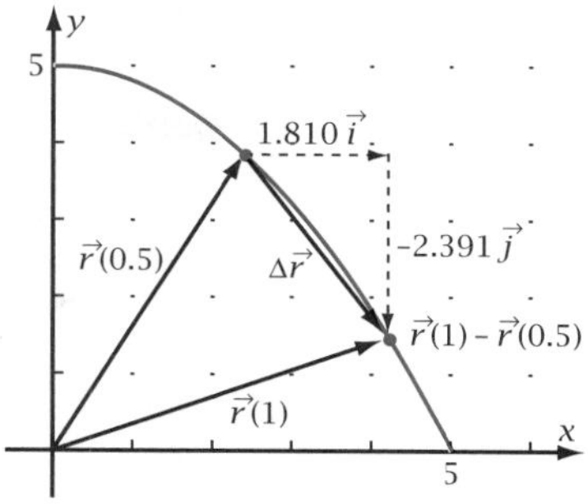


Figure 10-7j

c. $$t = 1 : \vec{v}_{av} = \frac{\vec{r}(1) - \vec{r}(0.5)}{1 - 0.5}$$

$$= \frac{1.81\ldots\vec{i} - 2.39\ldots\vec{j}}{0.5}$$

$$= 3.62\ldots\vec{i} - 4.78\ldots\vec{j}$$

$$t = 0.6 : \vec{v}_{av} = \frac{\vec{r}(0.6) - \vec{r}(0.5)}{0.6 - 0.5}$$

$$= \frac{0.426\ldots\vec{i} - 0.444\ldots\vec{j}}{0.1}$$

$$= 4.26\ldots\vec{i} - 4.44\ldots\vec{j}$$

Figure 10-7k shows these average vectors plotted on the diagram in Figure 10-7j. You plot them by counting spaces on the dot paper.

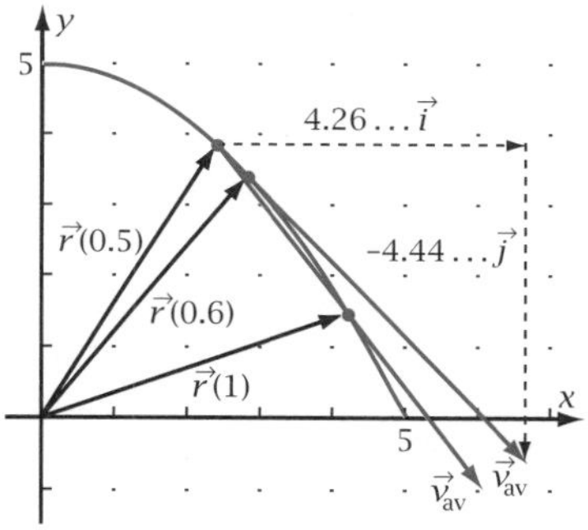


Figure 10-7k

d. $\vec{v}(t) = \vec{r}\,'(t) = (5\cos t)\vec{i} + (-10\cos t\sin t)\vec{j}$

$\therefore\ \vec{v}(0.5) = 4.38\ldots\vec{i} - 4.20\ldots\vec{j}$

Figure 10-7l shows that $\vec{v}$ is tangent to the path at the position $\vec{r}(0.5)$. The average velocity vectors approach $\vec{v}$ as a limit as $\Delta t$ approaches zero.

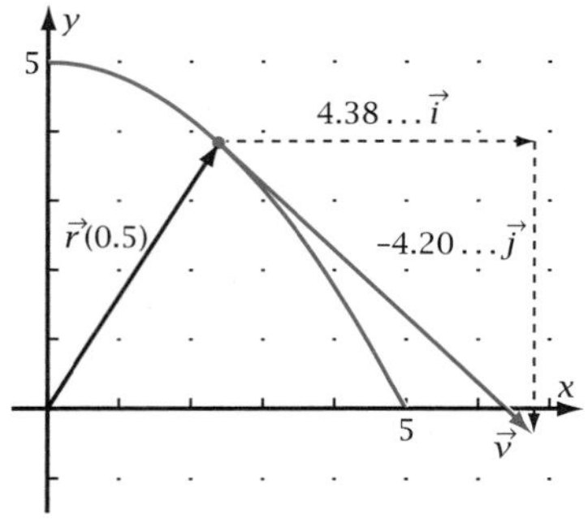


Figure 10-7l

e. $$\text{Speed} = |\vec{v}(0.5)| = \sqrt{(4.38\ldots)^2 + (-4.20\ldots)^2} = 6.079\ldots$$

Thus the object is traveling at about 6.1 ft/sec. ■

Example 2 shows how to find the acceleration vector and how it helps interpret the motion.

■ ***Example 2*** Given the vector equation

$$\vec{r}(t) = (5\sin t)\vec{i} + (5\cos^2 t)\vec{j}$$

for the position of a moving object, as in Example 1, do the following:

a. Write vector equations for the velocity vector, $\vec{v}(t)$, and the acceleration vector, $\vec{a}(t)$.

b. On a graph of the path of the object, sketch the position vector $\vec{r}(4)$ at time $t = 4$. From the head of $\vec{r}(4)$, sketch the vectors $\vec{v}(4)$ and $\vec{a}(4)$.

c. How fast is the object going at time $t = 4$?

d. Compute $\vec{a}_t(4)$, the *tangential component* of the acceleration (parallel to the path).

e. Is the object speeding up or slowing down at $t = 4$? How are you able to tell? At what rate is it speeding up or slowing down?

f. Compute $\vec{a}_n(4)$, the *normal component* of acceleration (perpendicular to the path). Toward which side of the path does $\vec{a}_n(4)$ point? What effect does this component have on the motion of the object?

**Solutions**

a. The velocity is found as in Example 1. The acceleration is found by differentiating the velocity vector.

$$\vec{v}(t) = \vec{r}\,'(t) = (5\cos t)\vec{i} + (-10\cos t\sin t)\vec{j}$$
$$= (5\cos t)\vec{i} + (-5\sin 2t)\vec{j}$$
$$\vec{a}(t) = \vec{v}\,'(t) = (-5\sin t)\vec{i} + (-10\cos 2t)\vec{j}$$

From trigonometry, $2\sin t\cos t = \sin 2t$.

b. Substituting 4 for $t$ gives

$$\vec{r}(4) = -3.78\ldots\vec{i} + 2.13\ldots\vec{j}$$
$$\vec{v}(4) = -3.26\ldots\vec{i} - 4.94\ldots\vec{j}$$
$$\vec{a}(4) = 3.78\ldots\vec{i} + 1.45\ldots\vec{j}$$

Figure 10-7m shows $\vec{v}(4)$ and $\vec{a}(4)$ drawn on a graph plotted as in Example 1. The vectors are drawn by counting spaces on the dot paper. Note that although $\vec{v}(4)$ is tangent to the path, the acceleration is at an angle to the path.

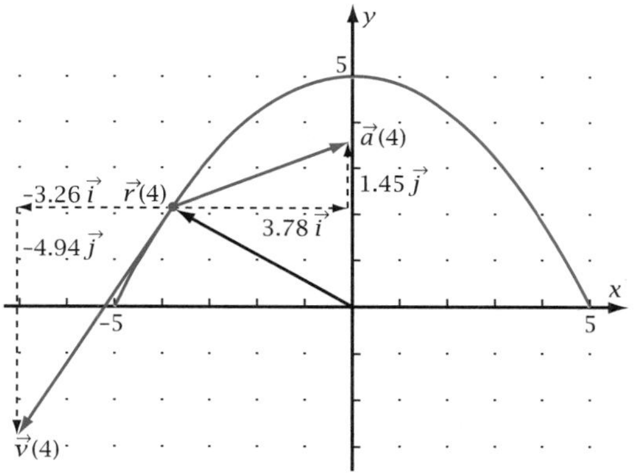


Figure 10-7m

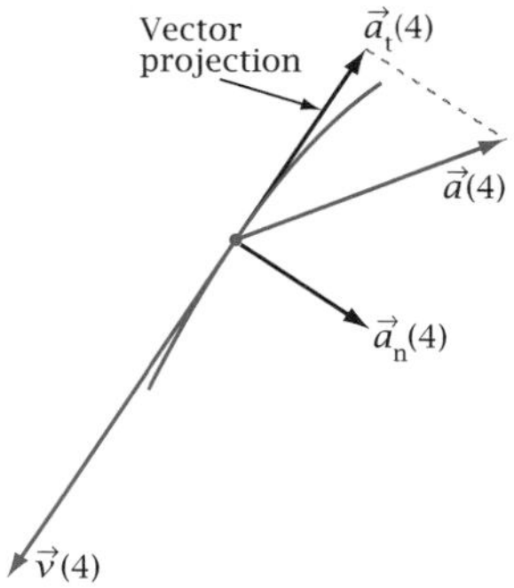


Figure 10-7n

c. Speed $= |\vec{v}(4)|$

$$= \sqrt{(5\cos 4)^2 + (-5\sin 8)^2}$$
$$= 5.928\ldots$$

Thus the object is going about 5.93 ft/sec.

d. The tangential acceleration, $\vec{a}_t(4)$, parallel to the path, is the **vector projection** of $\vec{a}(4)$ on $\vec{v}(4)$ (Figure 10-7n). First find the scalar projection, $P$.

$$P = \frac{\vec{a}(4)\cdot\vec{v}(4)}{|\vec{v}(4)|} = \frac{(-5\sin 4)(5\cos 4) + (-10\cos 8)(-5\sin 8)}{5.928\ldots} = -3.2998\ldots$$

To find a vector in the direction of $\vec{v}(4)$ with length 3.2998 ..., pointed the other way, multiply the scalar projection, −3.2998 ... by a unit vector in the direction of $\vec{v}(4)$.

$$\vec{a}_t(4) = P\frac{\vec{v}(4)}{|\vec{v}(4)|}$$

$$\vec{a}_t(4) = (-3.2998\ldots)\frac{(5\cos 4)\vec{i} + (-5\sin 8)\vec{j}}{5.928\ldots}$$

$$\vec{a}_t(4) = 1.818\ldots\vec{i} + 2.753\ldots\vec{j}$$

e. Since the tangential acceleration points in the direction opposite to $\vec{v}(4)$, the object is slowing down when $t = 4$. Both the obtuse angle between $\vec{v}(4)$ and $\vec{a}(4)$ (Figure 10-7n) and the negative value of P, the scalar projection of $\vec{a}(4)$ on $\vec{v}(4)$, reveal this fact. The rate at which the object is slowing equals the magnitude of $\vec{a}_t(4)$, namely, $|P|$, or 3.2998 .... So the object is slowing down at about 3.3 (ft/sec)/sec when $t = 4$.

f. As shown in Figure 10-7n, the normal acceleration, $\vec{a}_n(4)$, perpendicular to the path, equals the vector that, when added to $\vec{a}_t(4)$, gives $\vec{a}(4)$. Therefore,

$$\begin{aligned}\vec{a}_n(4) &= \vec{a}(4) - \vec{a}_t(4) = (3.78\ldots\vec{i} + 1.45\ldots\vec{j}) - (1.818\ldots\vec{i} + 2.753\ldots\vec{j})\\ &= 1.96\ldots\vec{i} - 1.29\ldots\vec{j}.\end{aligned}$$

The normal component of acceleration will always point toward the concave side of the graph, as shown in Figure 10-7n. It is responsible for pulling the object out of a straight-line path and into a curved path. ■

From Example 2, you can reach the following conclusions about acceleration vectors.

**Property: Components of the Acceleration Vector**

- The acceleration points toward the concave side of the path of the object.
- The scalar projection, $P$, of $\vec{a}$ on $\vec{v}$ tells the magnitude of the **tangential component** of acceleration, $\vec{a}_t$, which acts along the path.
- $|P|$ is equal to the **rate of change of speed** of the object.
- If $P > 0$, or the angle between $\vec{a}$ and $\vec{v}$ is acute, the object is speeding up.
- If $P < 0$, or the angle between $\vec{a}$ and $\vec{v}$ is obtuse, the object is slowing down.
- The **normal component** of acceleration, $\vec{a}_n$, changes the direction of motion. Since $\vec{a} = \vec{a}_t + \vec{a}_n$, the normal component can be found by $\vec{a}_n = \vec{a} - \vec{a}_t$.

In Example 3, you will find the distance traveled by an object moving in a curved path .

**Example 3** For the object in Example 1, $\vec{r}(t) = (5\sin t)\vec{i} + (5\cos^2 t)\vec{j}$. Find the distance traveled by the object in the time interval [0, 4].

**Solution** Recognize that a vector equation is the same as two parametric equations. The distance the object travels thus equals the arc length of a parametric curve (Section 8-7).

$$dL = \sqrt{x'(t)^2 + y'(t)^2}\,dt = \sqrt{(5\cos t)^2 + (-10\cos t \sin t)^2}\,dt$$

$$L = \int_0^4 \sqrt{(25 + 100\sin^2 t)\cos^2 t}\,dt$$

$$= 19.7245\ldots \approx 19.72 \text{ ft} \qquad \text{By numerical integration}$$

Check: A circle of radius 5 approximates the curve. A 4-radian arc of the circle has length $(4/2\pi)(2\pi \cdot 5) = 20$, which compares well with 19.72. ■

# Problem Set 10-7

### *Do These Quickly*

The following problems are intended to refresh your skills. You should be able to do all ten problems in less than five minutes.

**Q1.** Integrate: $\int x \sin x\, dx$

**Q2.** Differentiate: $x^2 e^{3x}$

**Q3.** Integrate: $\int 2^x\, dx$

**Q4.** Evaluate: $\dfrac{5^{2001}}{5^{1998}}$

**Q5.** Find $\int x^3\, dx$ if the integral equals 11 when $x = 2$.

**Q6.** Find $dy/dx$ if $x = e^{3t}$ and $y = \tan 6t$.

**Q7.** The function in Problem Q6 is called a(n) —?— function.

**Q8.** Integrate: $\int \ln x\, dx$

**Q9.** In polar coordinates, the graph of $r = \theta$ is a(n) —?—.

**Q10.** Simplify: $e^{2\ln x}$

1. *Parabolic Path Problem I:* An object moves along the parabolic path (Figure 10-7o)

$$\vec{r}(t) = (10\sin 0.6t)\vec{i} + (4\cos 1.2t)\vec{j},$$

where distance is in feet and time is in seconds.

a. Find equations for $\vec{v}(t)$ and $\vec{a}(t)$.

b. Calculate $\vec{r}(0.5)$, $\vec{v}(0.5)$, and $\vec{a}(0.5)$. On a photocopy of Figure 10-7o, plot $\vec{r}$ as a position vector, and plot $\vec{v}$ and $\vec{a}$ with their tails at the head of $\vec{r}$. Explain why the three vectors are reasonable.

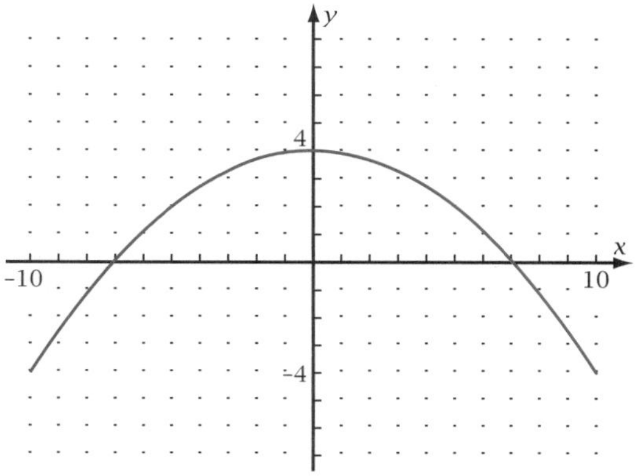

Figure 10-7o

c. Based on the graphs of the vectors in 1b, does the object seem to be speeding up or slowing down at time $t = 0.5$ sec? How do you tell?

d. Verify your answer to 1c by finding the tangential and normal components of $\vec{a}(0.5)$. Sketch these components on the diagram in 1b starting at the tail of $\vec{a}$.

e. At what rate is the object speeding up or slowing down at $t = 0.5$?

f. Calculate $\vec{r}(7)$, $\vec{v}(7)$, and $\vec{a}(7)$. Sketch these vectors on the diagram of 1b. At time $t = 7$, does the object seem to be speeding up or slowing down?

g. Show that at time $t = 0$ the acceleration vector is perpendicular to the path. How do you interpret this fact in terms of motion of the object at $t = 0$?

2. *Parabolic Path Problem II:* An object moves along the parabolic path (Figure 10-7p),

$$\vec{r}(t) = (8\cos 0.8t)\vec{i} + (6\sin 0.4t)\vec{j},$$

where distance is in feet and time is in seconds.

a. Find equations for $\vec{v}(t)$ and $\vec{a}(t)$.

b. Calculate $\vec{r}(1)$, $\vec{v}(1)$, and $\vec{a}(1)$. On a photocopy of Figure 10-7p, plot $\vec{r}$ as a position vector, and plot $\vec{v}$ and $\vec{a}$ with their tails at the head of $\vec{r}$. Explain why the three vectors are reasonable.

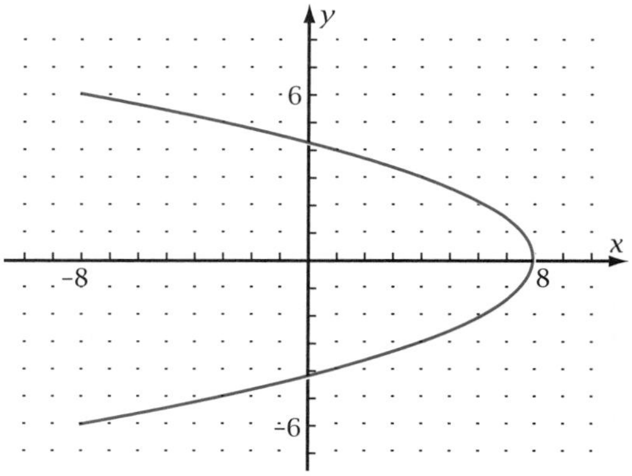

Figure 10-7p

c. Based on the graphs of the vectors in 2b, does the object seem to be speeding up or slowing down at time $t = 1$ sec? How do you tell?

d. Verify your answer to 2c by finding the tangential and normal components of $\vec{a}(1)$. Sketch these components on the diagram in 2b starting at the tail of $\vec{a}$.

e. At what rate is the object speeding up or slowing down at $t = 1$?

f. Calculate $\vec{r}(10.5)$, $\vec{v}(10.5)$, and $\vec{a}(10.5)$. Sketch these vectors on the diagram of 2b. At time $t = 10.5$, does the object seem to be speeding up or slowing down?

g. What is the first positive value of $t$ at which the object is stopped? What is the acceleration vector at that time? Plot this vector on the diagram in 2b. Surprising?

3. *Elliptical Path Problem:* An object moves along the elliptical path (Figure 10-7q),

$$\vec{r}(t) = (10\cos \tfrac{\pi}{6}t)\vec{i} + (6\sin \tfrac{\pi}{6}t)\vec{j},$$

where $t$ is in seconds and distances are in feet.

a. On your grapher, plot the path followed by the heads of the velocity vectors if their tails are placed at the heads of the respective position vectors. You can use parametric mode to plot $\vec{r} + \vec{v}$. Sketch the result on a photocopy of Figure 10-7q.

b. Sketch the velocity vectors for each integer value of $t$ from 0 through 12. You may find their beginnings by tracing the $\vec{r}$ vector and their ends by tracing $\vec{r} + \vec{v}$.

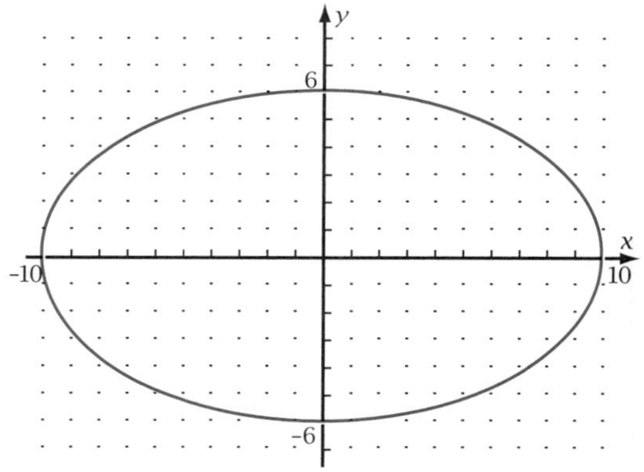

Figure 10-7q

c. Prove that the heads of the velocity vectors in 3b lie along an ellipse.

d. On your grapher, plot the path followed by the heads of the acceleration vectors when their tails are placed at the heads of the respective position vectors. Sketch the result on your diagram from 3a.

e. Sketch the acceleration vectors as you did for the velocity vectors in 3b. What seems to be true about the direction of each of these acceleration vectors?

4. *Spiral Path Problem:* An object moves on the spiral path (Figure 10-7r),

$$\vec{r}(t) = (0.5t\cos t)\vec{i} + (0.5t\sin t)\vec{j},$$

where distance is in miles and time is in hours.

a. Find vector equations for $\vec{v}(t)$ and $\vec{a}(t)$.

b. Find the position, velocity, and acceleration at $t = 8.5$ and at $t = 12$. On a photocopy of Figure 10-7r, plot $\vec{r}(8.5)$ and $\vec{r}(12)$, thus showing that these vectors really do terminate on the path.

c. Plot $\vec{v}(8.5)$ and $\vec{a}(8.5)$ starting at the head of $\vec{r}(8.5)$. Do the same for $\vec{v}(12)$ and $\vec{a}(12)$. Explain why these velocity vectors have the proper relationships to the path.

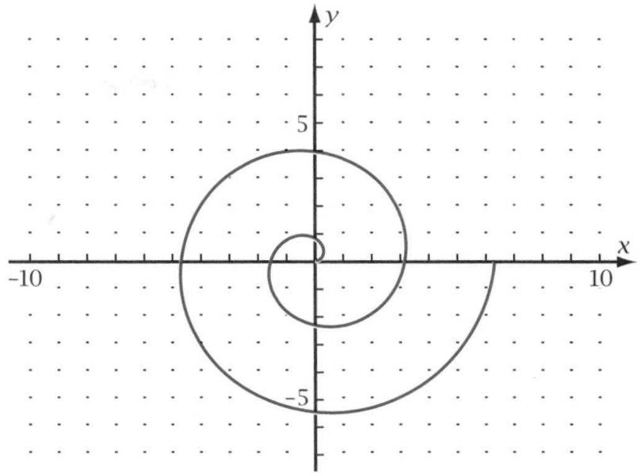

Figure 10-7r

d. At $t = 8.5$ and at $t = 12$, is the object speeding up or slowing down? How do you tell?

e. Find the tangential and normal components of the acceleration vector at $t = 12$. Show these components on the diagram from 4b.

f. How fast is the object going at $t = 12$ hr? At what rate is the speed changing then?

g. On your grapher plot the path followed by the heads of the acceleration vectors when they are placed with their tails at the heads of the respective position vectors. What geometrical figure does the path appear to be? Prove algebraically that your conjecture is correct.

5. *Parabolic Path Problem III:* An object moves along the parabola $y = x^2$. At various times, $t$, the object is at various points $(x, y)$, where $x$ and $y$ are in centimeters and $t$ is in seconds.

a. Write the position vector $\vec{r}(x)$ as a function of $x$ alone (and the two unit vectors $\vec{i}$ and $\vec{j}$, of course!). Then find the velocity vector $\vec{v}(x)$ as a function of $x$ and $dx/dt$.

b. Assume that the object moves in such a way that $x$ decreases at a constant rate of 3 cm/sec. Find $\vec{v}(2)$. How fast is the object moving when $x = 2$?

c. Sketch the graph of the parabola and draw $\vec{r}(2)$ and $\vec{v}(2)$ at the point (2, 4). Explain why the graph of $\vec{v}(2)$ is reasonable.

d. Find the acceleration vector, $\vec{a}(x)$, and evaluate $\vec{a}(2)$. Sketch $\vec{a}(2)$ on your graph.

e. Find the tangential and normal components of acceleration at $x = 2$. Show these components on your graph. Based on the graphs, why are your answers reasonable?

f. When $x = 2$, is the object speeding up or slowing down? Justify your answer.

g. The object changes its motion and goes in such a way that its speed along its curved path is 5 units per minute. Write an expression in terms of $x$ for $dL$, the differential of arc length along the curve. Find $dx/dt$ when $x = 2$.

6. *Velocity Vector Limit Problem:* An object moves along one petal of the four-leafed rose shown in Figure 10-7s.

$$\vec{r} = (12 \sin t \cos 0.5t)\vec{i} + (12 \sin t \sin 0.5t)\vec{j}$$

On a photocopy of this diagram, plot $\vec{r}(1)$. From the end of $\vec{r}(1)$, plot the average velocity difference quotient vectors,

$$\vec{q}(t) = \frac{\vec{r}(t) - \vec{r}(1)}{t - 1}$$

for $t = 2$, $t = 1.5$, and $t = 1.1$. Then plot the velocity vector, $\vec{v}(1)$. How does the velocity vector relate to the path of the object and to the average velocity vectors?

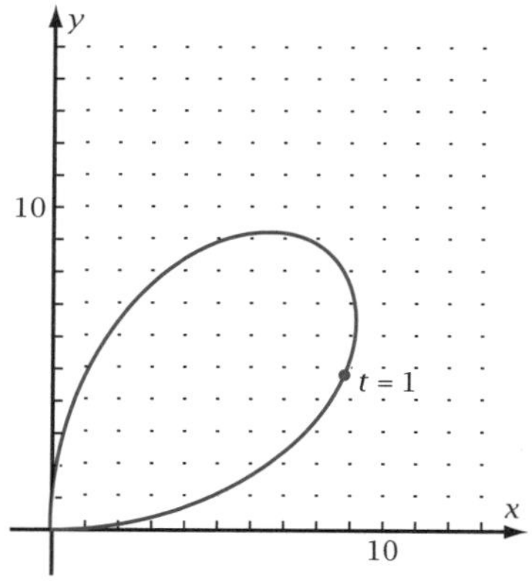


Figure 10-7s

7. Find the distance traveled by the object in Problem 1 from time $t = 0$ to $t = 2$.

8. Find the distance traveled by the object in Problem 3 in one complete cycle.

9. *Baseball Problem:* Sol Teen pitches a baseball. As it leaves his hand, it moves horizontally toward home plate at 130 ft/sec (about 90 mi/hr), so its velocity vector at time $t = 0$ sec is

$$\vec{v}(0) = -130\vec{i} + 0\vec{j}.$$

The minus sign is used since the distance from the plate is decreasing. As the ball moves, it drops vertically due to the acceleration of gravity. The vertical acceleration is 32 (ft/sec)/sec. Assuming that there is no loss of speed due to air resistance, its acceleration vector is

$$\vec{a}(t) = 0\vec{i} - 32\vec{j}.$$

a. Write an equation for $\vec{v}(t)$, the velocity as a function of time.

b. When Sol releases the ball at time $t = 0$ sec, it is at $y = 8$ ft above the playing field and $x = 60.5$ ft from the plate. Write the position vector, $\vec{r}(t) = x(t)\vec{i} + y(t)\vec{j}$.

c. Sol's sister, Phyllis, stands at the plate ready to hit the ball. How long does it take the ball to reach the plate, at $x = 0$? As it passes over the plate, will it be in Phyllis's strike zone, between $y = 1.5$ ft and $y = 4.5$ ft above the plate? Show how you reach your conclusion.

d. Sol pitches another time. Phyllis hits the ball, making it leave a point 3 ft above the plate at an angle of 15° to the horizontal, going at a speed of 200 ft/sec. What are the initial horizontal and vertical velocities? Assuming that the horizontal velocity stays constant and the vertical velocity is affected by gravity as above, write the position vector $\vec{r}(t)$ as a function of the number of seconds since she hit the ball.

e. Will Phyllis make a home run with the hit in 9d? The fence for which it is heading is 400 ft from the plate, and 10 ft high. You may do this by plotting the position graph in parametric mode and seeing where the ball is when $x = 400$.

10. *Sinusoidal Path Problem:* An object moves along the graph of $y = \sin x$ (Figure 10-7t), where $x$ and $y$ are in meters and $t$ is minutes. Its $x$-acceleration is 3 m/min$^2$, a constant. At time $t = 0$, the object is at the point (0, 0) and has velocity equal to the zero vector.

    a. Find $\vec{r}(t)$, the position vector as a function of time.

    b. How fast is the object moving when it is at the point $(6, \sin 6)$?

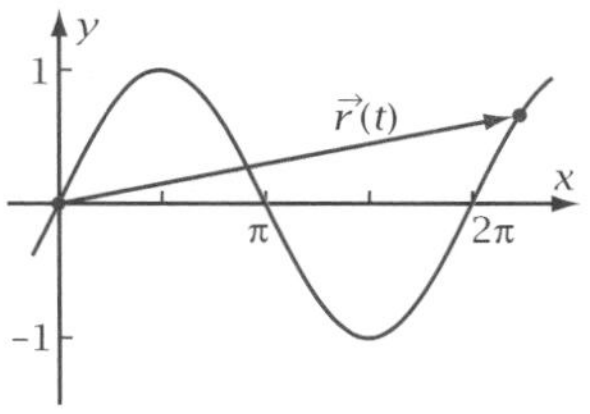


Figure 10-7t

11. *Figure Skating Problem:* One figure roller skaters do in competition has a large loop and a small loop (Figure 10-7u). Specifications by the Roller Skating Rink Operations Association of America require the outer loop to be 240 cm from the origin where the loops cross and the inner loop to be 60 cm from the origin. The figure closely resembles a *limaçon* with polar equation

$$d = a + b\cos t,$$

where $d$ is the directed distance from the origin at angle $t$ radians and $a$ and $b$ are constants.

    a. At $t = 0$, $d = 240$. At $t = \pi$, $d = -60$ so that the point is on the positive $x$-axis. Find the particular equation of this limaçon.

    b. Suppose that Annie Lips skates with an angular velocity of 1 rad/sec. So $t$ is also her time in seconds, and her position vector is

$$\vec{r}(t) = (d\cos t)\vec{i} + (d\sin t)\vec{j},$$

    where $d$ is given by the equation in 11a. Find Annie's velocity vector at time $t = 1$. How fast is she going at that time?

    c. Find Annie's acceleration vector at $t = 1$. Find the tangential and normal components of the acceleration. Is she speeding up or slowing down at this time? At what rate?

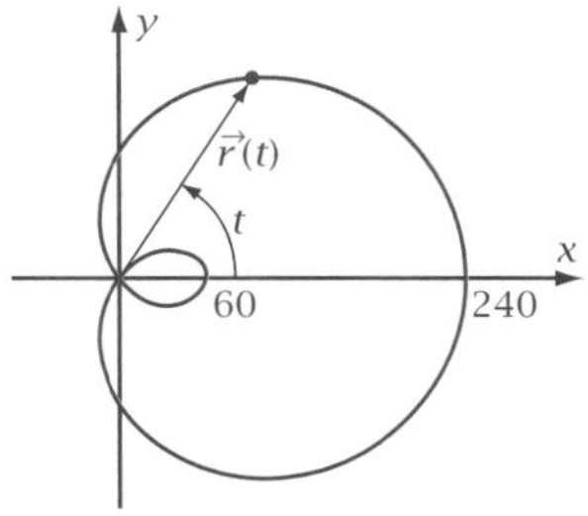


Figure 10-7u

12. *River Bend Problem:* A river meanders slowly across the plains (Figure 10-7v). A log floating on the river has position vector

$$\vec{r}(t) = (0.5t + \sin t)\vec{i} + (4\cos 0.5t)\vec{j},$$

where distances are in miles and $t$ is in hours.

    a. When $t = 14$, what are the log's velocity and acceleration vectors? How fast is it going? What are its tangential and normal acceleration vectors? Is it speeding up or slowing down? At what rate?

    b. How far does the log move along its curved path from $t = 0$ to $t = 14$? What is its average speed for this time interval?

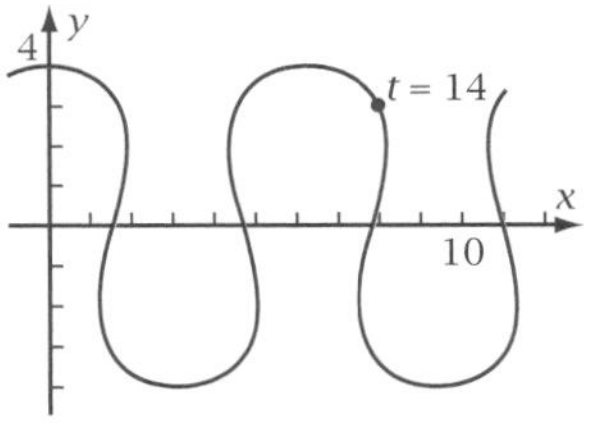


Figure 10-7v

13. *Roller Coaster Problem:* Assume that a roller coaster track is a prolate cycloid (Figure 10-7w) and that the position of a car on the track (in feet) at time $t$ seconds is

$$\vec{r}(t) = (5t - 12\sin t)\vec{i} + (15 + 12\cos t)\vec{j}.$$

a. Write the velocity and acceleration vectors as functions of $t$.

b. Find the velocity and acceleration vectors at the point shown, where $t = 2.5$ sec. Plot these vectors on a photocopy of Figure 10-7w, starting at the point on the graph.

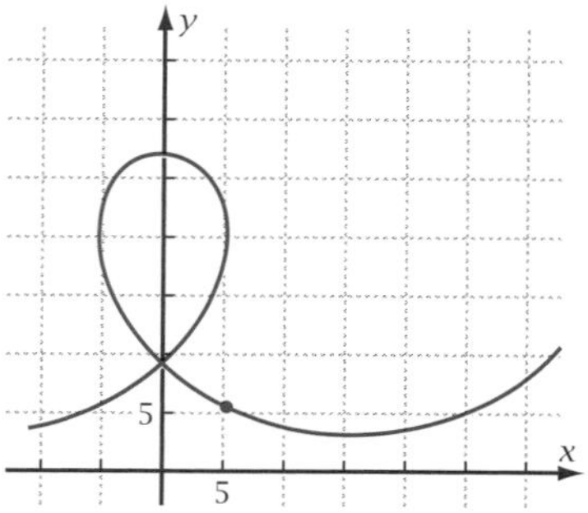


Figure 10-7w

c. Find the tangential and normal components of the acceleration vector at $t = 2.5$ sec.

d. Analyze the motion of the roller coaster at $t = 2.5$ sec. For instance, how can you tell that the velocity vector is reasonable? Is the normal component of acceleration reasonable? How fast is the roller coaster going? Is it speeding up or slowing down?

e. Show that the acceleration vector is straight down when the roller coaster is at a high point, and straight up when it is at a low point.

f. How long is the track from one high point to the next?

14. *Dot Product Problem:* The dot product of two vectors is defined to be

$$\vec{v}_1 \cdot \vec{v}_2 = |\vec{v}_1||\vec{v}_2|\cos\theta.$$

If $\vec{v}_1 = x_1\vec{i} + y_1\vec{j}$ and $\vec{v}_2 = x_2\vec{i} + y_2\vec{j}$, show as in Figure 10-7x that

$$\vec{v}_1 \cdot \vec{v}_2 = x_1x_2 + y_1y_2.$$

Assume the distributive property, $\vec{a} \cdot (\vec{b} + \vec{c}) = \vec{a} \cdot \vec{b} + \vec{a} \cdot \vec{c}$. You will need to figure out what $\vec{i} \cdot \vec{i}$, $\vec{j} \cdot \vec{j}$, and $\vec{i} \cdot \vec{j}$ equal, based on the angles between these unit vectors.

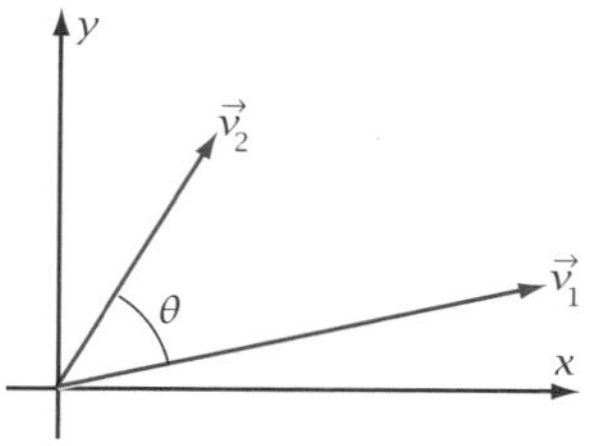


Figure 10-7x

15. *Three-Dimensional Vector Problem:* A three-dimensional vector (Figure 10-7y) can be resolved into three mutually perpendicular components. If $\vec{i}$, $\vec{j}$, and $\vec{k}$ are unit vectors in the $x$-, $y$-, and $z$-directions, respectively, then position vector $\vec{r}$ from the origin to the point $(x, y, z)$ can be written

$$\vec{r} = x\vec{i} + y\vec{j} + z\vec{k}.$$

Suppose that a moving object's position is given by the vector function

$$\vec{r}(t) = (10\sin 0.8t)\vec{i} + (10\cos 0.6t)\vec{j} + (6t^{0.5})\vec{k}.$$

Find the velocity and acceleration vectors at time $t = 1$. At that time, is the object speeding up or slowing down? Justify your answer.

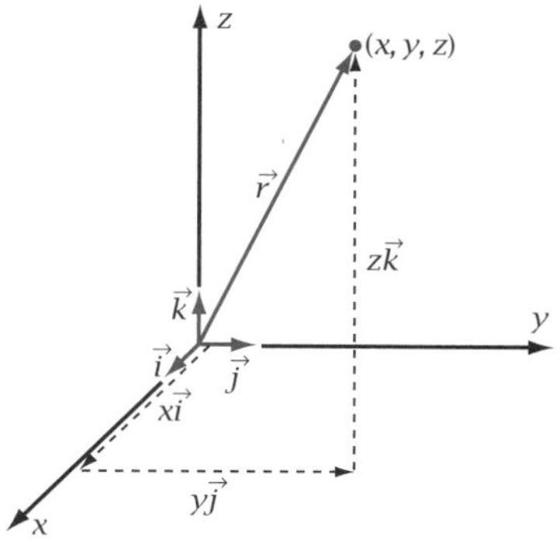


Figure 10-7y

16. *Curvature Project:* Figure 10-7z shows an object moving with velocity $\vec{v}$ along a path. The velocity makes an angle $\phi$ (Greek letter "phi") with the positive $x$-axis. The curvature of the path is defined to be the rate of change of $\phi$ with respect to distance, $s$, along the path. That is, $\kappa$ (lower case Greek letter "kappa") is given by

$$\kappa = d\phi/ds.$$

a. Explain why $d\phi/ds = (d\phi/dt)(dt/ds)$.

b. Explain why $\tan\phi = dy/dx$, which equals $(dy/dt)/(dx/dt)$.

c. Let $x'$ and $x''$ be the first and second derivatives of $x$ with respect to $t$, and similarly for $y$. Show that the following is true.

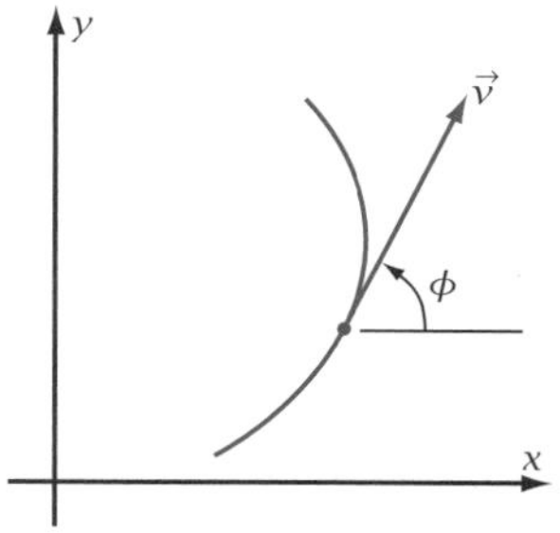


Figure 10-7z

**Technique: Calculation of Curvature**

$$\frac{d\phi}{ds} = \frac{x'y'' - x''y'}{|\vec{v}|^3}$$

where the derivatives are taken with respect to $t$.

d. Figure 10-7aa shows the ellipse

$$x = 5\cos t$$
$$y = 3\sin t.$$

Show that the maximum curvature is at each end of the major axis.

e. Show that the curvature of a circle,

$$x = r\cos t$$
$$y = r\sin t$$

is constant.

f. Show that the curvature of this line is zero.

$$x = 5\cos^2 t$$
$$y = 3\sin^2 t$$

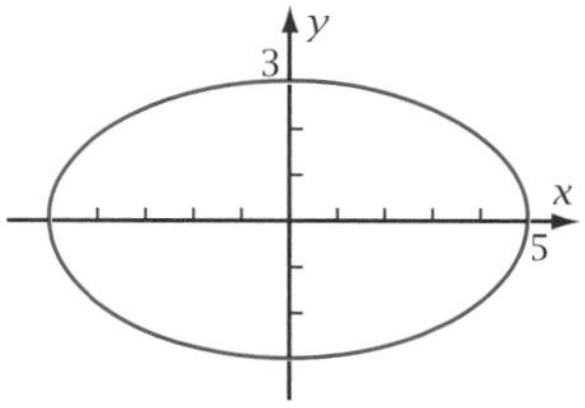


Figure 10-7aa

g. The **radius of curvature** is defined to be the reciprocal of the curvature. Find the radius of curvature of the ellipse in 15d at the right-most vertex, (5, 0).

h. On your grapher, plot the ellipse in Figure 10-7aa. Then plot a circle tangent to the ellipse at (5, 0), on the concave side of the ellipse, with radius equal to the radius of curvature. Sketch the result. This circle is called the **osculating circle** ("kissing" circle). Appropriately, it is the circle that best fits the curve at the point of tangency.

# 10-8 Chapter Review and Test

In this chapter you have studied applications of calculus to motion. You distinguished between distance traveled by a moving object and displacement from its starting point. You made precise the concept of average velocity and extended it to other average values. Next, you learned how to calculate the rate of change of a variable quantity from a related rate. You extended your study of maximum and minimum values to problems involving motion, and then to other similar problems. Finally, you applied the concepts to objects moving in a plane, using vectors as a tool.

The Review Problems are numbered according to the sections of this chapter. The Concepts Problems allow you to apply your knowledge to new situations. The Chapter Test is typical of a classroom test.

## Review Problems

R0. Update your journal with the things you have learned since the last entry. You should include such things as those listed here.

- The one most important thing you have learned in studying Chapter 10
- Which boxes you have been working on in the "define, understand, do, apply" table.
- The distinction among displacement, velocity, and acceleration
- How to find average rates
- How to use rates of change to find extreme values of functions
- How to find a rate that is related to another rate
- How to analyze motion of objects moving in two dimensions
- Any techniques or ideas about calculus that are still unclear

R1. *Popeye and Olive Problem:* Olive Oyl is on a conveyor belt moving 3 ft/sec toward the sawmill. At time $t = 0$, Popeye rescues her and starts running the other direction along the conveyor belt. His velocity with respect to the ground, $v$ ft/sec, is given by

$$v = \sqrt{t} - 3.$$

When does Popeye's velocity become positive? How far have he and Olive moved toward the sawmill at this time? What is their net displacement from the starting point at $t = 25$? What total distance did they go from $t = 0$ to $t = 25$?

R2. a. The velocity of a moving object is given by $v(t) = 2^t - 8$ cm/min.
   i. Graph velocity versus time. Sketch the result.
   ii. Find the net displacement between $t = 1$ and $t = 4$.
   iii. Find the total distance traveled between $t = 1$ and $t = 4$.

b. *Acceleration Data Problem:* An object initially going 30 ft/sec has the following accelerations in (feet per second) per second measured at 5-sec intervals.

| time | acceleration |
|---|---|
| 0 | 2 |
| 5 | 8 |
| 10 | 1 |
| 15 | 0 |
| 20 | −10 |
| 25 | −20 |

Find the estimated velocities at the ends of the time intervals. For each entry in the table, tell whether the object was speeding up, slowing down, or neither at that instant.

R3. a. *Average Velocity Problem:* An object moves with velocity $v(t) = \sin(\pi t/6)$. Find the average velocity on the time interval:
   i. $[0, 3]$
   ii. $[3, 9]$
   iii. $[0, 12]$

b. *Average Value Problem:* For the function $f(x) = 6x^2 - x^3$,
   i. Find the average value of $f(x)$ on the interval between the two $x$-intercepts.
   ii. Sketch a graph showing the geometrical significance of this average value.
   iii. Show that the average value is not equal to the average of the two values of $f(x)$ at the end points of the interval.

R4. *Rover's Tablecloth Problem:* Rover grabs the tablecloth and starts backing away at 20 cm/sec. A glass near the other end of the tablecloth (Figure 10-8a) moves toward the edge and finally falls off. The table is 80 cm high, Rover's mouth is 10 cm above the floor, and 200 cm of tablecloth separate Rover's mouth from the glass. At the instant the glass reached the table's edge, was it going faster or slower than Rovers 20 cm/sec? By how much?

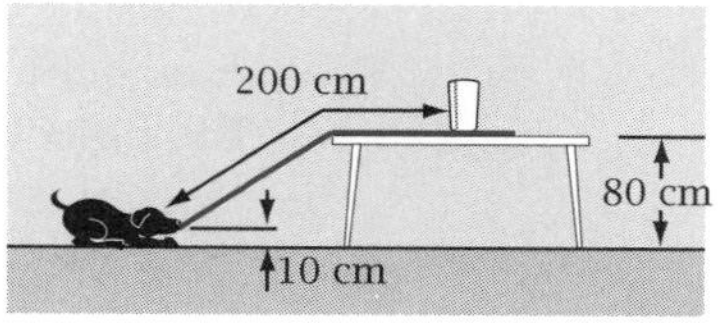

Figure 10-8a

R5. a. *Campus Cut-Across Problem:* Juana Cross makes daily trips from the Math Building to the English Building. She has three possible routes (Figure 10-8b):
   - Along sidewalk all the way
   - Straight across the grass
   - Angle across to the other sidewalk

   She figures her speed is 6.2 ft/sec on the sidewalk and 5.7 ft/sec across the grass. Which route takes the least time? Explain.

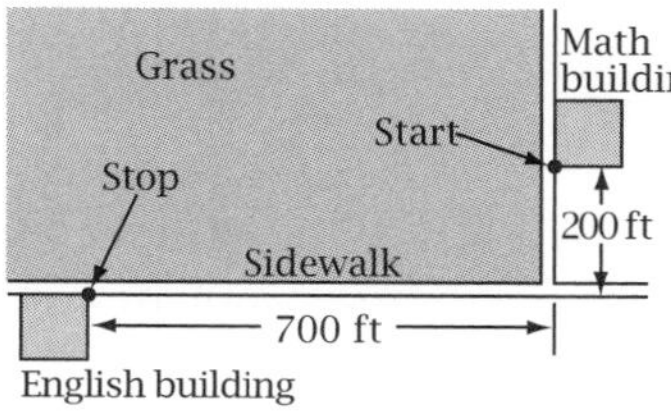

Figure 10-8b

b. *Resort Island Causeway Problem:* Moe Tell owns a resort on the beach. He purchases an island 6 km offshore, 10 km down the beach (Figure 10-8c). So that his guests may drive to the island, he plans to build a causeway from the island to the beach, connecting to a road along the beach to the hotel. The road will cost \$5 thousand per kilometer, and the bridge will cost \$13 thousand per kilometer. What is the minimum cost for the road and causeway system? How much money is saved by using the optimum path over what it would cost to build a causeway from the hotel straight to the island?

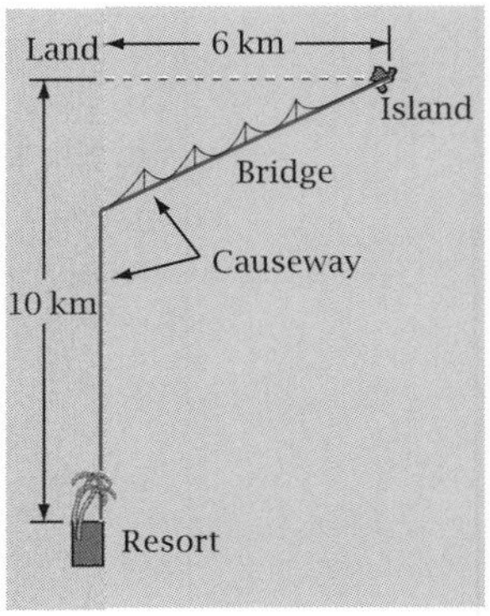


Figure 10-8c

R6. a. An object's acceleration is given by $a(t) = 6t - t^2$ in the interval [0, 10]. Find the following:

i. The maximum and minimum accelerations for $t$ in [0, 10]

ii. The maximum and minimum velocities for $t$ in [0, 10], assuming $v(0) = 0$

iii. The maximum and minimum displacements from the starting point for $t$ in [0, 10]

b. *Inflation Problem:* Saul T. O'Tile lives in a third-world country where the inflation rate is very high. Saul saves at a rate of 50 pillars (the currency in his country) a day. But the value of money is decreasing exponentially with time in such a way that at the end of 200 days a pillar will purchase only half of what it would at the beginning.

i. Write an equation for the purchasing power of the money Saul has saved as a function of the number of days since he started saving.

ii. On what day will Saul's accumulated savings have the maximum total purchasing power? Justify your answer.

R7. a. Make a sketch showing how the velocity and acceleration vectors are related to each other and to the curved path of an object moving in a plane if

i. The object is speeding up

ii. The object is slowing down.

b. An object moves along the hyperbola shown in Figure 10-8d. The position vector at any time $t$ minutes is given by

$$\vec{r} = (5\cosh t)\vec{i} + (3\sinh t)\vec{j}.$$

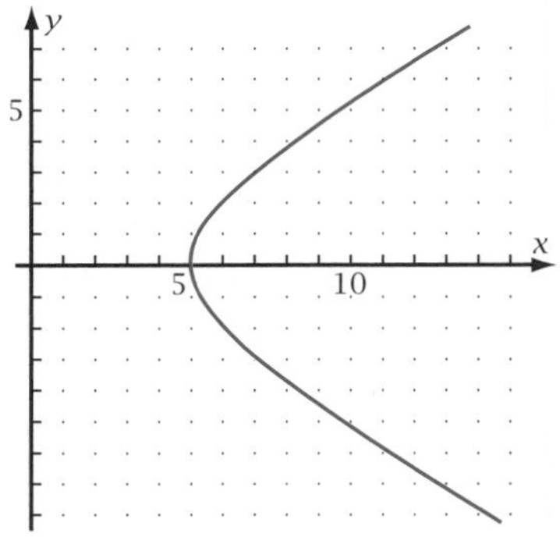


Figure 10-8d

i. Find the position, velocity, and acceleration vectors for the object at time $t = 1$.

ii. Draw these vectors at appropriate places on a photocopy of the object's path.

iii. At time $t = 1$, how fast is the object moving? Is it speeding up or slowing down? At what rate?

iv. How far does the object move between $t = 0$ and $t = 1$?

v. Show that if the tails of the velocity vectors are placed at the respective points on the path, then their heads lie on one of the asymptotes of the hyperbola.

## Concepts Problems

C1. *One-Problem Test on Linear Motion and Other Concepts:* A particle moves up and down the $y$-axis with velocity $v$ feet per second given by

$$v = t^3 - 7t^2 + 15t - 9$$

during the time interval [0, 4]. At time $t = 0$, its position is $y = 4$.

a. Sketch the velocity-time graph.

b. At what time(s) is the particle stopped?

c. At what time is the velocity the maximum? The minimum? Justify your answers.

d. At what time(s) does the velocity-time graph have a point of inflection?

e. What is happening to the particle at the point(s) of inflection?

f. Find the position, $y$, as a function of time.

g. Sketch the position-time graph.

h. At what time is $y$ the maximum? The minimum? Justify your answers.

i. At what time(s) does the position-time graph have a point of inflection?

j. What is happening to the particle at the point(s) of inflection?

k. Is $y$ ever negative? Explain.

l. What is the net displacement of the particle from $t = 0$ to $t = 4$?

m. How far does the particle travel from $t = 0$ to $t = 4$?

n. What is the average velocity from $t = 0$ to $t = 4$?

o. What is the average speed from $t = 0$ to $t = 4$?

C2. *New York to Los Angeles Problem:* What is the shortest time in which a person could possibly get from New York to Los Angeles? If you ignore such things as getting to and from airports, the kind of vehicle to be used, and so forth, the problem reduces to how much stress the human body can take from acceleration and deceleration ("$g$ forces"). Recall that an acceleration of $1g$ is the same as the acceleration due to gravity.

a. From what you have heard in the media or elsewhere, about how many $g$ can the human body withstand?

b. About how far is it from New York to Los Angeles?

c. You must be stopped both at the beginning of the trip and at the end. What, then, is the minimum length of time a human being could take to get from New York to Los Angeles?

C3. *Spider and Clock Problem:* A spider sitting on a clock face attaches one end of its web at the "12," 25 cm from the center of the clock. As the second hand passes by, she jumps onto it and starts crawling toward the center at a rate of 0.7 cm/sec (Figure 10-8e). As the clock turns, the spider spins more web. The length of this web depends on the number of seconds the spider has been crawling and can be calculated using the law of cosines. Find the rate of change of this length at the instant the spider has been crawling for 10 sec.

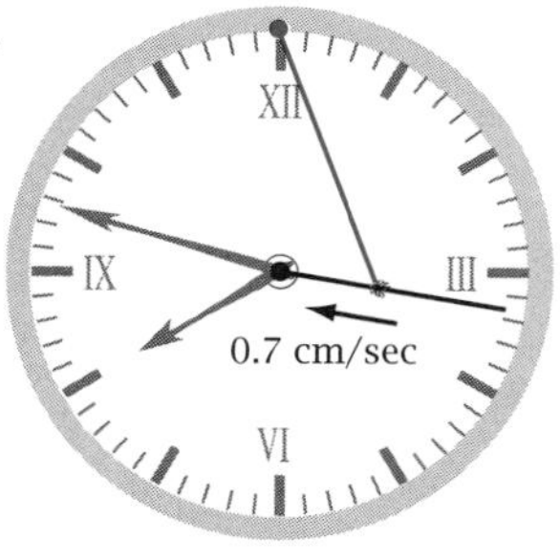

Figure 10-8e

C4. *Submerging Cone Problem:* A cone of base radius 5 cm and altitude 12 cm is being lowered at 2 cm/min, vertex down, into a cylinder of radius 7 cm that has water 15 cm deep in it (Figure 10-8f). As the cone dips into the water, the water level in the cylinder rises. Find the rate at which the level is rising when the vertex of the cone is

a. 10 cm from the bottom of the cylinder

b. 1 cm from the bottom of the cylinder

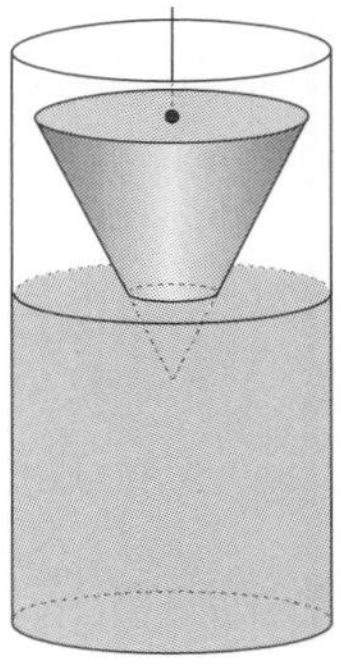

Figure 10-8f

C5. *The Horse Race Theorem:* Sir Vey and Sir Mount run a horse race. They start at time $t = a$ at the same point. At the end of the race, time $t = b$, they are tied. Let $f(t)$ be Sir Vey's distance from the start, and $g(t)$ be Sir Mount's distance from the start. Assuming that $f$ and $g$ are differentiable, prove that there was a time $t = c$ between $a$ and $b$ at which each knight was going exactly the same speed.

C6. *Hemispherical Railroad Problem:* A mountain has the shape of a perfect hemisphere with a base radius of 1000 ft (unlikely in the real world, but it makes an interesting problem!). A railroad track is to be built to the top of the mountain. Since the train can't go straight up, the track must spiral around the mountain (Figure 10-8g). The steeper the track spirals, the shorter it will be, but the slower the train will go. Suppose that the velocity of the train is given by

$$v = 30 - 60\sin\theta,$$

where $v$ is in feet per second and $\theta$ is the (constant) angle the track makes with the horizontal. If the track is built in the optimum way, what is the minimum length of time the train could take to get to the top?

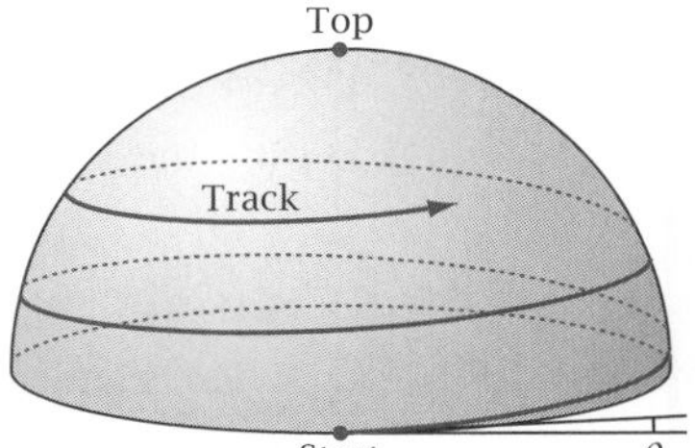


Figure 10-8g

## Chapter Test

T1. *Truck Passing Problem:* You accelerate your car to pass a truck, giving it a velocity

$$v = \sqrt{t} + 60,$$

where $v$ is velocity in feet per second and $t$ is time in seconds since you started to pass. Find out how far you go in the 25 sec it takes you to get around the truck.

T2. *Power Line Problem:* Ima Hunter builds a camp house in the country that she wants to supply with electricity. The house is 3 mi from the road. The electrical contractor tells her it will cost \$2520 (\$360 a mile) to run the power line 7 mi along the highway to the point nearest the camp house and \$2400 (\$800 a mile) more to run it the 3 mi from the highway to the camp house. You believe that Ima could save money by making the line cut off from the highway before the 7-mi point and angle across to the house. How should the power line be run to minimize its total cost? How much could Ima save over the \$4920 the contractor proposes?

T3. For the function $f(x) = x^3 - 4x + 5$, find the maximum, the minimum, and the average value of the function on the interval [1, 3]. Sketch a graph showing the geometrical significance of the average value.

T4. An object moving along a line has velocity $v(t) = 10(0.5 - 2^{-t})$ ft/sec.

a. Find the distance it travels and its net displacement from the starting point for the time interval [0, 2].

b. Find its acceleration at time $t = 0$.

c. At time $t = 0$, was the particle speeding up or slowing down? Justify your answer.

T5. An object is moving at 50 cm/sec at time $t = 0$. It has accelerations of 4, 6, 10, and 13 (cm/sec)/sec at times $t = 0$, 7, 14, and 21 sec, respectively. Approximately what was the object's average velocity for the 21-sec time interval? About how far did the object go?

Figure 10-8h shows the path of an object moving with vector equation

$$\vec{r}(t) = (10\cos 0.4t)\vec{i} + (10\sin 0.6t)\vec{j}$$

where distance is in miles and time is in hours.

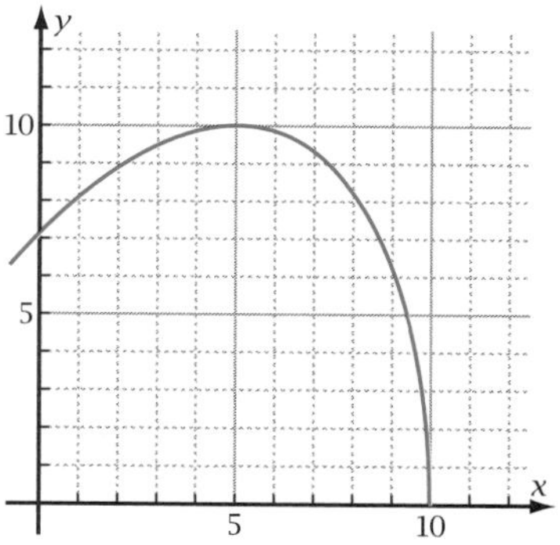

Figure 10-8h

T6. Find an equation for $\vec{v}(t)$.

T7. Find an equation for $\vec{a}(t)$.

T8. Find $\vec{r}(2)$. Make a photocopy of the graph in Figure 10-8h and draw $\vec{r}(2)$ on it.

T9. Find $\vec{v}(2)$. On the photocopy, plot this vector starting at the object's position when $t = 2$. How is this vector related to the path of the object?

T10. Find $\vec{a}(2)$. On the photocopy, plot this vector starting at the object's position when $t = 2$.

T11. Sketch the components of $\vec{a}(2)$, one of them directed tangentially to the path, and the other normal to it.

T12. Based on the components of $\vec{a}(2)$, would you expect that the object is slowing down or speeding up when $t = 2$? How can you tell?

T13. At what rate is the object speeding up or slowing down when $t = 2$?

T14. Explain why the normal component of $\vec{a}(2)$ is pointing toward the concave side of the path.

T15. Find the distance the object travels between $t = 0$ and $t = 2$.

CHAPTER

# 11 The Calculus of Variable-Factor Products

I-beams used in construction must be stiff so that they do not bend too much. The stiffness depends on the shape of the beam's cross-section. Stiffness is measured by the second moment of area of the cross-section, which is defined to be area times the square of the distance from the centroid of the cross-section. Since different parts of the cross-section are at different distances from the centroid, definite integrals are used to compute the stiffness of a given type of beam.

# Mathematical Overview

A definite integral gives a way to find the product of $x$ and $y$, where $y$ varies. In Chapter 11 you will apply integrals to

- work = force × displacement
- force = pressure × area
- mass = density × volume
- moment = displacement × quantity

You will do the applications in four ways.

**Graphically** The logo at the top of each even-numbered page of this chapter reminds you that work equals force times displacement.

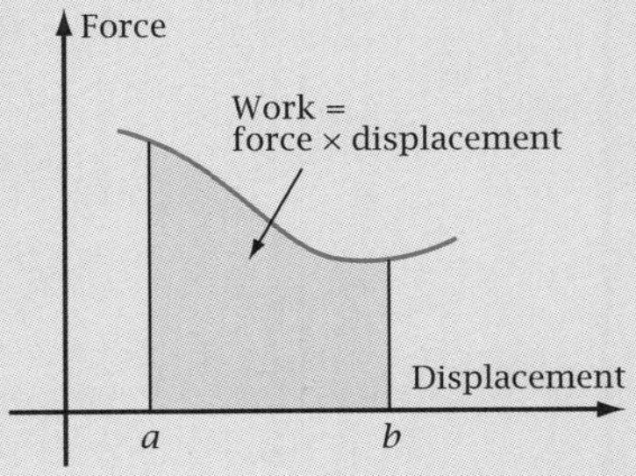


**Numerically**

| force | disp. | work |
|---|---|---|
| 50 | 10 | 0 |
| 53 | 12 | 103 |
| 58 | 14 | 214 |
| 70 | 16 | 342 |
| 90 | 18 | 502 |
| ... | ... | ... |

**Algebraically** $M_y = \int_a^b x \cdot dA$, the definition of moment of area.

**Verbally** *We calculated the balance point of a piece of cardboard by finding its centroid. Then we showed that we were right by cutting out the cardboard. It actually did balance on a pencil point placed at the calculated centroid!*

# 11-1 Review of Work—Force Times Displacement

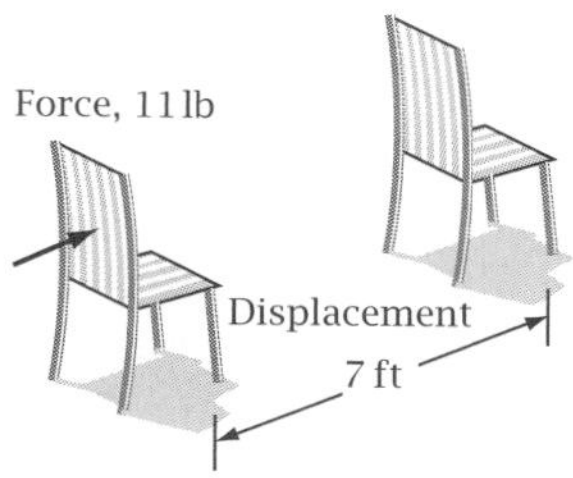


Figure 11-1a

In previous chapters you have run across the fact that the **work** done in moving an object from one place to another equals the force with which it is pushed or pulled times the displacement through which it moves. For instance, if you push a chair 7 feet across the floor with a force of 11 pounds (Figure 11-1a) you do 77 **foot-pounds** of work.

In Problem Set 11-1, you will refresh your memory about how to compute the work done if the force is variable. As you study this chapter you will see how the thought process you use for this one application can be used for many others. You will learn such things as how to find the balance point of a solid object, and how to calculate volumes and masses of objects quickly, without actually doing any integration.

**OBJECTIVE**

By yourself or with your study group, find the work done in moving a chair across the floor if the force you exert on it varies as you push.

## Exploratory Problem Set 11-1

*Chair Work Problem:* Suppose that you push a chair across the floor with a force

$$F = 20xe^{-0.5x},$$

where $F$ is the force in pounds and $x$ is the distance in feet the chair has moved since you started pushing.

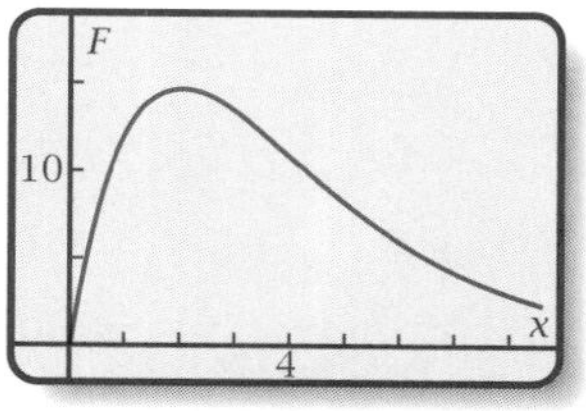


Figure 11-1b

1. Figure 11-1b shows the graph of $F$. On a photocopy of this graph, draw a narrow vertical strip of width $\Delta x = 0.2$ centered at $x = 4$. Approximately what is the force at any value of $x$ in this strip? Approximately how much work is done in moving the chair a distance $\Delta x$ at $x = 4$?
2. Write an equation for $dW$, the work done in moving the chair a distance of $dx$ feet when the chair is at point $x$, where the force is given by the equation above.
3. Add up all the $dW$'s from $x = 0$ to $x = 7$. That is, find the definite integral of $dW$.
4. How much work was done in moving the chair from $x = 0$ to $x = 7$?
5. If you continue to push the chair with the force shown and it continues to move, what limit would the amount of work approach as $x$ approaches infinity?

# 11-2 Work Done by a Variable Force

In ordinary English the word *work* is used in different contexts and with different meanings. For instance, you may feel that you did a lot of work on your calculus assignment last night. Physically, however, the word *work* has a precise definition.

It is the product of the *force* applied to an object and the *displacement* the object moves as a result of that force. For instance, if you push a chair 7 ft across the floor by exerting a force of 11 lb, you have done 77 ft-lb of work, as you saw in Section 11-1.

> **Definition: Work**
>
> If an object moves a certain displacement as a result of being acted upon by a certain force, then the amount of work done is given by
>
> $$\text{Work} = (\text{force})(\text{displacement}).$$

In most real-world situations, the force does not remain constant as the object moves. By now you should realize that finding the work under these conditions is a job for definite integration!

**OBJECTIVE**

Given a situation in which a varying force acts on an object, or where different parts of the object move through different displacements, be able to calculate the amount of work done.

There are two ways to analyze a work problem.

1. Move the whole object a small part of the displacement.
2. Move a small part of the object the whole displacement.

The following two examples show how this analysis can be done.

**■ Example 1**

**Move the whole object through a small displacement**. A ship is at anchor in 80 ft of water. The anchor weighs 5000 lb, and the chain weighs 20 lb/ft (Figure 11-2a). The anchor is to be pulled up as the ship gets under way.

a. How much force must be exerted to lift the anchor as it comes aboard the ship? Write an equation expressing force in terms of the displacement, $y$, of the anchor from the bottom of the ocean.

b. How much work must be done to raise the anchor the 80 ft from the bottom to the point where it comes aboard the ship?

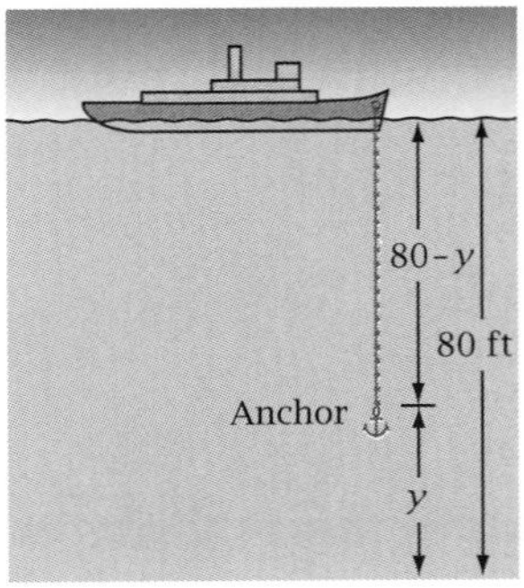


Figure 11-2a

**Solutions**

a. When the anchor is at the bottom and neglecting buoyancy, you must pull with enough force to lift the 5000-lb anchor and the 80 ft of chain. Letting $F$ stand for force,

$$F = (20)(80) + 5000 = 6600 \text{ lb}.$$

At the ship, the only force is that needed to lift the 5000-lb anchor.

$$F = 5000 \text{ lb}$$

In between, the force varies linearly with the length of the chain. If $y$ is the displacement from the bottom to the anchor, then this length is equal to $(80 - y)$. Therefore,

$$F = 20(80 - y) + 5000$$
$$= 6600 - 20y.$$

b. If the anchor is raised a small displacement, $dy$, the force would be essentially constant, the same as at some sample point in that particular subinterval. So the work, $dW$, done in lifting the anchor this small displacement would be

$$dW = F\,dy$$
$$= (6600 - 20y)\,dy.$$

The total amount of work, $W$, can be found by adding up the $dW$'s, then taking the limit as $dy$ goes to zero. You should recognize by now that this process is definite integration.

$$W = \int_0^{80} (6600 - 20y)\,dy$$
$$= 6600y - 10y^2 \Big|_0^{80}$$ You could integrate numerically.
$$= 464{,}000 \text{ ft-lb}$$

■

■ ***Example 2*** **Move a small part of the object the whole displacement.** A conical tank has a top diameter of 10 ft and an altitude of 15 ft (Figure 11-2b). It is filled to the top with liquid of density $k$ lb/ft$^3$. A pump takes suction from the bottom of the tank and pumps the liquid up to a level 8 ft above the top of the tank. Find the total amount of work done.

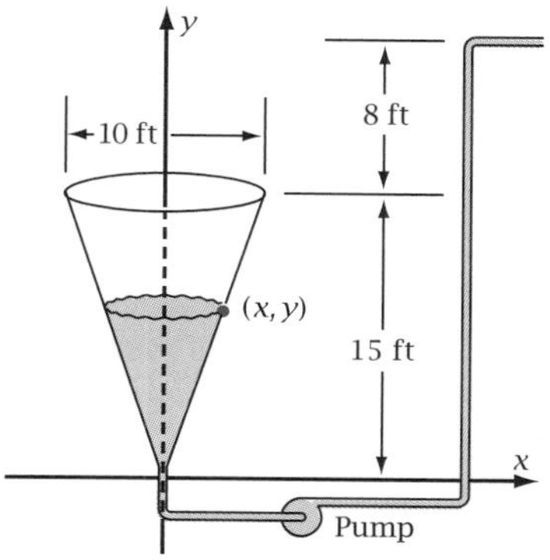


Figure 11-2b

***Solutions***

The first thing to realize is that the amount of work done lifting any small volume of liquid is independent of the path the liquid takes. It depends only on how far the volume is displaced upward from where it starts to where it finishes. Liquid at a sample point, $(x, y)$ travels down through the tank, through the pump, and up to the discharge 8 ft above the top of the tank (and thus 23 ft above the bottom of the tank, where $y = 0$). So its net displacement is equal to $(23 - y)$.

If you "slice" the liquid horizontally, liquid at each point in the slice will be displaced essentially the same distance as that at the sample point. The force, $dF$, needed to lift the water the displacement $(23 - y)$ is equal to the weight of the slice, namely, $k\,dV$. Letting $W$ stand for amount of work, the work done in lifting one slice is

$$\begin{aligned} dW &= (k\,dV)(23 - y) \\ &= k\pi x^2(23 - y)\,dy. \qquad \text{Substitute } \pi x^2\,dy \text{ for } dV \text{ and commute.} \end{aligned}$$

The element of the cone where the sample point $(x, y)$ is located is a line segment through the origin, containing the point (5, 15). So its slope is $15/5 = 3$, and its equation is

$$y = 3x, \quad \text{or} \quad x = \frac{y}{3}.$$

$$\begin{aligned} dW &= k\pi\left(\frac{y}{3}\right)^2(23 - y)\,dy \qquad \text{Substitute } y/3 \text{ for } x. \\ &= \frac{k\pi}{9}(23y^2 - y^3)\,dy \\ W &= \frac{k\pi}{9}\int_0^{15}(23y^2 - y^3)\,dy \qquad \text{Add up the } dW\text{'s and take the limit (that is, integrate).} \\ &= \frac{k\pi}{9}\left(\frac{23}{3}y^3 - \frac{1}{4}y^4\right)\Big|_0^{15} \qquad \text{You could integrate numerically.} \\ &= \frac{5875k\pi}{4} = 4614.214\ldots k \end{aligned}$$

If the liquid were water, with density $k = 62.4$ lb/ft$^3$, the total work would be about 287,927 ft-lb. ■

*Note:* Work is an equivalent physical quantity to energy. For instance, the work done compressing a spring is stored in that spring as energy. Foot-pounds of work can be converted directly to joules or calories by the appropriate conversion factors. Although first moment of force, called torque, also has the units (distance)(force), torque is not the same physical quantity as work. For this reason, torque is usually called "pound-feet" rather than foot-pounds (see Section 11-4).

## Problem Set 11-2

### *Do These Quickly*

The following problems are intended to refresh your skills. You should be able to do all ten problems in less than five minutes.

**Q1.** What is the area under one arch of $y = \sin x$?

**Q2.** What is the area under $y = 4 - x^2$ from $x = -2$ to $x = 2$?

**Q3.** Find a velocity equation if the acceleration is $a = \tan t$.

**Q4.** Find the acceleration equation if the velocity is $v = \ln t$?

**Q5.** Name the theorem that allows definite integrals to be calculated by antiderivatives.

**Q6.** $\sum f(x)\,dx$ is a —?— sum.

**Q7.** What is the average value of $y = \sin x$ for one complete cycle?

**Q8.** Name the technique for integrating $\int e^x \cos x\,dx$.

**Q9.** Name the technique for finding $dy/dx$ if $x^3y^5 = x\sin^2 y$.

**Q10.** Name the quick method for resolving an expression into partial fractions.

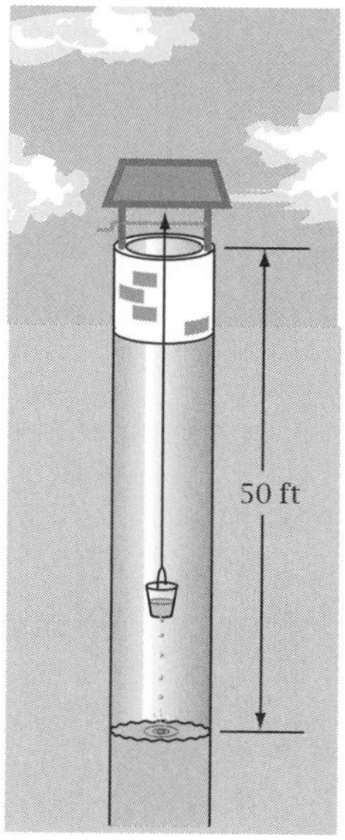


Figure 11-2c

1. *Leaking Bucket Problem:* Miss Hapse pulls a bucket of water up from the bottom of the well (Figure 11-2c). When she starts pulling, she exerts a force of 20 lb. But by the time she gets it to the top, 50 ft up, enough water has leaked out so that she pulls with only 12 lb. Assume that both the rate she pulls the bucket and the rate the water leaks are constant, so the force she exerts decreases linearly with displacement from the bottom. How much work did Miss Hapse do in pulling the bucket out of the well?

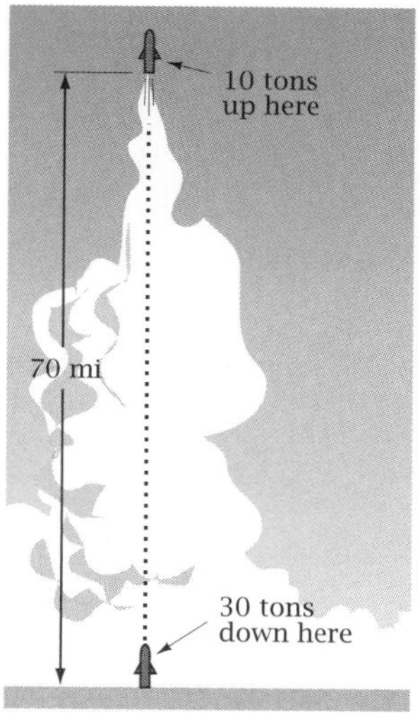


Figure 11-2d

2. *Spaceship Problem:* A spaceship on the launch pad weighs 30 tons (Figure 11-2d). By the time it reaches an altitude of 70 mi, it weighs only 10 tons because 20 tons of fuel have been used. Assume that the weight of the spaceship decreases linearly with displacement above the earth.
   a. How many mile-tons of work were done in lifting the spaceship to an altitude of 70 mi?
   b. The rocket engines exert a constant thrust (that is, force) of 90 tons. How much work was done by the engines in lifting the spaceship to 70 mi? What do you think happens to the excess energy from part a?

3. *Spring Problem:* It takes work to compress a spring (work = force × displacement). However, the amount of force exerted while compressing the spring varies, and is directly porportional to the displacement, $s$, the spring has been compressed (Figure 11-2e). This property is known as Hooke's Law. Let $k$ be the proportionality constant. Find the work required to compress a spring from $s = 0$ to $s = 10$.

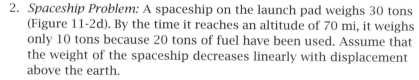

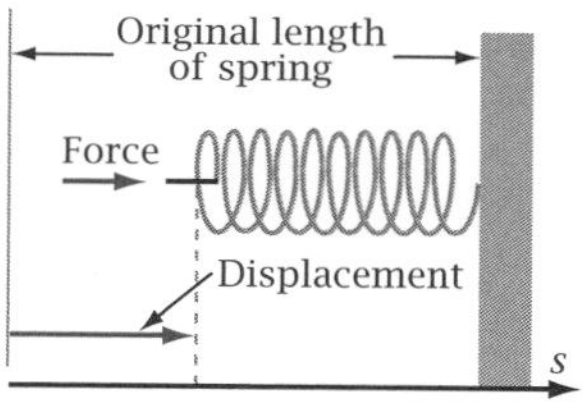


Figure 11-2e

4. *Table Moving Problem:* You push a table across the floor. At first, you push hard to get it moving, then ease off as it starts to move. The force drops to zero at a displacement of 4 ft, where the table stops. Assume that the force, $F$ lb, is given by

$$F = -x^3 + 6x^2 - 12x + 16,$$

where $x$ is the number of ft the table has been displaced.

a. Sketch the graph of $F$ and show that it really does have these properties.

b. How much work is done pushing the table the 4ft?

5. *Conical Reservoir Problem:* A conical reservoir 30 ft in diameter and 10 ft deep is filled to the top with water of density 62.4 lb/ft$^3$. Find the work done in pumping all of this water to a level of 7 ft above the top of the reservoir.

6. *Paraboloidal Tank Problem:* A tank is made in the shape of the paraboloid formed by rotating about the $y$-axis the graph of $y = x^2$ from $x = 0$ to $x = 4$ (Figure 11-2f). The tank is filled with benzene, an organic liquid whose density if 54.8 lb/ft$^3$. Find the work done in pumping a full tank of benzene to a level of 10 ft above the top of the tank.

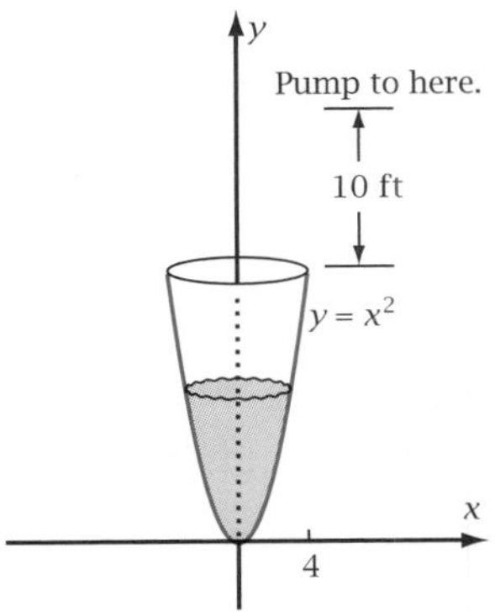

Figure 11-2f

7. *Spherical Water Tower Problem:* A spherical water tower 40 ft in diameter has its center 120 ft above the ground (Figure 11-2g). A pump at ground level fills the tank with water of density 62.4 lb/ft$^3$.

a. How much work is done in filling the tank half full?

b. Quick! How much work is done in filling the tank completely? (Be careful!)

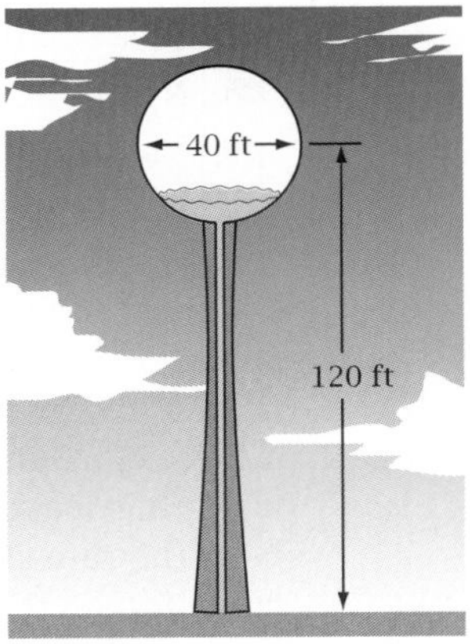

Figure 11-2g

8. *Flooded Ship Problem:* A compartment in a ship is flooded to a depth of 16 ft with sea water of density 67 lb/ft$^3$ (Figure 11-2h). The vertical bulkheads at both ends of the compartment have the shape of the region above the graph of

$$y = 0.0002x^4,$$

where $x$ and $y$ are in ft. The compartment is 15 ft long. How much work must the bilge pumps do to pump all of the water over the side of the ship, 30 ft above the bottom?

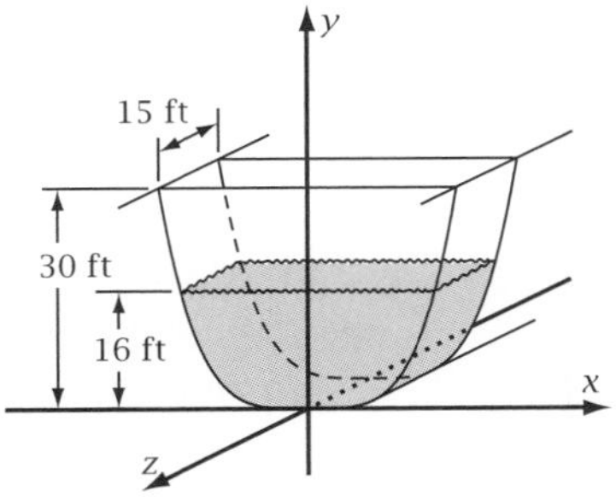

Figure 11-2h

9. *Carnot Cycle Problem:* An automobile engine works by burning gasoline in its cylinders. Assume that a cylinder in a particular engine has diameter 2 in. (Figure 11-2i). When the spark plug fires, the pressure inside the cylinder is 1000 psi (pounds per square inch), and the volume is at its minimum, 1 in$^3$. As the piston goes out, the hot gases expand adiabatically (that is, without losing heat to the surroundings). The pressure drops according to the equation

$$p = k_1 V^{-1.4},$$

where $p$ is pressure, $V$ is volume, and $k_1$ is a proportionality constant. When the piston is farthest out, and the volume is 10 in$^3$,

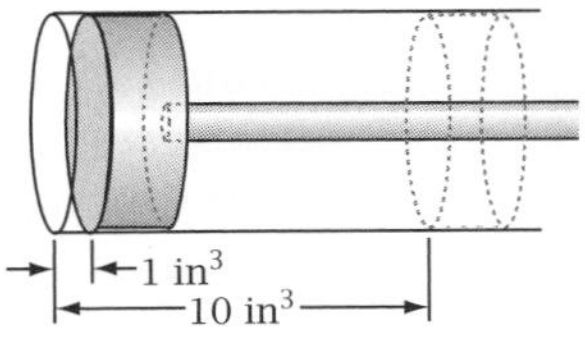

Figure 11-2i

the exhaust valve opens and the pressure drops to atmospheric pressure, 15 psi. As the piston comes back, the cool gases are compressed and the cycle is repeated. For compression, $p = k_2V^{-1.4}$, where $k_2$ is a different proportionality constant.

a. Find the work done on the piston by the expanding hot gas.

b. Find the work done by the piston as it compresses the cool gas.

c. Find the net amount of work done. This is the amount of work that is available for moving the car.

d. How is "Carnot" pronounced? Who was Carnot?

# 11-3 Mass of a Variable-Density Object

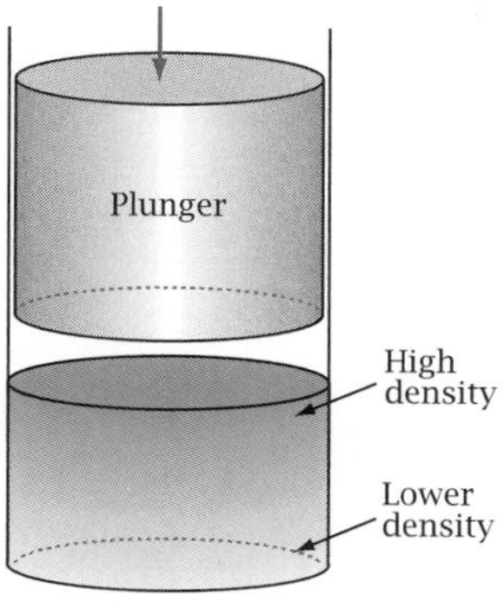

Figure 11-3a

The density of an object is defined to be the mass per unit volume. For instance, water has a density of 1 g/cm$^3$; iron, 7.86 g/cm$^3$; and uranium, 18.5 g/cm$^3$. Since density is calculated by dividing the mass of an object by its volume, the mass is equal to density times volume.

$$\text{Mass} = (\text{density})(\text{volume})$$

The density of a real object may vary from point to point within the object. For example, the density of the materials composing the earth varies from about 12 g/cm$^3$ at the center of the earth to about 4 g/cm$^3$ at the surface.

As another example, uranium oxide pellets, used as fuel in nuclear reactors, are made by compacting uranium oxide powder with a press (Figure 11-3a). The powder closer to the plunger in the press compacts to a higher density than that farther away.

In this section you will explore ways of predicting the mass of an object if you know how its density behaves at various places.

***OBJECTIVE***

Given a function specifying the density of an object at various places within that object, calculate the total mass of the object.

Example 1 shows how definite integration can be used to calculate the total mass of a hypothetical object where the density varies using techniques you know. Your purpose is to apply these techniques to real-world problems.

**Example 1** A solid is formed by rotating about the $x$-axis the region under the graph of $y = x^{1/3}$ from $x = 0$ to $x = 8$. Find the mass of the solid if the density, $\rho$ (Greek letter "rho")

a. Varies axially (in the direction of the axis of rotation), being directly proportional to the square of the distance from the $yz$-plane.

b. Varies radially (in the direction of the radius), being directly proportional to the distance from the $x$-axis.

**Solutions**

a. Figure 11-3b shows the solid. A vertical slice of the rotated region generates a disk parallel to the $yz$-plane. So each point in the disk has essentially the same density as at the sample point $(x, y)$. Letting $m$ stand for mass and $V$ stand for volume, the mass of a representative slice is as follows.

$$dm = \rho dV$$

$$\rho = kx^2$$

$\rho$ is directly proportional to the square of $x$, the distance from the $yz$-plane.

$$dV = \pi y^2\,dx$$

By geometry, volume = (cross-sectional area) (length).

$$\therefore dm = kx^2 \cdot \pi y^2\,dx$$

Substitute for $\rho$ and for $dV$.

$$= k\pi x^2 (x^{1/3})^2\,dx = k\pi x^{8/3}\,dx$$

$$\therefore m = \int_0^8 k\pi x^{8/3}\,dx$$

Add the $dm$'s and find the limit. That is, integrate.

$$= \frac{3}{11} k\pi x^{11/3} \Big|_0^8$$

$$= \frac{6144}{11} k\pi$$

(Find the actual mass by substituting for $k$ and doing the arithmetic.)

b. Since the density varies radially (with the distance from the $x$-axis), slicing the rotated region horizontally will produce a constant density within the slice. Rotating slices parallel to the axis of rotation produces cylindrical shells, as shown in Figure 11-3c. Again, picking a sample point on the curve, the mass of a representative shell is as follows.

$$dm = \rho dV$$

$$= ky \cdot 2\pi y(8 - x)\,dy$$

$\rho = ky$ and $dV = 2\pi y(8 - x)\,dy$.

$$= 2k\pi y^2(8 - y^3)\,dy = 2k\pi(8y^2 - y^5)\,dy$$

$$m = 2k\pi \int_0^2 (8y^2 - y^5)\,dy$$

Add the $dm$'s and find the limit. Why are the bounds 0 to 2?

$$= 2k\pi \left(\frac{8}{3}y^3 - \frac{1}{6}y^6\right) \Big|_0^2$$

$$= 2k\pi \left(\frac{64}{3} - \frac{32}{3} - 0 + 0\right) = \frac{64}{3} k\pi$$

■

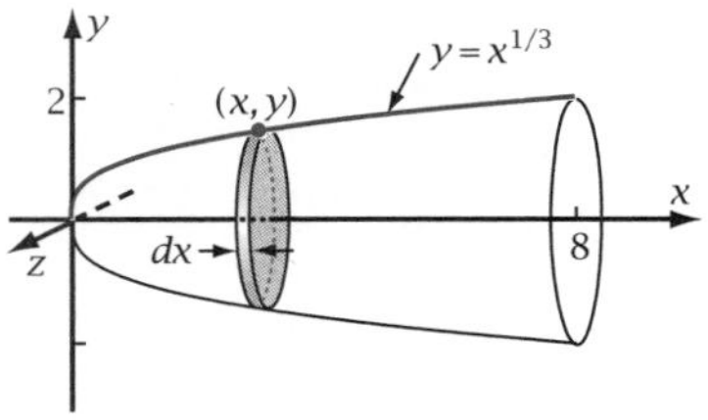


Figure 11-3b

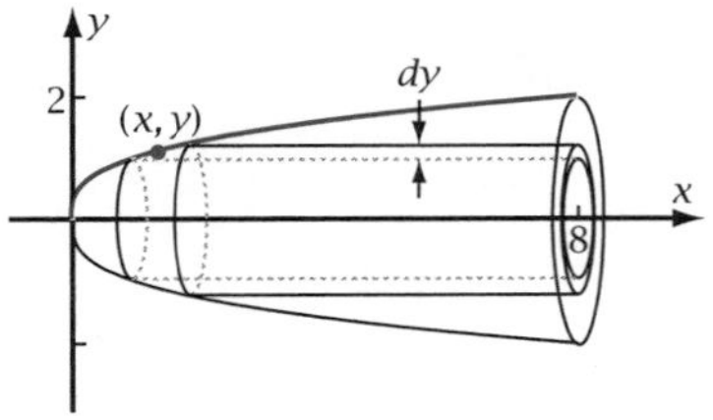


Figure 11-3c

*Note:* Part b of the example shows the real reason for slicing objects into cylindrical shells. If the density varies radially, it will be constant (essentially) at all points in the shell. Slicing into plane slices would give a slice in which the density varies.

## Problem Set 11-3

### *Do These Quickly*

The following problems are intended to refresh your skills. You should be able to do all ten problems in less than five minutes.

**Q1.** What is the volume of a cone inscribed in a 6-$cm^3$ cylinder?

**Q2.** What is the volume of a paraboloid inscribed in a 6-$cm^3$ cylinder?

**Q3.** $y$ varies linearly with $x$. $y$ is 12 if $x = 0$ and 20 if $x = 2$. Find $y$ if $x = 3$.

**Q4.** Sketch the graph: $y = \sin x$.

**Q5.** Sketch the graph: $y = \ln x$.

**Q6.** Sketch the graph: $y = 2^x$.

**Q7.** Sketch the graph: $y = x^2$.

**Q8.** Density = (—?—)/(—?—)

**Q9.** Work = (—?—)(—?—)

**Q10.** If $y = \sin^{-1}x$, then $y'$ = —?—.

1. The region bounded by the graph of $y = \ln x$, the $x$-axis, and the line $x = 3$ is rotated about the line $x = 0$ to form a solid. Find the mass of the solid if
   a. The density varies inversely with the distance from the axis of rotation.
   b. The density varies linearly with $y$, being 5 when $y = 0$, and 7 when $y = 1$.
2. The region bounded by the graph of $y = \sin x$ and the $x$-axis, between $x = 0$ and $x = \pi$, is rotated about the $y$-axis to form a solid. The density of the solid varies directly with the distance from the axis of rotation. Find the mass of the solid.
3. The region under the graph of $y = 9 - x^2$ is rotated about the $y$-axis to form a solid. Find the mass of the solid if
   a. The density is a constant, $k$.
   b. The density is constant in any thin horizontal slice but varies directly with the square of $y$ in the $y$-direction.
   c. The density does not vary in the $y$-direction but is directly proportional to the quantity $(1 + x)$, where $x$ is the distance between the sample point and the axis of rotation.
   d. Which of the solids in 3a, b, and c has the greatest mass? Assume that the constant $k$ is the same in all three parts.
4. The region bounded by the graphs of $y = \sqrt{x}$ and $y = 0.5x$ is rotated about the $x$-axis to form a solid. Find the mass of the solid if
   a. The density varies axially, being directly proportional to the distance between the sample point and the $yz$-plane.
   b. The density varies radially, being directly proportional to the square of the distance between the sample point and the axis of rotation.

5. *Two Cone Problem:* Two cones have the same size, base radius 3 in. and altitude 6 in. (Figure 11-3d). Both have the same weight densities at their two ends, 50 oz/in$^3$ and 80 oz/in$^3$, but one has the higher density at the base and the other has the higher density at the vertex. In both, the density varies linearly with the distance from the plane of the base.
   a. Without performing any calculations, predict which cone has the higher mass. Explain your reasoning.
   b. Confirm (or refute!) your prediction by calculating the mass of each cone.

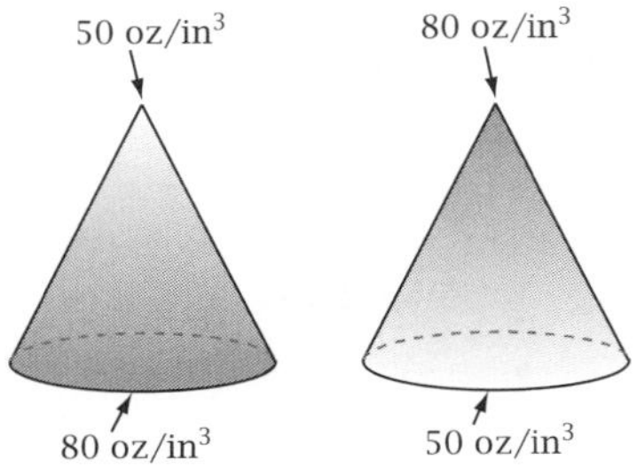

Figure 11-3d

6. *Two Cylinder Problem:* Two cylinders have the same shape, 3-in. radius and 6-in. altitude (Figure 11-3e). One has density 50 oz/in$^3$ along the axis, and 80 oz/in$^3$ at the walls. The other has density 80 oz/in$^3$ along the axis, and 50 oz/in$^3$ at the walls. In both cylinders the density varies linearly with the distance from the axis.
   a. Without performing any calculations, predict which cylinder has the higher mass. Explain.
   b. Confirm (or refute!) your prediction by calculating the mass of each cylinder.

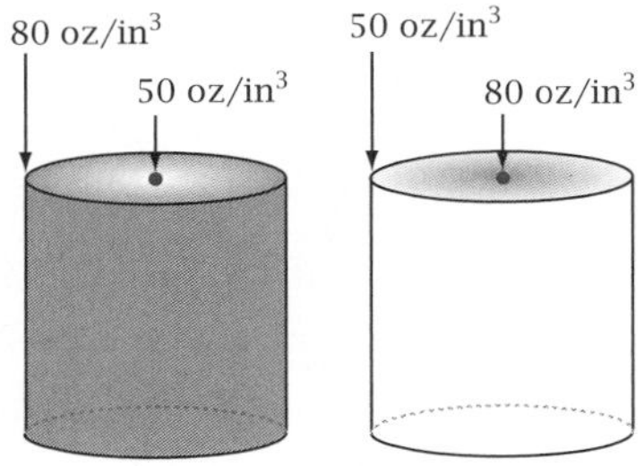

Figure 11-3e

7. The region bounded by the graphs of $y = 4 - 2x^2$, $y = 3 - x^2$, and $x = 0$ (Figure 11-3f) is rotated about the $x$-axis to form a solid. Both $x$ and $y$ are in centimeters. The density varies directly as the square of the distance from the $yz$-plane (that is, the "base" of the solid). Find the mass of the solid.

8. The region in Problem 7 (Figure 11-3f) is rotated about the $y$-axis to form a different solid. The density decreases exponentially with distance from the $y$-axis, according to the equation $\rho = e^{-x}$. Find the mass of the solid.

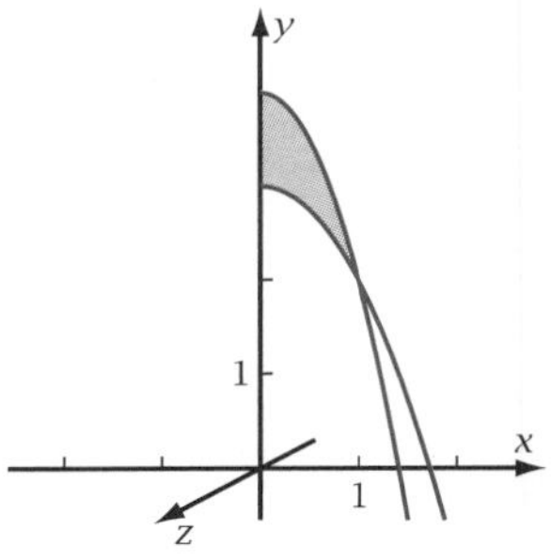

Figure 11-3f

9. *Uranium Fuel Pellet Problem:* Uranium oxide is used as a fuel in nuclear power plants that generate electricity. Powdered uranium oxide is compressed into pellets as shown in Figure 11-3a. The compressing makes the pellets slightly denser at the top than they are at the bottom. Suppose that the cylindrical pellets have a base diameter of 1 cm and an altitude of 2 cm. Assume that the density is constant in the radial direction, but varies with $y$, the distance from the bottom of the pellet (as shown in the table), being 9 g/cm$^3$ at the bottom and 10 g/cm$^3$ at the top. Predict the mass of the pellet, taking into consideration the variable density.

| $y$ (cm) | density (g/cm$^3$) |
|---|---|
| 2.0 | 10.0 |
| 1.6 | 9.9 |
| 1.2 | 9.8 |
| 0.8 | 9.6 |
| 0.4 | 9.4 |
| 0 | 9.0 |

10. The "triangular" region in the first quadrant bounded by the graphs of $y = 4 - x^2$, $y = 4x - x^2$, and $x = 0$, is rotated about various axes to form various solids.

   a. Find the mass of the solid formed by rotating the region about the $y$-axis if the density varies directly with $x$, the distance from the $y$-axis.

   b. Find the mass of the solid formed by rotating the region about the $x$-axis if the density varies directly with $x$, the distance from the $yz$-plane.

   c. Find the mass of the solid in 10a if the density varies directly with $y$, the distance from the $xz$-plane, instead of with $x$.

11. Find the mass of a sphere of radius $r$ if

   a. The density varies directly with the distance from a plane through the center.

   b. The density varies directly with the distance from one of its diameters.

   c. The density varies directly with the distance from the center. (Use *spherical* shells.)

12. *Mass of the Earth Problem:* The density of the earth is about 12 g/cm$^3$ at its center, and about 4 g/cm$^3$ at its surface. Assume that the density varies linearly with the distance from the center. Find the mass of the earth.
*Useful information:*
   - 1 mi = 5280 ft; 1 ft = 12 in; 2.54 cm = 1 in.
   - Radius of the earth is about 3960 mi.
   - Slice into spherical shells.

13. The region under the graph of $y = e^x$ from $x = 0$ to $x = \pi/2$ is rotated about the $y$-axis to form a solid. The density is given by $\rho = \cos x$. Find the mass of the solid.

14. *Buckminster's Elliptical Dome Problem:* Architect Buckminster Fuller (1895–1983) once proposed that a dome should be built over Manhattan Island and an air-conditioning system be built to regulate the temperature, remove air pollution, and so forth. Your job is to find out how much air would be inside such a dome. Figure 11-3g shows what that dome might look like. Assume that the dome is a half-ellipsoid 8 mi long, 2 mi wide, and 1/2 mi high.

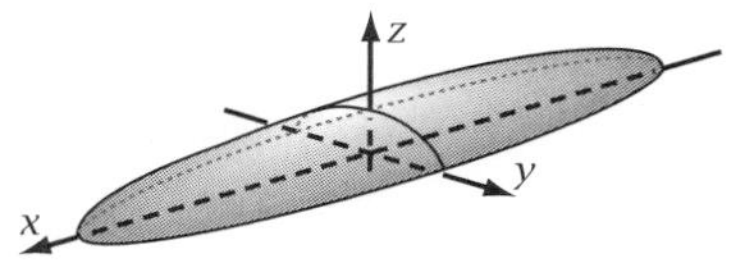

Figure 11-3g

   a. The three-dimensional equation for an ellipsoid is

$$\left(\frac{x}{a}\right)^2 + \left(\frac{y}{b}\right)^2 + \left(\frac{z}{c}\right)^2 = 1,$$

   where $a$, $b$, and $c$ are the $x$-, $y$-, and $z$-radii, respectively. Show that any cross section of the ellipsoid parallel to the $xy$-plane is an ellipse.

   b. The weight density of air at sea level ($z = 0$) is about 0.08 lb/ft$^3$. But it decreases with altitude according to the equation $\rho = 0.08e^{-0.2z}$, where $z$ is in mi. Find the mass of air inside the dome. How many tons is this?

   c. Suppose that you assume the density of the air is constant throughout the dome, 0.08 lb/ft$^3$. How many more lb of air would you have assumed are in the dome than are actually there? Surprising?!

   d. The volume of a (whole) ellipsoid is $V = (4/3)\pi abc$. See if you can derive this formula by integrating the $dV$ from this problem.

# 11-4 Moments, Centroids, Center of Mass, and the Theorem of Pappus

If you hold a meter stick at one end and hang a weight on it, the force caused by the weight twists the meter stick downwards (Figure 11-4a). The farther from your hand you hang the weight, the more the twisting. Doubling the displacement doubles the twisting for a given weight. And doubling the weight hung at the same displacement also doubles the twisting. The amount of twisting is given the name **torque**, pronounced "tork." The torque with respect to an axis through your hand is defined to be the amount of force created by the weight, multiplied by the displacement from your hand perpendicular to the direction of the force.

**Torque = (force)(displacement)**

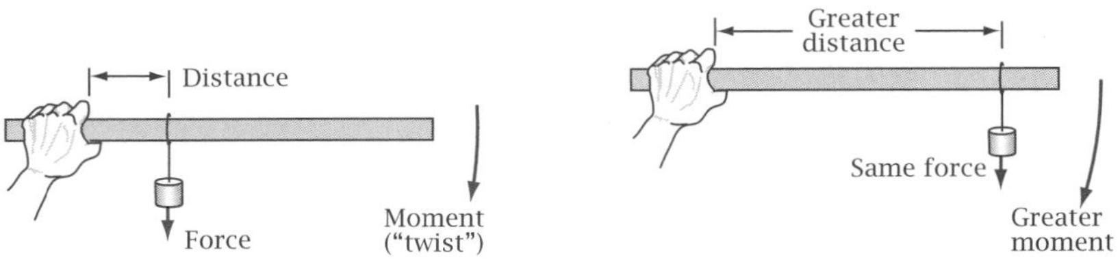


Figure 11-4a

Torque is just one example of a more general concept called **moment**. The word comes from the Latin *movere*, "to move," and *momentum*, "moving power." The moment of a physical quantity equals the magnitude of that quantity, multiplied by some power of the displacement from a reference point, line, or plane to the place where the quantity is located.

**Definition: nth Moment**

$n$th moment of quantity = (magnitude of quantity)(displacement)$^n$

The torque produced by the weight in Figure 11-4a is thus the *first* moment of *force* with respect to an *axis* through your hand. You can find any order moment of any quantity with respect to a point, line, or plane. Some moments have interesting meanings in the real world. Others are of interest just in the mathematical world. In this section you will explore first and second moments of mass, volume, arc length, and area. You will use the results to calculate the **center of mass** of a solid, the point where all of the mass could be concentrated to produce the same first moment, and the related **centroid**, which is a center of volume, length, or area. Calculus is used if parts of the object are at different displacements.

**OBJECTIVE**

Given the description of a solid or a plane region, find its first or second moment of volume, area, or mass with respect to a point, line, or plane, and its center of mass, volume, or area.

**■ Example 1**

A solid paraboloid has the shape of the solid formed by rotating about the $y$-axis the region in Quadrant I above the graph of $y = x^2$ and below the line $y = 9$ (Figure 11-4b).

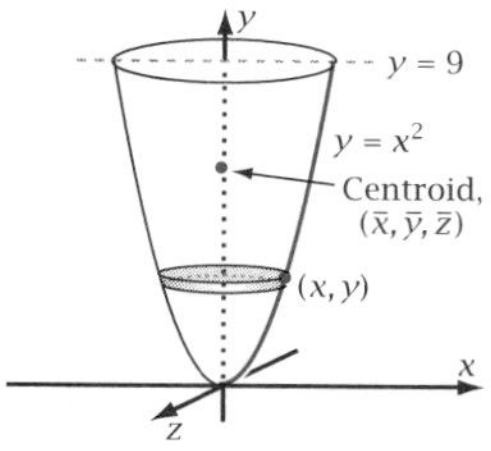


Figure 11-4b

a. Find the volume of the solid if the dimensions are in centimeters.

b. Find $M_{xz}$, the first moment of volume with respect to the $xz$-plane.

c. Find $\overline{y}$ ("$y$ bar"), the $y$-coordinate of the centroid, at which $\overline{y}\cdot$volume$= M_{xz}$ from step b.

d. At the centroid $(\overline{x}, \overline{y}, \overline{z})$, $\overline{x}\cdot$volume$= M_{yz}$, and $\overline{z}\cdot$volume$= M_{xy}$, where the moments are with respect to the $yz$- and $xy$-planes, respectively. Explain why both $\overline{x}$ and $\overline{z}$ are zero for this solid.

**Solutions**

a. Let $V$ stand for volume. Slicing perpendicular to the $y$-axis gives

$$dV = \pi x^2\,dy = \pi y\,dy.$$
$$V = \int_0^9 \pi y\,dy$$
$$= \frac{\pi}{2}y^2\Big|_0^9$$
$$= 40.5\pi = 127.234\ldots\text{cm}^3$$

b. Let $M_{xz}$ stand for the moment with respect to the $xz$-plane. Slicing perpendicular to the $y$-axis as in part a makes the slice parallel to the $xz$-plane, so every point in the slice has approximately the same displacement from the $xz$-plane as the sample point $(x, y)$.

$$dM_{xz} = y\,dV \qquad \text{Moment = (displacement)(volume)}$$
$$= y\cdot \pi y\,dy = \pi y^2\,dy \qquad \text{Substitute for } dV.$$
$$M_{xz} = \int_0^9 \pi y^2\,dy \qquad \text{Add up the } dM\text{'s and take the limit (integrate)}$$
$$= \frac{\pi}{3}y^3\Big|_0^9 = 243\pi = 763.407\ldots\text{cm}^4 \qquad \text{The units are (cm)(cm}^3\text{).}$$

c.
$$\overline{y}\cdot 40.5\pi = 243\pi \qquad (\overline{y})\text{(volume) = moment}$$
$$\overline{y} = \frac{243\pi}{40.5\pi} = 6\text{ cm} \qquad \text{The units are (cm}^4\text{)/(cm}^3\text{).}$$

Note that the centroid is two-thirds of the way up from the vertex to the base. This fact is to be expected since the solid is wider near the base.

d. The displacement is a directed distance. Since the solid is symmetrical with respect to the $xy$- and $yz$-planes, there is just as much negative moment on one side of the plane as there is positive moment on the other side. The moments with respect to these planes are thus zero. So the $x$- and $z$-coordinates of the centroid are also zero, and the centroid lies on the $y$-axis. ■

The word *centroid* means "center-like." The centroid of an object is a geometrical center.

## Definition: Centroid

The **centroid** of a solid is the point $(\bar{x}, \bar{y}, \bar{z})$ at which

$$\bar{x}V = M_{yz},\ \bar{y}V = M_{xz},\ \text{and}\ \bar{z}V = M_{xy},$$

where $V$ is volume, and $M_{yz}$, $M_{xz}$, and $M_{xy}$ are the first moments of volume of the solid with respect to the $yz$-, $xz$-, and $xy$-planes, respectively.

Centroids for plane regions and curves (center of area and center of arc length) are similarly defined. For instance, a region of area $A$ in the $xy$-plane has a centroid at a displacement from the $y$-axis given by $\bar{x}A = M_y$. A curve of length $L$ in the $xy$-plane has a centroid at a displacement from the $x$-axis given by $\bar{y}L = M_x$.

If a solid has a uniform density, its center of mass, or balance point, will be at the centroid. If the density of the solid is not uniform, the center of mass can be at a place other than the centroid. Example 2 shows how to calculate the center of mass.

**Example 2** Suppose that the solid in Example 1 has a density that is constant radially but varies axially, being equal to $y^{1/2}$ g/cm$^3$.

a. Find the mass of the solid.

b. Find the first moment of mass with respect to the $xz$-plane.

c. Find the $y$-coordinate of the center of mass, the point $(\bar{x}, \bar{y}, \bar{z})$ for which $(\bar{y})$(mass) = moment of mass with respect to the $xz$-plane. Show that the answer is reasonable.

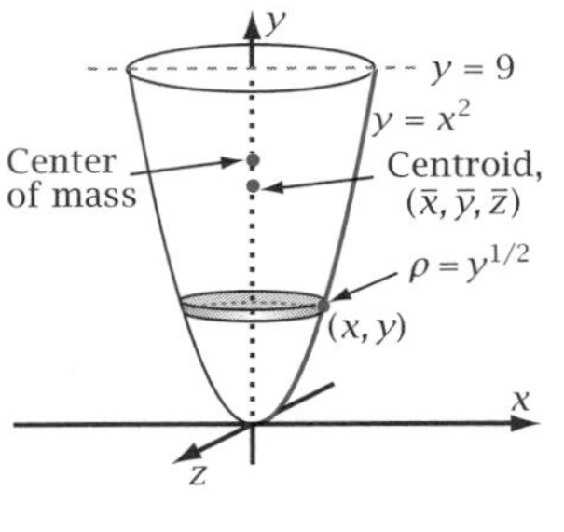


Figure 11-4c

**Solutions**

a. Figure 11-4c shows the solid, sliced horizontally as in Example 1. Since the density varies only axially and all points in the slice are about the same displacement from the $xz$-plane, the mass, $dm$, of any slice is the density at the sample point times the volume of the slice.

$$dm = \rho\, dV = y^{1/2}\pi y\, dy = \pi y^{3/2}\, dy \qquad \text{From Example 1, } dV = \pi y\, dy.$$

$$m = \int_0^9 \pi y^{3/2}\, dy = \tfrac{2}{5}\pi y^{5/2}\Big|_0^9 = 97.2\pi \approx 305.4 \text{ g} \qquad \text{Units are (g/cm}^3\text{)(cm}^3\text{).}$$

b. Let $M_{xz}$ stand for the first moment of mass with respect to the $xz$-plane. All points in a slice are about the same displacement from this plane. So the moment of the slice, $dM_{xz}$, equals the displacement from the $xz$-plane to the sample point, times the mass of the slice.

$$dM_{xz} = y\,dm = y\pi y^{3/2}\,dy = \pi y^{5/2}\,dy$$

$$M_{xz} = \int_0^9 \pi y^{5/2}\,dy = \frac{2}{7}\pi y^{7/2}\Big|_0^9 = \frac{4374\pi}{7} \approx 1963.0 \text{ cm-g}$$ Units are (cm)(g).

c. The $y$-coordinate of the center of mass, $\bar{y}$, is found using the fact that (displacement from center of mass)(total mass) = moment.

$$\bar{y} \cdot m = M_{xz}$$

$$\bar{y} = \frac{4374\pi/7}{97.2\pi} = 6\tfrac{3}{7} = 6.428\ldots \text{ cm}$$ Units are [(cm)(g)]/(g).

The answer is reasonable because it is a little larger than 6 cm, the $y$-coordinate of the centroid. Since the density is greater near the base than at the top of the solid, the center of mass is closer to the base than is the centroid. ■

Example 3 shows how to extend the concept of moment and centroid to a plane region.

**Example 3** Let $R$ be the region in Quadrant I bounded by the graph of $y = 3\cos x$ and the two coordinate axes, where $x$ and $y$ are in inches.

a. Find the first moment of area of $R$ with respect to the $y$-axis.

b. Find the first moment of area of $R$ with respect to the $x$-axis.

c. Find the centroid of $R$, the point $(\bar{x}, \bar{y})$ at which $(\bar{x})$(area) = first moment with respect to the $y$-axis, and $(\bar{y})$ (area) = first moment with respect to the $x$-axis.

**Solutions**

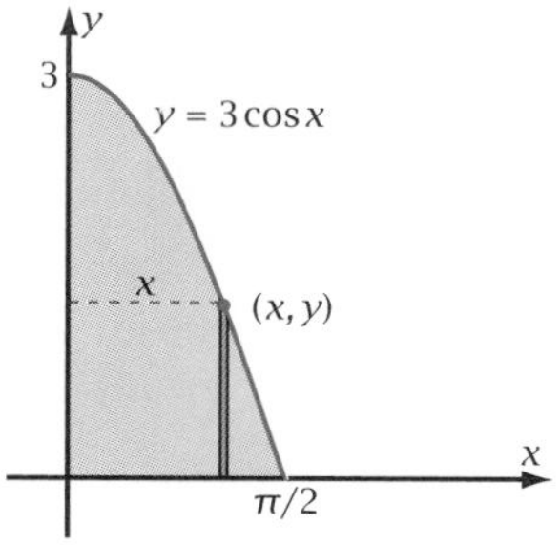

Figure 11-4d

a. Figure 11-4d shows the region $R$. Slicing parallel to the $y$-axis gives strips in which all points are about the same displacement from the $y$-axis. Use $A$ for area and $M_y$ for moment with respect to the $y$-axis. The moment, $dM_y$, of a strip of area $dA$ is

$$dM_y = x\,dA = x(3\cos x)\,dx$$
$$= 3x\cos x\,dx.$$
$$M_y = \int_0^{\pi/2} 3x\cos x\,dx$$
$$= 3x\sin x + 3\cos x\,\Big|_0^{\pi/2} = \tfrac{3\pi}{2} + 0 - 0 - 3 = 1.71238\ldots\text{in}^3$$ Why are the units $\text{in}^3$?

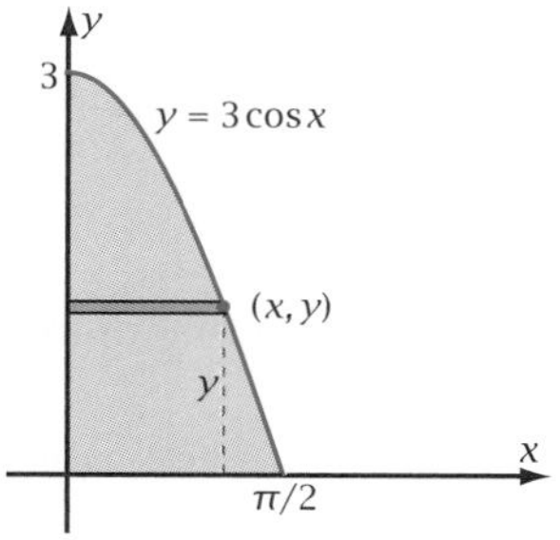

Figure 11-4e

b. To find $M_x$, the moment with respect to the $x$-axis, slice horizontally (Figure 11-4e). That way, each point in the strip will be about the same displacement from the $x$-axis.

$$dM_x = y\,dA = y(x\,dy)$$

You could put $\cos^{-1}(y/3)$ in place of $x$ and integrate from 0 to 3. If you are integrating algebraically, it is easier to substitute $3\cos x$ for $y$ and $-3\sin x\,dx$ for $dy$. Since $x$ is $\pi/2$ when $y$ is 0, and 0 when $y$ is 3, the limits of integration are $\pi/2$ to 0.

$$M_x = \int_{\pi/2}^{0} (3\cos x)(x)(-3\sin x\, dx)$$

$$= -9\int_{\pi/2}^{0} x\cos x\sin x\, dx = -\tfrac{9}{2}\int_{\pi/2}^{0} x\sin 2x\, dx$$

$$= -\tfrac{9}{2}\left(-\tfrac{1}{2}x\cos 2x + \tfrac{1}{4}\sin 2x\right)\Big|_{\pi/2}^{0}$$

$$= -\tfrac{9}{2}(0 + 0 - \tfrac{\pi}{4} + 0) = \tfrac{9\pi}{8} = 3.534291\ldots \approx 3.53 \text{ in}^3$$

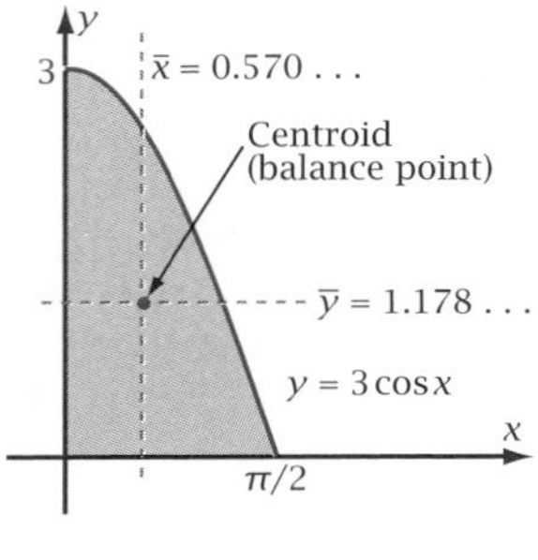


Figure 11-4f

c. To find the centroid, you need to find the area of the region first. You can either integrate $3\cos x$ from 0 to $\pi/2$ or recall that the area under a half-arch of $y = \cos x$ equals 1 so that the total area is 3.

$$\bar{x}A = M_y$$

$$\bar{x} = \frac{3\pi/2 - 3}{3} = 0.570796\ldots \approx 0.57 \text{ in.}$$

$$\bar{y}A = M_x$$

$$\bar{y} = \frac{9\pi/8}{3} = 1.178097\ldots \approx 1.18 \text{ in.}$$

■

Figure 11-4f shows the location of the centroid, point (0.57 . . ., 1.178 . . .).

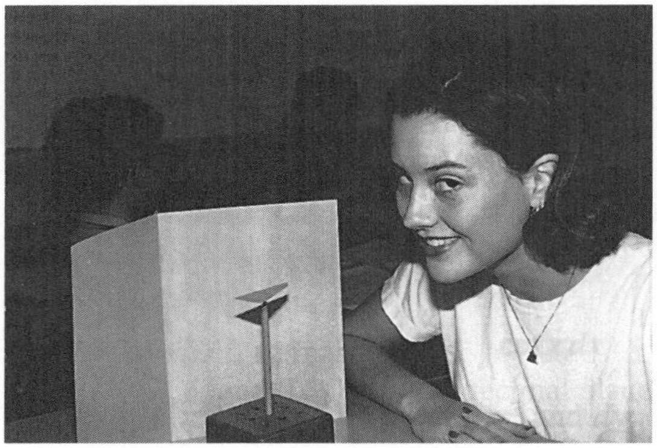

The photograph shows the region in Example 3 drawn on cardboard. The cutout will balance on a pencil point placed at the centroid!

The last example for this section shows you the meaning of second moment.

**■ Example 4** For the region $R$ in Example 3,

a. Find the second moment of area of the region with respect to the $y$-axis.

b. Find $\bar{x}$, the $x$-coordinate of the center of second moment, which is the displacement from the $y$-axis for which

(Displacement)$^2$(area) = second moment.

**Solutions**

a. Slice parallel to the $y$-axis as previously shown in Figure 11-4d so that points in a strip will be about the same displacement from that axis.

$$dM_y = x^2\, dA = x^2(3\cos x\, dx)$$ Second moment = (area) (square of displacement)

$$M_y = \int_0^{\pi/2} 3x^2\cos x\, dx = 1.402203\ldots \text{ in}^4$$ Why are the units in$^4$?

b. To find the center of second moment, you must use the fact that displacement squared times area equals second moment.

$$(\bar{x})^2 A = M_y (\bar{x})^2(3) = 1.402203\ldots$$

$$\bar{x} = \sqrt{\frac{1.402203\ldots}{3}} = 0.683667\ldots \approx 0.68 \text{ in.}$$

Why do the units come out inches?

The "stiffness"of a beam is related to the second moment of area of a region that has the cross-sectional shape of the beam. The resistance of a uniform flat plate to being rotated about an axis is related to the second moment of area about that axis. The higher the second moment, the more difficult it is to start the region rotating, or stop it once it gets started. For this reason the second moment of area is sometimes called the **moment of inertia** of the region. The displacement to the center of second moment from the axis of reference is called the **radius of gyration**. The same terms apply to second moments of volume or mass of a solid figure.

# Problem Set 11-4

### *Do These Quickly*

The following problems are intended to refresh your skills. You should be able to do all ten problems in less than five minutes.

**Q1.** Evaluate $-x^2$ if $x$ is 5.

**Q2.** Evaluate $x^2$ if $x$ is $-11$.

**Q3.** Write $\sin 2x$ in terms of functions of $x$.

**Q4.** Write $\cos^2 x$ in terms of $\cos 2x$.

**Q5.** Resolve into partial fractions: $1/[(x-2)(x-5)]$

**Q6.** Integrate: $\int dx/[(x-2)(x-5)]$

**Q7.** Differentiate: $y = 1/[(x-2)(x-5)]$

**Q8.** What hypothesis of Rolle's theorem is not a hypothesis of the mean value theorem?

**Q9.** Write the definition of indefinite integral.

**Q10.** Is $f(x) = x^3 - 7x$ increasing or decreasing at $x = 2$?

1. *Paraboloid Problem:* The region in Quadrant I under the graph of $y = 9 - x^2$ is rotated about the $y$-axis to form a solid. Assume that dimensions are in centimeters.
   a. Find the volume of the solid.
   b. Find its first moment of volume with respect to the $xz$-plane.
   c. Find its centroid.

2. *Ellipsoid Problem:* A half-ellipsoid is formed by rotating about the $x$-axis the region in the first quadrant bounded by (Figure 11-4g)

$$\left(\frac{x}{12}\right)^2 + \left(\frac{y}{5}\right)^2 = 1 \text{ (dimensions in feet).}$$

   a. Confirm by appropriate integration that the volume is $\frac{2}{3}\pi(12)(5^2)$.
   b. Find the first moment of volume with respect to the $yz$-plane.
   c. Find the centroid.

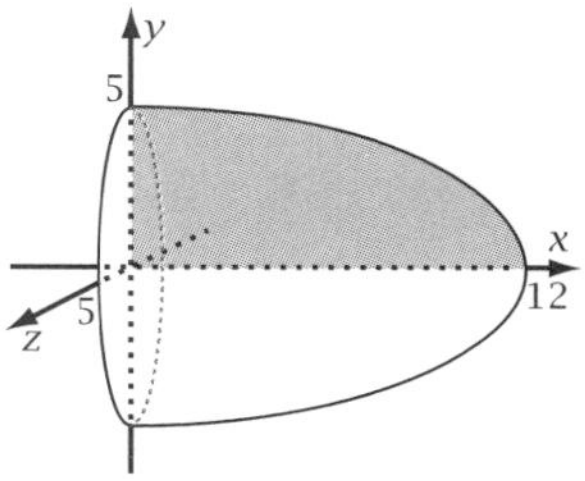

Figure 11-4g

3. *Paraboloid Mass Problem:* The paraboloid in Problem 1 has density (g/cm$^3$) that is constant in the radial direction, but directly proportional to the cube root of $y$ in the axial direction.
   a. Find the mass of the solid.
   b. Find the first moment of mass of the solid with respect to the xz-plane.
   c. Find the center of mass.
   d. True or false: "The center of mass of a solid is always at the centroid."
4. *Ellipsoid Mass Problem:* The half-ellipsoid in Problem 2 has a weight density (lb/ft$^3$) that is constant in the radial direction, but varies directly with $x$ in the axial direction.
   a. Find the weight of the solid.
   b. Find the first moment of weight of the solid with respect to the $yz$-plane.
   c. Find the center of weight (which is the same as the center of mass in this case).
   d. True or false: "The center of mass of a solid is always at the centroid."

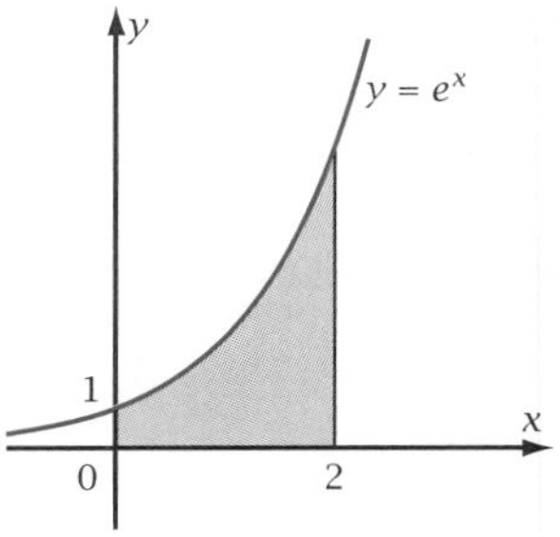

Figure 11-4h

5. *Exponential Region and Solid Problem:* Let $R$ be the region under the graph of $y = e^x$ from $x = 0$ to $x = 2$ (Figure 11-4h).
   a. Find the $x$-coordinate of the centroid of $R$.
   b. $R$ is rotated about the $x$-axis to form a solid. Find the $x$-coordinate of the centroid.
   c. True or false: "The centroid of a region and the centroid of the solid formed by rotating that region have the same $x$-coordinate."

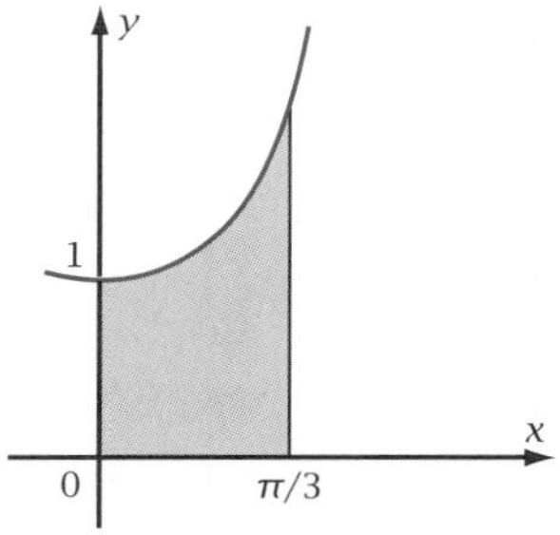

Figure 11-4i

6. *Secant Curve Region Problem:* Let $R$ be the region under the graph of $y = \sec x$ from $x = 0$ to $x = \pi/3$ (Figure 11-4i).
   a. Find the $x$-coordinate of the centroid of $R$.
   b. $R$ is rotated about the $x$-axis to form a solid. Find the $x$-coordinate of the centroid.
   c. True or false: "The centroid of a region and the centroid of the solid formed by rotating that region have the same $x$-coordinate."
7. *Centroid of a Triangle Experiment:* Prove that the centroid of a triangle is located one-third of the way up from the base (Figure 11-4j). Then draw a triangle on cardboard, draw lines one-third of the way from each base, and cut out the triangle. If your work is done accurately, you should find that the lines intersect at one point and that you can balance the triangle on the point of a pencil placed at that point.

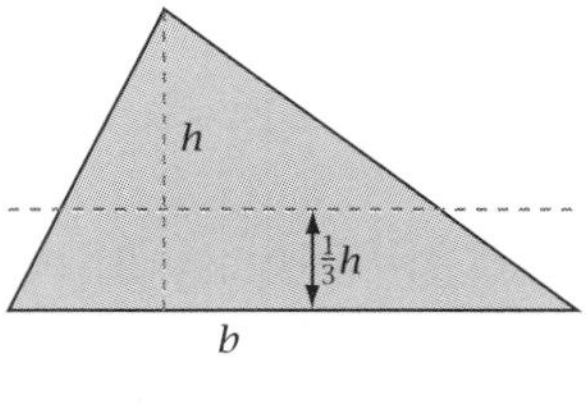

Figure 11-4j

8. *Centroid Cut-Out Experiment:* Let $R$ be the region under the graph of $y = x^{2/3}$ from $x = 0$ to $x = 2$, where $x$ and $y$ are in centimeters.
   a. Find the area of $R$.
   b. Find the first moment of $R$ with respect to the $x$-axis.
   c. Find the first moment of $R$ with respect to the $y$-axis.
   d. Find the coordinates of the centroid of $R$.

e. Plot an accurate graph of $R$ on an index card or graph paper. Mark the centroid. Then cut out the region and try to balance the region on a pencil point at the centroid.

9. *Second Moment of Area Problem:* Let $R$ be the region under the graph of $y = \sin x$ from $x = 0$ to $x = \pi$ (Figure 11-4k), where $x$ and $y$ are in centimeters.

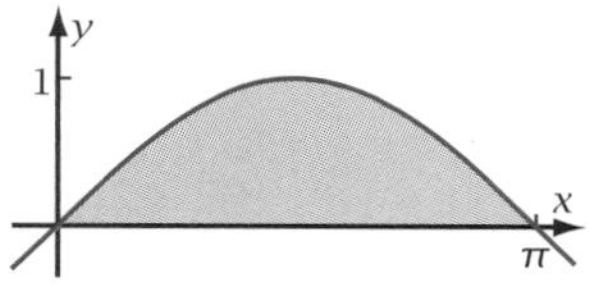

Figure 11-4k

a. Show that the centroid of $R$ is at $x = \pi/2$.

b. Find the second moment of area of the region with respect to the $y$-axis.

c. Find the radius of gyration (displacement to center of second moment) of $R$ with respect to the $y$-axis.

10. *Second Moments for Plane Regions Problem:* Find the second moment of area for the following shapes (Figure 11-4l):

a. A rectangle of base $B$ and height $H$, with respect to an axis along the base.

b. A rectangle of base $B$ and height $H$, with respect to an axis through the centroid, parallel to the base.

c. A triangle of base $B$ and altitude $H$, with respect to an axis along the base.

d. A triangle of base $B$ and altitude $H$, with respect to an axis parallel to the base, one-third of the way to the opposite vertex (that is, through the centroid).

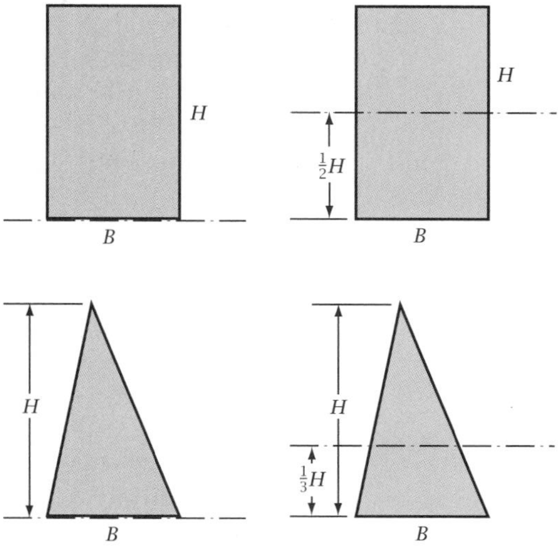

Figure 11-4l

11. *Second Moments for Solid Figures:* Find the second moment of volume and radius of gyration for these solids (Figure 11-4m):

a. A cylinder of radius $R$ and altitude $H$, with respect to its axis.

b. A cone of base radius $R$ and altitude $H$, with respect to its axis.

c. A sphere of radius $R$, with respect to a diameter.

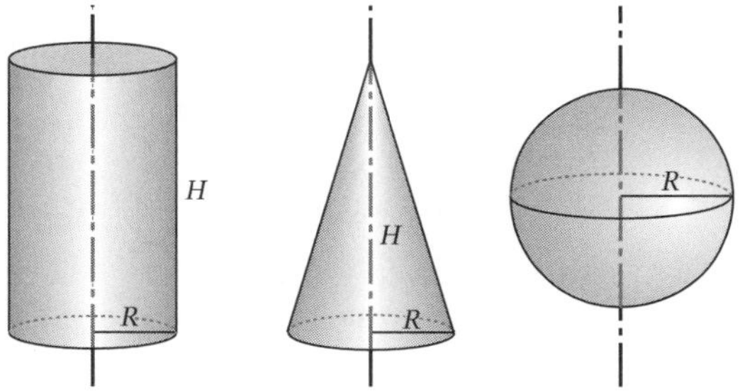

Figure 11-4m

12. *Rotation of Solids Problem:* The amount of resistance an object has to starting or stopping rotation is measured by its second moment of mass with respect to the axis of rotation. If the density is constant, the second moment of mass equals the density times the second moment of volume. Suppose that 1000 $cm^3$ of clay is made into a sphere, and another 1000 $cm^3$ is made into a cylinder whose diameter equals its altitude (Figure 11-4n). Which one has higher resistance to rotating? Justify your answer.

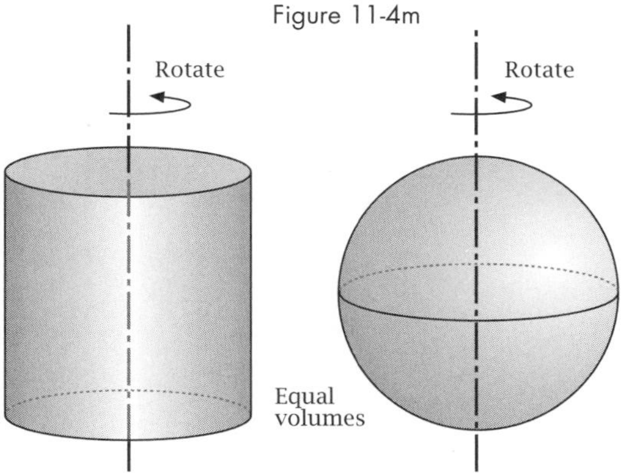

Figure 11-4n

13. *Beam Moment Problem:* The stiffness of a beam is directly proportional to the second moment of area of the beam's cross section with respect to an axis through the centroid of the cross section. In this problem you will investigate the stiffness of beams with the same cross-sectional area but with different shapes.

  a. Prove that if a rectangle has base $B$ and altitude $H$, then the second moment of area with respect to an axis through the centroid and parallel to the base is equal to $BH^3/12$.

  b. Find the stiffness of a 2″ by 12″ beam (Figure 11-4o) if it is
    i. turned on edge.
    ii. lying flat.
  Use $k$ for the proportionality constant. Based on the results, tell why boards used for floor joists in houses are turned on edge rather than being laid flat.

  c. An I-beam is made with the same cross-sectional area as the 2″ by 12″ in 13b. Find its stiffness if
    i. all three parts (two flanges and one web) are 4 in. wide.
    ii. the two flanges are 2″ by 4″, but the web is 1″ by 8″.

  d. Does increasing an I-beam's depth without changing the cross-sectional area make much change in the beam's stiffness? What physical limitations keep people from making a beam very tall and thus very stiff?

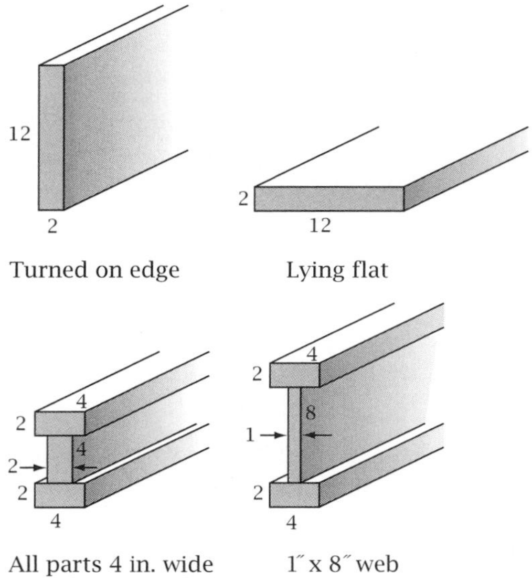

Figure 11-4o

14. *Introduction to the Theorems of Pappus:* The region $R$ under the graph of $y = x^3$ from $x = 0$ to $x = 2$ is rotated about the $y$-axis to form a solid (Figure 11-4p).

  a. Find the area of $R$.

  b. Find the volume of the solid using vertical slices of $R$.

  c. Find the first moment of area of $R$ with respect to the $y$-axis. What do you notice about the integral?

  d. Find the $x$-coordinate of the centroid of $R$.

  e. A theorem of Pappus states that the volume of a solid of revolution equals the area of the region being rotated times the distance the centroid of the region travels. Show that this problem confirms the theorem.

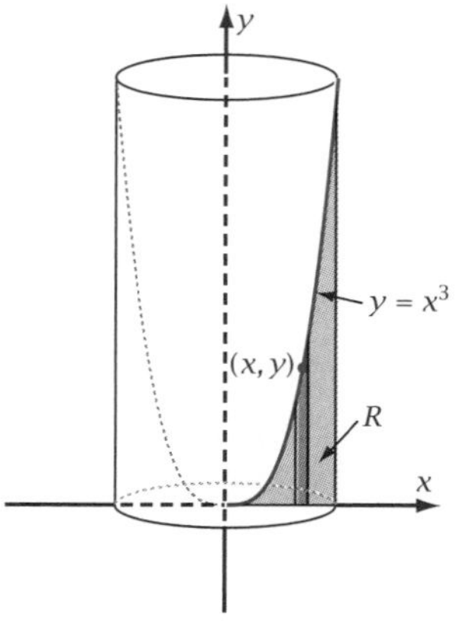

Figure 11-4p

15. *Theorem of Pappus Problem:* Pappus was a Greek mathematician who lived in Alexandria in the fourth century A.D. One of his theorems states the following.

> **Theorem: The Theorem of Pappus for Volumes**
>
> The volume, $V$, of a solid of revolution is given by
>
> $$V = 2\pi\bar{R}A,$$
>
> where $A$ is the area of the region being rotated, $\bar{R}$ is the displacement from the axis of rotation to the centroid of the region, and the region is not on both sides of the axis of rotation. The quantity $2\pi\bar{R}$ is thus the distance the centroid travels as the region rotates.

In Problem 14, you saw an example of this theorem. In this problem you will use the theorem, once forward and once backward.

a. *Toroid Problem:* A toroid (Figure 11-4q) is formed by rotating a circle of radius $r$ about an axis $R$ units from the center of the circle, where $r \le R$. Find the volume of the toroid.

b. *Centroid of a Semicircle:* A semicircle of radius $r$ is rotated about its diameter to form a sphere (Figure 11-4r). You know formulas for the area of a semicircle and for the volume of a sphere. Use these facts to find the displacement from the center of a semicircle to its centroid.

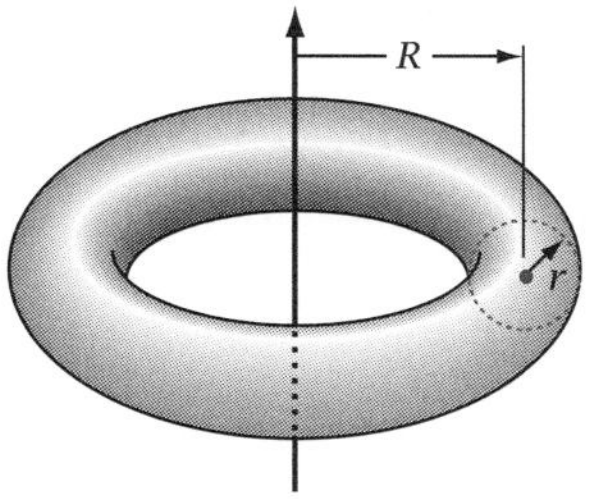


Figure 11-4q

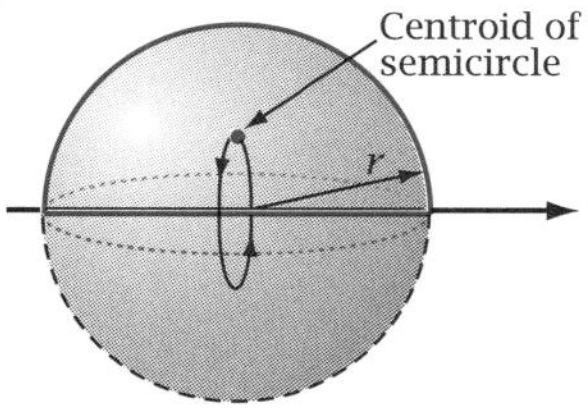


Figure 11-4r

16. *Theorem of Pappus Proof:* Prove the theorem of Pappus for volumes.

# 11-5 Force Exerted by a Variable Pressure—Center of Pressure

Pressure exerted by a fluid such as air or water is defined to be the force exerted by the fluid per unit area. For instance, water in your home's pipes is usually at a pressure of 40 to 100 psi (lb/in$^2$). The air in a scuba diving tank is compressed to about 3000 psi. This means that each square inch of the tank's wall is pushed with a force of 3000 lb. As a result of the definition of pressure,

**Force = (pressure)(area).**

In many real-world situations, the pressure acting on a surface is different at various places on the surface. For instance, the pressure acting on an airplane's wings is usually higher near the middle of the wing than it is at either the leading or trailing edge. So the total force, which holds up the plane, must be found by integrating rather than just by multiplying.

In this section you will learn how to calculate the force exerted by a variable pressure. You will also calculate the **moment of force**, and use it to find the **center of pressure**, where the entire force could be concentrated to produce the same moment.

**OBJECTIVE**

Given a region and a function specifying the pressure acting on the region, be able to calculate the total force, the moment of force, and the center of pressure.

**Example 1**

*Weir Problem:* A weir (a small dam) is to be built across a stream. When finished, the weir will have a vertical parabolic cross section the shape of the region above the graph of $y = x^2$ and below the line $y = 4$, where $x$ and $y$ are in feet (Figure 11-5a). The pressure at any sample point below the surface of the water will be directly proportional to the displacement from the surface to that point. The proportionality constant is the density of water, 62.4 lb/ft$^3$.

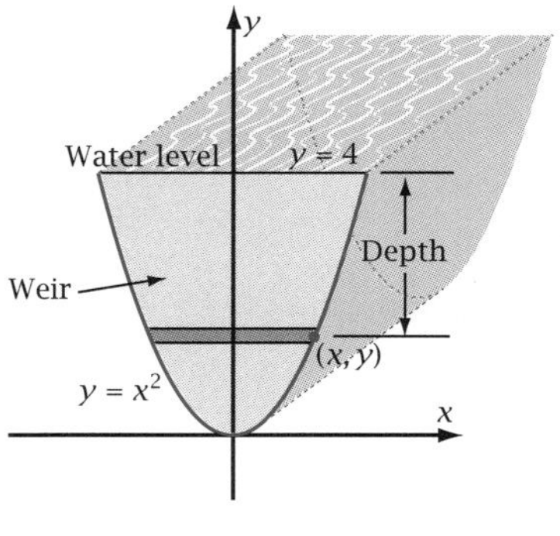


Figure 11-5a

a. Predict the total force acting on the weir when the water is all the way to the top.

b. Find the first moment of force with respect to the $x$-axis.

c. Find the "center of pressure," the point on the face of the weir where the entire force could be applied to produce the same moment with respect to the $x$-axis.

d. The weir face is wider at the top, so you would expect the center of pressure to be more than halfway up. But the pressure is greater toward the bottom, so you would also expect the center of pressure to be less than halfway up. Based on your answer to part c, which of these two competing effects predominates?

***Solutions***

a. Slice the region parallel to the $x$-axis so that the pressure will be essentially constant at any point in the slice. Pick a sample point $(x, y)$ in the slice and on the graph. Let $F$ stand for force, $p$ for pressure, and $A$ for area. By the definition of pressure,

$$dF = p\,dA.$$

Since pressure varies directly with depth, $(4 - y)$, the pressure at the sample point will be

$$p = k(4 - y),$$

where $k = 62.4$ lb/ft$^3$, which will be substituted at the end to get a numerical answer. Since $dA = 2x\,dy = 2y^{1/2}\,dy$, you can write

$$dF = 2k(4 - y)y^{1/2}\,dy.$$

To find the total force acting on the weir's face, you add up all the $dF$'s and take the limit as $dy$ goes to zero. This process is, of course, definite integration.

$$F = \int_0^4 2k(4 - y)y^{1/2}\,dy$$

$$F = 2k\left(\tfrac{8}{3}y^{3/2} - \tfrac{2}{5}y^{5/2}\right)\Big|_0^4$$

$$= \frac{256k}{15} = \frac{(256)(62.4)}{15}$$

$$= 1064.96, \text{ or about } 1065 \text{ lb}$$

b. The first moment of force with respect to the $x$-axis is defined to be the product of the force and the displacement from the $x$-axis to the point where the force is acting. Fortunately, all points in the horizontal slice (Figure 11-5a) are essentially the same displacement from the $x$-axis as the sample point $(x, y)$. Using $M$ for moment, the moment acting on the slice is

$$dM = y\,dF = y \cdot p\,dA,$$

where $y$ and $p$ are both measured at the sample point.

$$dM = y \cdot 2k(4 - y)y^{1/2}\,dy \qquad \text{Substitute for } p \text{ and } dA.$$

$$= 2k(4y^{3/2} - y^{5/2})\,dy$$

$$\therefore M = 2k\int_0^4 (4y^{3/2} - y^{5/2})\,dy \qquad \text{Add the } dM\text{'s and take the limit (that is, integrate).}$$

$$= 2k\left(\tfrac{8}{5}y^{5/2} - \tfrac{2}{7}y^{5/2}\right)\Big|_0^4$$

$$= \frac{1024k}{35} = \frac{(1024)(62.4)}{35} = 1825.645\ldots, \text{ or about } 1826 \text{ lb-ft.}$$

c. By the definition of center of pressure, its vertical coordinate, $\overline{y}$, is the number for which

$$\overline{y}F = M.$$

$$\therefore \overline{y} = \frac{1024k/35}{256k/15} = \frac{12}{7}, \text{ or } 1\frac{5}{7} \text{ ft}$$

By symmetry, the $x$-coordinate, $\overline{x}$, of the center of pressure is zero, so the center of pressure is at $(0, 1\frac{5}{7})$.

d. The center of pressure is less than halfway up, meaning that the increasing pressure at greater depths predominates over the decreasing area. ■

As you learned in Section 11-4, the first moment of force with respect to an axis is called torque. In part b of Example 1 above, the 1826 lb-ft is the amount of torque exerted by the water on the dam face. It measures the amount of twisting the force does on the dam face, tending to make it rotate about the $x$-axis and fall over.

## Problem Set 11-5

### *Do These Quickly*

The following problems are intended to refresh your skills. You should be able to do all ten problems in less than five minutes.

**Q1.** The geometrical center of a solid is called its —?—.

**Q2.** The point where all the mass of a solid could be concentrated is called its —?—.

**Q3.** The displacement from an axis to the center of second moment with respect to that axis is called the —?—.

**Q4.** The process of adding up parts of a physical quantity then taking the limit as the size of the parts goes to zero is called —?—.

**Q5.** The process of finding the antiderivative is called —?—.

**Q6.** Density equals —?— divided by —?—.

**Q7.** Simplify: $(x^{1/3})(x^{1/6})$

**Q8.** Integrate: $\int \sec x \, dx$

**Q9.** Differentiate: $y = \tan^{-1} x$

**Q10.** $(0.5)(e^x + e^{-x})$ is defined to be —?—.

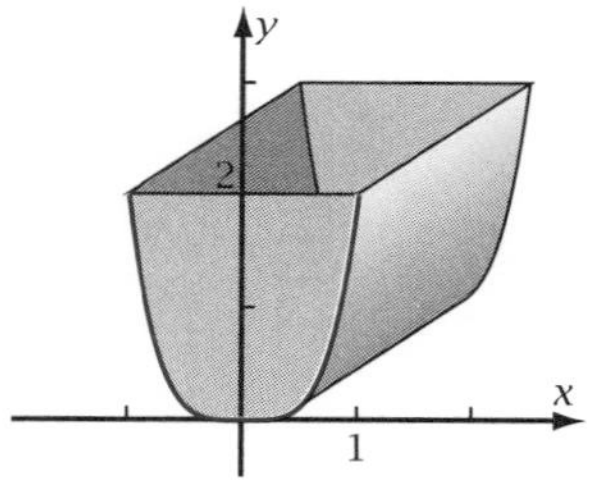

Figure 11-5b

1. *Trough Problem:* A trough has a vertical end in the shape of the region above the graph of $y = 2x^4$ and below the line $y = 2$, where $x$ and $y$ are in feet (Figure 11-5b). The trough is filled with liquid of density $k$ lb/ft$^3$.

   a. Find the force acting on the end of the trough. Recall that force = (pressure)(area), and the pressure at a point varies directly with the displacement from the surface of the liquid to that point.

   b. The force in 1a causes a moment with respect to the $x$-axis. However, different points on the end of the trough are at different displacements from the $x$-axis. Find the moment of force with respect to the $x$-axis.

c. Find the center of pressure, where the entire force could be concentrated to produce the same moment with respect to the $x$-axis.

2. *Dam Problem:* At its narrowest point, Scorpion Gulch is 20 ft wide and 100 ft deep. A dam at this point has its vertical face in the shape of the region bounded by the graphs of $y = x^2$ and $y = 100$, where $x$ and $y$ are in ft. Answer the following questions.

   a. Confirm that the dam is 20 ft wide at the top.

   b. Find the area of the vertical dam face.

   c. When the gulch is filled with water to the top of the dam, the greatest force will be exerted. It is important to know whether this force will be large enough to rip the dam from its foundations. Find this total force.

   d. The dam could also fail by being pushed over. The first moment of force with respect to the $x$-axis is the quantity that the dam must withstand to prevent this. Find the first moment of force with respect to the $x$-axis.

   e. How far above the bottom of Scorpion Gulch could the entire force be concentrated to produce the same moment as in 2d?

3. *Ship's Bulkhead Problem:* A bulkhead on a ship is a vertical wall that separates two compartments. Bulkheads are often designed so that they will withstand the water pressure if the compartment on one side of it gets flooded. Suppose that a bulkhead is to go all the way across a ship (Figure 11-5c). The bulkhead is to be 40 ft wide at the top and 32 ft from bottom to top. The cross section of the ship where the bulkhead will go is in the shape of the quartic ellipse

$$\left(\frac{x}{20}\right)^4 + \left(\frac{y-32}{32}\right)^4 = 1$$

where $y$ is the vertical displacement (in ft) from the bottom of the ship to the sample point and $x$ is the horizontal displacement (also in ft) from the center line of the ship to the sample point.

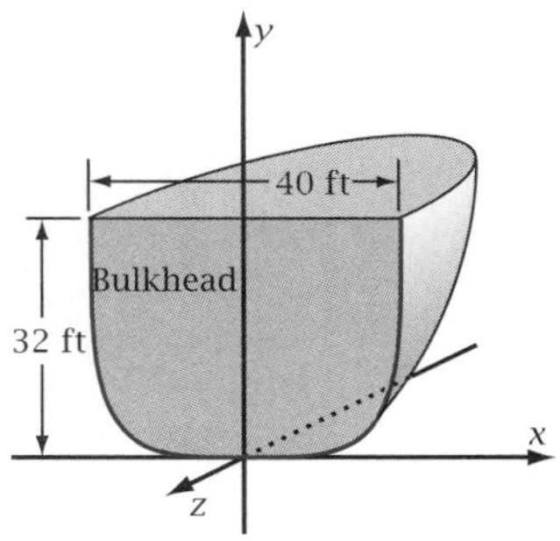

Figure 11-5c

   a. Find the area of the bulkhead.

   b. Find the force that the bulkhead must be designed to withstand from water pressure if the compartment on one side is filled to 32 ft with seawater of density 67 lb/ft$^3$.

   c. The bulkhead must also be designed to withstand the torque caused by this force. Find the torque with respect to the $x$-axis, taking into account that different parts of the force act at different displacements from the axis.

   d. Find the center of pressure, at which the total force could be concentrated to produce the same torque.

   e. Find the centroid of the bulkhead. Is the center of pressure located at the centroid?

   f. When the ship is floating, the water outside is expected to come up to $y = 16$ ft. Assuming that the ship has a uniform cross section, the center of buoyancy of the ship is located at the centroid of the part of the bulkhead that lies below the water line. Find the center of buoyancy. (The center of mass of the ship must be below the center of buoyancy, or the ship will capsize. Ships often carry ballast, consisting of rock, metal scrap, lead, and so on, at the bottom for the specific purpose of lowering the center of mass.)

4. *Oil Truck Problem:* An oil truck has a tank the shape of an elliptical cylinder (Figure 11-5d). The tank is 12 ft wide and 6 ft high. Your job is to analyze the forces acting on the elliptical end of the tank.

   a. Write an equation for the ellipse using axes with origin at the ellipse's center.

   b. Suppose that the tank is half full. Find the force acting on the ellipse. Recall that pressure at a sample point is directly proportional to the point's displacement below the liquid's surface. The proportionality constant is the density of oil, 50 lb/ft$^3$. (If your answer comes out negative, see if you can find your mistake!)

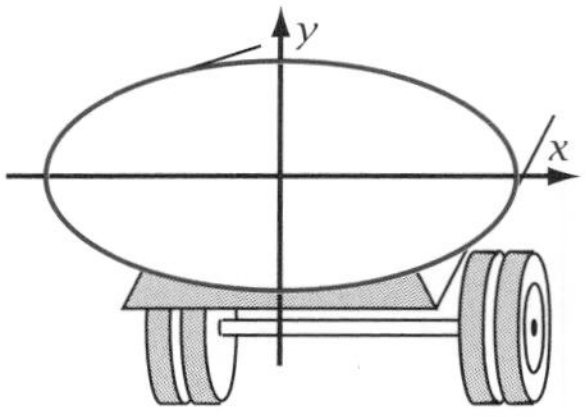

Figure 11-5d

5. *Airplane Wing Problem I:* An airplane wing has the shape of the region bounded by the graph of $y = 60\cos\frac{\pi}{20}x$ and the $x$-axis, where $x$ and $y$ are in ft.

   a. Find the area of the wing.

   b. Assume that the pressure pushing up on the wing when the plane is in flight is constant in the $y$-direction, but is directly proportional to the quantity $(10 - |x|)$ in the $x$-direction. Find the total force acting on the wing.

   c. In order for the plane to fly, each wing must lift 96 tons. What must the proportionality constant equal?

6. *Airplane Wing Problem II:* Suppose you have been hired by Fly-By-Night Aircraft Corporation. You are to analyze the forces that will act on the wings of a new plane. From the Design Department you find that, looking from the top, the wing's shape (Figure 11-5e) is the region bounded by the graph of $y = 100 - x^2$ and the $x$-axis, where $x$ and $y$ are in feet. The $x$-axis runs along the line where the wing joins the fuselage.

   a. The Research Department finds that in normal flight the pressure pushing up on the wings varies linearly with $x$. The pressure is 90 lb/ft$^2$ at the $y$-axis, and 20 lb/ft$^2$ at $x = 10$. Find the total force acting on the wing.

   b. Find the first moment of force with respect to the $y$-axis.

   c. For proper balance you need to know where in the $x$-direction the force could be concentrated to produce the same first moment of force. Find the $x$-coordinate of the center of pressure.

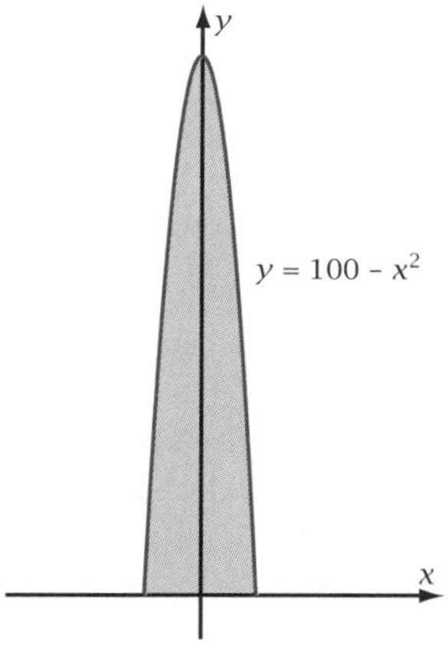

Figure 11-5e

   d. During a certain banking maneuver, the pressure pattern changes. It becomes directly proportional to $y$, and does not vary in the $x$-direction. The pressure is 60 lb/ft$^2$ at $y = 50$. Find the total force acting on the wing.

   e. Find the first moment of force in 6d with respect to the $x$-axis.

   f. The first moment of force in 6e measures the amount of twisting needed to make the plane bank. How far out on the wing could the total force be concentrated and produce the same first moment with respect to the $x$-axis?

7. *Double-Integration Airplane Wing Problem:* The place where an airplane's wing joins the fuselage must be designed to withstand the bending torque caused by air pressure acting on the wing. The stiffness of this joint is measured by the second moment of area of the joint with respect to a horizontal axis. Suppose that a new design of plane is to have a cross section as shown in Figure 11-5f. The equation of the curve is

$$y = 0.25(x - 4) - (x - 4)^{1/3}.$$

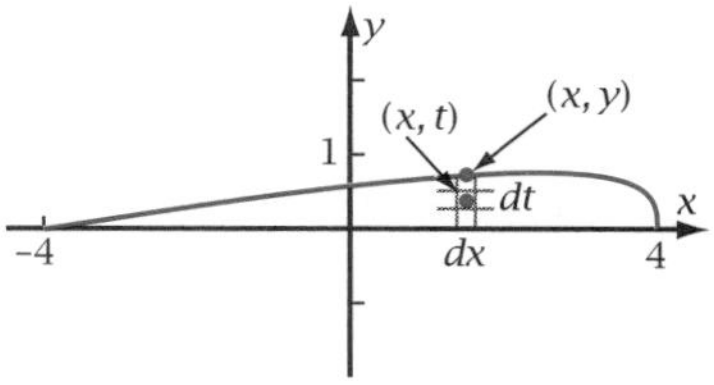

Figure 11-5f

Your mission is to calculate the second moment of area of this region with respect to the $x$-axis.

a. Slice the region vertically into strips of width $dx$. Slice each strip horizontally, forming rectangles of dimensions $dx$ by $dt$. Find the moment of a strip by finding the moment of a rectangle, then integrating from $t = 0$ to $t = y$. Recall that $x$ and $dx$ will be constants with respect to this integration.

b. Find the total second moment of the region by adding up the moments of the vertical strips and taking the limit (that is, by integrating with respect to $x$).

8. *Double Integration Variable Pressure Problem:* A variable pressure acts on the region bounded by the curve $y = e^{-x}$ and the lines $y = 1$ and $x = \ln 5$. Find the force acting on this region if

a. The pressure is constant in the $y$-direction but varies directly with the square of $x$.

b. The pressure is constant in the $x$-direction but varies inversely with $y$.

c. The pressure varies both directly with the square of $x$ and inversely with $y$. To solve this problem, you must slice one way, then slice the slice the other way. One integration gives $dF$. A second integration gives $F$. See Figure 11-5g for suggestions.

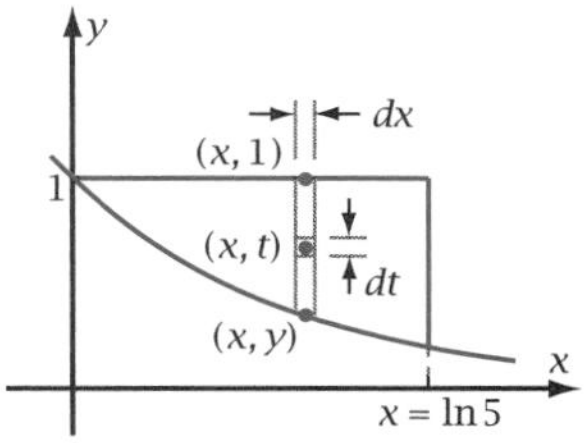

Figure 11-5g

9. Problems 7 and 8 involve *double integrals.* Why do you suppose this name is used?

10. *Floodgate Problem:* A vertical floodgate at the bottom of a dam has the shape of the region bounded by the graph of $y = 5\tan^2(\pi/8)x$ and the line $y = 5$, where $x$ and $y$ are in feet (Figure 11-5h). The lake behind the dam is filled with water to the level where $y = 20$ ft.

a. Find the area of the floodgate.

b. Find the total force acting on the floodgate.

c. The force acting on one side of the floodgate makes it difficult to open. The force with which the equipment must pull up on the gate equals the coefficient of friction between the gate and the dam multiplied by the force of the water acting on the gate. Experience shows that this force is about 10,000 lb. What does the coefficient of friction equal?

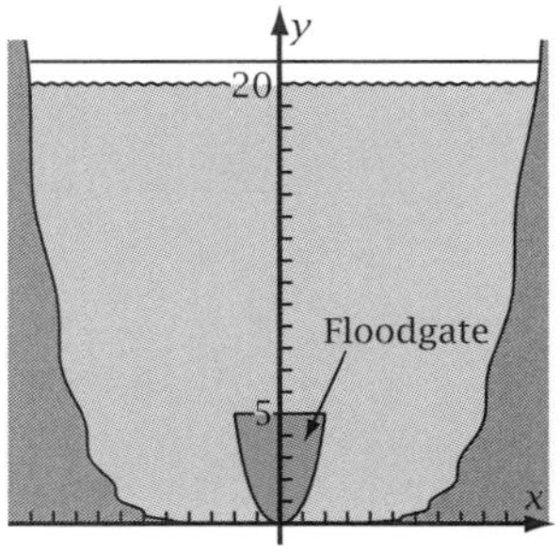

Figure 11-5h

# 11-6 Other Variable-Factor Products

The area of a rectangular region equals its length times its width. For the region in Quadrant I bounded by the graph of $y = 4 - x^2$ (Figure 11-6a), the length and width vary. If you slice the region into horizontal strips, you are taking a small amount of length, $dy$, in which the width is essentially constant. If you slice into vertical strips, you are taking a small amount of width, $dx$, in which the length is essentially constant. In the former case, $dA = x\,dy$. In the latter case, $dA = y\,dx$. Integrating either one gives the exact area by adding the areas of the strips and taking the limit.

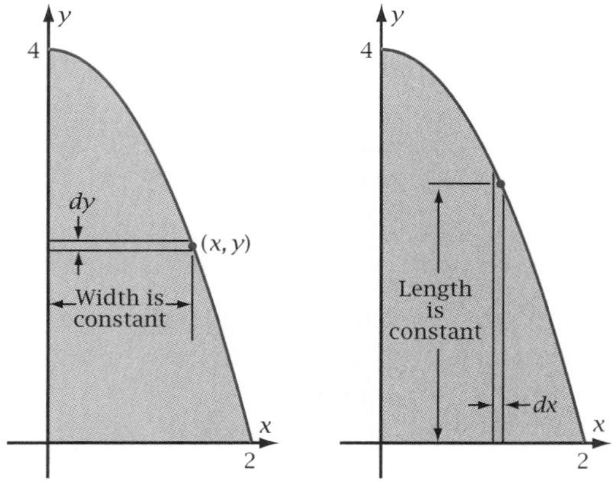


Figure 11-6a

Most applications of definite integration involve similar reasoning. A product has one or both factors that vary. You take a small amount of one quantity (slice) in which the other quantity is essentially constant, evaluate the "constant" quantity at a sample point in the strip, and find the product. The trick is in deciding which factor to slice. For example, volume = (cross-sectional area)(altitude). For plane slices (Figure 11-6b left), you take a small amount of altitude, $dy$, in which the cross-sectional area, $\pi x^2$, is constant. For cylindrical shells you take a small amount of cross-sectional area, $2\pi x\,dx$, in which the altitude, $y$, is constant (Figure 11-6b, right).

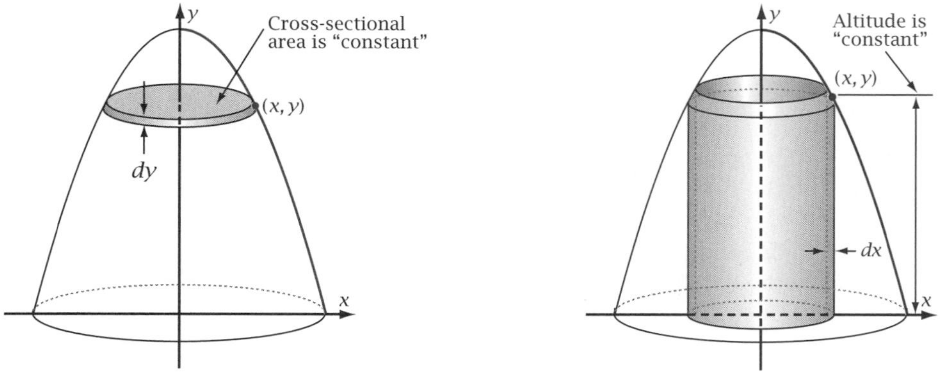


Figure 11-6b

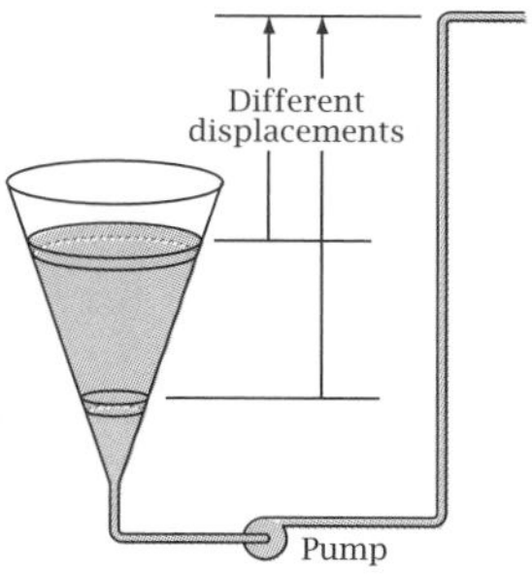

Figure 11-6c

Slicing may be easier one way than another. Work = (force)(displacement) or $W = (F)(D)$. If the whole object is moved the same amount, you should take small displacements, $dD$, in which the force is essentially constant, so $dW = F\,dD$. But different parts of a fluid may move different amounts. So it is preferable to take small amounts of force (that is, weight) for which the displacement is constant. In this case, $dW = D\,dF$ (Figure 11-6c).

In this section you will work problems in which one factor of a product varies. You will be expected to read and interpret the definition of each physical quantity, then translate it into the appropriate mathematics. It is the ability to see the underlying similarities in seemingly different phenomena that will enable you to make intelligent applications of mathematics.

***OBJECTIVE***

Given a real-world situation in which a product has a factor that varies, calculate the value of the product.

***Some Variable-Factor Products***

- Distance = (rate)(time)
- Area = (width)(length)
- Volume = (cross-sectional area)(height)
- Work = (force)(displacement)
- Force = (pressure)(area)
- Mass = (density)(volume)
- Moment = (displacement)$^n$(mass, volume, area, force, and so on)
- Worth of a region = (price)(area)

# Problem Set 11-6

### *Do These Quickly*

The following problems are intended to refresh your skills. You should be able to do all ten problems in less than five minutes.

**Q1.** $\int x^{100}\,dx =$ —?—

**Q2.** $\int_{-1}^{1} \tan x\,dx =$ —?—

**Q3.** $\int \ln x\,dx =$ —?—

**Q4.** Write $2\sin x \cos x$ in terms of a trigonometric function of $2x$.

**Q5.** Work = —?—

**Q6.** If $y = \tan^{-1} 3x$, then $y' =$ —?—.

**Q7.** $y = x^3 + 6x^2$ has a point of inflection at $x =$ —?—.

**Q8.** $\dfrac{d}{dx}(\sec^2 x) =$ —?—

**Q9.** If $y = \cos 3x$, then $d^2y/dx^2 =$ —?—.

**Q10.** What figure is the graph of $3x^2 - 7y^2 = 39$ ?

1. *Heat Capacity Problem:* The number of calories (heat, as energy) required to warm a substance from temperature $T_1$ to temperature $T_2$ equals the "heat capacity" of the substance (calories per degree) times the change in temperature $(T_2 - T_1)$, where $T$ is in degrees. Unfortunately, most substances have heat capacities that vary with temperature. Assume that calculus foeride (a rare, tough substance!) has a heat capacity given by

$$C = 10 + 0.3T^{1/2},$$

where $C$ is in calories per degree and $T$ is in degrees. How many calories would be needed to warm a gram of calculus foeride from 100° to 900°?

2. *Phoebe's Speeding Problem:* Phoebe is caught speeding. The fine is \$3.00 per minute for each mile per hour above the 55 mph speed limit. Since she was clocked at speeds up to 64 mph during a 6-minute period, the judge fines her

$$(3.00)(\text{time})(\text{mph over } 55) = (3.00)(6)(64 - 55) = \$162.$$

Phoebe is good at calculus. She argues that her speed varied over the 6 minutes. It was 55 mph at $t = 0$ and $t = 6$, and was 64 mph only at $t = 3$. She figures that her speed, $v$, was

$$v = 55 + 6t - t^2.$$

   a. Show that this equation gives the correct speeds at the times 0, 3, and 6 minutes.

   b. What should Phoebe propose to the judge as a more reasonable fine?

3. *Tunnel Problem:* The amount of money it takes to dig a tunnel equals the length of the tunnel times the cost per unit length. However, the cost per unit length increases as the tunnel gets longer because of the expense of carrying workers and tools in, and carrying dirt and rock out. Assume that the price per foot varies quadratically with the number of feet, $x$, from the beginning of the tunnel.

   a. Find the particular equation for the price per foot if the following prices are known:

| $x$ | price |
|---|---|
| 0 | \$500 |
| 100 | \$820 |
| 200 | \$1180 |

   b. Find the cost per foot for digging at a point 700 feet from the beginning of the tunnel.

   c. Find the total number of dollars for digging a tunnel 1000 feet long if the workers start at one end and dig through to the other end.

   d. How much money could be saved by starting the 1000-foot tunnel from both ends and meeting in the middle?

4. *Water Pipe Problem:* The flow rate of water through a pipe (cubic inches per second) equals the velocity of the water (in inches per second) times the cross-sectional area of the pipe.

   a. Show that velocity times cross-sectional area gives the right units for flow rate.

b. In real pipes, the flow rate varies at different points across the pipe, being a maximum at the center and dropping to zero at the pipe walls (Figure 11-6d). Assume that the velocity, $v$, through any cross-section of a 4-inch diameter pipe is given by

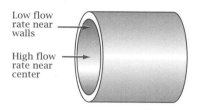

$$v = 4 - x^2,$$

where $x$ is the number of inches from the center of the pipe, and $v$ is in inches per second. Show that the velocity really is a maximum at the center and zero at the pipe walls.

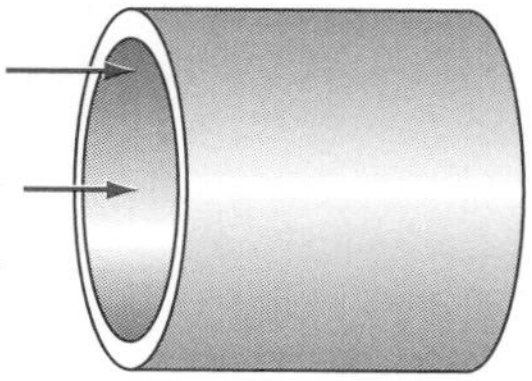

Figure 11-6d

c. What is the flow rate in cubic inches per second?

d. How many gallons per minute (gpm) are flowing through the pipe? (There are 231 cubic inches in a gallon.)

e. How many gpm would be flowing through the pipe if all the water were moving at the maximum velocity?

f. As far as the mathematics is concerned, this problem is identical to some other kind of problem you have worked. Which kind?

5. *Wire-Pulling Problem:* Yank Hardy tries to pull down a tree. He attaches one end of a long wire to the tree, and the other end to the bumper of his Jeep. As he drives the Jeep slowly away, the wire stretches tighter and tighter, and finally breaks. At first the force increases linearly with $x$, the number of inches the wire stretches. At $x = 2$ inches the wire "yields" (that is, begins to break). The table shows the forces to the point where the wire breaks at $x = 5$.

| $x$ (inches) | force (pounds) | |
|---|---|---|
| 0 | 0 | |
| 0.5 | 150 | |
| 1 | 300 | |
| 1.5 | 450 | |
| 2 | 600 | (before yielding) |
| 2 | 450 | (after yielding) |
| 2.5 | 470 | |
| 3 | 440 | |
| 3.5 | 420 | |
| 4 | 410 | |
| 4.5 | 390 | |
| 5 | 330 | (breaks) |

a. Plot the graph of force versus $x$.

b. Describe the behavior of the force function at $x = 2$.

c. Find the work done in stretching the wire from $x = 0$ to $x = 2$.

d. Find the work done in stretching the wire from $x = 2$ to $x = 5$.

e. Find the total work done in breaking the wire.

f. Is it possible for a discontinuous function to be integrable? Explain.

6. *Variable Attraction Problem:* A solid paraboloid is formed by rotating about the $y$-axis the region in Quadrant I bounded by the graph of $y = 4 - x^2$ (Figure 11-6e), where $x$ and $y$ are in centimeters. The solid has a uniform density of $k$ g/cm$^3$.

   a. Find the mass of the solid.

   b. The solid is attracted by a force that is inversely proportional to the square root of the distance from the base of the solid, and directly proportional to the mass. That is,

   $$\text{Force} = (\text{constant})(\text{mass})(y^{-1/2}).$$

   But different parts of the solid are at different distances from the base. By appropriate slicing, find the total force exerted on this solid.

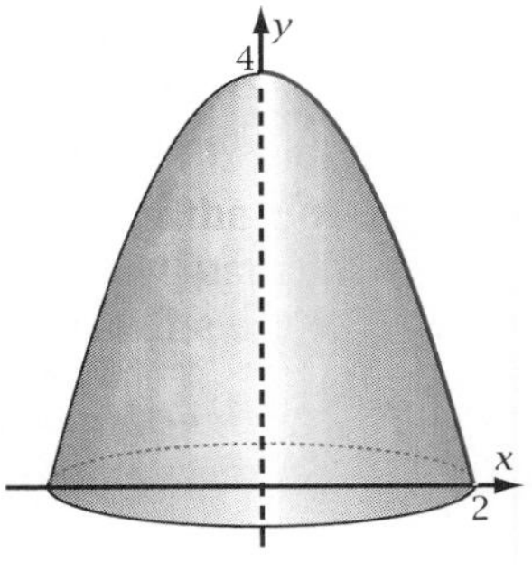

Figure 11-6e

7. *Moment of Inertia Problem:* The second moment of mass of an object with respect to an axis is defined to be the mass times the square of the distance between the object and the axis. It is sometimes called the moment of inertia because it measures how difficult it is to start or stop rotating the solid around the axis. Find the second moment of mass of the solid in Problem 6 with respect to the $y$-axis.

8. *Degree-Days Problem:* Engineers who design heating and air conditioning systems use a quantity called degree-days to measure how much above or below normal the weather has been. For example, if the temperature is 10 degrees above normal for 2 days, then the weather has been $(+10)(2) = +20$ degree-days. If it is 30 degrees below normal for half a day, the weather has been $(-30)(1/2) = -15$ degree-days. However, the temperature varies throughout the day, so degree-days should be calculated by calculus rather than by arithmetic. Suppose that one morning the temperature starts out at normal, and 6 hours later has risen 20° above normal, and that any time $D$ days after the morning reading, the temperature, $T$, is

   $$T = 20 \sin 2\pi D.$$

   a. Show that this equation gives the right values of $T$ for times $D = 0$ and $D = 1/4$.

   b. Find the number of degree-days between $D = 0$ and $D = 1/4$.

9. *Rocket Car Problem:* Iona Carr is building a rocket powered car that she plans to use in racing. In this problem you are to help Iona figure out the car's speed, and the distance it will travel in a given time. The car, with Iona in it and a full load of fuel, will have a mass of 2000 kilograms. When the engine is running it will develop 7000 N (newtons) of thrust, which means the car will be pushed with a constant force of 7000 N. You recall from physics that force = (mass)(acceleration), and 1 N is 1 kg-m/sec$^2$. However, the car uses fuel at a rate of 5 kg/sec, so its mass is decreasing.

   a. Write an equation expressing mass as a function of time.

   b. Write an equation expressing acceleration as a function of time.

   c. The answer to part b is a differential equation because acceleration is the derivative of velocity. Solve the differential equation for velocity as a function of time if $v(0) = 0$.

   d. Twenty seconds after the car starts, how fast will it be going? How far will it have gone?

10. *Field Worth Problem:* Ann Aggie has a tract of land the shape of the "triangular" region in Quadrant I bounded by the $y$-axis and by the graphs of $y = 4 - x^2$ and $y = 4x - x^2$ (Figure 11-6f) where $x$ and $y$ are in kilometers. The land's value per square kilometer is directly proportional to its distance from the railroad tracks (along the $y$-axis), being \$200 thousand per square kilometer at the point farthest from the tracks. To the nearest thousand dollars, what is the total worth of the land? How much less is this than it would be if the entire tract were worth \$200,000 per square kilometer?

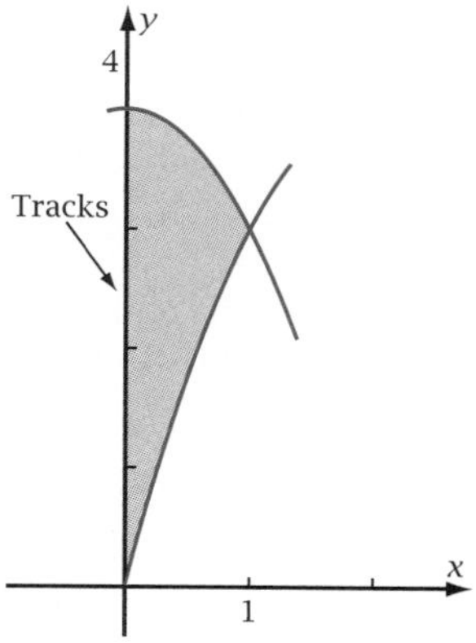

Figure 11-6f

11. *Sinusoidal Land Tract Problem:* A tract of land has the shape of the region in Quadrant I under the graph of $y = \cos x$ (Figure 11-6g). Find the total worth of the land if the worth per square unit is

   a. constant in the $y$-direction, but directly proportional to $x$ in the $x$-direction.

   b. constant in the $x$-direction, but directly proportional to $y$ in the $y$-direction.

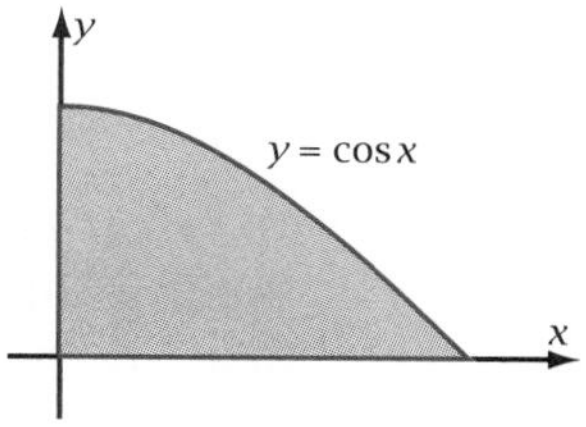

Figure 11-6g

12. *Painted Wall Problem:* Calvin has a contract to paint the wall of a new auditorium. The wall is the shape of the region under the graph of $y = 9 - x^2$, where $x$ and $y$ are in meters, and the $x$-axis runs along the ground. Since it is harder to paint higher up he charges a price per square meter that is directly proportional to the square of the distance above the ground. At a point 2 m above the ground, he charges \$12 per square meter. What total amount will Calvin charge for the job?

13. *City Land Value Problem:* Suppose that you have been hired by the Tax Assessor's Office in the town of Scorpion Gulch. You are to calculate the total worth of all land within the city limits. The town is circular, with a radius of 3 kilometers. You find that land is worth \$10 million per square kilometer right at the center of town, and \$1 million per square kilometer at the edge of town. Find the total worth of the land assuming that the price per square kilometer

   a. varies linearly with the distance from the center of town.

   b. varies exponentially with the distance from the center of town.

   c. is given by the table of values below.

   d. This problem is mathematically equivalent to another type of problem you have worked. What kind of problem?

   e. What real-world reason(s) can you think of to explain the pattern of the data in 13c?

| distance (km) | million \$/km$^2$ | distance (km) | million \$/km$^2$ |
|---|---|---|---|
| 0 | 10 | 1.8 | 8 |
| 0.3 | 12 | 2.1 | 5 |
| 0.6 | 15 | 2.4 | 3 |
| 0.9 | 14 | 2.7 | 2 |
| 1.2 | 13 | 3 | 1 |
| 1.5 | 10 | | |

14. *Diving Board Problem:* Calvin sits on the end of a diving board (Figure 11-6h). His anatomy exerts a pressure on the diving board that is constant in the $z$-direction (perpendicular to the page), and is equal to

$$p = 150[(x-8)^{1/2} - 0.5(x-8)]$$

(in pounds per square foot) in the $x$-direction. The diving board is 2 feet wide in the $z$-direction.

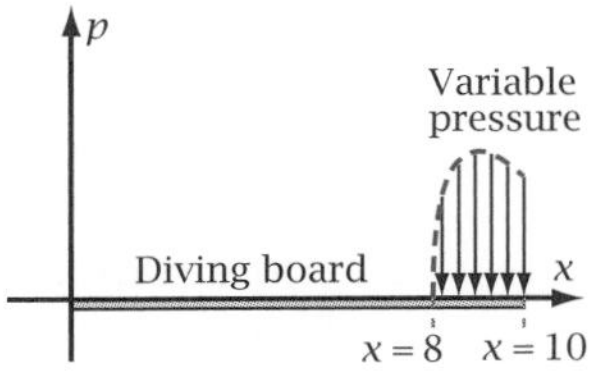

Figure 11-6h

a. To the nearest pound, how much does Calvin weigh?

b. What is the average pressure Calvin exerts in the interval between $x = 8$ and $x = 10$?

c. To the nearest pound-foot, find Calvin's first moment of force with respect to the $yz$-plane.

d. Calvin wishes to exert the same first moment by standing on tip-toes at some point near the end of the board. Where should he stand?

15. *Skewness Problem:* Figure 11-6i shows the graphs of

$$f(x) = 9 - x^2 \quad \text{and} \quad g(x) = -\tfrac{1}{3}x^3 - x^2 + 3x + 9.$$

The region under each graph has the same area, as you will show in 15b, below. But the region under the $g$ graph is "skewed" to the right. In this problem you will calculate the "skewness," which is used in statistics to measure how "unbalanced" a region is.

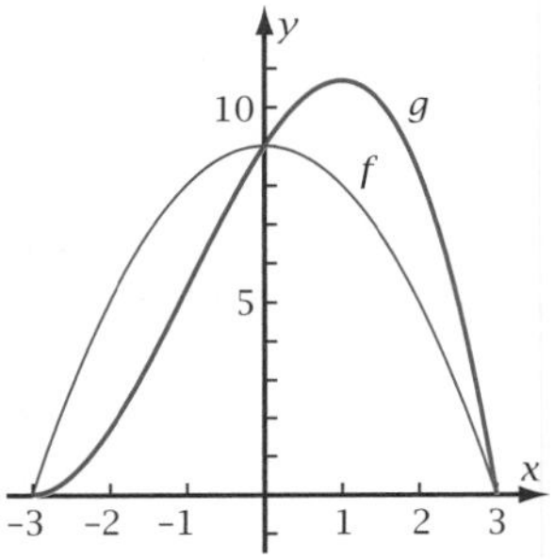

Figure 11-6i

a. Show that the only $x$-intercepts of both functions $f$ and $g$ are $-3$ and 3 (Figure 11-6i).

b. Show that the regions under the two graphs have equal area. How do the properties of definite integrals between symmetrical limits help you calculate the area easily?

c. At what value of $x$ in the interval $[-3, 3]$ do the maxima of the $f$ and $g$ graphs occur?

d. Find the $x$-coordinate of the centroid of the region under the $g$ graph. Recall that this is the number $\bar{x}$ such that $(\bar{x})$(area) = first moment of area of the region with respect to the $y$-axis.

e. True or false: "The centroid of the region is on a vertical line through the maximum on the $g$ graph."

f. True or false: "There is just as much area to the left of the centroid as there is to the right."

g. The **skewness** of a region is defined to be the third moment of area of the region with respect to a vertical line through the centroid. Calculate the skewness of the region under the graph of function $g$.

h. Show that the skewness of the region under the parabola, function $f$, is equal to zero. Why is the word *skewness* appropriate in this case?

i. Sketch the graph of a region whose skewness has the opposite sign from that under the graph of function $g$.

16. *Moment of Arc Length Problem:* You have found moments of area, mass, and volume. It is also possible to find moments of length. Figure 11-6j shows the arc of the parabola $y = x^2$ from $x = 0$ to $x = 2$. The moment, $dM_y$, of the arc $dL$ with respect to the $y$-axis is the length, $dL$, times its distance, $x$, from the $y$-axis. That is,

$$dM_y = x\,dL.$$

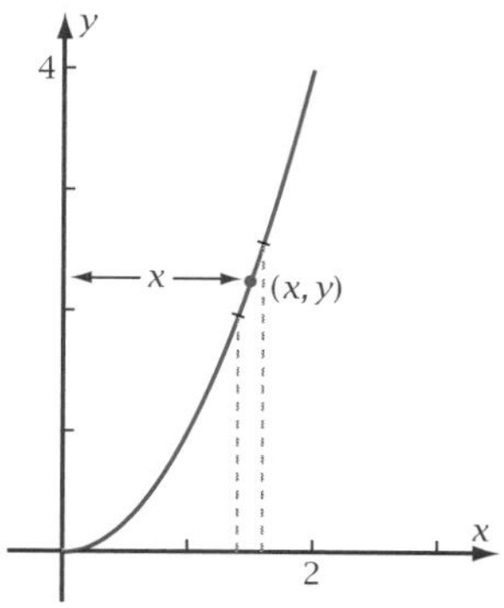

Figure 11-6j

a. Find $dM_y$ explicitly in terms of $x$ and $dx$.

b. Find the total moment of the parabolic arc with respect to the $y$-axis.

c. Find the length of the parabolic arc.

d. Find the $x$-coordinate of the centroid of the parabolic arc. This point would be the center of mass of a thin, uniform wire bent in the shape of the arc.

e. Find the surface area of the paraboloid formed by rotating the arc about the $y$-axis.

f. What interesting thing do you notice about the integral in 16e?

17. *Another Theorem of Pappus Problem:* In Section 11-4 you learned the theorem of Pappus for volumes. The theorem states the volume of a solid of revolution equals the area of the region being rotated times the distance traveled by the centroid of that region. There is a similar theorem for surface area.

> **Theorem: The Theorem of Pappus for Surfaces**
>
> The area, $S$, of a surface of revolution is given by
>
> $$S = 2\pi \overline{R} L,$$
>
> where $L$ is the length of the curve being rotated, and $\overline{R}$ is the displacement from the axis of rotation to the centroid of the curve, and the curve is not on both sides of the axis of rotation. The quantity $2\pi\overline{R}$ is thus the distance the centroid travels as the curve rotates.

Demonstrate that this theorem is true for the paraboloid in 16e.

18. *Application of Pappus' Other Theorem:* A toroidal surface (like an inner tube) is formed by rotating a circle of radius $r$ about an axis (Figure 11-6k) $R$ units from the center of the circle. It is hard to find the surface area of the toroid directly by integration, but easy by using the theorem of Pappus for surfaces. Find a formula for the area of a toroidal surface in terms of $r$ and $R$.

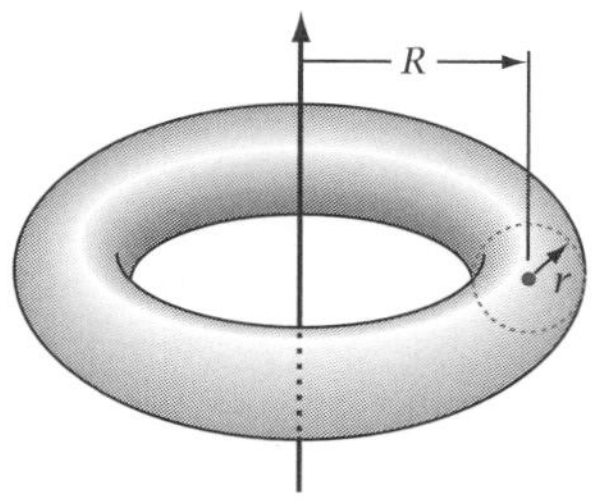

Figure 11-6k

# 11-7 Chapter Review and Test

In this chapter you have applied definite integration to problems involving a product of two quantities, where one of the quantities is a variable. By now you should be able to take any such situation, familiar or unfamiliar, and perform the appropriate mathematics. The ability to see similarities among seemingly dissimilar phenomena is the key to intelligent application of mathematics.

The Review Problems are numbered according to the sections of this chapter. The Concepts Problems allow you to apply your knowledge to new situations. The Chapter Test is more like a classroom test.

## Review Problems

R0. Update your journal with what you've learned since the last entry. You should include such things as those listed here.

- The one most important thing you have learned in studying Chapter 11
- Which boxes you have been working on in the "define, understand, do, apply" table
- Physical quantities that can be calculated as products, such as work, moment, and mass
- Centroid, center of mass, center of gravity, center of pressure, and so on
- Any techniques or ideas about calculus that are still unclear

R1. *Work Problem:* In Miss Calculate's first-grade classroom, Manuel Dexterity drags Bob Tail across the floor. Manuel pulls hard at first, then eases off. The force he exerts (Figure 11-7a) is given by

$$F = 30e^{-0.2x},$$

where $F$ is in pounds and $x$ is Bob's displacement in feet from the starting point. The work Manuel does is the force times the displacement. Find the number of foot-pounds of work he does in dragging Bob from $x = 0$ to $x = 10$ ft.

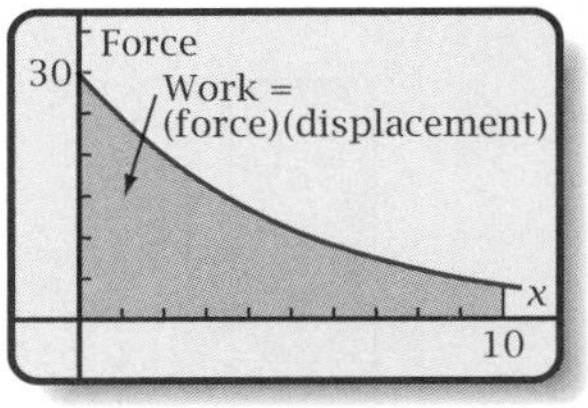

Figure 11-7a

R2. a. *Magnet Problem:* A magnet repels another magnet with a force inversely proportional to the square of their distance apart. That is, $F = k/x^2$, where $F$ is in pounds and $x$ is in inches. Find the work done in moving the magnets from 3 in. apart to 1 in. apart.

b. *Conical Cup Problem:* Phil LaRupp puts a 10 in. long straw into a conical cup filled to the top with root beer (Figure 11-7b). The cup has a top diameter of 6 in., and an altitude of 7 in. The root beer has a density of 0.036 lb/in$^3$. How much work will Phil do in raising all the liquid in the cup to the top of the straw?

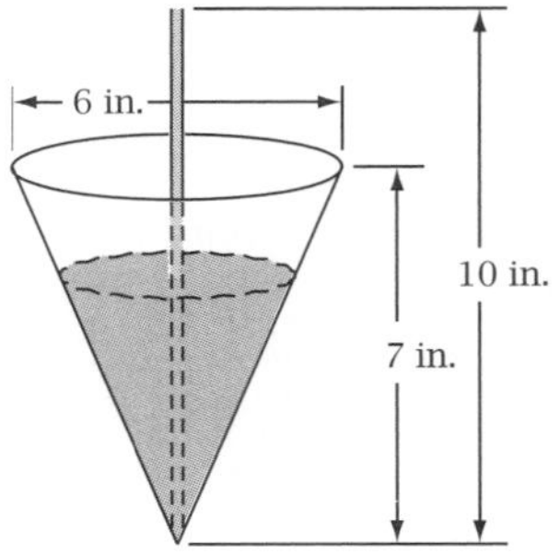

Figure 11-7b

R3. *Variable Density Problem:* The region in Quadrant I bounded by the graph of $y = 8 - x^3$ is rotated about the $y$-axis to form a solid. Find the mass of the solid if the density

a. is constant in the radial direction but equal to $ky$ in the $y$-direction, where $k$ is a proportionality constant.

b. is constant in the axial direction but equals $e^x$ in the radial direction.

R4. a. *Triangle Centroid Problem:* Figure 11-7c shows a triangle of base $b$ and altitude $h$. Write an equation for the width of the triangle in terms of $y$, the distance from the base to a sample point. Find the first moment of area of the region inside the triangle with respect to its base. Show that the centroid is one-third of the distance from the base to the opposite vertex.

b. *Second Moment of Volume Problem:* The region under the graph of $y = e^x$ from $x = 0$ to $x = 1$ is rotated about the $y$-axis to form a solid. Find the second moment of volume of the solid with respect to the $y$-axis.

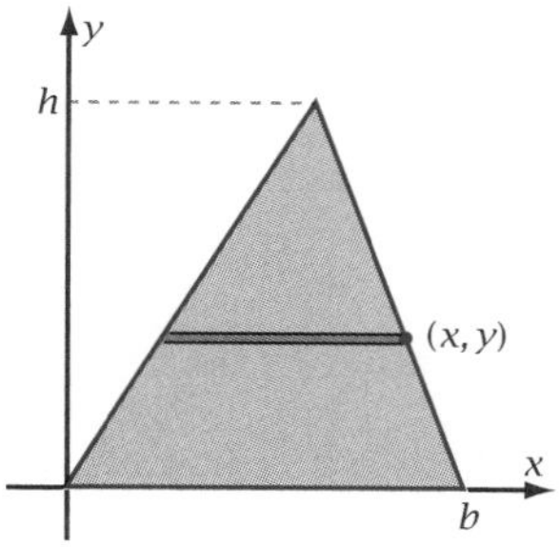

Figure 11-7c

R5. *Wind Force Problem:* A well-known tower has the shape of a slender pyramid (Figure 11-7d). The base of the pyramid, at ground level, is a square of length 150 ft. The building is 400 ft tall. When the wind blows, the pressure acting on the triangular face of the building is greater at the top than at the bottom because the wind speed increases with altitude. Assume that the pressure due to the wind is given by

$$p = 200(1 - e^{-0.01y}),$$

where $p$ is in pounds per square foot, and $y$ is the height in feet above the ground. Assume also that the face of the building is a vertical triangle of base 150 ft and altitude 400 ft. Calculate the total force of the wind acting on that face.

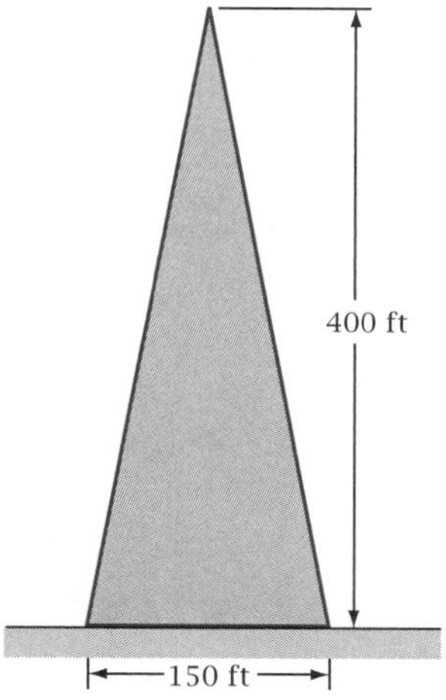

Figure 11-7d

R6. *Oil Well Problem:* Suppose you work for a company that plans to drill a well to a depth of 50,000 ft, farther than anyone has ever drilled before. Your job is to estimate the cost of drilling. From historical records you find that it costs about \$30 per foot to drill at the surface, and about \$50 per foot at a depth of 10,000 ft.

a. Assume that the number of dollars per foot varies exponentially with depth. Write the particular equation expressing cost per foot in terms of depth.

b. The total cost of the well will be the cost per foot times the number of feet. Since the cost per foot varies, you realize that this is a job for calculus! Your boss needs the estimated cost of the well. What are you going to tell him?

## Concepts Problems

C1. *Cubic Parabola Region Problem:* The following problems concern a region in the $xy$-plane of an $xyz$-coordinate system. The region is bounded by the graphs of $y = x^3$, $y = 8$, and $x = 0$ (Figure 11-7e).

a. Find the area of the region.

b. Find the first moment of area of the region with respect to
   i. The $x$-axis.
   ii. The $y$-axis.

c. Find the centroid of the region.

d. Find the volume of the solid generated by rotating the region
   i. About the $x$-axis.
   ii. About the $y$-axis.
   iii. About the line $x = 3$.

e. Show that for each of the solids in C1d, the volume is equal to the area of the region times the distance traveled by the centroid of the region as it rotates to form the solid.

f. Find the first moment of volume with respect to the $xz$-plane for the solid in C1d, part ii.

g. Find the centroid of the solid in C1d, part ii.

h. Does the $y$-coordinate of the centroid of the solid in C1d, part ii equal the $y$-coordinate of the centroid of the region?

i. Find the mass of the solid in C1d, part ii if the density varies directly with the square of the distance from the $y$-axis.

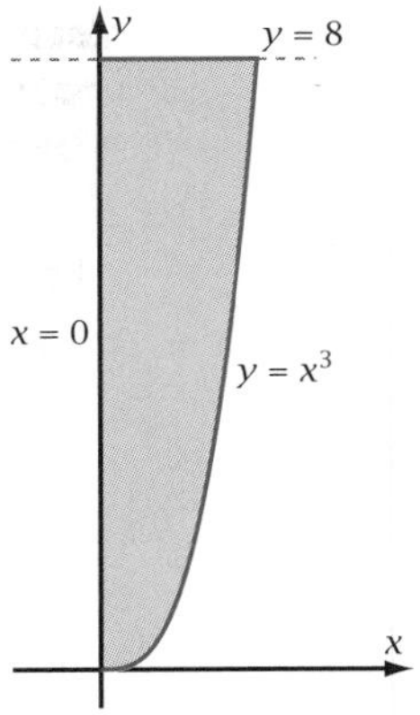


Figure 11-7e

j. Find the second moment of mass of the solid in C1d, part ii with respect to the $y$-axis.

k. Find the force acting perpendicular to the region due to a pressure equal to $(3 - x)$ in the $x$-direction (and constant in the $y$-direction).

l. Find the work done by moving the region from $z = 1$ to $z = 3$. Assume that the force in C1k acts on the region when it is at $z = 1$, and that the force varies inversely with the square of $z$ as the region moves in the $z$-direction, and acts in the positive $z$-direction.

m. Suppose that the object in C1d, part ii is made of a substance with a heat capacity of 0.3 cal/g/°C and a density of 5.8 g/cm$^3$, and that its dimensions are in centimeters. Suppose also that the object is warmed from 0°C to a temperature that is constant in the radial direction but is given by $T = 10 - y$ in the axial direction. Find the amount of heat needed to cause this temperature change.

C2. *Moment vs. Volume Problem:* Show that finding the first moment of the area of a region with respect to the $y$-axis is mathematically equivalent to finding the volume by cylindrical shells for the solid formed by rotating that region about the $y$-axis, provided that the region is not on both sides of the axis of rotation.

C3. *Paraboloid Moment Conjecture Problem:* A solid paraboloid is formed by rotating about the $y$-axis the region in Quadrant I under the graph of $y = 9 - x^2$. Show that the first moment of volume of the solid with respect to the plane of its base equals the second moment of volume of the solid with respect to its axis. Does this property hold in general for any solid paraboloid? Justify your answer.

C4. *Infinitesimals of Higher Order:*

a. Figure 11-7f shows a lower Riemann sum for $y = mx$, where $m \neq 0$. The area of each strip is $dA \approx y\,dx$, the area of the rectangle. The length of each piece of graph is $dL \approx dx$. Both approximations become exact as $\Delta x$ approaches zero. Show that on integrating from $a$ to $b$, $dA \approx y\,dx$ gives the exact area of the region, but $dL \approx dx$ does not give the exact length.

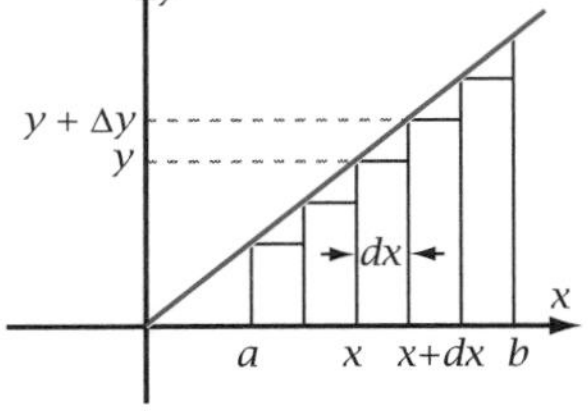


It works for area, but not for length.

Figure 11-7f

b. Figure 11-7g shows the cone formed by rotating about the $x$-axis the graph of $y = mx (m \neq 0)$ from $x = 0$ to $x = h$. Plane sections cut the cone into frustums of volume $dV \approx \pi y^2\, dx$. Each frustum has area $dS \approx 2\pi y\, dx$. Both approximations become exact as $\Delta x$ approaches zero. Show that on integrating from 0 to $h$, $dV \approx \pi y^2\, dx$ gives the exact volume of the cone, but $dS \approx 2\pi y\, dx$ does not give the exact area.

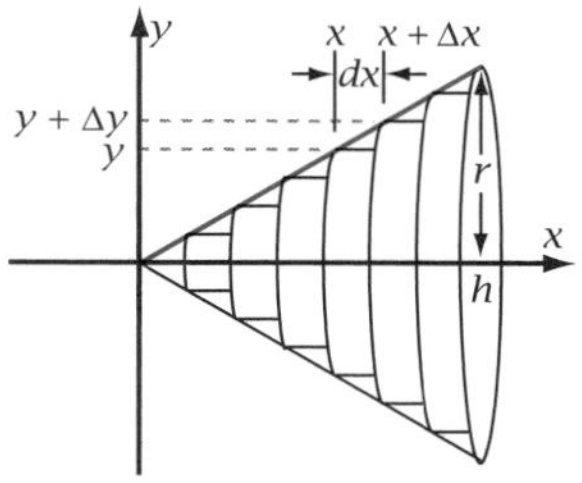


It works for volume, but not for surface area.

Figure 11-7g

c. Find the exact area of a strip in Figure 11-7f and the exact volume of a frustum in Figure 11-7g. [The volume of a frustum of altitude $dx$ is $V = (\pi/3)(R^2 + Rr + r^2)(dx)$, where $R$ is the larger radius and $r$ is the smaller radius of the frustum.]

d. A quantity such as $2\pi y\, dx$ that approaches zero as $\Delta x$ approaches zero is called a **first-order infinitesimal**. A quantity such as $0.5\Delta y\, dx$ that is the product of two or more first-order infinitesimals is called a **higher-order infinitesimal**. Show that the approximations $dA \approx y\, dx$ and $dV \approx \pi y^2\, dx$ differ from the exact values in C4c only by infinitesimals of higher order.

e. You recall that the differential of arc length is $dL = \sqrt{dx^2 + dy^2}$. The approximation $dL \approx dx = \sqrt{dx^2}$ leaves out the first-order infinitesimal $\sqrt{dy^2}$. Make a conjecture about how accurate a differential of a quantity must be so that it yields the exact value when it is integrated.

f. The second-order infinitesimal $0.5\Delta y\, dx$ appears in the exact value of the area of the strip in Figure 11-7f in C4d. The limit of the Riemann sum of such a higher-order infinitesimal equals zero. Give a reason for each step in this example of that statement.

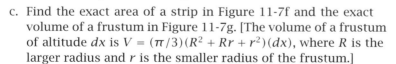

$$\sum 0.5\Delta y\, dx = 0.5\Delta y \sum dx$$
$$= 0.5\Delta y(b - a)$$
$$\therefore \lim_{\Delta x \to 0} \sum 0.5\Delta y\, dx = 0.5(0)(b - a) = 0$$

> ***Property: Infinitesimals of Higher Order***
>
> If $dQ \approx \Delta Q$ leaves out only infinitesimals of higher order, then
>
> $\int_a^b dQ$ is exactly equal to $Q$.

## Chapter Test

T1. A packing case is dragged across the floor from $x = 0$ to $x = 10$ ft. As it moves it becomes damaged, causing the force needed to move it to increase as shown in the table. Find the exponential function that best fits these data. Use the function to find the total amount of work done.

| $x$ | force (lb) |
|---|---|
| 0 | 30 |
| 2 | 34 |
| 4 | 38 |
| 6 | 43 |
| 8 | 49 |
| 10 | 55 |

T2. For the region under the graph of $y = e^x$ from $x = 0$ to $x = 2$, where $x$ and $y$ are in inches,

a. Find the first moment of area with respect to the $y$-axis. Tell the units in your answer.

b. Find the second moment of area with respect to the $y$-axis. Tell the units in your answer.

c. Find the $x$-coordinate of the centroid of the region. Tell the units in your answer.

T3. A solid is formed by rotating about the $x$-axis the region under the graph of $y = x^{1/2}$ from $x = 0$ to $x = 16$ where $x$ and $y$ are in centimeters. Its density is constant axially and equal to $3y$ radially (in grams per cubic centimeter). Find its mass.

T4. A trough 8 ft deep and 4 ft across has an end the shape of the region above the graph of $y = |x^3|$ (Figure 11-7h).

a. Find the total force acting on the end of the trough when it is full of water of density 62.4 lb/ft$^3$.

b. Find the center of pressure, where the force could be concentrated to produce the same moment.

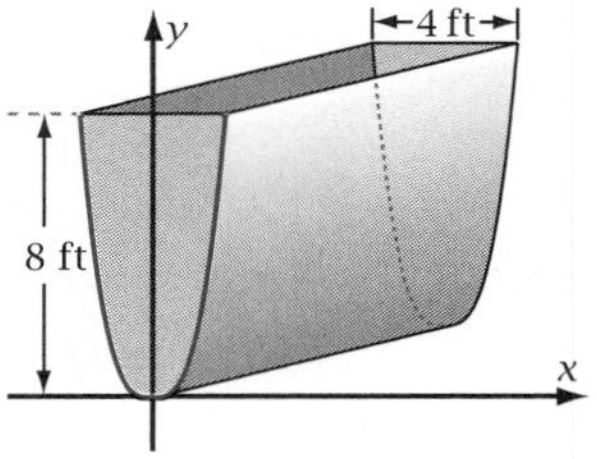


Figure 11-7h

T5. *Theater in the Round Problem:* A round theater is to be built with the stage at the center. The seats will be in circular rows starting at $r = 30$ ft from the center and ending at $r = b$ ft (Figure 11-7i).

a. The value of the seating area for any given performance is given by $v = 150/r$ (in dollars per square foot). Find the total value of the seating area in terms of the outer radius, $b$.

b. How big must the theater be in order to receive $60,000 for a performance?

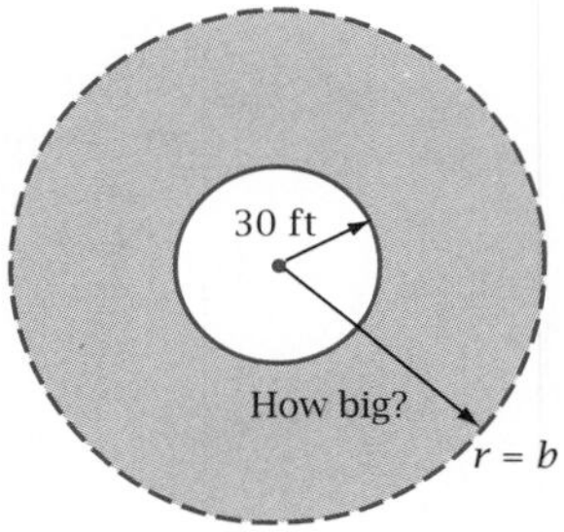


Figure 11-7i

CHAPTER

# 12 The Calculus of Functions Defined by Power Series

If you take regular doses of a medication, the amount in your system is the sum of what remains from the series of the doses you have taken. The limit of that series as the number of doses becomes large is important to know for determining long-term effects of the medication. Such limits can be found by calculus techniques.

## Mathematical Overview

How does a calculator find sines and logs when all it can do is add and multiply? In Chapter 12 you will see that these transcendental functions can be calculated as accurately as you please using "infinite polynomials" called power series. You will study these series in four ways.

**Graphically** The logo at the top of each even-numbered page of this chapter shows that the first few terms of a power series can fit the sine function close to $x = 0$.

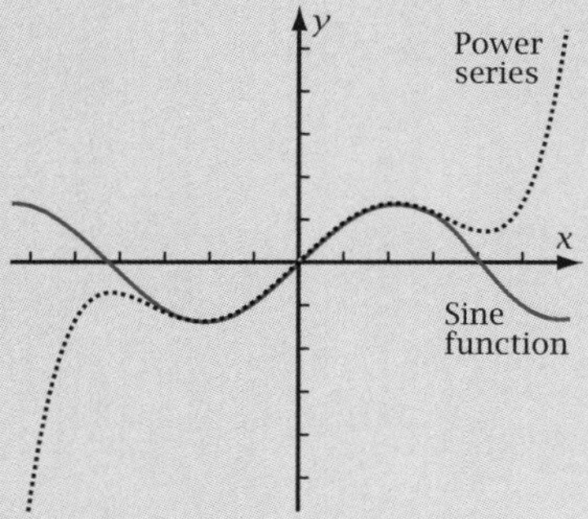


**Numerically** $\sin 0.6 = 0.56462473 \ldots$

| $n$ | series for sin 0.6 |
|---|---|
| 0 | 0.6 |
| 1 | 0.564 |
| 2 | 0.564648 |
| 3 | 0.564642445 ... |
| 4 | 0.564642473 ... |

**Algebraically** $\sin x = x - \frac{1}{3!}x^3 + \frac{1}{5!}x^5 - \ldots$, the Maclaurin series for sine.

**Verbally** *Perhaps the most surprising thing we learned about power series is that sometimes they converge as more and more terms are added, and sometimes they don't. For each power series there is an interval of x-values for which the series converges.*

# 12-1 Introduction to Power Series

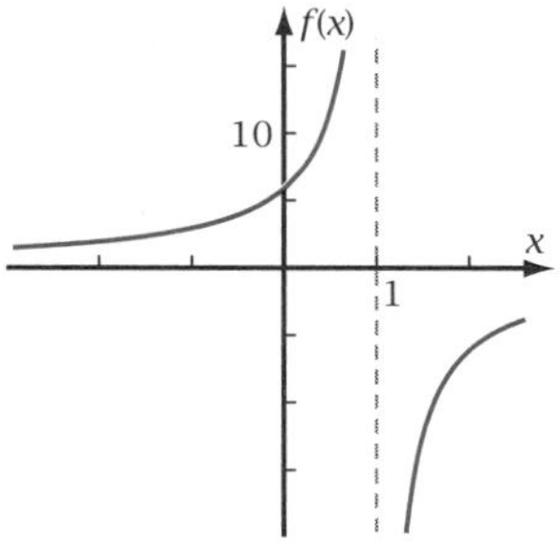

Figure 12-1a

Suppose that $f(x) = 6/(1 - x)$ (Figure 12-1a). If you divide $1 - x$ into 6, you get a "polynomial" that continues forever!

$$P(x) = 6 + 6x + 6x^2 + 6x^3 + 6x^4 + 6x^5 + \cdots$$

The result is called a **power series**. The word *series* indicates that there is an infinite number of terms. The word *power* tells us that each term contains a power of $x$.

**OBJECTIVE**

Find values of $P(x)$ for a given power series, and compare the results with the corresponding values of the function from which the power series originates.

The following problem set is designed to let you work toward this objective either on your own or with your study group following your test on Chapter 11.

## Exploratory Problem Set 12-1

Let $f(x) = 6/(1 - x)$ and let $P(x) = 6 + 6x + 6x^2 + 6x^3 + 6x^4 + 6x^5 + \cdots$.

1. On the same screen, plot $f(x)$ and the polynomial function $P_5(x)$ (the six terms of $P(x)$ through $6x^5$). Sketch the results. Use a friendly $x$-window from about $[-2, 2]$, and a $y$-window of $[-100, 100]$.
2. On the same screen as Problem 1, plot the polynomial function $P_6(x)$. From the graphs of $P_5$ and $P_6$, determine the $x$-values for which $P(x)$ is close to $f(x)$ and the $x$-values for which the graph of $P$ bears little or no resemblance to the graph of $f$.
3. Show that $P_6(0.5)$ is closer to $f(0.5)$ than $P_5(0.5)$ is, but that $P_6(2)$ is not closer to $f(2)$ than $P_5(2)$ is.
4. If the limit of the sum of a series as you add more and more terms is equal to the corresponding value of $f(x)$, then the series is said to **converge** to $f(x)$. Otherwise, the series is said to **diverge** (or to converge to some other number). Make a conjecture about the interval of values of $x$ for which the series $P(x) = 6 + 6x + 6x^2 + 6x^3 + 6x^4 + 6x^5 + \cdots$ converges to $f(x) = 6/(1 - x)$.
5. Write the values of $P_0(1)$, $P_1(1)$, ..., $P_4(1)$. Write the values of $P_0(-1)$, $P_1(-1)$, ... , $P_4(-1)$. Tell why each series diverges. Does this result affect your conjecture in Problem 4?
6. By how much do $P_5(0.5)$ and $P_5(-0.5)$ differ from the respective values of $f(0.5)$ and $f(-0.5)$? How do these differences compare with $6x^6$, the first term of the series that is left out of the sum?
7. Each term of $P(x)$ after the first is equal to the preceding term multiplied by the same number, $x$, in this case. What name is given to this type of series? What name is given to the multiplier $x$?

# 12-2 Geometric Sequences and Series as Mathematical Models

In Problem Set 12-1, you saw how the rational function $f(x) = 6/(1 - x)$ could be expanded as a series, $6 + 6x + 6x^2 + 6x^3 + \cdots$. Any term after the first can be generated by multiplying the preceding term by the same number, $x$ in this case. Thus the series fits the definition of geometric series you may have learned in algebra. In this section you will reverse the process, and see how a geometric series can be represented, at least in some instances, as a rational function. By so doing you will be able to analyze some functions in the real world in which the function values change **discretely** (by jumps) rather than continuously.

***OBJECTIVE***

Given a function defined by a geometric series, tell whether or not the series can be written as a rational algebraic function, and if so, write an equation for that target function.

### *Background*

A **geometric series** is defined to be a series $t_1 + t_2 + t_3 + t_4 + \cdots$ for which there is a constant, $r$, called the **common ratio** such that $t_n = rt_{n-1}$ for any integer $n > 1$. The numbers $t_1, t_2, t_3, \ldots$ are called **terms** of the series, hence the letter "$t$." The variable $n$ is called the **term index**. If $n$ starts at 1, the term index is the same as the term number. The ***n*th partial sum**, $S_n$, of a geometric series is the indicated sum of the first $n$ terms. By clever algebra it is possible to derive a closed formula (no ellipsis, ...) for $S_n$ as a function of the first term, $t_1$, and the common ratio, $r$.

$$S_n = t_1 + t_2 + t_3 + t_4 + \cdots + t_{n-1} + t_n$$

$$S_n = t_1 + rt_1 + r^2t_1 + r^3t_1 + \cdots + r^{n-2}t_1 + r^{n-1}t_1$$
Each term is $r$ times the preceding term.

$$rS_n = rt_1 + r^2t_1 + r^3t_1 + r^4t_1 + \cdots + r^{n-1}t_1 + r^nt_1$$
Multiply both sides of the equation by $r$.

$$S_n - rS_n = t_1 - r^nt_1$$
Subtract the third equation from the second one. The middle terms "telescope."

$$S_n = t_1 \cdot \frac{1 - r^n}{1 - r}$$

### *A Convergent Geometric Series—Drug Dosage*

Suppose that a person takes 500 mg of vitamin C every 8 hours. Assume that at the end of any 8-hr period, only 60% of the vitamin C present at the beginning of the period remains in the person's system. At the end of the first 8-hr period, only 300 mg of the original 500 remains. After the second dose, the amount jumps to 800 mg. Immediately after the $n$th dose, the amount of vitamin C remaining in the system is the sum of the 500 mg from the last dose and the remains of each previous dose.

$$S_n = 500 + 300 + 180 + 108 + \cdots$$
180 is 60% of 300; 108 is 60% of 180, and so forth.

$$= 500 + 500(0.6) + 500(0.6^2) + 500(0.6^3) + \cdots + 500(0.6^{n-1})$$

This series is geometric, with first term 500 and common ratio 0.6. After 10 doses,

$$S_{10} = 500 \cdot \frac{1 - 0.6^{10}}{1 - 0.6} = 1242.441\ldots$$

The person would have only about 1240 mg of vitamin C in his or her system, in spite of having taken a total of 5000 mg.

If the person continues taking the 500 mg doses for a long time, does the amount in the body become arbitrarily high? To find out, it is instructive to look at the partial sums graphically and numerically. As shown in Figure 12-2a, the amount of vitamin C rapidly levels off toward 1250. As shown in the accompanying table, the partial sums stay the same for more and more decimal places. For both of these reasons the sequence of partial sums converges to 1250. As you saw in Section 12-1, if the sequence of partial sums converges, then the series converges also.

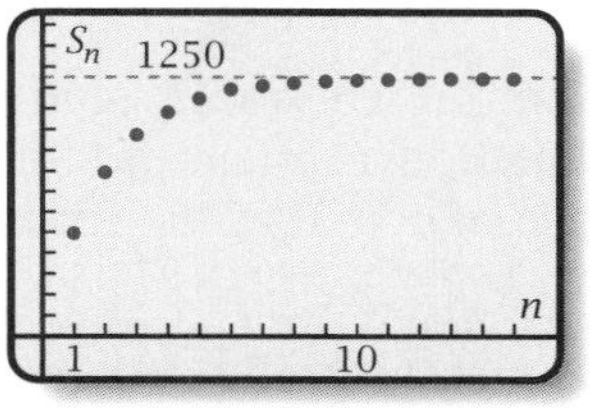

Figure 12-2a

| $n$ | $S_n$ |
|---|---|
| 25 | 1249.996446 ... |
| 26 | 1249.997867 ... |
| 27 | 1249.998720 ... |
| 28 | 1249.999232 ... |
| 29 | 1249.999539 ... |
| 30 | 1249.999723 ... |
| 31 | 1249.999834 ... |
| 32 | 1249.999900 ... |

From the formula for $S_n$, you can tell algebraically that the series converges to 1250. Take the limit of $S_n$ as $n$ approaches infinity.

$$\lim_{n \to \infty} S_n = \lim_{n \to \infty} 500 \cdot \frac{1 - 0.6^n}{1 - 0.6} = 500 \cdot \frac{1}{1 - 0.6}$$ Because $0.6^n$ approaches zero.

$$= 1250$$

So the amount of vitamin C in the person's system never exceeds 1250 mg, no matter how long the dosage is continued.

A geometric series will converge if the common ratio $r$ is a proper fraction (that is, $|r| < 1$). This is because the term $r^n$ in the formula for $S_n$ approaches zero as a limit as $n$ approaches infinity. The number $S$ to which the series converges is given by

$$S = \lim_{n \to \infty} t_1 \cdot \frac{1 - r^n}{1 - r} = t_1 \cdot \frac{1}{1 - r}.$$

### *A Divergent Geometric Sequence—Compound Interest*

In Chapter 7, you saw that an exponential function can be used as a mathematical model for invested money if the interest is compounded continuously. A sequence is more appropriate if the interest is compounded at discrete intervals such as once a day, once a month, or once a quarter. Suppose you invest \$500 in a savings account that pays 6% per year interest compounded quarterly. For the first 3 months you have only the initial \$500. Then \$7.50 is added to the account, 1.5% of the \$500 (a fourth of 6%), and you have \$507.50 for the next 3 months. At the end of the second quarter the account increases by \$7.6125, which is 1.5% of the \$507.50.

To find a pattern in the amounts, observe how the \$507.50 can be calculated.

$$500 + 500(0.015) = 500(1 + 0.015) = 500(1.015) \qquad \text{After the first quarter.}$$

Repeating the computation for the second quarter without simplifying 500(1.015) gives

$$\begin{aligned} &500(1.015) + 500(1.015)(0.015) \\ &\quad = 500(1.015)(1 + 0.015) = 500(1.015)^2. \qquad \text{Second quarter.} \end{aligned}$$

The amounts are terms in a geometric sequence with first term 500 and a common ratio 1.015.

| | | | | | | |
|---|---|---|---|---|---|---|
| 500, | 500(1.015), | $500(1.015)^2$, | $500(1.015)^3$, | $500(1.015)^4$, | ... | Dollars in the account. |
| 0 | 1 | 2 | 3 | 4 | ... | Quarters |

The exponent of 1.015 equals the number of quarters. After 10 years the amount would be

$$t_{40} = 500(1.015)^{40} = 907.0092\ldots \approx \$907.01 \qquad \text{Why 40, why not 10?)}$$

The amount of interest earned in the 10 years would be \$407.01, the difference between the \$907.01 and the initial investment of \$500. In this instance it is more convenient to start $n$ at 0 instead of 1 so that the term index will equal the number of quarters elapsed.

Note that the sequence diverges because the common ratio is greater than 1. This fact can be useful in the real world. For instance, it alerts bankers to the consequences of money left in dormant accounts. If the \$500 had been invested by George Washington the year he died, 1799, his heirs could claim \$74,439,561.08 in 1999!

### *Words Associated with Sequences and Series*

The following boxes summarize pertinent definitions and properties concerning sequences and series.

#### *Definitions: Vocabulary Associated with Sequences and Series*

A **sequence** is an infinite ordered set of numbers.
Example: 2, 3, 5, 7, 11, 13, 17, 19, 23, ... The sequence of primes.

A **series** is the indicated sum of the terms of a sequence.
Example: $2 + 3 + 5 + 7 + 11 + 13 + 17 + 19 + 23 + \cdots$ The series of primes.

The **terms** of a sequence or series, $t_1, t_2, t_3, \ldots, t_n, \ldots$, are the numbers that appear in the sequence or series.

The **term index** is the variable integer subscript $n$ used to calculate the term value. If $n$ starts at 1, the term index is also equal to the term number.

A **partial sum** of a series is the sum of a finite number of terms in the series.
Example: $S_4 = 2 + 3 + 5 + 7 = 17$ Fourth partial sum of the series of primes.

### Definitions

The **sequence of partial sums** for a series is the sequence whose terms are the first partial sum, the second partial sum, the third partial sum, and so on.

Example: For the series of primes, above, the sequence of partial sums is
$S_1, S_2, S_3, S_4, S_5, S_6, S_7, S_8, \ldots = 2, 5, 10, 17, 28, 41, 58, 77, \ldots.$

A *sequence* **converges to $L$** if its $n$th term approaches a finite limit $L$ as $n$ approaches infinity. If the sequence does not converge, it is said to **diverge.**

Examples: $1, 1\frac{1}{2}, 1\frac{3}{4}, 1\frac{7}{8}, 1\frac{15}{16}, \ldots$ converges to 2.

$2, 3, 5, 7, 11, 13, \ldots$ (the sequence of primes) diverges.

$1, 0, 1, 0, 1, 0, 1, \ldots$ diverges **by oscillation.**

A *series* **converges** if and only if its sequence of partial sums converges.

Example: $1 + \frac{1}{2} + \frac{1}{4} + \frac{1}{8} + \frac{1}{16} + \cdots$ converges since its sequence of partial sums is $1, 1\frac{1}{2}, 1\frac{3}{4}, 1\frac{7}{8}, 1\frac{15}{16}, \ldots,$ which converges to 2.

A **geometric series** is a series for which each term after the first term is given by $t_n = r \cdot t_{n-1}$ for some constant $r$ called the **common ratio.**

### Properties of Geometric Series

The $n$th partial sum of a geometric series is given by

$$S_n = t_1 \cdot \frac{1 - r^n}{1 - r}.$$

A geometric series converges if $|r| < 1$.

The number to which a convergent geometric series converges is $S = t_1 \cdot \dfrac{1}{1 - r}$.

## Problem Set 12-2

### Do These Quickly

The following problems are intended to refresh your skills. You should be able to work all ten problems in less than five minutes.

**Q1.** Definition: $L$ is the limit of $f(x)$ as $x$ approaches infinity if and only if —?—.

**Q2.** "If $g(x) = \int f(x)\,dx$, then $\int_a^b f(x)\,dx = g(b) - g(a)$" is a statement of —?—.

**Q3.** $(d/dx)\int_a^x f(t)\,dt = f(x)$ is a statement of —?—.

**Q4.** . . . such that $f'(c) = [f(b) - f(a)]/(b - a)$ is part of the conclusion of —?—.

**Q5.** Instantaneous rate of change of a function is the physical meaning of —?—.

**Q6.** $(d/dx)(x \cos x) =$ —?—

**Q7.** $\int x \cos x\,dx =$ —?—

**Q8.** The differential of area in polar coordinates is $dA =$ —?—.

**Q9.** What function has the graph shown in Figure 12-2b?

**Q10.** What function has the graph shown in Figure 12-2c?

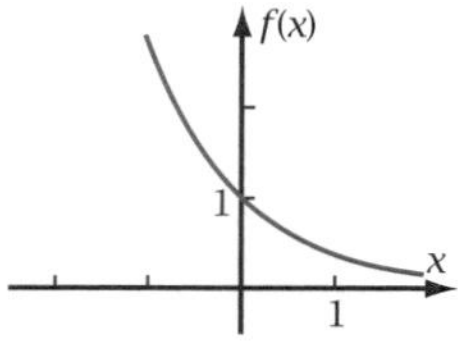

Figure 12-2b

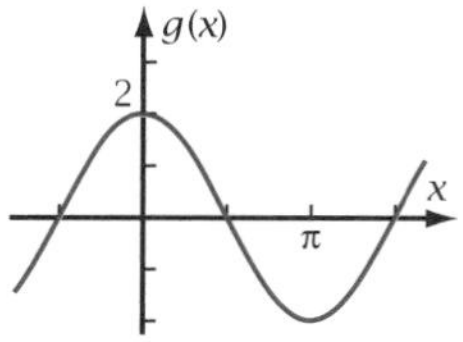

Figure 12-2c

1. Write the first few terms of the geometric series with first term 200 and common ratio −0.6. Write the corresponding partial sums. Plot the graph of the partial sums and sketch the result. To what number does the series converge? Show this number on the graph. What is the first value of the term number, $n$, for which the partial sum is within 0.0001 of the limit? What can you say about the proximity of $S_n$ to the limit for greater values of $n$?

2. Write the first few terms of the geometric series with first term 30 and common ratio 1.1. Write the corresponding partial sums. Give numerical and graphical evidence that the series diverges. For instance, what does $S_{100}$ equal? What meaning does the algebraic formula $S = t_1/(1 - r)$ have for this series?

3. *Drug Dosage Problem:* Suppose you have been hired by a pharmaceutical company. One of your projects is to determine the recommended dose rates for a new nasal allergy spray. For the drug to be effective but safe, the amount in the person's body should be between 50 and 80 $\mu$g (micrograms). Research has shown that each 6 hours the amount of drug remaining in the body is 80% of what it was at the beginning of the 6-hr period. Each puff of the spray delivers 7 $\mu$g of the drug.

   a. Suppose that a person uses one puff of the spray each 6 hours. Write a geometric series for the amount of drug remaining in the person's system after $n$ puffs. How soon would the amount in the person's system exceed 50 $\mu$g? Would the amount ever exceed 80 $\mu$g?

   b. Describe the effects of using two, three, or four puffs each 6 hours. For instance, how soon will be amount exceed 50 $\mu$g? Will it ever exceed 80 $\mu$g?

   c. Using the spray each 6 hours is inconvenient. Could several puffs of the spray be taken twice a day or just once a day and have the levels stay between 50 and 80 $\mu$g? Give evidence to support your answer.

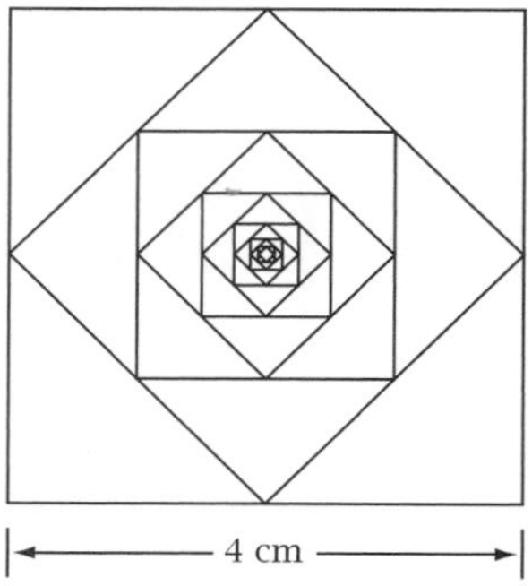

Figure 12-2d

4. *Inscribed Squares Problem:* Figure 12-2d shows an outer square of side 4 cm. The midpoints of the sides of the square are the vertices for an inscribed square. More squares are inscribed using the same pattern, *forever!*

a. Show that the perimeters of the squares form a geometric sequence.

b. The total perimeter of all the squares is a geometric series. Find the tenth partial sum of the series.

c. Does the series for the total perimeter converge, or does the total perimeter approach infinity?

d. The sum of the areas of the squares is also a geometric series. Does this series converge, or does the sum of the areas become infinite?

5. *Compound Interest Problem:* Meg A. Buck invests a million dollars in a certificate of deposit (CD) that earns 9% interest a year, compounded once a month.

a. Write a geometric sequence for the amounts the CD is worth after 0, 1, 2, and 3 mo.

b. How much will the CD be worth at the end of the first year? How much interest will have been earned?

c. How do you explain the fact that after 12 mo the term index is 12, but there are 13 terms in the sequence?

d. The **annual percentage rate** (APR) an investment earns is the amount of interest for 1 yr expressed as a percentage of the worth of the investment at the beginning of the year. What is the APR for Meg's CD?

e. When will Meg's CD be worth 2 million dollars?

6. *Regular Deposits Problem:* Ernest Lee invests \$100 a month in an individual retirement arrangement (IRA). The interest rate is 10.8% per year, compounded monthly. After 0 months, Ernest has only the first \$100 in the IRA. After 1 month, he has \$200, plus interest on the first \$100. After $n$ months, he has \$100 invested the last month, plus \$100 with 1 month's interest for the preceding month, plus \$100 with 2 months' interest, and so forth.

a. Write the amount Ernest has at the end of 5 months as a partial sum of a geometric series.

b. The 5 (months) in 6a is the term index. How many terms are in the partial sum? Why is the number of terms not equal to the term index?

c. How much will Ernest have after 10 years? How much of this is principal and how much is interest?

7. *Bouncing Ball Problem:* A superball is catapulted from floor level. It rises to 10 ft above the floor then starts back down. On the next bounce it rises to 9 ft above the floor. On each subsequent bounce it rises to 90% of the maximum height on the previous bounce (Figure 12-2e).

a. The ball travels 20 ft vertically before the first bounce. Write the first few terms of the sequence of distances the ball travels between bounces.

b. Calculate the fourth partial sum of the series of distances corresponding to the sequence in 7a.

c. To what number does the series in 7b converge? What does this fact imply for the total distance the ball travels as it comes to rest?

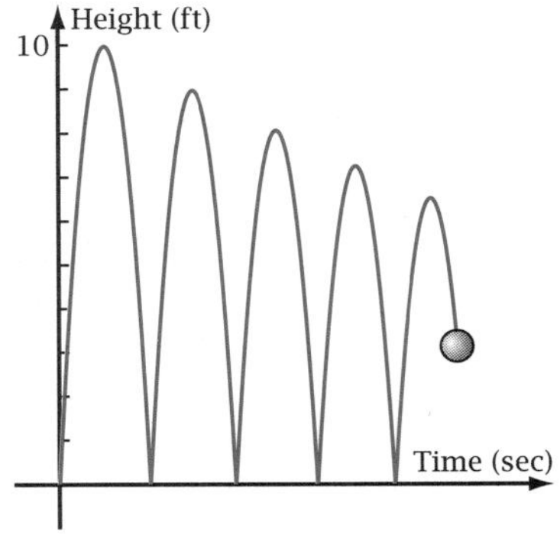


Figure 12-2e

d. From physics you learn that the distance an object drops from rest under the influence of gravity is $d = (1/2)gt^2$. If $d$ is in feet and $t$ is in seconds, then $g \approx 32.2$ ft/sec$^2$. The time taken for an up-and-down cycle is twice the time to fall from a high point. How long does it take the ball to make the 20-ft first up-and-down cycle? How long does it take to make the 18-ft second cycle?

e. According to this mathematical model the ball makes an infinite number of bounces before it comes to rest. Does this infinite number of bounces take an infinite length of time, or does the model predict that the ball eventually comes to rest? Explain.

8. *Snowflake Curve Problem:* A figure called the **snowflake curve** is generated as shown in Figure 12-2f. An equilateral triangle has the one-third points marked on each side. For the first iteration the middle one-third of each side is erased and two line segments equal to the length of the erased segment are added to form sides of smaller equilateral triangles. In the second iteration the process is repeated. Each old segment is replaced with four new segments, each of which is one-third as long as the segment they replace. The snowflake curve is the figure that results from taking the limit as the number of iterations approaches infinity. This limit was first considered by Helge von Koch in 1904.

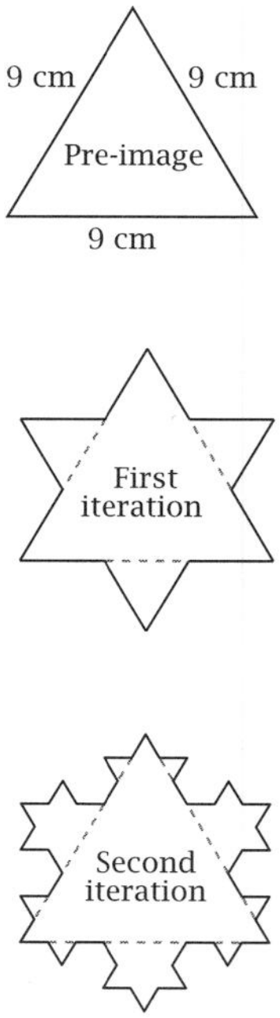

Figure 12-2f

a. Suppose that the pre-image (the original triangle) has sides 9 cm long. Write the total length of the curve at the first, second, and third iterations. How can the length at one particular iteration be generated from the length at the previous iteration?

b. Does the sequence of total lengths in 8a converge or diverge? What does the answer tell you about the total length of the snowflake curve? Surprising?

c. The area enclosed by each iteration is a partial sum of a geometric series. Write the first few terms of this series. Does the series converge or diverge? If it converges, tell the limit to which it converges. If it diverges, tell how you know it diverges.

d. The snowflake curve is a classic example of a **fractal curve**. It is so "fractured" that it is more than one-dimensional but less than two-dimensional. Its dimension is a "fraction" equal to about 1.26. The curve is continuous everywhere but differentiable nowhere. For more about such curves, see, for example, Benoit Mendelbrot's book, *The Fractal Geometry of Nature*, published by W.H. Freeman and Company in 1983.

*9. *Derivatives of a Geometric Series:* In this problem you will consider the derivatives of the geometric series from Problem Set 12-1 and see how they relate to the rational algebraic function from which the series was derived.

Let $P(x) = 6 + 6x + 6x^2 + 6x^3 + 6x^4 + 6x^5 + \cdots$.

Let $f(x) = 6/(1 - x)$.

Assume that the derivatives of a series can be found by differentiating each term. Write series for $P'(x)$, $P''(x)$, and $P'''(x)$. [$P'''(x)$ is the **third derivative**, the derivative of $P''(x)$.] Show that $P'(0), P''(0)$, and $P'''(0)$ equal the corresponding values of $f'(0), f''(0)$, and $f'''(0)$. How do you suppose $P^{(n)}(0)$ relates to $f^{(n)}(0)$, the ***n*th derivative**?

*This problem prepares you for the next section.

# 12-3 Power Series for an Exponential Function

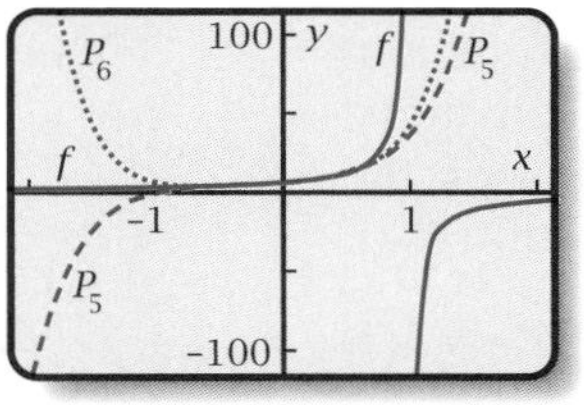

Figure 12-3a

In Section 12-1, you saw that the function

$$f(x) = \frac{6}{1-x}$$

could be written as a power series,

$$P(x) = 6 + 6x + 6x^2 + 6x^3 + 6x^4 + \cdots.$$

Figure 12-3a shows that for values of $x$ between $-1$ and 1, the more terms of the series used, the closer the $P$ graph is to the $f$ graph.

Values of $f(x) = 6/(1-x)$ can be calculated directly. Values of the elementary transcendental functions cannot be calculated directly using only a finite number of operations of algebra, namely, $+, -, \times$, and $\div$. Fortunately, it is possible to express many of these functions as power series. Partial sums of these series can be used to calculate $\sin x$, $\ln x$, $e^x$, and so forth to as many decimal places as you need. In this section you will derive a power series for $f(x) = 5e^{2x}$.

***OBJECTIVE***

Given a particular exponential function, derive a power series that fits the function for values of $x$ close to zero.

In the following problem set you will accomplish this objective.

## Problem Set 12-3

### *Do These Quickly*

The following problems are intended to refresh your skills. You should be able to do all 10 in less than 5 minutes.

***Q1.*** Write 1/3 as a repeating decimal.

***Q2.*** Write 4/9 as a repeating decimal.

***Q3.*** Write 0.6666 . . . (repeating) as a ratio of two integers.

***Q4.*** Write $0.4 + 0.04 + 0.004 + 0.0004 + \cdots$ as a ratio of two integers.

***Q5.*** Write the next term of the arithmetic series $1 + 5 + 9 + \cdots$.

***Q6.*** Write the next term of the geometric series $1 + 5 + 25 + \cdots$.

***Q7.*** First moment of mass = —?— times —?—.

***Q8.*** Center of volume is called —?—.

***Q9.*** Do the integration: $\int x^{-1}\,dx$

***Q10.*** Differentiate: $y = \sec 2x$

1. Let $f(x) = 5e^{2x}$. Find $f'(x)$, $f''(x)$, $f'''(x)$, and $f^{(4)}(x)$, the first, second, third, and fourth derivatives of $f(x)$.
2. Function $f$ is locally linear at $x = 0$. Let $P_1$ be the linear function $P_1(x) = c_0 + c_1x$ that best fits $f(x)$ at $x = 0$. ($c_0$ and $c_1$ are used for the constants rather than $b$ and $m$ so that

you will see a pattern later.) Find the values of $c_0$ and $c_1$ that make $P_1(0) = f(0)$ and $P_1'(0) = f'(0)$.

3. Function $f$ is also **locally quadratic** at $x = 0$. That is, there is a quadratic function $P_2(x) = c_0 + c_1x + c_2x^2$ that best fits $f(x)$ at $x = 0$. Find the values of the constants $c_0$, $c_1$, and $c_2$ that make $P_2(0) = f(0)$, $P_2'(0) = f'(0)$, and $P_2''(0) = f''(0)$. How do the values of $c_0$ and $c_1$ compare to the corresponding values for the linear function $P_1$?

4. Function $f$ is also **locally cubic** and **locally quartic** at $x = 0$. Find equations for the cubic and quartic functions,

$$P_3(x) = c_0 + c_1x + c_2x^2 + c_3x^3 \text{ and}$$
$$P_4(x) = c_0 + c_1x + c_2x^2 + c_3x^3 + c_4x^4,$$

that best fit $f(x)$ at $x = 0$. For these equations, $P_3(0)$ and $P_4(0)$ must equal $f(0)$, and the first three derivatives (for $P_3$) or the first four derivatives (for $P_4$) must equal the corresponding derivatives of $f$ at $x = 0$. How do the coefficients $c_0$, $c_1$, and $c_2$ compare with those for the quadratic and linear functions in Problems 2 and 3?

5. Plot graphs of $f$, $P_3$, and $P_4$ on the same screen. Use a friendly window of about $[-2, 2]$ for $x$ and a window of $[-20, 100]$ for $y$. Sketch the results.

6. For what range of values of $x$ is the graph of $P_4$ indistinguishable from the graph of $f$ on your grapher?

7. Show that the value of $P_4(1)$ is closer to the actual value of $f(1)$ than the value of $P_3(1)$ is.

8. In Problem 4, you should have found that for the fourth derivative $P_4^{(4)}(0)$ to equal $f^{(4)}(0)$, the value of $c_4$ was given by

$$24c_4 = 80 \Rightarrow c_4 = \frac{80}{24}.$$

Write the 80 as the product of 5 and a power of 2. Write the 24 as a factorial. What pattern do you notice?

9. Show that $c_3$, $c_2$, $c_1$, and even $c_0$ follow the pattern in Problem 8.

10. Let $P(x)$ be the power series $P(x) = c_0 + c_1x + c_2x^2 + c_3x^3 + c_4x^4 + c_5x^5 + \cdots$. Note that $P_3(x)$ and $P_4(x)$ are partial sums of this series. Make a conjecture about the values of $c_5$ and $c_6$ such that $P_5(x)$ and $P_6(x)$ best fit $f(x)$ at $x = 0$.

11. In previous courses you probably learned how to express series in $\Sigma$ (sigma) notation. For instance,

$$\sum_{n=0}^{\infty} \frac{1}{n+1} x^n = 1 + \tfrac{1}{2}x + \tfrac{1}{3}x^2 + \tfrac{1}{4}x^3 + \cdots.$$

The expression $1/(n+1) \cdot x^n$ is evaluated for each integer value of $n$ starting at 0, and going to infinity, and the terms are added. Use what you have learned in this problem set to write in $\Sigma$ notation the series for $P(x)$ that best fits $f(x) = 5e^{2x}$.

# 12-4 Power Series for Other Elementary Functions

In Sections 12-1 and 12-3, you saw that two quite different functions could be represented in similar form as power series, at least for values of $x$ close to zero.

Rational function: $f(x) = \dfrac{6}{1-x}$ Series: $P(x) = 6 + 6x + 6x^2 + 6x^3 + 6x^4 + 6x^5 + \cdots$

Exponential function: $f(x) = 5e^{2x}$ Series: $5 + 10x + 10x^2 + \frac{20}{3}x^3 + \frac{10}{3}x^4 + \frac{4}{3}x^5 + \cdots$

The two series have the same form. The only difference is the values of the coefficients, all 6's for one series and 5, 10, 10, 20/3, ... for the other.

The process of finding the right coefficients for a particular function is called **expanding the function as a power series.** If a function and the series match each other at $x = 0$, the function is said to be **expanded about $x = 0$.**

***OBJECTIVE***

Given an elementary function, find the first few terms of the power series that best fits the function, find a pattern that allows you to write more terms of the series, write the series in sigma notation, and plot the graph to see how well the series fits the function.

A power series can be written in the following general form.

**Definition: Power Series**

A power series for $f(x)$ expanded about $x = 0$ can be written

$$P(x) = c_0 + c_1x + c_2x^2 + c_3x^3 + c_4x^4 + c_5x^5 + \cdots,$$

where $c_0, c_1, c_2, \ldots$ stand for constant coefficients.

Informally: A power series is a "polynomial" with an infinite number of terms.

**Example 1**

By equating derivatives, show that the following are the first three nonzero terms of the power series for $f(x) = \sin x$ expanded about $x = 0$.

$$x - \frac{1}{3!}x^3 + \frac{1}{5!}x^5$$

**Solution**

Let $P(x) = c_0 + c_1x + c_2x^2 + c_3x^3 + c_4x^4 + c_5x^5 + \cdots$

In order for $P(x)$ to fit $f(x) = \sin x$ at $x = 0$, the function value and each derivative of $f(x)$ must equal the corresponding function value and derivative of $P(x)$ at $x = 0$. Assume that the series can be differentiated termwise.

$$P(x) = c_0 + c_1x + c_2x^2 + c_3x^3 + c_4x^4 + c_5x^5 + c_6x^6 + \cdots \Rightarrow P(0) = c_0$$

$$P'(x) = c_1 + 2c_2x + 3c_3x^2 + 4c_4x^3 + 5c_5x^4 + 6c_6x^5 + \cdots \Rightarrow P'(0) = c_1$$

$$P''(x) = 2c_2 + 6c_3x + 12c_4x^2 + 20c_5x^3 + 30c_6x^4 + \cdots \Rightarrow P''(0) = 2c_2$$

$$P'''(x) = 6c_3 + 24c_4x + 60c_5x^2 + 120c_6x^3 + \cdots \Rightarrow P'''(0) = 6c_3 = 3!c_3$$

$$P^{(4)}(x) = 24c_4 + 120c_5x + 360c_6x^2 + \cdots \Rightarrow P^{(4)}(0) = 24c_4 = 4!c_4$$

$$P^{(5)}(x) = 120c_5 + 720c_6x + \cdots \Rightarrow P^{(5)}(0) = 120c_5 = 5!c_5$$

[Recall that 3! (three factorial) is the product of the first three counting numbers, $1 \cdot 2 \cdot 3$.] For the function, the derivatives of $f(x)$ are as follows.

$$\begin{aligned}
f(x) &= \sin x &&\Rightarrow f(0) = 0\\
f'(x) &= \cos x &&\Rightarrow f'(0) = 1\\
f''(x) &= -\sin x &&\Rightarrow f''(0) = 0\\
f'''(x) &= -\cos x &&\Rightarrow f'''(0) = -1\\
f^{(4)}(x) &= \sin x &&\Rightarrow f^{(4)}(0) = 0\\
f^{(5)}(x) &= \cos x &&\Rightarrow f^{(5)}(0) = 1
\end{aligned}$$

Equating the function values and corresponding derivatives of $f$ and $P$ gives

$$\begin{aligned}
&c_0 = 0\\
&c_1 = 1\\
&2c_2 = 0 \Rightarrow c_2 = 0\\
&3!c_3 = -1 \Rightarrow c_3 = -\tfrac{1}{3!}\\
&4!c_4 = 0 \Rightarrow c_4 = 0\\
&5!c_5 = 1 \Rightarrow c_5 = \tfrac{1}{5!}
\end{aligned}$$

Thus the sum of the first three nonzero terms is

$P(x) = x - \frac{1}{3!}x^3 + \frac{1}{5!}x^5$, Q.E.D. ■

Once you have found derivatives for the series, you can remember the pattern and use it when you are called upon to expand other functions as series by equating derivatives.

**Property: Derivatives of a Power Series**

If $P(x) = c_0 + c_1x + c_2x^2 + c_3x^3 + c_4x^4 + c_5x^5 + \cdots + c_nx^n + \cdots$, then $P(0) = c_0,\ P'(0) = c_1,\ P''(0) = 2!c_2,\ \ldots,\ P^{(n)}(0) = n!c_n, \ldots$.

All you have to do to expand a function $f$ as a power series about $x = 0$ is find the values of $f(0), f'(0), f''(0), \ldots, f^{(n)}(0), \ldots$, set them equal to the above values of $P(0)$ and derivatives, and solve for the values of $c$.

■ ***Example 2*** For the series $\sin x = x - \frac{1}{3!}x^3 + \frac{1}{5!}x^5 - \cdots$

a. Demonstrate that you understand the pattern in the series by writing the next three terms.

b. Write the series using sigma notation.

***Solutions***

a. The exponents of $x$ are the odd integers. Each coefficient is the reciprocal of the factorial of the exponent. The signs alternate, with the first term being positive. Thus,

$$\sin x = x - \frac{1}{3!}x^3 + \frac{1}{5!}x^5 - \frac{1}{7!}x^7 + \frac{1}{9!}x^9 - \frac{1}{11!}x^{11} + \cdots.$$

b. The series can be written in sigma notation this way:

$$\sum_{n=0}^{\infty}(-1)^n \frac{1}{(2n+1)!} x^{2n+1}.$$

This symbol is pronounced, "the sum from $n = 0$ to infinity of $(-1)^n x^{2n+1}/(2n+1)!$." It means to let $n = 0, 1, 2, 3, \ldots$ and add up the resulting terms. The secret to finding a formula for $t_n$ (the term with index $n$) is writing the values of $n$ under the terms. In this case it is helpful to start $n$ at 0 rather than 1.

$$x - \frac{1}{3!}x^3 + \frac{1}{5!}x^5 - \frac{1}{7!}x^7 + \cdots.$$

0 1 2 3

Write the values of the term index, $n$, under the respective terms.

By comparing the values of $n$ with numbers in the terms, you can see that the exponent and denominator in each term are one more than twice the value of $n$. The factor $(-1)^n$ makes the signs alternate. The index of summation, $n$, could start at 0, 1, or whatever number you feel is appropriate. For instance, the answer above could be written

$$\sum_{n=1}^{\infty}(-1)^{n+1} \frac{1}{(2n-1)!} x^{2n-1}$$

Alternative form. ■

■ ***Example 3***

a. Plot the sixth partial sum of the power series for $\sin x$ expanded about $x = 0$.

b. Find, approximately, the interval of $x$-values for which the sixth partial sum is within 0.0001 unit of the value of the sine function.

c. Find a wider interval for which the ninth partial sum is within 0.0001 unit of $\sin x$.

***Solutions***

a. The sixth partial sum is $S_5(x)$ since the index of summation starts at $n = 0$.

$$S_5(x) = x - \frac{1}{3!}x^3 + \frac{1}{5!}x^5 - \frac{1}{7!}x^7 + \frac{1}{9!}x^9 - \frac{1}{11!}x^{11}$$

A time-efficient way to enter the partial sum uses the formula for the $n$th term that was found in Example 2 and the grapher's sequence commands. For a typical grapher you can enter the formula this way:

$y_1 = \text{SUM SEQUENCE}\ ((-1)\verb|^|n/(2n+1)! * x\verb|^|(2n+1), n, 0, 5, 1).$

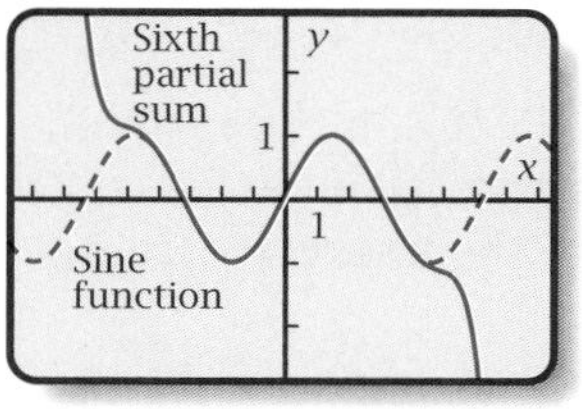


Figure 12-4a

The sequence command tells the grapher to generate a set of numbers using the formula inside the parentheses. The $n$ after the comma tells the grapher that $n$ is the index of summation. The last three numbers tell the grapher to start $n$ at 0, end it at 5, and increase it by steps of 1 each time (thus giving six terms). The sum command tells the grapher to add up the terms of the sequence it has calculated. The grapher performs this computation for each value of $x$ in the window you specify. Figure 12-4a shows the result.

| $x$ | $\sin x -$ sum |
|---|---|
| $-4$ | $-0.0100020...$ |
| $-3$ | $-0.0002454...$ |
| $-2$ | $-0.00000129...$ |
| $-1$ | $-0.000000000159...$ |
| 0 | 0 |
| 1 | $0.000000000159...$ |
| 2 | $0.00000129...$ |
| 3 | $0.0002454...$ |
| 4 | $0.0100020...$ |

b. A table of values of the differences between $\sin x$ and the series quickly shows the interval of $x$-values. Enter $(\sin x - y_1)$ as $y_2$. From the table you can see that if $x$ is between $-2$ and 2, the absolute value of the difference is less than 0.0001. By exploring the interval between 2 and 3 with another table, stepping $x$ by 0.1, you can find that the series is within 0.0001 unit of $\sin x$ for $-2.7 < x < 2.7$.

The answer can also be found using the solve feature of your grapher. If you have entered $\sin x$ as $y_1$ and the partial sum as $y_2$, then set $(y_1 - y_2) - 0.0001$ equal to 0. The result is $x \approx 2.7986 \ldots$. By symmetry, the interval is $-2.7986\ldots < x < 2.7986\ldots$.

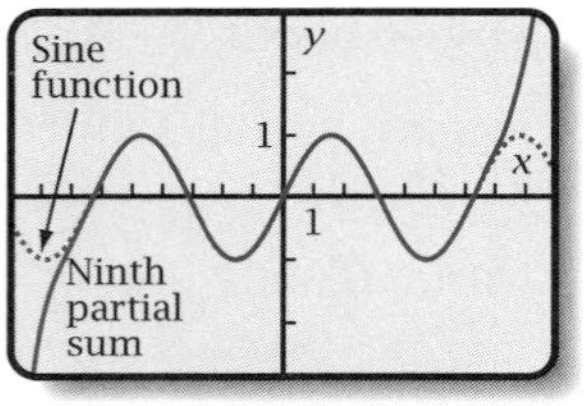

Figure 12-4b

c. The ninth partial sum is $S_8(x)$. If you are using the sequence commands, you can change the 5 in part (a) to 8. The grapher will then calculate 9 terms of the series, starting at $n = 0$, for each value of $x$. The resulting graph is as in Figure 12-4b. Numerically, as in part (b) you can find that the ninth partial sum is within 0.0001 of $\sin x$ if

$$-4.8974\ldots < x < 4.8974\ldots$$

Power series relate to functions the way decimals relate to irrational numbers. For instance,

$$\pi = 3.141592653\ldots \quad \text{and} \quad \sqrt{7359} = 85.7846140\ldots.$$

The human mind can grasp the size of the approximation 85.78... more easily than it can grasp the exact value, $\sqrt{7359}$. Similarly, a computer can calculate values of $\sin x$ from a power series more easily than it can calculate them directly from a definition of sine.

The more decimal places you use for a number such as $\pi$, the more accurate the approximation is. In many cases, the more terms you use for the partial sum of a series, the better the partial sum fits the function values. As was shown in Figure 12-4b, the ninth partial sum of the series above seems to coincide with $\sin x$ for $-7 < x < 7$. The sixth partial sum in Figure 12-4a coincides only for about $-4 < x < 4$.

## Problem Set 12-4

### *Do These Quickly*

The following problems are intended to refresh your skills. You should be able to do all ten problems in less than five minutes.

**Q1.** Sketch the graph of $y = \sin x$.

**Q2.** Sketch the graph of $y = \cos x$.

**Q3.** Sketch the graph of $y = e^x$.

**Q4.** Sketch the graph of $y = \ln x$.

**Q5.** Sketch the graph of $y = \cosh x$.

**Q6.** Sketch the graph of $y = \tan^{-1} x$.

**Q7.** In the expression $3x^5$, the number 5 is called the —?—.

**Q8.** In the expression $3x^5$, the number 3 is called the —?—.

**Q9.** The expression $x^5$ is called a —?—.

**Q10.** The area of the region between the graph of $y = 9 - x^2$ and the $x$-axis equals —?—.

1. *Exponential Function Series Problem:*
   a. Show by equating derivatives that the power series expansion for $e^x$ about $x = 0$ is
   $$P(x) = 1 + x + \tfrac{1}{2!}x^2 + \tfrac{1}{3!}x^3 + \cdots.$$
   b. Write the next two terms of the series.
   c. Write the series using sigma notation.
   d. Plot the fourth partial sum of the series. On the same screen plot $y = e^x$. Use a window of $[-3, 3]$ for $x$ and $[-2, 10]$ for $y$. Sketch the result.
   e. For what interval of $x$-values are the two graphs indistinguishable from each other?
   f. For what interval of $x$-values is the fourth partial sum within 0.0001 unit of $e^x$?
   g. For what wider interval is the ninth partial sum of the series within 0.0001 of $e^x$?

2. *Cosine Function Series Problem:*
   a. Show by equating derivatives that the power series expansion for $\cos x$ about $x = 0$ is
   $$P(x) = 1 - \tfrac{1}{2!}x^2 + \tfrac{1}{4!}x^4 - \tfrac{1}{6!}x^6 + \tfrac{1}{8!}x^8 - \cdots.$$
   b. Write the next three terms of the series.
   c. Write the series using sigma notation. Start the index of summation at $n = 0$.
   d. Figure 12-4c shows the graph of the fifth partial sum, $S_4(x)$. Plot this graph on your grapher. Then plot $y = \cos x$ on the same screen. Sketch both graphs.
   e. Plot the graph of the eighth partial sum, $S_7(x)$. For what interval of $x$-values is the $S_7(x)$ graph indistinguishable from that of $y = \cos x$? Sketch the result.
   f. For what interval of $x$ is the eighth partial sum within 0.0001 unit of $\cos x$?
   g. Give a reason why the series for $P(x)$ agrees with the properties of the cosine function.

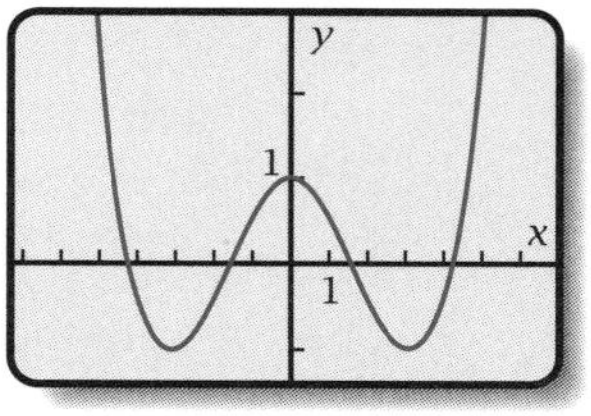

Figure 12-4c

3. *Sine Series Problem:* Let $P(x) = x - \frac{1}{3!}x^3 + \frac{1}{5!}x^5 - \frac{1}{7!}x^7 + \cdots$, which is the sine series.
   a. Show that $S_3(0.6)$, the fourth partial sum, is approximately equal to $\sin 0.6$.
   b. The **tail** of a power series is the series of terms left after a given partial sum. Write the value of $\sin 0.6$ to as many places as your calculator gives. Use this number to evaluate, approximately, the tail of the $P(0.6)$ series for $S_1(0.6)$, $S_2(0.6)$, and $S_3(0.6)$. Show that in each case, the value of the tail of the series is *less* in magnitude than the absolute value of the *first* term of the tail.
   c. Assuming that your observation in 3b about the tail of the series is correct for all values of $n$, figure out how many terms of the series for $P(0.6)$ it would take to get a partial sum that estimates sin 0.6 correct to at least 20 decimal places.

4. *Hyperbolic Sine and Cosine Series Problem:* Let $P(x) = \sum_{n=0}^{\infty} \frac{1}{(2n+1)!}x^{2n+1}$.
   a. Write the first four terms of the series (through $n = 3$).
   b. Show by equating derivatives that the series $P(x)$ represents $\sinh x$.
   c. Show that $S_3(0.6)$, the fourth partial sum of the series, is approximately equal to sinh 0.6.
   d. For what interval of $x$-values is $S_3(x)$ within 0.0001 unit of $\sinh x$?
   e. Assume that the derivative of the series equals the sum of the derivatives of the terms. Differentiate each term of the series for $P(x)$ to get a series for $P'(x)$.
   f. Since the derivative of $\sinh x$ is $\cosh x$, the series you found in 4e should be the series for $\cosh x$. Demonstrate that this is true by showing that the value of $P'(0.6)$ is approximately equal to $\cosh 0.6$. Use the fourth partial sum of the derivative series.
   g. Integrate the series for $P(x)$ term-by-term to get a power series for $\int P(x)\,dx$. Show that the result is the series for $\cosh x$ in 4f if the integration constant is picked appropriately.

5. *Natural Log Series Problem:* Let $P(x) = (x-1) - \frac{1}{2}(x-1)^2 + \frac{1}{3}(x-1)^3 - \frac{1}{4}(x-1)^4 + \cdots$. This series is the power series for $\ln x$ expanded about $x = 1$.
   a. By equating derivatives, show that $P(x)$ and $\ln x$ have the same function value at $x = 1$, and the same first, second, and third derivative values at $x = 1$.
   b. Write the next two terms of the series.
   c. Write the series using sigma notation. Start the index of summation at $n = 1$.
   d. Figure 12-4d shows the graph of the fourth partial sum of the series. The graph fits $y = \ln x$ reasonably well when $x$ is close to 1. Plot $y = \ln x$ and $S_{10}(x)$, the tenth partial sum of the series, on the same screen. Sketch.
   e. By appropriate use of the TRACE or TABLE feature, compare $S_{10}(1.2)$, $S_{10}(1.95)$, and $S_{10}(3)$ with the values of $\ln 1.2$, $\ln 1.95$, and $\ln 3$. For what interval of $x$-values does the tenth partial sum of the series seem to fit the ln function? Is this interval much larger than that for the fourth partial sum in Figure 12-4d?

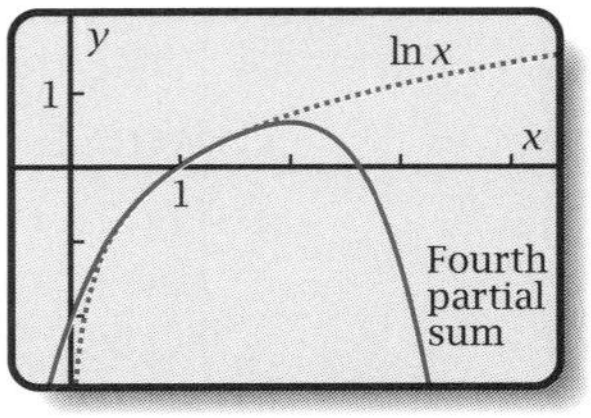

Figure 12-4d

6. *Convergence and Divergence Problem:* From Problem Set 12-1 you recall that a series converges to $f(x)$ for a particular value of $x$ if the partial sums of $P(x)$ approach the value of $f(x)$ as the number of terms in the partial sum approaches infinity. In Problem

5 the series $P(x)$ converges to $\ln x$ when $x = 1.2$ and $x = 1.95$. But the series diverges for $x = 3$. In this problem you will see reasons why this is true.

a. Make a table of values for the first few terms of $P(3)$. What is happening to the absolute value of the terms?

b. By appropriate use of l'Hospital's rule, show that the absolute value of the $n$th term for $P(3)$ approaches infinity as $n$ approaches infinity. Explain how this fact tells you that the series for $P(3)$ cannot possibly converge.

c. Make a table of values for the first few terms of $P(1.2)$. Show that these terms approach zero for a limit as $n$ approaches infinity, and thus the series could converge.

d. In Problem 3 it was observed that the value of the tail of a series which remained after the $n$th partial sum was smaller in absolute value than the absolute value of the first term of the tail. Is this observation true for $P(1.2)$. Justify your answer.

7. *Inverse Tangent Series Problem:*

a. Let $f(x) = \tan^{-1}x$. Let $P(x)$ be the power series

$$P(x) = \sum_{n=0}^{\infty} (-1)^n \frac{1}{2n+1} x^{2n+1}$$

Write out the first few terms of the series.

b. Plot the graph of $f$ and the graphs of the sixth and seventh partial sums on the same screen. For what values of $x$ do the partial sums represent the graph of $f$ quite well? For what values of $x$ do the partial sum graphs bear little or no resemblance to the graph of $f$?

# 12-5 Taylor and Maclaurin Series, and Operations on These Series

In Problem 5 of Problem Set 12-4, it was stated that the expansion of $\ln x$ about $x = 1$ is

$$\ln x = (x-1) - \tfrac{1}{2}(x-1)^2 + \tfrac{1}{3}(x-1)^3 - \tfrac{1}{4}(x-1)^4 + \cdots.$$

The coefficients can be found by equating derivatives at $x = 1$ as you will see in Example 1 of this section. In general, if function $f$ is expanded about $x = a$, then the coefficients are

$$c_0 = f(a),\ c_1 = f'(a),\ c_2 = \frac{f''(a)}{2!},\ c_3 = \frac{f'''(a)}{3!}, \ldots.$$

The powers are $(x-a)^n$ rather than $x^n$ because $(x-a)$ equals zero when $x = a$. The result is called the **Taylor series expansion of $f(x)$ about $x = a$** after the British mathematician Brook Taylor (1685–1731). If $a = 0$, the Taylor series is called the **Maclaurin series expansion of $f(x)$** after the Scottish mathematician Colin Maclaurin (1698–1746), although neither Taylor nor Maclaurin was the first to publish this kind of series.

### *Taylor Series and Maclaurin Series*

If $f$ is a function with differentiable derivatives, then $f(x)$ can be written as a Taylor series expansion about $x = 1$ as follows:

$$f(x) = f(a) + f'(a)(x-a) + \frac{f''(a)}{2!}(x-a)^2 + \frac{f'''(a)}{3!}(x-a)^3 + \cdots + \frac{f^{(n)}(a)}{n!}(x-a)^n + \cdots$$

If $a = 0$, the series is called a Maclaurin series.

**OBJECTIVE** Given the Taylor series for $e^x$, $\sin x$, $\cos x$, $\sinh x$, $\cosh x$, $\ln x$, $1/(1-x)$, and $\tan^{-1}x$, perform operations on these series to derive power series for related functions.

To accomplish the objective efficiently, it is a good idea to memorize the following eight series. These are the series you derived in Sections 12-1 through 12-4.

### *Eight Well-Known Power Series*

$$e^x = 1 + x + \tfrac{1}{2!}x^2 + \tfrac{1}{3!}x^3 + \tfrac{1}{4!}x^4 + \cdots = \sum_{n=0}^{\infty} \frac{1}{n!}x^n$$

$$\sin x = x - \tfrac{1}{3!}x^3 + \tfrac{1}{5!}x^5 - \tfrac{1}{7!}x^7 + \cdots = \sum_{n=0}^{\infty} (-1)^n \frac{1}{(2n+1)!}x^{2n+1}$$

$$\cos x = 1 - \tfrac{1}{2!}x^2 + \tfrac{1}{4!}x^4 - \tfrac{1}{6!}x^6 + \cdots = \sum_{n=0}^{\infty} (-1)^n \frac{1}{(2n)!}x^{2n}$$

$$\sinh x = x + \tfrac{1}{3!}x^3 + \tfrac{1}{5!}x^5 + \tfrac{1}{7!}x^7 + \cdots = \sum_{n=0}^{\infty} \frac{1}{(2n+1)!}x^{2n+1}$$

$$\cosh x = 1 + \tfrac{1}{2!}x^2 + \tfrac{1}{4!}x^4 + \tfrac{1}{6!}x^6 + \cdots = \sum_{n=0}^{\infty} \frac{1}{(2n)!}x^{2n}$$

$$\ln x = (x-1) - \tfrac{1}{2}(x-1)^2 + \tfrac{1}{3}(x-1)^3 - \tfrac{1}{4}(x-1)^4 + \cdots = \sum_{n=1}^{\infty} (-1)^{n+1}\tfrac{1}{n}(x-1)^n$$

$$\frac{1}{1-x} = 1 + x + x^2 + x^3 + x^4 + \cdots = \sum_{n=0}^{\infty} x^n \quad \text{(A geometric series.)}$$

$$\tan^{-1}x = x - \tfrac{1}{3}x^3 + \tfrac{1}{5}x^5 - \tfrac{1}{7}x^7 + \cdots = \sum_{n=0}^{\infty} (-1)^n \frac{1}{2n+1}x^{2n+1}$$

**■ Example 1** Show by equating derivatives that the Taylor series for $\ln x$ expanded about $x = 1$ is

$$\ln x = (x-1) - \tfrac{1}{2}(x-1)^2 + \tfrac{1}{3}(x-1)^3 - \tfrac{1}{4}(x-1)^4 + \cdots.$$

**Solution** So that $P(1)$ will equal $c_0$, $P'(1)$ will equal $c_1$, and so forth, the series is written in powers of $(x-1)$ instead of in powers of $x$ as before.

$$P(x) = c_0 + c_1(x-1) + c_2(x-1)^2 + c_3(x-1)^3 + c_4(x-1)^4 + \cdots.$$

[If you were to use $P(x) = c_0 + c_1x + c_2x^2 + \cdots$, then $P(1)$ would equal $c_0 + c_1 + c_2 + \cdots$ instead of just $c_0$.] Equating derivatives gives

$$\begin{array}{lllllll}
f(x) = \ln x & \Rightarrow & f(1) = 0 & \Rightarrow & c_0 = 0 & & \\
f'(x) = 1/x = x^{-1} & \Rightarrow & f'(1) = 1 & \Rightarrow & c_1 = 1 & & \\
f''(x) = -x^{-2} & \Rightarrow & f''(1) = -1 & \Rightarrow & 2!c_2 = -1 & \Rightarrow & c_2 = -\frac{1}{2} \\
f'''(x) = +2x^{-3} & \Rightarrow & f'''(1) = 2 & \Rightarrow & 3!c_3 = 2 & \Rightarrow & c_3 = \frac{1}{3} \\
f^{(4)}(x) = -6x^{-4} & \Rightarrow & f^{(4)}(1) = -6 & \Rightarrow & 4!c_4 = -6 & \Rightarrow & c_4 = -\frac{1}{4} \\
f^{(5)}(x) = +24x^{-5} & \Rightarrow & f^{(5)}(1) = 24 & \Rightarrow & 5!c_5 = 24 & \Rightarrow & c_5 = \frac{1}{5}
\end{array}$$

$$\therefore \ln x = (x-1) - \tfrac{1}{2}(x-1)^2 + \tfrac{1}{3}(x-1)^3 - \tfrac{1}{4}(x-1)^4 + \cdots, \text{Q.E.D}$$ ■

■ ***Example 2*** Expand $f(x) = \sin x$ as a Taylor series about $x = \pi/3$.

***Solution***

$$f(x) = \sin x \Rightarrow f(\tfrac{\pi}{3}) = \sin\tfrac{\pi}{3} = \tfrac{\sqrt{3}}{2}$$

$$f'(x) = \cos x \Rightarrow f'(\tfrac{\pi}{3}) = \cos\tfrac{\pi}{3} = \tfrac{1}{2}$$

$$f''(x) = -\sin x \Rightarrow f''(\tfrac{\pi}{3}) = -\sin\tfrac{\pi}{3} = -\tfrac{\sqrt{3}}{2}$$

$$f'''(x) = -\cos x \Rightarrow f'''(\tfrac{\pi}{3}) = -\cos\tfrac{\pi}{3} = -\tfrac{1}{2}, \text{ and so forth.}$$

$$\therefore \sin x = \sqrt{3}/2 + (1/2)(x-\pi/3) - \left[\tfrac{\sqrt{3}/2}{2!}\right][(x-\pi/3)^2]$$
$$-\left[\tfrac{1/2}{3!}\right][(x-\pi/3)^3] + \left[\tfrac{\sqrt{3}/2}{4!}\right][(x-\pi/3)^4] + \cdots.$$ ■

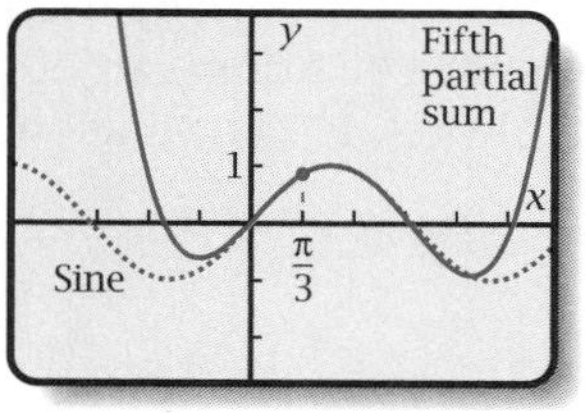


Figure 12-5a

Example 2 shows that once you have found the derivatives for the function you are expanding, you can just substitute them directly into the formula for the Taylor series. It isn't necessary to equate derivatives.

Figure 12-5a shows that the fifth partial sum in Example 2 fits $\sin x$ well if $x$ is in a neighborhood of $\pi/3$.

It is usually easier to derive a series by starting with one of the known series than it is to calculate derivatives of $f(x)$. Examples 3–6 show you ways this can be done.

■ ***Example 3*** Write the first few terms of the Maclaurin series for $\sin(3x)^2$.

***Solution*** Take the known series for $\sin x$, and replace the $x$ with $(3x)^2$. The rest is algebra.

$$\sin(3x)^2 = (3x)^2 - \tfrac{1}{3!}[(3x)^2]^3 + \tfrac{1}{5!}[(3x)^2]^5 - \tfrac{1}{7!}[(3x)^2]^7 + \cdots$$
$$= 3^2x^2 - \tfrac{3^6}{3!}x^6 + \tfrac{3^{10}}{5!}x^{10} - \tfrac{3^{14}}{7!}x^{14} + \cdots$$ ■

■ ***Example 4*** Write the first few terms of the Maclaurin series for $g(x) = \dfrac{1}{1+x^3}$.

***Solution*** This series can be derived by performing long division, or by substituting $(-x^3)$ for $x$ in the geometric series from $1/(1-x)$.

$$g(x) = 1 + (-x^3) + (-x^3)^2 + (-x^3)^3 + (-x^3)^4 + \cdots$$
$$= 1 - x^3 + x^6 - x^9 + x^{12} - \cdots$$ ■

**Example 5** By appropriate operations show that the Maclaurin series for $\tan^{-1}x$ is

$$\tan^{-1}x = x - \tfrac{1}{3}x^3 + \tfrac{1}{5}x^5 - \tfrac{1}{7}x^7 + \cdots.$$

**Solution** If you start the process of equating derivatives, the result is

$$f(x) = \tan^{-1}x$$
$$f'(x) = \frac{1}{1+x^2}.$$

The expression for the first derivative can be expanded as a Maclaurin series by substituting $-x^2$ for $x$ in the geometric series from $1/(1-x)$, as in Example 4.

$$f'(x) = 1 - x^2 + x^4 - x^6 + \cdots$$

The series for $\tan^{-1}x$ can be found by integrating, assuming that an infinite series can be integrated termwise.

$$\begin{aligned}\tan^{-1}x &= \int (1 - x^2 + x^4 - x^6 + \cdots)\,dx \\ &= x - \tfrac{1}{3}x^3 + \tfrac{1}{5}x^5 - \tfrac{1}{7}x^7 + \cdots + C\end{aligned}$$

Since $\tan^{-1}0 = 0$, the constant of integration $C$ is also zero. Thus

$$\tan^{-1}x = x - \tfrac{1}{3}x^3 + \tfrac{1}{5}x^5 - \tfrac{1}{7}x^7 + \cdots, \text{ Q.E.D.}$$

■

**Example 6** Write a power series for $f(x) = \int_0^x t\cos t^5\,dt$. Evaluate the sixth partial sum at $x = 0.8$.

**Solution** The technique is to write a series for the integrand, then integrate term by term. As in Example 5, assume that the sum of an infinite number of terms can be integrated termwise, which is true in this case, but not always. First, replace $x$ with $t^5$ in the Maclaurin series for cosine.

$$\cos t^5 = 1 - \tfrac{1}{2!}t^{10} + \tfrac{1}{4!}t^{20} - \tfrac{1}{6!}t^{30} + \cdots$$

Then multiply each term by $t$, and integrate.

$$t\cos t^5 = t - \tfrac{1}{2!}t^{11} + \tfrac{1}{4!}t^{21} - \tfrac{1}{6!}t^{31} + \cdots$$

$$f(x) = \int_0^x \left(t - \tfrac{1}{2!}t^{11} + \tfrac{1}{4!}t^{21} - \tfrac{1}{6!}t^{31} + \cdots\right)dt$$

$$f(x) = \tfrac{1}{2}t^2 - \tfrac{1}{12\cdot 2!}t^{12} + \tfrac{1}{22\cdot 4!}t^{22} - \tfrac{1}{32\cdot 6!}t^{32} + \cdots \Big|_0^x$$

$$f(x) = \tfrac{1}{2}x^2 - \tfrac{1}{12\cdot 2!}x^{12} + \tfrac{1}{22\cdot 4!}x^{22} - \tfrac{1}{32\cdot 6!}x^{32} + \cdots$$

To find $S_6(0.8)$, substitute and do the arithmetic. For decimals longer than your calculator can handle, add and subtract column-wise, as shown here.

$$S_6(0.8) = \tfrac{1}{2}0.8^2 - \tfrac{1}{12\cdot 2!}0.8^{12} + \tfrac{1}{22\cdot 4!}0.8^{22} - \tfrac{1}{32\cdot 6!}0.8^{32} + \tfrac{1}{42\cdot 8!}0.8^{42} - \tfrac{1}{52\cdot 10!}0.8^{52}$$

$$\begin{aligned} = \ &0.3200000000000\ldots \\ &-0.0028633115306\ldots \\ &+0.0000139748061\ldots \\ &-0.0000000343872\ldots \\ &+0.0000000000502\ldots \\ &\underline{-0.0000000000000484\ldots} \\ = \ &0.31715062893851\ldots \end{aligned}$$

Add the digits column-wise. For instance, for the 13th decimal place, add $0 - 6 + 1 - 2 + 2 - 0$ to obtain $-5$. Write down 5 and carry 1.

■

The answer could, of course, be found numerically. But the series takes only six terms to give 13-place accuracy. As you will see in the following section, it is possible to determine the accuracy of an integral if you use a series rather than a Riemann sum or other numerical methods.

## Problem Set 12-5

### *Do These Quickly*

The following problems are intended to refresh your skills. You should be able to do all 10 in less than 5 minutes.

**Q1.** Evaluate: 4!

**Q2.** Evaluate: 3!

**Q3.** Evaluate: 4!/4

**Q4.** What does $n$ equal if $4!/4 = n!$?

**Q5.** If $m!/m = n!$, then $n =$ —?—.

**Q6.** $0! = m!/m$. What does $m$ equal?

**Q7.** Why does 0! equal 1?

**Q8.** Why is $(-1)!$ infinite?

**Q9.** Differentiate: $f(x) = \sqrt{x^2 - 7}$

**Q10.** Integrate: $\int \sinh x\, dx$

For Problems 1–8, write from memory the power series.

1. $f(u) = e^u$
2. $f(u) = \ln u$
3. $f(u) = \sin u$
4. $f(u) = \cos u$
5. $f(u) = \cosh u$
6. $f(u) = \sinh u$
7. $f(u) = (1 - u)^{-1}$
8. $f(u) = \tan^{-1} u$

For Problems 9–24, derive a power series for the given function. Write enough terms of the series to show the pattern.

9. $x \sin x$
10. $x \sinh x$
11. $\cosh x^3$
12. $\cos x^2$
13. $\ln x^2$
14. $e^{-x^2}$
15. $\int_0^x e^{-t^2}\, dt$
16. $\int_0^x \sin t^3\, dt$
17. $\int_0^x t^2 \sin t^5\, dt$
18. $\int_1^x \ln t^3\, dt$
19. $\int_0^x \frac{1}{t} \sinh t^2\, dt$
20. $\int_0^x \cos t^{0.5}\, dt$
21. $\dfrac{1}{x^4 + 1}$
22. $\dfrac{9}{x^2 + 3}$
23. $\int_0^x \frac{1}{t^4 + 1}\, dt$
24. $\int_0^x \frac{9}{t^2 + 3}\, dt$

For Problems 25–30, expand the function as a Taylor series about the given value of $x$. Write enough terms to reveal clearly that you have seen the pattern.

25. $f(x) = \sin x$, about $x = \pi/4$

26. $f(x) = \cos x$, about $x = \pi/4$

27. $f(x) = \ln x$, about $x = 1$

28. $f(x) = \log x$, about $x = 10$

29. $f(x) = (x - 5)^{7/3}$, about $x = 4$

30. $f(x) = (x + 6)^{4.2}$, about $x = -5$.

31. Find the Maclaurin series for $\cos 3x$ by equating derivatives. Compare the answer, and the ease of getting the answer, with the series you obtain by substituting $3x$ for $x$ in the cosine series.

32. Find the Maclaurin series for $\ln(1 + x)$ by equating derivatives. Compare the answer, and the ease of finding the answer, with the series you obtain by substituting $(1 + x)$ for $x$ in the Taylor series for $\ln x$, expanded about $x = 1$.

33. *Accuracy for* ln *x Series Value:* Estimate ln 1.5 using $S_4$ (1.5), fourth partial sum of the Taylor series. How close is your answer to the real answer? How does the error in the series value compare with the first term of the tail of the series, $t_5$, which is the first term left out in the partial sum?

34. *Accuracy Interval for* ln *x Series:* Find the interval of values of $x$ for which the fourth partial sum of the Taylor series for ln $x$ gives values that are within 0.001 unit of ln $x$.

35. *Inverse Tangent Series and an Approximation for $\pi$:* You recall that $\tan(\pi/4) = 1$. Thus $\tan^{-1} 1 = \pi/4$. In this problem you will use the inverse tangent series to estimate $\pi$.

    a. Write the first few terms of the Maclaurin series for $\tan^{-1} 1$. Then use the appropriate features of your grapher to find the 10th partial sum of this series. Multiply by 4 to find an approximate value of $\pi$. How close does this approximation come to $\pi$?

    b. Find another approximation for $\pi$ using the 50th partial sum of the series in 35a. Is this approximation much better than the one using the 10th partial sum?

    c. By appropriate trigonometry, show that

    $$\tan^{-1} 1 = \tan^{-1} \tfrac{1}{2} + \tan^{-1} \tfrac{1}{3}.$$

    Use the result to write $\pi/4$ as a sum of the Maclaurin series. Estimate the value of $\pi$ by finding the tenth partial sums of the two series. Comment on how much better this method is for estimating $\pi$ than the methods of 35a and 35b.

36. *Tangent Series Problem:* You recall that $\tan x = (\sin x)/(\cos x)$. Long divide the Maclaurin series for $\sin x$ by that for $\cos x$ to get a power series for $\tan x$. Use enough terms of both sine and cosine series to find four terms of the tangent series. Show by calculator that the fourth partial sum for tan 0.2 is close to tan 0.2.

37. *Taylor Series Proof Problem:* Prove by mathematical induction that for all positive integers $n$, the $n$th derivative of the general Taylor series is equal to $f^{(n)}(a)$.

38. *Historical Problem:* What were Taylor's and Maclaurin's first names? When did they live in relation to Newton and Leibniz, who invented calculus?

*39. *Ratio of Terms Problem:* A Taylor series usually gives better and better approximations for values of a function the more terms you use. For some series this is true only for certain values of $x$. For instance, the series for the natural logarithm,

$$\ln x = \sum_{n=1}^{\infty} (-1)^{n+1} \frac{1}{n} (x-1)^n,$$

converges to $\ln x$ only for $0 < x \le 2$. If $x$ is outside this **interval of convergence**, the series does not converge to a real number. It diverges and thus cannot represent $\ln x$. In this problem you will investigate the ratio of a term in this series to the term before it, and try to discover a way to find from this ratio whether or not the series converges.

a. As shown above, formula for $t_n$, the $n$th term in the series for $\ln x$, is

$$t_n = (-1)^{n+1} \frac{1}{n} (x-1)^n.$$

Let $r_n$ be the ratio $|t_{n+1}/t_n|$. Find a formula for $r_n$ in terms of $x$ and $n$.

b. Calculate $r_{10}$ for $x = 1.2$, $x = 1.95$, and $x = 3$.

c. Let $r$ be the limit of $r_n$ as $n$ approaches infinity. Find an equation for $r$ in terms of $x$.

d. Evaluate $r$ for $x = 1.2$, $x = 1.95$, and $x = 3$.

e. Make a conjecture: "The series converges to $\ln x$ whenever the value of $x$ makes $r$ —?—, and diverges whenever the value of $x$ makes $r$ —?—."

f. If your conjecture is correct, you can use it to show that the series converges if $x$ is in the interval $0 < x < 2$. Check your conjecture by showing that it gives this interval.

40. *Journal Problem:* Update your journal with what you've learned since the last entry. Include such things as those listed here.
- The one most important thing you've learned since the last journal entry.
- The difference between a sequence and a series.
- The distinction between term index and term number.
- The definition of geometric series.
- The meaning of power series, and for what purpose they may be useful.
- What it means for a series to converge and to diverge.
- Anything about series that is still unclear.

---

*This problem prepares you for the next section.

# 12-6 Interval of Convergence for a Series—The Ratio Technique

A series converges to a certain number if the limit of the $n$th partial sum is that number as $n$ approaches infinity. Power series often converge if $x$ is within 1 unit of $a$, the constant about which the series is expanded. For instance the series

$$\ln x = (x-1) - \tfrac{1}{2}(x-1)^2 + \tfrac{1}{3}(x-1)^3 - \tfrac{1}{4}(x-1)^4 + \cdots = \sum_{n=1}^{\infty} (-1)^{n+1}\tfrac{1}{n}(x-1)^n$$

converges when $x = 1.6$. The quantity $(x - 1)$ equals 0.6, and the powers $0.6^n$ approach zero rapidly as $n$ gets large. But if $x = 4$, the quantity $(x - 1)$ is 3, and the powers $3^n$ become infinitely large as $n$ approaches infinity. You can see what happens from a table of values.

| $n$ | $n$th term, $x = 1.6$ | $n$th term, $x = 4$ |
|---|---|---|
| 1 | 0.6 | 3 |
| 2 | −0.18 | −4.5 |
| 3 | 0.072 | 9 |
| 4 | −0.0324 | −20.25 |
| 5 | 0.015552 | 48.6 |
| 6 | −0.007776 | −121.5 |
| 7 | 0.00399908... | 312.428... |
| ... | ... | ... |
| 20 | −0.00000182... | −174339220.05 |

Figure 12-6a shows what happens to the partial sums of the natural logarithm series. The left-hand graph shows that the partial sums for $x = 1.6$ converge rapidly to a number around 0.5 as $n$ approaches infinity. The right-hand graph shows that the partial sums for $x = 4$ diverge.

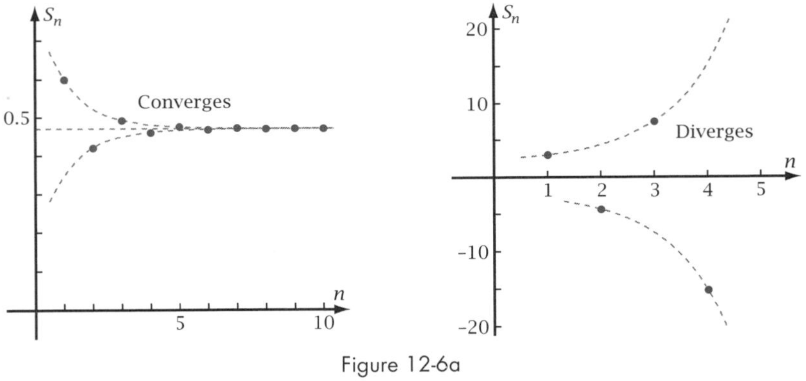

Figure 12-6a

Surprisingly, the series for $\sin x$,

$$\sin x = x - \frac{1}{3!}x^3 + \frac{1}{5!}x^5 - \frac{1}{7!}x^7 + \cdots = \sum_{n=0}^{\infty} (-1)^n \frac{1}{(2n+1)!}x^{2n+1},$$

converges no matter how large $x$ is! At $x = 10$, for instance, the power $10^{2n+1}$ is very large. But the denominator, $(2n + 1)!$, is much larger. If $n = 20$, then $(2n + 1)! = 41! = 3.3\ldots \times 10^{49}$, which is 300 million times as big as $10^{41}$. In this section you will develop a method called the **ratio technique** (sometimes called the

**ratio test**) for finding precisely the **interval of convergence**—that is, the interval of $x$-values for which a power series converges.

***OBJECTIVE***

Given a power series in $x$, use the ratio technique to find the interval of convergence.

The ratio technique is based on bounding the given series with a convergent geometric series. To see how the technique works, consider the series for $\ln x$ when $x = 1.6$.

$$\begin{aligned}\ln 1.6 &= (1.6 - 1) - \tfrac{1}{2}(1.6 - 1)^2 + \tfrac{1}{3}(1.6 - 1)^3 - \tfrac{1}{4}(1.6 - 1)^4 + \cdots \\ &= 0.6 - \tfrac{1}{2}(0.6)^2 + \tfrac{1}{3}(0.6)^3 - \tfrac{1}{4}(0.6)^4 + \cdots\end{aligned}$$

If you take the ratios of the absolute values of adjacent terms, $|t_{n+1}/t_n|$, you get the sequence

$$\begin{array}{llllllll} \tfrac{1}{2}(0.6), & \tfrac{2}{3}(0.6), & \tfrac{3}{4}(0.6), & \tfrac{4}{5}(0.6), & \tfrac{5}{6}(0.6), & \tfrac{6}{7}(0.6), & \tfrac{7}{8}(0.6), & \tfrac{8}{9}(0.6), \ldots \\ = 0.3, & 0.4, & 0.45, & 0.48, & 0.5, & 0.514\ldots, & 0.525, & 0.5333\ldots, \ \ldots \end{array}$$

A given term in the ln 1.6 series is formed by multiplying the preceding term by the appropriate one of these ratios. So each term is less than 0.6 times the preceding term.

Pick a geometric series with common ratio between 0.6 and 1, say $r = 0.7$, and with the first term equal to a term in the tail, say $|t_4| = 0.0324$. Since $|r| < 1$, the geometric series converges to

$$S = \frac{0.324}{1 - 0.7} = 0.108.$$

As shown in Figure 12-6b, the geometric series is an upper bound for the absolute values of the terms in the tail of the ln 1.6 series. Starting the geometric series at $t_{20}$ gives an upper bound of $|t_{20}|/0.3$, which equals 0.00000609.... Since the terms of the ln 1.6 series alternate in sign and approach zero as $n$ approaches infinity, a lower bound for the tail is $-0.00000609\ldots$. Since the bounds for the tail can be made as close to zero as you like, the series converges.

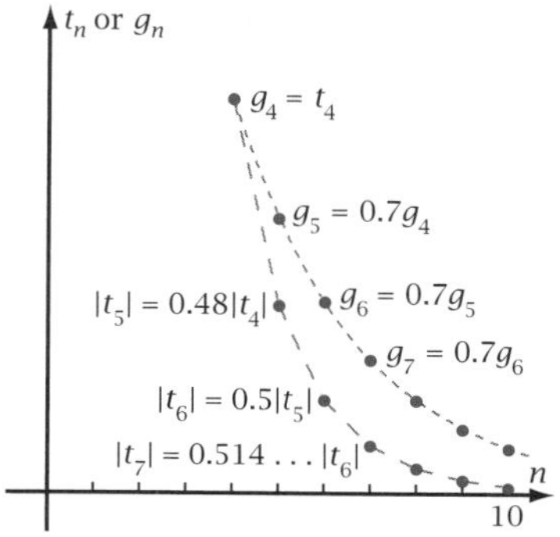


Figure 12-6b

In general, a power series will converge if the ratio of the absolute values of adjacent terms can be kept less than some number $R$, and $R$ is less than 1. In that case you can always find a geometric series with common ratio between $R$ and 1 that converges and is an upper bound for the tail of the series.

One way to show that there is such a number $R$ is to take the limit, $L$, of the ratios of adjacent terms. As shown in Figure 12-6c, if $L < 1$, then you can pick an epsilon small enough so that $R = L + \epsilon$ is also less than 1. Then any geometric series with common ratio $r$ between $R$ and 1, and with a suitable first term, will be an upper bound for the tail of the given series.

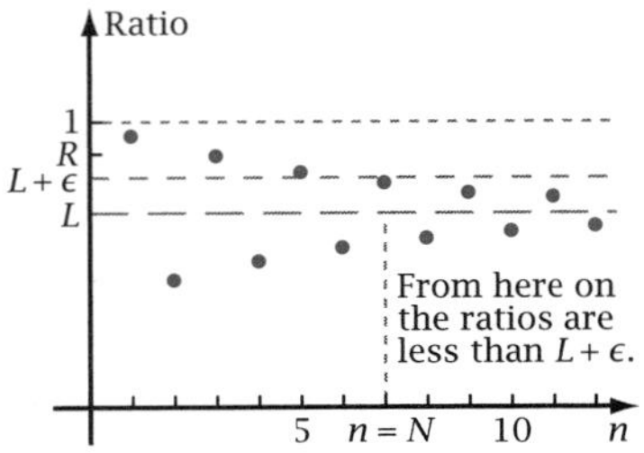


Figure 12-6c

This fact can be used as a relatively simple way to find the interval of values of $x$ for which a series converges. Example 1 shows you how this technique is used with the series for $\ln x$.

**■ Example 1** Find the interval of convergence for $\ln x = \sum_{n=1}^{\infty} (-1)^{n+1}\frac{1}{n}(x-1)^n$.

**Solution**

$$L = \lim_{n\to\infty}\left|\frac{t_{n+1}}{t_n}\right| = \lim_{n\to\infty}\left|\frac{(-1)^{n+2}(x-1)^{n+1}}{(n+1)}\cdot\frac{n}{(-1)^{n+1}(x-1)^n}\right|$$

$$= \lim_{n\to\infty}\left|\frac{(x-1)(n)}{n+1}\right|$$ What happens to $(-1)^{n+1}$ and $(-1)^{n+2}$?

$$= |x-1|\lim_{n\to\infty}\frac{n}{n+1}$$ Since $|x-1|$ is independent of $n$.

$$= |x-1|\tfrac{1}{1}$$ By l'Hospital's rule, first embedding $t_n$ in a continuous function.

$$= |x-1|$$

So the series will converge if

$$|x-1| < 1 \Rightarrow -1 < x-1 < 1 \Rightarrow 0 < x < 2.$$ (Open) interval of convergence. ■

Here is a formal statement of the ratio technique used in Example 1.

> ***Technique: The Ratio Technique for Convergence of Series***
>
> For the series $\sum_{n=1}^{\infty} t_n$, if $L = \lim_{n\to\infty}\left|\frac{t_{n+1}}{t_n}\right|$, then:
>
> i. The series converges if $L < 1$.
>
> ii. The series diverges if $L > 1$.
>
> iii. The series may either converge or diverge if $L = 1$.

The interval of convergence in Example 1, $0 < x < 2$, goes $\pm 1$ unit either side of $x = 1$, the value of $x$ about which the series is expanded. The half-width of the interval of convergence is called the **radius of convergence**. The word *radius* is used because if $x$ is allowed to be a complex number, the series converges for all $x$ inside a circle of that radius (Figure 12-6d).

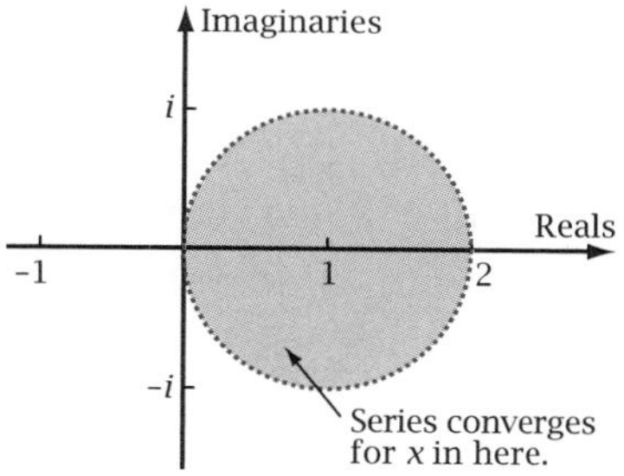


Figure 12-6d

**■ *Example 2*** For the series $\sum_{n=1}^{\infty} \frac{n}{3^n}(x-5)^n$,

a. Write out the first few terms.

b. Find the interval of convergence.

c. Find the radius of convergence.

***Solutions***

a. $\frac{1}{3}(x-5) + \frac{2}{9}(x-5)^2 + \frac{3}{27}(x-5)^3 + \frac{4}{81}(x-5)^4 + \cdots$

b.
$$\begin{aligned} L &= \lim_{n\to\infty} \left| \frac{t_{n+1}}{t_n} \right| \\ &= \lim_{n\to\infty} \left| \frac{(n+1)(x-5)^{n+1}}{3^{n+1}} \cdot \frac{3^n}{n(x-5)^n} \right| \\ &= \lim_{n\to\infty} \left| \frac{n+1}{n} \cdot \frac{1}{3}(x-5) \right| \\ &= |x-5| \lim_{n\to\infty} \left| \frac{n+1}{3n} \right| \\ &= |x-5|\tfrac{1}{3} \end{aligned}$$

The series will converge if $L < 1$.

$$|x-5|\tfrac{1}{3} < 1 \Rightarrow |x-5| < 3 \Rightarrow -3 < x-5 < 3 \Rightarrow 2 < x < 8$$

c. The radius of convergence is the distance from the midpoint of the interval of convergence to one of its endpoints.

Radius of convergence is 3. ■

If $x$ equals the number at an endpoint of the interval of convergence, the limit of the ratio of terms equals 1. The series may or may not converge in this case. In Section 12-7, you will learn tests for convergence that can be used when the ratio technique doesn't work. Example 3 shows you that the radius of convergence of a series is zero if the limit of the ratio of terms is infinite.

**Example 3** For the series $\sum_{n=1}^{\infty} \frac{n!}{n^4}(x-3)^n$,

a. Write out the first few terms.

b. Show that though the first few terms decrease in value, the radius of convergence is zero.

c. For what one value of $x$ does the series converge?

**Solutions**

a. $(x-3) + \frac{1}{8}(x-3)^2 + \frac{2}{27}(x-3)^3 + \frac{3}{32}(x-3)^4 + \cdots$

b. Note that the factorials simplify nicely when you divide adjacent terms.

$$L = \lim_{n\to\infty}\left|\frac{t_{n+1}}{t_n}\right| = \lim_{n\to\infty}\left|\frac{(n+1)!(x-3)^{n+1}}{(n+1)^4}\cdot\frac{n^4}{n!(x-3)^n}\right|$$

$$= \lim_{n\to\infty}\left|\frac{(n+1)(n!)}{n!}\cdot\left(\frac{n}{n+1}\right)^4(x-3)\right|$$

$$= |x-3|\lim_{n\to\infty}\left|(n+1)\left(\frac{n}{n+1}\right)^4\right|$$

Since $n/(n+1)$ goes to 1 as $n$ approaches infinity, its fourth power also goes to 1. Thus the quantity inside the absolute value sign approaches the other $(n+1)$, and $L$ is infinite for all values of $x$ not equal to 3. The radius of convergence is thus equal to zero, Q.E.D.

c. If $x = 3$, the series becomes $0 + 0 + 0 + \cdots$, which converges to zero. So 3 is the only value of $x$ for which the series converges. ■

From Example 3 there follow two special cases.

> **Special Cases: Zero and Infinite Radius of Convergence**
>
> For a power series in $(x-c)^n$ with radius of convergence $r$:
>
> If $r = 0$, the series converges only at $x = c$.
>
> If $r$ is infinite, the series converges for all values of $x$.

# Problem Set 12-6

### Do These Quickly

The following problems are intended to refresh your skills. You should be able to do all ten problems in less than five minutes.

**Q1.** $x - x^3/3! + x^5/5! - x^7/7! + \cdots =$ -?-

**Q2.** $x + x^3/3! + x^5/5! + x^7/7! + \cdots =$ -?-

**Q3.** $1 - x + x^2/2! + x^3/3! + x^4/4! - \cdots =$ -?-

**Q4.** $1 + x + x^2/2! + x^3/3! + x^4/4! + \cdots =$ -?-

**Q5.** $1 + x + x^2 + x^3 + x^4 + x^5 + \cdots =$ -?-

**Q6.** Integrate: $\int \cos 2x\, dx$

**Q7.** Differentiate: $f(x) = \tan 3x$

**Q8.** Find the limit as $x$ approaches zero of $f(x) = \cos 4x$.

**Q9.** Find the limit as $x$ approaches zero of $g(x) = (1+x)^{1/x}$.

**Q10.** (Force)(displacement) = —?—

For Problems 1–6,

a. Write out the first few terms.

b. Find the interval of convergence.

c. Find the radius of convergence.

1. $\sum_{n=1}^{\infty} \frac{n}{4^n} x^n$

2. $\sum_{n=1}^{\infty} \frac{x^n}{n \cdot 2^n}$

3. $\sum_{n=1}^{\infty} \frac{(2x+3)^n}{n}$

4. $\sum_{n=1}^{\infty} \frac{(5x-7)^n}{2n}$

5. $\sum_{n=1}^{\infty} \frac{n^3}{n!}(x-8)^n$

6. $\sum_{n=1}^{\infty} \frac{n!}{n^4}(x+2)^n$

For Problems 7–12, show that these familiar series for the transcendental functions converge for all real values of $x$.

7. $\sin x = x - \frac{1}{3!}x^3 + \frac{1}{5!}x^5 - \frac{1}{7!}x^7 + \cdots$

8. $\cos x = 1 - \frac{1}{2!}x^2 + \frac{1}{4!}x^4 - \frac{1}{6!}x^6 + \cdots$

9. $\sinh x = x + \frac{1}{3!}x^3 + \frac{1}{5!}x^5 + \frac{1}{7!}x^7 + \cdots$

10. $\cosh x = 1 + \frac{1}{2!}x^2 + \frac{1}{4!}x^4 + \frac{1}{6!}x^6 + \cdots$

11. $e^x = 1 + x + \frac{1}{2!}x^2 + \frac{1}{3!}x^3 + \frac{1}{4!}x^4 + \cdots$

12. $e^{-x} = 1 - x + \frac{1}{2!}x^2 - \frac{1}{3!}x^3 + \frac{1}{4!}x^4 - \cdots$

13. Show that the series $0! + 1!x + 2!x^2 + 3!x^3 + \cdots$ converges only for the trivial case, $x = 0$.

14. Mae Danerror writes out the first few terms of the series

$$\sum_{n=0}^{\infty} \frac{n!}{100^n} = 1 + 0.01x + 0.0002x^2 + 0.000006x^3 + \cdots.$$

She figures that since the coefficients are getting small so fast, the series is bound to converge, at least if she picks a value of $x$ such as 0.7, which is less than 1. Show Mae that she is wrong, and that the series converges only for the trivial case, $x = 0$.

15. Amos Take evaluates the Maclaurin series for cosh 10 and gets

$$\cosh 10 = \sum_{n=0}^{\infty} \frac{1}{(2n)!} \cdot 10^{2n} = 1 + 50 + 416.666\ldots + 1388.888\ldots + \cdots.$$

He figures that since the terms are increasing so fast, the series could not possibly converge. Show Amos his mistake by showing him that the series does actually converge, even though the terms increase for a while.

16. For the Taylor series for ln 0.1 expanded about $x = 1$, construct a table of values showing the term index, $n$; the term value, $t_n$; and the absolute value of the ratio of terms, $|t_{n+1}/t_n|$. Make a conjecture about what number the ratio seems to be approaching as $n$ approaches infinity. By taking the limit of the ratio, show that your conjecture is correct, or change the conjecture.

17. *Inverse Tangent Series Problem:* The series

$$P(x) = x - \frac{x^3}{3} + \frac{x^5}{5} - \frac{x^7}{7} + \cdots$$

converges to $\tan^{-1}x$ for certain values of $x$.

a. Find the open interval of convergence of the series.

b. On the same screen, plot the graphs of $\tan^{-1}x$ and the fourth and fifth partial sums of the series. How do the graphs confirm what you found algebraically in 17a.

c. Evaluate the fourth partial sum of the series for $x = 0.1$.

d. Find the value of the tail of the series after the fourth partial sum by comparing your answer to 17c with the value of $\tan^{-1}0.1$ you obtain with your calculator.

e. Show that the remainder of the series in 17d is less in magnitude than the absolute value of the first term of the tail of the series.

18. *Volume Problem:* Figure 12-6e shows the solid generated by rotating about the $y$-axis the region under the graph of $y = x^2 \sin 2x$ from $x = 0$ to $x = 1.5$.

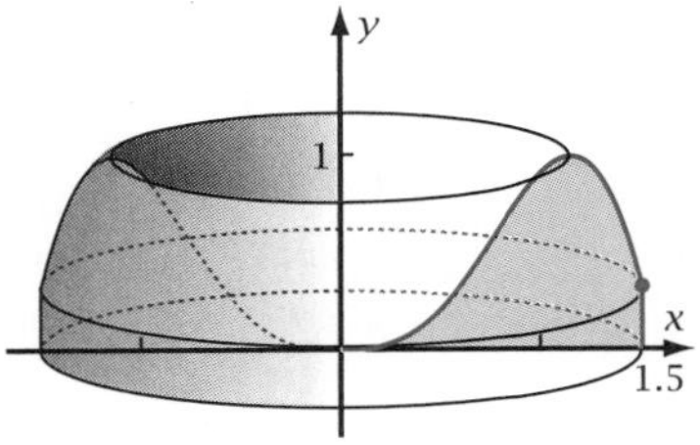

Figure 12-6e

a. Find the volume of this solid. Do the integrating numerically, and write all the decimal places your grapher will give you.

b. Find the volume exactly by integrating by parts then using the fundamental theorem.

c. Evaluate your answer to 18b. Write all the decimal places your calculator will give you. How does this exact answer compare with the numerical answer you got in 18a.

d. Write the integrand for the indefinite integral in 18a as a Maclaurin series. Then do the integration.

e. Show that $x = 1.5$ is in the interval of convergence for the integrated series in 18d.

f. Estimate the volume of the solid by evaluating the first five non-zero terms of the series in 18d. How does this estimate compare with the exact answer in 18b?

g. The integrated series in 18d is an alternating series whose terms decrease in value and approach zero as $n$ approaches infinity. Thus the remainder of the series after a given partial sum is no larger in magnitude than the absolute value of the first term of the tail following that partial sum. How many terms of the series would you need to use in order to estimate the volume correct to 10 decimal places?

19. *The Error Function:* Figure 12-6f shows the **normal distribution curve**, sometimes used to "curve" grades. Its equation is

$$y = \frac{2}{\sqrt{\pi}}e^{-t^2}.$$

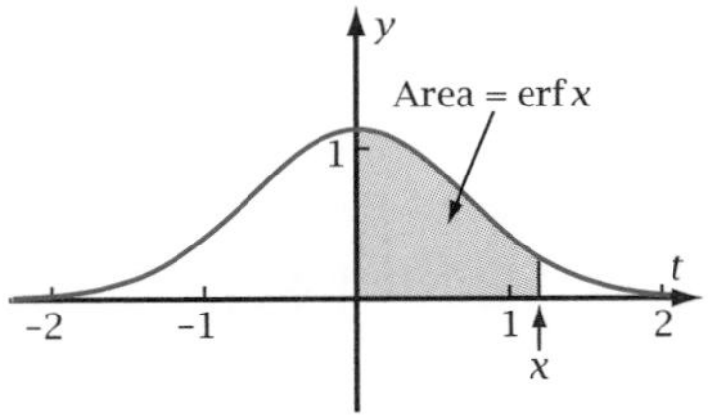

Figure 12-6f

The area of the region under the graph from zero to infinity turns out to be 1. So the area from $t = 0$ to $t = x$ is the fraction of a normally distributed population that is within $x$ units of zero. The resulting integral is called the **error function** of $x$, written $\operatorname{erf} x$.

$$\operatorname{erf} x = \frac{2}{\sqrt{\pi}}\int_0^x e^{-t^2}\,dt$$

The fundamental theorem cannot be used to evaluate erf $x$ since $e^{-t^2}$ is not the derivative of an elementary function. But a power series can be used. Let

$$f(x) = \int_0^x e^{-t^2}\,dt.$$

a. Find the Maclaurin series for $f(x)$. Write enough terms to show clearly the pattern.

b. On the same screen, plot the sixth partial sum of the series for $f(x)$ and the value of $f(x)$ by numerical integration. Use an $x$-window of about $-5 \le x \le 5$. For what interval of $x$-values does the partial sums graph fit the numerical integration graph reasonably well?

c. Does the series in 19a converge for all values of $x$? Justify your answer.

d. Does erf $x$ really seem to approach 1 as $x$ approaches infinity? How do you tell?

20. *The Sine-Integral Function:* The function

$$f(x) = \int_0^x \frac{\sin t}{t}\,dt$$

is called the **sine-integral function of x**, abbreviated Si $x$ (no pun intended!) Since the antiderivative of $(\sin t)/t$ is not an elementary transcendental function, values of Si $x$ cannot be found directly using the fundamental theorem. Power series give a way to do this.

a. Write a power series for the integrand by a time-efficient method. Integrate the series to find a power series for Si $x$.

b. Is the radius of convergence for the Si $x$ series the same as that for the integrand series?

c. Find the third partial sum of the series for Si 0.6. How does this value compare with the value you get by numerical integration?

d. Plot the graph of Si $x$ by numerical integration. On the same screen, plot the graph of the tenth partial sum of the series for Si $x$. Use an $x$-window of about $-12$ to 12. For what interval do the partial sums seem to fit the numerical integration values reasonably well?

21. *The Root Technique:* A series of positive terms can be shown to converge if *the nth root of the nth term approaches a constant less than 1* for its limit as $n$ approaches infinity. Figure 12-6g shows such a series.

Let $L = \lim_{n\to\infty} \sqrt[n]{t_n}$ where $L < 1$.

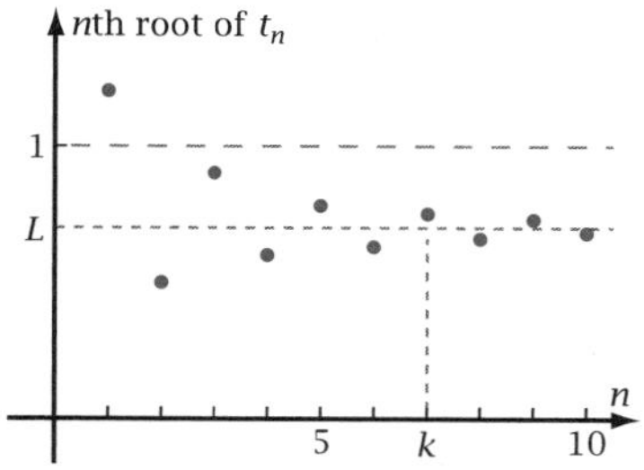

Figure 12-6g

a. Show that for any number $\epsilon > 0$ there is a number $k$ such that if $n > k$ then $\sqrt[n]{t_n} < L + \epsilon$.

b. Show that $\epsilon$ can be made small enough so that $L + \epsilon$ is also less than 1.

c. Show that for all integers $n > k$, $t_n < (L + \epsilon)^{n-k}$

d. Show that the tail of the series after $t_n$ is bounded above by a convergent geometric series.

e. Explain how the above reasoning verifies that the series converges.

The result of Problem 21 is called the **root technique**, or **root test**, stated as follows:

> ***Technique: The Root Technique for Convergence of Series***
>
> For the series $\sum_{n=1}^{\infty} t_n$, if $L = \lim_{n\to\infty} \sqrt[n]{|t_n|}$ then:
>
> i. The series is *absolutely convergent* if $L < 1$,
>
> ii. The series is *absolutely divergent* if $L > 1$,
>
> iii. The series may either converge or diverge if $L = 1$.

22. *A Special Limit Problem:* To use the root technique it helps to know the limit of the $n$th root of $n$.

    Let $L = \lim_{n\to\infty} \sqrt[n]{n}$

    Prove that $L = 1$. (Try taking $\ln L$, finding its limit, then raising $e$ to that power to get $L$.)

> ***Property: Limit of the nth Root of n***
>
> $$\lim_{n\to\infty} \sqrt[n]{n} = 1$$

23. Use the root technique to show that the open interval of convergence of the Taylor series for $\ln x$ is $0 < x < 2$.
24. Use the root technique to show that $\sum_{n=1}^{\infty} \dfrac{1}{n^n} x^n$ converges for all values of $x$.
25. Use the root technique to show that $\sum_{n=1}^{\infty} n^n x^n$ converges only for $x = 0$.
26. *"Which One Wins?" Problem:* In Problems 13 and 24, you showed that $\sum_{n=1}^{\infty} n!x^n$ converges for no values of $x$ except $x = 0$, and that $\sum_{n=1}^{\infty} \dfrac{1}{n^n} x^n$ converges for all values of $x$. For what values of $x$ does $\sum_{n=1}^{\infty} \dfrac{n!}{n^n} x^n$ converge?

# 12-7 Convergence of Series at the Ends of the Convergence Interval

In Section 12-6, you learned the ratio technique for finding the interval of $x$-values for which a power series converges. Since the limit of the ratios of terms values is 1 or $-1$ at the endpoints of the interval, other techniques are needed to test for convergence there.

***OBJECTIVE***

> Given a series of constants for which the ratio technique is inconclusive, prove either that the series converges or that it diverges.

To accomplish this objective, it is helpful for you to consolidate your knowledge about the tail and the remainder of a series.

### Definitions: Tail and Remainder of a Series

The **tail** of a series is the indicated sum of the terms remaining in the series beyond the end of a particular partial sum.

Example:

$2 + 3 + 5 + 7 | + 11 + 13 + 17 + 19 + 23 + \cdots$ The series of primes.

4th partial sum | —— Tail ——→

The **remainder** of a series, $R_n$, is the value of the tail after partial sum $S_n$, provided the tail converges.

Examples:

For $1 + \frac{1}{2} + \frac{1}{4} + \frac{1}{8} + \frac{1}{16} + \cdots$, $R_5 = \frac{1}{16}$ because $S_5 = 1\frac{15}{16}$, the series converges to 2, and $2 - 1\frac{15}{16} = \frac{1}{16}$.

For the series of primes, $R_4$ is infinite because the series diverges.

See the box in Section 12-2 for other vocabulary relating to series.

## Convergence of Sequences

There is one major property of sequences that leads to several methods of testing for convergence. You might think at first that a sequence converges if there is an upper bound for the terms of the sequence. Not true! The sequence

$$2, 3, 2, 3, 2, 3, 2, 3, \ldots$$

is bounded above by 3, and does not converge. It diverges by oscillation. However, a sequence such as

$$\frac{1}{2}, \frac{2}{3}, \frac{3}{4}, \frac{4}{5}, \frac{5}{6}, \ldots$$

does converge since the terms are *strictly increasing* as well as being bounded above (Figure 12-7a). The number 1 is an upper bound for the terms because the numerators are always less than the denominators. Term $t_n = n/(n+1)$ can be made arbitrarily close to 1 by picking a large enough value of $n$. Beyond that value of $n$, the terms are even closer to 1 since they are strictly increasing. Thus 1 is the limit of $t_n$ as $n$ approaches infinity.

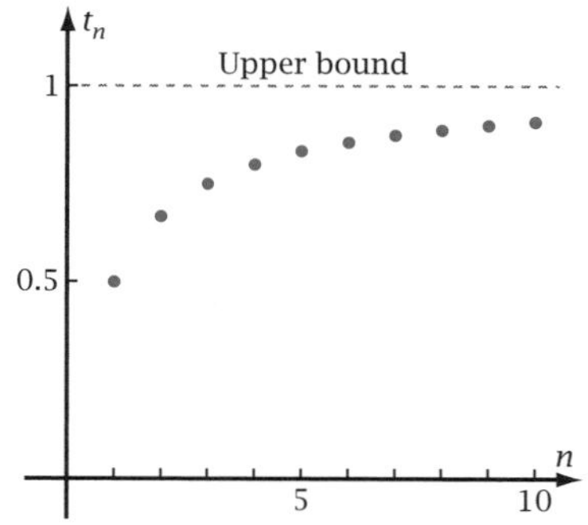

Figure 12-7a

In Problem 23 of Problem Set 12-7, you will prove that a sequence converges if its terms are bounded above and are strictly increasing.

**Property: Convergence of Sequences**

If a sequence $\{t_1, t_2, t_3, \ldots, t_n, \ldots\}$ is increasing and bounded above, then the sequence converges.

### *Some p-Series Converge, and Others Don't*

The series $1 + \frac{1}{8} + \frac{1}{27} + \frac{1}{64} + \cdots$ is called a $p$-**series** because each denominator is a power of the term number. In this case, $p = 3$. The tail of the series following the terms shown is

$$\frac{1}{5^3} + \frac{1}{6^3} + \frac{1}{7^3} + \cdots.$$

Figure 12-7b shows how the terms of a series can be bounded above by an improper integral. The sequence $\{t_n\}$ is said to be *embedded* in the continuous function $f(x) = 1/x^3$ because $f(x) = t_n$ whenever $x = n$. Drawing 1 unit to the left of the graph at each point gives inscribed rectangles, each of whose area equals $t_n$. So the integral of $1/x^3$ from 4 to infinity,

$$\int_4^\infty \frac{1}{x^3}\,dx$$

is an upper bound for the tail of the series starting at $n = 5$. The tail is a lower Riemann sum for the integral. Integrating gives

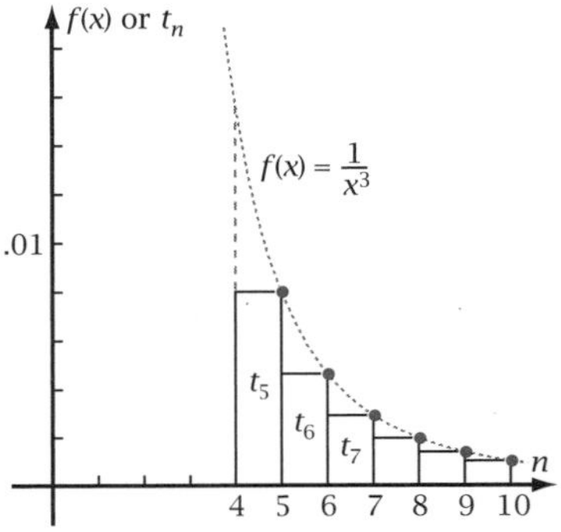

Figure 12-7b

$$\sum_{n=5}^{\infty} \frac{1}{n^3} < \int_4^\infty \frac{1}{x^3}\,dx = \lim_{b\to\infty}\left(-\frac{1}{2}x^{-2}\,\Big|_4^b\right) = \lim_{b\to\infty}\left(-\frac{1}{2}b^{-2} + \frac{1}{2}\cdot 4^{-2}\right) = \frac{1}{32}.$$

The sequence of partial sums in the tail is increasing because each term is positive and is bounded above by $1/32$. Thus the series converges because the tail converges. In addition, you know that $1/32$ is an upper bound for $R_4$, the remainder after partial sum $S_4$.

The $p$-series

$$\frac{1}{1^{0.6}} + \frac{1}{2^{0.6}} + \frac{1}{3^{0.6}} + \frac{1}{4^{0.6}} + \cdots$$

diverges, even though the terms,

$$1 + 0.659753\ldots + 0.517281\ldots + 0.435275\ldots + \cdots,$$

are decreasing and approach zero for a limit. Figure 12-7c shows the tail after four terms embedded in $f(x) = 1/x^{0.6}$. Drawing rectangles 1 unit to the right of the graph at each point makes the tail an upper Riemann sum for a divergent improper integral.

$$\sum_{n=5}^{\infty} \frac{1}{n^3} > \int_5^\infty \frac{1}{x^{0.6}}\,dx = \lim_{b\to\infty}\left(2.5x^{0.4}\,\Big|_5^b\right)$$
$$= \lim_{b\to\infty}(2.5b^{0.4} - 4.759\ldots) = \infty$$

Since the tail is bounded below by infinity, the tail is also infinite. Thus the series diverges. The $p$-series will converge if $p > 1$ because the exponent $-p + 1$ in $b^{-p+1}$ will still be negative after the integration. The series will diverge if $p < 1$ because the exponent $-p + 1$ in $b^{-p+1}$ will be positive after integration. If $p = 1$, the series becomes a divergent harmonic series, as shown below.

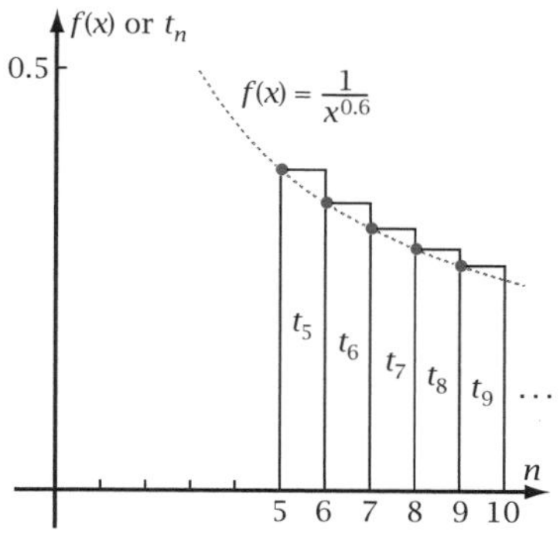


Figure 12-7c

**Property: Convergence of a p-Series**

The $p$-series $\sum_{n=1}^{\infty} \frac{1}{n^p} = \frac{1}{1^p} + \frac{1}{2^p} + \frac{1}{3^p} + \frac{1}{4^p} + \cdots$ converges if $p > 1$, and diverges if $p \le 1$.

### The Harmonic Series Diverges

The series

$$1 + \tfrac{1}{2} + \tfrac{1}{3} + \tfrac{1}{4} + \tfrac{1}{5} + \tfrac{1}{6} + \cdots$$

is called a **harmonic series**. Its terms are the reciprocals of the terms in an arithmetic series. The partial sums,

$$1,\ 1\tfrac{1}{2},\ 1\tfrac{5}{6},\ 2\tfrac{1}{12},\ 2\tfrac{17}{60}, \ldots,$$

are increasing. But they are not bounded above. As shown in Figure 12-7d, the tail after five terms can be embedded in $f(x) = 1/x$, and the series written as an upper Riemann sum.

$$\sum_{n=6}^{\infty} \frac{1}{n} > \int_6^{\infty} \frac{1}{x}\,dx = \lim_{n\to\infty}(\ln b - \ln 6) = \infty$$

Since the tail is bounded below by infinity, the tail is also infinite. Thus the series diverges.

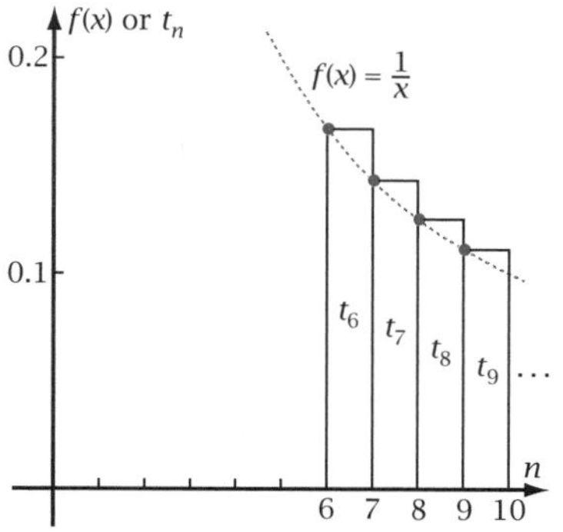


Figure 12-7d

### The Alternating Harmonic Series Converges

The series

$$1 - \tfrac{1}{2} + \tfrac{1}{3} - \tfrac{1}{4} + \tfrac{1}{5} - \tfrac{1}{6} + \cdots,$$

is called an **alternating harmonic series**. The partial sums,

$$1, \tfrac{1}{2}, \tfrac{5}{6}, \tfrac{7}{12}, \tfrac{47}{60}, \tfrac{37}{60}, \ldots,$$

get bigger and smaller. But as shown in Figure 12-7e, they seem to be converging toward some number between 1/2 and 1.

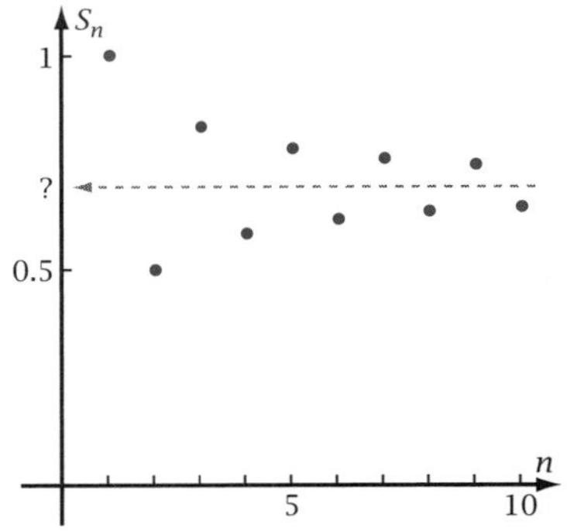

Figure 12-7e

Associating pairs of terms gives

$$\left(1 - \tfrac{1}{2}\right) + \left(\tfrac{1}{3} - \tfrac{1}{4}\right) + \left(\tfrac{1}{5} - \tfrac{1}{6}\right) + \left(\tfrac{1}{7} - \tfrac{1}{8}\right) + \cdots$$

$$= \tfrac{1}{2} + \tfrac{1}{12} + \tfrac{1}{30} + \tfrac{1}{56} + \cdots$$

Since each term of the series of differences is positive, the sequence of even-numbered partial sums is strictly increasing. That is,

$$S_2, S_4, S_6, S_8, \ldots = 0.5, 0.58333\ldots,$$

$$0.61666\ldots,\ 0.634523\ldots,\ \ldots$$

Associating another way gives

$$1 - \left(\tfrac{1}{2} - \tfrac{1}{3}\right) - \left(\tfrac{1}{4} - \tfrac{1}{5}\right) - \left(\tfrac{1}{6} - \tfrac{1}{7}\right) - \left(\tfrac{1}{8} - \tfrac{1}{9}\right) + \cdots = 1 - \tfrac{1}{6} - \tfrac{1}{20} - \tfrac{1}{42} - \tfrac{1}{72} - \cdots.$$

Since each term after the first is subtracted from 1, the odd-numbered partial sums are bounded above by 1.

$$S_1,\ S_3,\ S_5,\ S_7,\ S_9, \ldots = 1, 0.83333\ldots,\ 0.78333\ldots,\ 0.75952\ldots,\ 0.74563\ldots,\ \ldots$$

Thus the sequence of even-numbered partial sums converges because it is increasing and bounded above. The odd-numbered partial sums approach the same limit since the terms approach zero. By computer, the limit is 0.693147..., which happens to equal ln 2.

In general, a strictly alternating series will converge if the absolute values of its terms decrease uniformly toward zero for a limit.

### Property: Alternating Series Convergence Test

If a series $t_1 - t_2 + t_3 - t_4 + \cdots$ has the following properties,

- the terms in the tail are strictly alternating in sign,
- the terms in the tail are strictly decreasing in absolute value, and
- the limit of $t_n$ is zero as $n$ approaches infinity,

then the series converges.

Corollary: The remainder is bounded by the first term of the tail, $|R_n| < |t_{n+1}|$.

A formal proof of the theorem would duplicate in general the reasoning in the preceding example.

### *Absolute Convergence of a Series*

If the signs of the terms are not strictly alternating, or if all the terms are positive, it is more difficult to prove convergence. What is normally done is to consider all terms to be positive (which makes the sequence of partial sums increasing), then look for an upper bound. If the series of absolute values of terms converges, the series is said to be **absolutely convergent**.

### *Definition: Absolute and Conditional Convergence*

A series $t_1 + t_2 + t_3 + t_4 + \cdots$ is said to be absolutely convergent if the series of absolute values of the terms,

$$|t_1| + |t_2| + |t_3| + |t_4| + \cdots$$

converges.

If a series converges but is not absolutely convergent, then it is said to be **conditionally convergent**.

Absolute convergence may be considered to be a "worst case." It is most difficult to make a series converge if all terms have the same sign. If a series is absolutely convergent, it converges even though some of its signs may be negative and some positive.

There are several ways to establish upper bounds for a series of positive terms. These methods, or tests for convergence, are summarized in the following box. You will see why some of these tests work in Problem Set 12-7.

### *Properties: Tests for Convergence of a Series of Constants*

- **Increasing Series Test**
  *Converges* if the tail is bounded above by a convergent integral or series.
  *Diverges* if the tail is bounded below by a divergent integral or series.

- **Alternating Series Test**
  *Converges* if these three conditions apply:

  **1.** The terms in the tail are strictly alternating in sign.
  **2.** The absolute values of the terms in the tail are strictly decreasing.
  **3.** The limit of $t_n$ is 0 as $n$ approaches infinity.

  Upper bound for the remainder: |tail| < |first term of tail|.

- ***n*th Term Test** *Diverges* if $\lim_{n \to \infty} t_n \neq 0$.

- **Geometric Series Test**
  *Converges* if |common ratio| < 1.
  *Diverges* if |common ratio| ≥ 1.

- ***p*-Series Test**
  *Converges* if $p > 1$.
  *Diverges* if $p \leq 1$.

- **Harmonic Series Test**
  *Diverges* if all signs are the same.

Armed with these properties, you can now determine the convergence of power series at the endpoints of the interval of convergence, where the ratio technique is inconclusive.

**■ Example 1** The open interval of convergence for the Taylor series for $\ln x$ expanded about $x = 1$ is $0 < x < 2$. Determine whether or not the series converges at $x = 0$ and at $x = 2$.

**Solution** The series for $\ln x$ is $\ln x = (x-1) - \frac{1}{2}(x-1)^2 + \frac{1}{3}(x-1)^3 - \frac{1}{4}(x-1)^4 + \cdots$. At $x = 0$, the series becomes $-1 - \frac{1}{2} - \frac{1}{3} - \frac{1}{4} - \cdots$, which diverges because it is the opposite of the divergent harmonic series. At $x = 2$, the series becomes $1 - \frac{1}{2} + \frac{1}{3} - \frac{1}{4} + \cdots$, which converges because it meets the hypotheses of the alternating series test.

$\therefore$ the complete interval of convergence is $0 < x \leq 2$. ■

**■ Example 2** Find the complete interval of convergence of the power series $\sum_{n=0}^{\infty} \dfrac{2^n(x-1)^n}{\ln(n+2)}$.

**Solution** By the ratio technique,

$$L = \lim_{n\to\infty} \left| \frac{2^{n+1}(x-1)^{n+1}}{\ln(n+3)} \cdot \frac{\ln(n+2)}{2^n(x-1)^n} \right|$$

$$= 2|x-1| \lim_{n\to\infty} \left| \frac{\ln(n+2)}{\ln(n+3)} \right| \to \frac{\infty}{\infty} \qquad \text{l'Hospital's rule applies.}$$

$$= 2|x-1| \lim_{n\to\infty} \left| \frac{n+3}{n+2} \right| \to \frac{0}{0} \qquad \text{l'Hospital's rule applies again.}$$

$$= 2|x-1| \cdot 1 = 2|x-1|$$

$$L < 1 \iff 2|x-1| < 1 \iff \tfrac{1}{2} < x < \tfrac{3}{2}$$

At $x = \frac{1}{2}$, the series is

$$\frac{1}{\ln 2} - \frac{1}{\ln 3} + \frac{1}{\ln 4} - \frac{1}{\ln 5} + \cdots,$$

which converges because it meets the hypotheses of the alternating series test. At $x = \frac{3}{2}$, the series is

$$\frac{1}{\ln 2} + \frac{1}{\ln 3} + \frac{1}{\ln 4} + \frac{1}{\ln 5} + \cdots,$$

for which the terms starting at $1/\ln 3$ are larger than $\frac{1}{3} + \frac{1}{4} + \frac{1}{5} + \cdots$, a divergent harmonic series.

$\therefore$ the complete interval of convergence is $\frac{1}{2} \leq x < \frac{3}{2}$. ■

Sometimes it is necessary for you to tell whether or not a given series of constants converges, even if the series does not come from the endpoint of a Taylor series. Examples 3–5 show you how to determine whether such series converge.

**■ Example 3** Determine whether or not the series converges. $\sum_{n=1}^{\infty} \left(1 + \dfrac{1}{n^2}\right)$

**Solution** The series begins $2 + 1.25 + 1.1111\ldots + 1.0625 + \cdots$

$\therefore$ the series diverges because $t_n$ approaches 1, not 0, as $n$ approaches infinity. ■

■ **Example 4** Determine whether or not the series converges. $\sum_{n=0}^{\infty} \frac{n}{n^2+7}$

**Solution** The series begins $0 + \frac{1}{8} + \frac{2}{11} + \frac{3}{16} + \frac{4}{23} + \frac{5}{32} + \frac{6}{43} + \cdots$, which is equal to

$$0 + 0.125 + 0.1818\ldots + 0.1875 + 0.17391\ldots + 0.15625 + 0.13953\ldots + \cdots.$$

The series might converge because the terms are decreasing after a while and approach 0. (The $n^2$ in the denominator dominates the $n$ in the numerator, as you could tell by l'Hospital's rule). Since it's reasonably easy to integrate the given function, you can compare the series with an improper integral. The lower limit of integration can be any nonnegative number, since only the tail of the series is in question.

$$\int_0^{\infty} \frac{x}{x^2+7}\,dx = \lim_{b\to\infty} \int_0^b \frac{x}{x^2+7}\,dx$$
$$= \lim_{b\to\infty} \tfrac{1}{2}\ln|x^2+7|\Big|_0^b$$
$$= \lim_{b\to\infty} \tfrac{1}{2}\ln|b^2+7| - \tfrac{1}{2}\ln 7 = \infty$$

$\therefore$ the series diverges because the tail could be bounded below by a divergent integral. ■

■ **Example 5** Determine whether or not the series converges. $\sum_{n=0}^{\infty} \frac{1}{n^2+7}$

**Solution** The series begins $\frac{1}{7} + \frac{1}{8} + \frac{1}{11} + \frac{1}{16} + \frac{1}{23} + \cdots$.

The series might converge because the terms decrease and approach 0 as a limit ($t_n$ approaches the form $1/\infty$). Each term after the first one in the given series is smaller than the corresponding term of a convergent $p$-series.

| | | | |
|---|---|---|---|
| $p$-series: | $\sum_{n=1}^{\infty} \frac{1}{n^2}$ | $=$ | $1 + \frac{1}{4} + \frac{1}{9} + \frac{1}{16} + \cdots$ |
| Value of $n$: | | | 1 2 3 4 |
| Given series: | $\sum_{n=0}^{\infty} \frac{1}{n^2+7}$ | $=$ | $\frac{1}{7} + \frac{1}{8} + \frac{1}{11} + \frac{1}{16} + \frac{1}{23} + \cdots$ |

$\therefore$ the series converges since the partial sums are increasing and bounded above by the limit of a convergent $p$-series. ■

# Problem Set 12-7

### *Do These Quickly*

The following problems are intended to refresh your skills. You should be able to do all ten problems in less than five minutes.

**Q1.** $7 + 14 + 28 + 56 + \cdots$ are terms of a —?— series.

**Q2.** The next term in the series in Q1 is found from the preceding term by —?—.

**Q3.** The number 2 for the series in Q1 is called the —?— of the series.

**Q4.** $(x-1) - \frac{1}{2}(x-1)^2 + \frac{1}{3}(x-1)^3 - \cdots$ is the Taylor series expansion for —?—.

**Q5.** The first three terms in the Maclaurin series expansion of $\cos 2x$ are —?—.

**Q6.** The coefficient of $x^6$ in the Maclaurin series expansion of $f(x) = \sin x^2$ is —?—.

**Q7.** If the interval of convergence is $3 < x < 8$, then the radius of convergence is —?—.

**Q8.** The open interval of convergence for $\sum_{n=0}^{\infty} \frac{(x-4)^n}{3^n}$ is —?—.

**Q9.** The volume of the solid formed by rotating the region under the graph of $y = 9 - x^2$ about the $y$-axis is —?—.

**Q10.** If $\vec{r}(t) = (e^{2t})\vec{i} + (\sin 3t)\vec{j}$, then $\vec{v}(t) =$ —?—.

1. *Vocabulary Problem I:* For the series $\sum_{n=1}^{\infty} \frac{6}{n!}$
   a. Write the first five terms of the series.
   b. Calculate the first five terms of the sequence of partial sums.
   c. Write the first three terms of the tail of the series after the fifth partial sum.
   d. Are the terms of the series increasing or decreasing?
   e. Are the partial sums of the series increasing or decreasing?

2. *Vocabulary Problem II:* Explain why a series of positive terms always has an increasing sequence of partial sums, even if the term values themselves are decreasing.

3. *Vocabulary Problem III:* For the series $\sum_{n=1}^{\infty} (-1)^{n+1} \frac{6}{n!}$
   a. Write the first five terms of the series.
   b. Calculate the first five terms of the sequence of partial sums.
   c. Write the first three terms of the tail of the series after the fifth partial sum.
   d. What is the effect of the $(-1)^{n+1}$ factor in the formula for the series?
   e. Show that the sequence of even-numbered partial sums is increasing.
   f. Show that the sequence of partial sums is bounded above by the first term of the series.

4. *Vocabulary Problem IV:* The series $6 - 3 + 1 - 0.25 + 0.05 - \cdots$ from Problem 3, above, converges to $3.792723\cdots$. If the series $6 + 3 + 1 + 0.25 + 0.05 + \cdots$ also converges, then the former series is said to be —?— convergent. If the series $6 + 3 + 1 + 0.25 + 0.05 + \cdots$ does not converge, then the series $6 - 3 + 1 - 0.25 + 0.05 - \cdots$ is said to be —?— convergent.

For Problems 5 through 14, find the interval of convergence for the given power series, including convergence or divergence at the endpoints of the interval.

5. $\sum_{n=1}^{\infty} n(x-3)^n$

6. $\sum_{n=1}^{\infty} \frac{5^n x^n}{n^2}$

7. $\sum_{n=1}^{\infty} \frac{x^n}{n}$

8. $\sum_{n=4}^{\infty} \frac{(-1)^n (x-6)^n}{n 2^n}$

9. $\sum_{n=1}^{\infty} \frac{(-1)^{n+1}(x+5)^{2n}}{2n}$

10. $\sum_{n=1}^{\infty} \frac{(x+1)^n}{n^2}$

11. $\sum_{n=0}^{\infty} \frac{\ln(n+1)}{n+1} x^n$

12. $\sum_{n=1}^{\infty} 5(x-3)^n$

13. $\sum_{n=0}^{\infty} \frac{4^n}{x^n}$

14. $\sum_{n=1}^{\infty} \frac{1}{x^n}$

15. *Upper Bound by Convergent Improper Integral:* Given $S = \sum_{n=1}^{\infty} \frac{1}{n^2}$.

a. Write the first five terms of the series, and calculate the fifth partial sum, $S_5$.

b. The tail of the series after $S_5$ is

$$R_5 = \sum_{n=6}^{\infty} \frac{1}{n^2} = \frac{1}{36} + \frac{1}{49} + \frac{1}{64} + \cdots.$$

Figure 12-7f shows that the tail is a lower sum for the improper integral

$$\int_5^{\infty} \frac{1}{x^2}\,dx$$

Why is the lower limit of summation 6, but the lower limit of integration is only 5?

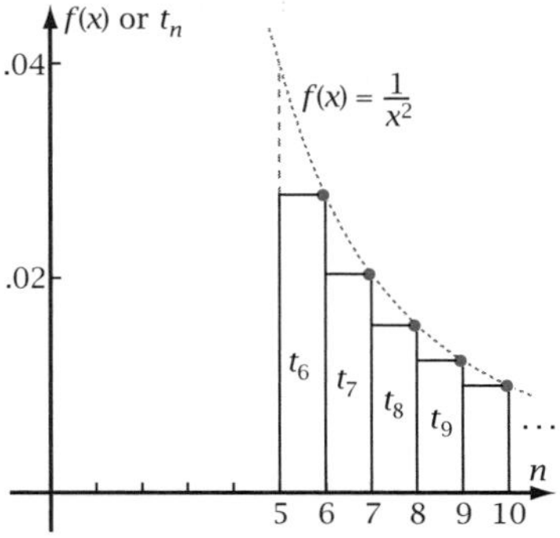


Figure 12-7f

c. By evaluating the improper integral, find an upper bound for the tail of the series.

d. Explain how the above reasoning allows you to conclude that the original series converges.

e. Estimate the number to which the series converges by summing the first 1000 terms.

f. Find an upper bound for the remainder of the series in part (e).

g. True or false: "The remainder of the series is close to the value of the first term of the tail."

h. Complete: "The value of the series using 1000 terms has no more than a -?-% error."

i. How many terms would it take to guarantee that the value of the series is correct to the sixth decimal place (error less than 0.0000005)?

16. *Divergence by Comparison with Divergent Improper Integral:* Consider the series $\sum_{n=1}^{\infty} \frac{1}{n}$.

a. Find $S_5$, the fifth partial sum of the series.

b. The tail after $S_5$ is

$$R_5 = \sum_{n=6}^{\infty} \frac{1}{n} = \frac{1}{6} + \frac{1}{7} + \frac{1}{8} + \cdots$$

The improper integral $\int_6^{\infty} \frac{1}{x}\,dx$ is a lower bound for this tail (Figure 12-7g). Evaluate the integral. How does the result tell you that the series diverges?

c. Why would it be futile to try to evaluate this series by computer?

d. True or false: "If the terms of a series approach zero for a limit as $n$ aproaches infinity, then the series converges."

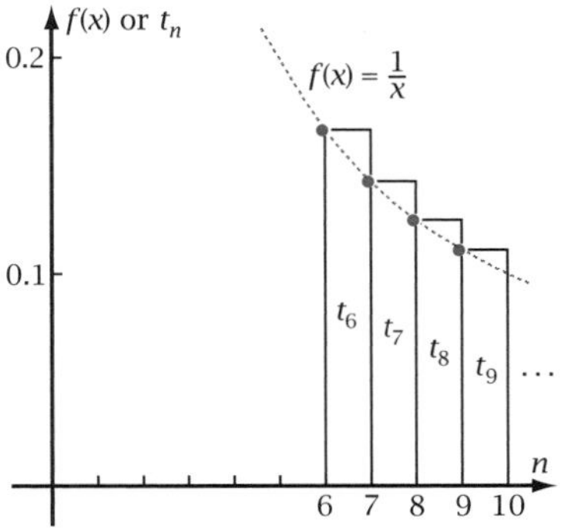


Figure 12-7g

17. *Integral Test Problem:* Use the results of Problems 15 and 16 to explain the following:

> **Technique: The Integral Test for Convergence of Series**
>
> Given $S = \sum_{n=0}^{\infty} f(n)$ and $I = \int_a^{\infty} f(x)\,dx$ where $f(x)$ decreases monotonically to 0.
>
> $S$ converges if $I$ converges, and $S$ diverges if $I$ diverges.

18. *Follow-Up Problem:* In Problem 15, you concluded that

$$\frac{1}{36} + \frac{1}{49} + \frac{1}{64} + \cdots$$

converges because it is a lower sum for an improper integral. You could also have made the series an upper sum for the integral

$$\int_a^b \frac{1}{x^2}\,dx$$

as shown in Figure 12-7h. Explain why you learn nothing about the convergence of this series by making it an upper sum.

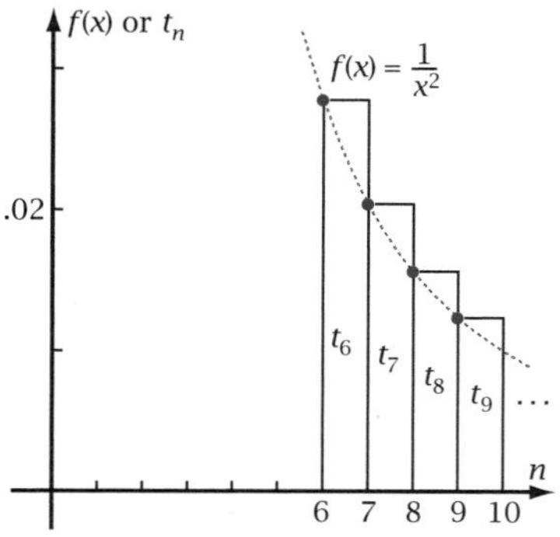

Figure 12-7h

19. *The Factorial Reciprocal Series Converges:* Suppose that 1 is substituted for $x$ in the Maclaurin series for $e^x$. The result is the series of reciprocals of factorials.

$$\sum_{n=0}^{\infty} \frac{1}{n!} = \frac{1}{0!} + \frac{1}{1!} + \frac{1}{2!} + \frac{1}{3!} + \frac{1}{4!} + \frac{1}{5!} + \frac{1}{6!} + \cdots$$

a. Explain why it would be difficult to find an upper bound for the tail of the series using an improper integral.

b. Comparing the given series with the geometric series with first term 1 and ratio $\frac{1}{2}$ shows

| Term index, $n$: | 0 | 1 | 2 | 3 | 4 | 5 | 6 | ... |
|---|---|---|---|---|---|---|---|---|
| Given: | $1+$ | $1+$ | $\frac{1}{2}+$ | $\frac{1}{6}+$ | $\frac{1}{24}+$ | $\frac{1}{120}+$ | $\frac{1}{720}+$ | $\cdots$ |
| Geometric: | $1+$ | $\frac{1}{2}+$ | $\frac{1}{4}+$ | $\frac{1}{8}+$ | $\frac{1}{16}+$ | $\frac{1}{32}+$ | $\frac{1}{64}+$ | $\cdots$. |

|—— Tail ——→ (from term $n = 4$ on)

From term $t_4$ on, the geometric series terms are upper bounds for the terms of the given series. To what number does the tail of the geometric series converge?

c. Find an upper bound for the remainder of the given series after $S_3$, the fourth partial sum.

d. Find an upper bound for the entire given series.

e. Explain how the reasoning in 19a–d allows you to conclude that the given series converges.

20. *Comparison Test for the Exponential Function Series:* The following are the first seven terms of the Maclaurin series for $e^{0.6}$.

| $n$: | 0 | 1 | 2 | 3 | 4 | 5 | 6 | ... |
|---|---|---|---|---|---|---|---|---|
| $e^{0.6}=$ | $1\,+$ | $0.6\,+$ | $0.18\,+$ | $0.036\,+$ | $0.0054\,+$ | $0.000648\,+$ | $0.0000648+$ | $\cdots$ |

|←— 5th partial sum (terms $n = 0$ to $4$) —→|—— Tail (from term $n = 5$ on) ——→

a. Show how the seventh term, $t_6$, is calculated.

b. Show that the fifth partial sum, $S_4$, differs from the actual value of $e^{0.6}$ by more than $t_5$, the first term of the tail, but not by much more.

c. Show that each term of the geometric series

$$0.000648 + 0.0000648 + \cdots$$

with common ratio 0.1 is an upper bound for the corresponding term in the tail.

d. To what value does the geometric series in 19c converge?

e. Based on your answer to 19d, what number is an upper bound for the sum of the tail of the series? What number is an upper bound for the entire series? Show that the latter number is just above $e^{0.6}$.

21. *Alternating Series Remainders Property Problem:* The following are the first four terms of the Maclaurin series for sin 0.6:

$$\begin{array}{lccccc} n: & 0 & 1 & 2 & 3 & \cdots \\ \sin 0.6 = & 0.6 & -\,0.036 & +\,0.000648 & -\,0.000005554285714\cdots & +\cdots \end{array}$$

a. Show how $t_3$, the fourth term, is calculated.

b. Calculate $S_1$ and $S_2$, the second and third partial sums, respectively.

c. Calculate $R_1$ and $R_2$, the remainders after $S_1$ and $S_2$ (the values of the tail), by finding the difference between the partial sum and the value of sin 0.6 by calculator. Show that in both cases, the magnitude of the remainder is less than the absolute value of the first term of the tail.

d. Use the appropriate property to prove that the series for sin 0.6 converges.

22. *Infinite Overhang Problem:* Figure 12-7i shows a pile of blocks. The top block sits so that its center of mass is exactly on the edge of the second one down. The third block is placed under the center of mass of the first two. The fourth is placed under the center of mass of the first three, and so on.

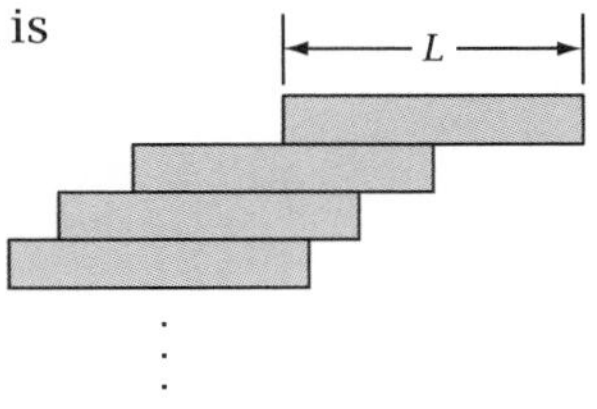

Figure 12-7i

a. Show that the overhangs of the blocks are terms in the harmonic sequence $\frac{1}{2}L, \frac{1}{4}L, \frac{1}{6}L, \frac{1}{8}L, \ldots$ where $L$ is the length of each block. To find the centroid of a particular pile, find the sum of the moments of the blocks by summing each one's moment with respect to the $y$-axis, then dividing by the number of blocks. You must, of course, find the centroid of one pile before you can find the centroid of the next.

b. What depth of pile is the first to have its top block projecting entirely beyond its bottom block?

c. Explain why, in theory at least, it would be possible to make a pile of blocks with *any* desired overhang, using nothing but gravity to hold the pile together.

d. If you pile up a normal 52-card deck the way the blocks are piled in this problem, by how many card-lengths would the top card be offset from the bottom card?

23. *Convergence of Sequences Proof:* Figure 12-7j shows a sequence

$$\{t_1,\ t_2,\ t_3, \ldots, t_n, \ldots\}$$

that is increasing and bounded above. Prove that the sequence converges. You use the **least upper bound postulate** (which states that any set of real numbers that is bounded above has a least upper bound) to establish the existence of a least upper bound, $L$, then prove that $L$ is the limit of the sequence.

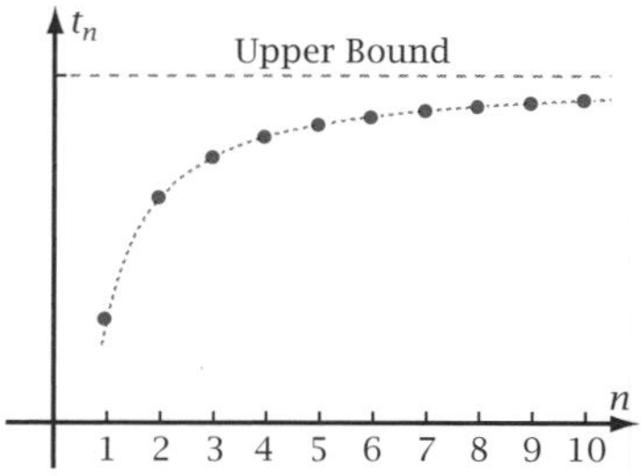

Figure 12-7j

24. *Sequences vs. Series Problem:* Explain why the sequence 1.9, 1.99, 1.999, 1.9999, ... converges, but the series $1.9 + 1.99 + 1.999 + 1.9999 + \cdots$ does not converge.

For Problems 25–30, determine whether the series converges or diverges. Justify your answer.

25. $\displaystyle\sum_{n=0}^{\infty} \frac{3}{4^n}$

26. $\displaystyle\sum_{n=0}^{\infty} \frac{3^n}{4^n}$

27. $\displaystyle\sum_{n=0}^{\infty} \frac{1}{(2n+1)!}$

28. $\displaystyle\sum_{n=0}^{\infty} \frac{1}{(-3)^n}$

29. $\displaystyle\sum_{n=2}^{\infty} \frac{n^3}{n^4 - 1}$

30. $\displaystyle\sum_{n=0}^{\infty} \sin n$

31. *Journal Problem:* Update your journal with things you have learned since the last entry. Include such things as those listed here.
    - The one most important thing you have learned since your last journal entry.
    - The way you find an interval of convergence for a power series.
    - The ways you can determine convergence at the endpoints of the interval of convergence.
    - What you understand better, now, about the meaning of convergence.
    - Any techniques or ideas about series that are still unclear.

# 12-8 Error Analysis for Series

From time to time in this chapter you have estimated the remainder of a series, the value of the tail of the series after a certain number of terms. This remainder represents the error in the value of a function that you get by using a partial sum of the series. For certain alternating series you found that the entire tail is bounded by the first term of the tail. In this section you will learn about the *Lagrange form* for the remainder of a Taylor series, an expression similar to the first term of the tail. Joseph Louis Lagrange (1736–1813) applied mathematics in many areas, including the motion of planets, and helped set up the French metric system.

**OBJECTIVE**

Given a series, determine the number of terms needed to obtain an approximation for the limit to which the series converges correct to a specified accuracy.

The general term of the Taylor series expansion of $f(x)$ about $x = a$ is

$$t_n = \frac{f^{(n)}(a)}{n!}(x-a)^n.$$

The first term of the tail of a Taylor series is $t_{n+1}$. For any value of $x$ in the interval of convergence, it turns out that there is a value of $c$ between $a$ and $x$ for which $R_n(x)$ is given by

$$R_n(x) = \frac{f^{(n+1)}(c)}{(n+1)!}(x-a)^{n+1}.$$

The only difference between this remainder and the first term of the tail is that $f^{(n+1)}(a)$ is replaced by $f^{(n+1)}(c)$. Usually this derivative is awkward to calculate. Often, though, an upper bound, $M$, can be found for it. If this is the case, an upper bound can be found for the remainder. Finding the value of $n$ that gives a remainder sufficiently small allows you to determine how many terms to use to get the desired accuracy in the partial sum representing $f(x)$.

### Property: Lagrange Form of the Remainder of a Taylor Series

If $f(x)$ is expanded as a Taylor series about $x = a$ and $x$ is a number in the interval of convergence, then there is a number $c$ between $a$ and $x$ such that the remainder $R_n$ after the partial sum $S_n$ is given by

$$R_n = \frac{f^{(n+1)}(c)}{(n+1)!}(x-a)^{n+1}.$$

If $M$ is the maximum value of $f^{(n+1)}(x)$ on the interval between $a$ and $x$, then

$$|R_n| \le \frac{M}{(n+1)!}|x-a|^{n+1}.$$

The property is an extension of the mean value theorem, which concludes that there is a number $c$ between $a$ and $x$ for which

$$f'(c) = \frac{f(x) - f(a)}{x-a}.$$

Multiplying by $(x - a)$ gives

$$f(x) - f(a) = f'(c)(x-a).$$

As shown in Figure 12-8a, $f(x) - f(a)$ is the error in using $f(a)$ as an approximation for $f(x)$.

Solving this equation for $f(x)$ gives

$$f(x) = f(a) + f'(c)(x-a).$$

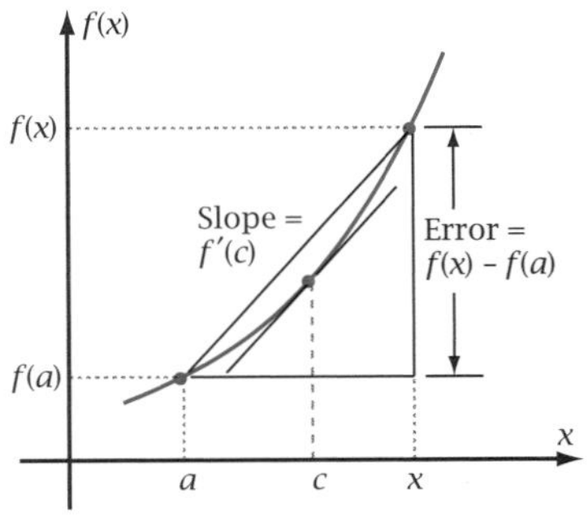

Figure 12-8a

In this form you can see that $f(a)$ is the first term ($n = 0$) of the Taylor series expansion of $f(x)$ about $x = a$, and $f'(c)(x - a)$ is the Lagrange form of the remainder after $n = 0$. You will be asked to supply the algebraic details of the derivation in Problem 21 of Problem Set 12-8.

**Example 1**

a. Estimate $e^2$ using the 11th partial sum ($n = 10$) of the Maclaurin series for $e^x$.

b. Use the Lagrange form of the remainder to estimate the accuracy of using this partial sum.

c. How does this estimate of the remainder (part b) compare with the value calculated by subtracting $S_{10}$ from the value of $e^2$ on your calculator?

**Solutions**

a. $S_{10} = \sum_{n=0}^{10} \frac{1}{n!} 2^n = 7.3889470\ldots$

b. All derivatives of $e^x$ are equal to $e^x$. Since you are estimating $e^2$ from scratch, you should not assume that $e$ is known to be 2.718 .... However, you know that $e < 3$. So a value of $M$ is $3^2$, and thus $f^{(n+1)}(x) < 9$ for all $x$ between 0 and 2.

$$|R_{10}| < \frac{9}{11!}(2-0)^{11} = 0.0004617\ldots$$

Thus $S_{10}$ may be off by as much as 5 in the fourth decimal place and thus should match $e^2$ to $\pm 1$ in the third decimal place.

c. $e^2 = 7.38905609\ldots$ By calculator.

$S_{10} = 7.38899470\ldots$ From part a.

The difference is 0.00006138..., which is significantly less than the upper bound 0.0004617... by Lagrange's form. Note that although the difference has zeros in the first four decimal places, the partial sum and the more precise value of $e^2$ still differ by 1 in the third decimal place. ■

**Example 2**

How many terms of the Maclaurin series for $\sinh x$ are needed to estimate $\sinh 4$ correct to five decimal places? Confirm your answer by subtracting the partial sum from $\sinh 4$ using your calculator.

**Solution**

The general term of the series is $t_n = \frac{1}{(2n+1)!}x^{2n+1}$, where $n$ is the term index.

All derivatives of $\sinh x$ are either $\cosh x$ or $\sinh x$. Both functions are increasing on the interval [0, 4], with $\cosh x > \sinh x$. Thus the derivatives are all bounded by $\cosh 4$. Because you are trying to estimate $\sinh 4$, you should not assume that you know $\cosh 4$ exactly. However, $2 < e < 3$, so $\cosh 4 < 0.5(3^4 + 2^{-4}) = 40.53125 < 41$, which means that the absolute values of the derivatives are bounded by $M = 41$.

$$|R_n| = \frac{41}{(2n+3)!}4^{2n+3}$$ Why $2n + 3$?

To get five-place accuracy, $|R_n|$ should have zeros in the first five decimal places and no more than 5 in the sixth place. That is, $|R_n| < 0.000005$. Using the table feature,

| $n$ | $41/(2n+3)! \cdot 4^{2n+3}$ |
|---|---|
| 7 | 0.001980319... |
| 8 | 0.000092646... |
| 9 | 0.000003529... |

The 0.000003529... for $n = 9$ is the first value less than 0.000005. Therefore, you should use at least 10 terms (because the term index, $x$, starts at 0).

$\sinh 4 = 27.28991719\ldots$ By calculator.

$S_9 = 27.28991711\ldots$

Difference = 0.000000088..., which is considerably less than 0.000005. ■

**■ Example 3** For the Taylor series for $\ln x$ expanded about $x = 1$, how many terms would be needed in the partial sum to compute $\ln 1.4$ to five decimal places?

**Solution**

$$\ln 1.4 = (1.4-1) - \tfrac{1}{2}(1.4-1)^2 + \tfrac{1}{3}(1.4-1)^3 - \cdots$$
$$= 0.4 - 0.08 + 0.021333\ldots - \cdots$$

Since this series meets the requirements of the alternating series test, $|R_n| < |t_{n+1}|$.

Make $\dfrac{1}{n+1}(0.4^{n+1}) < 0.000005$.

$n < 9.731\ldots < 10$ Solve numerically for $n$.

Use 10 terms. Because the term index starts at 1, it is equal to the term number.

As a check, $S_{10} = 0.336469445\ldots$, and $\ln 1.4 - S_{10} = 0.00000279\ldots$, which checks. ■

**■ Example 4** For the Maclaurin series for $e^2$ in Example 1, find approximately the value of $c$ for which the Lagrange form is equal to the remainder $R_{10}$.

**Solution**

$$R_{10} = \frac{f^{(11)}(c)}{11!}(2-0)^{11} = \frac{e^c}{11!}\cdot 2^{11} = 0.00006138\ldots$$ From Example 2.

$$\therefore e^c = \frac{0.00006138\ldots \cdot 11!}{2^{11}} = 1.1965\ldots$$

$c = \ln 1.1965\ldots = 0.1794\ldots$, which is between 0 and 2. ■

**■ Example 5** Estimate the remainder of the $p$-series $\sum_{n=1}^{\infty} \dfrac{1}{n^{1.02}}$ after 20 terms.

**Solution**

Since this is a series of constants not necessarily related to a Taylor series, the Lagrange form of the remainder does not apply. Instead, compare the tail of the series with an improper integral that is an upper bound.

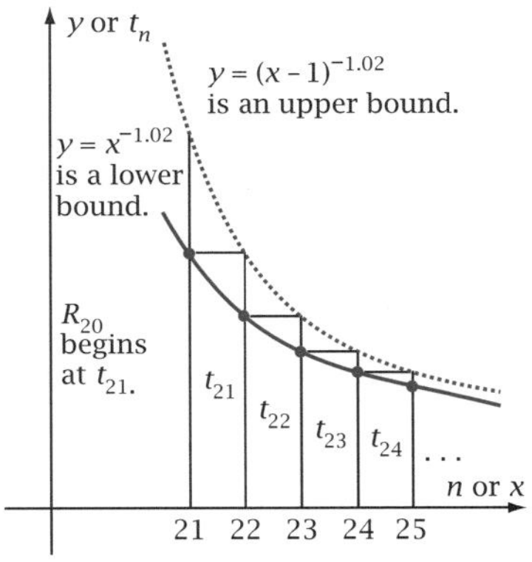

Figure 12-8b

Figure 12-8b shows the first few terms of the tail starting at term $t_{21}$. The area of each rectangle in the histogram equals the respective term value, and thus the sum of their areas equals the value of the tail, $R_{20}$. The area under the graph of $y = x^{-1.02}$ is a lower bound for $R_{20}$ since the rectangles form an upper Riemann sum. If the graph is shifted one space to the right, the equation is $y = (x - 1)^{-1.20}$, and the area under the shifted graph is an upper bound for $R_{20}$. The areas of each region can be expressed as an improper integral whose value is an upper or lower bound.

$$R_{20} = \sum_{n=21}^{\infty} \frac{1}{n^{1.02}} > \int_{21}^{\infty} x^{-1.02}\,dx = \lim_{b\to\infty}(-50x^{-0.02}\,\Big|_{21}^{b}) = \lim_{b\to\infty}(-50b^{-0.02} + 50 \cdot 21^{-0.02})$$

$$= 0 + 47.04631\ldots = 47.04631\ldots$$

Similarly, $R_{20} < \int_{21}^{\infty} (x-1)^{-1.02}\,dx = \lim_{b\to\infty}[-50(b-1)^{-0.02} + 50 \cdot 20^{-0.02}] = 47.09224\ldots$

So $R_{20}$ is between 47.046... and 47.092.... Since $S_{20}$ is only 3.50977..., the series is nowhere close to converging after just 20 terms. ■

# Problem Set 12-8

### *Do These Quickly*

The following problems are intended to refresh your skills. You should be able to do all ten problems in less than five minutes.

**Q1.** The radius of convergence of a power series can be found using the —?— technique.

**Q2.** A geometric series converges if and only if —?—.

**Q3.** The Maclaurin series for $\cos x$ converges for what values of $x$?

**Q4.** The Taylor series for $\ln x$, expanded about $x = 1$, has what radius of convergence?

**Q5.** Write the first four non-zero terms of the Maclaurin series for $\tan^{-1} x$.

**Q6.** Sketch a partial sum of the Maclaurin series for sine compared to the actual sine graph.

**Q7.** Do the integrating: $\int \sec x\,dx$

**Q8.** Differentiate: $y = \tan x$

**Q9.** Do the integrating: $\int \sec^2 x\,dx$

**Q10.** Which two people are credited with having invented the calculus?

For Problems 1 through 4,

a. Find the indicated partial sum.

b. Use the Lagrange form of the remainder to estimate the number of decimal places to which the partial sum in part (a) is accurate.

c. Confirm your answer to part (b) by subtracting the partial sum from the calculator value.

1. $\cosh 4$ using the sixth partial sum ($n = 5$) of the Maclaurin series
2. $\sinh 5$ using the tenth partial sum ($n = 9$) of the Maclaurin series
3. $e^3$ using the 15th partial sum of the Maclaurin series
4. $\ln 0.7$ using 8 terms of the Taylor series expansion about $x = 1$

For Problems 5 through 8, use the Lagrange form of the remainder to find the number of terms needed in the partial sum to estimate the function value to the specified accuracy.

5. $\sinh 2$ to 6 decimal places using the Maclaurin series
6. $\cosh 3$ to 8 decimal places using the Maclaurin series

7. $\ln 0.6$ to 7 decimal places using the Taylor series expansion about $x = 1$
8. $e^{10}$ to 5 decimal places using the Maclaurin series

For Problems 9 and 10 calculate the value of $c$ in the appropriate interval for which the Lagrange form of the remainder is equal to the remainder calculated by subtracting the partial sum from the function value by calculator.

9. $\cosh 2$ using 5 terms ($S_4$)
10. $e^5$ using 20 terms ($S_{19}$)

For Problems 11 and 12 show that the hypotheses of the alternating series test apply to the function, then find the number of terms needed in the partial sum to get the specified accuracy.

11. $\cos 2.4$ to 6 decimal places using the Maclaurin series
12. $e^{-2}$ to 7 decimal places using the Maclaurin series
13. *p-Series Problem I:* For the $p$-series $\sum_{n=1}^{\infty}(1/n^3)$ find an upper bound for the tail of the series after 10 terms. How does this estimate of the error introduced by stopping at $S_{10}$ compare with the value of $t_{11}$? How many terms would be needed to ensure that the partial sum is correct to at least five decimal places?
14. *p-Series Problem II:* The series

$$1 + \frac{1}{\sqrt{2}} + \frac{1}{\sqrt{3}} + \frac{1}{\sqrt{4}} + \cdots$$

is a $p$-series. Explain why the method of Problem 13 would not be appropriate for estimating the remainder of this series.

15. *p-Series Problem III:* Amos Take wants to calculate the limit to which $\sum_{n=1}^{\infty}(1/n^{1.05})$ converges. With his grapher he calculates $S_{99} = 4.69030101\ldots$. Show Amos that although he has used many terms of the series, his answer is nowhere close to the value to which the series converges.
16. *Ratio Technique and p-Series Problem:* The ratio technique can be used to determine whether or not a series of constants converges. If the limit of the ratio of adjacent terms is less than 1 in absolute value, then the series converges. Show that the ratio technique *never* gives conclusive results for a $p$-series.
17. *Geometric Series as an Upper Bound Problem:* In Example 1 of this section you saw that the error in calculating $e^2$ using the eleventh partial sum ($S_{10}$) of the Maclaurin series could be estimated using the Lagrange form of the remainder. The error can also be estimated by bounding the tail of the series with a convergent geometric series that has first term equal to $t_{11}$ (the first term of the tail) and common ratio equal to $t_{12}/t_{11}$. Which method gives a better estimate of the error, the geometric series or the Lagrange remainder?
18. *Values of $e^x$ from Values of $e^{-x}$ Problem:* The value of $e^2$ can be calculated by first finding the value of $e^{-2}$, then taking the reciprocal. After the first few terms the series for $e^{-2}$ meets the hypotheses for the alternating series test. Thus the error for any partial sum is bounded by the first term of the tail of the series after that partial sum. Estimate the error in the estimate of $e^{-2}$ using the eleventh partial sum ($S_{10}$). Then estimate $e^2$ by calculating $1/S_{10}$. Is the error in the answer any smaller than the error in using $S_{10}$ directly for $e^2$ as in Example 1 of this section?

19. Sin $x$ *for Any Argument Using a Value of* $x$ *in* $[0, \pi/4]$ *Problem:* As you have seen, the Maclaurin series for $\sin x$ converges more slowly the farther $x$ is away from 0. Suppose that you wanted to compute sin 250.

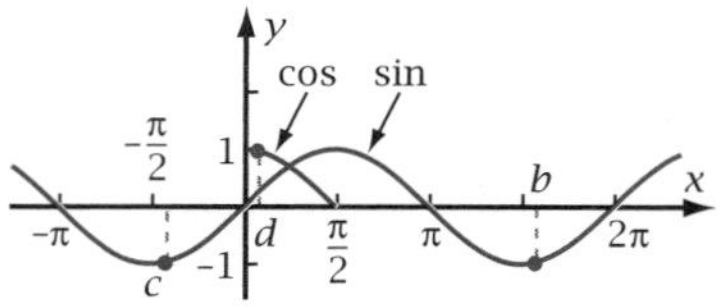

Figure 12-8c

a. The values of $\sin x$ repeat themselves with a period of $2\pi$. Find a number $b$ in $[0, 2\pi]$ for which $\sin b = \sin 250$.

b. Each value of $\sin x$ for $x$ in $[0, 2\pi]$ is equal to a value of $\sin c$ for some number $c$ in $[-\pi/2, \pi/2]$ (Figure 12-8b). Find the value of $c$ for which $\sin c = \sin 250$.

c. Each value of $\sin x$ for $x$ in $[-\pi/2, \pi/2]$ is equal to $\pm \sin d$ or $\pm \cos d$ for some number $d$ in $[0, \pi/4]$ (Figure 12-8c). Find the value of $d$ for which $\sin 250 = \pm \sin d$ or $\pm \cos d$. Demonstrate that your value of $d$ gives the correct answer for sin 250.

d. Show that the technique of this problem can be used to calculate values of $\sin x$ correct to at least 10 decimal places using just six terms of the appropriate Maclaurin series. How many terms are needed to calculate sin 250 to 10 places directly from the series?

e. *Project:* Write a program to calculate $\sin x$ correct to 10 decimal places by Maclaurin series using the technique of this problem. Programs similar to this are used internally by calculators to evaluate sines and cosines efficiently.

20. The National Bureau of Standards *Handbook of Mathematical Functions* lists the value of sin 1 to 23 decimal places as 0.84147 09848 07896 50665 250. (The spaces are used in lieu of commas for ease of reading.) How many terms of the Maclaurin series for $\sin x$ would have to be used to get this accuracy? How many terms would it take if the technique of Problem 19 were used?

21. *Derivation of the Lagrange Form of the Remainder:* Earlier in this section you saw that the conclusion of the mean value theorem leads to a special case of the Lagrange form of the remainder. If function $f$ has derivatives of all orders, as do exponential, trigonometric, hyperbolic, and many other functions, then the mean value theorem applies to each derivative.

a. Show that applying the mean value theorem to $f'(x)$ on the interval $[a, x]$ gives

$$f'(x) = f'(a) + f''(c)(x - a)$$

for some number $c$ between $x$ and $a$.

b. Assume that $a$ and $c$ are constants and $x$ is the variable. Integrate both sides of the differential equation in part (a) with respect to $x$. Use the point $(a, f(a))$ as the initial condition. Show that the answer can be transformed to

$$f(x) = f(a) + f'(a)(x - a) + \tfrac{1}{2}f''(c)(x - a)^2.$$

c. You should recognize that the first two terms of the right-hand side of the equation in part (b) are terms in the Taylor series expansion of $f(x)$ about $x = a$, and the third term is the Lagrange form of the remainder. By applying the mean value theorem to $f''$ on the interval $[a, x]$ and integrating twice show that there is a number $c$ in $(a, x)$ for which

$$f(x) = f(a) + f'(a)(x - a) + \tfrac{1}{2!}f''(a)(x - a)^2 + \tfrac{1}{3!}f'''(c)(x - a)^3.$$

d. Without actually doing the algebra, name the mathematical technique that could be used to prove for any integer $n > 0$ that there is a number $c$ in the interval

$(a, x)$ for which the Lagrange form of the remainder is exactly equal to the error in using the partial sum $S_n(x)$ of the Taylor series as an approximation for $f(x)$.

22. *A Pathological Function:* Figure 12-8d shows the function

$$f(x) = \begin{cases} e^{-x^{-2}}, & \text{if } x \neq 0 \\ 0, & \text{if } x = 0 \end{cases}$$

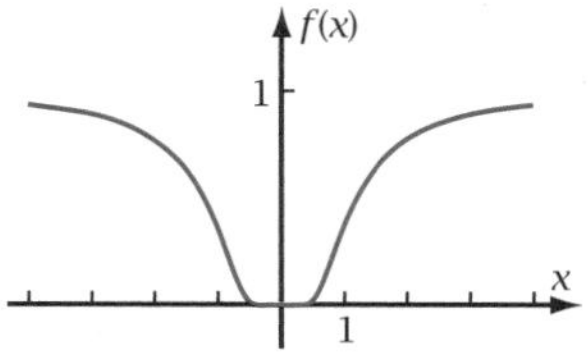

Figure 12-8d

Function $f$ has derivatives of all orders at $x = 0$, and each derivative equals zero there.

a. By equating derivatives, show that the Maclaurin series for $f(x)$ would be $0 + 0x + 0x^2 + 0x^3 + \cdots$.

b. Show that the Maclaurin series converges for all values of $x$, but that it does not converge to $f(x)$ except at $x = 0$.

c. Substitute $-x^{-2}$ for $x$ in the Maclaurin series for $e^x$. Write the first four terms of the power series and simplify.

d. The resulting power series is called a **Laurent series**, the name applied to a power series in which some powers can have negative exponents. By finding a partial sum of the series, make a conjecture about whether or not the Laurent series evaluated at $x = 2$ converges to $f(2)$.

23. *The Maclaurin Series for $e^x$ Converges to $e^x$:* If you worked Problem 22 you found that a Maclaurin series can converge, but not to the target function. Use the Lagrange form of the remainder to show that the Maclaurin series for $e^x$ does converge to $e^x$ for all values of $x$ by showing that the remainder of the series approaches zero as $n$ approaches infinity.

# 12-9 Chapter Review and Test

In this chapter you have seen how a function can be expanded as a power series. There are two advantages to doing this. First, it allows you to calculate values of transcendental functions by doing only the four operations of arithmetic. Calculators and computers use series internally to calculate values of sines, logs, and so forth. Second, it allows you to determine how accurate a numerical integral is. If $x$ is within the interval of convergence, you can get any desired accuracy by using enough terms of the series.

The Review Problems are numbered according to the sections of this chapter. The Concepts Problems allow you to apply your knowledge to new situations. The Chapter Test is more like a typical classroom test your instructor might give you.

## Review Problems

R0. Update your journal with the things you have learned since the last entry. You should include such things as those listed here.

- The one most important thing you have learned in studying Chapter 12.
- Which boxes you have been working on in the "define, understand, do, apply" table.
- How to write from memory some special, well-known series.

- How you find a power series for a given function, either by equating derivatives or by operating on another known series.
- What it means for a sequence or series to converge.
- How you determine the accuracy of a function value found by series.
- Any ideas about series that are still unclear.

R1. Let $f(x) = \frac{9}{1-x}$ and let $P_n(x) = 9 + 9x + 9x^2 + 9x^3 + 9x^4 + 9x^5 + \cdots + 9x^n$. On the same screen, plot $f(x)$, $P_5(x)$, and $P_6(x)$. Sketch the results. For what values of $x$ does $P_n(x)$ seem to be close to $f(x)$, and for what values of $x$ does the graph of $P$ bear little resemblance to the graph of $f$? Show that $P_6(0.4)$ is closer to $f(0.4)$ than $P_5(0.4)$ is. Show that $P_5'(0)$, $P_5''(0)$, and $P_5'''(0)$ equal $f'(0)$, $f''(0)$, and $f'''(0)$, respectively. What kind of series is $P_n(x)$ a subseries of?

R2. a. *Biceps Problem:* You start an exercise program to increase the size of your biceps. The first day you find that the circumference of each bicep increases by 3 mm. You assume that the amount of increase on each subsequent day will be only 90% of the amount of increase the day before. By how much do you predict your biceps will have increased after 10 days? At the limit, what will be the total increase in each bicep?

b. *Present Value Problem:* You win \$10 million in the state lottery! However, you will receive only \$0.5 million now, and \$0.5 million a year for the next 19 years (20 payments). How much money must the state invest now so that they will have \$0.5 million to pay you at the beginning of the 20th year? Assume that the state can get 10% per year interest, compounded annually, on their investment. How much money, total, must the state invest now to make all 19 future payments? This amount is called the **present value** of your remaining \$9.5 million.

R3. Let $P(x)$ be the power series $c_0 + c_1x + c_2x^2 + c_3x^3 + c_4x^4 + \cdots$. Let $f(x) = 7e^{3x}$. By equating derivatives find the values of $c_0$, $c_1$, $c_2$, and $c_3$ that make $P(0)$, $P'(0)$, $P''(0)$, and $P'''(0)$ equal $f(0)$, $f'(0)$, $f''(0)$, and $f'''(0)$, respectively.

R4. For a–c, show that the fourth partial sum, $S_3(0.12)$ is close to $f(0.12)$.

a. $e^x = 1 + x + \frac{1}{2!}x^2 + \frac{1}{3!}x^3 + \frac{1}{4!}x^4 + \cdots$

b. $\cos x = \sum_{n=0}^{\infty} (-1)^n \frac{1}{(2n)!} x^{2n}$

c. $\sinh x = x + \frac{1}{3!}x^3 + \frac{1}{5!}x^5 + \frac{1}{7!}x^7 + \cdots$

d. Show that the 20th partial sum of $\sum_{n=1}^{\infty} (-1)^{n+1} \frac{1}{n}(x-1)^n$ gives values close to $\ln x$ if $x = 1.7$, but not if $x = 2.3$.

R5. a. What is the difference between a Maclaurin series and a Taylor series?

b. Write the Maclaurin series for $\ln(x+1)$ by performing appropriate operations on the Taylor series for $\ln x$.

c. Integrate the series in R5b to find a Maclaurin series for $\int \ln(x+1)\,dx$.

d. Show that the series in R5c is equivalent to the one you would obtain by finding the antiderivative of $\ln(x + 1)$ and writing that as a Maclaurin series.

e. Write the first few terms of a power series for $\int_0^x t \cos t^2 \, dt$.

f. Write $\tan^{-1} x$ as the definite integral of an appropriate function from 0 to $x$. Write the integrand as a Maclaurin series. Then write the first few terms of the corresponding Maclaurin series for $\tan^{-1} x$.

g. Suppose that $f$ is a function whose derivatives of all orders are defined for all real values of $x$. If $f(3) = 5$, $f'(3) = 7$, $f''(3) = -6$, and $f'''(3) = 0.9$, write the first four terms of the Taylor series for $f(x)$ expanded about $x = 3$.

R6. a. Write out the first few terms of $\sum_{n=1}^{\infty} (-3)^{-n}(x - 5)^n$.

b. Find the (open) interval convergence and radius of convergence of the series in R6a.

c. Show that the Maclaurin series for $\cosh x$ converges for all values of $x$.

d. Write the fifth five terms of the Maclaurin series for $e^{1.2}$. Then calculate the error in using the fifth partial sum to approximate $e^{1.2}$ by subtracting the partial sum from $e^{1.2}$ by calculator. How does the error compare to the value of the first term in the tail of the series after the fifth partial sum?

e. On the same screen plot the graphs of $\ln x$, the Taylor series about $x = 1$ for $\ln x$ using 10 terms, and the same series using 11 terms. Sketch the graphs. Then write a paragraph stating how the graphs relate to the interval of convergence.

R7. a. Find the tenth partial sum of the geometric series with $t_1 = 1000$ and common ratio 0.8.

b. By how much does the tenth partial sum in R7a differ from the limit to which the series converges?

c. The rest of the series in R7a following the tenth partial sum is called the —?— of the series.

d. The value of the rest of the series, R7b, is called the —?— of the series.

e. Use an appropriate improper integral to find an upper bound for the remainder of the $p$-series

$$1 + \frac{1}{8} + \frac{1}{27} + \frac{1}{64} + \cdots$$

after the tenth term.

f. Explain how your result in R7e can be used to prove that the $p$-series

$$1 + \frac{1}{8} + \frac{1}{27} + \frac{1}{64} + \cdots$$

converges.

g. Show that there is a convergent geometric series that is an upper bound for the tail of the series $2/1! + 4/2! + 8/3! + 16/4! + 32/5! + \cdots$ after a suitable number of terms.

h. Show that the alternating harmonic series

$$1 - \frac{1}{2} + \frac{1}{3} - \frac{1}{4} + \frac{1}{5} - \frac{1}{6} + \cdots$$

converges.

i. Find an upper bound for the remainder of the series in R7h after 10,000 terms.

j. Find the complete interval of convergence, including the endpoints.

i. $\displaystyle\sum_{n=1}^{\infty} \frac{10^n(x-3)^n}{n^2}$  ii. $\displaystyle\sum_{n=1}^{\infty} \frac{(-1)^n(x+1)^n}{n \cdot 2^n}$

k. Tell whether or not the following series of constants converge. Justify your answer.

i. $\displaystyle\sum_{n=0}^{\infty} \frac{10}{n!}$  ii. $\displaystyle\sum_{n=1}^{\infty} (n^{-3} + 5^{-1})$

R8. a. Use the Lagrange form of the remainder to estimate the error in using the fourth partial sum of the Maclaurin series to estimate $\cosh 2$.

b. It is desired to calculate $e^3$ using enough terms of the Maclaurin series to get a 20 decimal place accuracy. Use the Lagrange form of the remainder to calculate the number of terms that should be used.

c. The Maclaurin series for $\cosh x$ converges for all values of $x$. Use the Lagrange form of the remainder to show that the value the series converges to when $x = 4$ really is equal to $\cosh 4$.

d. Calculate, approximately, the number $c$ in the interval $(0, 0.6)$ for which the Lagrange form is equal to the remainder of the Maclaurin series for $\sinh 0.6$ after the fourth partial sum ($n = 3$).

e. Use the fact that the Taylor series for $\ln x$ is alternating if $x$ is between 1 and 2 to find the number of terms of the series needed to compute ln 1.3 to 20 decimal places.

f. Use an improper integral to find an upper bound on the remainder of the $p$-series

$$\sum_{n=1}^{\infty} \frac{1}{p^4}$$

after the 50th partial sum ($n = 50$).

## Concepts Problems

C1. *Series with Imaginary Numbers Problem:* If you substitute $ix$ for $x$ in the Maclaurin series for cosine and sine, you get some startling results! In this problem you will see how these results lead to another similarity between trigonometric functions and hyperbolic functions.

a. Substitute $ix$ (where $i$ is $\sqrt{-1}$) for $x$ in the Maclaurin series for cosine. When you simplify, you should find that $\cos ix$ is real-valued and equals $\cosh x$.

b. Substitute $ix$ for $x$ in the Maclaurin series for sine. You should find that each term has $i$ as a factor. Factor out the $i$ to show that $\sin ix = i \sinh x$.

c. Substitute $ix$ for $x$ in the Maclaurin series for $e^x$. Use the result and the answers to C1a and b to show that the following formula is true.

$$e^{ix} = \cos x + i \sin x$$

d. Show that $e^{i\pi} = -1$. This one short formula combines four of the most mysterious numbers of mathematics!

C2. *Practical Calculation of Pi Problem:* In Problem 35 of Problem Set 12-5 you computed $\pi$ by using the Maclaurin series for $\tan^{-1} x$ to compute $\pi/4$, which equals $\tan^{-1} 1$. You made use of the composite argument property from trigonometry,

$$\tan(A + B) = \frac{\tan A + \tan B}{1 - \tan A \tan B},$$

to show that

$$\tan^{-1}\tfrac{1}{2} + \tan^{-1}\tfrac{1}{3} = \tfrac{\pi}{4},$$

thus obtaining more accuracy with fewer terms. Show that the double series

$$4\tan^{-1}\tfrac{1}{5} - \tan^{-1}\tfrac{1}{239}$$

also converges to $\pi/4$. How many terms of this series would be needed to get $\pi$ correct to the number of decimal places reported in William Shaaf's booklet *Computation of Pi* (Yale University Press, 1967), namely,

$$\pi = 3.14159\ 26535\ 89793\ 23846\ 26433\ 83279\ 50288\ 41971\ 69399\ 37510\ldots.$$

C3. *Series Solution of a Differential Equation:* In future courses on differential equations you will learn to solve a differential equation directly in terms of a power series. In this problem you will get a preview of the technique used. Consider the second-order differential equation

$$y'' + 9xy = 0$$

with initial conditions $y' = 7$ and $y = 5$ when $x = 0$.

a. Assume that there is a power series equal to $y$. That is,

$$y = \sum_{n=0}^{\infty} c_n x^n = c_0 + c_1x + c_2x^2 + c_3x^3 + c_4x^4 + c_5x^5 + c_6x^6 + \cdots.$$

Assuming that the series can be differentiated termwise, write equations for $y'$ and $y''$.

b. Use the two initial conditions in the appropriate places to evaluate $c_0$ and $c_1$.

c. Substituting the series for $y$ and $y''$ into the original differential equation and combining terms with equal powers of $x$ gives

$$2c_2 + 6c_3x + 12c_4x^2 + 20c_5x^3 + 30c_6x^6 + \cdots$$
$$+9x(c_0 + c_1x + c_2x^2 + c_3x^3 + c_4x^4 + c_5x^5 + c_6x^6 + \cdots) = 0$$
$$2c_2 + (6c_3 + 9c_0)x + (12c_4 + 9c_1)x^2 + (20c_5 + 9c_2)x^3 + (30c_6 + 9c_3)x^4 + \cdots = 0$$

Since the right-hand side of the equation is zero, each coefficient on the left-hand side must equal zero. Use this fact to calculate the values of $c_2$ through $c_6$.

d. Use the terms of the series through the sixth power to compute $y$ when $x = 0.3$.

e. Just for fun, see if you can tell whether or not the series you found in C3d converges when $x = 0.3$.

## Chapter Test

T1. You know that the $p$-series $\sum_{n=1}^{\infty} 2/n^3$ converges. Suppose you evaluate the series by adding up the first 1000 terms. The tail of the series, starting at term number 1001, represents the error involved if you stop at 1000 terms. By comparing with a convergent improper integral, find an upper bound for the tail of the series.

T2. Based on your answer to Problem T1, to how many decimal places could you guarantee the answer to be accurate if you stop after 1000 terms?

T3. By equating derivatives, show that the Taylor series for $\ln x$ expanded about $x = 1$ is

$$\ln x = (x-1) - \tfrac{1}{2}(x-1)^2 + \tfrac{1}{3}(x-1)^3 - \tfrac{1}{4}(x-1)^4 + \cdots.$$

T4. Let $f(x) = \int_0^x \frac{1}{1+t^3}\, dt$. Write a power series for $f(x)$.

T5. Find the interval of convergence of the series in Problem T4.

T6. Find an approximation for $f(0.6)$ using 20 terms of the series from Problem T4.

T7. Find an approximation for $f(0.6)$ in Problem T4 by numerical integration.

T8. Find $f(0.6)$ in Problem T4 exactly, using the fundamental theorem. To how many decimal places are the answers to Problems T6 and T7 correct?

T9. Demonstrate that the error in the value of $f(0.6)$ by series in Problem T6 is less than the first term in the tail of the series.

T10. Write a power series for $\cosh x$. Express the answer in sigma notation.

T11. Use the Lagrange form of the remainder to find the number of terms of the series in Problem T10 needed to estimate $\cosh 3$ correct to 10 decimal places.

T12. Write a power series for $\sin(x^2)$. Write the answer in sigma notation.

T13. Show that the geometric series $1000 + 999 + \cdots$ converges, but the geometric series $0.0001 + 0.0002 + \cdots$ does not converge.

T14. Find the open interval of convergence and the radius of convergence:

$$\sum_{n=1}^{\infty} \frac{(2x-5)^n}{3n}$$

T15. Does the series in T14 converge or diverge at the endpoints of the interval of convergence? Justify your answer.

# 12-10 Cumulative Reviews

In this section are several cumulative reviews that may be considered to be "rehearsals" for your final exam. Each review touches on most of the concepts and techniques of calculus, particularly those of the second half of the book.

## Problem Set 12-10

**Cumulative Review No. 1—The Dam Problem**

Suppose you are hired as a mathematician by Albee Dam Construction Company, which has been awarded a contract to build a dam across Scorpion Gulch. The following questions pertain to your part in this project. Before Mr. Albee will allow you to work on his dams, he must be sure that you know some of the fundamental definitions, theorems, and techniques of mathematics. These are contained in Problems 1 through 5.

1. There are four major concepts of calculus. Name those concepts, and state their definitions.

2. Define each of the following:
   a. Continuity of a function at a point
   b. Continuity of a function on an interval
   c. Convergence of a sequence
   d. Convergence of a series
   e. Natural logarithm
   f. The exponential $a^x$ where $a > 0$

3. Mr. Albee is satisfied with your knowledge of definitions, and proceeds to quiz you on your knowledge of various properties. State the following:
   a. The mean value theorem
   b. The intermediate value theorem
   c. The squeeze theorem
   d. The uniqueness theorem for derivatives
   e. The limit of a product property
   f. The integration by parts formula
   g. The fundamental theorem of calculus
   h. The Lagrange form of the remainder
   i. The chain rule for parametric functions
   j. The polar differential of arc length

4. To make sure you know enough algebraic techniques, Mr. Albee asks you to find the following limits, derivatives, and integrals.
   a. $f'(x)$, if $f(x) = \int_3^x \sqrt{1 + \operatorname{sech} t}\, dt$
   b. $f'(x)$, if $f(x) = a^x$
   c. $f'(x)$, if $f(x) = x^a$
   d. $f'(x)$, if $f(x) = x^x$
   e. $\int e^{6x} \cos 3x\, dx$
   f. $\int \cosh^5 x \sinh x\, dx$
   g. $\int \sec^3 x\, dx$
   h. $\int (\sin 5x)^{-1} \cos 5x\, dx$
   i. $\lim_{x \to 0} \dfrac{\cos 7x - 1}{13x^2}$
   j. $\lim_{x \to 0} (1 - x)^{3/x}$

5. Mr. Albee wants to be sure you know graphical and numerical methods.
   a. Figure 12-10a shows the slope field for
   $$\frac{dy}{dx} = 0.2x - 0.3y + 0.3$$
   On a photocopy of the figure, sketch the particular solution containing (1, 8).
   b. Use Euler's method with $\Delta x = 0.5$ to estimate the value of $y$ for the solution in 5a if $x = 9$. How does your answer compare with your graphical solution?

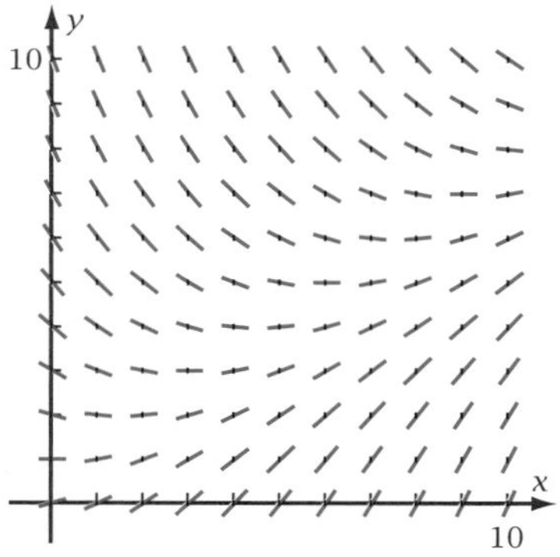


Figure 12-10a

You pass your preliminary tests and start to work on the dam project. At the dam site, Scorpion Gulch has a parabolic cross-section whose shape is the graph of $y = 0.1x^2$, where $x$ and $y$ are in yards. The back face of the dam (where the water will be) is vertical, and lies in the $xy$-plane (Figure 12-10b). The front face slopes in such a way that the thickness is $z = 30$ yards at the bottom of the gulch (where $y = 0$), and $z = 10$ yards at the top of the dam. The dam is to be 40 yards high.

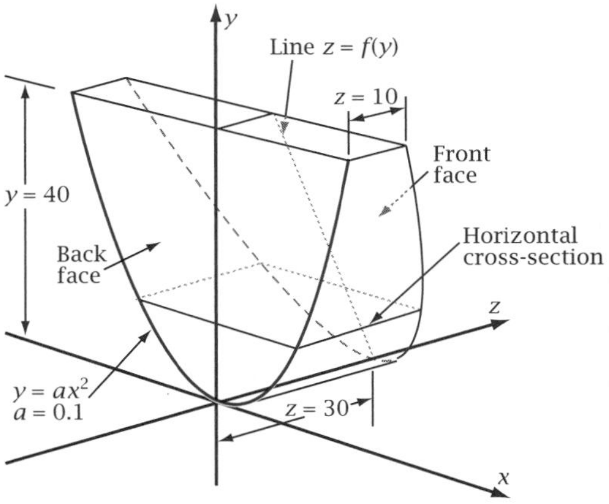


Figure 12-10b

6. Your first project is to analyze the forces that the water will exert on the vertical back face of the dam when the lake is full (i.e., 40 yards deep). Assume that the water density is $k$ pounds per cubic yard.
   a. Write an equation for the pressure in terms of $y$.
   b. Find the area of the dam's back face.
   c. Find the force exerted by the water on the back face of the dam.
   d. Find the first moment of this force with respect to the $x$-axis.
   e. Find the "center of pressure." This is the point on the back face at which the entire force could be concentrated to produce the same first moment with respect to the $x$-axis.

7. Your next project is to determine some of the physical characteristics of the dam itself.
   a. Find a linear equation expressing the thickness of the dam, $z$, in terms of the altitude, $y$.
   b. At what $y$-value will the dam's *horizontal* cross-sectional area be a maximum? a minimum?
   c. A cement mixer truck holds 5 cubic yards of concrete. How many truckloads of concrete should you order when it is time to pour the dam?
   d. Find the length of the joint between the dam's back face and the sides of the gulch.

8. The dam is finished. A speedboat on the lake behind the dam moves with vector equation

$$\vec{r} = (100\cos 0.03t)\vec{i} + (50\sin 0.03t)\vec{j}$$

   where distances are in feet. How fast is the boat going when $t = 50$ seconds?

9. The waves from the boat displace the water's surface according to the equation $z = (\sin t)/t$. The average displacement over the time interval $[0, t]$ involves the sine integral function,

$$\operatorname{Si} t = \int_0^t \frac{\sin u}{u}\,du$$

   Write Si $t$ as a power series. Use the ratio technique to determine the interval of convergence. Estimate the error in calculating Si 0.6 using just the first three non-zero terms of the series. Calculate Si 0.6 by numerical integration on your grapher.

10. The drain in the dam has a cross-section the shape of the polar curve $r = 5 + 4\cos\theta$ where $r$ is in feet. Find the area of the drain's cross-section.

11. At time $t = 0$ hours, the drain is opened. Initially water flows out at 5 million gallons per hour. But the rate is directly proportional to the amount of water remaining. There were 300 million gallons of water behind the dam at $t = 0$. Predict the amount remaining at $t = 10$.

**Cumulative Review No. 2—The Ship Problem**

After graduation you apply for work at Sinkin Ship Construction Company. Mr. Sinkin gives you the following preliminary test to see how much calculus you know.

1. Define derivative.
2. Define definite integral.
3. State the mean value theorem.
4. Find $f'(x)$ if $f(x) = \int_3^x g(t)\,dt$.
5. Integrate: $\int \tanh^5 x \operatorname{sech}^2 x\,dx$
6. Integrate: $\int x \sinh 2x\,dx$
7. Integrate: $\int \dfrac{3x + 14}{(x + 3)(x - 2)}\,dx$
8. Write the Maclaurin series for $\int \dfrac{\sinh x}{x}\,dx$.
9. Find the (open) interval of convergence for this series:

$$\sum_{n=1}^{\infty} \frac{n(x - 5)^n}{3^n}$$

10. Evaluate the improper integral $\int_0^1 x^{-0.998}\,dx$.
11. Find the average value of $y = x^2$ on the interval [3, 9].
12. Given $f(x) = x^2$. If $\delta = 0.01$, is this small enough to keep $f(x)$ within 0.08 unit of $f(4)$ when $x$ is within $\delta$ units of 4? Justify your answer.

Mr. Sinkin is satisfied with your work on these questions and assigns you to the design team for a new ship. The hull of this ship is shown in Figure 12-10c.

13. The volume of the ship equals the cross-sectional area times the length. At the forward end of the ship, the cross-sectional area varies with $x$, the distance from the bow. Write an integral for the volume of the part of the ship from $x = 2$ to $x = 10$. Then evaluate the integral approximately by Simpson's rule, given the cross-sectional areas shown in the table. Dimensions are in feet and square feet.

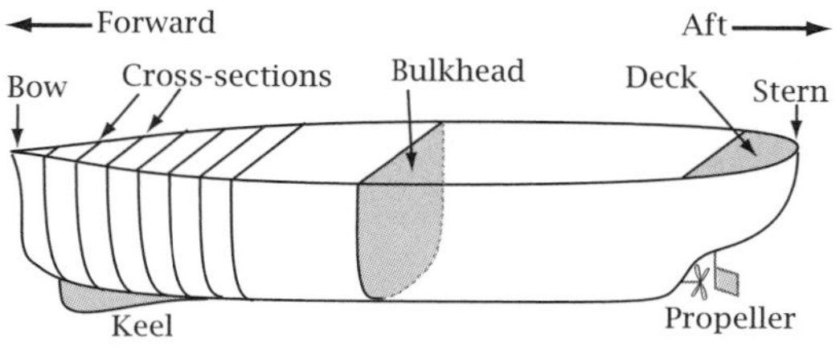


Figure 12-10c

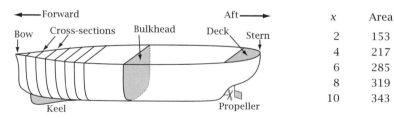

| $x$ | Area |
|---|---|
| 2 | 153 |
| 4 | 217 |
| 6 | 285 |
| 8 | 319 |
| 10 | 343 |

14. The propeller will have four blades the shape of the four-leaved rose $r = 4\sin 2\theta$, where $r$ is in feet. Find the area of one blade.

15. At the stern of the ship, the deck has a shape similar to the region bounded by the ellipse

$$\left(\tfrac{x}{5}\right)^2 + \left(\tfrac{y}{3}\right)^2 = 1$$

between $x = 1$ and $x = 5$. Find the area of this region.

Your next project is to analyze a vertical bulkhead (a wall) that goes across the ship. The bulkhead has the shape of the region that lies above the graph of $y = 0.0016x^4$ and below the line $y = 16$.

16. Find the area of the bulkhead.

17. The welders who will install the bulkhead need to know the length of the graph of $y = 0.0016x^4$ that forms the edge of the bulkhead. Find this length.

18. The bulkhead must be strong enough to withstand the force of the water if the compartment on one side of the bulkhead becomes flooded. You recall that force equals pressure times area, and that the pressure at any point below the water's surface is proportional to that point's distance from the surface. The proportionality constant is 62.4 pounds per cubic foot, the density of water. Find to the nearest 100 pounds the force exerted by the water.

A vertical keel is to extend below the bottom of the ship. When turned upside down, the keel is similar in shape to the region under the graph of $y = (\ln x)/x$, for $x \geq 1$.

19. Find the limit of $y$ as $x$ approaches infinity.

20. Find the $x$-coordinate of the maximum of the function. Justify your answer.

21. Find the $x$-coordinate(s) of all points of inflection of the graph.

22. Sketch the graph, consistent with your answers above.

The radar equipment needs values of natural logarithms to 20 decimal places.

23. Show that the Taylor series for $\ln x$ expanded about $x = 1$ converges for $0 < x \leq 2$.

24. How many terms of the series would be needed to calculate ln 1.4 to 20 decimal places?

Your last project is analysis of the motion of the ship.

25. In linear motion the velocity of the ship is given by a differential equation whose slope field is shown in Figure 12-10d. Describe the way the velocity changes if the ship starts from $v = 0$ ft/sec at $t = 0$ min. How would the velocity differ if somehow the ship were given an initial velocity of 50 ft/sec?

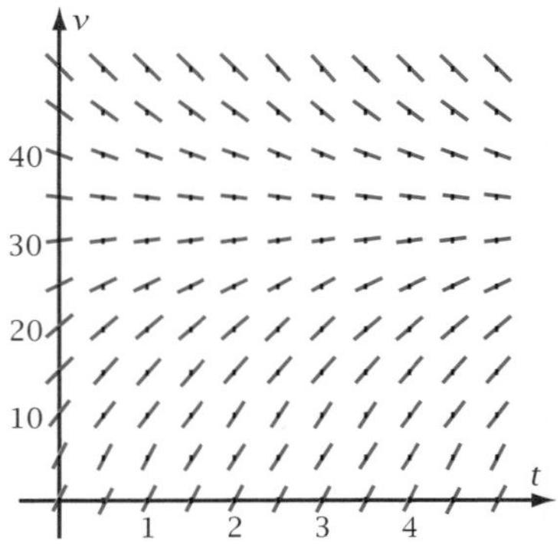

Figure 12-10d

26. In a sharp turn, the position vector of the ship is given by $\vec{r} = (\ln t)\vec{i} + (\sin 2t)\vec{j}$. Find the acceleration vector.

**Cumulative Review No. 3—Routine Problems**

Calculus involves four fundamental concepts. In the first four problems you are to demonstrate that you understand these concepts.

1. Demonstrate that you understand the definition of limit by sketching the graph of a function that has a limit $L$ as $x$ approaches $c$, and showing an epsilon neighborhood of $L$ and a corresponding delta neighborhood of $c$ that is clearly smaller than is necessary.
2. Write the formal definition of derivative. Then tell a graphical meaning of the derivative, and a physical meaning of the derivative.
3. Write the definition of $\int f(x)\,dx$.
4. Write the definition of $\int_r^s f(t)\,dt$.

The definition of limit is not used to find limits. So other techniques are developed.

5. There is a technique for finding "interesting" limits of the form $0/0$ or $\infty/\infty$. Name this technique, and use it to evaluate

$$\lim_{x\to 0} \frac{x\cos x}{1-e^{5x}}.$$

The definition of derivative is awkward to use. So you develop shortcuts.

6. Find $y'$ if $y = \tan(\sin 5x)$. Name the property that allows you to differentiate such "composite functions."
7. Products and powers can be differentiated logarithmically. Find $y'$ if

$$y = (5x-3)(2x+7)^4(x-9).$$

8. Formulas for derivatives of inverse cicrular functions are found by implicit differentiation. Do this for the inverse tangent function.

In Problems 9 through 12 you will demonstrate your knowledge of certain basic techniques and when to use them. Integrate.

9. $\int \sin^7 x \cos x\,dx$
10. $\int \sqrt{x^2+9}\,dx$
11. $\int \dfrac{3x-11}{x^2+2x-3}\,dx$
12. $\int \sin^{-1} x\,dx$

Definite integrals are hard to evaluate using the definition. Fortunately, there is a theorem relating definite integrals to indefinite ones.

13. Name and state the theorem that relates definite and indefinite integrals.
14. The mean value theorem plays a key role in the proof of the theorem in Problem 13. Demonstrate that you understand what the mean value theorem says by sketching an appropriate graph.

The techniques of calculus can be applied to problems in the real and mathematical worlds.

15. If $f(x) = \int_3^x h(t)\,dt$, find $f'(x)$.
16. Given: $f(x) = xe^{-x}$ for $x \ge 0$. Find the $x$-coordinates of all points of inflection.
17. Find the length of the graph of $y = \sin x$ from $x = 0$ to $x = 2$.

18. The integral $\int_0^{16} x^{-3/4}\,dx$ is improper.
   a. Show that the integral converges.
   b. Use the result to find the average value of $y = x^{-3/4}$ from $x = 0$ to $x = 16$.

19. Find the area of the region inside the circle with polar equation $r = 10\cos\theta$ from $\theta = 0.5$ to $\theta = 1$.

20. A particle travels in the $xy$-plane in such a way that its position vector is

$$\vec{r} = t^2\vec{i} + 3t^{-1}\vec{j}.$$

At time $t = 1$, what is its velocity vector? How fast is it going? Is the particle's distance from the origin increasing or decreasing? At what rate?

21. The region in Quadrant I bounded by the coordinate axes and the graph of $y = \cos x$ is rotated about the $y$-axis to form a solid. Find its volume.

22. A rectangle in the first quadrant has one corner at the origin, and the diagonally opposite corner on the line $y = -1.5x + 6$.
   a. Show that the rectangle has maximum area when $x = 2$.
   b. If the rectangle and line are rotated about the $y$-axis to form a cylinder inscribed in a cone, show that a different value of $x$ produces the maximum-volume cylinder.

23. The crew's compartment in a space ship has an irregular shape due to all the equipment in it. Cross sections at various distances from the bottom of the compartment have areas as follows (feet and square feet):

| distance | area |
|---|---|
| 3 | 51 |
| 5 | 37 |
| 7 | 41 |
| 9 | 63 |
| 11 | 59 |

Use Simpson's rule to estimate the volume of the crew's compartment between 3 and 11 ft.

24. The error function, used in "curving" grades, is defined by

$$\operatorname{erf} x = 2\pi^{1/2}\int_0^x e^{-t^2}\,dt.$$

   a. Write the first few terms of the Maclaurin series for the integral in erf $x$.
   b. Use the ratio technique to prove that the series for erf $x$ converges for all values of $x$.

# FINAL EXAMINATION

This section contains an examination that may be considered to be a "dress rehearsal" for the exam your instructor will give you. We suggest that you make the rehearsal as realistic as possible by putting yourself under simulated test conditions and giving yourself a two-hour time limit. No answers are provided in the back of the book.

### *A Guided Tour Through Calculus*

Calculus involves two basic concepts:

a. Instantaneous rates of change, and

b. Products in which one factor's value depends on the other factor.

Both of these are based on the underlying concept of limit. They are linked together by the fundamental theorem, which allows you to calculate limits of Riemann sums by using antiderivatives. On this test it will be your objective to answer the questions in a way that demonstrates that you understand these concepts and their relationships.

1. The first problem you encountered was finding the instantaneous rate of change of a function at a given point. Find, approximately, the derivative of $f(x) = \sin x$ at $x = 1$ by finding how much $\sin 1$ differs from $\sin 1.1$, $\sin 1.01$, and $\sin 1.001$, and doing the appropriate division.
2. Later, you found techniques for calculating derivatives exactly. Find $f'(1)$ if $f(x) = \sin x$. Show that the three approximate values of $f'(1)$ you calculated in Problem 1 are converging toward the value of $f'(1)$ you calculated in this problem.
3. The intuitive idea of "instantaneous rate of change" is made precise by a formal definition of derivative. Write both forms of this definition, one for $f'(x)$, and one for $f'(c)$, where $c$ is a particular value of $x$.
4. The definition of derivative in Problem 3 involves the concept of limit. The limit of $f(x)$ as $x$ approaches $c$ is the number $f(x)$ can be kept close to, just by keeping $x$ close enough to $c$. Suppose that $f(x) = e^x$. What does the limit of $f(x)$ equal as $x$ approaches 2? How close would you have to keep $x$ to 2 in order for $f(x)$ to be within 0.1 unit of this limit?
5. The intuitive idea of "closeness" is made precise in the formal definition of limit. Write this definition.
6. The quantities epsilon and delta from the definition of limit appear in Problem 4, above. Which one is epsilon, and which is delta?
7. Your intuitive introduction to variable-factor products came from the distance = rate × time equation. Draw an appropriate graph which shows that if the rate is constant, the distance can be represented as the area of a rectangle.
8. If the rate varies, the distance can still be represented as the area of the region under a graph. Suppose that the rates shown in the table have been measured at the given times. Plot the graph of rate vs. time. Find the distance traveled between 1.0 and 2.8 by counting squares.

| Time | Rate |
|---|---|
| 1.0 | 7 |
| 1.3 | 9 |
| 1.6 | 13 |
| 1.9 | 12 |
| 2.2 | 10 |
| 2.5 | 8 |
| 2.8 | 5 |

9. More recently you have learned ways to calculate definite integrals such as in Problem 8, without having to draw the graph and count. Find the distance using Simpson's rule. Show that it is approximately the same as the distance you found by counting squares.
10. In Problems 8 and 9 you knew no equation for rate in terms of time. If you do know such an equation, there are other ways to calculate the distance. Suppose that $v(t) = te^{-t}$. Find the distance traveled between $t = 0$ and $t = 2$ by calculating a Riemann sum with $n = 5$ increments, taking sample points at the midpoint of each subinterval.
11. You now know the fundamental theorem of calculus, which allows you to calculate limits of Riemann sums exactly, using antiderivatives. Find, exactly, the distance traveled in Problem 10. By what percentage does the Riemann sum in Problem 10 differ from the exact value?
12. State the fundamental theorem of calculus.
13. The proof of the fundamental theorem relies on the mean value theorem. Show that the mean value theorem does apply to $f(x) = x^{2/3}$ on the inverval $[0, 1]$, in spite of the fact that $f$ is not differentiable at $x = 0$. Calculate the point $x = c$ in the interval $(0, 1)$ at which the conclusion of the mean value theorem is true. Then plot the graph accurately, and show that the line through $(c, f(c))$ with slope $f'(c)$ really does satisfy the requirements of the mean value theorem.
14. In order to use the fundamental theorem, you must be reasonably good at finding indefinite integrals. Write an integral that can be evaluated by the given technique, and do the integration.

    a. Partial fractions.

    b. Trigonometric substitution.
15. Sometimes integration by parts results in the same integral appearing on both sides of the equals sign. Show how this situation can be handled by doing the integration for $\int \sec^3 x\, dx$.
16. In addition to their role in evaluating definite integrals, indefinite integrals have applications in their own right. For instance, if you know how a function changes, you can find an equation for the function itself. Suppose that the instantaneous rate of change of $y$ with respect to $x$ is directly proportional to $y$. Write the appropriate differential equation and solve it to express $y$ in terms of $x$.

17. Definite integrals arise from variable-factor products. The volume of a solid is equal to its cross-sectional area times its height. Sketch the solid formed by rotating about the $y$-axis the region in Quadrant I under the graph of $y = 4 - x^2$. Then slice the height in such a way that the cross-sectional area is (essentially) constant at any point in the slice.

18. Sketch the solid in Problem 17 again, and draw a slice using cylindrical shells. Show that this method slices the cross-sectional area so that the height is (essentially) constant at any point in the slice.

19. You recall that the moment of a quantity is the magnitude of that quantity times a distance from a reference point, line, or plane. Find the first moment of area of the region in Problem 17 with respect to the $y$-axis. Use the result to find the $x$-coordinate of the centroid of the region.

20. Once you understand the concept of variable-factor products, you can analyze any such problem, even when the quantities are unfamiliar. For instance, the number of calories needed to warm a substance from temperature $T_1$ to temperature $T_2$ equals the "heat capacity" of the substance (calories per degree) times the change in temperature, $T_2 - T_1$. Unfortunately, most real substances have heat capacities that vary with temperature. Assume that calculus foeride (a rare, tough substance!) has a heat capacity given by

$$C = 10 + 0.3T^{1/2},$$

where $C$ is in calories per degree and $T$ is in degrees celsius. How many calories would be needed to warm the calculus foeride from 100° to 900°F?

21. Definite integrals can be applied to the mathematical world. For instance, a function might be defined as a definite integral. As you may recall, the sine-integral function, Si $x$, is defined as

$$\text{Si } x = \int_0^x \frac{\sin u}{u}\, du$$

a. Write an equation for Si′$x$.

b. Expand the integrand as a Maclaurin series, then integrate to get a series for Si $x$.

c. Evaluate Si 0.7 approximately, using the first two nonzero terms of the series.

d. Find an upper bound for the tail of the series that is left after the first two terms. Based on this result, tell to how many decimal places you can guarantee that your answer in 21c is correct.

e. Prove that the series for Si $x$ converges for all values of $x$.

22. Parametric equations can be used to apply calculus to vector functions. Suppose that an object is moving in such a way that its position vector, $\vec{r}$, is given by

$$\vec{r} = (t^3)\vec{i} + (t^2)\vec{j}.$$

Plot accurately the path of the object from $t = 0$ to $t = 1$. Show the location of the object when $t = 0.5$. Calculate the velocity and acceleration vectors when $t = 0.5$. Plot these two vectors with their tails at the object. Is the object speeding up or slowing down? Explain.

23. Calculus can be applied to figures in polar coordinates. Figure FE-1 shows the polar graph of

$$r = \cos \theta$$

from $\theta = 0$ to $\theta = \pi/2$. Slicing the region as shown gives a wedge of angle $d\theta$. Any point on the graph that is within the angle $d\theta$ has (essentially) the same radius as at the sample point. The area of the wedge is approximately equal to the area of a sector of a circle of radius $r$. The sector, of course, is $d\theta/(2\pi)$ of the area of a circle of radius $r$. Use this information to find $dA$, the area of the wedge, in terms of $\theta$. Then find the area from $\theta = 0$ to $\theta = \pi/6$ by adding the $dA$'s and taking the limit as $d\theta$ approaches 0 (i.e., definite integrating).

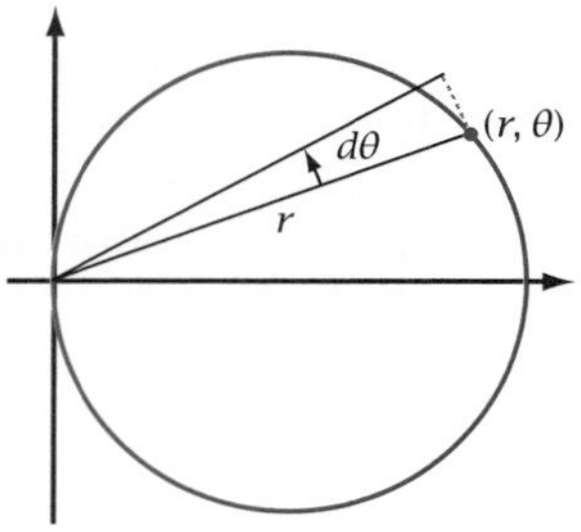


Figure FE-1

# Appendix A: Summary of Properties of Trigonometric Functions

1. *Reciprocal*

$$\cot x = \frac{1}{\tan x} \text{ or } \tan x \cot x = 1$$

$$\sec x = \frac{1}{\cos x} \text{ or } \cos x \sec x = 1$$

$$\csc x = \frac{1}{\sin x} \text{ or } \sin x \csc x = 1$$

2. *Quotient*

$$\tan x = \frac{\sin x}{\cos x} = \frac{\sec x}{\csc x}$$

$$\cot x = \frac{\cos x}{\sin x} = \frac{\csc x}{\sec x}$$

3. *Pythagorean*

$$\cos^2 x + \sin^2 x = 1$$

$$1 + \tan^2 x = \sec^2 x$$

$$\cot^2 x + 1 = \csc^2 x$$

4. *Odd-Even*

$\sin(-x) = -\sin x$ (odd)

$\cos(-x) = \cos x$ (even)

$\tan(-x) = -\tan x$ (odd)

$\cot(-x) = -\cot x$ (odd)

$\sec(-x) = \sec x$ (even)

$\csc(-x) = -\csc x$ (odd)

5. *Cofunction*

$$\cos(90^\circ - \theta) = \sin\theta;\ \cos\left(\frac{\pi}{2} - x\right) = \sin x$$

$$\cot(90^\circ - \theta) = \tan\theta;\ \cot\left(\frac{\pi}{2} - x\right) = \tan x$$

$$\csc(90^\circ - \theta) = \sec\theta;\ \csc\left(\frac{\pi}{2} - x\right) = \sec x$$

6. *Composite-Argument*

$\cos(A - B) = \cos A \cos B + \sin A \sin B$

$\cos(A + B) = \cos A \cos B - \sin A \sin B$

$\sin(A - B) = \sin A \cos B - \cos A \sin B$

$\sin(A + B) = \sin A \cos B + \cos A \sin B$

$$\tan(A - B) = \frac{\tan A - \tan B}{1 + \tan A \tan B}$$

$$\tan(A + B) = \frac{\tan A + \tan B}{1 - \tan A \tan B}$$

7. *Double-Argument*

$\sin 2x = 2 \sin x \cos x$

$\cos 2x = \cos^2 x - \sin^2 x = 1 - 2\sin^2 x$

$\quad = 2\cos^2 x - 1$

$$\tan 2x = \frac{2\tan x}{1 - \tan^2 x}$$

$$\cos^2 x = \frac{1}{2}\left(1 + \cos 2x\right)$$

$$\sin^2 x = \frac{1}{2}\left(1 - \cos 2x\right)$$

8. *Half-Argument*

$$\sin\frac{1}{2}x = \pm\sqrt{\frac{1}{2}\left(1 - \cos x\right)}$$

$$\cos\frac{1}{2}x = \pm\sqrt{\frac{1}{2}\left(1 + \cos x\right)}$$

$$\tan\frac{1}{2}x = \pm\sqrt{\frac{1 - \cos x}{1 + \cos x}}$$

$$= \frac{\sin x}{1 + \cos x} = \frac{1 - \cos x}{\sin x}$$

9. *Sum and Product*

$2\cos A \cos B = \cos(A + B) + \cos(A - B)$

$2\sin A \sin B = -\cos(A + B) + \cos(A - B)$

$2\sin A \cos B = \sin(A + B) + \sin(A - B)$

$2\cos A \sin B = \sin(A + B) - \sin(A - B)$

$$\cos x + \cos y = 2\cos\tfrac{1}{2}\left(x + y\right)\cos\tfrac{1}{2}\left(x - y\right)$$

$$\cos x - \cos y = -2\sin\tfrac{1}{2}\left(x + y\right)\sin\tfrac{1}{2}\left(x - y\right)$$

$$\sin x + \sin y = 2\sin\tfrac{1}{2}\left(x + y\right)\cos\tfrac{1}{2}\left(x - y\right)$$

$$\sin x - \sin y = 2\cos\tfrac{1}{2}\left(x + y\right)\sin\tfrac{1}{2}\left(x - y\right)$$

10. *Linear Combination of Sine and Cosine*

$A\cos x + B\sin x = C\cos(x - D)$; where

$C = \sqrt{A^2 + B^2}$, $\cos D = \frac{A}{C}$, and $\sin D = \frac{B}{C}$.

# Appendix B: Answers to Selected Problems

## CHAPTER 1

### Problem Set 1-1

*The Concept of Instantaneous Rate*

1. *Pendulum Problem*
   a. 95 cm, Q.E.D.
   b. $t = 5.1$, rate $\approx 26.34$ cm/sec
   $t = 5.01$, rate $\approx 27.12$ cm/sec
   $t = 5.001$, rate $\approx 27.20$ cm/sec
   So the instantaneous rate of change at $t = 5$ is about 27.20 or 27.21 cm/sec.
   c. Instantaneous rate involves division by zero.
   d. For $t = 1.5$ to 1.501, rate $\approx -31.42$ cm/sec. The pendulum is *approaching* the wall. Since rate of change is negative the distance is decreasing.
   e. The instantaneous rate of change is the *limit* of the average rates as the time interval approaches zero. It is called the *derivative.*
   f. Before $t = 0$ the pendulum was not yet moving. For large values of $t$ the pendulum's motion will die out due to friction.

### Problem Set 1-2

*Rates of Change by Equation, Graph, or Table*

1. a. Increasing slowly.
   b. Increasing fast.
3. a. Decreasing fast.
   b. Decreasing slowly.
5. a. Increasing fast.
   b. Increasing slowly.
   c. Decreasing slowly.
   d. Increasing fast.
7. a. Increasing slowly.
   b. Increasing slowly.
   c. Increasing slowly.
9. a. Increasing fast.
   b. Neither increasing nor decreasing.
   c. Increasing fast.
   d. Increasing slowly.
11. a. $x = 1.5$: rate $\approx 6.0$ cm/min. Increasing.
    b. $x = 3.0$: rate $\approx 6.8$ cm/min. Increasing.
    c. $x = 4.0$: rate $\approx -0.3$ cm/min. Decreasing.
13. *Rolling Tire Problem*
    a. i. $-1.0$ in./sec. ii. 0.0 in./sec. iii. 1.15 in./sec.
    b. 1.7 sec, since $y = 0$ at that time.
15. a. Quadratic (or polynomial).
    b. $f(3) = 30$
    c. Increasing at about 11.0. (2.99 to 3.01)
17. a. Exponential. b. $f(2) = 9$
    c. Increasing at about 9.89. (1.99 to 2.01)
19. a. Rational algebraic. b. $f(4) = -1$
    c. Decreasing at about 1.00. (3.99 to 4.01)
21. a. Linear (or polynomial).
    b. $f(5) = -8$
    c. Decreasing at 3. (Exact)
23. a. Circular (or trigonometric).
    b. $f(2) = 0.90929\ldots$
    c. Decreasing at about 0.416. (1.99 to 2.01).
25. *Accurate Graph of a Cubic Function Problem*

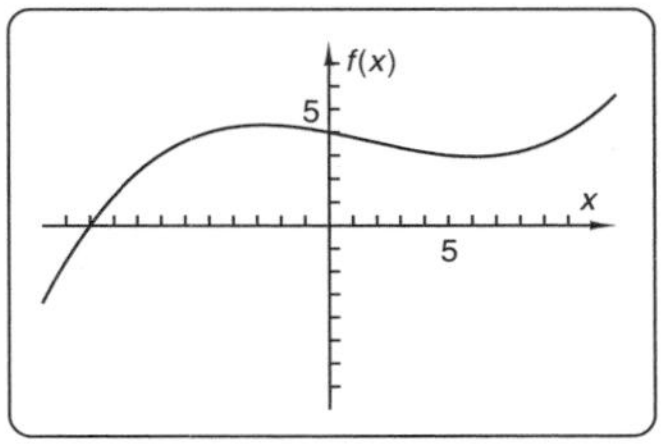


    a. $f(x)$ is increasing fast when the graph slopes steeply upward.
    b. $f(x)$ is decreasing for about $-3 < x < 6$.
    c. False. $f(x)$ is positive, but decreasing between $x = -3$ and $x = 6$.
    d. $f(x)$ is decreasing fastest at about $x = 1$ or 2.
27. See definition in text.

### Problem Set 1-3

*One Kind of Integral of a Function*

1. a. Approximately 30.8
   b. Approximately 41.8

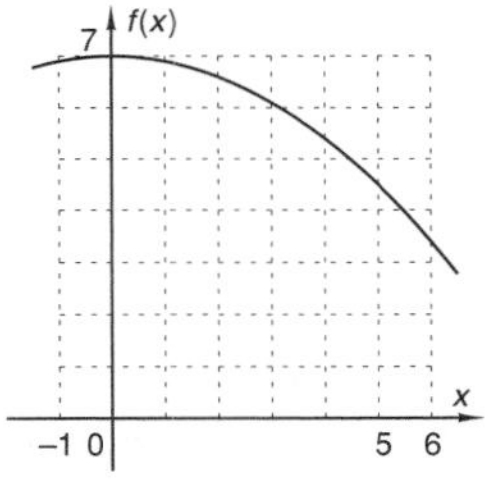


3. a. Approximately 2.0
   b. Approximately 1.0

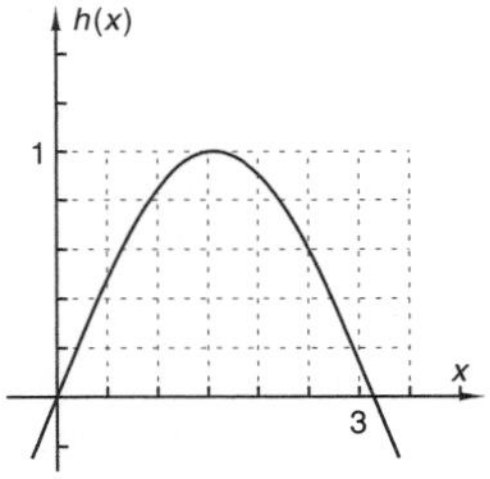


5. Distance $\approx 680$ feet.
7. Derivative $\approx 3.42\ldots$

9. *Sports Car Problem*

a. Graph.

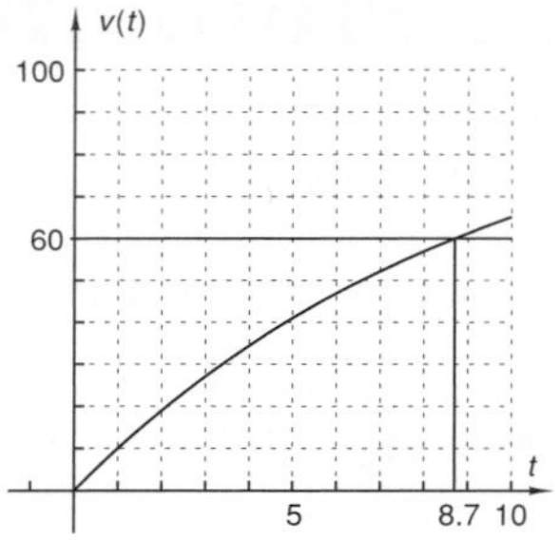


b. Range is $0 \le y < 100$.

c. $x \approx 8.7$ sec.

d. Distance $\approx$ 300 ft.

e. Rate $\approx$ 6.2 (ft/sec)/sec

f. Acceleration.

11. About 7.1 cm

13. See text meaning of definite integral.

### Problem Set 1-4

*Definite Integrals by Trapezoids, from Equations and Data*

1. *Spaceship Problem*

a. Graph.

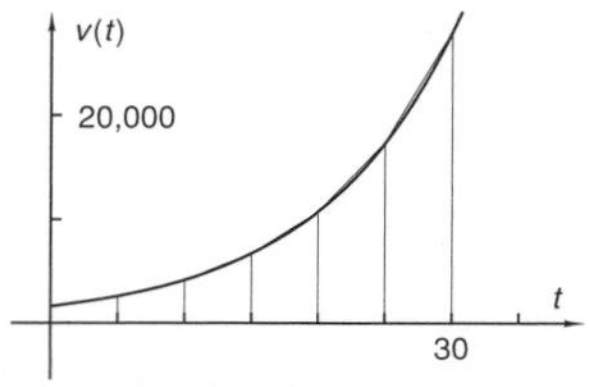


b. Distance = rate times time. Since the vertical axis represents distance and the horizontal axis represents time, their product (i.e., the area) represents distance.

c. Graph. Distance $\approx$ 281,000 ft.

d. Definite integral.

e. Yes, it will be going fast enough. $v(30) = 27{,}919.04\ldots > 27{,}000$.

3. *Aircraft Carrier Landing Problem*
Distance $\approx$ 396 feet. No danger of running off!

5. Integral $\approx$ 70.8

7. Programs will vary, depending on calculator.

9. a. 30.8125
b. 41.7095
c. 41.766095

11. *Trapezoidal Rule Error Problem*
If the trapezoids wind up being circumscribed outside the region bounded by the graph, the trapezoids enclose too much area and the trapezoidal rule overestimates the integral. If the trapezoids wind up being inscribed inside the region the rule underestimates the integral. Thus for Problem 9 the rule *underestimates*, and for Problem 10 it *overestimates.*

13. *Football Problem*
Integral $\approx$ *227.8 in*$^3$
The integral will have units $(\text{in}^2)(\text{in.}) = \text{in}^3$. So the integral represents the *volume* of the football.

15. *Derivative from Graph Problem*

a. Derivative $\approx -5.6$.

b. Derivative $\approx 5.6$

Note the different scales on the two axes.

17. *Meaning of Limits Problem*

a. $f(5)$ would involve division by zero.

b. $f(x) = 2(x + 5)$, $x \ne 5$.
$f(4.9) = 19.8$, $f(5.1) = 20.2$

c. Both are close to 20.

d. $f(4.99) = 19.98$, $f(5.01) = 20.02$
Both are close to 20.

e. "If $x$ is within 0.01 unit of 5, then $f(x)$ is within 0.02 unit of $L$."

### Problem Set 1-5

*Limit of a Function*

1. Has a limit, 3.

3. Has a limit, 3.

5. Has no limit.

7. Has a limit, 7.

9. Has no limit.

11. *Definition of Limit, Problem 1:*

a. See text definition of limit.

b. $f(4) = 3(4) - 7 = 5$, Q.E.D.

c. Keep $x$ within 0.2 unit of 4.

d. Graph.

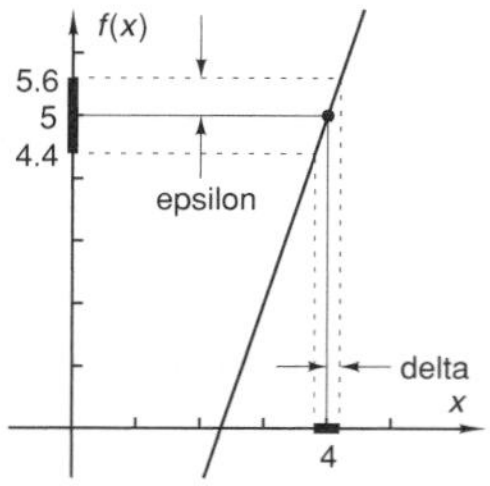


e. e.g., Let $x = 4.1$. Then $f(4.1) = 5.3$, which is within 0.6 unit of 5.

f. $\delta = \epsilon/3 = (0.00012)/3 = 0.00004$

13. *Definition of Limit, Problem 3:*

a. $f(x) = \dfrac{(x^2 - 6x + 13)(x - 2)}{x - 2}$

$f(2) = \dfrac{(5)(0)}{(0)} = \dfrac{0}{0}$, Q.E.D.

The limit is 5. Substitute 2 for $x$ into the simplified expression, $f(x) = x^2 - 6x + 13$, $x \neq 2$

b. $f(1.995) = 5.010025$, $f(1.996) = 5.008016$; $f(2.005) = 4.990025$, $f(2.006) = 4.988025$. If $x$ is within 0.004 unit of 2, then.... You must use the value of $x$ that is closer to 2.

c. $f(x) = 4.99$: $x = 2.00501256\ldots$
$f(x) = 5.01$: $x = 1.99501243\ldots$
$1.99501243\ldots < x < 2.00501256\ldots$

d. Graph (exaggerated to show concept)

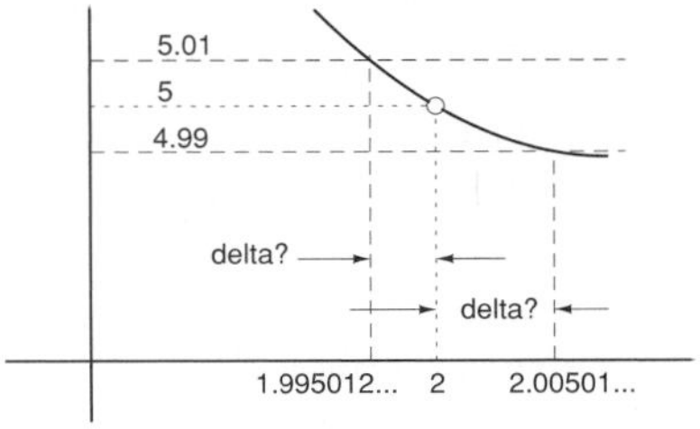


e. Delta = 0.00498756...

f. $L = 5$, $c = 2$, epsilon = 0.01, delta = 0.00498756...

15. *One-Sided Limit Problem*

a. The quantity $|x - 2|/(x - 2)$ changes from $-1$ to 1 at $x = 2$, thus causing the jump.

b. From the left, the limit is 3.

c. From the right, the limit is 5.

d. Pick any value of epsilon less than 1. No matter what number you claim to be the limit, there are values of $x$ on one side of 2 or the other which make $f(x)$ come out more than epsilon units away from that number.

17. Derivative $\approx -0.1111$ using $r(-3.01)$ and $r(-2.99)$

19. *Don't Believe Everything You See Problem!*
"Look, Ima. The two curves are so close together that the grapher can't tell the difference. But you should realize that by using TRACE on the two graphs, you will see a slight difference in the $y$-values for the two graphs at the same $x$-value. Or you could use a wider window, thus showing the curve of the sine graph away from the straight of the linear graph."

## Problem Set 1-6

*Calculus Journal*

1. Answers will vary.

## Problem Set 1-7

*Chapter Review and Test*

### Review Problems

R1. *Bungee Jumping Problem*

a. $t = 4$: $d \approx 15.4$ ft.

b. From 4 to 4.1, average rate $\approx -29.3$ ft/sec
From 3.9 to 4, average rate $\approx -40.1$ ft/sec
Instantaneous rate $\approx -34.7$ ft/sec
Going down. Distance from water is decreasing.

c. Instantaneous rate $\approx 70.8$

d. Going up at about 70.8 ft/sec.

e. Derivative.

R2. a. Instantaneous rate of change of a function.

b. $x = -4$: Decreasing fast
$x = 1$: Increasing slowly
$x = 3$: Increasing fast
$x = 5$: Neither increasing nor decreasing

c. $f(2) = 25$. Derivative $\approx 40.2$.

d. $t = 2$: 3.25 m/sec
$t = 18$: 8.75 m/sec
$t = 24$: 11.5 m/sec
Speed is constant, 7 m/sec, from $t = 6$ to 16 sec. At $t = 24$, Mary is giving her final spurt toward the finish line.

R3. a. Graph.

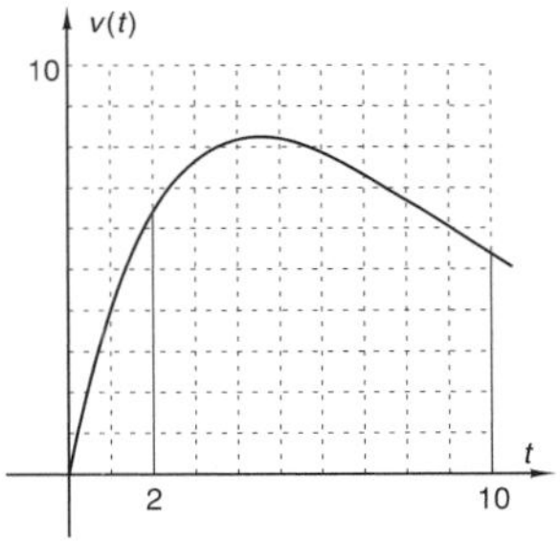


b. Distance $\approx 58.1$ ft.

c. Definite integral

R4. a. Graph is correct.

b. Integral $\approx 15.0$

c.

| $x$ | $f(x)$ |
|---|---|
| 1.0 | 5.3 |
| 1.5 | 5.575 |
| 2.0 | 5.6 |
| 2.5 | 5.375 |
| 3.0 | 4.9 |
| 3.5 | 4.175 |
| 4.0 | 3.2 |

Integral $\approx 14.9375$

R5. a. See definition of limit in text.

b. Limit = $-10$

c. Delta = 0.00498756...

d. e.g., Let $x = 3.004$.
$f(3.004) = -10.007984$, which is within 0.01 unit of $-10$.

e. Graph. (example)

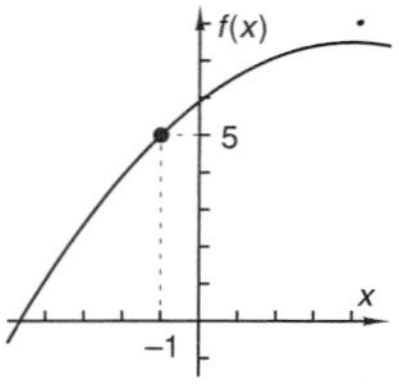


R6. The journal gives you a chance to summarize things you have learned and condense the class notes you have taken. Since it also gives you a chance to write down unanswered questions, you do *not* have to know the answers to everything you write.

## CHAPTER 2

### Exploratory Problem Set 2-1

*Numerical Approach to the Definition of Limit*

1. a. Grapher graph agrees with text graph.

   b.

| $x$ | $f(x)$ |
|---|---|
| 1.9995 | 2.920629947... |
| 1.9996 | 2.926319370... |
| 1.9997 | 2.933056704... |
| 1.9998 | 2.941519645... |
| 1.9999 | 2.953584111... |
| 2 | 3 |
| 2.0001 | 3.046415888... |
| 2.0002 | 3.058480354... |
| 2.0003 | 3.066943295... |
| 2.0004 | 3.073680629... |
| 2.0005 | 3.079370052... |

   c. $1.9997 \le x \le 2.0003$.

   d. $1.9999 \le x \le 2.0001$.

   e. Yes. To make $3 - 0.01 < f(x) < 3 + 0.01$, keep $x$ in the interval $2 - 0.01^3 < x < 2 + 0.01^3$. That is, $1.999999 < x < 2.000001$ (but $x \ne 2$).

   f. $L = 3$, $c = 2$, epsilon = 0.07, and delta = 0.0003.

   g. Keep $x$ in the interval $2 - \text{epsilon}^3 < x < 2 + \text{epsilon}^3$.

3. Graphs. No limit. Graph cycles infinitely as it approaches $x = 3$.

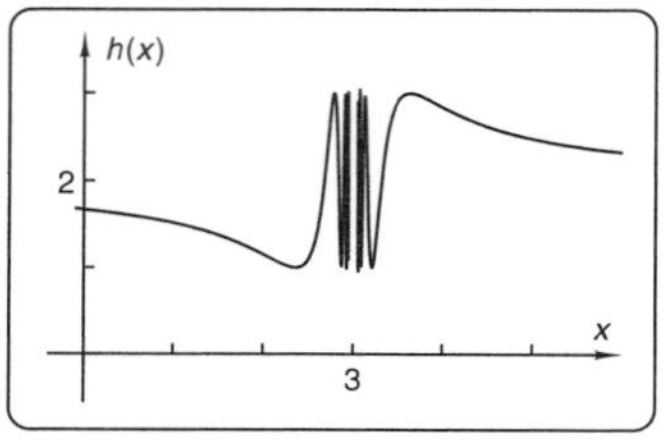


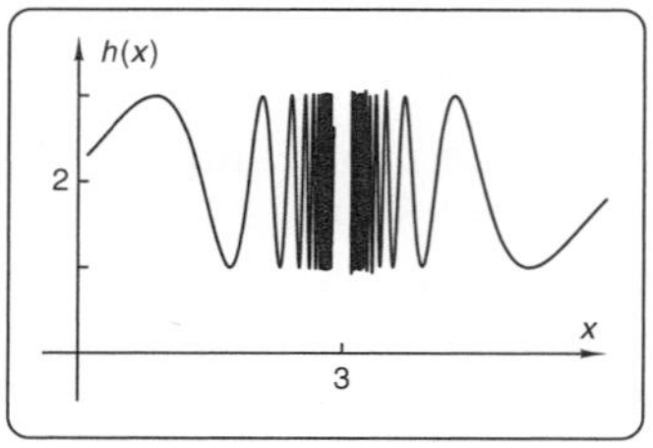


### Problem Set 2-2

*Graphical and Algebraic Approach to the Definition of Limit*

1. $\lim_{x\to3} f(x) = 5$. For $\epsilon = 0.5$, $\delta \approx 0.2$ or 0.3.

3. $\lim_{x\to6} f(x) = 4$. For $\epsilon = 0.7$, $\delta \approx 0.5$ or 0.6. (The right side is the more restrictive.)

5. $\lim_{x\to5} f(x) = 2$. For $\epsilon = 0.3$, $\delta \approx 0.5$ or 0.6. (The right side is more restrictive.)

7. a. Graph. (Same as Problem 1.)
   b. $\lim_{x\to3} f(x) = 5$.
   c. Graph is symmetrical about $x = 3$.
   Max. $\delta = 3 - (3 + \sin^{-1}(-0.25)) = 0.25268\ldots$.
   d. Max. $\delta = \sin^{-1}(\epsilon/2)$, which is positive for any positive value of $\epsilon$.

9. a. Graph. (Same as Problem 3.)
   b. $\lim_{x\to6} f(x) = 4$.
   c. The right side is more restrictive.
   Max. $\delta = (7 - (2.3/3)^3) - 6 = 0.5493\ldots$.
   d. Max. $\delta = 1 - ((3 - \epsilon)/3)^3$, which is positive for all positive values of $\epsilon$.

11. a. Graph. (Same as Problem 5.)
    b. $\lim_{x\to5} f(x) = 2$.
    c. The right side is more restrictive.
    Max. $\delta = (5 + \sqrt{0.3}) - 5 = 0.54772\ldots$.
    d. Max. $\delta = \sqrt{\epsilon}$, which is positive for all $\epsilon > 0$.

13. *Limits Applied to Derivatives Problem*
    a. $m(t) = \dfrac{3t^2 - 48}{t - 4}$
    b. Graph. Removable discontinuity at $x = 4$.

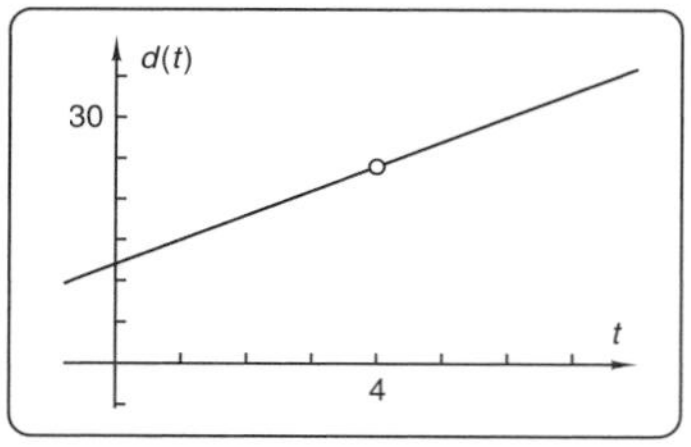


    c. Limit = 24 ft/sec.
    d. $m(t) = 3t + 12$, if $t \ne 4$.
    Keep $t$ within 0.04 unit of 4.

### Problem Set 2-3

*The Limit Theorems*

1. *Limit of a Function Plus a Function Problem*
   Graph.

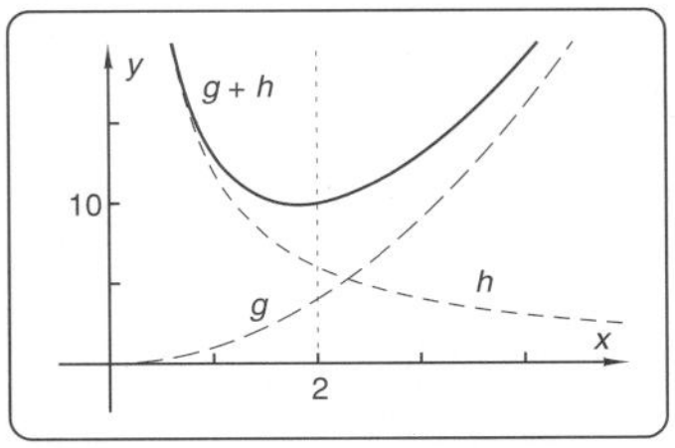


$\lim_{x\to 2} f(x) = 10$, $\lim_{x\to 2} g(x) = 4$, and $\lim_{x\to 2} h(x) = 6$.
$\therefore \lim_{x\to 2} f(x) = \lim_{x\to 2} g(x) + \lim_{x\to 2} h(x)$, Q.E.D.
Example: Use each 0.01 from $x = 1.97$ to 2.03.

| $x$ | $f(x)$ |
|---|---|
| 1.97 | 9.9722... |
| 1.98 | 9.9810... |
| 1.99 | 9.9902... |
| 2.00 | 10 |
| 2.01 | 10.0102... |
| 2.02 | 10.0209... |
| 2.03 | 10.0322... |

All of these $f(x)$ values are close to 10.

3. *Limit of a Constant Problem*
Graph.

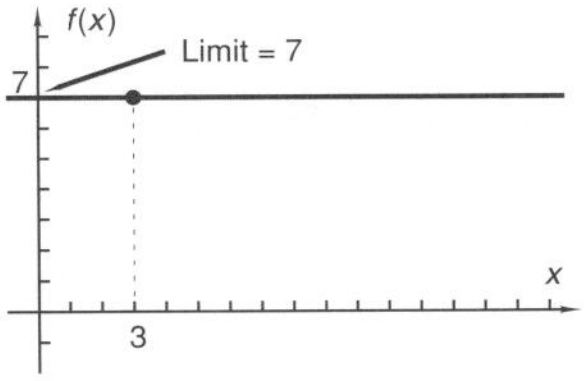


The limit is 7 since $f(x)$ is *always* close to 7, no matter what value $x$ takes on. (It shouldn't bother you that $f(x) = 7$ for $x \neq 3$, if you think of the definition of limit for a while.)

5. *Limit of a Product Problem*
$1.5^2 = 2.25$ and $\tan 1.5 = 14.101419\ldots$
$\therefore f(1.5) = (2.25)(14.10\ldots) = 31.72819\ldots$

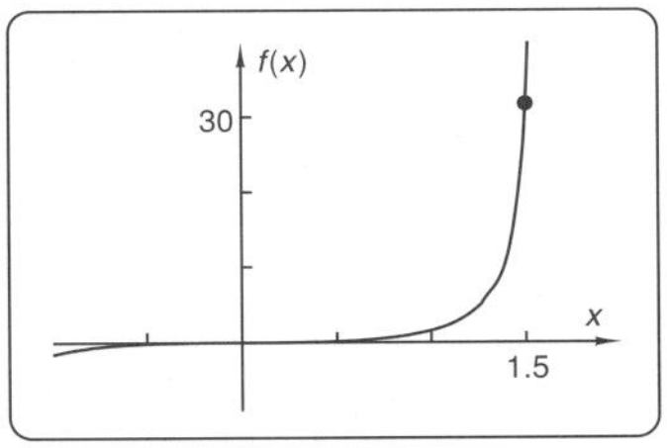


By tracing on the graph or by table close to $x = 1.5$, with an increment of 0.000001,
$f(1.499980) = 31.71835\ldots$
$f(1.500020) = 31.73803\ldots$
Since both of these are within 0.01 of the limit, and the next increment of 0.000001 gives values further away, let $\delta = 0.000020$.
If $x = 1.5 + \delta$ then $x^2$ is within 0.0000600004 of $1.5^2$ and $\tan x$ is within 0.0039981... of $\tan 1.5$.

7. a. Graph.

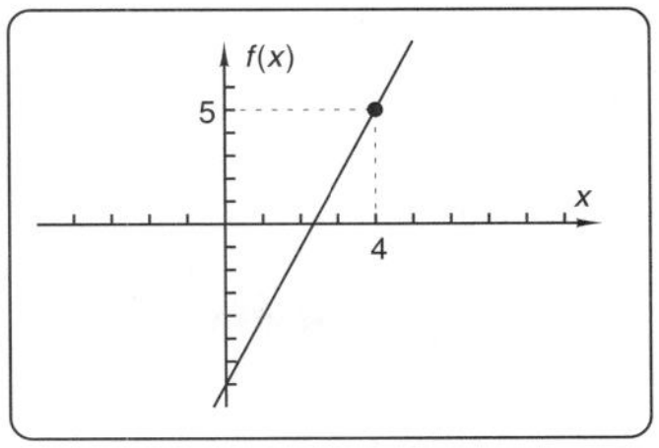


b. $\lim_{x\to 4} f(x) = 5$.
c. *Proof:*

$$\lim_{x\to 4} f(x) = \lim_{x\to 4}(3x - 7)$$
$$= \lim_{x\to 4} 3x + \lim_{x\to 4}(-7)$$
Limit of a sum.
$$= 3\lim_{x\to 4} x - 7$$
Limit of a constant times a function, and limit of a constant.
$$= 3 \cdot 4 - 7 = 5, \text{Q.E.D.} \ldots \text{Limit of } x.$$

9. a. Graph.

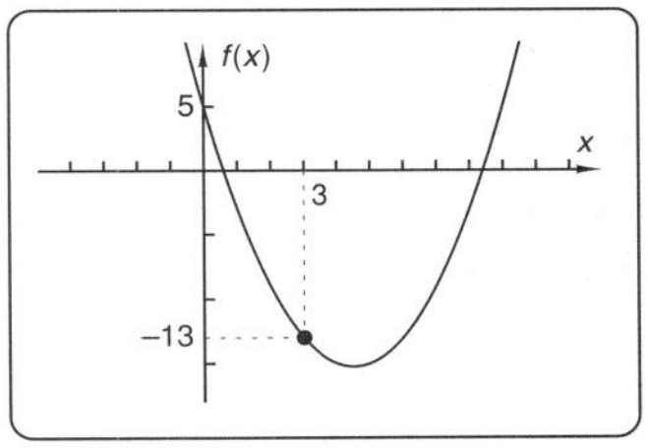


b. $\lim_{x\to 3} f(x) = -13$
c. *Proof:*

$$\lim_{x\to 3} f(x) = \lim_{x\to 3}(x^2 - 9x + 5)$$
$$= \lim_{x\to 3} x^2 + \lim_{x\to 3}(-9x) + \lim_{x\to 3} 5$$
Limit of a sum.
$$= \lim_{x\to 3} x \cdot \lim_{x\to 3} x + (-9)\lim_{x\to 3} x + 5$$
Limit of a product, constant times function, and constant.
$$= 3 \cdot 3 + (-9)(3) + 5 = -13, \text{ Q.E.D.}$$
Limit of $x$.

11. a. Graph.

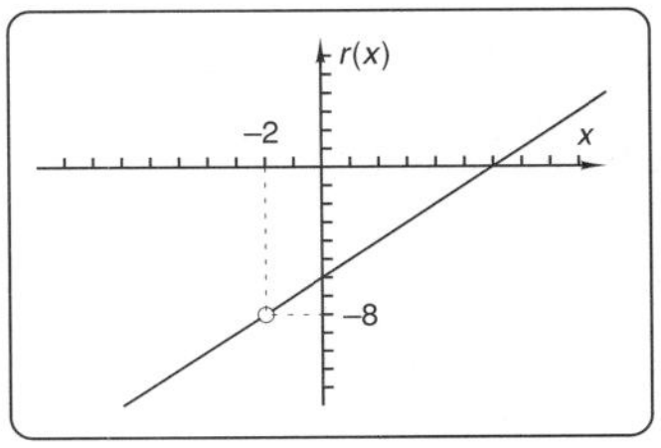

b. $r(x) = x - 6, x \neq -2$
$\lim_{x \to -2} r(x) = -8.$

c. *Proof:*

$\lim_{x \to -2} r(x) = \lim_{x \to -2}(x - 6)$
Since $x \neq -2$.
$= \lim_{x \to -2} x + \lim_{x \to -2}(-6)$
Limit of a sum.
$= -2 - 6 = -8$, Q.E.D.
Limit of $x$.

13. a. Graph.

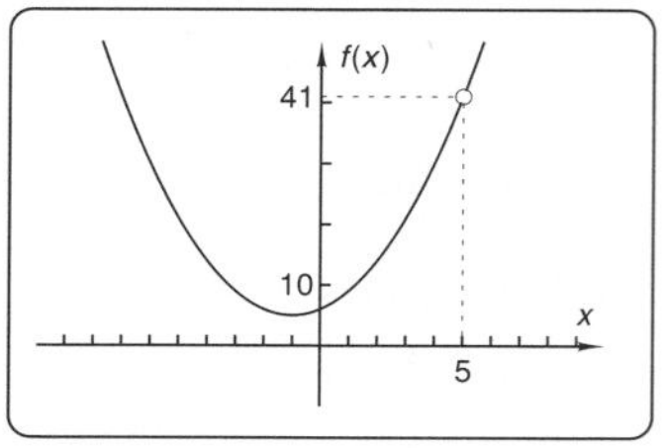


b. $f(x) = x^2 + 2x + 6, x \neq 5$
$\lim_{x \to 5} f(x) = 41.$

c. *Proof:*

$\lim_{x \to 5} f(x)$
$= \lim_{x \to 5}(x^2 + 2x + 6)$
Since $x \neq 5$.
$= \lim_{x \to 5} x^2 + \lim_{x \to 5}(2x) + \lim_{x \to 5} 6$
Limit of a sum.
$= \lim_{x \to 5} x \cdot \lim_{x \to 5} x + 2 \lim_{x \to 5} x + 6$
Limit of a product, limit of a constant
$= 5 \cdot 5 + 2 \cdot 5 + 6 = 41$, Q.E.D.
Limit of $x$.

15. a. Graph.

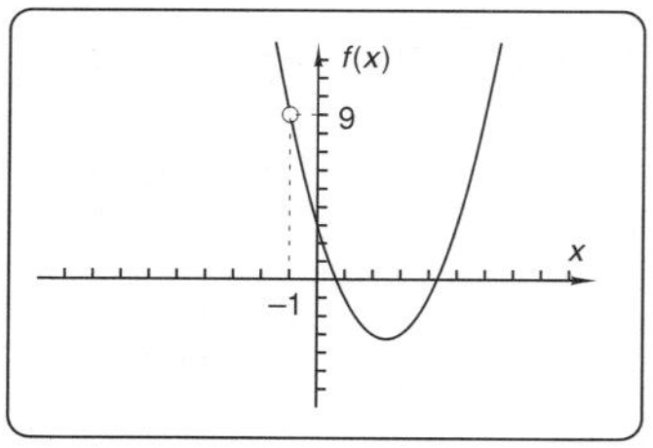


b. $f(x) = x^2 - 5x + 3, x \neq -1$
$\lim_{x \to -1} f(x) = 9.$

c. *Proof:*

$\lim_{x \to -1} f(x)$
$= \lim_{x \to -1}(x2 - 5x + 3)$
Since $x \neq -1$.
$= \lim_{x \to -1} x^2 + \lim_{x \to -1}(-5x) + \lim_{x \to -1} 3$
Limit of a sum.
$= \lim_{x \to -1} x \cdot \lim_{x \to -1} x$
$+(-5) \lim_{x \to -1} x + 3$
Limit of a product and a constant.
$= (-1)(-1) + (-5)(-1) + 3 = 9$, Q.E.D.
Limit of $x$.

17. a. Graph.

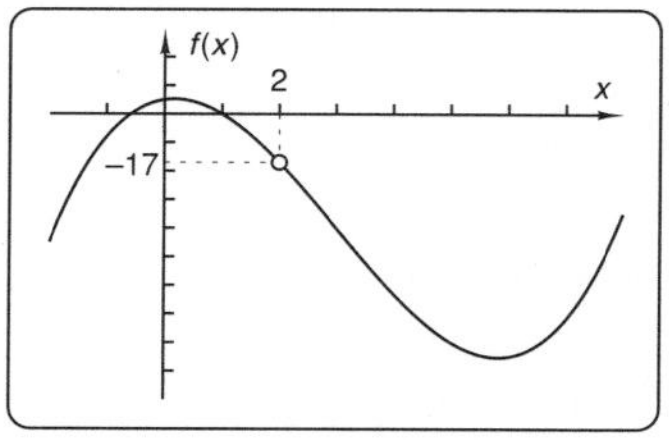


b. $f(x) = x^3 - 9x^2 + 3x + 5, x \neq 2$
$\lim_{x \to 2} f(x) = -17$

c. *Proof:*

$\lim_{x \to 2} f(x)$
$= \lim_{x \to 2}(x^3 - 9x^2 + 3x + 5)$
Since $x \neq 2$.
$= \lim_{x \to 2} x^3 + \lim_{x \to 2}(-9x^2)$
$+ \lim_{x \to 2} 3x + \lim_{x \to 2} 5$
Limit of a sum.
$= \lim_{x \to 2} x \cdot \lim_{x \to 2} x \cdot \lim_{x \to 2} x$
$-9 \lim_{x \to 2} x \cdot \lim_{x \to 2} x$
$+3 \lim_{x \to 2} x + 5$
Limit of a product and a constant.
$= 2 \cdot 2 \cdot 2 + (-9)(2 \cdot 2) + 3 \cdot 2 + 5$
$= -17$, Q.E.D.
Limit of $x$.

19. *Limit of a Composite Function Problem*

a. Graph. $y$ is close to 1 when $x$ is close to 0.

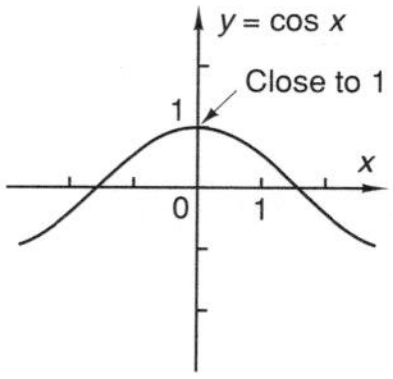


b. Graph. $y$ is close to $\tan 1 = 1.557\ldots$ when $x$ is close to 1.

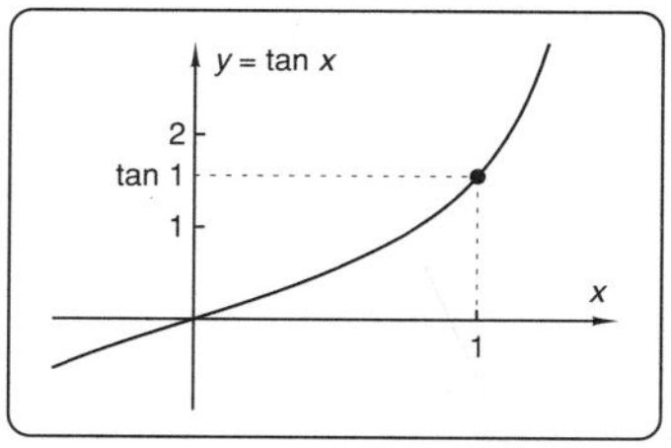


c. Graph. $y$ stays close to $\tan 1 = 1.557\ldots$ when $x$ is close to 0.

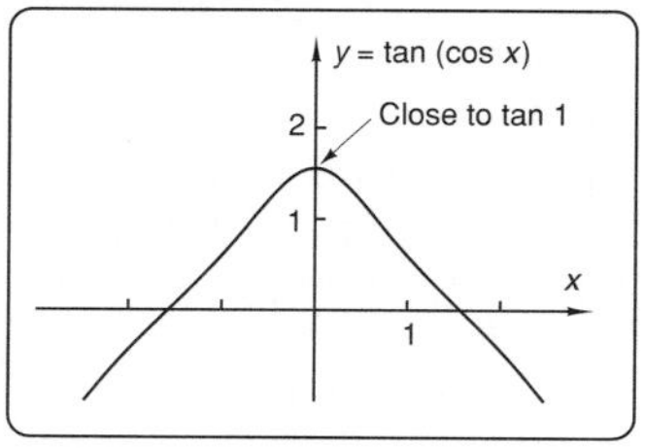

d. $\lim_{x \to 0} \cos x = 1$. $\lim_{u \to 1} \tan u = 1.55\ldots$.
$\lim_{x \to 0} \tan(\cos x) = 1.55\ldots$.

21. *Exact Derivative Problem*

a. Derivative $\approx 12.61$

b. $\dfrac{x^3 - 8}{x - 2} = \dfrac{(x-2)(x^2+2x+4)}{x-2} = x^2 + 2x + 4,$

provided $x \neq 2$.
This expression approaches 12.

*Proof:*

$\lim_{x \to 2}(x^3 - 8/x - 2) = \lim_{x \to 2}(x^2 + 2x + 4)$
Since $x \neq 2$.
$= \lim_{x \to 2} x^2 + \lim_{x \to 2} 2x + \lim_{x \to 2} 4$
Limit of a sum.
$= \lim_{x \to 2} x \cdot \lim_{x \to 2} x + 2 \lim_{x \to 2} x + 4$
Limit of a product and limit of a constant.
$= 2 \cdot 2 + 2 \cdot 2 + 4 = 12$, Q.E.D
Limit of $x$.

c. Graph. The line appears to be tangent to the graph of $f$ at $(2, 8)$.

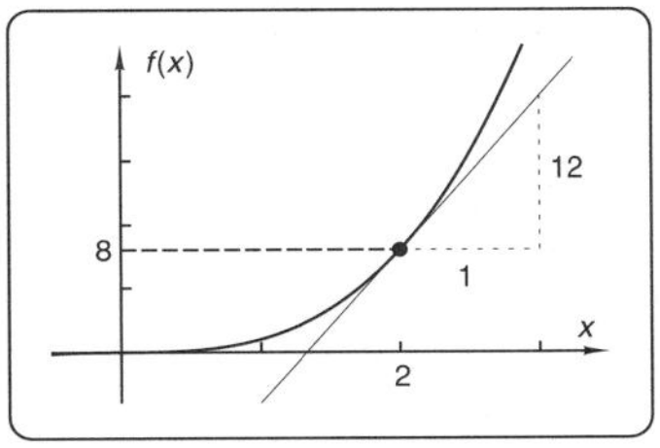


23. Integral $\approx 11.8235\ldots$ ($n = 100$)

25. *Journal Problem* (Not selected.)

## Problem Set 2-4

*Continuity*

1. a. Has right and left limits.
   b. Has no limit.
   c. Discontinuous. Has no limit.

3. a. Has right and left limits.
   b. Has a limit.
   c. Continuous.

5. a. Has right and left limits.
   b. Has a limit.
   c. Continuous.

7. a. Has right and left limits.
   b. Has a limit.
   c. Continuous. (Note that the $x$-value, $-3$, is *not* at the asymptote.)

9. a. Has right and left limits.
   b. Has a limit.
   c. Discontinuous. No value for $f(-6)$.

11. a. Has no right and left limits.
    b. Has no limit.
    c. Discontinuous. No limit. No value for $f(-2)$.

13. a. Has right and left limits.
    b. Has a limit.
    c. Continuous. (Note that the $x$-value, 5, is *not* at the discontinuity.)

15. a. Has right and left limits.
    b. Has a limit.
    c. Discontinuous. $f(1) \neq$ limit.

17. a. Has right and left limits.
    b. Has no limit.
    c. Discontinuous. No limit.

19. a. Has right and left limits.
    b. Has a limit.
    c. Discontinuous. No $f(c)$.

21. Graph. (example)

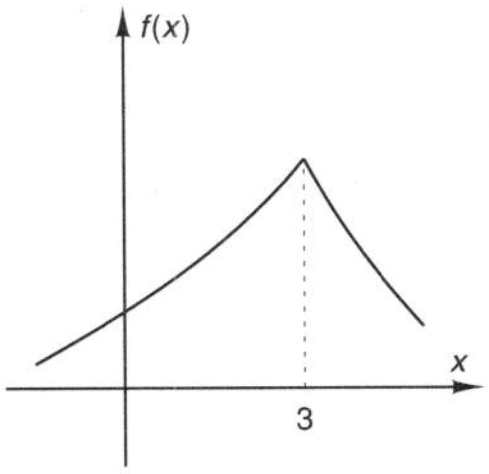


23. Graph. (example)

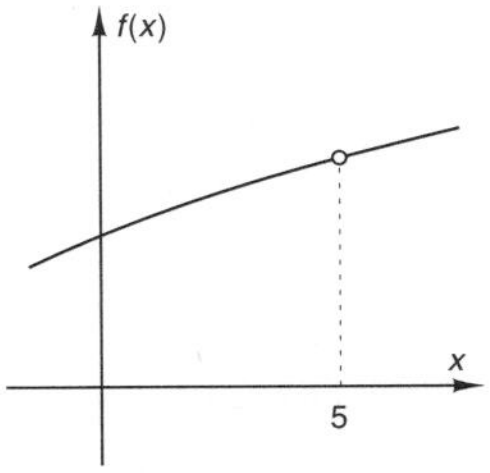


25. Graph. (example)

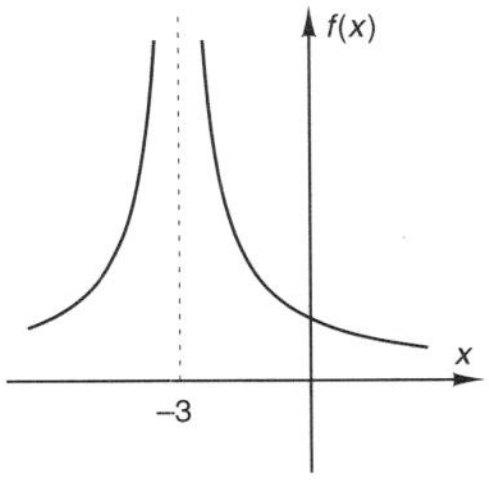


27. Graph. (example)

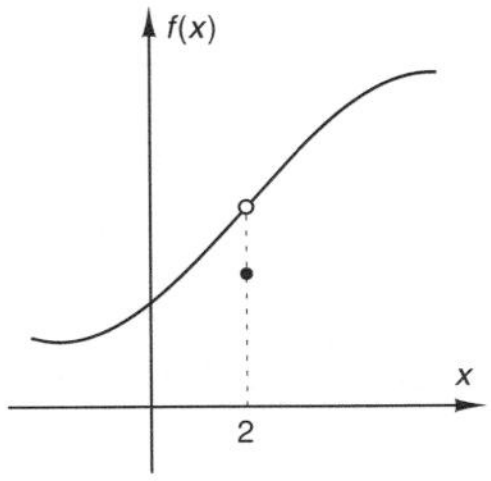


29. Graph. (example)

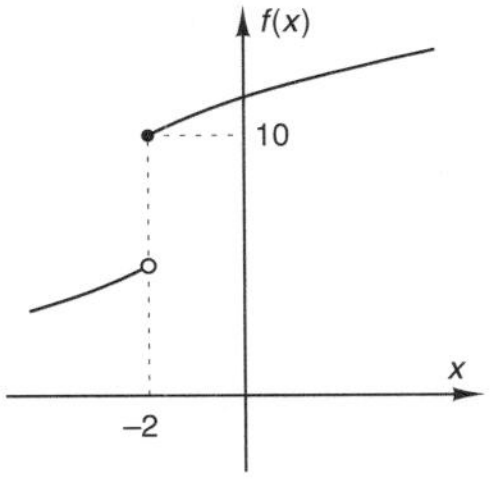


31. Graph. (example)

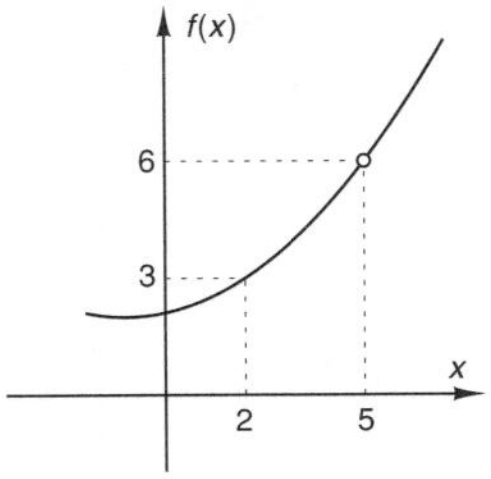

33. Graph. (example)

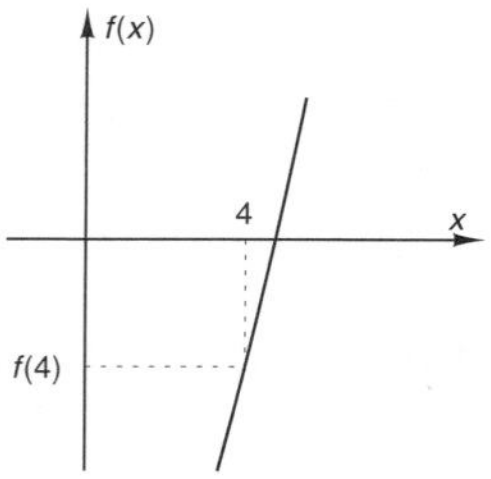


35. Graph. (example)

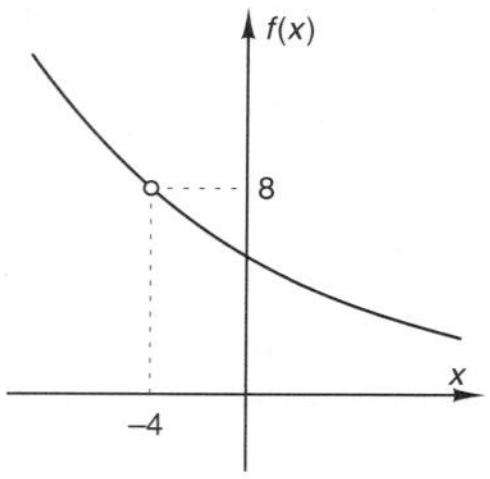


37. Graph. (example)

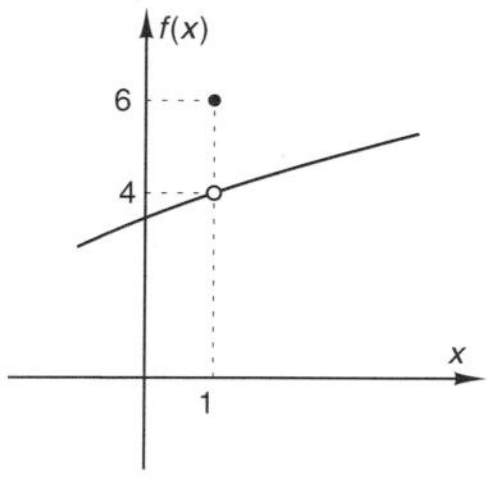


39. Graph. (example)

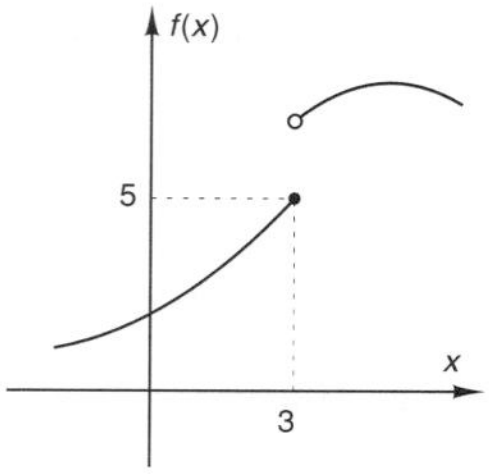


41. Graph. (example)

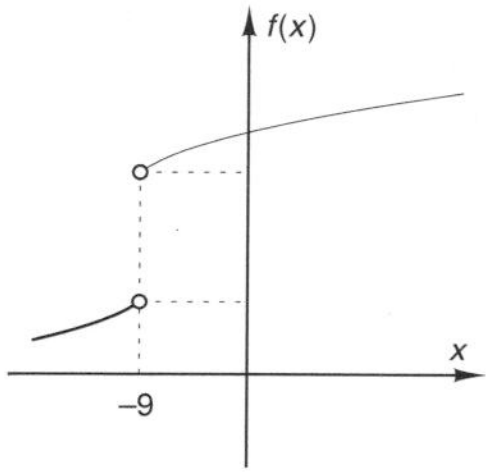


43. Discontinuous at $x = -3$.

45. Discontinuous at $x = \pi/2 + \pi n$, where $n$ stands for an integer.

47. Graph. Discontinuous. $\lim_{x \to 2} f(x) = 2$ and $f(2) = 3$.

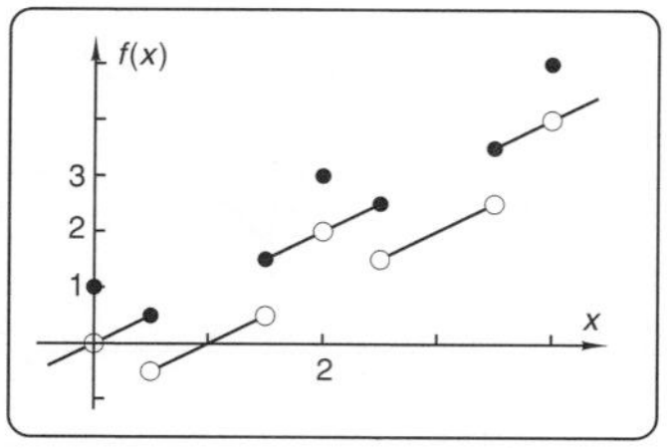


49. Graph. Discontinuous because $s(x)$ has no limit as $x \to 2^-$.
(No real function values to the left of $x = 2$)

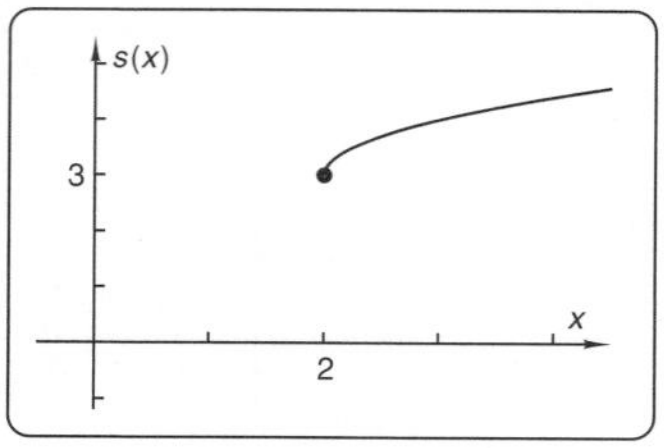


51. Graph. Discontinuous. There is no value of $h(2)$.

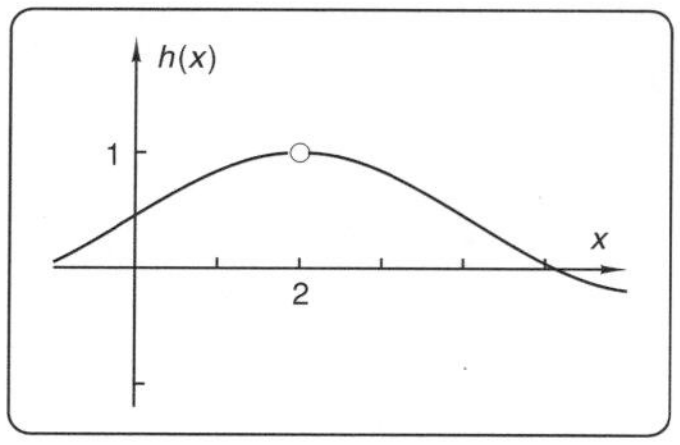


53. a. Graph.
Not continuous
(No value for $f(2)$)

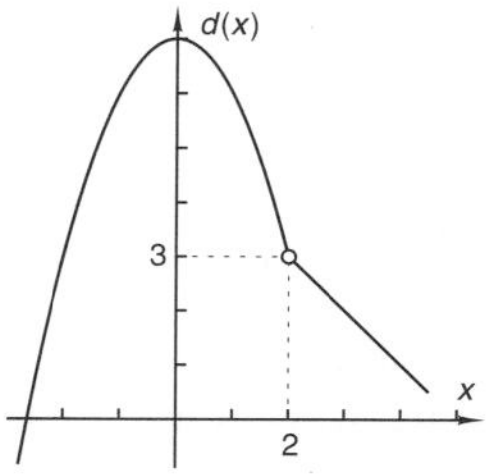


b. $\lim_{x \to 2^-} d(x) = 3$,
$\lim_{x \to 2^+} d(x) = 3$,
Limit = 3.

55. a. Graph.
Not continuous

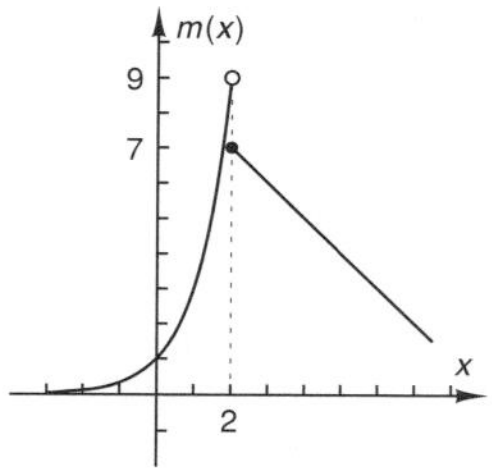


b. $\lim_{x \to 2^-} m(x) = 9$,
$\lim_{x \to 2^+} m(x) = 7$,
No limit.

57. a. Graph. Not continuous

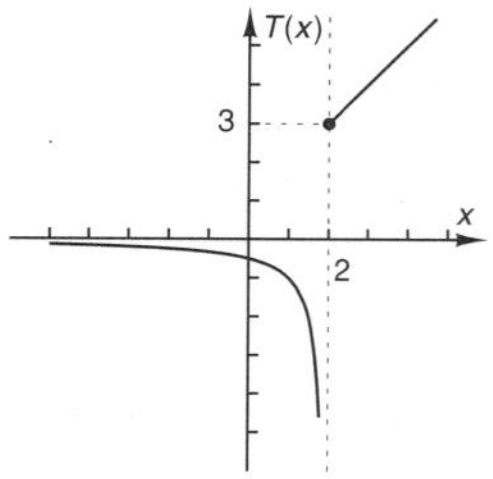


b. $\lim_{x \to 2^-} T(x)$: none.
$\lim_{x \to 2^+} T(x) = 3$,
No limit.

59. $k = 1.3$. Graph.

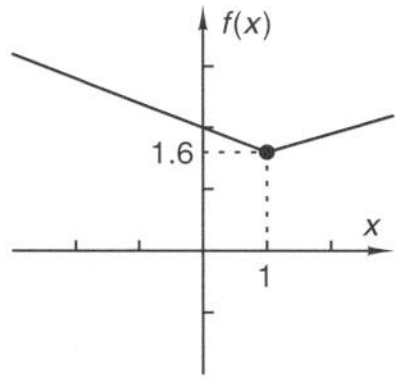


61. $k = 2.5$. Graph.

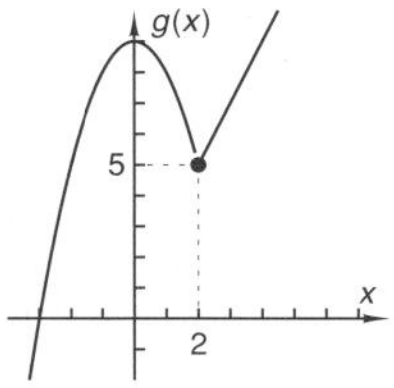


63. $k = -1/2$. Graph.

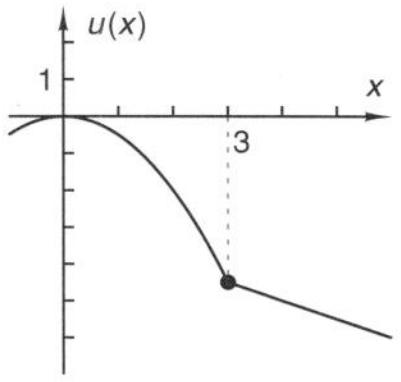


65. $k = -1$ or 2. Graphs.

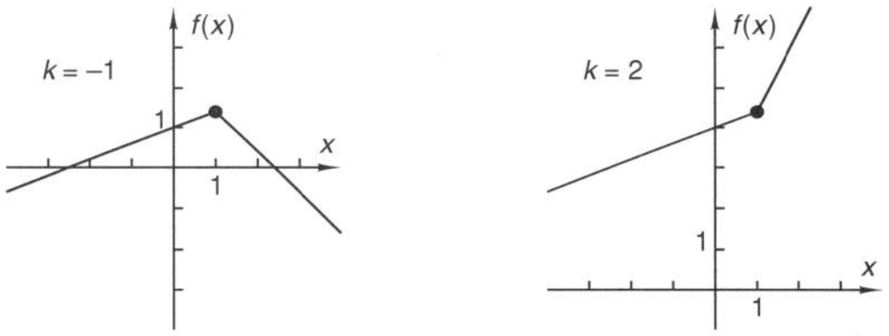


67. *Two Constants Problem*

a. $b - 1 = a$.

b. $a = -1 \Rightarrow b = 0$. Graph. Continuous at $x = 1$.

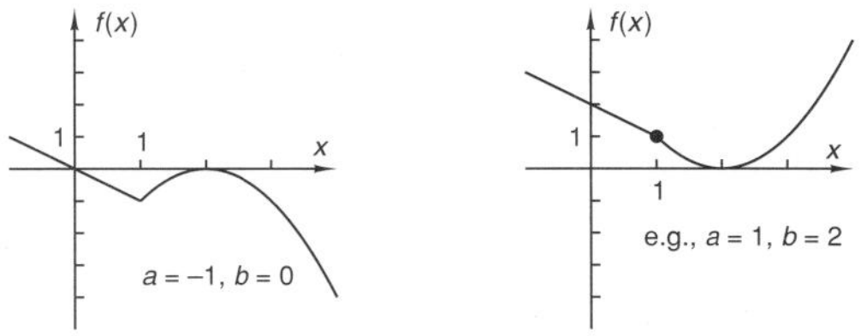


c. e.g., $a = 1 \Rightarrow b = 2$. Graph, above. Continuous at $x = 1$.

69. *Continuity of Polynomial Functions*
For any value of $c$, $P(c)$ is determined by addition and multiplication. Since the set of real numbers is closed under multiplication and addition, $P(c)$ will be a *unique, real* number for any real value $x = c$. $P(c)$ is the *limit* of $P(x)$ as $x$ approaches $c$ by the properties of the limit of a product of functions (for powers of $x$), limit of a constant times a function (for multiplication by the coefficients), and limit of a sum (for the individual terms). Therefore, $P$ is continuous for all values of $x$.

## ***Problem Set 2-5***

*Limits Involving Infinity*

1. Graph. (example)

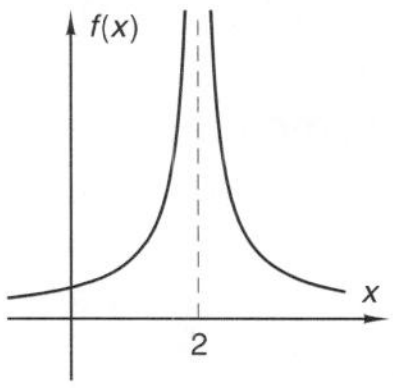


3. Graph. (example)

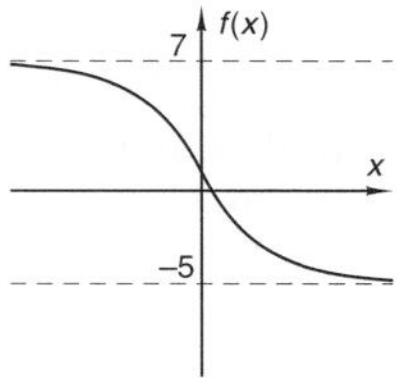


5. a. Graph.

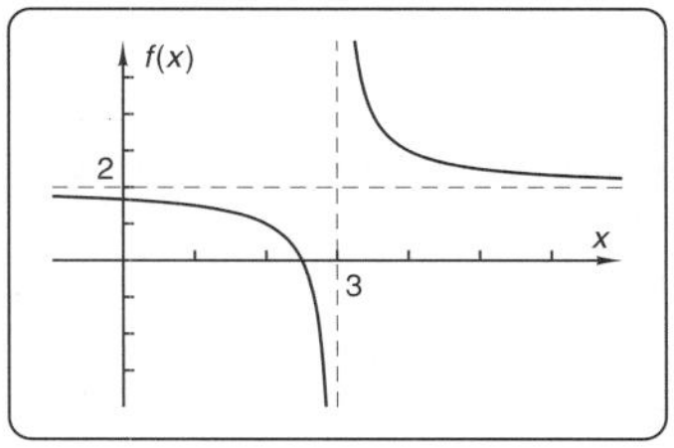

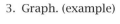

b. $\lim_{x \to 3^+} f(x) = \infty$, $\lim_{x \to 3^-} f(x) = -\infty$, $\lim_{x \to 3} f(x)$, none, $\lim_{x \to \infty} f(x) = 2$, $\lim_{x \to -\infty} f(x) = 2$

c. $\delta = 1/98$

d. $D = 1003$

7. a. Graph.

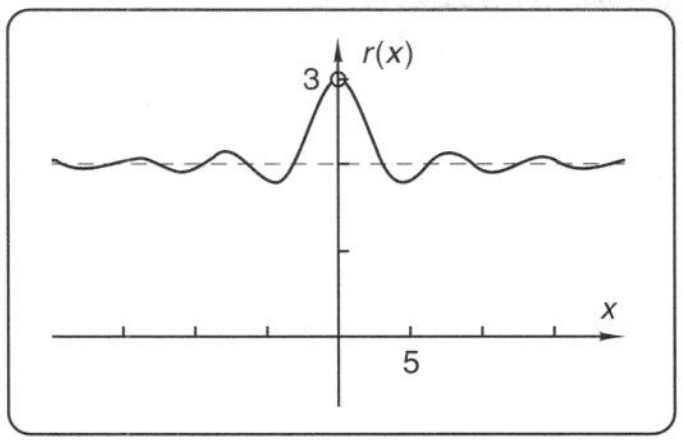


b. $\lim_{x \to \infty} r(x) = 2$

c. $D = 1000$

d. The line $y = 2$ is *not* an asymptote since the graph crosses this line an infinite number of times as $x$ increases.

e. $\lim_{x \to 0} r(x) = 3$. By zooming in on the graph around $x = 0$ you can see that $r(x)$ is very close to 3 when $x$ is close to, but not equal to, zero.

9. The limit is infinite. $Y$ is unbounded as $x$ approaches infinity. If there were a number $E$ such that $\log x < E$ for all $x > 0$, then you could let $x = 10^{2E}$, so that $\log x = \log 10^{2E} = 2E$, which is greater than $E$ which was assumed to be an upper bound.

11. *Limits Applied to Integrals Problem*

a. The definite integral is the product of the independent and dependent variables. Since distance = (rate)(time), the integral represents distance in this case.

b. $T_9 = 17.8060005\ldots$
$T_{45} = 17.9819616\ldots$
$T_{90} = 17.9935649\ldots$
$T_{450} = 17.9994175\ldots$

c. The exact answer is 18. It is a limit since the sums can be made as close to it as you like, just by making the number of trapezoids large enough (and thus their widths close to zero). The sums are smaller than the integral since each trapezoid is inscribed under the graph, and thus leaves out a part of its respective strip of the region.

d. $T_n$ is within exactly 0.01 unit of 18 when it equals 17.99, which occurs between $n = 45$ and $n = 90$.
By experimentation,
$T_{67} = 17.9900158\ldots$
$T_{66} = 17.9897900\ldots$
Therefore the approximation is within 0.01 units of 18 for any value of $n \ge 67$.

13. *Searchlight Problem*
Length $= 100 \sec x = 100/\cos x$
$x$ must be within $0.100167\ldots$ unit of $\pi/2$.

## Problem Set 2-6

*The Intermediate Value Theorem and Its Consequences*

1. $f$ is continuous because it is a polynomial function.
$f(1) = 18,\ f(4) = 3.$
Since 8 is between 18 and 3, there is a number $x = c$ between 1 and 4 for which $f(c) = 8$, Q.E.D.
Graph. $c = 1.4349\ldots$

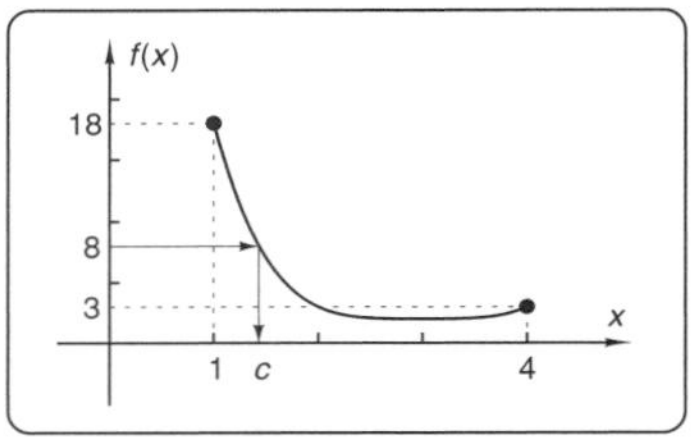


3. *Converse of the Intermediate Value Theorem?*
   a. For $1 \le y < 2$ or for $5 < y \le 8$, the conclusion would be true. But for $2 \le y \le 5$ it would be false since there are no values of $x$ in [1, 5] which give these values for $f(x)$.
   b. The conclusion of the theorem is true since every number $y$ in [4, 6] is a value of $g(x)$ for some value of $x$ in [1, 5].

5. Let $f(x) = x^2$.
Since $f$ is a polynomial function, it is continuous and thus the intermediate value theorem applies.
Since $f(1) = 1$ and $f(2) = 4$, there is a number $c$ between 1 and 2 such that $f(c) = 3$. By the definition of square root, $c = \sqrt{3}$, Q.E.D.

7. The intermediate value theorem is called an existence theorem since it tells you that a number such as $\sqrt{3}$ *exists.* It does not tell you how to calculate that number.

9. *Foot Race Problem*
Let $f(t)$ = Jesse's speed − Kay's speed.
$f(1) = 20 - 15 = 5$, which is *positive.*
$f(3) = 17 - 19 = -2$, which is *negative.*
Since the speeds are assumed to be continuous, $f$ is also continuous, and the intermediate value theorem applies.
Thus, there is a value of $t$ between 1 and 3 for which $f(t) = 0$, meaning that Jesse and Kay are going exactly the same speed at that time.
The *existence* of the time tells you neither what that time is, nor what the speed is. An existence theorem such as the intermediate value theorem does not tell these things.

11. *Cosine Function Problem*
The intermediate value theorem *cannot* be used on the cosine function until it has been proved that cos is *continuous.* Once it has been proved (Chapter 3), you can conclude that there is a number $c = \cos^{-1} 0.6 = 0.92729521\ldots.$

13. *The Extreme Value Theorem*
This means that a function graph has a high point and a low point on any interval in which the function is continuous. Graph.

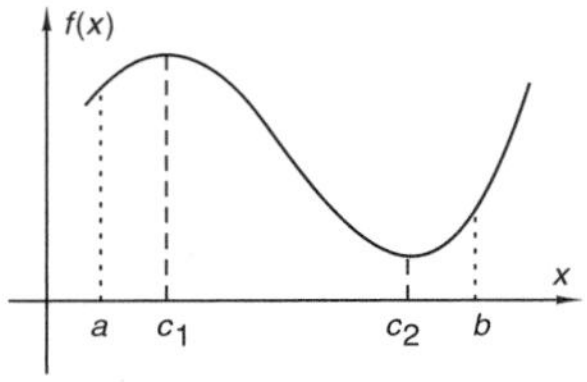


If the function is *not* continuous, there might be a point missing where the maximum or minimum would have been. Graph.

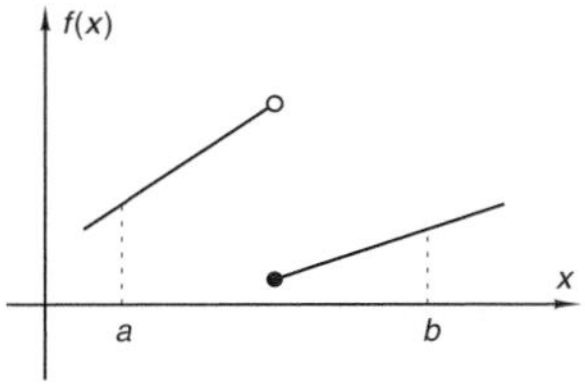


Another possibility would be a graph with a vertical asymptote somewhere between $a$ and $b$.

## Problem Set 2-7

*Chapter Review and Test*

R0. (Not selected.)

R1. a. See text definition of limit.
   b. Graph. $f(2) = 0^{1/5} + 3 = 3$, Q.E.D.

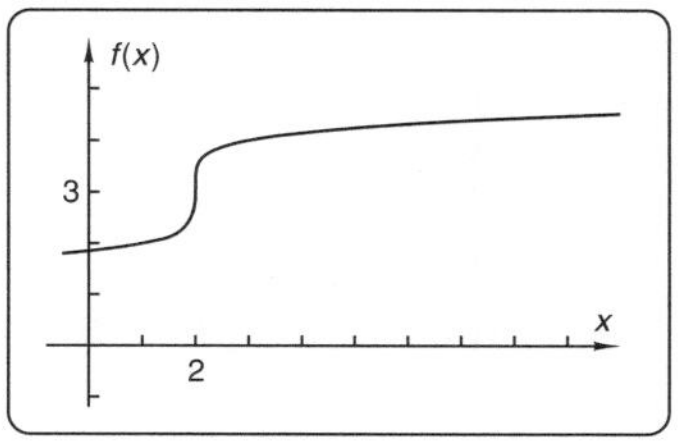


| $x$ | $f(x)$ |
|---|---|
| 1.9995 | 2.78132... |
| 1.9996 | 2.79087... |
| 1.9997 | 2.80256... |
| 1.9998 | 2.81794... |
| 1.9999 | 2.84151... |
| 2 | 3 |
| 2.0001 | 3.15848... |
| 2.0002 | 3.18205... |
| 2.0003 | 3.19743... |
| 2.0004 | 3.20912... |
| 2.0005 | 3.21867... |

Keep $x$ within 0.0003 unit of 2.

c. Graph. Graph has a *cusp* and a *minimum point.* There *is a limit.*

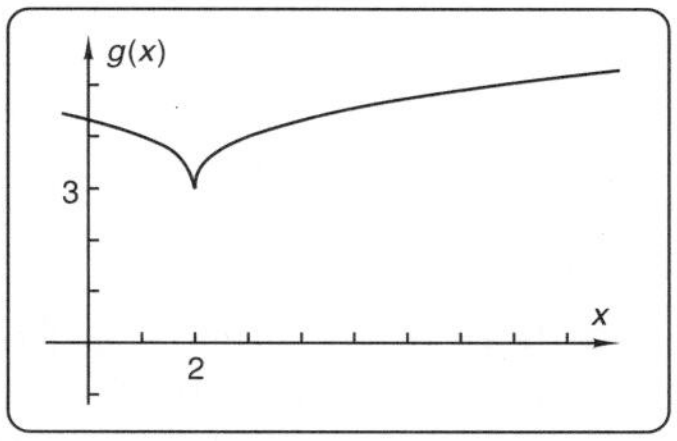


R2. a. Maximum value of $\delta$ is 0.00032.

b. Graph is symmetrical about $x = 2$.
Let $f(x) = 3 + \epsilon$.
$(x - 2)^{1/5} + 3 = 3 + \epsilon$
$(x - 2) = \epsilon^5$
Let $\delta = \epsilon^5$, which is positive for all $\delta > 0$.

c. $\lim_{x \to 2} f(x) = 3$. Maximum $\delta$ is 0.6 or 0.7.

d. Left side of $x = 2$ is more restrictive.
Maximum value of $\delta$ is 0.64.

e. Let $f(x) = 3 - \epsilon$.
$2 + \sqrt{x - 1} = 3 - \epsilon$
$x = (1 - \epsilon)^2 + 1$
Let $\delta = 2 - ((1 - \epsilon)^2 + 1) = 1 - (1 - \epsilon)^2$ which is positive for all positive $\epsilon < 1$.

R3. a. See the limit property statements in the text.

b. Graph.

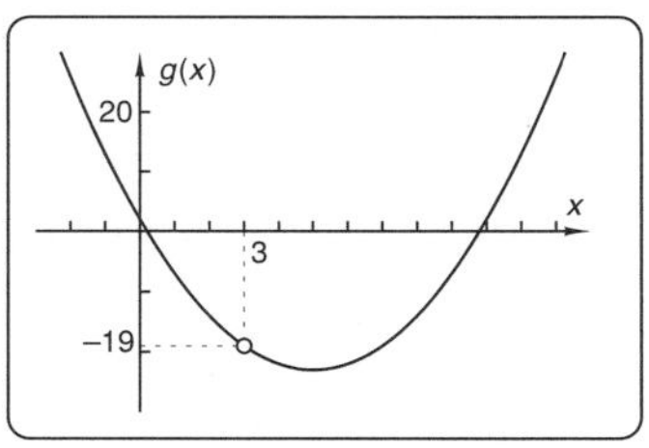


$g(x) = x^2 - 10x + 2, x \neq 3$
$\lim_{x \to 3} g(x) = -19$, which agrees with the graph.

c. The part of the definition is, "..., but not equal to $c$, ...." Since the definition restricts $x$ away from 3, the quantity $(x - 3)$ in the denominator cannot equal zero. So you are allowed to cancel.

d. $m(x) = \dfrac{(x+3)(x-2)}{x-4}$

$\lim_{x \to 6} m(x) = \dfrac{(6+3)(6-2)}{(6-4)} = 18.$

*Proof:*

$$\lim_{x \to 6} m(x) = \frac{\lim_{x \to 6}(x+3)(x-2)}{\lim_{x \to 6}(x-4)}$$

Limit of a quotient.

$$= \frac{\lim_{x \to 6}(x+3) \cdot \lim_{x \to 6}(x-2)}{\lim_{x \to 6}(x-4)}$$

Limit of a product.

$$= \frac{9 \cdot 4}{2}$$

Limit of a linear function (3 times).

$= 18$, Q.E.D.

For limit as $x$ approaches 4, the property cannot be used since the denominator goes to zero. The property specifically excludes the denominator function having zero as its limit.

e. *Chuck's Rock Problem*
From 5 to 5.1 sec, average velocity $= -15.5$ m/sec.
av. vel. $= \dfrac{35t - 5t^2 - 50}{t - 5} = -5(t - 2)$, for $t \neq 5$.
instantaneous velocity = limit $= -5(5-2) = -15$ m/sec.
Rate is negative, so distance above starting point is getting smaller, which means the rock is going down.
Instantaneous velocity is a derivative.

R4. a. See text definition of continuity at a point.

b. i. Graph. (example)

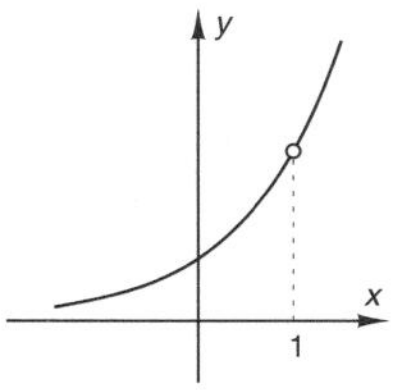


ii. Graph. (example)

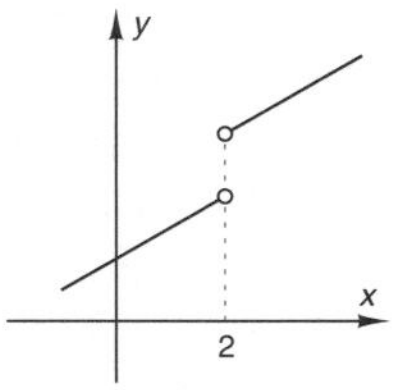


iii. Graph. (example)

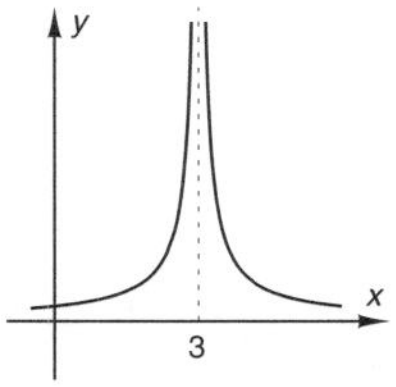


iv. Graph. (example)

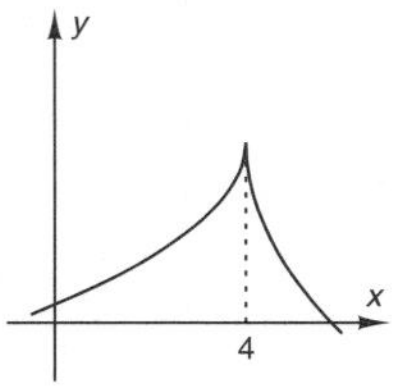

v. Graph. (example)

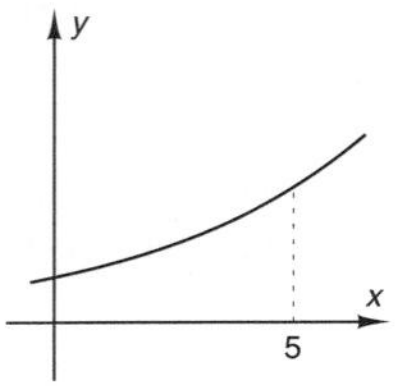


vi. Graph. (example)

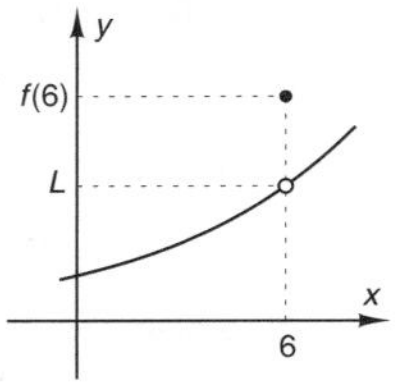


vii. Graph. (example)

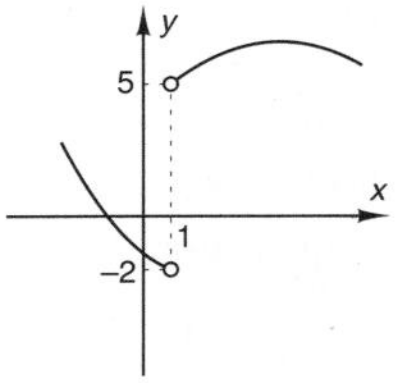


c. i. Graph.

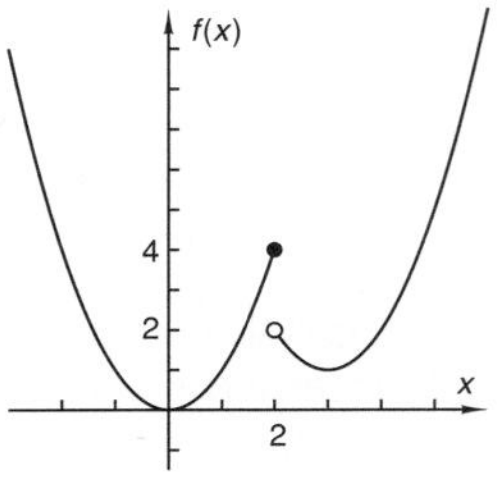


ii. The left limit is 4 and the right limit is 2. So $f$ is discontinuous at $x = 2$, Q.E.D.

iii. $k = 12$.

R5. a. See the text definition of infinite limit.

b. Graph. (example)

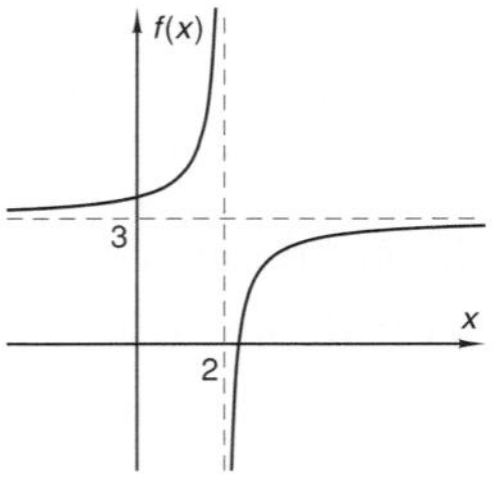


c. $f(x) = 6 - 2^{-x}$.
$\lim_{x\to\infty} f(x) = 6$ since $2^{-x}$ approaches zero.
Graph.

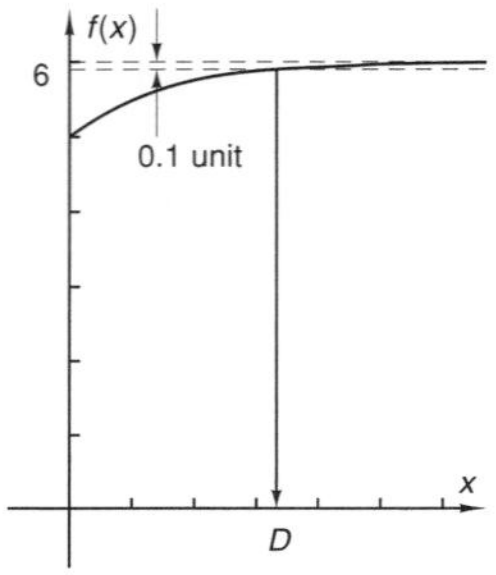


Let $D = 9.9653\ldots$. Keep $x > D$.

d.

| $n$ | trapezoidal rule |
|---|---|
| 50 | 467.9074... |
| 100 | 467.9669... |
| 200 | 467.9882... |
| 400 | 467.9958... |

The limit of these sums seems to be 468.
$D = 223$.

R6. a. See text statement of intermediate value theorem.
Basis is the completeness axiom.
See text statement of extreme value theorem.
The word is corollary.

b. $f(3) = 8$, $f(4) = -4$.
So $f(x) = 0$ for some $x$ between 3 and 4 by the intermediate value theorem.
The property is continuity.
The value of $x$ is approximately 3.7553.

c. Graph.

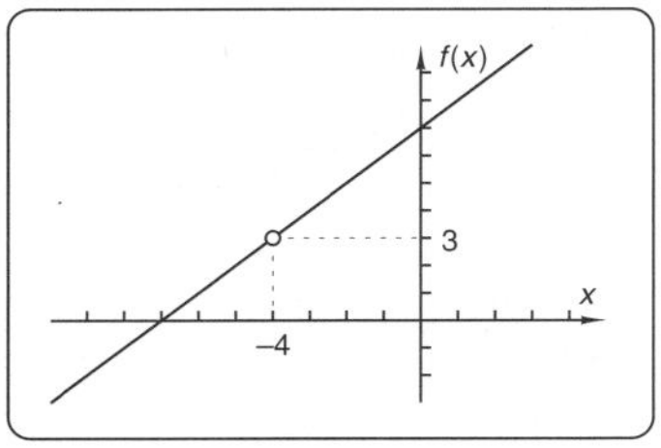


$f(-6) = 1$ and $f(-2) = 5$
Pick $y = 3$, and there is no value of $x$. This fact does not contradict the intermediate value theorem. Function $f$ does not meet the continuity hypothesis of the theorem.

## CHAPTER 3

### Exploratory Problem Set 3-1

*Graphical Interpretation of Derivative*

1. Graph is correct.

3. $m(x) = x - 3$, provided $x \neq 5$.

5. $m(5)$ has the form 0/0, which is an indeterminate form. It is undefined because of division by zero.

7. The line is tangent to the graph.

9. (Not selected.)

### Problem Set 3-2

*Difference Quotients, and One Definition of Derivative*

1. See text definition of derivative.

3. a. $f'(3) = 3.6$

b. Graph of the difference quotient, $m(x)$.

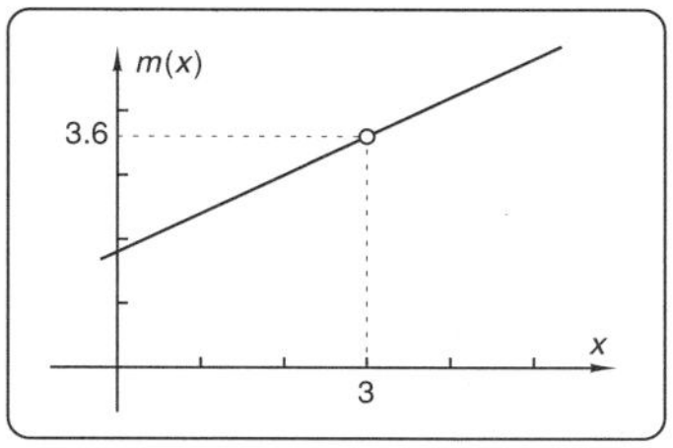


c. and d. Graph of the function and tangent line.

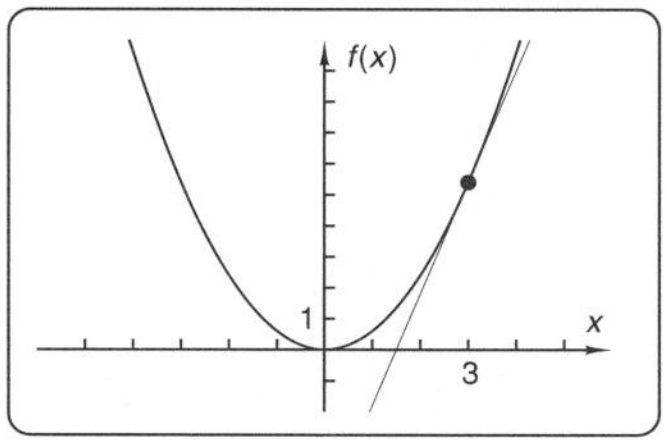


5. $f'(-2) = 1$

7. $f'(1) = -4$

9. $f'(3) = -0.7$

11. $f'(-1) = 0$

13. The derivative of a linear function equals the slope. The tangent line coincides with the graph.

15. a. First, find $f'(1)$; then plot a straight line through point $(1, f(1))$ using $f'(1)$ as the slope.
    b. Near the point $(1, f(1))$, which is $(1, 1)$, the tangent line and the curve appear coincidental.
    c. The curve appears to get closer and closer to the line and finally touch it at the point $(1, f(1))$.
    d. Near point $(1, 1)$ the curve looks linear.
    e. If a graph has local linearity, the graph near that point looks like the tangent line; therefore the derivative at that point could be said to equal the slope of the graph at that point.

17. a. Graph.

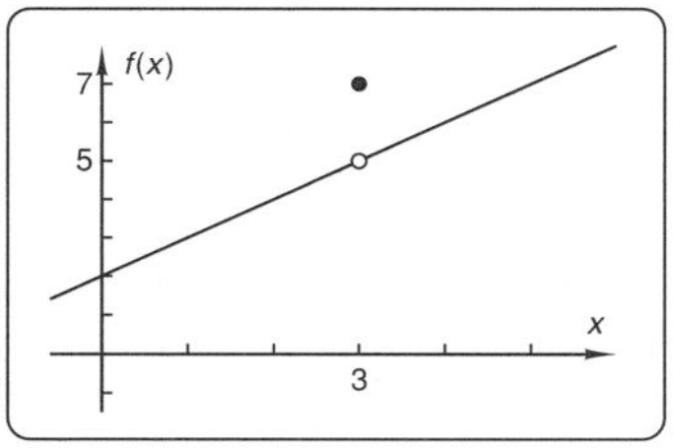


b. Difference quotient is

$$m(x) = \frac{x - 5}{x - 3}$$

Graph.

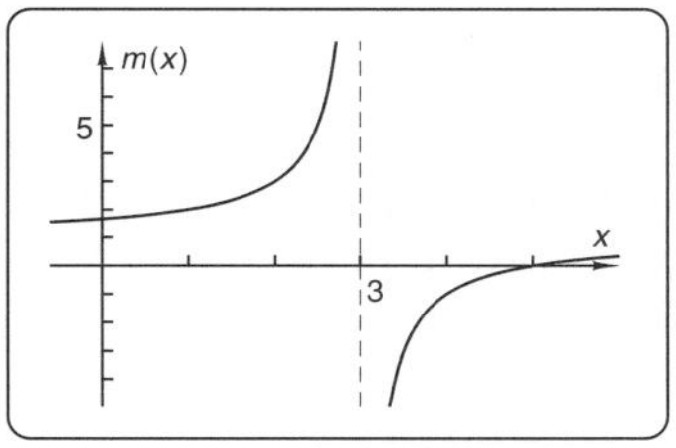


c.

| $x$ | $f(x)$ |
|---|---|
| 2.997 | 667.66... |
| 2.998 | 1001 |
| 2.999 | 2001 |
| 3.000 | error |
| 3.001 | −1999 |
| 3.002 | −999 |
| 3.003 | −665.66... |

The difference quotients are all large positive numbers on the left side of 3. On the right side they are large negative numbers. For a derivative to exist the difference quotient must approach the *same* number as $x$ gets closer to 3.

19. *Tangent Lines as Limits of Secant Lines*
    a. The tangent line on the graph has a slope of $-1$. $f'(x) = -1$, Q.E.D.
    b. Graph. As the $x$-distance between the point and 3 decreases, the secant lines (solid) approach the tangent line (dotted).

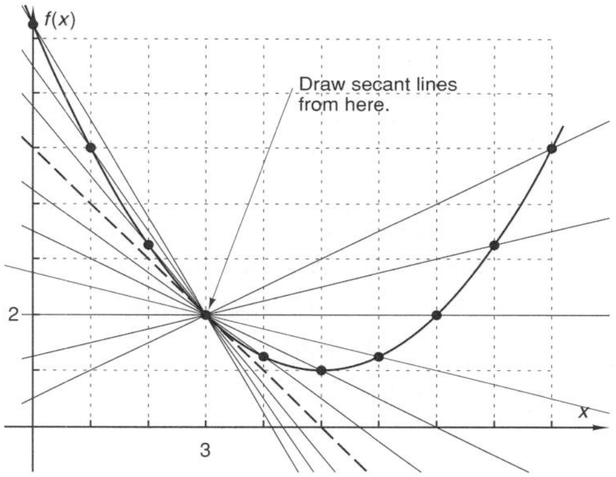


c. The same thing happens with secant lines from the left of $x = 3$. See graph, above.

d. Graph. $g(x) = 4 - 6|\cos \frac{\pi}{6}x|$

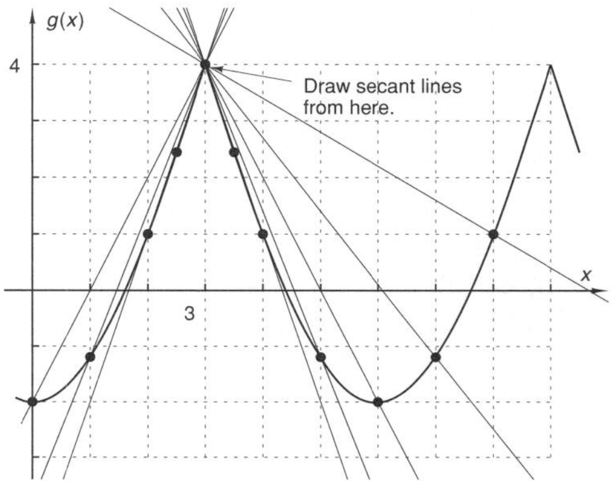


e. A derivative is a limit. Since the left and right limits are unequal, there is no derivative at $x = 3$.

f. $m(x) = \dfrac{-6|\cos\frac{\pi}{6}x|}{x-3}$. By table,

| $x$ | $m(x)$ |
|---|---|
| 2.9 | 3.1401... |
| 2.99 | 3.1415... |
| 3 | error |
| 3.01 | −3.1415... |
| 3.1 | −3.1401... |

Conjecture: The numbers are $\pi$ and $-\pi$.

### Problem Set 3-3

*Derivative Functions Numerically and Graphically*

1. *Cubic Function Problem #1*

a. Graph.

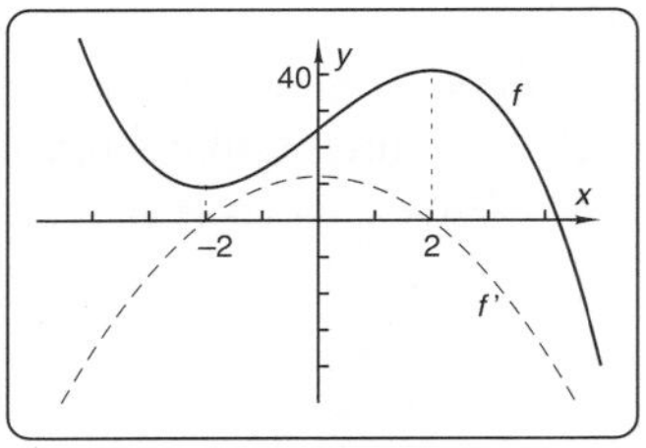


b. $f'(x)$ is positive for $-2 < x < 2$.
The graph of $f$ is increasing for these $x$-values.

c. $f(x)$ is decreasing for $x$ satisfying $|x| > 2$.
$f'(x) < 0$ for these values of $x$.

d. Where the $f'$ graph crosses the $x$-axis, the $f$ graph has a high point or a low point.

e. See the graph in part (a).

f. Conjecture: $f'$ is quadratic.

3. *Quartic Function Problem #1*

a. Graph.

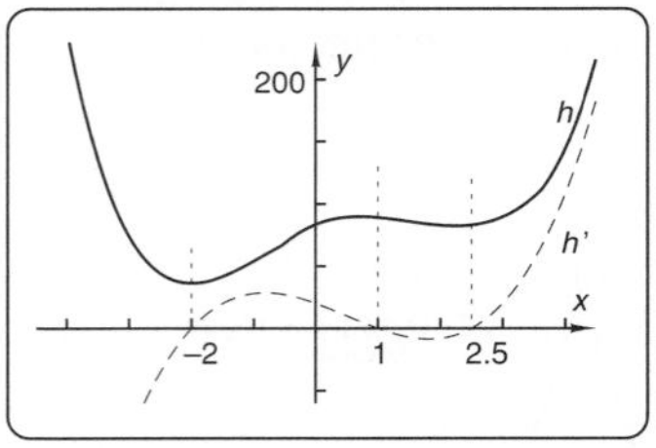


b. The $h'$ graph looks like a cubic function graph.
Conjecture: 7th degree function has a sixth degree function for its derivative.

c. By plotting the graph using a friendly window, then tracing, the zeros of $h'$ are −2, 1, 2.5.

d. If $h'(x) = 0$, the $h$ graph has a high point or a low point. This is reasonable because if $h'(x) = 0$, the rate of change of $h(x)$ is zero, which would happen when the graph stops going up and starts going down, or vice versa.

e. See graph in part (a).

5. *Sinusoid Problem #1*

a. Graph.

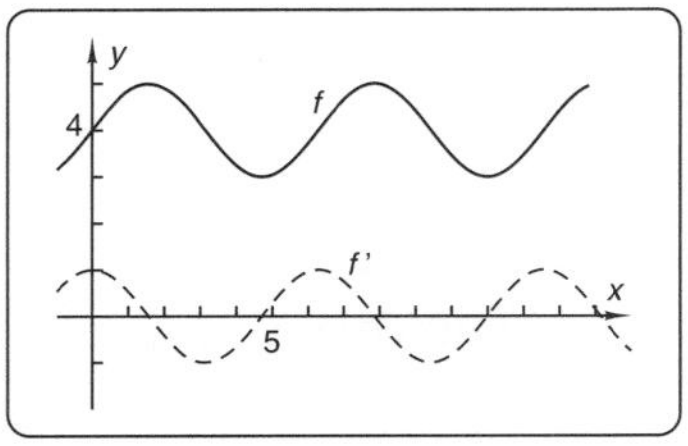


b. Amplitude = 1, period = $2\pi$ = 6.283...

c. The $f'$ graph has amplitude 1 and period $2\pi$.

d. Graph.

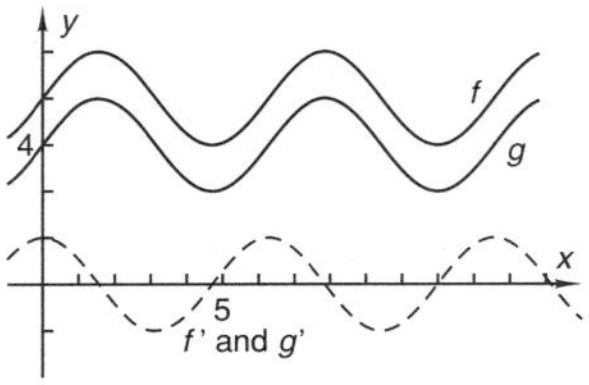


The graphs of $f$ and $g$ are the same shape, spaced 1 unit apart vertically. The graphs of $f'$ and $g'$ are identical! This is to be expected since the shapes of the $f$ and $g$ graphs are the same.

7. (Not selected)

9. *Tolerance Problem (Epsilon and Delta)*

a. Area is within 0.2401 in$^2$ of the nominal.

b. Let $x$ be the number of inches.
Keep $x$ within 0.0008 in. of 12 in.

c. The 0.02 in part (b) corresponds to $\epsilon$ and the 0.0008 corresponds to $\delta$.

11. *Difference Quotient Accuracy Problem*

a. $f'(1) = 2$.

b. Forward: 2.31
Backward: 1.71
Symmetric: 2.01
The symmetric difference quotient is closer to the actual because it is the average of the other two, and the other two span the actual derivative.

c. $f'(0) = -1$.

d. Forward: −0.99
Backward: −0.99
Symmetric: −0.99.
All three difference quotients are equal since $f(x)$ changes just as much from −0.1 to 0 as it does from 0 to 0.1.

e. The journal entry should note that in general the symmetric difference quotient is more accurate than either the forward or backward one, except when the function is increasing or decreasing at the same rate on both sides of $x = c$.

13. *Journal Problem* (Not selected)

## *Problem Set 3-4*

*Derivative of the Power Function, and Another Definition of Derivative*

1. $f'(x) = 20x^3$

3. $dv/dt = -0.581t^{-84}$

5. $M'(x) = 0$

7. $dy/dx = 0.6x - 8$

9. $\frac{d}{dx}(13 - x) = -1$

11. $dy/dx = 2.3x^{1.3} - 10x^{-3} - 100$

13. $dv/dx = 18x - 24$

15. $f'(x) = 24x^2 + 120x + 150$

17. $P'(x) = x - 1$

19. $f(x) = 7x^4$

$f'(x) = \lim_{h\to 0} \frac{7(x+h)^4 - 7x^4}{h}$

$= \lim_{h\to 0}(28x^3 + 42x^2h + 28xh^2 + 7h^3) = 28x^3$.
By formula, $f'(x) = 7 \cdot 4x^3 = 28x^3$, which checks.

21. $v'(t)$

$= \lim\limits_{h\to 0} \frac{[10(t+h)^2 - 5(t+h) + 7] - [10t^2 - 5t + 7]}{h}$

$= \lim\limits_{h\to 0} \frac{20th + 10h^2 - 5h}{h} = \lim\limits_{h\to 0}(20t + 10h - 5)$

$= 20t - 5$.
By formula, $v'(t) = 10 \cdot 2t - 5 = 20t - 5$, which checks.

23. *Misconception Problem*
Mae should realize that you differentiate *functions,* not values of functions. If you substitute a value for $x$ into $f(x) = x^4$, you get $f(3) = 3^4 = 81$, which is a *new* function, $g(x) = 81$. It is the derivative of $g$ that equals zero.
*Moral:* Differentiate *before* you substitute for $x$.

25. Graph. Dashed line is the derivative.

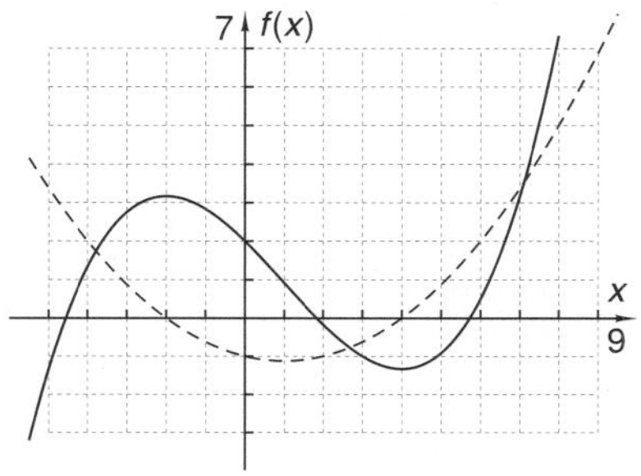


27. *Numerical vs. Exact Derivative Problem*

a. Graph.

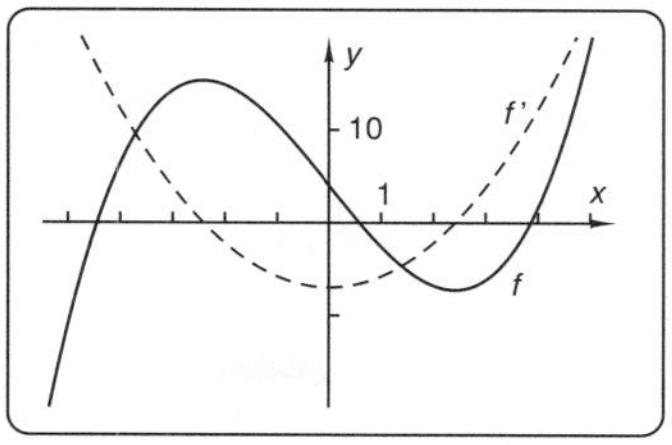


b. The graph of $f'$ is shown dotted in part (a).

c. There appear to be only two graphs because the exact and the numerical derivative graphs almost coincide.

d. $f(3) = -6.2$
$f'(3) = 3.8$ (by formula)
$f'(3) \approx 3.8000004$ (depending on grapher)
The two values of $f'(3)$ are almost identical!

29. $f(x) = x^{1/2} + 2x - 13$
$f'(x) = \frac{1}{2}x^{-1/2} + 2f'(4) = \frac{9}{4}$
Increasing by 9/4 $y$-units per $x$-unit at $x = 4$.

31. Decreasing by 1.5 $y$-units per $x$-unit at $x = 9$.

33. Graph. High and low points of the $f$ graph are at the $x$-intercepts of the $f'$ graph.

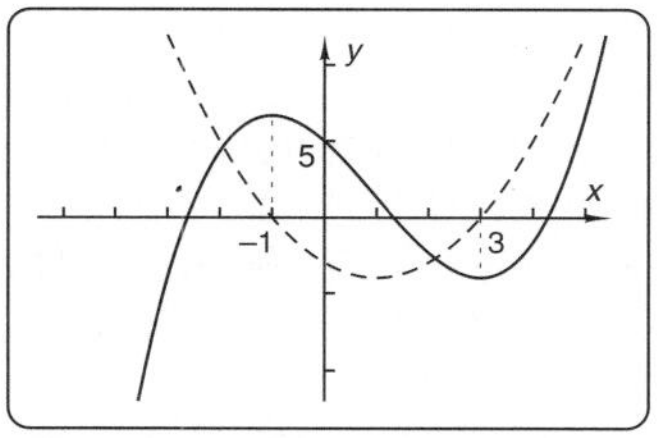


35. *Formula Proof Problem No. 1*
If $f(x) = k \cdot g(x)$, then $f'(x) = k \cdot g'(x)$.
*Proof:*
$f'(x) = \lim_{h\to 0} \frac{f(x+h) - f(x)}{h}$
$= \lim_{h\to 0} \frac{k \cdot g(x+h) - k \cdot g(x)}{h}$
$= \lim_{h\to 0} k \cdot \frac{g(x+h) - g(x)}{h}$
$= k \cdot \lim_{h\to 0} \frac{g(x+h) - g(x)}{h}$
$= k \cdot g'(x)$, Q.E.D.

37. *Derivative of a Power Formula*
If $f(x) = x^n$, then $f'(x) = nx^{n-1}$.
*Proof:*
$f'(x) = \lim_{h\to 0} \frac{(x+h)^n - x^n}{h}$
$= \lim_{h\to 0} \frac{x^n + nx^{n-1}h + \frac{1}{2}n(n-1)x^{n-2}h^2 + \cdots + h^n - x^n}{h}$
$= \lim_{h\to 0}(nx^{n-1} + \frac{1}{2}n(n-1)x^{n-2}h + \cdots + h^{n-1})$
$= nx^{n-1} + 0 + 0 + \cdots + 0$
$= nx^{n-1}$, which is from the second term in the binomial expansion of $(x + h)^n$, Q.E.D.

39. *Introduction to Antiderivatives*

a. $f(x) = x^3 - 5x^2 + 5x$

b. $g(x) = f(x) + 13$ is also an answer to part (a) since it has the same derivative as $f(x)$. The derivative of a constant is zero.

c. The name antiderivative is picked because it is an inverse operation of taking the derivative.

## Problem Set 3-5

*Displacement, Velocity, and Acceleration*

1. $v = 20t^3 - 7.2t^{1.4} + 7$, $a = 60t^2 - 10.08t^{0.4}$

3. $x = -t^3 + 13t^2 - 35t + 27$. Graph.
The object starts out at $x = 27$ ft when $t = 0$ sec. It moves to the left to $x \approx 0.16$ ft when $t \approx 1.7$ sec. It turns there and goes to the right to $x = 70$ ft when $t = 7$ sec. It turns there and speeds up, going to the left for all higher values of $t$.

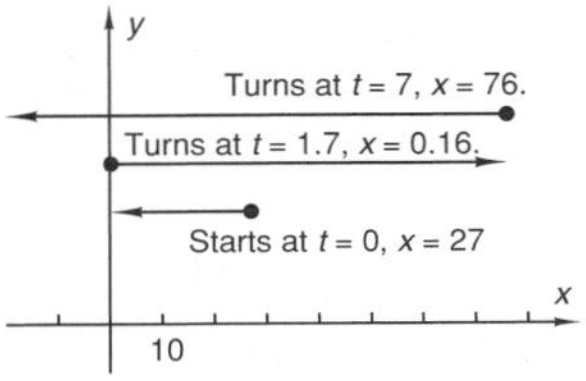


5. a. $v = -3t^2 + 26t - 35$, $a = -6t + 26$
   b. $x$ is decreasing at 12 ft/sec at $t = 1$.
   c. The object is slowing down at 20 (ft/sec)/sec since the velocity and acceleration are in opposite directions when $t = 1$.
   d. At $t = 7$, $x$ has a relative maximum since $v(7) = 0$ at that point and is positive just before $t = 7$ and negative just after.
   e. No, $x$ is never negative for $t$ in [0, 9]. It starts out at 27 ft, decreases to just above 0 around $t = 1.7$ sec, and does not become negative until some time between $t = 9.6$ and 9.7 sec.

7. *Car Problem*
   a. Graph.

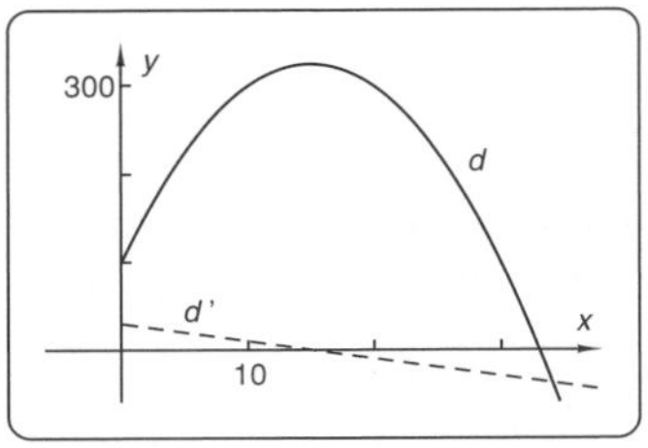


   b. Velocity is positive for $0 \le t < 15$.
   Calvin is going up the hill for the first 15 sec.
   c. At 15 seconds his car stopped.
   $d(15) = 324$, so distance is 324 feet.
   d. He'll be back at the bottom when $t = 33$ sec.
   e. Car runs out of gas 99 ft from the bottom.

9. *Velocity from Displacement Problem*
   a. $d'(1) = 18 - 9.8 = 8.2$
   $d'(3) = 18 - 9.8 \cdot 3 = -11.4$
   $d'$ is called velocity in physics.
   b. At $t = 1$ the football is going up at 8.2 m/sec.
   At $t = 3$ the football is going down at 11.4 m/sec.
   The ball is going up when the derivative is positive and coming down when the derivative is negative.
   The ball is going up when the graph slopes up and coming down when the graph slopes down.
   c. $d(4) = -21.2$, which suggests that the ball is going down at 21.2 m/sec. However, $d(4) = -6.4$, which reveals that the ball has gone underground. The function gives meaningful answers in the real world only if the domain of $t$ is restricted to values that make $d(t)$ non-negative.

11. *Average Rate vs. Instantaneous Rate Problem*
The average rate is defined to be the change in the dependent variable divided by the change in the independent variable (such as total distance divided by total time). Thus, the difference quotient is an average rate.
The instantaneous rate is the limit of this average rate as the change in the independent variable approaches zero.

## Problem Set 3-6

*Introduction to Sine, Cosine, and Composite Functions*

1. Graph.

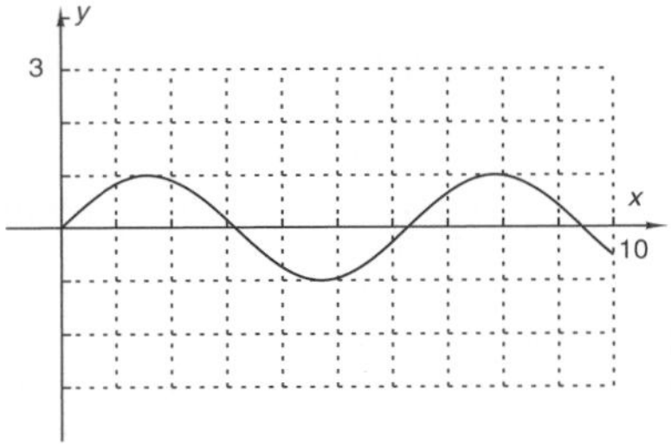


3. Conjecture: $g'(x) = 3\cos 3x$
Graph confirms conjecture.

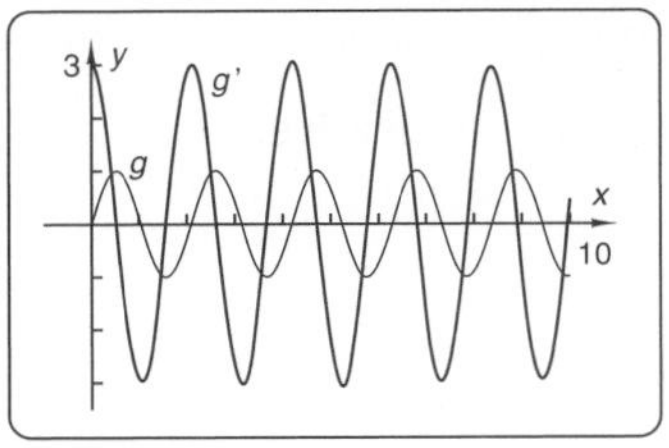


5. Conjecture: $t'(x) = 0.7x^{-0.3}\cos x^{0.7}$
Graph confirms conjecture!

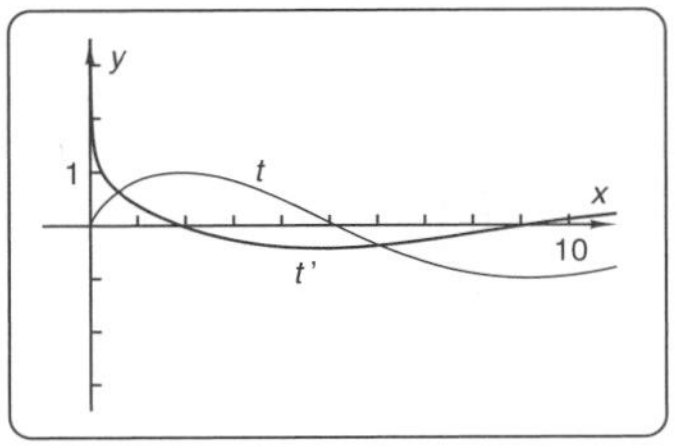

7. a. Inside: $3x$. Outside: sine.
   c. Inside: cube. Outside: sine.
   e. Inside: tangent. Outside: reciprocal.

### Problem Set 3-7

*Derivatives of Composite Functions—The Chain Rule*

1. a. Let $y = f(u), u = g(x)$.
   $\frac{dy}{dx} = \frac{dy}{du} \cdot \frac{du}{dx}$
   b. $y' = f'(g(x)) \cdot g'(x)$
   c. To differentiate a composite function, differentiate the outside function with respect to the inside function, then multiply by the derivative of the inside function with respect to $x$.
3. $f'(x) = -3 \sin 3x$
5. $g'(x) = -3x^2 \sin(x^3)$
7. $y' = -3 \cos^2 x \sin x$
9. $y' = 6 \sin^5 x \cos x$
11. $y' = -18 \cos 3x$
13. $\frac{d}{dx}(\cos^4 7x) = -28 \cos^3 7x \sin 7x$
15. $f'(x) = 160 \sin^{2/3} 4x \cos 4x$
17. $f'(x) = 35(5x+3)^6$
19. $y' = -72x^2(4x^3 - 7)^{-7}$
21. $y' = -200x \cos^{99}(x^2+3) \sin(x^2+3)$
23. *Graphical Verification Problem*
   $f'(x) = -\sin 0.2x$
   $f'(3) = -\sin 0.6 = -0.5646\ldots$ and $f(3) = 4.126\ldots$
   Line has equation $y = -0.5646\ldots x + 5.820\ldots$
   Graph. Line is tangent to graph.

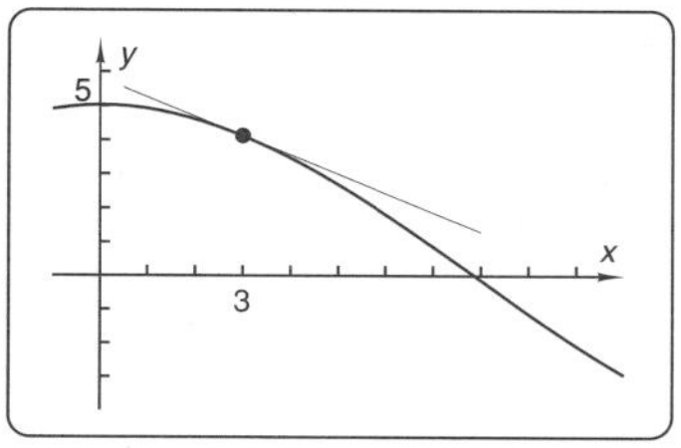


25. *Balloon Volume Problem*
   a. $\frac{dV}{dr} = 4\pi r^2$ (cm$^3$/cm), or cm$^2$.
   b. $r = 6t + 10$
   c. $\frac{dr}{dt} = 6$ cm/min
   d. $\frac{dV}{dt} = \frac{dV}{dr} \cdot \frac{dr}{dt}$
   When $t = 5$, $\frac{dV}{dr} = 6400\pi$.
   $\therefore \frac{dV}{dt} = 6400\pi \cdot 6 = 38400\pi$ cm$^3$/min.
   Since $dV/dr$ has units cm$^2$, and $dr/dt$ has units cm/min, $dV/dt$ has units cm$^2 \cdot \frac{\text{cm}}{\text{min}}$, which becomes cm$^3$/min, Q.E.D.
   e. $V = \frac{4\pi}{3}(6t+10)^3$
   $\therefore \frac{dV}{dt} = 24\pi(6t+10)^2$
   When $t = 5$, $\frac{dV}{dt} = 38400\pi$, which checks.

### Problem Set 3-8

*Proof and Application of Sine and Cosine Derivatives*

1. *Ferris Wheel Problem*
   a. Graph. $y(t) = 25 + 20 \cos \frac{\pi}{10}(t-3)$

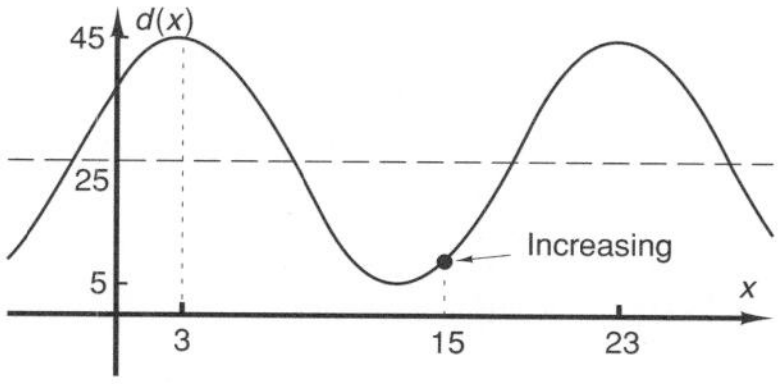


   b. $y'(t) = -2\pi \sin \frac{\pi}{10}(t-3)$
   c. $y'(15) = 3.69316\ldots$
   $y(t)$ is increasing at about 3.7 ft/sec.
   The seat is at $y(t) = 25$ ft above the ground then.
   d. The fastest $y(t)$ changes is $2\pi$, or 6.28 . . . ft/sec.
3. *Playground Problem*
   a. Curb has slope $(3.25 - 0.75)/44 = 2.5/44$.
   $\therefore$ equation is $f(x) = 0.75 + (2.5/44)x$
   b. Sinusoid has period 8 ft, so $B = 2\pi/8 = \pi/4$.
   Amplitude $= 0.5(0.75 - 0.25) = 0.25$ ft.
   Low end of ramp is a low point on the sinusoid.
   $\therefore$ sinusoidal axis is at $y = 0.25$ when $x = 0$, and goes up with slope 2.5/44.
   Sinusoid is at a low point when $x = 0$. So phase displacement is 0 if the cosine is *subtracted.*
   $\therefore$ equation is
   $g(x) = 0.25 + \frac{2.5}{44}x - 0.25 \cos \frac{\pi}{4}(x)$
   (There are other correct forms.)
   c. $g'(x) = \frac{2.5}{44} + \frac{\pi}{16} \sin \frac{\pi}{4}(x)$
   $g'(9) = \frac{2.5}{44} + \frac{\pi}{16} \sin \frac{\pi}{4}(9) = 0.1956\ldots$ ft/ft.
   Going *up* at about 0.2 vertical ft per horizontal ft
   $g'(15) = \frac{2.5}{44} + \frac{\pi}{16} \sin \frac{\pi}{4}(15) = -0.0820\ldots$ ft/ft.
   Going *down* at about 0.08 vertical ft per horizontal ft.
   Negative derivative implies $g(x)$ is getting smaller, and thus child is going down, and vice versa.
   d. By tracing the $g'$ graph, maximum value of $g'(x)$ is $0.2531\ldots$ ft/ft (about 14.2° up).
   Minimum is $-0.1395\ldots$ ft/ft (about 7.9° down).
5. *Pendulum Experiment* (Not selected)
7. *Squeeze Theorem, Numerically*
   a. Graph. $f(x) = -2x^2 + 8x - 2$, $g(x) = 2x^2 + 2$, $h(x) = 4x$. Limits are each equal to 4.

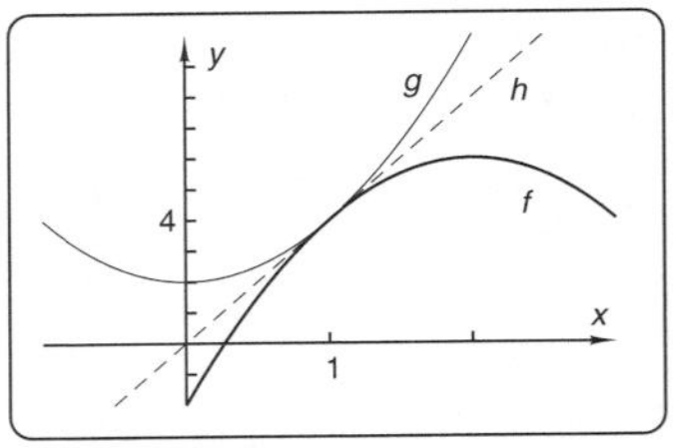


b. Each function is continuous since it is a polynomial function.
$f(x) \le h(x) \le g(x)$.

c.

| $x$ | $f(x)$ | $h(x)$ | $g(x)$ |
|---|---|---|---|
| 0.95 | 3.795 | 3.8 | 3.805 |
| 0.96 | 3.8368 | 3.84 | 3.8432 |
| 0.97 | 3.8782 | 3.88 | 3.8818 |
| 0.98 | 3.9192 | 3.92 | 3.9208 |
| 0.99 | 3.9598 | 3.96 | 3.9602 |
| 1.00 | 4 | 4 | 4 |
| 1.01 | 4.0398 | 4.04 | 4.0402 |
| 1.02 | 4.0792 | 4.08 | 4.0808 |
| 1.03 | 4.1182 | 4.12 | 4.1218 |
| 1.04 | 4.1568 | 4.16 | 4.1632 |
| 1.05 | 4.195 | 4.2 | 4.205 |

d. From the table, $\delta = 0.01$ or $0.02$ will work, but 0.03 is too large.

e. All the values of $h(x)$ are between the corresponding values of $f(x)$ and $g(x)$, and the three functions all approach 4 as a limit.

9. *Limit of Sine Problem* (See text proof.)

11. *Derivative of the Cosine Function* (See text proof.)

13. *Group Discussion Problem* (Not selected)

## Problem Set 3-9

*Antiderivatives and Indefinite Integrals*

1. $f(x) = x^7 + C$
3. $f(x) = \frac{1}{6}x^6 + C$
5. $f(x) = -\frac{1}{8}x^{-8} + C$
7. $f(x) = \sin x + C$
9. $f(x) = 8x^{9/2} + C$
11. $f(x) = -0.2\cos 5x + C$
13. $f(x) = \frac{1}{32}(4x+5)^8 + C$
15. $f(x) = \frac{1}{3}x^3 + 3x^2 - 5x + C$
17. $f(x) = \frac{1}{5}x^5 + 9.8$
19. $f(x) = \sin x + 4$
21. $f(x) = \frac{1}{3}x^3 - 4x^2 + 3x + \frac{113}{3}$
23. *Displacement Problem*
    a. $d(t) = 70t - 4.9t^2 + C$
    b. $d(t) = 70t - 4.9t^2 + 6$
    c. $d(5) = 233.5$ meters
    $d(6) = 249.6$ meters
    $d(9) = 239.1$ meters
    These three numbers show that $d(t)$ has a high point somewhere between 5 and 9.
    d. Arrow was highest, 256m, at about $t = 7.1$ sec.
25. *Derivative and Antiderivative Problem:*
    a. $g(x) = 0.3x^2 + C$
    b. i. $g(x) = 0.3x^2$
    ii. $g(x) = 0.3x^2 + 3$
    iii. $g(x) = 0.3x^2 + 5$
    c. Graph. All the graphs are obtained by shifting the solution function vertically through some displacement $C$. So all the graphs are "related" and thus can be called a family.

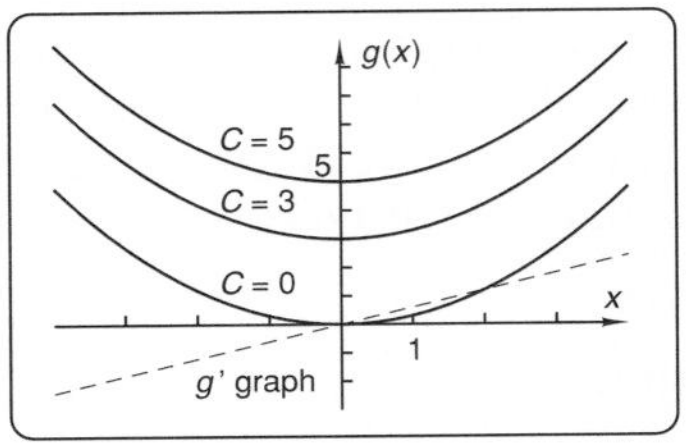


## Problem Set 3-10

*Chapter Review and Test*

### Review Problems

R0. (Not selected)

R1. a. $f'(2) \approx 12$

b. $m(x) = \frac{x^3-8}{x-2}$

$m(2)$ takes the indeterminate form 0/0.
By tracing the graph or constructing a table, the limit of $m(x)$ seems to be 12 as $x$ approaches 2.

c. $m(x) = x^2 + 2x + 4$.
$\lim_{x\to 2} m(x) = 12$

d. The answer to part (c) is exactly 12.
The answer to part (a) is approximately 12.

R2. a. $f'(c) = \lim\limits_{x\to c} \frac{f(x)-f(c)}{x-c}$

b. $f(x) = 0.4x^2 - x + 5$

$$f'(x) = \lim_{x\to 3} \frac{0.4x^2-x+5-5.6}{x-3}$$

$$= \lim_{x\to 3} \frac{(x-3)(0.4x+0.2)}{x-3}$$

$$= \lim_{x\to 3}(0.4x + 0.2) = 1.4$$

c. $m(x) = \frac{0.4x^2-x+0.6}{x-3}$. Graph.

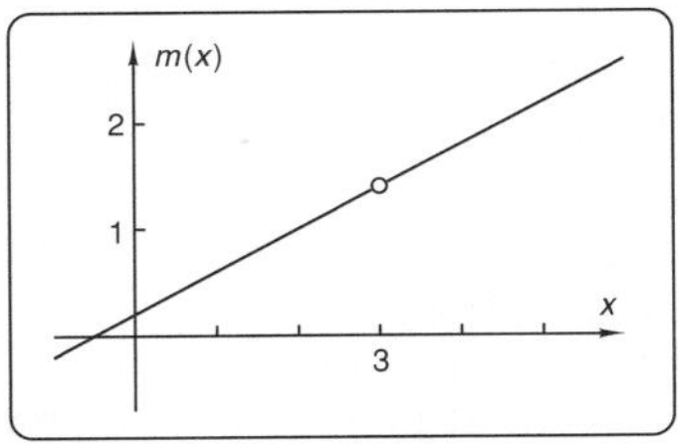


d. Line: $y = 1.4x + 1.4$. Graph.

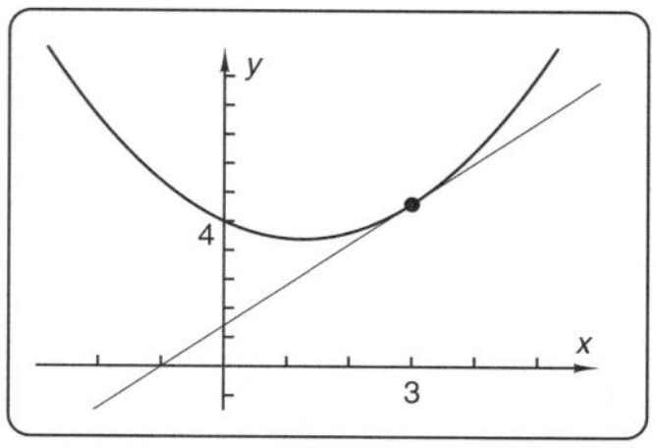


e. The line is tangent to the graph.

f. Yes, $f$ does have local linearity at $x = 3$. Zooming in on the point (3, 5.6) shows that the graph looks more and more like the line.

R3. a. Graph.

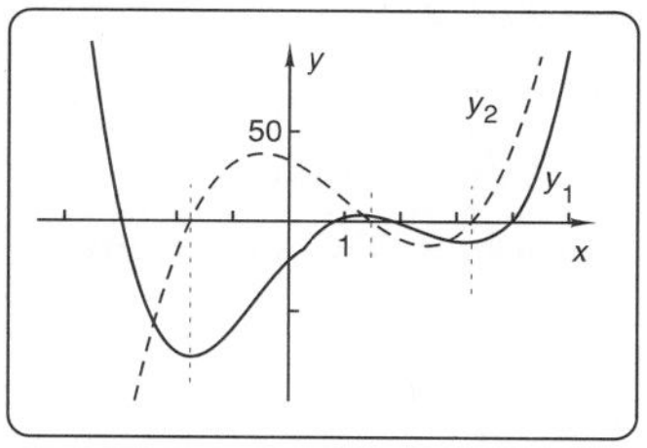


b. $y_2$ = numerical derivative. See graph in part (a).

c. The $y_1$ graph has a high point or a low point at each $x$-value where the $y_2$ graph is zero.

d. *Leaky Tire Problem*
Graph.

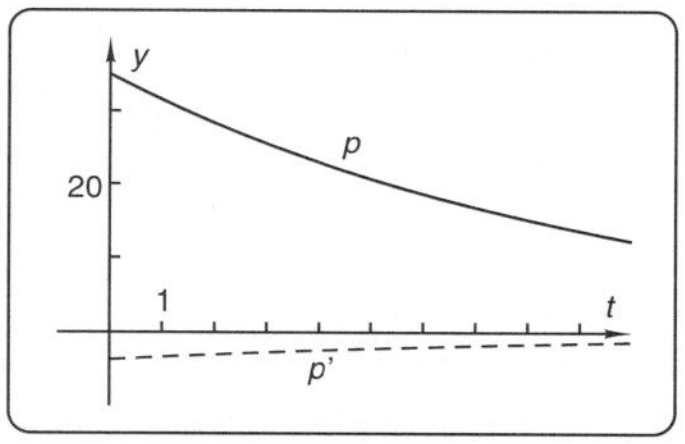


Decreasing at about 2.69 psi/hr when $t = 3$.
Decreasing at about 1.96 psi/hr when $t = 6$.
Decreasing at about 3.69 psi/hr when $t = 0$.
The units are psi/hr.
The sign of the pressure change is negative since the pressure is decreasing.
Yes, the rate of pressure change is getting closer to zero.

R4. a. See text definition of derivative.

b. Differentiate.

c. If $y = x^n$, then $y' = nx^{n-1}$.

d. See solution to Problem Set 3-4, Problem 35.

e. See the proof in Section 3-4.

f. $\frac{dy}{dx}$ is pronounced, "Dee $y$, dee $x$."
$\frac{d}{dx}(y)$ is pronounced, "Dee, dee $x$, of $y$."
Both mean the derivative of $y$ with respect to $x$.

g. i. $f'(x) = \frac{63}{5}x^8$
ii. $g'(x) = -28x^{-5} - \frac{1}{3}x - 1$
iii. $h'(x) = 0$

h. $f'(32) = 201.6$ exactly.
Numerical derivative is equal to or very close to 201.6.

i. Graph. (Dotted line.)

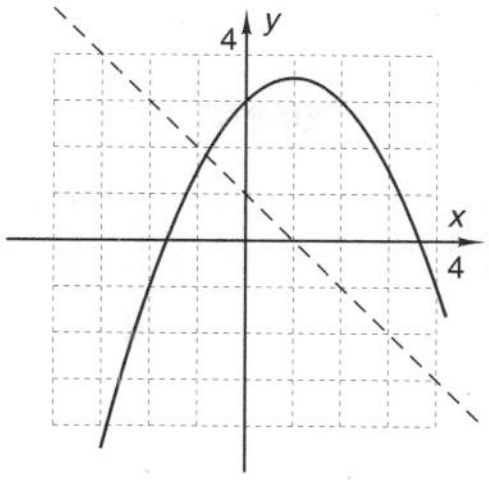


R5. a. $v = \frac{dx}{dt}$ or $x'(t)$.
$a = \frac{dv}{dt}$ or $v'(t)$, $a = \frac{d^2x}{dt^2}$ or $x''(t)$

b. *Spaceship Problem*
i. $v = -0.03t^2 + 1.8t - 25$
$a = -0.06t + 1.8$
ii. $a(15) = 0.9$ (km/sec)/sec
$v(15) = -4.75$ km/sec
The spaceship is slowing down at $t = 15$ since the velocity and acceleration have opposite signs.
iii. $v = -0.03t^2 + 1.8t - 25 = 0$
By SOLVE or quadratic formula,
$t = 21.835\ldots$ or $t = 38.164\ldots$.
The spaceship is stopped at about 21.8 and 38.2 seconds.
iv. $v = 0$ when $t = 50$. $v(50) = -10$.
Since the spaceship is going 10 km/sec when it reaches the surface, it is a crash landing!

R6. a. Graph.

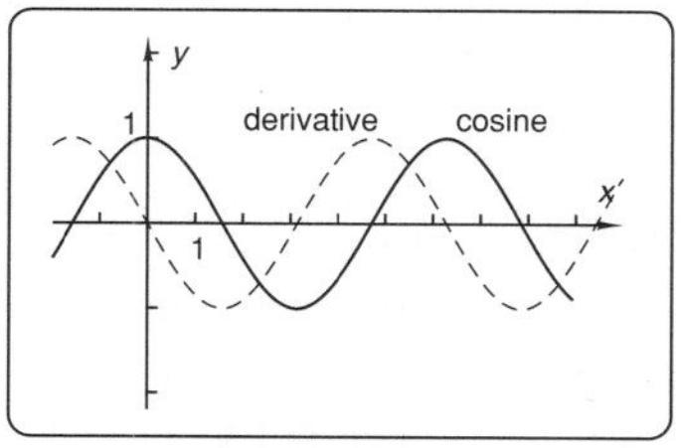


b. The graph of the derivative is the same as the sine graph, but inverted in the $y$-direction. Thus, $(\cos x)' = -\sin x$ is confirmed.

c. $\cos 1 = 0.5403023058\ldots$
Numerical derivative $\approx 0.5403022158\ldots$
The two are very close!

d. Composite function.
$f'(x) = -2x\sin(x^2)$

R7. a. i. $\frac{dy}{dx} = \frac{dy}{du} \cdot \frac{du}{dx}$
ii. $f(x) = g(h(x)) \Rightarrow f'(x) = g'(h(x)) \cdot h'(x)$
iii. The derivative of a composite function is the derivative of the outside function with respect to the inside function, times the derivative of the inside function with respect to $x$.

b. See the derivation in the text. This derivation constitutes a proof.
$\Delta u$ must be non-zero throughout the interval.

c. i. $f(x) = (x^2 - 4)^3$
$f'(x) = 3(x^2 - 4)^2 \cdot 2x = 6x(x^2 - 4)^2$

ii. $f(x) = x^6 - 12x^4 + 48x^2 - 64$
$f'(x) = 6x^5 - 48x^3 + 96x$
Expanding the answer to part (i) gives
$f'(x) = 6x^5 - 48x^3 + 96x$, which checks.

d. $f'(x) = -3x^2 \sin x^3$
$g'(x) = 5 \cos 5x$
$h'(x) = -6 \sin x \cos^5 x$
$k'(x) = 0$

e. *Shark Problem*
$\frac{dW}{dt} = \frac{dW}{dx} \cdot \frac{dx}{dt} = 1.8x^2 \cdot 0.4 = 0.72x^2$
If $x = 2$, $W = 0.6 \cdot 2^3 = 4.8$ lb
$dW/dt = 0.72(2^2) = 2.88$
Shark is gaining about 2.88 lb/day
If $x = 10$, $W = 0.6 \cdot 10^3 = 600$ lb
$dW/dt = 0.72(10^2) = 72$
Shark is gaining about 72 lb/day
The chain rule is used to get $dW/dt$ from $dW/dx$ by multiplying the latter by $dx/dt$.

R8. a. $\lim_{x \to 0} \frac{\sin x}{x} = 1$.

b.

| $x$ | $(\sin x)/x$ |
|---|---|
| −0.05 | 0.99958338541... |
| −0.04 | 0.99973335466... |
| −0.03 | 0.99985000674... |
| −0.02 | 0.99993333466... |
| −0.01 | 0.99998333341... |
| 0.00 | (No value) |
| 0.01 | 0.99998333341... |
| 0.02 | 0.99993333466... |
| 0.03 | 0.99985000674... |
| 0.04 | 0.99973335466... |
| 0.05 | 0.99958338541... |

The values approach 1 as $x$ approaches 0.

c. See text statement of squeeze theorem.
Squeeze $(\sin x)/x$ between $\cos x$ and $\sec x$.

d. See proof in text (Section 3-8).

e. $\cos x = \sin(\pi/2 - x)$
$\cos' x = \cos(\pi/2 - x)(-1) = -\sin x$, Q.E.D.

f. *Clock Problem*
$d(t) = 180 + 20 \cos \frac{\pi}{30} t$
$d'(t) = -\frac{2\pi}{3} \sin \frac{\pi}{30} t$
At 2, $t = 10$. $d'(10) \approx -1.81$ cm/sec.
At 3, $t = 15$. $d'(15) \approx -2.09$ cm/sec.
At 7, $t = 35$. $d'(35) \approx 1.05$ cm/sec.
At the 2 and 3, the tip is going down, so the distance from the floor is decreasing, which is implied by the negative derivatives.
At the 7, the tip is going up, as implied by the positive derivative.

R9. a. $f(x) = 6x^6 + C$

b. $y = -5 \cos 0.2x + 8$

c. *Distance Problem*
$y(t) = 4t^{3/2} + 100$
$y(60) = 1959.03\ldots$
$v(60) = 46.475\ldots$
She is about 1959 feet away from the house, going about 46.5 ft/sec 1 minute after she starts.

d. An antiderivative and an indefinite integral are the same thing.

## CHAPTER 4

### Exploratory Problem Set 4-1

*Combinations of Two Functions*

1. $f'(x) = -3 \sin x$, $g'(x) = 2 \cos x$

3. *Derivative of a Quotient of Two Functions*
Graph.

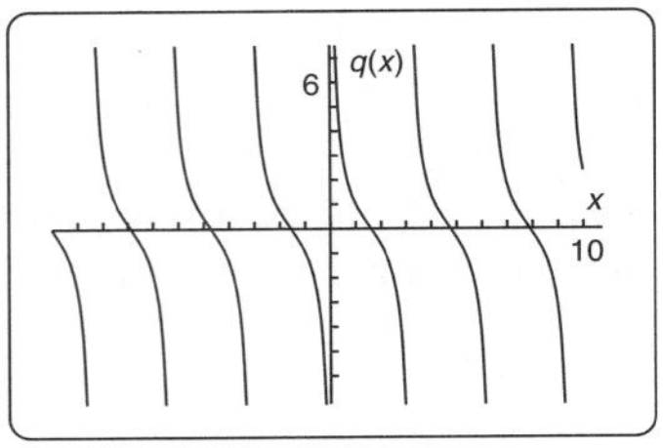


$q$ is the *cotangent* function.
$q'(2) = -1.8141\ldots$
$q(x)$ is decreasing at $x = 2$.
$f'(2)/g'(2) = 3.2775\ldots \neq f'(2)/g'(2)$.

5. *Derivative of a Parametric Function*
Graph. $x = 3 \cos t$, $y = 2 \sin t$

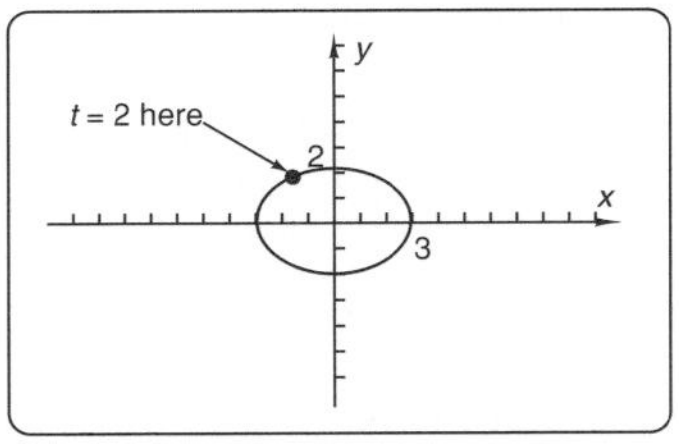


$\Delta x = -0.54466\ldots$, $\Delta y = -0.16618\ldots$
$dy/dx \approx \Delta y/\Delta x = 0.3051\ldots$
At $t = 2$, $\dfrac{dy/dt}{dx/dt} = \dfrac{2 \cos 2}{-3 \sin 2} = 0.3051\ldots$, which agrees with the difference quotient.
Also, from the graph in Problem 4, the slope of a line tangent to the graph at the point where $t = 2$ would be positive, and less than 1, which agrees with the value of $0.3051\ldots$ for the difference quotient.

### Problem Set 4-2

*Derivative of a Product of Two Functions*

1. $f'(x) = 3x^2 \cos x - x^3 \sin x$

3. $g'(x) = 1.5x^{0.5}\sin 7x + 7x^{1.5}\cos 7x$

5. $dy/dx = x^6(2x+5)^9(34x+35)$

7. $z' = 4x^3\cos^5 3x - 15x^4\cos^4 3x\sin 3x$

9. $(d/dx)[(4x-3)^6\sin 5x]$
$= 24(4x-3)^5\sin 5x + 5(4x-3)^6\cos 5x$

11. $y' = (6x+11)^3(5x-9)^6(330x+169)$

13. $P' = 10x(x^2-1)^9(x^2+1)^{14}(5x^2-1)$

15. $a'(t) = 12\cos 3t\cos 5t - 20\sin 3t\sin 5t$

17. $y' = -400\cos^7 5x\sin 5x\sin^5 8x$
$+ 400\cos^8 5x\sin^4 8x\cos 8x$

19. $z' = 3x^2(5x-2)^4\sin 6x + 20x^3(5x-2)^3\sin 6x$
$+6x^3(5x-2)^4\cos 6x$

21. $y' = -3\sin(3\sin x)\cos x$

23. *Product of Three Functions Problem*
If $y = uvw$, where $u$, $v$, and $w$ are differentiable functions of $x$, then $y' = u'vw + uv'w + uvw'$.

*Proof:*
$y = uvw = (uv)w$
$\therefore y' = (uv)'w + (uv)w' = (u'v + uv')w$
$+(uv)w'$
$= u'vw + uv'w + uvw'$, Q.E.D.

25. $z' = 5x^4\cos^6 x\sin 7x - 6x^5\cos^5 x\sin x\sin 7x$
$+7x^5\cos^6 x\cos 7x$

27. $y' = 4x^3(2x-3)^5\sin x\cos 2x$
$+10x^4(2x-3)^4\sin x\cos 2x$
$+x^4(2x-3)^5\cos x\cos 2x$
$-2x^4(2x-3)^5\sin x\sin 2x$

29. *Odd and Even Function Derivative Problem*
Prove that the derivative of an odd function is an even function, and the derivative of an even function is an odd function.

*Proof:*
For any function, the chain rule gives

$$\frac{d}{dx}f(-x) = f'(-x)\cdot(-1) = -f'(-x).$$

For an odd function,

$$\frac{d}{dx}f(-x) = \frac{d}{dx}(-f(x)) = -f'(x).$$
$$\therefore -f'(-x) = -f'(x) \text{ or } f'(-x) = f'(x),$$

and the derivative is an even function.
For an even function,

$$\frac{d}{dx}f(-x) = \frac{d}{dx}f(x) = f'(x).$$
$$\therefore -f'(-x) = f'(x) \text{ or } f'(-x) = -f'(x),$$

and the derivative is an odd function, Q.E.D.

31. *Derivative of a Power by Induction Problem*
Prove that if $f_n(x) = x^n$, then $f_n'(x) = nx^{n-1}$ for all integers $\geq 1$.

*Proof:* (by induction on $n$)
If $n = 1$, then $f_1(x) = x^1$, which implies that $f_1'(x) = 1 = 1x^0$, which anchors the induction. Assume that for some integer $n = k > 1$, $f_k'(x) = kx^{k-1}$.
For $n = k+1$, $f_{k+1}(x) = x^{k+1} = (x^k)(x)$.
By the derivative of a product property, $f_{k+1}'(x) = (x^k)'(x) + (x^k)(x)' = (x^k)'(x) + x^k$.
Substituting for $(x^k)'$ from the induction hypothesis, $f_{k+1}'(x) = (kx^{k-1})(x) + x^k = kx^k + x^k = (k+1)x^k = (k+1)x^{(k+1)-1}$, completing the induction.
$\therefore f_n'(x) = nx^{n-1}$ for all integers $\geq 1$, Q.E.D.

33. *Confirmation of the Product Property*

a. Graph. $f(x) = x^3\cdot\sin x$, with the graph of $f'$. $f'$ should have been sketched.

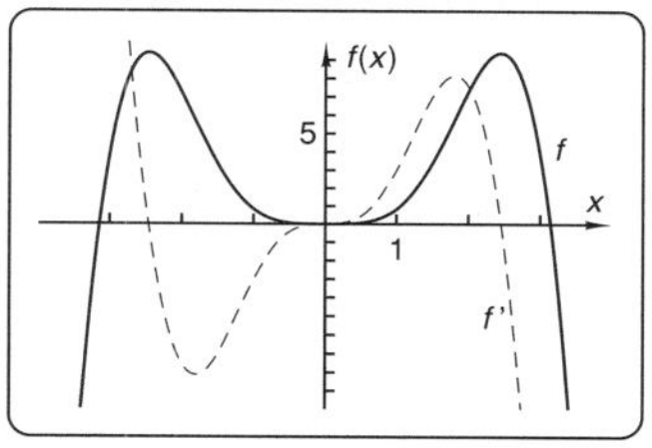


b. $f'(x) = 3x^2\sin x + x^3\cos x$
Graph in part (a) is correct.

c. The numerical derivative graph duplicates the algebraic derivative graph, as in part (a), thus showing that the algebraic derivative is right.

35. *Pole Dance Problem*

a. $A = LW$

$$\frac{dA}{dt} = \frac{dL}{dt}\cdot W + L\cdot\frac{dW}{dt}$$

b. At $t = 4$, $dA/dt = 7.132\ldots$, so $A$ is increasing.
At $t = 5$, $dA/dt = -4.949\ldots$, so $A$ is decreasing.

## Problem Set 4-3

*Derivative of a Quotient of Two Functions*

1. $f'(x) = \dfrac{3x^2\sin x - x^3\cos x}{\sin^2 x}$

3. $g'(x) = \dfrac{-3x\cos^2 x\sin x - 5\cos^3 x}{x^6}$

5. $y' = \dfrac{10\cos 10x\cos 20x + 20\sin 20x\sin 10x}{\cos^2 20x}$

7. $y' = \dfrac{57}{(6x+5)^2}$

9. $\dfrac{dz}{dx} = \dfrac{(8x+1)^5(120x+141)}{(5x-2)^{10}}$

11. $P' = \dfrac{60x^2 - 98x + 62}{(3x^2 + 6x - 8)^2}$

13. $\dfrac{d}{dx}(60x^{-4/3}) = -80x^{-7/3}$

15. $r'(x) = -36x^{-4}$

17. $v'(x) = \dfrac{7 \sin 0.5x}{\cos^2 0.5x}$

19. $e'(x) = \dfrac{-1}{x^2} = -x^{-2}$

21. $W'(x) = 150x^2(x^3 - 1)^4$

23. $T'(x) = \sec^2 x$ ("$T$" is for "tangent function.")

25. $C'(x) = -\csc x \cot x$ ("$C$" is for "cosecant function.")

27. *Black Hole Problem*

a. $v(1) = 500$ mph
$v(2) = 1000$ mph
$v(3) = 1000/0$. No value for $v(3)$.

b. $a(t) = \dfrac{1000}{(3 - t)^2}$

c. $a(1) = 250$ mph/hr
$a(2) = 1000$ mph/hr
$a(3) = 1000/0$. No value for $a(3)$.

d. Graph.

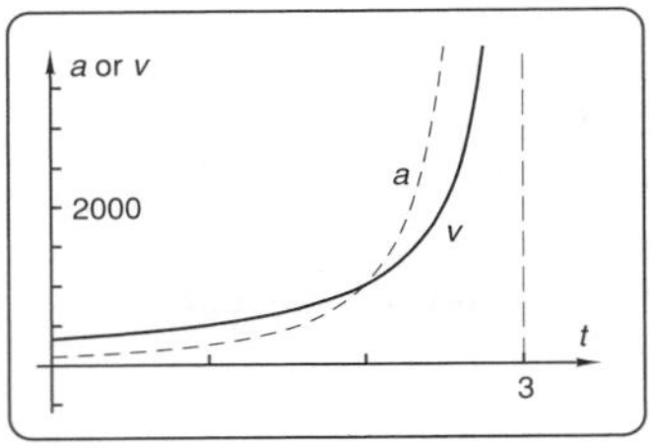


e. Range is $0 \le t < 1.585\ldots$.

29. *Confirmation of Quotient Formula Problem*

$$f(x) = \frac{3x + 7}{2x + 5} \Rightarrow f'(x) = \frac{1}{(2x + 5)^2}$$

$f'(4) = 0.005917159\ldots$

For 4.1, $f'(4) \approx 0.005827505\ldots$

For 4.01, $f'(4) \approx 0.005908070\ldots$

For 4.001, $f'(4) \approx 0.005916249\ldots$

$f'(4)$ (exact) $= 0.005917159\ldots$

Difference quotients are approaching $f'(4)$.

31. *Derivative Proof for Negative Integer Exponents*
If $y = x^n$, where $n$ is a negative integer, then $y' = nx^{n-1}$.

*Proof:*

Let $n = -p$, where $p$ is a positive integer.

$$\therefore y = x^{-p} = \frac{1}{x^p}.$$

$$\therefore y' = \frac{0 \cdot x^p - 1 \cdot px^{p-1}}{x^{2p}}$$ since $p$ is a positive integer.

$$= -\frac{px^{p-1}}{x^{2p}} = -px^{p-1-2p} = -px^{-p-1}.$$

Replacing $-p$ with $n$ gives

$y' = nx^{n-1}$, Q.E.D.

33. Not selected.

## Problem Set 4-4

*Derivatives of the Other Trigonometric Functions*

1. $f'(x) = 5 \sec^2 5x$

3. $y' = 7 \sec 7x \tan 7x$

5. $g'(x) = -11 \csc^2 11x$

7. $r'(x) = -20 \csc 20x \cot 20x$

9. $(d/dx)(y) = 20 \tan^4 4x \sec^2 4x$

11. $(d/dx)(3 \cot^6 8x) = -144 \cot^5 8x \csc^2 8x$

13. $y' = 40 \sec^{5/4} 4x \tan 4x$

15. $v' = 7x^{-8} \csc(x^{-7}) \cot(x^{-7})$

17. $dp/dx = \sec x \tan^2 x + \sec^3 x$

19. $y' = -3x^{-4} \cot x - x^{-3} \csc^2 x$

21. $y' = \sec^2 x - \csc^2 x$

23. $y' = \sec x \tan x$

25. $y' = \dfrac{35x^6 \cot 14x + 70x^7 \csc^2 14x}{\cot^2 14x}$

27. $w' = 3 \sec^2(\sin 3x) \cdot \cos 3x$

29. $S'(x) = 0$

31. $A'(x) = 2x \cos x^2$

33. $F'(x) = 2 \sin x \cos x$

35. $C'(x) = \cos(\sin x) \cdot \cos x$

37. *Derivative of the Cotangent Problem*

$$y = \cot x = \frac{\cos x}{\sin x} \Rightarrow$$

$$y' = \frac{-\sin x \cdot \sin x - \cos x \cdot \cos x}{\sin^2 x}$$

$$= \frac{-1}{\sin^2 x} = -\csc^2 x \qquad \text{or:}$$

$$y = \frac{1}{\tan x} = (\tan x)^{-1} \Rightarrow$$

$$y' = -1 \cdot (\tan x)^{-2} \cdot \sec^2 x = -\csc^2 x$$

39. *Confirmation of Tangent Derivative Formula:*

a. See graph in part (b).

b. $f(x) = \tan x \Rightarrow f'(x) = \sec^2 x$. Graph.

Predicted graph should be close to actual one.

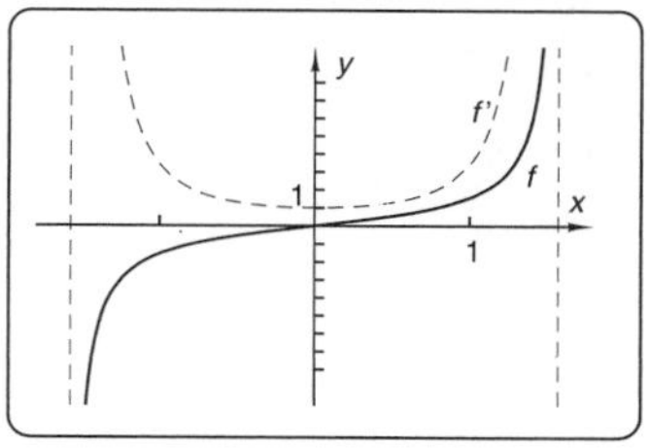


c. $\dfrac{\tan 1.01 - \tan 0.99}{2(0.01)} = 3.42646416\ldots$

$\tan' 1 = \sec^2 1 = (1/\cos 1)^2 = 3.42551882\ldots$
Difference quotient is within 0.001 of actual.

41. *Light on the Monument Problem*

a. $y/10 = \tan x \Rightarrow y = 10\tan x$, Q.E.D.

b. At $x = 1$, $y$ is increasing at $34.2551\ldots$, or about 34.3 ft/radian, which is $0.5978\ldots$ ft/degree.

c. At $y = 535$, $y$ is increasing at about 28,632.5 ft/radian.

43. a. $y = \sin x + C$ b. $y = -\dfrac{1}{2}\cos 2x + C$

c. $y = \dfrac{1}{3}\tan 3x + C$ d. $y = -\dfrac{1}{4}\cot 4x + C$

e. $y = 5\sec x + C$

## Problem Set 4-5

*Derivatives of Inverse Trigonometric Functions*

*For Problems 1 through 4, see Figure 4-5d.*

1. Graph, $y = \cos^{-1} x$ 3. Graph, $y = \csc^{-1} x$

5. The principal branch of the inverse cotangent function goes from 0 to $\pi$ so that the function will be continuous.

7. $\sin(\sin^{-1} 0.3) = 0.3$

9. $y = \sin^{-1} x \Rightarrow \sin y = x \Rightarrow \cos y \cdot y' = 1 \Rightarrow$

$y' = \dfrac{1}{\cos y} = \dfrac{1}{\sqrt{1 - x^2}}$, Q.E.D.

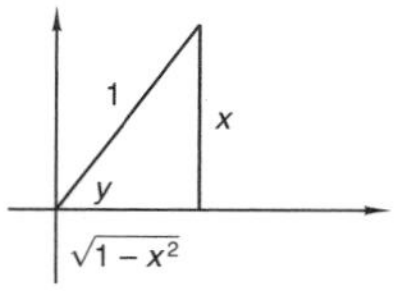


[Since $\sin y$ = (opposite leg)/(hypotenuse), put $x$ on the opposite leg and 1 on the hypotenuse. Adjacent leg = $\sqrt{1 - x^2}$, and $\cos y$ = (adjacent)/(hypotenuse).]

11. $y = \csc^{-1} x \Rightarrow \csc y = x \Rightarrow -\csc y \cot y \cdot y' \Rightarrow$

$y' = -\dfrac{1}{\csc y \cot y} = -\dfrac{1}{x\sqrt{x^2 - 1}}$ if $x > 0$

If $x < 0$, then $y$ is in QIV. So both $\csc y$ and $\cot y$ are negative, and thus their product is positive.

$\therefore y' = -\dfrac{1}{|x|\sqrt{x^2 - 1}}$, Q.E.D.

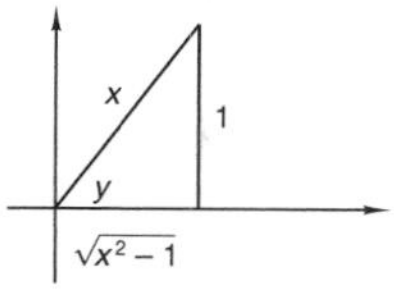


[Since $\csc y$ = (hypotenuse)/(opposite leg), put $x$ on the hypotenuse, 1 on the opposite leg. Adjacent leg = $\sqrt{x^2 - 1}$, and $\csc y = x$ and $\cot y$ = (adjacent)/(opposite).]

13. $y' = \dfrac{4}{\cos y} = \dfrac{4}{\sqrt{1 - 16x^2}}$

15. $y' = -\dfrac{0.5x^{-0.5}}{\csc^2 y} = -\dfrac{0.5x^{-0.5}}{1 + x}$

17. $y' = \dfrac{1}{3 \sec y \tan y} = \dfrac{3}{|x|\sqrt{x^2 - 9}}$

19. $y' = \dfrac{10x}{\sqrt{1 - 25x^4}}$

21. $g'(x) = 2\sin^{-1} x \cdot \dfrac{1}{\sqrt{1 - x^2}}$

23. $v' = \sin^{-1} x$. The surprise is that you now have seen a formula for the antiderivative of the inverse sine.

25. *Radar Problem*

a. $\tan\theta = x/100$, so $\theta = \tan^{-1}(x/100)$, Q.E.D.

b. $\dfrac{d\theta}{dx} = \dfrac{100}{10000 + x^2}$, $\dfrac{d\theta}{dt} = \dfrac{100}{10000 + x^2} \cdot \dfrac{dx}{dt}$

c. Truck is going 104 ft/sec $\approx$ 71 mph.

27. *Numerical Answer Check Problem*

| $x$ | numerical derivative | algebraic derivative |
|---|---|---|
| −0.8 | −1.666671... | −1.666666... |
| −0.6 | −1.250000... | −1.25 |
| −0.4 | −1.091089... | −1.091089... |
| −0.2 | −1.020620... | −1.020620... |
| 0 | −1.000000... | −1 |
| 0.2 | −1.020620... | −1.020620... |
| 0.4 | −1.091089... | −1.091089... |
| 0.6 | −1.250000... | −1.25 |
| 0.8 | −1.666671... | −1.666666... |

*The precise value for the numerical derivative will depend on the tolerance to which the grapher is set.

29. *General Derivative of the Inverse of a Function*

a. $y = \sin^{-1} x \Rightarrow \sin y = x \Rightarrow \cos y \cdot y' = 1 \Rightarrow$

$y' = \dfrac{1}{\cos y}$, Q.E.D.

b. $y' = \dfrac{1}{\cos(\sin^{-1} x)} = \dfrac{1}{\cos(\sin^{-1} 0.6)} = 1.25$

$y' = \dfrac{1}{\sqrt{1-x^2}} = \dfrac{1}{\sqrt{1-0.6^2}} = \dfrac{1}{0.8} = 1.25$, Q.E.D.

c. $y = f^{-1}(x) \Rightarrow f(y) = x \Rightarrow f'(y) \cdot \dfrac{d}{dx}(y) = 1 \Rightarrow$

$\dfrac{d}{dx}(y) = \dfrac{1}{f'(y)} \Rightarrow \dfrac{d}{dx}(f^{-1}(x)) = \dfrac{1}{f'(f^{-1}(x))}$,

Q.E.D.

d. $f(x) = x^3 + x = 10$

$(x-2)(x^2+2x+5) = 0$

$x = 2$ (only) $\therefore h(10) = 2$.

Since $h(x) = f^{-1}(x)$ and $f'(x) = 3x^2 + 1$,

$h'(10) = \dfrac{1}{f'(h(10))} = \dfrac{1}{f'(2)} = \dfrac{1}{3 \cdot 2^2 + 1} =$

$1/13$

### Problem Set 4-6

*Differentiability and Continuity*

1. Continuous.
3. Neither.
5. Neither.
7. Both.
9. Neither.
11. Continuous.

13. a. Graph. (example) b. (Equations will vary.)

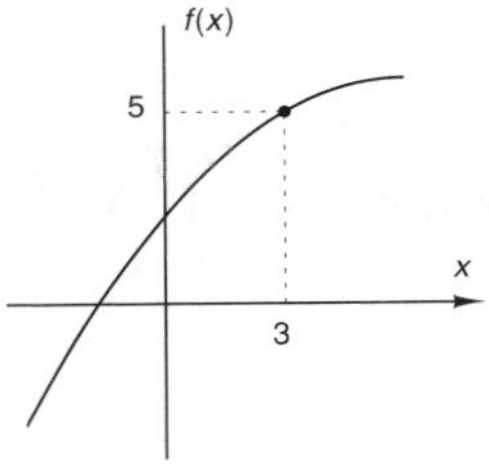


15. a. Graph. (example) b. (Equations will vary.)

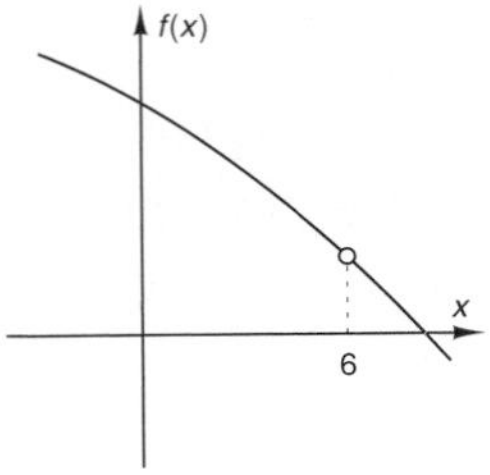


17. a. Graph (example) b. (Equations will vary.)

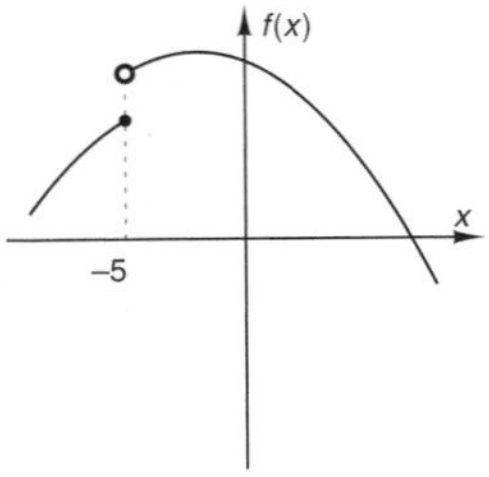


19. a. Graph. (example) b. (Equations will vary.)

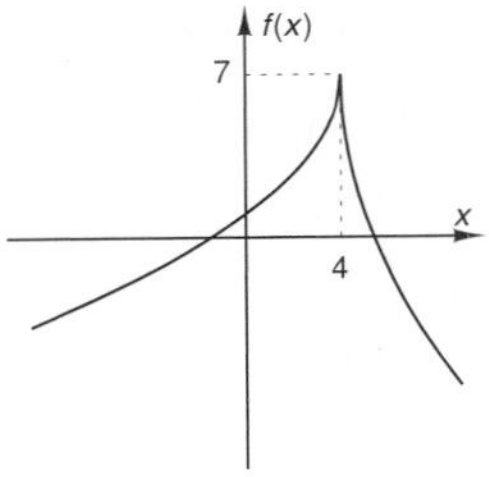


21. Graph. Continuous

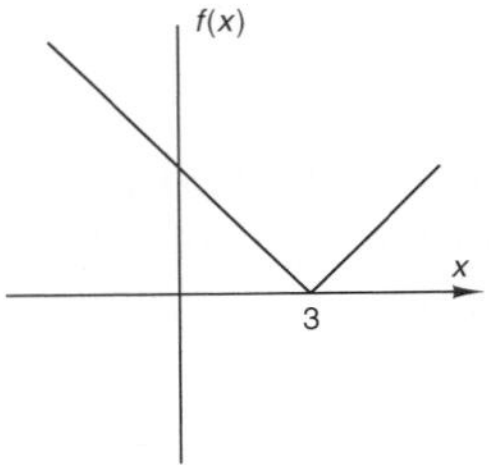


23. Graph. Both

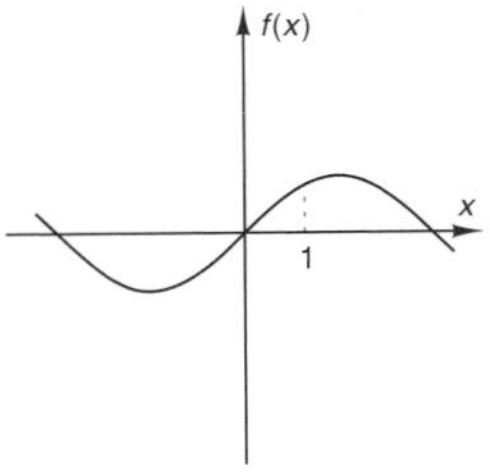


25. Graph. Neither

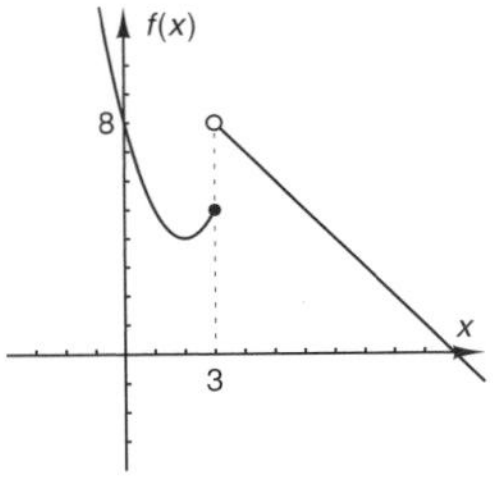


27. Graph. Neither

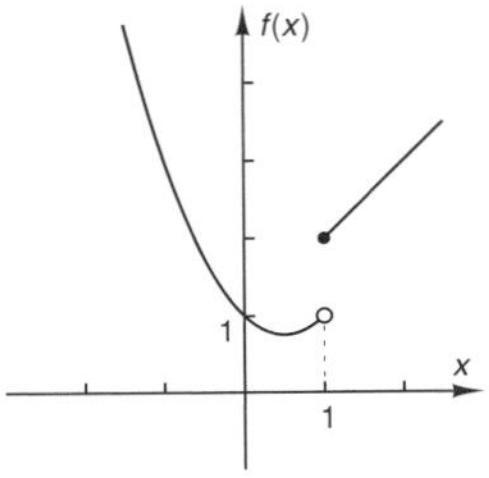

29. Graph. Neither

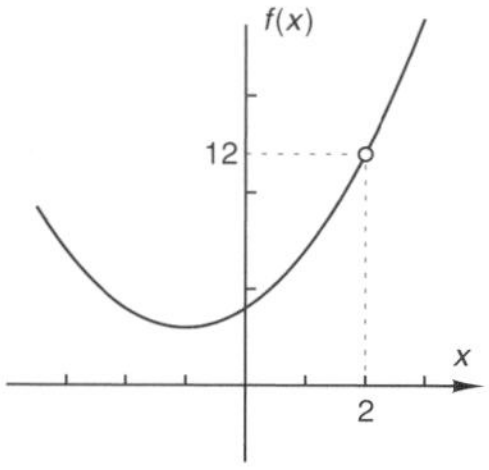


31. $a = -1.5$, $b = 2.5$. Graph.

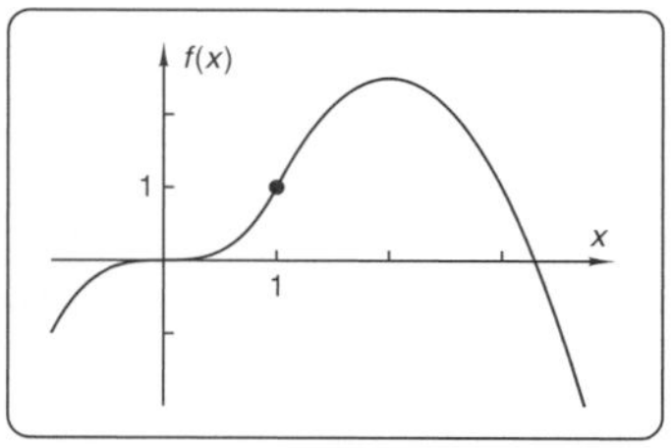


33. $a = -0.5$, $b = 16$. Graph.

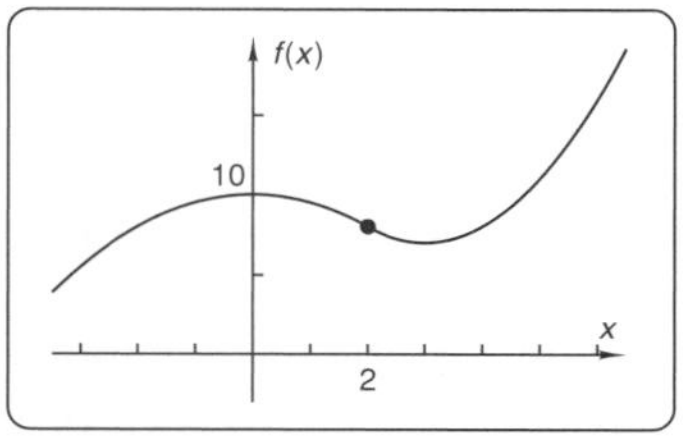


35. *Railroad Curve Problem*

a. $a = 1/30000$, $b = -200/3$
Check: Graph shows that $y$ is differentiable at $x = 100$ with these values of $a$ and $b$.

b. Rate of change of slope is $(y')'$, abbreviated $y''$.

$$y'' = 0 \text{ if } x < 0 \text{ and } y'' = 6ax \text{ if } x > 0.$$

Both of these quantities approach zero as $x$ approaches zero. Since $y'' = 6ax$ for $x > 0$, the slope increases uniformly with $x$ for positive values of $x$, Q.E.D.

37. $f'(x) = \begin{cases} 2x, & \text{if } x < 2 \\ 2x, & \text{if } x > 2 \\ \text{undefined}, & \text{if } x = 2 \end{cases}$

Taking the left and right limits gives

$$\lim_{x \to 2^-} f'(x) = 2 \cdot 2 = 4$$
$$\lim_{x \to 2^+} f'(x) = 2 \cdot 2 = 4$$

Using the definition of derivative, taking the limit from the left,

$$f'(x) = \lim_{x \to 2^-} \frac{x^2 + 1 - 4}{x - 2} \to \frac{1}{0},$$

which is infinite.

The same thing happens from the right. As the following graph shows, the secant lines become vertical as $x$ approaches 2 from either side.

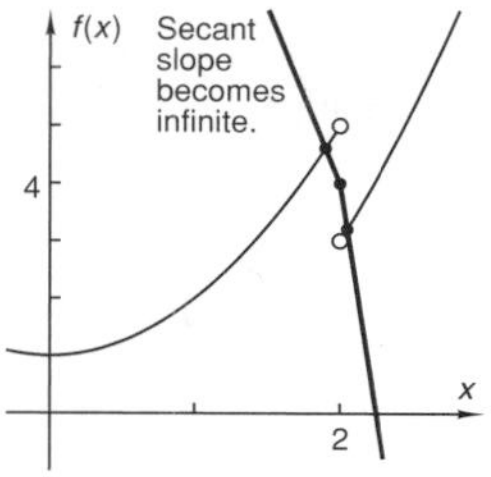


Thus $f$ is not differentiable at $x = 2$, even though the right and left limits of $f'(x)$ are equal to each other. The function must be continuous if it is to have a chance of being differentiable.

39. *Continuity Proof Problem*

a. $y = mx + b \Rightarrow y' = m$, which is independent of $x$.
$\therefore$ linear functions are differentiable for all $x$.
$\therefore$ linear functions are continuous for all $x$.

b. $y = ax^2 + bx + c \Rightarrow y' = 2ax + b$, which exists for all $x$ by the closure axioms.
$\therefore$ quadratic functions are differentiable for all $x$.
$\therefore$ quadratic functions are continuous for all $x$.

c. $y = 1/x = x^{-1} \Rightarrow y' = -x^{-2}$, which exists for all $x \neq 0$ by closure and multiplicative inverse axioms.
$\therefore$ the reciprocal function is differentiable for all $x \neq 0$.
$\therefore$ the reciprocal function is continuous for all $x \neq 0$.

d. $y = x \Rightarrow y' = 1$, which is independent of $x$.
$\therefore$ the identity function is differentiable for all $x$.
$\therefore$ the identity function is continuous for all $x$.

e. $y = k \Rightarrow y' = 0$, which is independent of $x$.
$\therefore$ constant functions are differentiable for all $x$.
$\therefore$ constant functions are continuous for all $x$.

## Problem Set 4-7

*Derivative of a Parametric Function*

1. *Parabola Problem*

a.

| $t$ | $x$ | $y$ |
|---|---|---|
| −3 | −1 | −6 |
| −2 | 0 | −1 |
| −1 | 1 | 2 |
| 0 | 2 | 3 |
| 1 | 3 | 2 |
| 2 | 4 | −1 |
| 3 | 5 | −6 |

b. Graph.

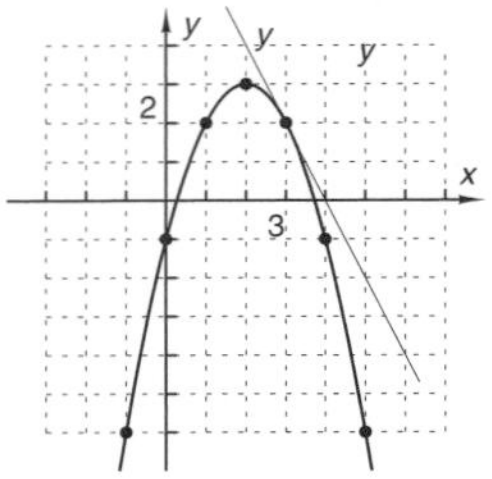


c. $\dfrac{dy}{dx} = -2t$

If $t = 1$, $dy/dx = -2$, and $(x, y) = (3, 2)$.
Line through (3, 2) with slope $-2$ is tangent to the graph. See part (b)

d. $x = 2 + t \Rightarrow t = x - 2 \Rightarrow y = 3 - (x - 2)^2$
This is the Cartesian equation of a parabola because only one of the variables is squared.

e. By direct differentiation, $dy/dx = -2(x - 2)$. At $(x, y) = (3, 2)$, $dy/dx = -2(3 - 2) = -2$, which agrees with part (c).
$dy/dx = -2(x - 2) = -2(2 + t - 2) = -2t$, which agrees with part (a).

3. *Ellipse Problem*

a. Graph. $x = 3\cos t$, $y = 5\sin t$

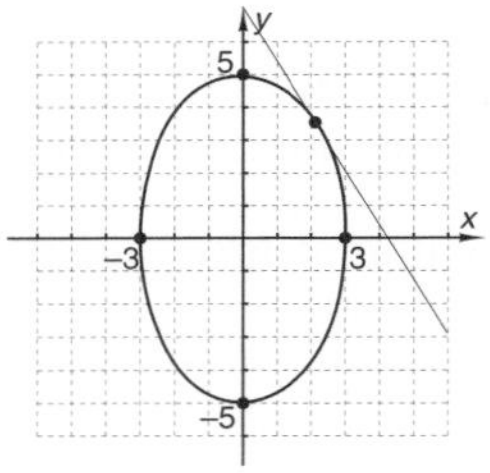


b. $\dfrac{dy}{dx} = \dfrac{5\cos t}{-3\sin t}$

c. If $t = \pi/4$, $(x, y) = (2.121\ldots, 3.535\ldots)$, $dy/dx = -5/3$.
Graph, part (a). The line is tangent to the graph.

d. False. The line from $(0, 0)$ to $(2.1\ldots, 3.5\ldots)$ does not make an angle of 45° with the $x$-axis. [This shows that the $t$ in parametric functions is not the same as the $\theta$ in polar coordinates.]

e. Tangent line is horizontal if $dy/dx = 0$.
$\therefore \cos t = 0$ and $\sin t \neq 0$.
This happens at $t = \pi/2, 3\pi/2, \ldots$.
Points are $(0, 5)$, $(0, -5)$.
Tangent line is vertical if $dy/dx$ is infinite.
$\therefore \sin t = 0$ and $\cos t \neq 0$.
This happens at $t = 0, \pi, 2\pi, \ldots$.
Points are $(3, 0)$, $(-3, 0)$. See graph in part (a).

f. $(x/3)^2 + (y/5)^2 = 1$, which is a standard form of the equation of an ellipse centered at the origin, with $x$-radius 3 and $y$-radius 5.

5. *Circle Problem*

a. Graph.

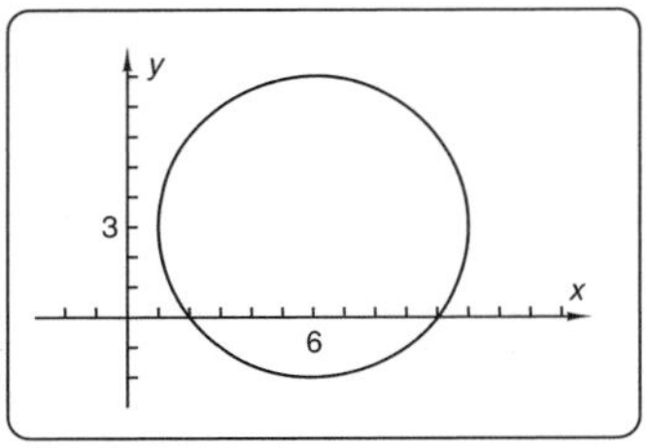


b. $dy/dx = -\cot t$

c. $dy/dx = 0$ if $t = 0.5\pi, 1.5\pi, 2.5\pi, \ldots$
$dy/dx$ is infinite if $t = 0, \pi, 2\pi, \ldots$
At a point where $dy/dx$ is infinite, $dx/dt$ must be 0. If $dy/dt \neq 0$, $dy/dx$ is infinite. If $dy/dt = 0$, $dy/dx$ is indeterminate, and could be infinite.

d. $\dfrac{x-6}{5} = \cos t$ and $\dfrac{y-3}{5} = \sin t$

$$\left(\frac{x-6}{5}\right)^2 + \left(\frac{y-3}{5}\right)^2 = \cos^2 t + \sin^2 t$$

$$\left(\frac{x-6}{5}\right)^2 + \left(\frac{y-3}{5}\right)^2 = 1$$

This is a standard form of the equation of a circle centered at $(6, 3)$ with radius 5.

e. The 6 and 3 added in the original equations are the $x$- and $y$-coordinates of the center, respectively.
The coefficients, 5, for cosine and sine in the original equations are the $x$- and $y$-radii, respectively. Since the $x$- and $y$-radii are equal, the graph is a circle.

7. *Deltoid Problem*

a. Grapher confirms figure in text.

b. $\dfrac{dy}{dx} = \dfrac{\cos t - \cos 2t}{-\sin t - \sin 2t}$

c. Cusps occur where both $dx/dt$ and $dy/dt = 0$. Graphical solution shows that this occurs at $t = 0$, $t = 2\pi/3$, $t = 4\pi/3$, $t = 2\pi, \ldots$.

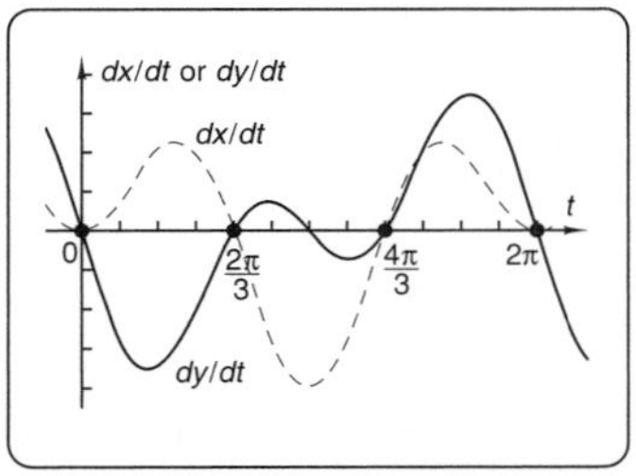


At $t = 0, 2\pi, \ldots$, the tangent appears to be horizontal. At $t = 2\pi/3, 4\pi/3, \ldots$, there appears to be a tangent line but not horizontal.
A numerical solution shows the following values as $t$ approaches $2\pi/3$.

| $t$ | $dy/dx$ |
|---|---|
| $2\pi/3 - 0.1$ | $-1.547849\ldots$ |
| $2\pi/3 - 0.01$ | $-1.712222\ldots$ |
| $2\pi/3 - 0.001$ | $-1.730052\ldots$ |
| $2\pi/3$ | Indeterminate |
| $2\pi/3 + 0.001$ | $-1.734052\ldots$ |
| $2\pi/3 + 0.01$ | $-1.752225\ldots$ |
| $2\pi/3 + 0.1$ | $-1.951213\ldots$ |

$dy/dx$ seems to be approaching about $-1.732$ as $t$ approaches $2\pi/3$.
The exact answer is $-\sqrt{3}$, which you can find with l'Hospital's rule when you study Section 6-8.

9. *Involute Problem*

   a. $x = \cos t + t \sin t$
   $y = \sin t - t \cos t$
   Grapher confirms figure in text.

   b. $\dfrac{dy}{dx} = \dfrac{t \sin t}{t \cos t} = \tan t$

   c. At $t = \pi$, $dy/dx = \tan \pi = 0$.
   The string will be pointing straight up from the $x$-axis. The diagram shows that the tangent to the graph is horizontal at this point.

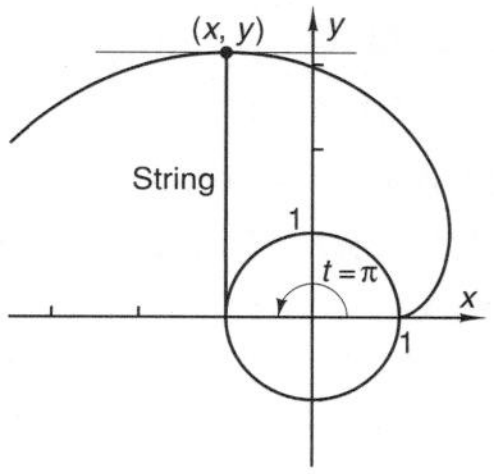


11. *Pendulum Project*
    Not selected

13. *Lissajous Curves*

    a. Grapher confirms figure in text.

    b. Graph. ($x = \cos 4t, y = \sin t$)

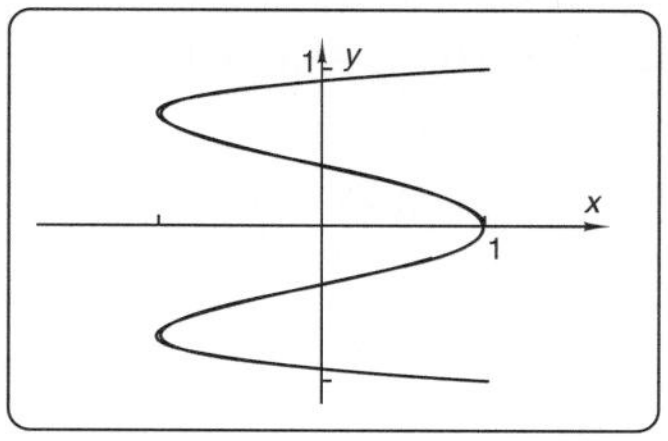


   c. If $n$ is an even number, the graph comes to end points and retraces its path, making two complete cycles as $t$ goes from 0 to $2\pi$.
   If $n$ is an odd number, the graph does not come to end points. It makes one complete cycle as $t$ goes from 0 to $2\pi$.

   d. i. Graph. ($x = \cos 5t, y = \sin t$)

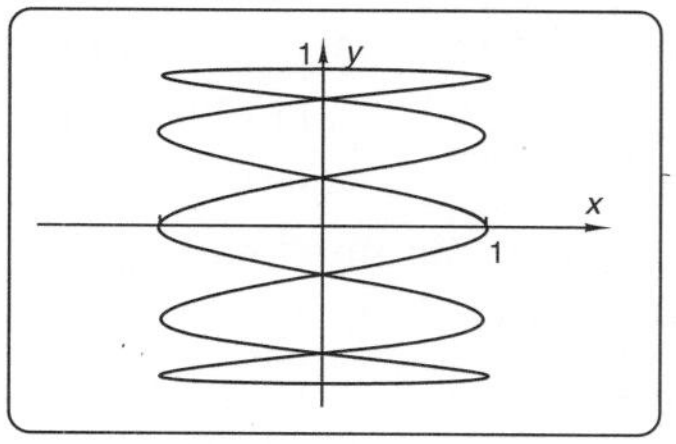


   ii. Graph. ($x = \cos 6t, y = \sin t$)

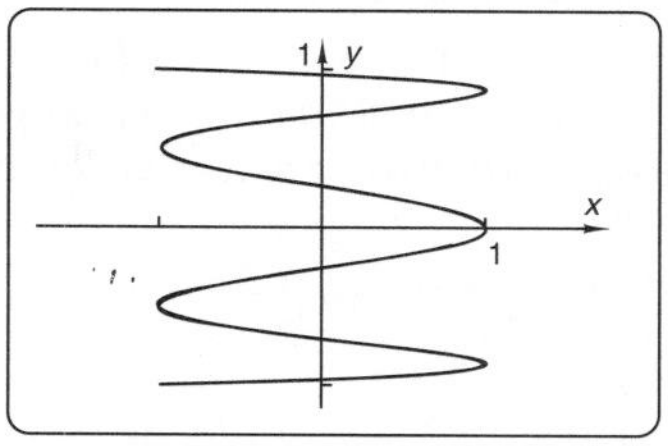


   e. See grapher graphs in part (d).

   f. Graph, $n = 1$. ($x = \cos t, y = \sin t$)

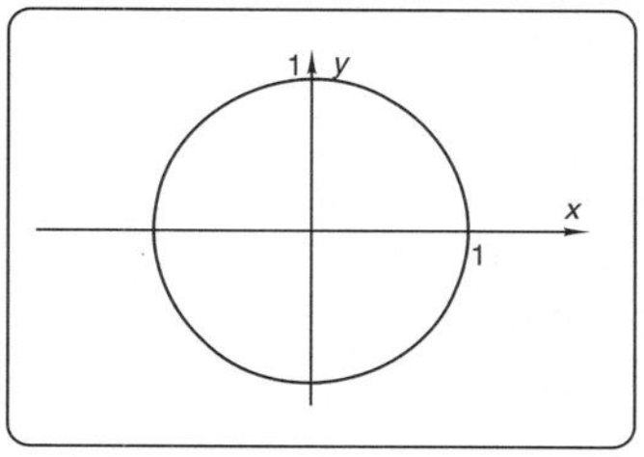


   Graph, $n = 2$. ($x = \cos 2t, y = \sin t$)

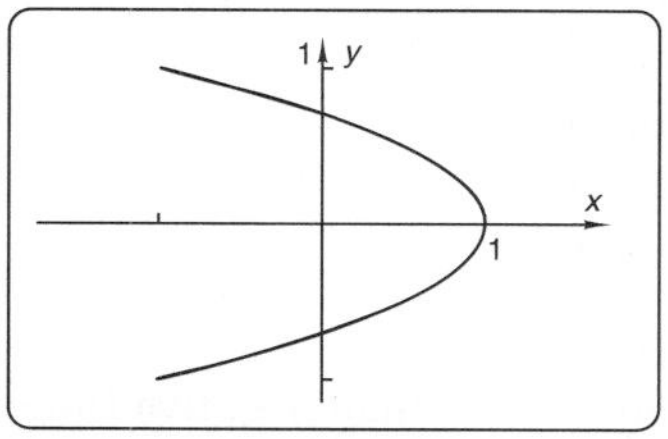


   If $n = 1$ the graph is a circle.
   If $n = 2$ the graph is a parabola.

## Problem Set 4-8

*Graphs and Derivatives of Implicit Relations*

1. $y' = -\dfrac{3x^2}{28y^3}$

3. $y' = \dfrac{2x^5y^9 + 1}{y^2 - 3x^6y^8}$

5. $y' = \dfrac{2\cos 2x - 1 - y}{x + 1}$

7. $y' = y^{0.5}/x^{0.5}$

9. $y' = -\dfrac{9x}{4y}$

11. $y' = \dfrac{1 - 15x^{14}y^{20}}{1 + 20x^{15}y^{19}}$

13. $y' = \dfrac{\cos x \sin x}{\cos y \sin y}$

15. $y' = -y/x$

17. $y' = \sec y$

19. $y' = -\sin y \tan y$

21. $y' = -\dfrac{1}{\sin y} = -\dfrac{1}{\sqrt{1 - x^2}}$

23. $y = x^{11/5} \Rightarrow y^5 = x^{11} \Rightarrow 5y^4 \cdot y' = 11x^{10} \Rightarrow$

$$y' = \frac{11x^{10}}{5y^4} = \frac{11x^{10}}{5(x^{11/5})^4} = \frac{11x^{10}}{5x^{44/5}} = \frac{11}{5}x^{6/5},$$

which is the answer obtained using the derivative of a power formula, Q.E.D.

25. *Circle Problem*

a. At $(-6, 8)$, $(-6)^2 + 8^2 = 100$, which shows that $(-6, 8)$ is on the graph, Q.E.D.

b. $dy/dx = -x/y$. At $(-6, 8)$, $dy/dx = 0.75$. A line at $(-6, 8)$ with slope 0.75 is tangent to the graph, showing that the answer is reasonable.

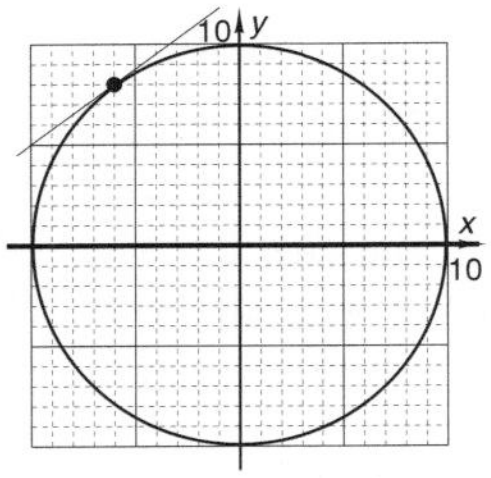


c. $\dfrac{dy}{dx} = -\dfrac{\cos t}{\sin t}$

At $x = -6$, $t = \cos^{-1}(-0.6)$
$\sin(\cos^{-1}(-0.6)) = 0.8$

$\therefore \dfrac{dy}{dx} = -\dfrac{-0.6}{0.8} = 0.75$, which agrees with part (b), Q.E.D.

27. *Cubic Circle Problem*

a. $dy/dx = -x^2/y^2$
$x = 0$: $dy/dx = 0$
The tangent is horizontal (see graph below).
$x = 2$: $dy/dx = -0.2732\ldots.$
The tangent line has a small negative slope, which agrees with the graph.
$x = 4$: $dy/dx$ is infinite.
The tangent line is vertical.

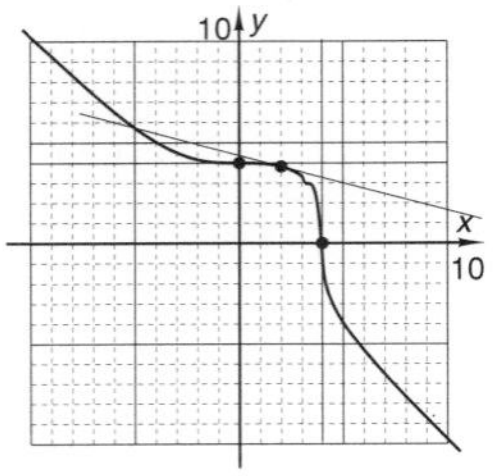


b. $y = x$: $dy/dx = -1$

c. $y = (64 - x^3)^{1/3}$
As $x$ becomes infinite, $(64 - x^3)^{1/3}$ gets closer to $(-x^3)^{1/3}$, which equals $-x$. The graph has a diagonal asymptote at $y = -x$, and $dy/dx \to -1$.

d. The name comes from analogy with the equation of a circle, such as $x^2 + y^2 = 64$.

## Problem Set 4-9

*Chapter Review and Test*

### Review Problems

R0. Not selected

R1. a. $x = g(t) = t^3 \Rightarrow g'(t) = 3t^2$
$y = h(t) = \cos t \Rightarrow h'(t) = -\sin t$
If $f(t) = g(t) \cdot h(t) = t^3 \cos t$, then, for example, $f'(1) = 0.7794\ldots$ by numerical differentiation.
$g'(1) \cdot h'(1) = 3(1^2) \cdot (-\sin 1) = -2.5244\ldots.$
$\therefore f'(t) \neq g'(t) \cdot h'(t)$, Q.E.D.

b. If $f(t) = g(t)/h(t) = t^3/\cos t$, then, for example, $f'(1) = 8.4349\ldots$ by numerical differentiation.
$g'(1)/h'(1) = 3(1^2)/(-\sin 1) = 3.5651\ldots.$
$\therefore f'(t) \neq g'(t)/h'(t)$, Q.E.D.

c. $y = \cos t$.
$x = t^3 \Rightarrow t = x^{1/3} \Rightarrow y = \cos(x^{1/3})$

$\dfrac{dy}{dx} = -\sin(x^{1/3}) \cdot \dfrac{1}{3}x^{-2/3}$

At $x = 1$, $\dfrac{dy}{dx} = -\sin 1 \cdot \dfrac{1}{3} = -0.280490\ldots$

If $x = 1$, then $t = 1^{1/3} = 1$.

$\therefore \dfrac{dy/dt}{dx/dt} = \dfrac{-\sin t}{3t^2} = \dfrac{-\sin 1}{3} = -0.280490\ldots,$

which equals $dy/dx$, Q.E.D.

R2. a. If $y = uv$, then $y' = u'v + uv'$.

b. See proof of product formula in text.

c. i. $f'(x) = 7x^6 \cos 3x - 3x^7 \sin 3x$
ii. $g'(x) = \cos x \sin 2x + 2 \sin x \cos 2x$
iii. $h'(x) = 15(3x - 7)^4(5x + 2)^2(8x - 5)$
iv. $s'(x) = 1000x^7$ (Be careful!)

d. $f(x) = (3x + 8)(4x + 7)$
i. $f'(x) = 3(4x + 7) + (3x + 8)(4) = \underline{24x + 53}$
ii. $f(x) = 12x^2 + 53x + 56$
$f'(x) = \underline{24x + 53}$, which checks.

R3. a. If $y = u/v$, then $y' = \dfrac{u'v - uv'}{v^2}$.

b. See proof of quotient formula in text.

c. i. $f'(x) = \dfrac{10x \cos 10x - 5 \sin 10x}{x^6}$

ii. $g'(x) = \dfrac{18(2x + 3)^8(5x - 11)}{(9x - 5)^5}$

iii. $h(x) = -1500x^2(100x^3 - 1)^{-6}$

d. $y = 1/x^{10}$
As a quotient:
$$y' = \frac{0 \cdot x^{10} - 1 \cdot 10x^9}{x^{20}} = \frac{-10}{x^{11}} = -10x^{-11}$$
As a power:
$y = x^{-10}$
$y' = -10x^{-11}$, which checks.

e. $t'(x) = \sec^2 x$
$t'(1) = 3.4255\ldots$

f. $m(x) = \dfrac{t(x) - t(1)}{x - 1} = \dfrac{\tan x - \tan 1}{x - 1}$

Graph.

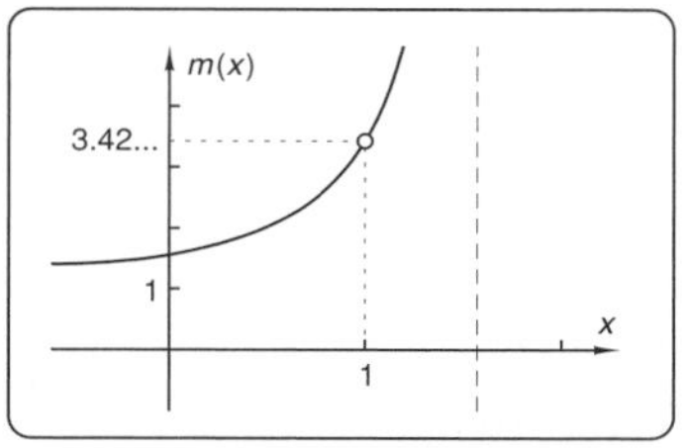


| $x$ | $m(x)$ |
|---|---|
| 0.997 | 3.40959... |
| 0.998 | 3.41488... |
| 0.999 | 3.42019... |
| 1 | no value |
| 1.001 | 3.43086... |
| 1.002 | 3.43622... |
| 1.003 | 3.44160... |

The values get closer to 3.4255... as $x$ approaches 1 from either side, Q.E.D.

R4. a. i. $y' = 7\sec^2 7x$

ii. $y' = -4x^3 \csc^2(x^4)$

iii. $y' = 3\sec x \tan x$

iv. $y' = -\csc x \cot x$

b. See derivation in text for $\tan' x = \sec^2 x$.

c. Graph. The graph is always sloping upward, which is connected to the fact that $\tan' x$ equals the square of a function, and is thus always positive.

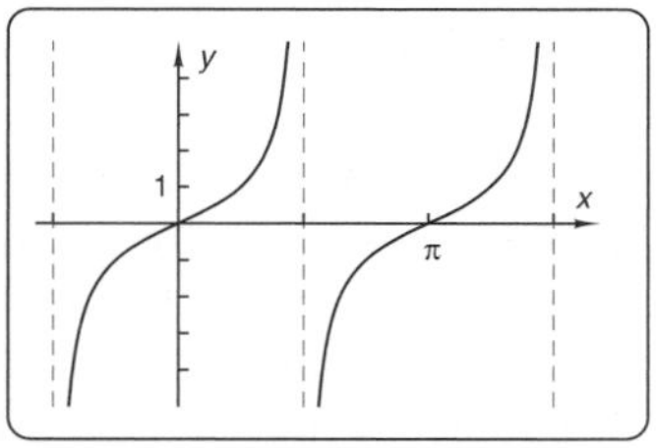


d. $f'(t) = 7\sec t \tan t$

$f'(1) = 20.17\ldots$

$f'(1.5) = 1395.44\ldots$

$f'(1.57) = 11038634.0\ldots$

There is an asymptote in the secant graph at $t = \pi/2 = 1.57079\ldots$. As $t$ gets closer to this value, secant changes very rapidly!

R5. a. i. $y' = \dfrac{3}{1 + 9x^2}$

ii. $\dfrac{d}{dx}(\sec^{-1} x) = \dfrac{1}{|x|\sqrt{x^2 - 1}}$

iii. $c'(x) = -\dfrac{2\cos^{-1} x}{\sqrt{1 - x^2}}$

b. Graph, $y = \sin^{-1} x$, plotted as

$x = \sin t$

$y = t$

$t$-window: $[-\pi/2, \pi/2]$

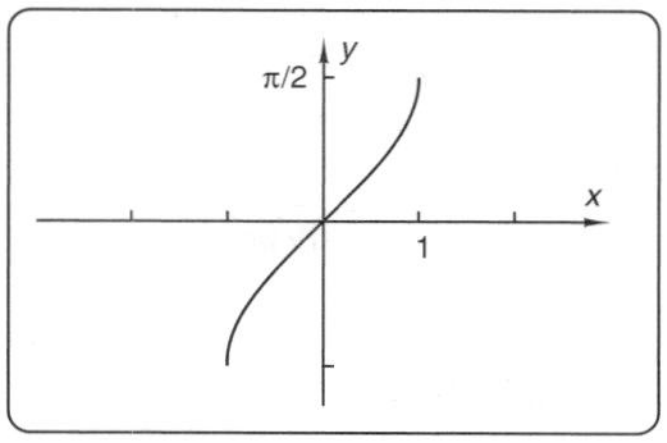


$y'(0) = \dfrac{1}{\sqrt{1 - 0^2}} = 1$, which agrees with the graph.

$y'(1) = \dfrac{1}{\sqrt{1 - 1^2}} = \dfrac{1}{0}$, which is infinite.

The graph becomes vertical as $x$ approaches 1 from the negative side. $y'(2)$ is undefined because $y(2)$ is not a real number.

R6. a. Differentiability implies continuity.

b. i. Graph. (example)

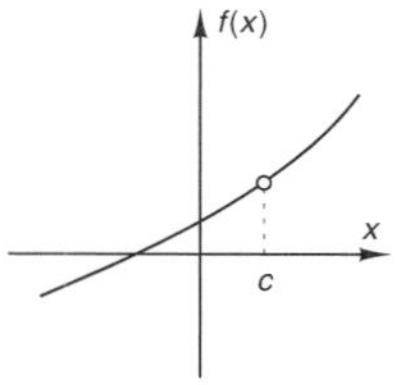


ii. Graph. (example)

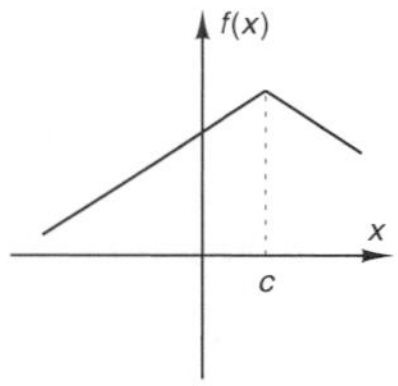


iii. Graph.

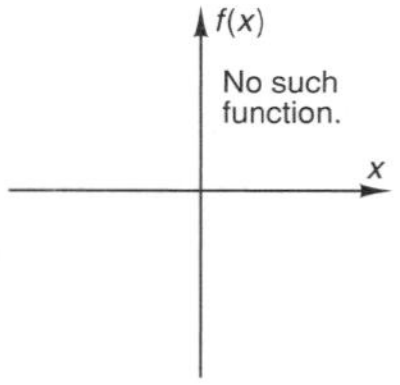


iv. Graph. (example)

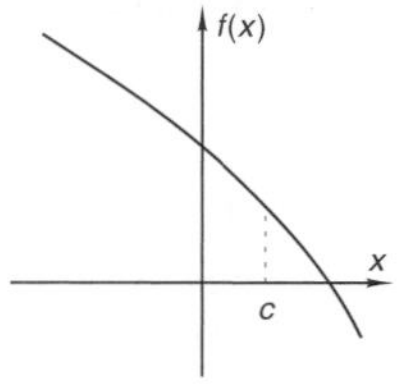


c. i. Graph.

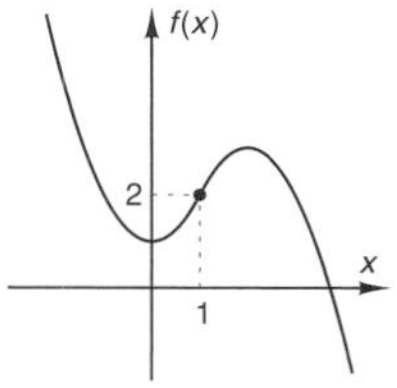


ii. $f$ is continuous at $x = 1$ because right and left limits both equal 2, which equal $f(1)$.

iii. $f$ is differentiable. Left and right limits of $f'(x)$ are both equal to 2, and $f$ is continuous at $x = 2$.

d. $a = 1$, $b = 0$

Graph, differentiable and continuous at $x = 0$.

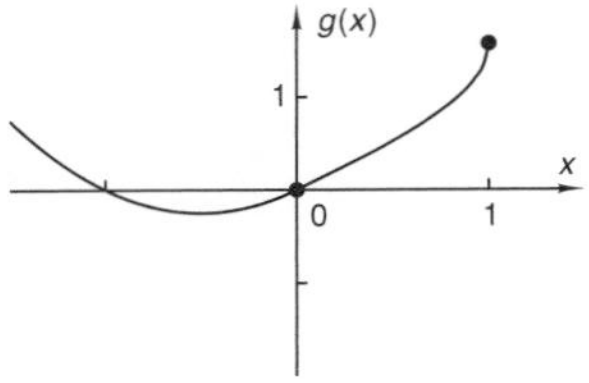


R7. a. $\dfrac{dy}{dx} = \dfrac{\sin t + t\cos t}{\cos t - t\sin t}$

Where the graph crosses the positive $x$-axis, $t = 2\pi, 4\pi, 6\pi, \ldots$
If $t = 6\pi$, $x = 6$ and $y = 0$.
$\therefore (6, 0)$ *is* on the graph.
If $t = 6\pi$, then $dy/dx = 6\pi$.
So the graph is *not* vertical where it crosses the $x$-axis. It has a slope of $6\pi = 18.84\ldots$.

b. *Ferris Wheel Problem*

$x = 20\sin\dfrac{\pi}{10}(t-3)$

$y = 25 + 20\cos\dfrac{\pi}{10}(t-3)$

$dx/dt = 2\pi\cos\dfrac{\pi}{10}(t-3)$

$dy/dt = -2\pi\sin\dfrac{\pi}{10}(t-3)$

When $t = 0$, $dy/dt = 5.0832\ldots$.
The Ferris wheel is going up at about 5.1 ft/sec.
When $t = 0$, $dx/dt = 3.6931\ldots$.
The Ferris wheel is going right at about 3.7ft/sec.

$\dfrac{dy}{dx} = \dfrac{dy/dt}{dx/dt}$

$dy/dx$ is first infinite at $t = 8$ sec.

R8. a. $y' = 24x^{-2/3}(12x^{1/3} + 7)^5$

b. $y' = \dfrac{dy}{dx} = \dfrac{4.5x^{3.5} - y^4\cos(xy)}{3y^2\sin(xy) + xy^3\cos(xy)}$

c. *Cissoid of Diocles Problem*

i. $\dfrac{dy}{dx} = \dfrac{3x^2 + y^2}{8y - 2xy}$

At $(2, 2)$, $dy/dx = 2$. At $(2, -2)$, $dy/dx = -2$. Lines at these points with these slopes are tangent to the graph (see diagram).

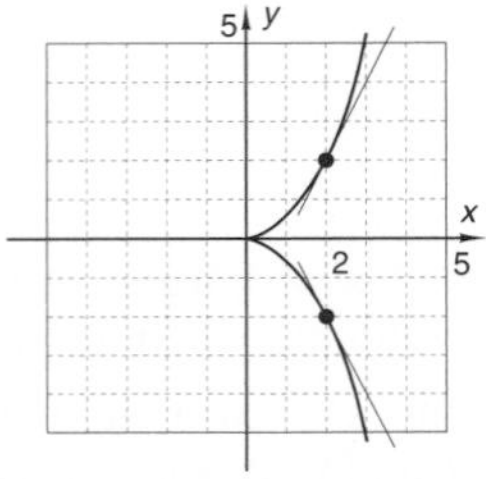


ii. At $(0, 0)$, $dy/dx$ has the indeterminate form $0/0$, which is consistent with the cusp.

iii. Asymptote is at $x = 4$.

## CHAPTER 5

### Exploratory Problem Set 5-1

A Definite Integral Problem

*Oil Well Problem*

1. $c(1000) \approx \$27.00/\text{ft}$
   $c(4000) \approx \$66.39/\text{ft}$
3. Average cost $\approx \$43.86/\text{ft}$
5. Average cost using Problem 4 $\approx 43.74$
   Average of $c(1000)$ and $c(4000)$ is 46.69.
   The average of $c(1000)$ and $c(4000)$ is significantly higher than the actual average figured either way.
7. The mathematical word for such a rate is the second derivative. The physical quantity is acceleration.

### Problem Set 5-2

Review of Antiderivatives

1. $f(x) = x^7 + C$
3. $f(x) = -\dfrac{1}{8}x^{-8} + C$
5. $f(x) = \sin x + C$
7. $f(x) = -\cot x + C$
9. $f(x) = \csc x + C$
11. $f(x) = -\dfrac{1}{5}\cos 5x + C$
13. $f(x) = \dfrac{1}{8}\tan 8x + C$
15. $f(x) = \dfrac{1}{32}(4x+5)^8 + C$
17. a. Each is an antiderivative of $y' = 5x^4$.

    b. The word is *congruent*.
    For any one value of $x$, each pair of points on $y = x^5 + 0.3$ and $y_2 = x^5 + 0.7$, for example, is the same *vertical* distance apart, 0.4. However, the graphs are not really parallel because the *perpendicular* distance from one to another is not constant.

    c. $f(x) = x^3 - 2x + C$
    For $(1, 0)$, $C = 1$
    $f(x) = x^3 - 2x + 1$ contains $(1, 0)$
    For $(1, 1)$, $C = 2$
    $f(x) = x^3 - 2x + 2$ contains $(1, 1)$
    For $(1, 2)$, $2 = 1^3 - 2 \cdot 1 + C \Rightarrow C = 3$
    $f(x) = x^3 - 2x + 3$ contains $(1, 2)$

    d. Graph.

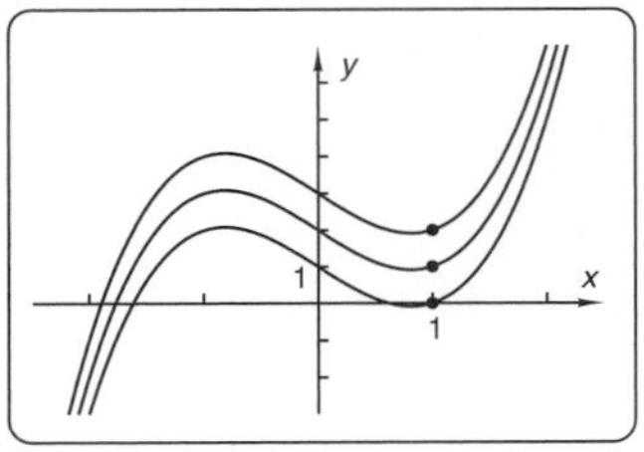

e. The constant $C$ affects the vertical position of the graph without affecting either its shape or its horizontal position. The antiderivative is a "family" of functions since there is more than just one function, but they look so much the same.

### Problem Set 5-3

*Linear Approximations and Differentials*

1. $y = 21.6x - 48.6$
   $x = 3.1$: Error $= 0.11042$
   $x = 3.001$: Error $= 0.0000108\ldots$
   $x = 2.999$: Error $= 0.0000107\ldots$

3. Local Linearity Problem #1
   $y = 2x - 1$
   Graph shows zoom by factor of 10.

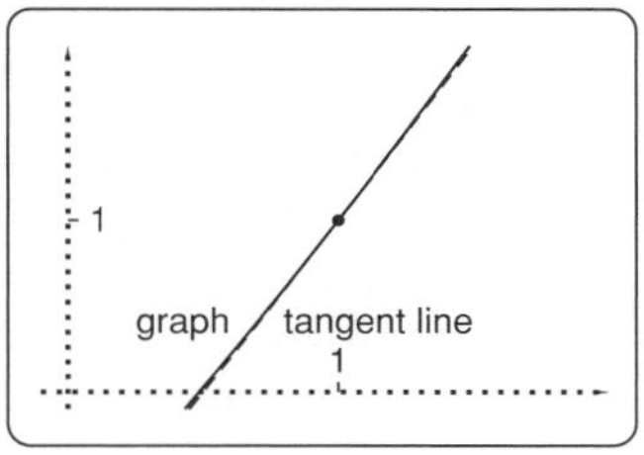


Local linearity describes the property of the function because if you keep $x$ close to 1 (in the "locality" of 1) the curved graph of the function looks like the straight graph of the tangent line.

5. *Steepness of a Hill Problem*
   a. Let $A$ be the number of radians in $\theta$ degrees.
   By trigonometry, $\tan A = \dfrac{x}{100} \Rightarrow A = \tan^{-1}\dfrac{x}{100}$
   Since 1 radian is $180/\pi$ degrees,
   $\theta = \dfrac{180}{\pi}\tan^{-1}\dfrac{x}{100}$, Q.E.D.
   b. $d\theta = \dfrac{1.8/\pi}{1 + (x/100)^2}\,dx$
   $x = 0: \quad d\theta = 0.5729\ldots dx$
   $x = 10: \quad d\theta = 0.5672\ldots dx$
   $x = 20: \quad d\theta = 0.5509\ldots dx$
   c. The error is $0.1492\ldots°$, which is about 1.3%.
   d. $0.5729\ldots$ is approximately 0.5. So multiplying by it is approximately equivalent to dividing by 2.
   For a 20% grade this estimate gives 10°, compared to the actual angle of $11.309\ldots°$, an error of about 11.6%.
   For a 100% grade this estimate gives 50°, compared to the actual angle of 45°, an error of about 11.1%.

7. $dy = 21x^2\,dx$
9. $dy = 28x^3(x^4 + 1)^6\,dx$
11. $dy = (6x + 5)\,dx$
13. $dy = 8.5x^{-2.7}\,dx$
15. $dy = 3\cos 3x\,dx$
17. $dy = 3\tan^2 x\sec^2 x\,dx$
19. $dy = (4\cos x - 4x\sin x)\,dx$
21. $dy = \left(x - \dfrac{1}{4}\right)dx$
23. $dy = -\sin(\sec x)\cdot\sec x\tan x\,dx$
25. $y = 5x^4 + C$
27. $y = -\dfrac{1}{4}\cos 4x + C$
29. $y = \dfrac{2}{7}(0.5x - 1)^7 + C$
31. $y = \tan x + C$
33. $y = 5x + C$
35. $y = 2x^3 + 5x^2 - 4x + C$
37. $y = \dfrac{1}{6}\sin^6 x + C$
39. a. $dy = 6(3x - 4)(2x - 5)^2(5x - 1)\,dx$
    b. $dy = -60.48$
    c. $\Delta y = -60.0218\ldots$
    d. $-60.48$ is close to $-60.0218\ldots$.

### Problem Set 5-4

*Formal Definition of Indefinite Integral*

1. $x^6 + C$
3. $\dfrac{1}{11}x^{11} + C$
5. $-\dfrac{4}{5}x^{-5} + C$
7. $20t^{5.1} + C$
9. $50p^{3/5} + C$
11. $\sin x + C$
13. $-\dfrac{1}{3}\cos 3m + C$
15. $\dfrac{4}{7}\sin 7x + C$
17. $\dfrac{1}{12}(4v + 9)^3 + C$
19. $-\dfrac{1}{20}(8 - 5x)^4 + C$
21. $-\dfrac{1}{21}(6 + 7b)^{-3} + C$
23. $\dfrac{1}{7}\sin^7 x + C$
25. $-\dfrac{1}{5}\cos^5\theta + C$
27. $\dfrac{1}{4\pi}\sin^4 \pi x + C$
29. $\dfrac{1}{3}x^3 + \dfrac{3}{2}x^2 - 5x + C$
31. $-r^{-1} + \dfrac{1}{3}r^3 + C$
33. $\dfrac{1}{7}x^7 + 3x^5 + 25x^3 + 125x + C$
35. $\tan x + C$
37. $-\dfrac{1}{3}\csc 3x + C$
39. $\dfrac{1}{8}\tan^8 x + C$
41. $-\dfrac{1}{9}\csc^9 x + C$
43. *Distance from Velocity Problem*
    $D(t) = 40t + \dfrac{10}{3}t^{3/2}$
    $D(10) = 505.4092\ldots \approx 505$ feet

45. *Integral of a Sum Property*
Prove that if $f$ and $g$ are functions that can be integrated, then $\int(f(x) + g(x))\,dx = \int f(x)\,dx + \int g(x)\,dx$.
*Proof:*
Let $h(x) = \int f(x)\,dx + \int g(x)\,dx$.
By the derivative of a sum property,
$h'(x) = \dfrac{d}{dx}\int f(x)\,dx + \dfrac{d}{dx}\int g(x)\,dx$
By the definition of indefinite integral applied twice to the right side of the equation,
$h'(x) = f(x) + g(x)$.
By the definition of indefinite integral applied in the other direction,
$h(x) = \int(f(x) + g(x))dx$.
By the transitive property, then, $\int(f(x)+g(x))dx = \int f(x)dx + \int g(x)dx$, Q.E.D.

47. *Introduction to Riemann Sums*
   a. Integral $\approx 50.75$
   b. Integral $\approx 50.9375$
   c. As shown in Figures 5-4a and 5-4b, the Riemann sum with 6 increments has smaller regions included above the graph and smaller regions excluded below the graph. So the Riemann sum should be closer to the integral.
   d. Conjecture: Exact value is 51.
   e. By trapezoidal rule with $n = 100$, integral $\approx 51.00045$, which agrees with the conjecture.
   f. The object went 51 ft.
   Average velocity = 17 ft/min.

## Problem Set 5-5

*Riemann Sums, and the Definition of Definite Integral*

1. $R_6 = 20.9375$
3. $R_8 = 23.97054\ldots$
5. $R_5 = 0.958045\ldots$
7. $L_4 = 0.73879\ldots$, $U_4 = 1.16866\ldots$
$M_4 = 0.92270\ldots$, $T_4 = 0.95373\ldots$
$\therefore M_4$ and $T_4$ are between $L_4$ and $U_4$, Q.E.D.
9. *Sample Point Problem*
   a. Take sample points at $x = 1, \pi/2, 2, 3, 4$, and 6.
   b. Take sample points at $x = 0, 1, 3, 4, 3\pi/2$, and 5.
   c. $U_6 = 21.71134\ldots$, $L_6 = 14.53372\ldots$
11. *Limit of Riemann Sums Problem*
   a. The program should give the values listed in text.
   b. $L_{100} = 20.77545$, $L_{500} = 20.955018$.
   $L_n$ seems to be approaching 21.
   c. $U_{100} = 21.22545$, $U_{500} = 21.045018$.
   $U_n$ also seems to be approaching 21.
   $f$ is *integrable* on $[1, 4]$ if $L_n$ and $U_n$ have the same limit as $n$ approaches infinity.
   d. The trapezoids are circumscribed around the region under the graph and thus contain more area (see left diagram). For rectangles, the "triangular" part of the region that is left out has more area than the "triangular" part that is included since the "triangles" have equal bases but unequal altitudes (see right diagram).

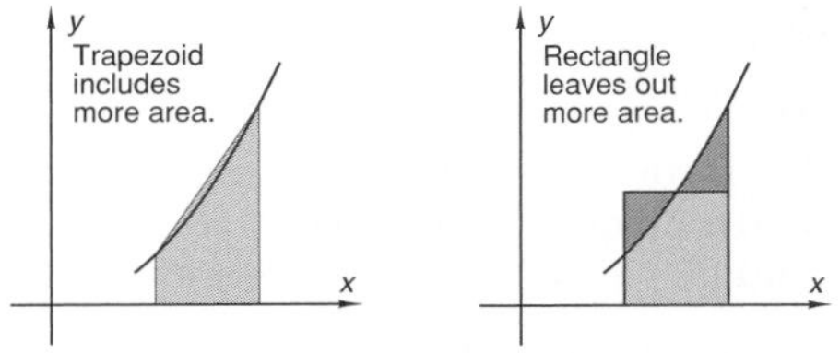


12. *Exact Integral of Square Function by Brute Force*
   a. $\int_0^3 x^2\,dx$
   $U_{100} = 9.13545$; $L_{100} = 8.86545$
   Conjecture: Integral equals 9 exactly.
   b. The sample points will be at the *right* of each interval, $1 \cdot 3/n, 2 \cdot 3/n, 3 \cdot 3/n, \ldots, n \cdot 3/n$.
   c. $U_n = (3/n)(1 \cdot 3/n)^2 + (3/n)(2 \cdot 3/n)^2 + (3/n)(3 \cdot 3/n)^2 + \cdots + (3/n)(n \cdot 3/n)^2$
   d. $U_n = (3/n)^3(1^2 + 2^2 + 3^2 + \cdots + n^2)$
   $= (3/n)^3(n/6)(n+1)(2n+1)$
   $= (4.5/n^2)(n+1)(2n+1)$
   $U_{100} = (4.4/100^2)(101)(201) = 9.13454$, which is correct.
   e. Using the formula, $U_{1000} = 9.013504\ldots$, which *does* seem to be approaching 9.
   h. $U_n = 4.5 \cdot \dfrac{n+1}{n} \cdot \dfrac{2n+1}{n}$
   $= 4.5(1 + 1/n)(2 + 1/n)$
   As $n$ approaches infinity, $1/n$ approaches zero.
   $\therefore U_n$ approaches $4.5(1 + 0)(2 + 0) = 9$
13. Not selected.

## Problem Set 5-6

*The Mean Value Theorem and Rolle's Theorem*

1. See statement of mean value theorem in text.
3. Graph, $g(x) = 6/x$; $[1, 4]$

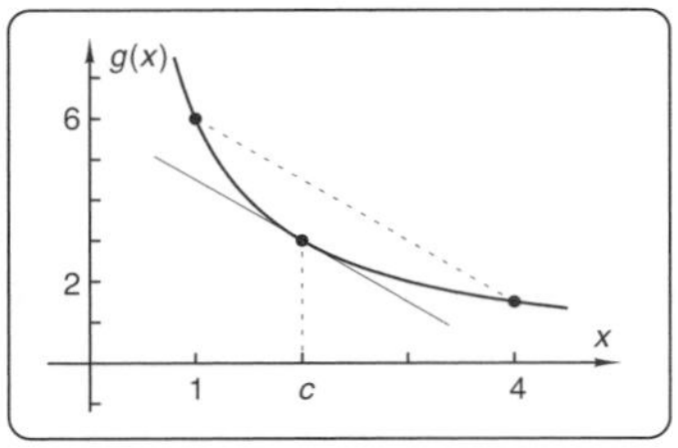


$c = 2$
Tangent at $x = 2$ parallels the secant line.

5. Graph, $c(x) = 2 + \cos x$; $\left[0, \dfrac{\pi}{2}\right]$

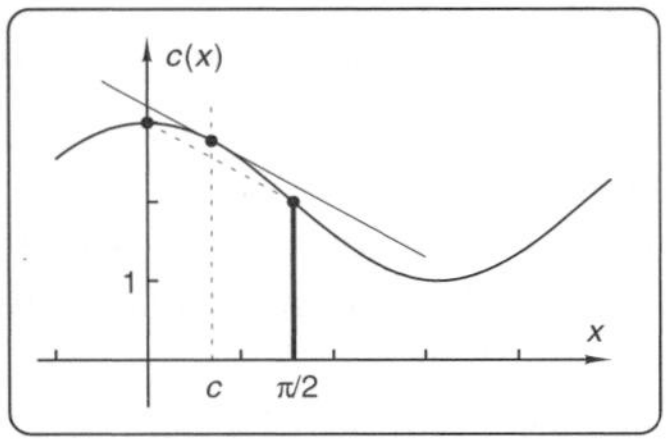


$c = 0.69010\ldots$
Tangent at $x = 0.690\ldots$ parallels the secant line.

7. Graph, $f(x) = x\cos x$

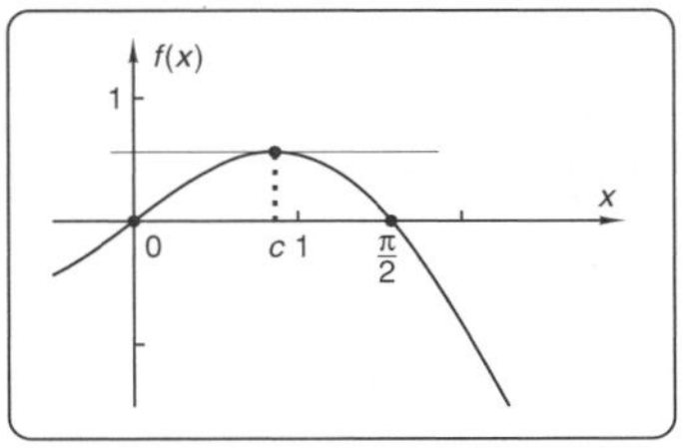


$f'(x) = \cos x - x\sin x$
$\therefore f$ is differentiable for all $x$.
$f(0) = f(\pi/2) = 0$
$\therefore$ hypotheses are met on $[0, \pi/2]$.
$c = 0.86033\ldots$
Horizontal line at $x = 0.86033\ldots$ is tangent.

9. Graph, $f(x) = (6x - x^2)^{1/2}$

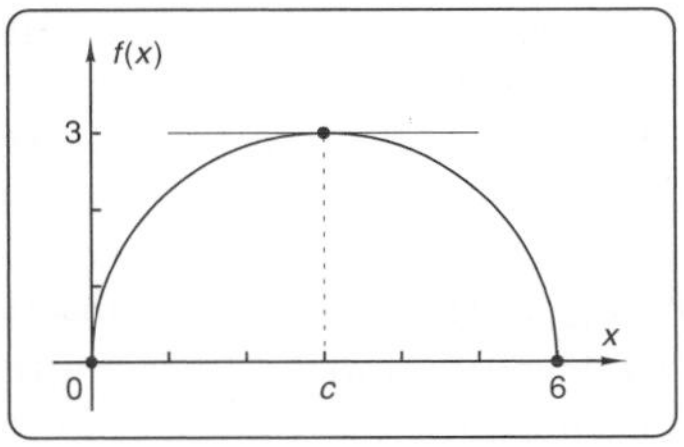


$f'(x) = (1/2)(6x - x^2)^{-1/2} \cdot (6 - 2x)$
$\therefore f$ is differentiable on $(0, 6)$.
$f$ is continuous at $x = 0$ and $x = 6$.
$f(0) = f(6) = 0$; interval is $[0, 6]$; $c = 3$
Horizontal line at $x = 3$ is tangent.

11. *Compound Interest Problem*
   a. \$74,357.52 Surprising!
   b. Average rate $\approx$ \$1,467.15 per year
   c. $d'(0) \approx$ \$86.18 per year
      $d'(50) \approx$ \$6,407.96 per year
      The average of these is \$3,247.07 per year, which does *not* equal the average in part (b).
   d. $t \approx 32.893\ldots$ years
      This time is not halfway between 0 and 50.

13. See Figure 5-6d.

15. Graph. (example)

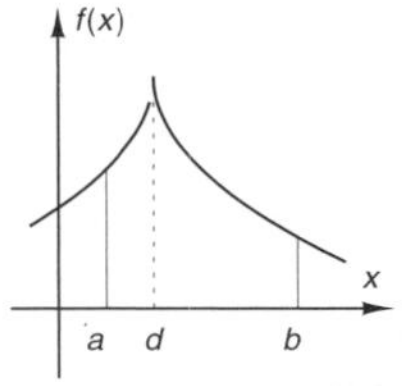


17. See Figure 5-6g.

19. $f(1) = -3 \neq 0$.
    Conclusion is not true.
    $f'(2) = 0$, but 2 is not in the interval $(0, 1)$.
    Graph.

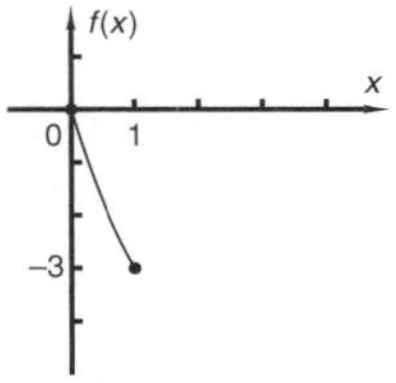


21. $f(2) = -4 \neq 0$.
    Conclusion is not true. $f'(2) = 0$, but 2 is not in the *open* interval $(0, 2)$.
    Graph.

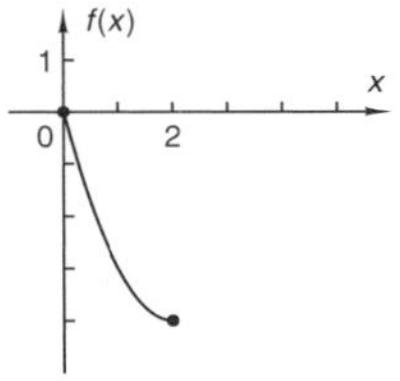


23. $f(3) = -3 \neq 0$.
    Conclusion is true.
    $f'(2) = 0$ and 2 is in the interval $(0, 3)$.
    Graph.

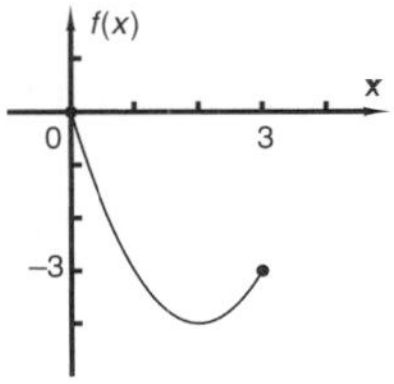


25. $f(0)$ does not exist.
    Conclusion is not true.
    $f'(x)$ never equals 0.
    Graph.

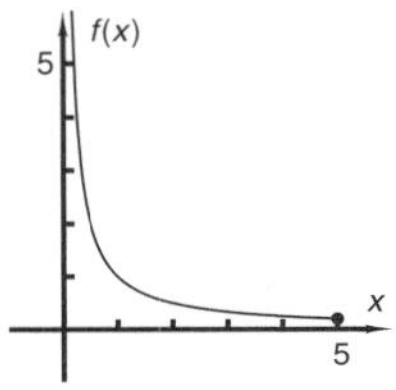

27. $f$ is not differentiable at $x = 3$. Conclusion is not true.
$f'(x)$ never equals 0. Graph.

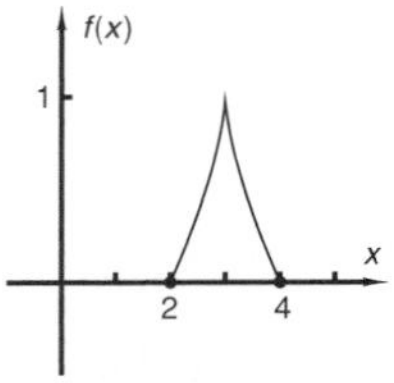


29. $g$ is discontinuous at $x = 2$. Thus the hypotheses of the mean value theorem are not met. The conclusion is *not* true for $[1, 3]$ because the tangent line would have to contain $(2, g(2))$, as shown in the left graph. The conclusion *is* true for $(1, 5)$ since the slope of the secant line is 1, and $g'(x) = 1$ at $x = 3$, which is in the interval $(1, 5)$. See the right graph.

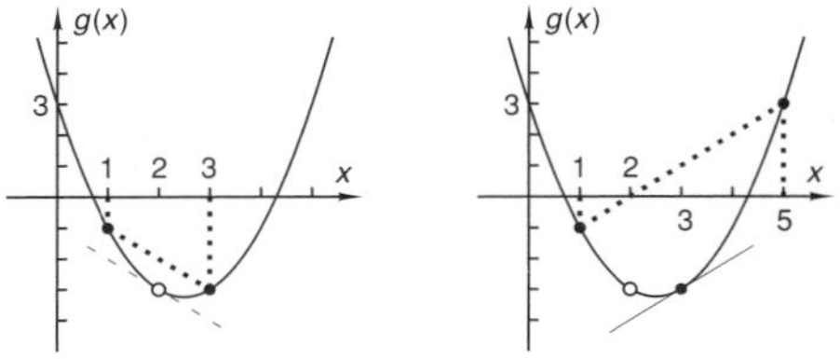


31. a. $f(x) = \begin{cases} 3x - 3, & \text{if } x \geq 3 \\ x + 3, & \text{if } x < 3 \end{cases}$

b. Graph.

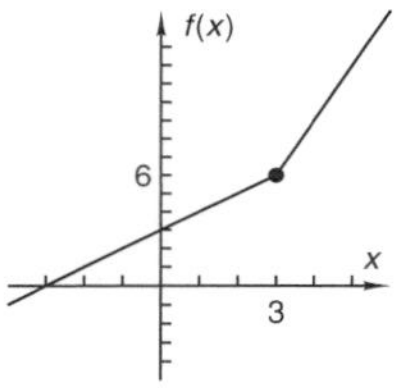


c. $f$ is continuous at $x = 3$. The right and left limits both equal 6.

d. $f$ is not differentiable at $x = 3$. The left limit of $f'(x)$ is 1 and right limit is 3.

e. $f$ is not differentiable at $x = 3$, which is in $(1, 6)$.

f. The secant line has slope $11/5$. The tangent line has slope either 1 or 3, and thus never $11/5$.

g. $f$ is integrable on $[1, 6]$. The integral equals 41.5, the sum of the areas of the two trapezoids shown in the diagram below.

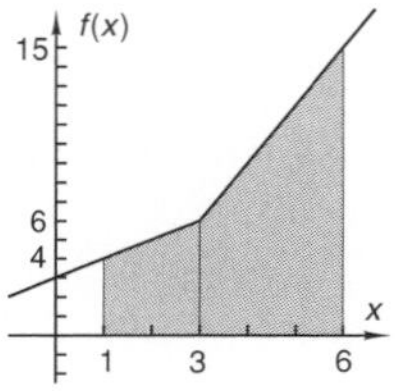


33. *Rolle's Theorem Proof Illustrated by Graph and Table*

a. Grapher graph agrees with Figure 5-6k.

b. At $x = 5$ the cosine is at a high point and the parabola $y = 25 - (x - 5)^2$ is also at a high point. $f(5) = 29$

c. $f'(x) = -2x^2 + 10x - 8\pi \sin(2\pi(x - 5))$; $f'(5) = 0$

d. Graph, difference quotient $y_2 = m(x)$.

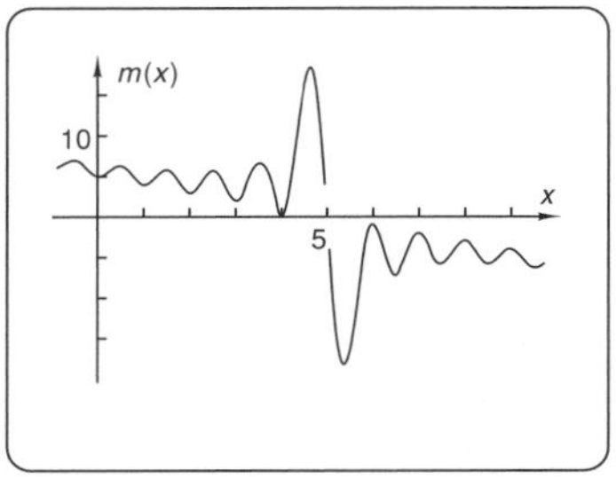


e.

| $x$ | $m(x)$ | $x$ | $m(x)$ |
|---|---|---|---|
| 2.0 | 3 | 5.5 | −16.5 |
| 2.5 | 5.7 | 6.0 | − 1 |
| 3.0 | 2 | 6.5 | − 6.833... |
| 3.5 | 6.8333... | 7.0 | − 2 |
| 4.0 | 1 | 7.5 | − 5.7 |
| 4.5 | 16.5 | 8.0 | − 3 |
| 5.0 | no value | | |

f. As shown in parts (d) and (e), the difference quotient is positive when $x$ is less than 5 and negative when $x$ is greater than 5. In the proof of Rolle's theorem the left limit of the difference quotient was shown to be positive or zero and the right limit was shown to be negative or zero. The unmentioned hypothesis is *differentiability* on the interval $(a, b)$. Function $f$ is differentiable on any interval containing $x = 5$. Since there is a value of $f'(5)$, both the left and right limits of the difference quotient must be equal. This number can only be zero, which establishes the conclusion of the theorem. The conclusion of Rolle's theorem *can* be true even if the hypotheses aren't met. For instance, $f(x) = 2 + \cos x$ has zero derivatives every $\pi$ units of $x$, although $f(x)$ is never equal to zero.

35. *Corollary of the Mean Value Theorem*
The hypotheses of the mean value theorem state that $f$ should be differentiable in the *open* interval $(a, b)$, and continuous at $x = a$ and $x = b$. If $f$ is differentiable in the *closed* interval $[a, b]$, then it is automatically continuous at $x = a$ and $x = b$ because differentiability implies continuity.

37. *Antiderivative of Zero*
By the definition of antiderivative (indefinite integral), $g(x) = \int 0\,dx$ if and only if $g'(x) = 0$. Any other function $f$ for which $f'(x) = 0$ differs from

$g(x)$ by a constant. Thus the antiderivative of 0 is a constant function, Q.E.D.

39. *Maximum and Minimum Values of Continuous Functions* The hypotheses of Rolle's theorem say that $f$ is *differentiable* on the *open* interval $(a, b)$. Since differentiability implies continuity, $f$ is also *continuous* on $(a, b)$. Combining this fact with the hypothesis of continuity at $a$ and at $b$ allows you to conclude that the function is continuous on the *closed* interval $[a, b]$.

41. Not selected.

## Problem Set 5-7

*Some Very Special Riemann Sums*

1. $T_3 = 4.6462643\ldots.$
   Since the curve is concave downward, it lies *above* each trapezoid, and thus encloses more area than the trapezoids. So the trapezoidal rule *underestimates* the actual area. See graph.

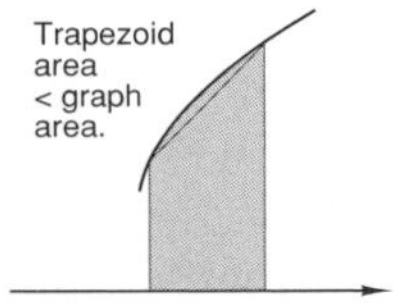


3. $R_3 = 4.66666667$ (Remarkable!)
   Answer is *between* the answer to Problem 1 (which is a *lower* bound) and the answer to Problem 2 (which is an *upper* bound).

5. $c \approx 1.24580513$
   This is the sample point used in Problem 4.

7. Conjecture: Exact area $= 4\frac{2}{3}$

9. $T_{100} = 4.0004$
   Conjecture: Integral = 4, exactly.

11. $c_1 = 0.31498026\ldots$
    $c_2 = 0.77680912\ldots$
    $c_3 = 1.26644925\ldots$
    $c_4 = 1.76182468\ldots$
    Each value of $c$ is within the respective interval.

13. Conjecture: Area $= g(2) - g(0)$
    $c = 1.25992\ldots$
    $f(c) = 2$ (exactly)
    $\therefore R_1 = (2)(2) = 4$, the exact answer.

## Problem Set 5-8

*The Fundamental Theorem of Calculus*

1. a. $I = \int_4^9 10x^{-1.5}\,dx$
   $= (-10/0.5)(9^{-0.5}) - (-10/0.5)(4^{-0.5})$
   $= -20/3 + 20/2 = \underline{10/3} = \underline{3.33333\ldots}$
   The $+C$ and $-C$ add up to zero.

   b. Graph, upper sum, $n = 5$.

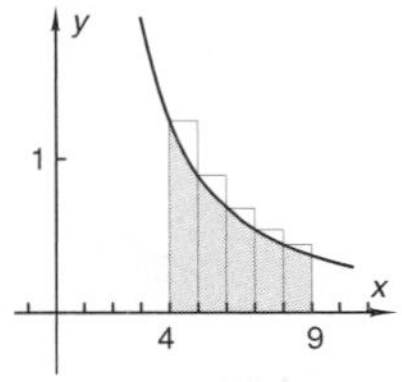


   c. Pick sample points at left ends of subintervals for $U_5$ and at right ends for $L_5$.
   $U_5 = 3.80673199\ldots$, $L_5 = 2.92710236\ldots$
   Average $= 3.36691717\ldots$
   Average *overestimates* the integral, $3.33333\ldots.$ This fact is consistent with the fact that the graph is concave *up*, and thus area above each lower rectangle is less than half the difference between each upper rectangle and lower rectangle.

   d. Use sample points at the midpoints.
   $M_{10} = 3.32911229\ldots$
   $M_{100} = 3.33329093\ldots$
   $M_{1000} = 3.33333290\ldots$
   Sums are converging toward 10/3.

3. See text statement of the fundamental theorem.

5. See the text proof of the fundamental theorem.

7. *Freeway Exit Problem*
   Distance $= \int_0^8 (100 - 20(t+1)^{1/2})\,dt = 453\frac{1}{3}$ feet

8. *The Fundamental Theorem Another Way*
   a. $M_{10} = 12.66753\ldots$
   b. $h(u)\Delta u$ and $h(u + \Delta u)\Delta u$ are terms in a lower and an upper sum, respectively, because $h(x)$ is increasing.
   $\therefore h(u)\Delta u < A(u + \Delta u) - A(u) < h(u + \Delta u)\Delta u$
   c. $h(u) < \dfrac{A(u + \Delta u) - A(u)}{\Delta u} < h(u + \Delta u)$
   But the limits of $h(u)$ and $h(u + \Delta u)$ both equal $h(u)$ since $h$ is continuous and $h(u)$ is independent of $\Delta u$. Therefore, by the squeeze theorem,
   $\lim_{\Delta u \to 0} \dfrac{A(u + \Delta u) - A(u)}{\Delta u} = h(u).$
   But the limit on the left is defined to be $dA/du$.
   $\therefore dA/du = h(u)$, Q.E.D.
   d. $dA = h(u)du$
   $A(u) = (2/3)u^{3/2} - 16/3.$
   e. $A(9) = 12\dfrac{2}{3}$ which agrees with $M_{10} = 12.667\ldots.$

9. a. Graph. (example) b. Graph. (example)

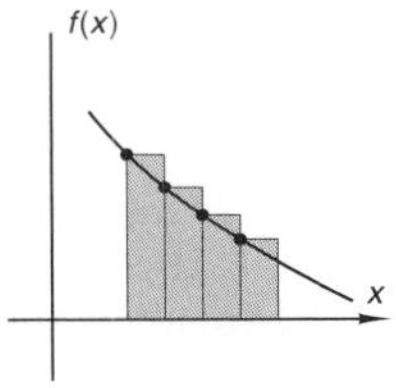


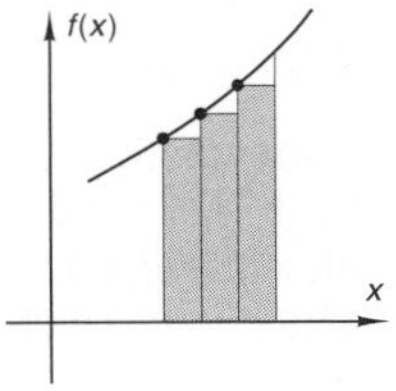

c. Graph. (example)

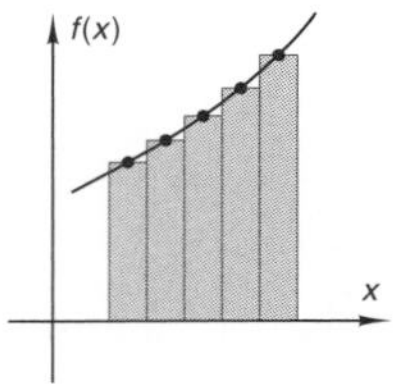


d. Graph. (example)

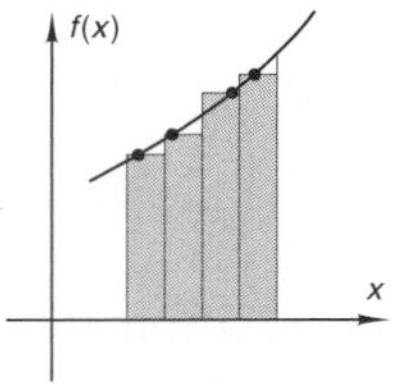


e. Graph. (example)

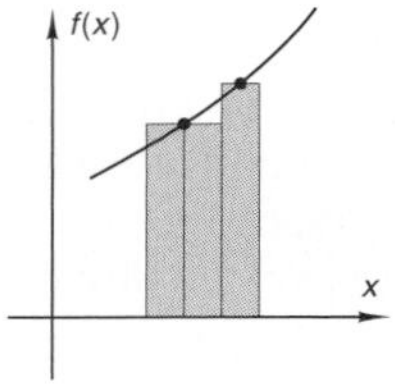


f. Graph. (example)

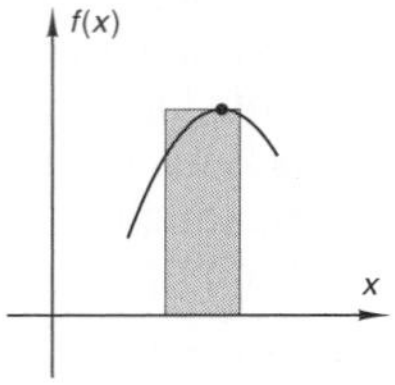


### Problem Set 5-9

*Definite Integral Properties and Practice*

1. 21
3. 125
5. 1116
7. 30
9. $10\frac{2}{3}$
11. $4\frac{1}{3}$
13. 8
15. $(7/6)\sqrt{3} - 1/2 = 1.52072\ldots$
17. $36388\frac{29}{35}$
19. $\frac{1}{4}(\sin^4 2 - \sin^4 1) = 0.045566\ldots$
21. $\frac{1}{3}(\sin 0.6 - \sin 0.3) = 0.0897074\ldots$
23. 20
25. no value
27. Integral $= -$(area)

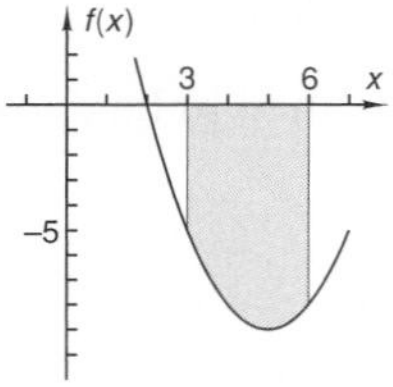


29. Integral $\neq$ area

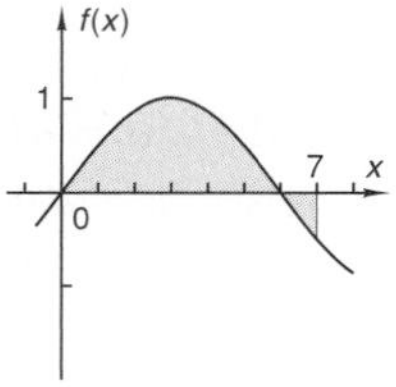


31. $\int_b^a f(x)\,dx = -7$
33. $\int_a^c g(x)\,dx = 25$
35. $\int_a^c f(x)\,dx + \int_a^c g(x)\,dx$ cannot be determined.
37. Converse:
"If $\int_a^b f(x)\,dx < \int_a^b g(x)\,dx$, then $f(x) < g(x)$ for all $x$ in $[a, b]$."
The converse can be shown to be false by any counterexample in which the area of the region under the $g$ graph is greater than the area under the $f$ graph, but the $g$ graph touches or crosses the $f$ graph somewhere in $[a, b]$. One counterexample is $f(x) = 1.5$ and $g(x) = 2 + \cos x$ on $[0, 2\pi]$. Graph.

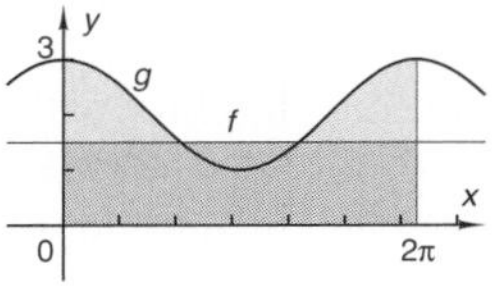


### Problem Set 5-10

*A Way to Apply Definite Integrals*

1. *Displacement Problem*
   a. Graph, showing a strip and a sample point $(t, v)$.

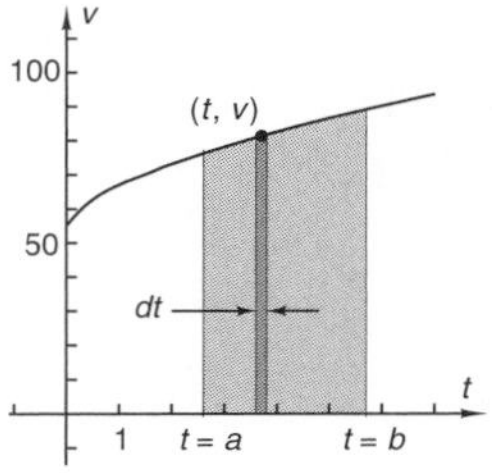


   b. $dy = v\,dt = (55 + 12t^{0.6})\,dt$
   c. $R = \sum dy = \sum(55 + 12t^{0.6})\,dt$
   d. Displacement $= \int_a^b (55 + 12t^{0.6})\,dt$
   e. 1st hour: Disp. $= \int_0^1 (55 + 12t^{0.6})\,dt = 62.5$ mi
   2nd hour: Disp. $= \int_1^2 (55 + 12t^{0.6})\,dt \approx 70.2$ mi.
   1st 2 hr.: Disp. $= \int_0^2 (55 + 12t^{0.6})\,dt = 132.735\ldots$, which equals the sum of the two integrals above.
   f. $v(2) \approx$ 73.2 mph.
   g. Approx. 4.134 hours.

3. *Work Problem*
   a. Graph, $F = 0.6x$, showing strip and sample point.

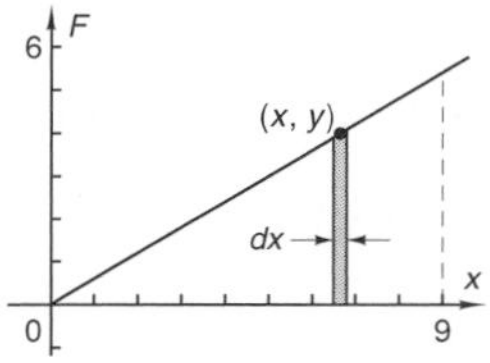


   b. $dW = F\,dx = 0.6x\,dx$
   c. $W = 24.3$ inch pounds
   d. $F(4.5) = 2.7$ pounds and $F(9) = 5.4$ pounds. So the force at $x = 9$ *is* twice the force at $x = 4.5$. Work done in stretching from 0 to 4.5 inch is 6.075 inch pounds. So the work done stretching from 0 to 9 inches is four times the work done stretching from 0 to 4.5 inches, *not* twice the work.

5. *Heat Problem*

a. Graph, $C = -0.016T^3 + 0.678T^2 + 7.45T + 796$, showing strip and sample point $(T, C)$.

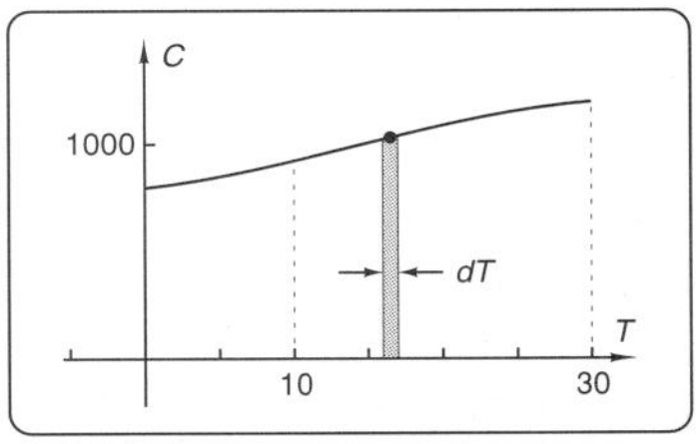


b. $dH = (-0.016T^3 + 0.678T^2 + 7.45T + 796)\,dT$

c. $H = \int_{10}^{30}(-0.016T^3 + 0.678T^2 + 7.45T + 796)\,dT$ $= 21,576$ Btu

d. 43,152,000 Btu
Integral of a constant times a function.

e. The mathematical model does *not* give reasonable answers beyond 3000° ($T = 30$). As stated in the text, the actual heat capacity rises slowly. The model indicates that it decreases rapidly. See graph.

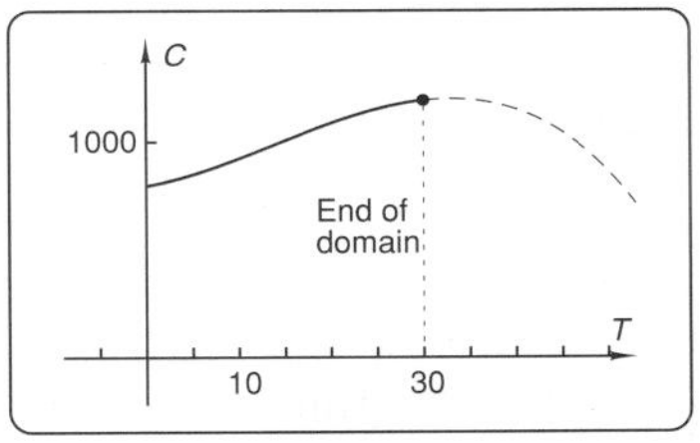


7. *Golf Course Problem*
Using trapezoids, area $\approx 3475$ ft$^2$.
The fundamental theorem cannot be used since the function is specified only by data, not by an equation whose antiderivative can be found.

## Problem Set 5-11

*Numerical Integration by Simpson's Rule and Grapher*

1. *Velocity Problem*

a. Distance $\approx 3.444\ldots \approx 3.4$ nautical miles

b. $T_6 = 3.7333\ldots \approx 3.7$ nautical miles

c. The answer by Simpson's rule should be closer since the graph is represented by curved segments instead of straight ones.

3. *Tensile Strength Test*

a. Graph, scatter plot of the data.

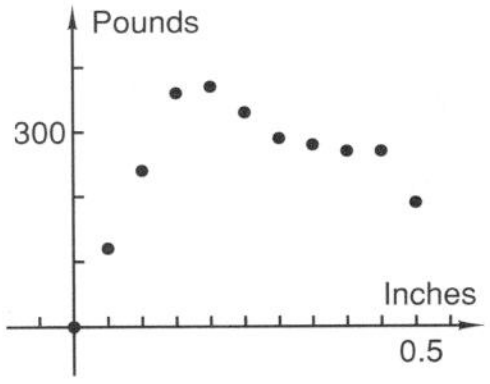


b. Work $\approx 132.8333\ldots \approx 132.8$ inch pounds

5. *Sine-Integral Function Problem*

a. Graph, $y = \text{Si}\,x$

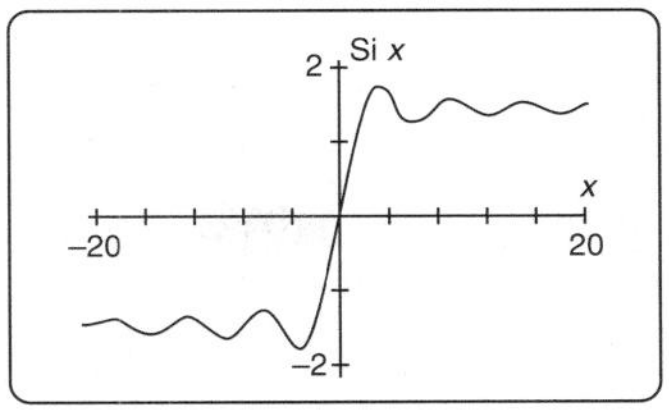


b. $(\sin x)/(x)$ approaches 1 as $x$ approaches 0.

c. Answers will vary depending on the grapher. The TI-82 gives $\text{Si}\,0.6 = 0.58812881$ using TRACE or 0.588128809608 using TABLE, both of which are correct to as many decimal places as NBS.

d. By TABLE, $\text{Si}\,x$ seems to be oscillating between about 1.53 and 1.61 when $x$ is between 20 and 30. The limit is somewhere between these two numbers, say about 1.57. The actual limit is $\pi/2$, which equals $1.570796\ldots$.

e. Graph, $f(x) = (\sin x)/(x)$, superimposed on $y = \text{Si}\,x$. The $f$ graph is positive, and greatest when $x$ is between $-\pi$ and $\pi$, which agrees with the large positive slope of the $\text{Si}\,x$ graph in this region. Each place the $\text{Si}\,x$ graph has a high or low point the $f(x)$ graph has a zero, corresponding to the zero slope of the $\text{Si}\,x$ graph.

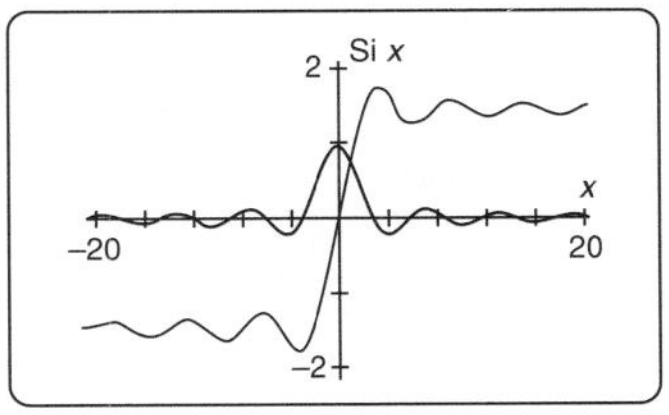


7. $\int_{0.3}^{1.4} \cos x\,dx \approx 0.689929523\ldots$

9. $\int_0^3 2^x\,dx \approx 10.0988965\ldots$

11. *Answer Check Problem*
$\sin 1.4 - \sin 0.3 = 0.689929523\ldots$, which agrees with Problem 7.

13. *Program for Simpson's Rule from Data*
Not selected.

15. *Relative Accuracy Problem*

a. $I = \int_0^{\pi} \sin x\,dx$

i. $S_{50} = 2.00000017\ldots$

ii. $T_{50} = 1.99934198\ldots$

iii. INTEGRATE: $I = 2$

iv. $I = -\cos x|_0^{\pi} = -(-1) + 1 = 2$

b. The built-in integrate function is closest, followed by Simpson's rule, then trapezoidal rule.

## Problem Set 5-12

*Chapter Review and Test*

### Review Problems

R0. Not selected

R1. Heat Capacity Problem

a. Heat needed is (Btu/degree)(degrees), which is a product of independent and dependent variables. Since (Btu/degree) varies, a definite integral must be used.

b. $C = -0.4 + 0.3 \log T$
By trapezoidal rule with $n = 100$, the amount of heat added from $T = 1000$ to $T = 5000$ is about 2527 Btu. (Exact answer: 2527.3016...)

c. Average $\approx 0.632$ Btu/degree

R2. a. $f(x) = 2.8x^{10/7} + C$

b. $f(x) = 5 \sin 2x + C$

c. $f(x) = -\dfrac{1}{24}(12x + 5)^{-2} + C$

R3. a. Linear function is $y = -\pi x + \pi$
At $x = 1.1$, Error $= -0.005142\ldots$
At $x = 1.001$, Error $= -0.000000005\ldots$

b. i. $dy = -10 \csc^5 2x \cot 2x\, dx$
ii. $dy = (x^4 + x^{-4})\, dx$
iii. $dy = -12(7 - 3x)^3\, dx$

c. i. $y = \sec x + C$
ii. $y = \dfrac{1}{18}(3x + 7)^6 + C$
iii. $y = 5x + C$

d. i. $dy = (2x + 5)^{-1/2}\, dx$
ii. $dy = 0.06$
iii. $\Delta y = 0.059644\ldots$
iv. 0.06 is close to 0.059644....

R4. a. See text definition of indefinite integral.

b. i. $7.2x^{5/3} + C$
ii. $\dfrac{1}{7} \sin^7 x + C$
iii. $\dfrac{1}{3}x^3 - 4x^2 + 3x + C$

R5. a. See text definition of integrability.

b. See text definition of definite integral.

c. i. $U_6 = 2.845332\ldots$
ii. $L_6 = 1.872703\ldots$
iii. $M_6 = 2.209073\ldots$
iv. $T_6 = 2.359108\ldots$

d. Graphs of $U_6$ and $L_6$, $M_6$, respectively.

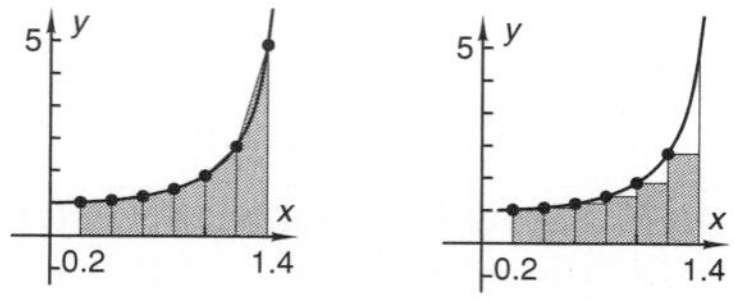


Graphs of $M_6$ and $T_6$, respectively.

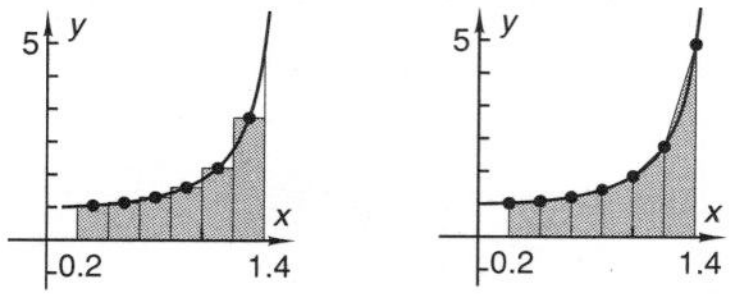


e. i. $U_n = (1 \cdot 5/n)(5/n) + (2 \cdot 5/n)(5/n) + (3 \cdot 5/n)(5/n) + \cdots + (n \cdot 5/n)(5/n) = (25/n^2)(1 + 2 + 3 + \cdots + n)$
ii. $U_n = (25/n^2)(0.5n)(n + 1) = 12.5(1 + 1/n)$
iii. $\lim_{n \to \infty} U_n = 12.5$ because $1/n \to 0$ as $n \to \infty$.
iv. Integral = area of triangle with base 5 and altitude 5, which is $(1/2)(5)(5) = 12.5$.

R6. a. The hypothesis is the "if" part of a theorem and the conclusion is the "then" part. (Hypo- means under, and -thesis means theme.)

b. Average velocity = 1.5 m/sec
Instantaneous velocity $= d'(t) = 0.75\pi \cos \dfrac{\pi}{4} t$
Instantaneous velocity equals average velocity at time $t = 1.12132\ldots \approx 1.12$ sec

c. Interval is $[0, 4]$, $c = 1$.
At $x = 0$, $g'(0)$ takes the form 1/0 which is infinite.
Thus, $g$ is not differentiable at $x = 0$. However, the function need not be differentiable at the end points of the interval, just at interior points.

d. See Figure 5-6c, left diagram.

e. See Figure 5-6c, right diagram.

f. See text derivation of Rolle's theorem.

g. Graph. Points are 1/8, 1/4, 3/8, 1/2, 5/8, 3/4, 7/8.

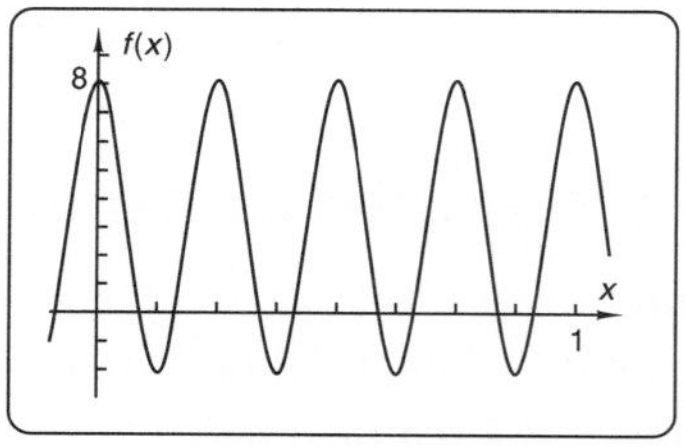


h. If $r'(x) = s'(x)$ for all $x$ in an interval, then $r(x) = s(x) + C$ for some constant $C$.

R7. $c_1 = 1.513915927\ldots$
$c_2 = 2.508338988\ldots$
$c_3 = 3.505954424\ldots$
$R_3 = (1.531\ldots)^{1.5} + (2.508\ldots)^{1.5} + (3.505\ldots)^{1.5} =$ 12.4, which is the exact value of the integral.

R8. a. Integral $= 92/3 = 30.666\ldots$

b. $T_{100} = 30.6656$, which is close to 92/3.

c. $M_{10} = 30.72$
$M_{100} = 30.6672$
$M_{1000} = 30.666672$
These Riemann sums are approaching 92/3.

R9. a. i. 4/5

ii. $(1/12)(19)^6 - (1/12)(12)^6 = 3671658.08\ldots$

iii. $2 - 5\pi$

b. Graph, $y = \sin x - 5$.
Integral is negative since each $y$-value in the Riemann sum is negative.

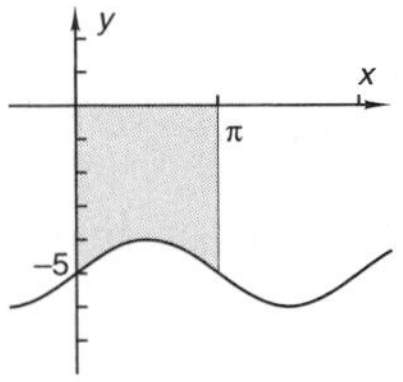


c. Integral = 80

d. Graph. Total area = sum of two areas.

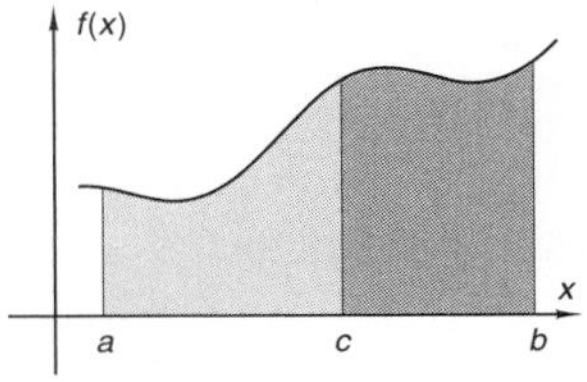


R10. *Displacement Problem*

a. Graph, showing strip and sample point $(t, v)$.

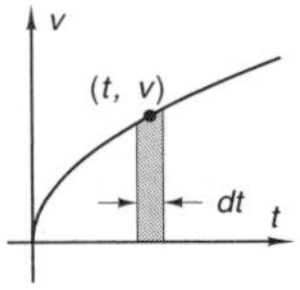


b. $dy = v\,dt = 150t^{0.5}\,dt$

c. $R = \sum 150t^{0.5}\,dt$

d. $\lim_{n\to\infty} R = \int_0^9 150t^{0.5}\,dt = 2700$ ft., a definite integral.

e. The 2700 in part (d) is the displacement, 2700 ft.
For $[0, 4]$, $y = 800$.
For $[4, 9]$, $y = 1900$.
Thus 2700 = 800 + 1900, Q.E.D.

R11. a. See text graph, Figure 5-11d.
Each parabola requires three points, thus taking two subintervals. Therefore, Simpson's Rule uses an even number of increments.

b. See graphs in Figures 5-11a and 5-11b.

c. Displacement = 67.6 m

d. Integral ≈ 6.0913
Graph. By counting squares, integral ≈ 6.

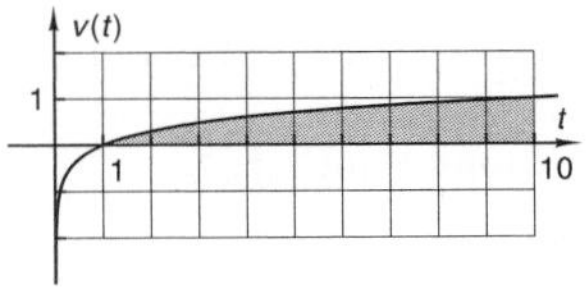


## CHAPTER 6

### Problem Set 6-1

*Integral of the Reciprocal Function, a Population Growth Problem*

1. The annual rate of population growth, $dP/dt$, is 5% (0.05) times the current population $P$.

3. $\int_0^{10} 0.05\,dt = 0.5$
Using the power function method on $\int P^{-1}\,dP$ gives $(1/0)P^0$, which involves division by zero.

5. From the answer to Problem 4 you can tell that the value of $N$ which makes the integral equal 0.5 is somewhere between 1500 and 2000. Setting the numerical integral between $t = 1000$ and $t = N$ equal to 0.5 and doing a numerical solution for $N$ gives
$N \approx 1648.72\ldots$, or about 1649 people.

7. The $P$ versus $t$ graph is non-linear. From $t = 0$ to $t = 10$ the population increased by 649 people. From $t = 10$ to $t = 20$ it increased by 1069 people.

### Problem Set 6-2

*Antiderivative of the Reciprocal Function*

1. Each value of $x$ uniquely determines the area; as $x$ increases, so does the area. Note that the area does not depend at all on $t$.

3. Graph, showing that each $\Delta t$ is negative and each value of $1/t$ is positive, so that the Riemann sums are negative, and thus the integral is negative.

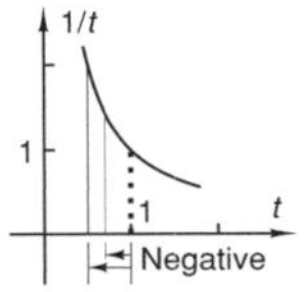


5. a. $g(3) + g(2) = 1.098617\ldots + 0.693142\ldots = 1.791759\ldots$, which equals $g(6)$.

b. $g(8) - g(2) = 2.079441\ldots - 0.693147\ldots = 1.386294\ldots$, which equals $g(4)$.

c. $3 \cdot g(2) = 3 \cdot 0.693147\ldots = 2.079441\ldots$, which equals $g(8)$.

d. $-g(2) = -0.69314\ldots = g(0.5) = g(1/2)$.

7. Graphs, $y = g(x)$ and $y = \log x$.

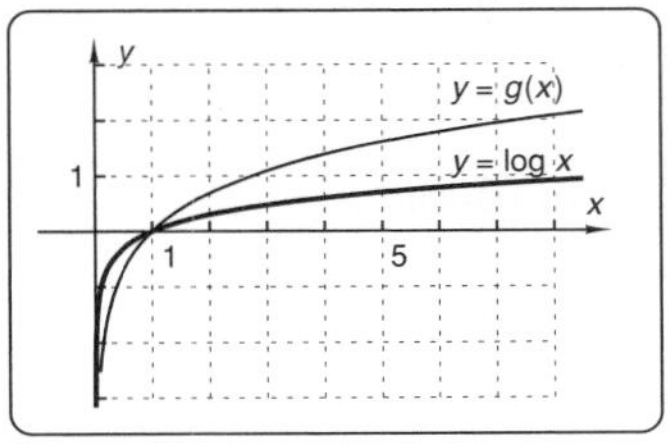

Both graphs have asymptotes at $x = 0$, $x$-intercepts of 1, slopes tending to zero as $x$ approaches infinity. Both are increasing and concave down.

9. $g'(3) \approx \dfrac{g(4) - g(2)}{2} \approx \dfrac{1.38629 - 0.69314}{2}$
$\approx 0.3466$
By numerical differentiation,
$(d/dx)(\ln x) \approx 0.33333$,
which is close to 0.3466.

11. Solving numerically for $g(b) = 1$ gives
$b \approx 2.71828\ldots$

## Problem Set 6-3

*Natural Logarithms, and Another Form of the Fundamental Theorem*

1. $y' = 1/x$
3. $f'(x) = 5/x$
5. $h'(x) = -12/x$
7. $r'(t) = 3/t$
9. $y' = (1/x)(\ln 4x + \ln 6x)$ or: $\dfrac{\ln 24x^2}{x}$
11. $y' = \dfrac{\ln 3x - \ln 11x}{x(\ln 3x)^2}$ or: $\dfrac{\ln(3/11)}{x(\ln 3x)^2}$
13. $p' = (\cos x)(\ln x) + (\sin x)(1/x)$
15. $y' = -\sin(\ln x) \cdot (1/x)$
17. $y' = -\tan x$ (Surprise!)
19. $T'(x) = \sec^2(\ln x) \cdot (1/x)$
21. $y' = -3(3x + 5)^{-2}$
23. $y' = 4x^3 \ln 3x + x^3$
25. $y' = -1/x$
27. $7 \ln |x| + C$
29. $\dfrac{1}{3} \ln |x| + C$
31. $\dfrac{1}{3} \ln |x^3 + 5| + C$
33. $-\dfrac{1}{6} \ln |9 - x^6| + C$
35. $\ln |1 + \sec x| + C$
37. $\ln |\sin x| + C$
39. $\ln 8 = 2.079441\ldots$
41. $\ln 30 = 3.401197\ldots$
43. $\dfrac{2}{3}(\ln 28 - \ln 9) = 0.756653\ldots$
45. $\dfrac{1}{6}(\ln x)^6 + C$
47. $f'(x) = \cos 3x$
49. $\tan^3 x$
51. $f'(x) = 2x \cdot 3^{x^2}$
53. $h'(x) = 3\sqrt{1 + (3x - 5)^2}$
55. Fundamental Theorem: $5 \ln 3 - 5 \ln 1 = \underline{5.493061\ldots}$
Midpoint Riemann sum: $M_{100} = 5.492987\ldots$
Trapezoidal rule: $T_{100} = 5.493209\ldots$
Numerical integration: $5.493061\ldots$
57. *Population Problem*
$\int_{1000}^{N} (1/P)\, dP = \ln N - \ln 1000$.
$N \approx 1649$ people.
59. *Radio Dial Derivative Problem*
a. $a = -35.934084\ldots$, $b = 9.0507041\ldots$
b.

| $f$ | $d$ cm | $d'$ part(c) |
|---|---|---|
| 53 | 0 | 0.1707 |
| 60 | 1.1227 | 0.1508 |
| 70 | 2.5197 | 0.1292 |
| 80 | 3.7265 | 0.1131 |
| 100 | 5.7461 | 0.0905 |
| 120 | 7.3962 | 0.0754 |
| 140 | 8.7914 | 0.0646 |
| 160 | 10.0 | 0.0565 |

The measured distances are close to the calculated distances.
c. $d'(f) = b/f = 9.0507/f$. See table in part (b).
d. $d'(f)$ is in cm/10 kHz.
e. $d'(f)$ decreases as $f$ gets larger; this is consistent with the spaces between the numbers getting smaller as $f$ increases.
61. Not selected.

## Problem Set 6-4

*ln x Really is a Logarithmic Function*

1. $\ln 6 + \ln 4 = 1.79175\ldots + 1.38629\ldots$
$= 3.17805\ldots$
$\ln 24 = 3.17805\ldots$ (checks)
3. $\ln 2001 - \ln 667 = 7.60140\ldots - 6.50279\ldots$
$= 1.09861\ldots$
$\ln(2001/667) = \ln 3 = 1.09861\ldots$ (checks)
5. $3 \ln 1776 = 3(7.48211\ldots) = 22.44635\ldots$
$\ln(1776^3) = \ln 5601816576 = 22.44635\ldots$ (checks)
7. See text proof of the uniqueness theorem.
9. Prove that $\ln(a/b) = \ln a - \ln b$ for all $a > 0$, $b > 0$.
*Proof:*
Let $f(x) = \ln(x/b)$, $g(x) = \ln x - \ln b$ for $x, b > 0$.
Then $f'(x) = (b/x)(1/b) = 1/x$, and $g'(x) = (1/x) - 0 = 1/x$.
$\therefore f'(x) = g'(x)$ for all $x > 0$.
$f(b) = \ln(b/b) = \ln 1 = 0$.
$g(b) = \ln b - \ln b = 0$.
$\therefore f(b) = g(b)$.
$\therefore f(x) = g(x)$ for all $x > 0$ by the uniqueness theorem.
$\therefore \ln(x/b) = \ln x - \ln b$ for all $x > 0$.
$\therefore \ln(a/b) = \ln a - \ln b$ for all $a > 0$ and $b > 0$, Q.E.D.
11. Prove that $\ln(a/b) = \ln a - \ln b$ for all $a > 0$, $b > 0$.
*Proof:*
$\ln(a/b) = \ln(a \cdot b^{-1}) = \ln a + \ln b^{-1}$
$= \ln a + (-1) \ln b = \ln a - \ln b$.
$\therefore \ln(a/b) = \ln a - \ln b$, Q.E.D.
13. *Base of Natural Logarithms Problem*
a. $y = \log_b x$ and $x = b^y$ are equivalent by the definition of logarithm.
b. $x$ would equal $b^1$, which equals $b$.
c. When $y = 1$, $x = b \approx 2.7183$.
d. This number is called "$e$."

## Problem Set 6-5

*Derivatives of Exponential Functions—Logarithmic Differentiation*

1. $f'(x) = 0.4^{2x} \cdot 2\ln 0.4$

3. $g'(x) = 4(7^x)\ln 7$

5. $c'(x) = x^5 \cdot 3^x(5/x + \ln 3)$

7. $y' = (\cos x)^{0.7x}(0.7\ln(\cos x) - 0.7x\tan x)$

9. $y' = (\csc 5x)^{2x}[2\ln(\csc 5x) - 10x\cot 5x]$

11. $f'(t) = t^{\sec t}(\sec t\tan t\ln t + (1/t)\sec t)$

13. $v' = (x^4 - 1)^x\left[\ln(x^4 - 1) + \dfrac{4x^4}{(x^4 - 1)}\right]$

15. $y' = 2^x\ln x[\ln 2 + 1/(x\ln x)]$

17. $y' = 5(3x - 4)^x[\ln(3x - 4) + 3x/(3x - 4)]$

19. a. $y' = 7/x$
    b. $y' = 7/x$ (checks)

21. a. $y' = \dfrac{12x - 19}{(3x + 4)(2x - 9)}$
    b. $y' = \dfrac{3}{3x + 4} + \dfrac{2}{2x - 9} = \dfrac{12x - 19}{(3x + 4)(2x - 9)}$

23. a. $y' = \dfrac{-54}{(5x + 2)(7x - 8)}$
    b. $y' = \dfrac{5}{5x + 2} - \dfrac{7}{7x - 8} = \dfrac{-54}{(5x + 2)(7x - 8)}$

25. From Problem 19, $y' = 7/x$
    At $x = 2$, $y' = 7/2 = 3.5$.
    $\dfrac{\ln 3(2.001)^7 - \ln 3(2)^7}{0.001} = 3.49912\ldots$, close to 3.5.

27. $y' = y\left(\dfrac{35}{5x + 11} + \dfrac{35}{7x - 3}\right)$

29. $y' = y\left(\dfrac{-20}{3 - 4x} + \dfrac{20}{7 + 5x}\right)$

31. $y' = y[4/(4x + 1) - 6\cot x]$

33. $-5\ln 3 = -5.493061\ldots$

35. *Continued Exponentiation Problem*
    a. $f'(x) = x^x(\ln x + 1)$
    b. $g'(x) = x^{x^x} \cdot x^x[(\ln x)^2 + \ln x + 1/x]$

37. *Compound Interest Problem*
    a. $m'(t) = 1000(1.06)^t(\ln 1.06)$
    $m'(0) = 58.27$ \$/year
    $m'(5) = 77.98$ \$/year
    $m'(10) = 104.35$ \$/year.
    b. $m(0) = \$1000.00$
    $m(5) = \$1338.23$
    $m(10) = \$1790.85$
    The rates are increasing. \$338.23 is earned between 0 and 5 years, \$452.62 is earned between 5 and 10 years, which agrees with the increasing derivatives shown in part (a).
    c. $\dfrac{m'(t)}{m(t)} = \dfrac{1000(1.06)^t(\ln 1.06)}{1000(1.06)^t} = \ln 1.06.$
    $\therefore m'(t)/m(t) = \ln 1.06$, a constant.
    d. $m(1) = 1060.00$. So you earn \$60.00.
    The rate starts out at only 58.27 \$/year, but has increased enough by year's end to make the total for the year equal \$60.00.

39. *Limit of an Interesting Expression:*
    Using TRACE or TABLE,

| $n$ | $(1 + 1/n)^n$ |
|---|---|
| 10 | 2.5937424601... |
| 100 | 2.7048138294... |
| 1000 | 2.7169239322... |
| 10000 | 2.7181459268... |
| 100000 | 2.7182682371... |
| 1000000 | 2.7182804693... |

The values are increasing toward $e$, the base of natural logarithms.

## Problem Set 6-6

*The Number e and the Derivative of Base b Logarithms*

1. $f'(x) = 1/(x\ln 3)$, $f'(5) = 0.182047\ldots$
   Graph, showing tangent with small positive slope.

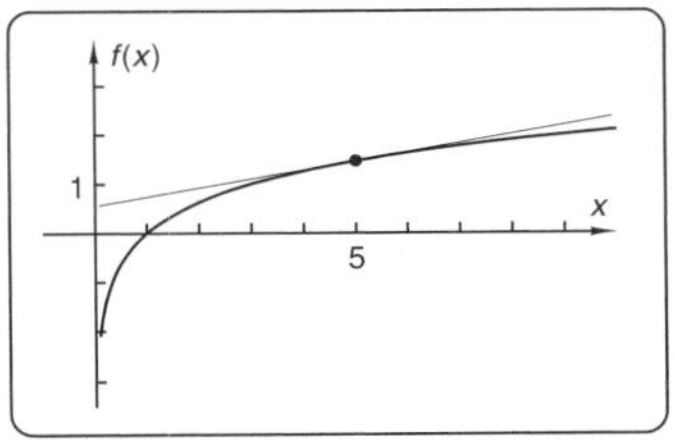


3. $f'(x) = 1/(x\ln 0.6)$, $f'(9) = -0.217512\ldots$
   Graph, showing tangent with small negative slope.

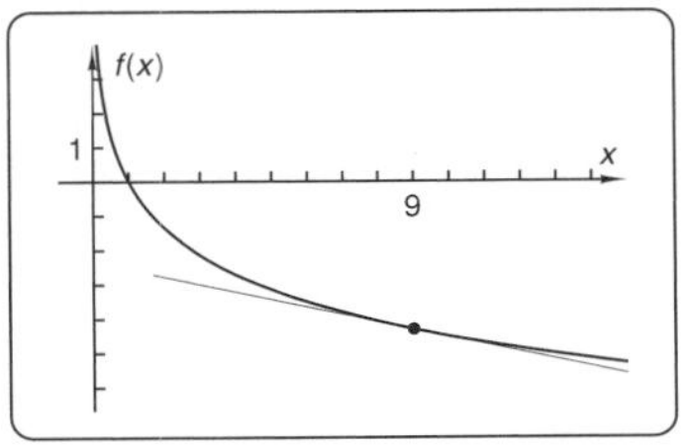


5. $f'(x) = 13/x$

7. $g'(x) = 40/x$

9. $T'(x) = (\cot x)/(\ln 5)$

11. $p'(x) = (2\ln x)/(x\ln 5)$

13. $y' = 1/(4\ln 10) = 0.108573620\ldots$
    Numerical derivative is 0.1085736... (checks)

15. $f'(x) = 1/(x\ln 0.9)$; $f'(2) = -4.7456\ldots$; graph:

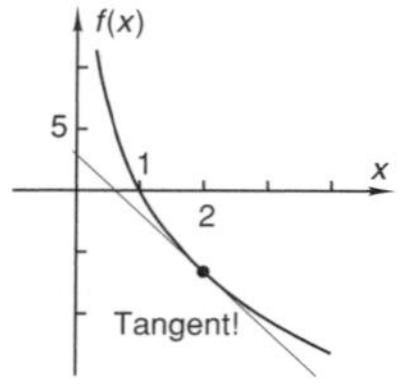


17. Not selected.

19. *Hours/Mile Lava Flow Problem*
   a. $y = 7 \cdot (2 - 0.9^x)$
      $dy/dx = 7(-0.9^x)(\ln 0.9)$
      $dy/dx = 0.737523\ldots(0.9^x)$
      $x = 0$: $dy/dx = 0.737\ldots$ mph
      $x = 1$: $dy/dx = 0.663\ldots$ mph
      $x = 5$: $dy/dx = 0.435\ldots$ mph
      $x = 10$: $dy/dx = 0.257\ldots$ mph
      Lava is slowing down. (Phew!)
   b. $y/7 = 2 - 0.9^x$
      $0.9^x = 2 - y/7$
      $x \ln 0.9 = \ln(2 - y/7)$
      $x = (1/\ln 0.9)[\ln(2 - y/7)]$
   c. $\dfrac{dx}{dy} = \dfrac{9.491221\ldots}{14 - y}$
      $y = 10$: $dx/dy = 2.372\ldots$ hours/mile
   d. If $x = 10$, then $dx/dy = 3.888651\ldots$
   e. $3.88\ldots$ is the reciprocal of $0.257\ldots$, the value of $dy/dx$ when $x = 10$, not when $y = 10$.

21. *Proof of the Change of Base Property*
   a. Definition of logarithm (algebraic).
   b. Take $\log_b$ of both sides.
   c. Log of a power property.
   d. Divide by $\log_b a$.
   e. Substitution.

23. Not selected.

25. *Limit and Function Interchange Journal Problem*
   A typical journal entry should include the fact that if the outside function is continuous and the inside function has a limit as $x$ approaches $c$, then $\lim f(g(x)) = f(\lim g(x))$. A simple example is $\lim_{x \to c} f(x) = f(\lim_{x \to c} x) = f(c)$, which is the definition of continuity. The property is used to reverse the log and the limit in finding the derivative of the logarithm function algebraically.

## Problem Set 6-7

*The Natural Exponential Function, the Inverse of ln*

1. $y' = 4e^{4x}$

3. $y' = -85e^{-5x}$

5. $f'(x) = -e^{-x}$

7. $h'(x) = x^2e^x(3 + x)$

9. $r'(t) = e^t \sin t + e^t \cos t$

11. $u' = 0$

13. $y' = 2e^{2u} \ln 3u + e^{2u} \cdot (1/u)$

15. $y' = \dfrac{\exp x \ln x - \exp x(1/x)}{(\ln x)^2}$

17. $y' = 4e^{\sec x} \cdot \sec x \tan x$

19. $f'(x) = -\csc e^x \cot e^x \cdot e^x$

21. $y' = 6$

23. $y' = 24x$

25. $g'(x) = 12$

27. $y' = 30015e^{15x}$

29. $y' = e^x - e^{-x}$

31. $u' = 14e^{2t}(5 + e^{2t})6$

33. $y' = 15x^2 \exp(5x^3)$

35. $y' = 0$

37. $f(x) = e^{0.4x} \Rightarrow f'(x) = 0.4e^{0.4x}$
   Algebraically: $f'(2) = 0.4e^{0.8} = 0.890216\ldots$
   Numerically: $f'(2) \approx 0.890216\ldots$ (checks)

39. $f'(x) = 5e^x(1 + x)$
   $f'(-1) = 0$, $f(-1) = -1.839\ldots$
   Graph: Line at $x = -1$ is tangent to the graph.

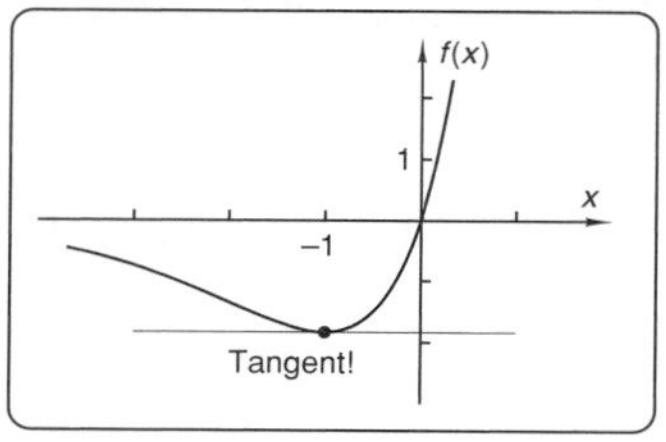


41. $\frac{1}{5}e^{5x} + C$

43. $6 \exp x + C$

45. $-\frac{3}{2}e^{-2x} + C$

47. $e^{\sin x} + C$

49. $\frac{1}{4}x^4 + C$

51. $\frac{1}{102}(1 + e^{2x})^{51} + C$

53. $9x + 6e^x + \frac{1}{2}e^{2x} + C$

55. a. $2.5(e^{0.8} - e^{0.4}) = 1.834290\ldots$
   b. Numerically, integral $\approx 1.834290\ldots$ (checks)

57. a. $e^2 + e^{-2} - 2 = 5.524391\ldots$
   b. Numerically, integral $\approx 5.524391\ldots$ (checks)

59. *Rabbit Population Problem*
   a. $R(t) = 60000e^{1.844\ldots t}$
   b. $R(5) \approx 607$ million rabbits.
   c. $t = -5.589\ldots$. So the first pair of rabbits was introduced about 5.6 years earlier, or in 1859.

61. *An Exponential Function Is Not a Power Function!* Counterexample: Let $f(x) = e^x$. Using the derivative of a power formula, $f'(x)$ would equal $xe^{x-1}$. Then $f'(0)$ would equal $0 \cdot e^0 = 0$. But the graph of $f(x) = e^x$ crosses the $y$-axis with a slope of $e^0 = 1$. So the derivative of a power formula produces a wrong answer.

63. *Zero/Zero Problem*

a. $\lim_{x\to 1} f(x) \to \dfrac{\ln 1 + \sin 0}{1 - e^0} \to \dfrac{0}{0}$, Q.E.D.

b. Graph.

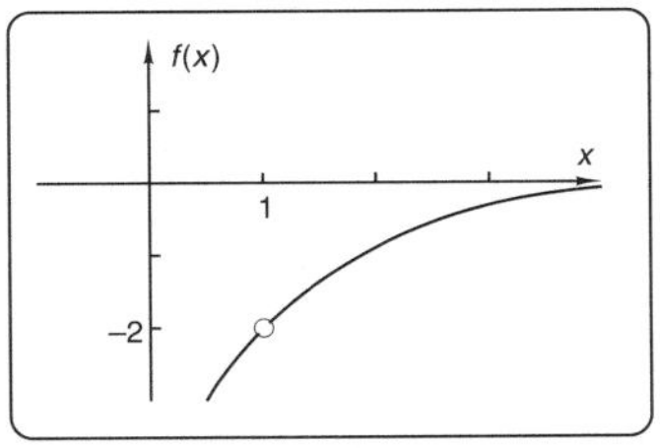


c. $f(x)$ appears to approach $-2$.

d. $\dfrac{d}{dx}(\ln x + \sin(x-1)) = 1/x + \cos(x-1)$;

At $x = 1$, $1/1 + \cos(1-1) = 1 + \cos 0 = 2$.

$\dfrac{d}{dx}(1 - e^{x-1}) = -e^{x-1}$; $-e^{1-1} = -e^0 = -1$

Ratio $= 2/(-1) = -2$, which equals the apparent limit!

## Problem Set 6-8

*Limits of Indeterminate Forms—l'Hospital's Rule*

1. Limit $= 10/3$. Graph.

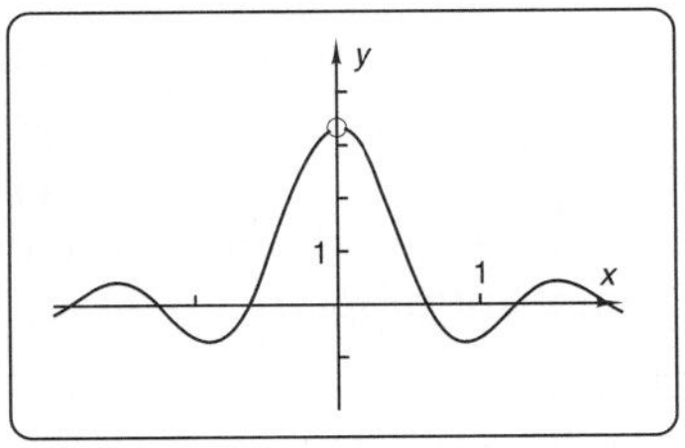


3. Limit $= 1$
5. Limit $= 1/2$
7. Limit $= \infty$
9. Limit $= 0$
11. Limit $= e/5$
13. Limit $= -26.43297\ldots$
15. Limit $= \infty$
17. Limit $= 3/4$
19. Limit $= 1/4$
21. Limit $= 1$
23. Limit $= 1$
25. Limit $= 1$
27. Limit $= e^3 = 20.085\ldots$
29. Limit $= 1/2$

31. *Infinity Minus Infinity Problem*

$f(x) = \sec^2 \dfrac{\pi}{2}x - \tan^2 \dfrac{\pi}{2}x$

Graph. Where secant and tangent are defined, the Pythagorean properties tell that $f(x) = 1$.

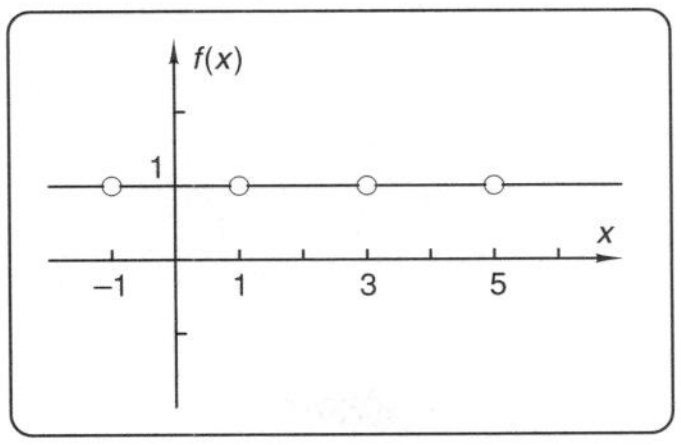


33. *Zero to the Zero Problem*

$L = \lim_{x\to 0^+} x^{k/(\ln x)} \to 0^0$

$\ln L = \lim_{x\to 0^+} [k/(\ln x) \cdot \ln x] = \lim_{x\to 0^+} k = k.$

$\therefore L = e^k$

Graph. The graph turns out to be a horizontal line $y = e^k$ defined for $x > 0$.

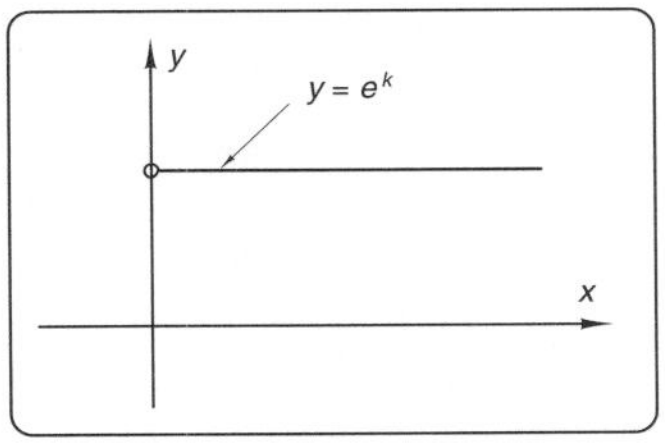


By the definition of a power,
$x^{k/(\ln x)} = (x^k)^{1/\ln x} = (e^{k \ln x})^{1/\ln x} = e^k$

35. *Continuous Compounding of Interest Problem*

a. For yearly compounding, $m(t) = 1000(1 + 0.06)^t$
For semi-annual compounding, $m(t) = 1000(1 + 0.06/2)^{2t}$ because there are two compounding periods per year, each of which gets half the interest rate.

b. $m(t) = 1000(1 + 0.06/n)^{nt}$
$\lim_{n\to\infty} m(t) = 1000e^{0.06t}$
When interest is compounded continuously, $m(t) = 1000e^{006t}$.

c.

| $t$ | $m(t)$, annual | $m(t)$, cont. | difference |
|---|---|---|---|
| 5 | 1,338.23 | 1,349.86 | 11.63 |
| 20 | 3,207.14 | 3,320.12 | 112.98 |
| 50 | 18,420.15 | 20,085.54 | 1,665.38 |

d. $m(t) = 1000e^{0.07t}$.

37. Not selected.

## Problem Set 6-9

*Derivative and Integral Practice for Transcendental Functions*

1. $y' = 3/(3x+4)$
3. $y' = 3$
5. $y' = -5\tan x$
7. $y' = -\tan(\tan x)\sec^2 x$
9. $y' = -(1/x)\sin(\ln x)$
11. $y' = 7e^{7x}$
13. $y' = 5x^4$
15. $y' = -e^x \sin e^x$
17. $y' = 5x^4 e^{x^5}$
19. $y' = \dfrac{e^x}{\cos y} = \dfrac{e^x}{\sqrt{1 - e^{2x}}}$

21. $y' = 1/x$

23. $y' = 1/x$

25. $y' = 2^x \ln 2$

27. $y' = 2x$

29. $y' = x^x(\ln x + 1)$

31. $y' = xe^x$

33. $y' = \frac{1}{2}(e^x + e^{-x})$

35. $y' = 5^x \ln 5$

37. $y' = \frac{x^{-8}}{\ln 2}(-7\ln x + 1)$

39. $y' = e^{-2x}(-2\ln 5x + 1/x)$

41. $y' = 1/x$

43. $y' = 1/x$

45. $y' = \frac{7}{x\ln 5}$

47. $y' = e^{\sin x}\cos x$

49. $y' = 0$

51. $y' = \cos x$

53. $y' = -\csc x \cot x$

55. $y' = \sec^2 x$

57. $\frac{1}{4}e^{4x} + C$

59. $\frac{1}{4}e^{x^4} + C$

61. $\frac{1}{6}(\ln x)^6 + C$

63. $\frac{5^x}{\ln 5} + C$

65. $\ln x$

67. $\frac{2^x}{\ln 2} + C$

69. $3\ln|x| + C$

71. $\frac{1}{10}(\ln x)^{10} + C$

73. $\frac{1}{2}x^2 + C$

75. $C$

77. $\frac{1}{2}\ln|\sec 2x + \tan 2x| + C$

79. $\frac{1}{4}\ln|\sin 4x| + C$

81. Limit = 0

83. Limit = $\pi/2$

85. Limit = $\frac{125}{6} = 20.8333\ldots$

87. Limit = $e^0 = 1$

89. Limit = $e^{-3/2} = 0.22313\ldots$

## Problem Set 6-10

*Chapter Review and Test*

### Review Problems

R0. Not selected.

R1. a. $dM/dt = 0.06M \Rightarrow M^{-1}\,dM = 0.06\,dt$
$\therefore \int_{100}^{x} M^{-1}\,dM = \int_0^5 0.06\,dt$, Q.E.D.
b. $x \approx 134.9858\ldots$
c. The interest would be \$34.99.

R2. a. Integrating $x^{-1}$ by the power rule results in division by zero: $\frac{x^{-1+1}}{-1+1} + C$.
b. $L(2) = 0.693\ldots$, which equals ln 2.
$L(3) = 1.098\ldots$, which equals ln 3.
$L(4) = 1.386\ldots$, which equals ln 4.
$L(8) = 2.079\ldots$, which equals ln 8.
$L(12) = 2.484\ldots$, which equals ln 12.
c. $L(3 \cdot 4) = 2.484\ldots = 1.098\ldots + 1.386\ldots$
$= L(3) + L(4)$
$L(12/3) = 1.386\ldots = 2.484\ldots - 1.098\ldots$
$= L(12) - L(3)$
$L(2^3) = L(8) = 2.079\ldots = 3 \cdot 0.693\ldots = 3L(2)$

R3. a. i. $y' = (3/x)(\ln 5x)^2$
ii. $f'(x) = 9/x$
iii. $y' = -\csc(\ln x)\cot(\ln x) \cdot (1/x)$
iv. $g'(x) = 2x \csc x^2$
b. i. $\ln|\sec x| + C$
ii. $10(\ln 3 - \ln 2) = 4.054651\ldots$
iii. $\frac{1}{3}\ln|x^3 - 4| + C$
c. *Memory Retention Problem*
i. $y(100) \approx 70$ names; 70% remembered
$y(1) = 1$ name; 100% remembered.
ii. $y' = \frac{101}{100 + x}$
$y'(100) = 0.505$ names/person
$y'(1) = 1$ name/person
iii. Paula has probably not forgotten any names as long as $x - y < 0.5$. After meeting 11 people she remembers about $10.53\ldots \approx 11$ names, but after meeting 12 people she remembers about $11.44\ldots \approx 11$ names.

R4. a. See text definition of ln.
b. See text definition of logarithm.
c. See text statement of the uniqueness theorem.
d. See text statement of ln of a power.
e. See text for ln of a quotient property, and see the solution for Problems 9 and 11, Problem Set 6-4, for proof of the quotient property.

R5. a. i. $y' = 100^x \cdot \ln 100$
ii. $f'(x) = (0.74\ln 10)(10^{0.2x})$
iii. $r'(t) = t^{\tan t}[\sec^2 t \ln t + (\tan t)/(t)]$
b. $y' = (5x - 7)^3(3x + 1)^5\left(\frac{15}{5x - 7} + \frac{15}{3x + 1}\right)$
c. *Vitamin C Problem*
i. From Figure 6-10b the maximum concentration is about 150 ppm at about 2 hours.
ii. $C(t)$ is increasing at about 58.7 ppm/hr when $t = 1$, and decreasing at about 24.2 ppm/hr when $t = 5$. The concentration is increasing if $C'(t)$ is positive and decreasing if it is negative.
iii. $C(t) = 50$ for $t \approx 0.2899\ldots$ and $t \approx 6.3245\ldots$. So $C(t) > 50$ for about 6 hours.

iv. Graph, $C_1(t) = 200t \cdot 0.3^t$

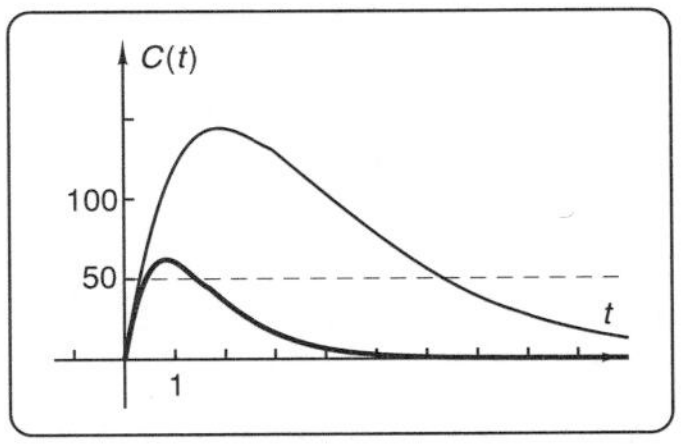


From the graph, the maximum is about 60 ppm around $t = 1$.
$C(t) = 50$ for $t \approx 0.409\ldots$ and $t = 1.473\ldots$.
$C(t) > 50$ for about 1.06 hours.
In conclusion, the concentration peaks *sooner* at a *lower* concentration, and stays above 50 ppm for a much *shorter* time.

R6. a. $e = \lim_{n\to 0}(1+n)^{1/n} = \lim_{n\to\infty}(1+1/n)^n$
b. $\log_e x = \ln x$
c. $\log_b x = \dfrac{\ln x}{\ln b}$
d. i. $y' = \dfrac{1}{x \ln 4}$
ii. $f'(x) = -\dfrac{\tan x}{\ln 2}$
iii. $y' = \log_5 9$
e. Not selected.

R7. a. i. $y = e^x$
ii. $y = \exp(-x)$
iii. $y = \ln x$

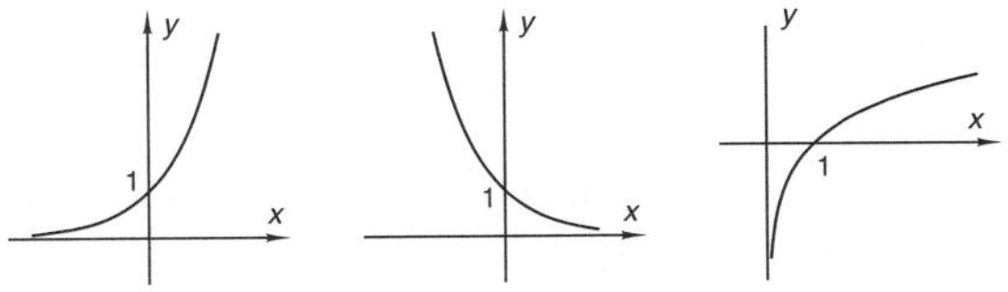


b. i. $f'(x) = x^{0.4}\exp(5x)\cdot(1.4+5x)$
ii. $g'(x) = -2e^{-2x}\cos e^{-2x}$
iii. $y' = 1$
c. i. $-5e^{-2x} + C$
ii. $-e^{\cos x} + C$
iii. $-10\exp(-0.2) + 10\exp(0.2) = 4.0267200\ldots$
d. The number $e$ is used as the base in calculus since the algebraic formulas for the derivatives are simpler.
Exponentials: $d(e^x)/dx = e^x$; $d(a^x) = a^x \cdot \ln a$
Logs: $d(\ln x)/dx = 1/x$; $d(\log_b x)/dx = (1/x)/\ln b$.
e. *Radioactive Decay Problem*
i. $p(5) = 88.2496\ldots$, so about 88% remains.
ii. $p'(0) = -2.5$. Decreasing at about 2.5%/year.
$p'(5) = -2.5e^{-0.125} = -2.2062\ldots$
Decreasing at about 2.2% per year.
iii. $t = 27.7258\ldots$, or about 28 years.
iv. $t = 460.5170\ldots$, or about 461 years.
f. *Chemotherapy Problem*
i. The exposure is the product of $C(t)$ and $t$, where $C(t)$ varies. Thus a definite integral must be used.
ii. $E(x) = 937.5(-e^{-0.16x} + 1)$
$E(5) = 516.25\ldots$ ppm · days
$E(10) = 748.22\ldots$ ppm · days
As $x$ grows very large, $E(x)$ seems to approach 937.5.
iii. $E'(x) = 150e^{-0.16x} = C(x)$
$E'(5) = 67.39\ldots$ ppm (or ppm · days) per day
$E'(10) = 30.28\ldots$ ppm

R8. a. Limit $= -2/5$
b. Limit $= 3$
c. Limit $= 0$
d. Limit $= e^{-2/\pi} = 0.529077\ldots$
e. Limit $= 48$ (Don't be fooled!)
f. Limit $= 1$
g. Examples of indeterminate forms:
$0/0, \infty/\infty, 0\cdot\infty, 0^0, 1^\infty, \infty^0, \infty - \infty$

R9. a. i. $y' = 28\cot 7x$
ii. $y' = x^{-4}e^{2x}(2x-3)$
iii. $y = \cos(2^x) \Rightarrow y' = -\sin(2^x)\cdot 2^x \ln 2$
iv. $y' = \dfrac{4}{x\ln 3}$
b. i. $(-1/1.7)e^{-1.7x} + C$
ii. $(1/\ln 2)2^{\sec x} + C$
iii. $\ln(5+\sin x) + C$ (No absolute value is needed.)
iv. $\ln 5$ (by definition!)
c. i. Limit $= \infty$
ii. Limit $= e^{-3} = 0.049787\ldots$

## Problem Set 6-11

*Cumulative Review, Chapters 1 Through 6*

1. $f'(3) \approx 5.549618\ldots$
2. $\int_{10}^{50} g(x)\,dx \approx 200$
3. $L = \lim_{x\to c} f(x)$ if and only if for any $\epsilon > 0$ there is a $\delta > 0$ such that if $x$ is within $\delta$ units of $c$ but not equal to $c$, then $f(x)$ is within $\epsilon$ units of $L$.
4. Graph. (example)

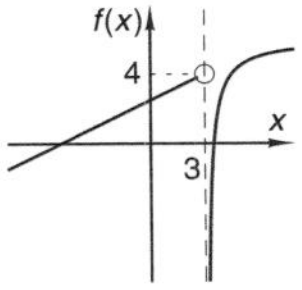


5. $f'(x) = \lim_{h\to 0}\dfrac{f(x+h)-f(x)}{h}$ or

$f'(c) = \lim_{x\to c}\dfrac{f(x)-f(c)}{x-c}$

6. $f(x) = x^3$

$f'(x) = \lim_{h\to 0} \dfrac{(x+h)^3 - x^3}{h}$

$= \lim_{h\to 0} \dfrac{x^3 + 3x^2h + 3xh^2 + h^3 - x^3}{h}$

$= \lim_{h\to 0}(3x^2 + 3xh + h^2) = 3x^2$, Q.E.D.

7. $f'(5) = 75$
$\Delta x = 0.01$: $f'(5) \approx 75.0001$
$\Delta x = 0.001$: $f'(5) \approx 75.000001$
The symmetric differences are getting closer to 75 as $\Delta x$ gets closer to zero, Q.E.D.

8. $f'(7) = 0.375 = 3/8$

9. Graph. Line with slope of 3/8 is tangent to the graph at $x = 7$.

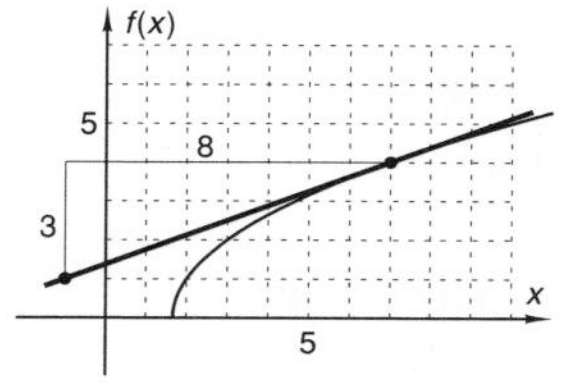


10. Optional graph showing upper sum, $U_6 = 24.875$.

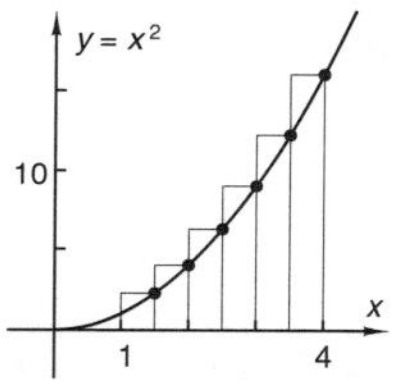


11. $M_{10} = 20.9775$, $M_{100} = 20.999775$
Sums seem to be approaching 21.

12. a. $-\dfrac{1}{6}\cos^6 x + C$

b. $\ln|x| + C$

c. $-\ln|\cos x| + C$

d. $\ln|\sec x + \tan x| + C$

e. $\dfrac{2}{9}(3x-5)^{3/2} + C$

13. Integral = 21, as conjectured in Problem 10.

14. Graph, example, showing tangent line parallel to secant line at $x = c$.

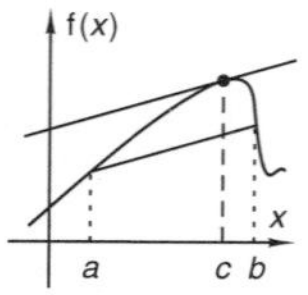


Statement:
If $f$ is differentiable on $(a, b)$ and continuous at $x = a$ and $x = b$, then there is a number $x = c$ in $(a, b)$ such that $f'(x) = \dfrac{f(b) - f(a)}{b - a}$.

15. $y = x^{9/7}$
Either:
$y^7 = x^9$
$7y^6y' = 9x^8$
$y' = \dfrac{9x^8}{7y^6} = \dfrac{9x^8}{7(x^{9/7})^6} = \dfrac{9}{7}x^{8-54/7}$
$= \dfrac{9}{7}x^{2/7} = \dfrac{9}{7}x^{9/7-1}$, as from the derivative of a power formula.

Or:
$\ln y = \dfrac{9}{7}\ln x \Rightarrow (1/y)y' = \dfrac{9}{7}(1/x) \Rightarrow$

$y' = \dfrac{9}{7}(1/x)\cdot y = \dfrac{9}{7}(1/x)\cdot x^{9/7} = \dfrac{9}{7}x^{2/7} = \dfrac{9}{7}x^{9/7-1}$,
as from the derivative of a power formula.

16. If $x^{-1}$ were the derivative of a power, then the power would have to be $x^0$. But $x^0 = 1$, and so its derivative equals 0, not $x^{-1}$. Thus $x^{-1}$ is not the derivative of a power, Q.E.D.

17. $f'(x) = \cos(3\tan x)\cdot \sec^2 x$

18. $f(x) = \int_1^x (1/t)\,dt \Rightarrow f'(x) = 1/x$, Q.E.D.

19. Prove $\ln x^a = a\ln x$ for any constant $a$ and all $x > 0$.

*Proof:*
Let $f(x) = \ln x^a$ and $g(x) = a\ln x$.
Then $f'(x) = \dfrac{1}{x^a}\cdot ax^{a-1} = a\cdot\dfrac{1}{x} = \dfrac{a}{x}$, and

$g'(x) = a\cdot\dfrac{1}{x} = \dfrac{a}{x}$

$\therefore f'(x) = g'(x)$ for all $x > 0$.
$f(1) = \ln(1^a) = \ln 1 = 0$, and $g(1) = a\ln 1 = 0$.
$\therefore f(1) = g(1)$.
$\therefore f(x) = g(x)$ for all $x > 0$, and thus $\ln x^a = a\ln x$ for all $x \geq 0$, Q.E.D.

20. $\dfrac{dy}{dx} = \dfrac{3\cos t}{-5\sin t}$

21. At $t = 2$, $(x, y) = (-2.08\ldots, 2.72\ldots)$, and $dy/dx = 0.2745\ldots$
Graph, showing that a line of slope $0.27\ldots$ at point $(-2.08\ldots, 2.72\ldots)$ is tangent to the curve.

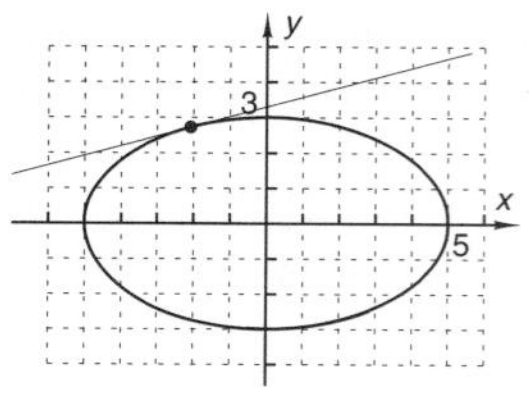


22. $v = (1 + t^2)^{-1}$

$a = -\dfrac{2t}{(1+t^2)^2}$

23. Limit = 3/5

24. $L = \lim_{n\to 0}(1+n)^{1/n} \to 1^\infty$

$\ln L = \lim_{n\to 0}\left(\frac{1}{n}\ln(1+n)\right) \to \infty \cdot 0$

$= \lim_{n\to 0}\frac{\ln(1+n)}{n} \to \frac{0}{0}$

$= \lim_{n\to 0}\frac{1/(1+n)}{1} = 1$

$\therefore L = e^1 = e$, Q.E.D.

25. Integral $\approx 556\frac{2}{3}$

26. Area of cross-section $= \pi y^2$.
Since the end of the radius is on a line through the origin with slope $r/h$, $y = (r/h)x$.

$\therefore \text{Area} = \pi\left[\left(\frac{r}{h}\right)x\right]^2 = \frac{\pi r^2}{h^2}x^2.$

Graph, showing Area as a function of $x$, with strip of width $dx$ and sample point $(x, y)$ on the graph within the strip.

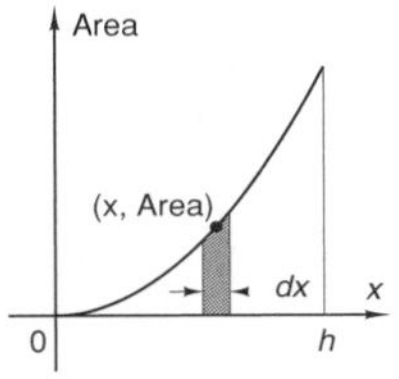


$dV = (\text{Area})\, dx$

$\therefore V = \int_0^h (\text{Area})\, dx = \int_0^h \frac{\pi r^2}{h^2}x^2\, dx$

$= \frac{\pi r^2}{h^2}\cdot\frac{1}{3}x^3\Big|_0^h = \frac{1}{3}\pi\frac{r^2}{h^2}(h^3 - 0^3) = \frac{1}{3}\pi r^2 h$, Q.E.D.

27. Not selected.

## CHAPTER 7

### Exploratory Problem Set 7-1

*Direct Proportion Property of Exponential Functions*

1.

| $t$ | $D(t)$ |
|---|---|
| 0 | 500 |
| 10 | 895.42 |
| 20 | 1603.57 |

3.

| $t$ | $R(t)$ |
|---|---|
| 0 | 0.0582689081... |
| 10 | 0.0582689081... |
| 20 | 0.0582689081... |

5. $f(x) = a\cdot b^x \Rightarrow f'(x) = a\cdot(\ln b)\cdot b^x$
$= (\ln b)(a\cdot b^x) = (\ln b)\cdot f(x)$
So $f'(x)$ is directly proportional to $f(x)$, Q.E.D.

### Problem Set 7-2

*Exponential Growth and Decay*

1. *Bacteria Problem*

a. $B$ = no. of millions of bacteria; $t$ = no. of hours.
$dB/dt = kB \Rightarrow \int dB/B = \int k\, dt$
$B = C_1 e^{kt}$

b. $B = 5e^{(1/3)\ln(7.5)t} = 5(7/5)^{t/3} = 5e^{0.112157\ldots t}$

c. Graph.

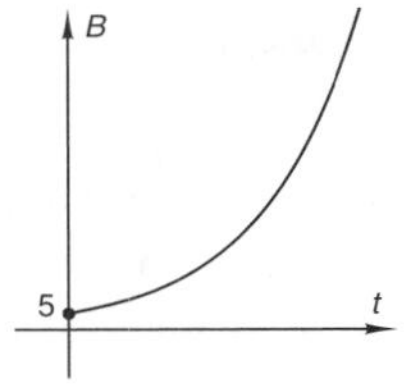


d. About 74 million.

e. $t = 47.24001\ldots$
About 47 hours since start.

3. *Chemical Reaction Problem*

a. $F$ = no. of mg; $t$ = no. of minutes.
$dF/dt = kF$
$F = 50(0.6)^{t/20} = 50e^{-0.025541\ldots t}$

b. Graph.

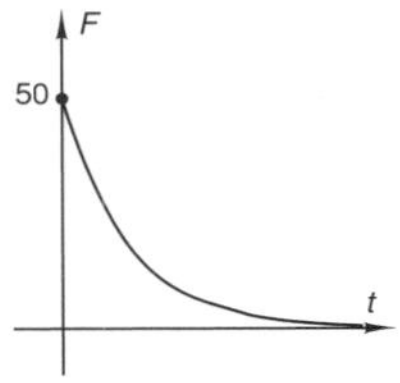


c. 10.8 mg

d. $t = 347.4323\ldots$ About 5 hr 47 min.

5. *Biological Half-Life Problem*

a. $dC/dt = kC$

b. $C = 0.00372e^{-0.0662277\ldots t}$

c. Either: $C = 0.015 \Rightarrow t = -21.05\ldots$, which is before the poison was inhaled,
Or: $t = -20 \Rightarrow C = 0.0139\ldots$, which is less than 0.015.
$\therefore$ concentration never was that high.

d. Graph.

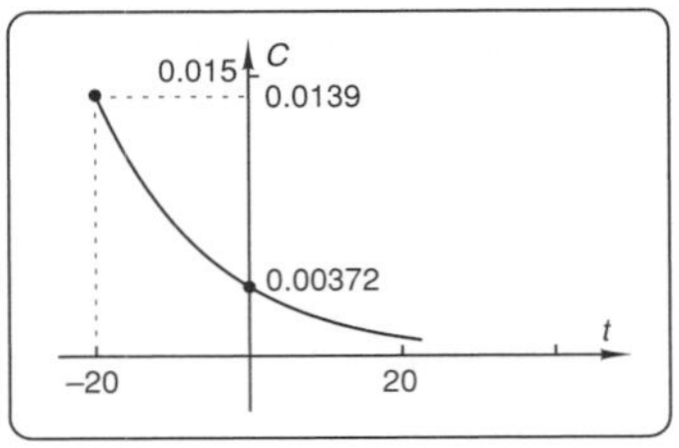


e. $t = 10.4661\ldots \approx 10.5$ hours.

7. *Compound Interest Problem No. 1*
$dM/dt = kM \Rightarrow M = Ce^{kt}$, where $C$ is the initial investment. $\therefore M$ varies exponentially with $t$.
Let $i$ = interest rate as a decimal.
$dM/dt = Ck\cdot e^{kt}$

At $t = 0$, $dM/dt = Ci$
$\therefore Ci = Ck \cdot e^0 \Rightarrow i = k$
Examples:
\$1000 at 7% for 5 years: \$1419.07
\$1000 at 7% for 10 years: \$2013.75
\$1000 at 14% for 5 years: \$2013.75
\$1000 at 14% for 10 years: \$4055.20
Leaving the money twice as long has the *same* effect as doubling the interest rate. Doubling the amount invested doubles the money at any particular time.

9. *Generalization Problem*
$dy/dx = ky \Rightarrow \int dy/y = \int k\,dx \Rightarrow \ln|y| = kx + C_1$
$|y| = e^{kx+C_1} \Rightarrow y = Ce^{kx}$, Q.E.D.

## Problem Set 7-3

*Other Differential Equations for Real World Applications*

1. *Sweepstakes Problem No. 1*
   a. $dM/dt = 100 - S$
   b. $S = kM \Rightarrow dM/dt = 100 - kM$ (which is positive)
   c. $\int \dfrac{dM}{100 - kM} = \int dt$
   $M = \dfrac{100}{k}(1 - e^{-kt})$
   d. $M = 5000(1 - e^{-0.02t})$
   e. Graph.

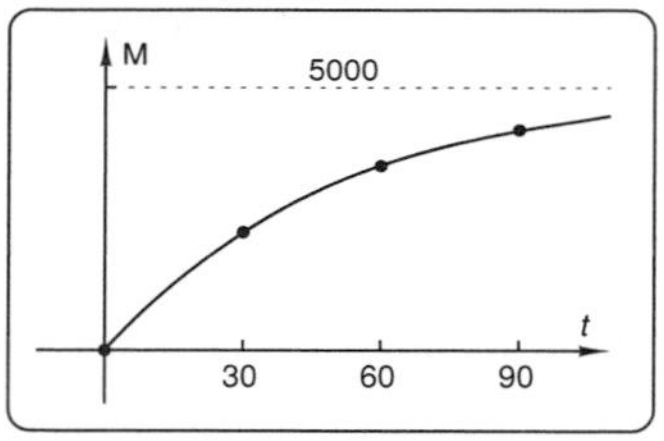


   f. $t = 30$: \$2255.94 (\$3000 in, \$744.06 spent)
   $t = 60$: \$3494.03 (\$6000 in, \$2505.97 spent)
   $t = 90$: \$4173.51 (\$9000 in, \$4826.49 spent)
   g. $t = 365$: (366 could be used.): $M = 4996.622\ldots$
   $\approx$ \$4996.62 in the account.
   $dM/dt = 0.06755\ldots$
   $M$ is increasing at about \$0.07 per day.
   h. $\lim_{t\to\infty} M = 5000$

3. *Electrical Circuit Problem*
   a. $E = RI + L(dI/dt)$
   b. $I = \dfrac{E}{R}(1 - e^{-(R/L)t})$
   c. $I = 11(1 - e^{-0.5t})$ Graph.

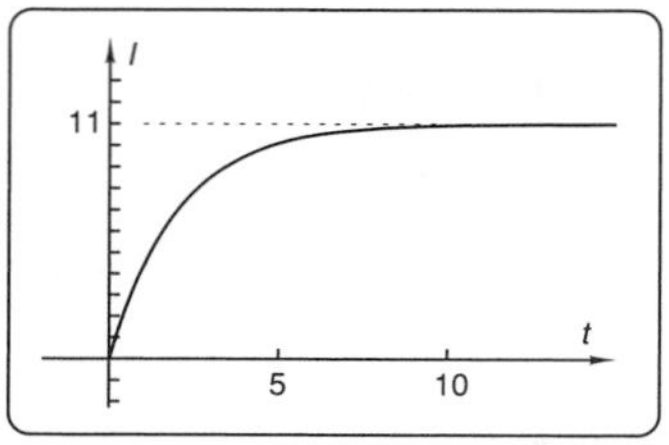


   d. i. $I = 4.3281\ldots \approx 4.33$ amps
   ii. $I = 10.9258\ldots \approx 10.93$ amps
   iii. $I = 11$ amps
   e. $t = -2\ln 0.05 \approx 6$ seconds

5. *Hot Tub Problem*
   a. $\dfrac{dV}{dt} = kV^{1/2}$
   b. $\int V^{-1/2}dV = k\int dt \Rightarrow$
   $2V^{1/2} = kt + C \Rightarrow V = \left(\dfrac{kt + C}{2}\right)^2$
   $V$ varies quadratically with $t$.
   c. Initial conditions $t = 0$; $V = 196$; $dV/dt = -28$:
   $196^{1/2} = \dfrac{k \cdot 0 + C}{2} \Rightarrow C = 28$
   and: $-28 = k \cdot 196^{1/2} \Rightarrow k = -2$
   $\therefore V = \left(\dfrac{-2t + 28}{2}\right)^2 \Rightarrow V = (t - 14)^2$
   d. False. Since $dV/dt = 2t - 28$, the water flows out at 28 only when $t = 0$. For instance, at $t = 5$, $dV/dt = -18$, which means water flows out at only 18 $ft^3$/sec. So it takes longer than 7 minutes to empty the tub.
   e. $0 = (t - 14)^2 \Rightarrow$ the tub is empty at $t = 14$ minutes.
   f. Graph.

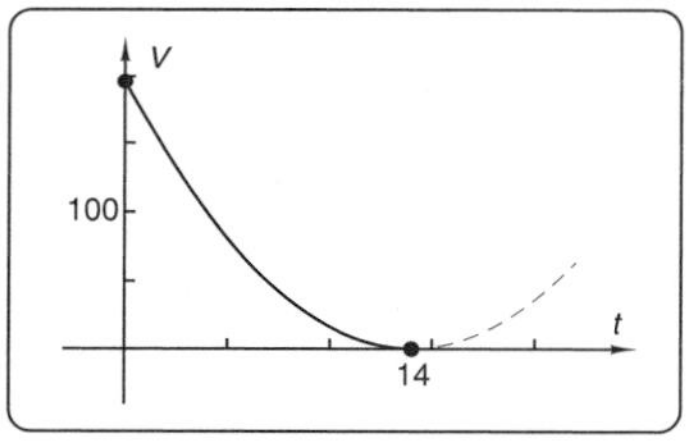


   g. See Problem Set 7-7, #C4.

7. *Differential Equation Generalization Problem*
   a. $n = 1, k = 1, C = -3$: $y = \pm 0.04978\ldots e^x$. Graph.

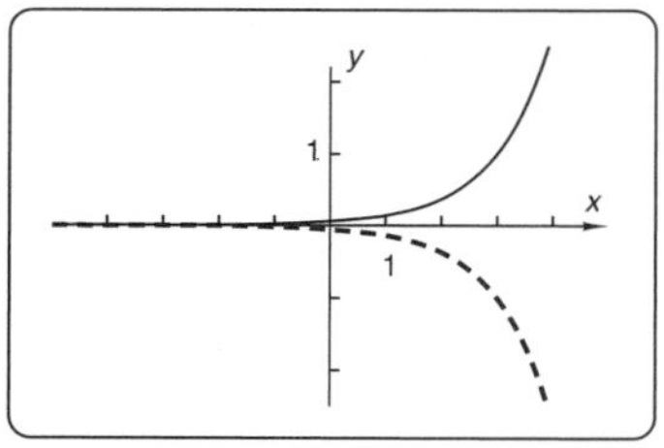


   b. $n = 0.5, k = 1, C = -3$: $y = \dfrac{1}{4}(x - 3)^2$. Graph.

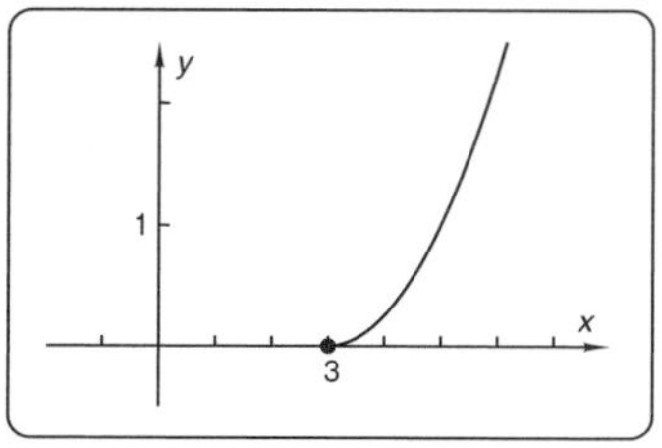

Note: $x \geq 3$ because the symbol $y^{0.5}$ stands for a positive number.

c. $n = -1$, $k = 1$, $C = -3$: $y = \pm\sqrt{2x - 6}$. Graph.

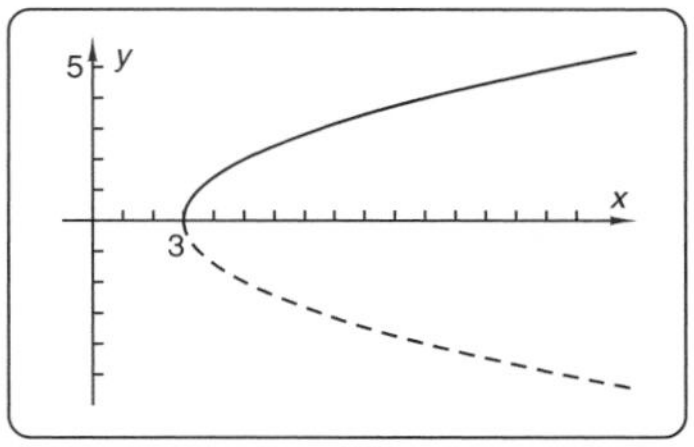


$n = -2$, $k = 1$, $C = -3$: $y = \sqrt[3]{3x - 9}$. Graph.

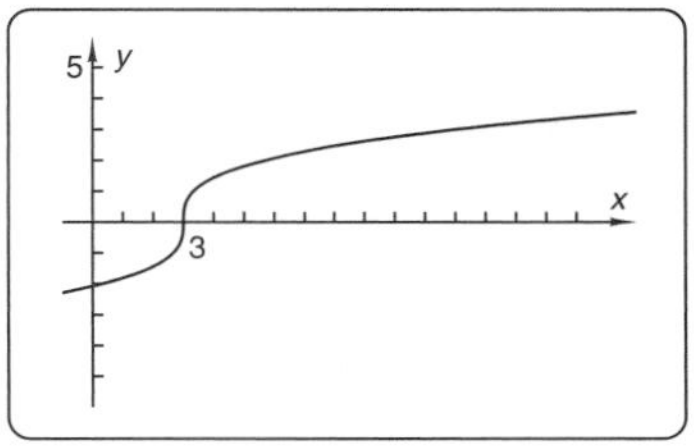


d. For $n > 1$, $\dfrac{dy}{dx} = ky^n \Rightarrow \int y^{-n}\,dy = k\int dx$

$\Rightarrow -\dfrac{y^{-(n-1)}}{n-1} = kx + C$ since $n > 1$, so

$$y = \frac{-1}{\sqrt[n-1]{(n-1)\cdot(kx + C)}},$$

which has a vertical asymptote at $x = -C/k$ since the denominator $= 0$ for this point.

Note that the radical will involve a $\pm$ sign when the root index is even (i.e., when $n$ is odd).

For $n = 2$, $k = 1$, $C = -3$: $y = -(x - 3)^{-1}$. Graph.

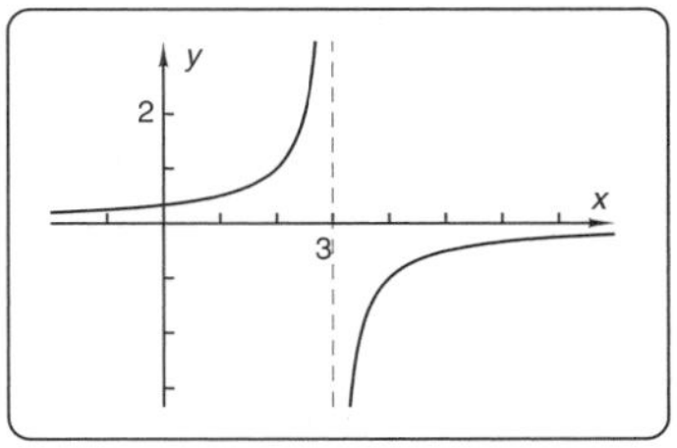


For $n = 3$, $k = 1$, $C = -3$: $y = \pm\dfrac{-1}{\sqrt{2x - 6}}$. Graph.

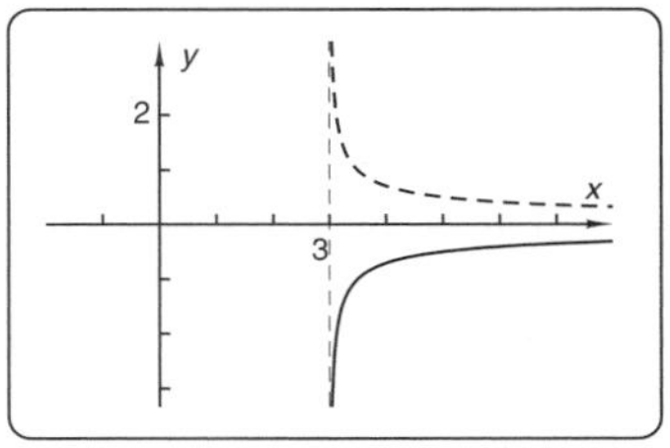


e. $n = 0$, $k = 1$, $C = -3$: $y = x - 3$, which is a linear function, Q.E.D. Graph.

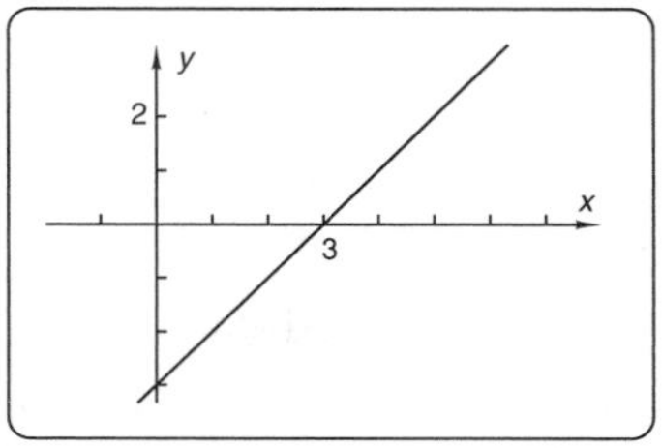


9. *Water Heater Project*

$T \approx 70 + 102.26\ldots(1 - e^{-0.02933\ldots t})$

Time data for various temperatures can be found by grapher, or by substituting for $T$ and solving for $t$.

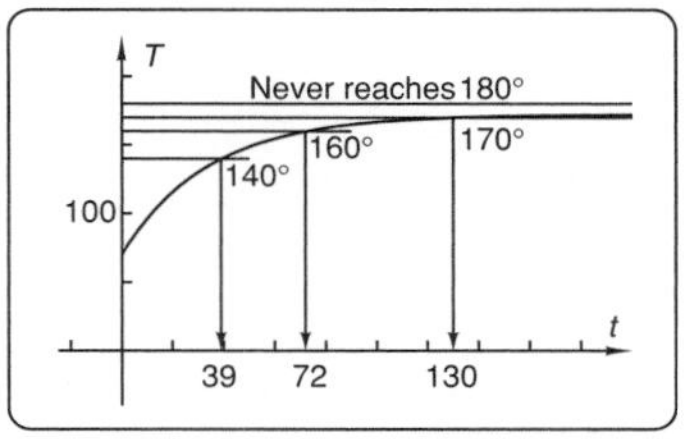


| $T$ | $t$ |
|---|---|
| 140° | 39 min. |
| 155° | 61 min. |
| 160° | 72 min. |
| 170° | 130 min. |
| 180° | Never! |

The limit of $T$ as $t$ increases is $70 + 102.26\ldots(1 + 0)$ which equals 172.26°. Thus, the temperature never reaches 180°.

When the heater turns off the differential equation becomes

$\dfrac{dT}{dt} = -kh(T - 70) \Rightarrow$

$T = 70 + C_2e^{-kht}$

Using $T = 160$ at time $t = 0$ when the heater turns off,

$T = 70 + 90e^{-0.02933\ldots t}$

To find the time taken to drop to 155°, substitute:

$155 = 70 + 90e^{-0.02933\ldots t}$

Solving numerically or algebraically gives $t = 1.9\ldots$. Thus it takes only 2 minutes for the temperature to drop 5°! By contrast, from the above table it takes 11 minutes ($t = 61$ to $t = 72$ in the table above) to warm back up from 155° to 160°.

The design of the heater is inadequate because it takes much longer to warm up by a certain amount than it does to cool back down again. Near 172° a slight increase in the thermostat setting for the heater makes a great increase in the time taken to reach that setting. For instance, it takes an hour (72 minutes to 130 minutes) to warm the 10 degrees from 160° to 170°. These inadequacies could be corrected most easily by adding more insulation. The resulting decrease in $h$ would make the heater cool more slowly, heat up faster, and reach the 180 degrees it currently cannot. Decreasing $h$ would also reduce the power consumption.

### ***Problem Set 7-4***

*Graphical Solution of Differential Equations Using Slope Fields*

1. a. At $(3, 5)$, $dy/dx = 3/10 = 0.3$.
   At $(-5, 1)$, $dy/dx = -5/2 = -2.5$.
   On the graph, the line at $(3, 5)$ slopes upward with a slope less than 1. At $(-5, 1)$ the line slopes downward with a slope much steeper than $-1$.

   b. Graph. The figure looks like one branch of a hyperbola opening in the $y$-direction. (The lower branch shown on the graph is also part of the solution, but you are not expected to find this graphically.)

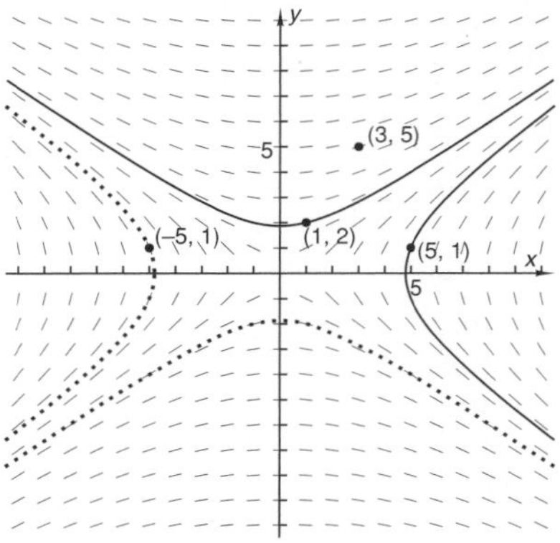


   c. Graph, above. The figure looks like the right-hand branch of a hyperbola opening in the $x$-direction. (The left-hand branch is also part of the solution, but you are not expected to find this graphically.)

   d. $x^2 - 2y^2 = 23$.
   This is the particular equation of a hyperbola opening in the $x$-direction, which confirms the observations in part (c).

3. a. Graph.

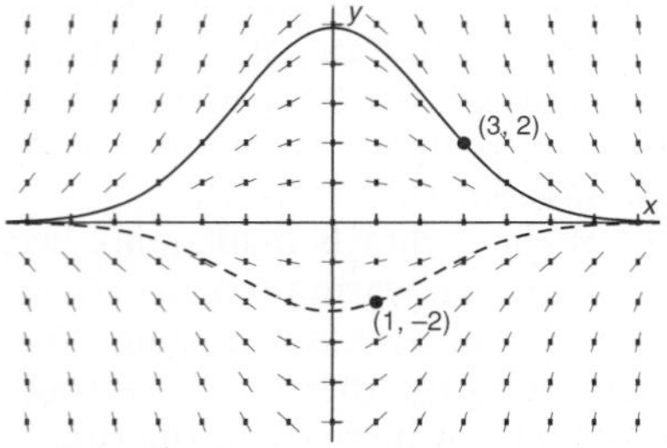


   b. $\dfrac{dy}{dx} = -0.2xy$

   Evidence: At $(1, 1)$ the slope was given to be $-0.2$, which is true for this differential equation. As $x$ or $y$ increase from this point, the slope gets steeper in the negative direction, which is also true for this differential equation. In quadrants I and III the slopes are all negative, and in quadrants II and IV they are all positive.
   (Note: The algebraic solution is $y = Ce^{-0.1x^2}$)

5. Graph. (differential equation is
   $dy/dx = (x/5)\sin(\pi y/8) + y/10$.)

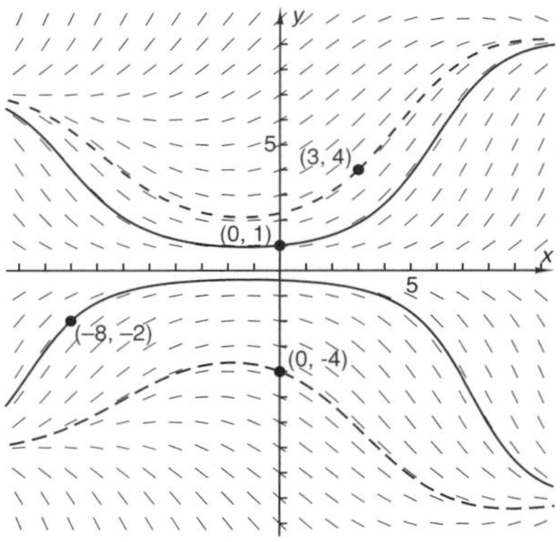


7. *Rabbit Population Problem*

   a. Graph. Initial condition $(0, 2)$

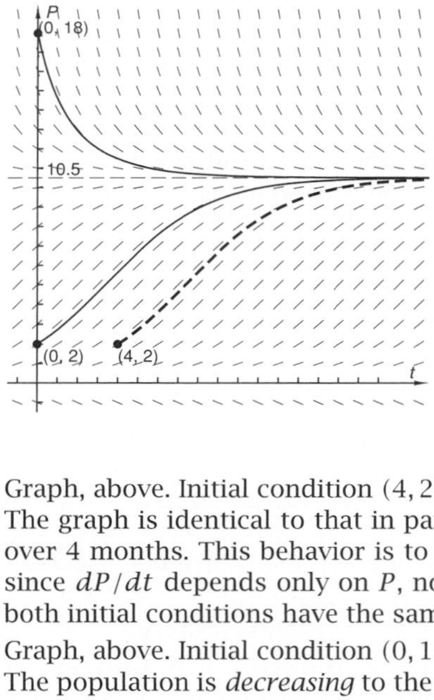


   b. Graph, above. Initial condition $(4, 2)$
   The graph is identical to that in part (a) shifted over 4 months. This behavior is to be expected since $dP/dt$ depends only on $P$, not on $t$, and both initial conditions have the same value of $P$.

   c. Graph, above. Initial condition $(0, 18)$
   The population is *decreasing* to the same asymptote, $P = 10.5$, as in parts (a) and (b).

   d. The asymptote at $P = 10.5$ indicates that the island can sustain only 1050 rabbits. If the population is lower than that, it increases. If the population is higher than that, it decreases. The number 10.5 is a value of $P$ that makes $dP/dt$ equal zero. Note that there is another asymptote at $P = 0$, which also makes $dP/dt$ equal zero.

9. *Escape Velocity Problem*

a. $ma = \dfrac{mg}{r^2}$ by hypothesis

$\dfrac{dv}{dt} = \dfrac{g}{r^2}$ divide by $m$; $a = \dfrac{dv}{dt}$

$\dfrac{dv}{dr} \cdot \dfrac{dr}{dt} = \dfrac{g}{r^2}$ chain rule

$\dfrac{dv}{dr} \cdot v = \dfrac{g}{r^2}$ $v = \dfrac{dr}{dt}$ ($r =$ distance)

$\dfrac{dv}{dr} = \dfrac{g}{r^2 v}$ divide by $v$.

b. $\dfrac{dv}{dr}(5, 2) = -1.2488$

$\dfrac{dv}{dr}(1, 10) = -6.244$

$\dfrac{dv}{dr}(10, 4) = -0.1561$

These slopes agree with those shown.

c. Graph. Initial condition $(r, v) = (1, 10)$
Spaceship stops about 4 earth radii, or about 25,000 km above the surface.

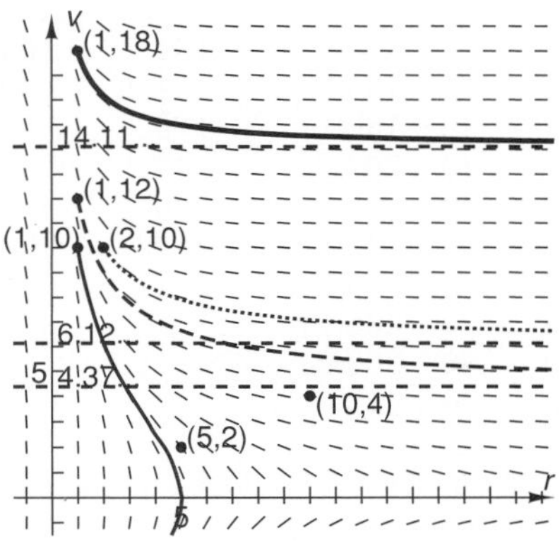


d. Graph above. Initial condition $(r, v) = (1, 12)$
The graph levels off between 4 and 5 km/sec.

e. Graph, above. Initial condition $(r, v) = (1, 18)$
The graph levels off at $v \approx 14$ km/sec. Here the spaceship loses about 4 km/sec of velocity, whereas it loses 7 or 8 km/sec when starting at 12 km/sec. Both cases lose the same amount of kinetic energy, which is proportional to $v^2$ (the change in $v^2$ is the same in both cases).

f. Graph, above. Initial condition $(r, v) = (2, 10)$
The graph levels off at about 6 km/sec, so the spaceship does escape. Alternatively note that the solution through $(2, 10)$ lies above the solution through $(1, 12)$.

## Problem Set 7-5

*Numerical Solution of Differential Equations by Euler's Method*

1. *How Euler's Method Works*

a. At $(0, 3)$, $dy/dx = 0$. At $x = 0.5$, $y \approx 3$.

b. At $(0.5, 3)$, $dy/dx = -0.0833\ldots$.
At $x = 1$, $y \approx 2.9583\ldots$.

c.

| $x$ | $y$ | slope | $dy$ |
|---|---|---|---|
| 1 | 2.9583... | −0.1690... | −0.0845... |
| 1.5 | 2.8738... | −0.2609... | −0.1304... |
| 2 | 2.7433... | −0.3645... | −0.1822... |
| 2.5 | 2.5610... | −0.4880... | −0.2440... |
| 3 | 2.3170... | −0.5463... | −0.3236... |
| 3.5 | 1.9933... | −0.8779... | −0.4385... |
| 4 | 1.5543... | −1.2866... | −0.6433... |
| 4.5 | 0.9110... | −2.4696... | −1.2348... |
| 5 | −0.3237... | 7.7213... | 3.8606... |
| 5.5 | 3.5368... | −0.7775... | −0.3887... |
| 6 | 3.1481... | −0.9529... | −0.4764... |
| 6.5 | 2.6716... | −1.2164... | −0.6082... |
| 7 | 2.0634... | −1.6962... | −0.8481... |

d. Graph.

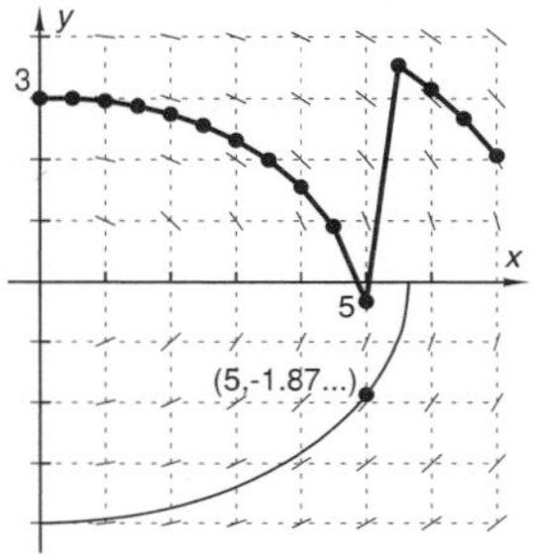


The values of $y$ follow the slope field through $x = 4.5$. At $x = 5$, $y$ becomes negative. As a result, $dy/dx$ is positive and the curve jumps up in the positive direction. Thus, for $x > 5$ the $y$-values by Euler's method are clearly wrong. Note that the values follow another curve that has initial condition $(5.5, 3.5368\ldots)$

3. *Accuracy of Euler's Method*

a. $y^2 = -\dfrac{1}{2}x^2 + 16 \Rightarrow y = -\sqrt{16 - 0.5x^2}$
The negative root is picked because $y$ is negative when $x = 0$.
For $x = 5$, $y = -\sqrt{3.5} = -1.8708\ldots$.
The point $(5, -1.87\ldots)$ is on the graph (see Problem 1, part (d)).

b. $\Delta x = 0.5$

| $x$ | $y$ |
|---|---|
| 0 | −4 |
| 1 | −3.9687... |
| 2 | −3.8097... |
| 3 | −3.5085... |
| 4 | −3.0292... |
| 5 | −2.2823... |
| 6 | −0.9420... |
| 7 | −1.8486... |

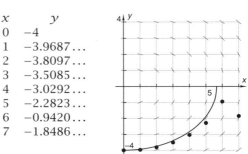

c. Graph, $\Delta x = 0.5$.

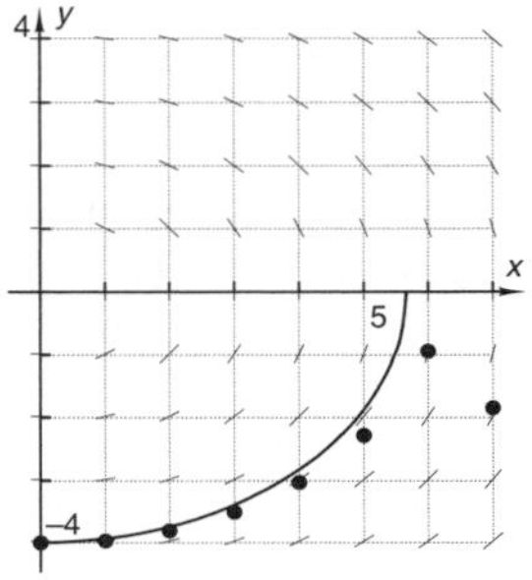

Euler's method gives a good approximation close to the starting point, but gets progressively worse farther away from the starting point. The answers are meaningless beyond the $x$-intercept, where the slope is infinite.

d. $\Delta x = 0.1$ Graph, $\Delta x = 0.1$

| $x$ | $y$ |
|---|---|
| 0 | −4 |
| 1 | −3.9434... |
| 2 | −3.7555... |
| 3 | −3.4155... |
| 4 | −2.8715... |
| 5 | −1.9696... |
| 6 | 0.7600... |
| 7 | 2.1652... |

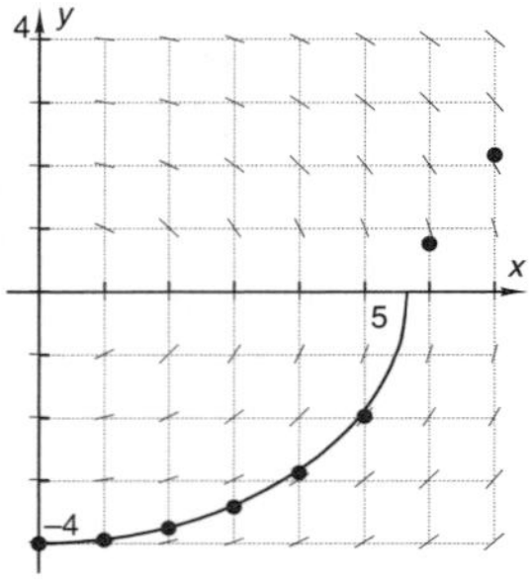


The approximation is better if $\Delta x$ is smaller. The values still diverge slightly from the actual values as $x$ gets farther from the starting point. For instance, if $x = 5$, $y \approx -1.9696\ldots$ by Euler's method compared to the exact value, $-1.8708\ldots$, from part 3(a). The method still fails beyond the $x$-intercept.

e. Using $\Delta x = 0.01$, $y \approx -1.8812\ldots$ when $x = 5$, which is quite close to $-\sqrt{3.5} = -1.8708\ldots$.

5. a–b. Graph, $\dfrac{dy}{dx} = -0.2xy$

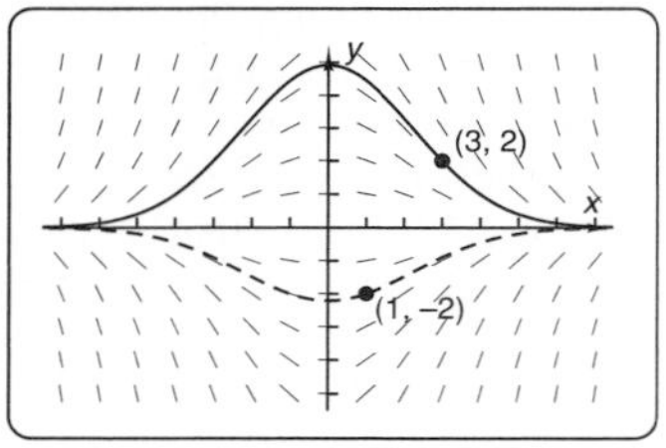


7. *U.S. Population Project*

a–b.

| year | $P$ | $\Delta P/\Delta t$ | $(\Delta P/\Delta t)/P$ |
|---|---|---|---|
| 1940 | 131.7 | | |
| 1950 | 151.4 | 2.38 | 0.01571... |
| 1960 | 179.3 | 2.59 | 0.01444... |
| 1970 | 203.2 | 2.36 | 0.01161... |
| 1980 | 226.5 | 2.275 | 0.01004... |
| 1990 | 248.7 | | |

c. Using linear regression on the values of $(\Delta P/\Delta t)/P$ without round-off gives
$$\frac{1}{P}\frac{\Delta P}{\Delta t} \approx 0.02802596\ldots - 0.0000792747\ldots P$$
The correlation coefficient is $r = -0.98535\ldots$
For the other types of regression:
$r = -0.978\ldots$ for logarithmic
$r = -0.981\ldots$ for exponential
$r = -0.981\ldots$ for power
Thus a linear function fits best because $r$ is closest to −1.

d. $\dfrac{1}{P}\dfrac{dP}{dt} \approx 0.02802596\ldots - 0.0000792747\ldots P$
$\Rightarrow \dfrac{dP}{dt} = P(0.02802596\ldots - 0.0000792747\ldots P)$

e. Graph.

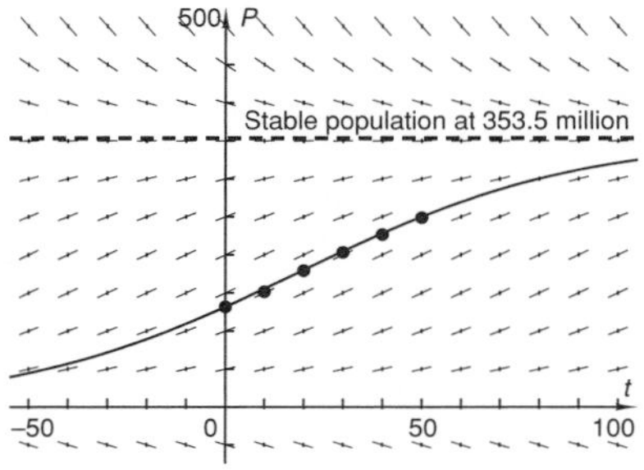


f.

| year | $t$ | Euler | actual* | Euler** |
|---|---|---|---|---|
| 1890 | −50 | 44.6... | 62.9 | 46.1... |
| 1900 | −40 | 56.9... | 76.0 | 58.3... |
| 1910 | −30 | 71.7... | 92.0 | 73.9... |
| 1920 | −20 | 89.2... | 105.7 | 90.1... |
| 1930 | −10 | 109.3... | 122.8 | 109.8... |
| 1940 | 0 | 131.7 | 131.7 | 131.7 |
| 1950 | 10 | 155.4... | 151.4 | 155.0... |
| 1960 | 20 | 180.1... | 179.3 | 179.2... |
| 1970 | 30 | 204.7... | 203.2 | 203.5... |
| 1980 | 40 | 228.2... | 226.5 | 226.9... |
| 1990 | 50 | 249.4... | 248.7 | 248.8... |
| 2000 | 60 | 269.3... | | |
| 2010 | 70 | 286.1... | | |
| 2020 | 80 | 300.2... | | |
| 2030 | 90 | 311.8... | | |
| 2040 | 100 | 321.1... | | |

*Data from *The World Book Encyclopedia*

**Note that although linear regression gives the "best" fit for $(\Delta P/\Delta t)/P$ vs. $P$, actually plotting the graph shows that the data point for 1960 is considerably out of line.

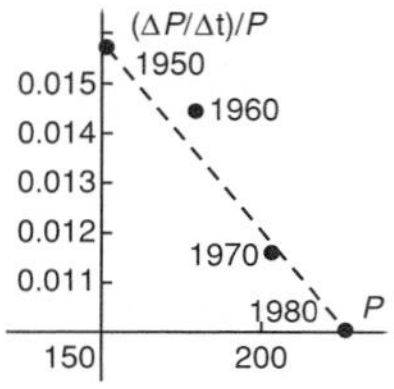


Using the two end points, 1950 and 1980, gives $(\Delta P/\Delta t)/P = 0.002716\ldots - 0.00007558\ldots P$
Using this equation gives populations much closer to the actual for the given years, as shown in the right-most column above. This is, of course, no guarantee that the later model fits any better in the future than the former one.

g. The population growth rate is zero if $dP/dt = 0$.
Let $P(0.02802596\ldots - 0.0000792747\ldots P) = 0$.
$P = 0$ or

$P = (0.02802596\ldots)/(0.0000792747\ldots) = 353.5\ldots$

Predicted ultimate population $\approx$ 353.5 million.

Differential equation: $P = 353.5\ldots$ makes $dP/dt = 0$.

Graph: $P = 353.5\ldots$ is a horizontal asymptote.

h. Graph, part (f). Data do follow the solution.

i. Example answer: "The predicted populations agree fairly well with the data for the six given years. The fit is exact for 1940 since this point was used as an initial condition. For the other five years the predicted populations are a bit higher than the actual population."

j. Actual data are underlined in the table in part (f).

k. The predicted population for 2000 from part (f) is 269.3... million. Using 469.3 million as an initial condition in 2000 gives the following predictions:

| year | $t$ | Euler |
|---|---|---|
| 2000 | 60 | 469.3 |
| 2010 | 70 | 433.9... |
| 2020 | 80 | 410.6... |
| 2030 | 90 | 394.8... |
| 2040 | 100 | 383.7... |

The logistic model predicts that the population will *drop*, approaching the ultimate value of 353.5 million from *above*. This behavior shows up in the slope field of part (c), since the slopes are *negative* for populations above 353.5.

9. Not selected.

## Problem Set 7-6

*Predator-Prey Population Problems*

1. $\dfrac{dR}{dt} = k_1R \Rightarrow \dfrac{dR}{R} = k_1\,dt \Rightarrow \ln|R| = k_1t + C$

$\Rightarrow |R| = e^Ce^{k_1t} \Rightarrow R = C_1e^{k_1t}$

$R$ is increasing since $k_1 > 0$.

3. $\dfrac{dR}{dt} = k_1R - k_3RF$

$\dfrac{dF}{dt} = -k_2F + k_4RF$

5. $dF/dR = 0.4017\ldots$

7. The populations vary periodically, and the graph is cyclical. The foxes reach their maximum 1/4 cycle after the rabbits.

9. $dF/dR = -0.5357\ldots$

11. The populations now spiral to a fixed point. The rabbit population stabilizes at the same value as in Problem 8, $R = 40$ (4000 rabbits), which is surprising. The stable fox population decreases from 25 to 15.

13. Graph. The slope at $(70, 15)$ is about $-0.4$.

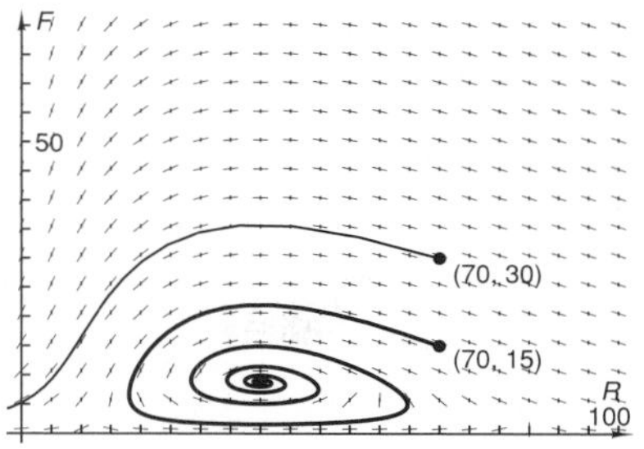


15. Graph in Problem 13, starting at $(70, 30)$. With this many foxes and hunters chasing rabbits, the rabbits become extinct. At this point the foxes have been reduced to just 5. After the rabbits become extinct, the foxes decrease exponentially with time, eventually becoming extinct themselves.

## Problem Set 7-7

*Chapter Review and Test*

### Review Problems

R0. Journal entries will vary.

R1. *Punctured Tire Problem*

$P(t) = 35(0.98^t)$

$P'(t) = 35(0.98^t)\ln 0.98$

| $t$ | $P(t)$ | $P'(t)$ | $P'(t)/P(t)$ |
|---|---|---|---|
| 0 | 35 | $-0.7070\ldots$ | $-0.2020\ldots$ |
| 10 | 28.597... | $-0.5777\ldots$ | $-0.2020\ldots$ |
| 20 | 23.366... | $-0.4720\ldots$ | $-0.2020\ldots$ |

$$\frac{P'(t)}{P(t)} = \frac{35(0.98^t)\ln 0.98}{35(0.98^t)} = \ln 0.98 = -0.2020\ldots,$$

which is a constant, Q.E.D.

R2. *Ramjet Problem*

a. $V =$ speed in mph, $t =$ time in seconds.

$\dfrac{dV}{dt} = kV$

b. $\int \dfrac{dV}{V} = k\int dt$

$\ln|V| = kt + C \Rightarrow |V| = e^{kt+C} = e^C \cdot e^{kt} \Rightarrow$

$V = C_1e^{kt}$

Mathematically, $C_1$ can be positive or negative, so the absolute value sign is not needed for $V$. In the real world $V$ is positive, which also makes the absolute value sign unnecessary.

c. $V = 400e^{0.005578\ldots t}$

d. $t = 112.68\ldots \approx$ 113 seconds

R3. a. $y = (3x + C)^2$

b. $y = (3x - 4)^2$

c. Graph.

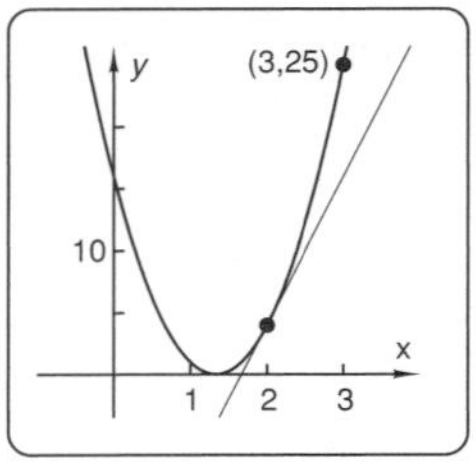


d. At $x = 2$, $y' = 12$ and $y = 4$.
A line through $(2, 4)$ with slope 12 is tangent to the graph, showing that 12 is reasonable.

e. *Memory Retention Problem*

i. $dN/dt = 100 - kN$
$N = 2210.6\ldots(1 - e^{-0.045236t})$

ii. About 1642 names.

iii. Brain saturates at about 2211 names.

iv. $t \approx 27$ days.

R4. a. At $(2, 5)$, $dy/dx = -1.75$.
At $(10, 16)$, $dy/dx = 0.675$
The slopes at $(2, 5)$ and $(10, 16)$ agree with these numbers as shown on the graph in part (b).

b. Graph, initial conditions $(1, 8)$ and $(1, 12)$.

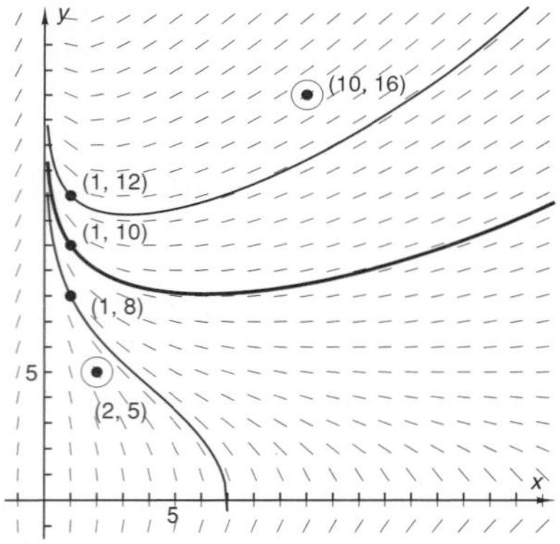


The solution containing $(1, 8)$ crosses the $x$-axis near $x = 7$, converges asymptotically to the $y$-axis as $x$ approaches zero, and is symmetric across the $x$-axis. The solution containing $(1, 12)$ goes to infinity as $x$ goes to infinity.

c. Graph, initial condition $(1, 10)$.
The solution containing $(1, 10)$ behaves more like the one containing $(1, 12)$, although a slight discrepancy in plotting may make it seem to go the other way.

R5. a. Table, initial condition $(1, 9)$, $\Delta x = 1$

| $x$ | $y(\Delta x = 1)$ | $y(\Delta x = 0.1)$ |
|---|---|---|
| 1 | 9 | 9 |
| 2 | 7.227... | 7.707... |
| 3 | 6.205... | 6.949... |
| 4 | 5.441... | 6.413... |
| 5 | 4.794... | 5.999... |
| 6 | 4.200... | 5.662... |
| 7 | 3.616... | 5.377... |
| 8 | 3.007... | 5.130... |
| 9 | 2.326... | 4.910... |
| 10 | 1.488... | 4.712... |
| 11 | 0.2185... | 4.529 ... |
| 12 | −8.091... | 4.359 ... |
| 13 | | 4.199... |
| 14 | | 4.045... |
| 15 | | 3.896... |
| 16 | | 3.750... |
| 17 | | 3.604... |
| 18 | | 3.457... |
| 19 | | 3.306... |
| 20 | | 3.150... |
| 21 | | 2.986... |
| 22 | | 2.811... |
| 23 | | 2.621... |
| 24 | | 2.410... |
| ... | | ... |
| 28.9 | | 0.1344... |
| 29 | | −0.3796... |

Graph.

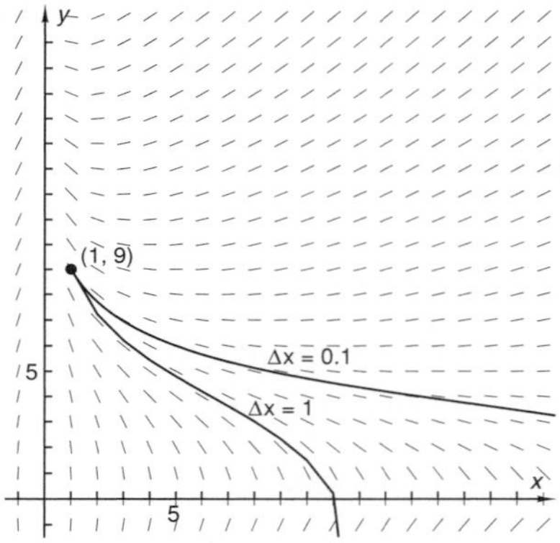


For $\Delta x = 1$, the graph crosses the $x$-axis at about $x = 11$, and for $\Delta x = 0.1$, the graph crosses the $x$-axis at about $x = 28.9$.

b. Table in part (a), $\Delta x = 0.1$
Graph in part (a) shows different pattern.

c. The accuracy far away from the initial condition is very sensitive to the size of the increment. For instance, in part (a) the first step took the graph so far down that it crosses the $x$-axis before running off the edge of the grid. The greater accuracy with $\Delta x = 0.1$ shows that the graph actually does not cross the $x$-axis before $x = 20$.

d. Graph crosses the $x$-axis close to $x = 28.9$.

R6. *Predator-Prey Problem*

a. $\dfrac{dy}{dx} = \dfrac{-0.5(x-6)}{(y-7)}$
$dy = 0$ when $x = 6$ and $dx = 0$ when $y = 7$.
So the stable point is $(6, 7)$, corresponding to the present population of 600 Xaltos natives and 7000 yaks.

b. Graph, initial condition $(9, 7)$.

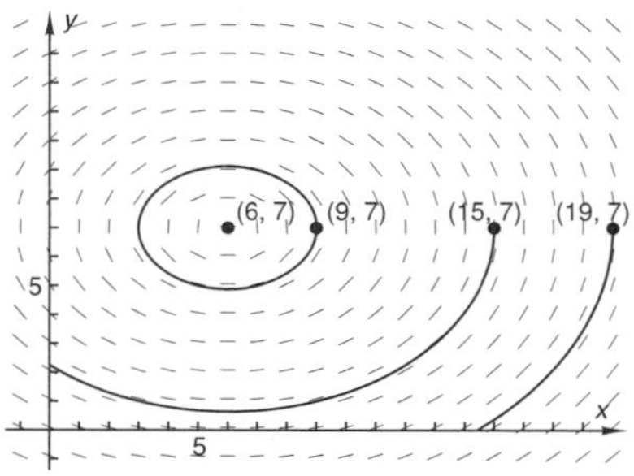


Suddenly there are too many predators for the number of prey, so the yak population declines. Since $y$ is decreasing from $(9, 7)$, the graph follows a clockwise path.

c. Graph, initial condition $(19, 7)$, in part (b).
The graph crosses the $x$-axis at $x \approx 14.4$, indicating that the yaks are hunted to extinction. (The Xaltos would then starve or become vegetarian!)

d. Graph, initial condition $(15, 7)$, in part (b).
The graph never crosses the $x$-axis, but crosses the $y$-axis at $y \approx 2.3$, indicating that the yak population becomes so sparse that the predators become extinct. (The yak population would then explode!)

## Problem Set 7-8

*Cumulative Review, Chapters 1 through 7*

*Rocket Problem*

1. Graph, showing strip and sample point.
$v(t)\,dt$ represents the distance traveled in time $dt$.

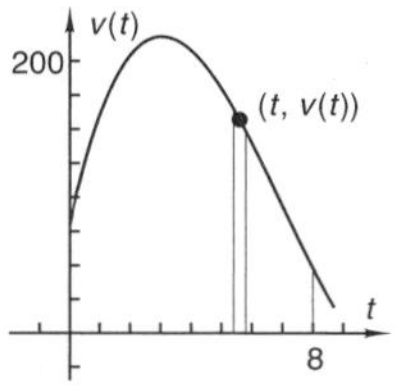


2. Definite integral

3. 1280 mi

4. $M_{100} = 1280.0384$
$M_{1000} = 1280.000384$
The Riemann sums seem to be approaching 1280 as $n$ increases. Thus, the 1280 that was found by purely algebraic methods seems to give the correct value of the limit of the Riemann sum.

5. Graph, showing the upper sum $U_8$.

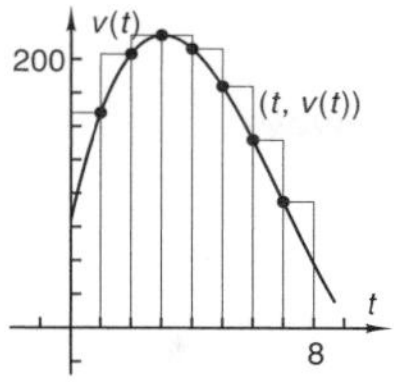


6. Any Riemann sum is bounded by the corresponding lower and upper sums. That is,
$L_n \le R_n \le U_n$.
By the definition of integrability, the limits of $L_n$ and $U_n$ are equal to each other, and to the definite integral. By the squeeze theorem, then, the limit of $R_n$ is also equal to the definite integral.

7. Definition: $\int_a^b f(x)\,dx = \lim_{\Delta x \to 0} L_n = \lim_{\Delta x \to 0} U_n$ provided that the two limits are equal.
Fundamental theorem: If $f$ is integrable on $[a, b]$, and $g(x) = \int f(x)\,dx$, then $\int_a^b f(x)\,dx = g(b) - g(a)$.

8. Numerically, the integral equals 1280.
By counting, there are approximately 52 squares.
Thus the integral $\approx 52(25)(1) = 1300$.

9. $\Delta t = 0.1$: $v'(4) \approx -19.9$ (mi/min)/min
$\Delta t = 0.01$: $v'(4) \approx -19.9999$ (mi/min)/min

10. $f'(c) = \lim_{x \to c} \dfrac{f(x) - f(c)}{x - c}$ or
$f'(x) = \lim_{\Delta x \to 0} \dfrac{f(x + \Delta x) - f(x)}{\Delta x}$

11. $v'(t) = 3t^2 - 42t + 100 \Rightarrow v'(4) = -20$

12. *Slowing down.* $v'(4) < 0 \Rightarrow$ velocity is decreasing.

13. Graph, showing line of slope $-20$ through $(4, 208)$. The line is tangent to the graph.

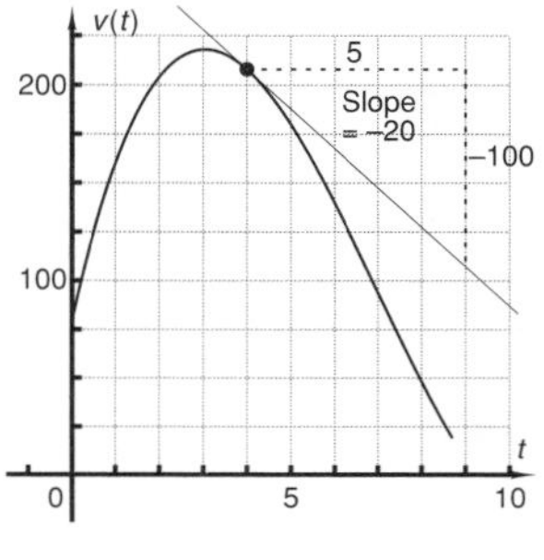


14. Acceleration

15. $v'(t) = 0 \iff t = 10.958\ldots$ or $3.041\ldots$
So the maximum is *not* at exactly $t = 3$.

16. $v''(t) = 6t - 42$

*Compound Interest Problem*

17. $\dfrac{dm}{dt} = km$

18. $\int \dfrac{dm}{m} = k\int dt \Rightarrow \ln|m| = kt + C \Rightarrow$
$|m| = e^{kt+C} \Rightarrow m = C_1e^{kt}$

19. Exponentially

20. General

21. $m = 10{,}000e^{\ln(1.09)t} = 10{,}000(1.09)^t$

22. False. The rate of increase changes as the amount in the account increases. At $t = 10$,
$m = 10{,}000(1.09)^{10} \approx 23{,}673.64$.
The amount of money would grow by \$13,673.64, not just \$9,000.

*Discrete Data Problem*

23. Integral $\approx 1022$

24. By symmetric difference quotient, $y' \approx 1.75$.

*Mean Value Theorem Problem*

25. See text statement of Rolle's theorem.

26. Graph. (example)

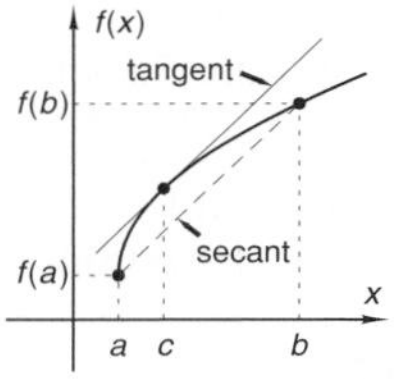


*Graphing Problems*

27. Graph.

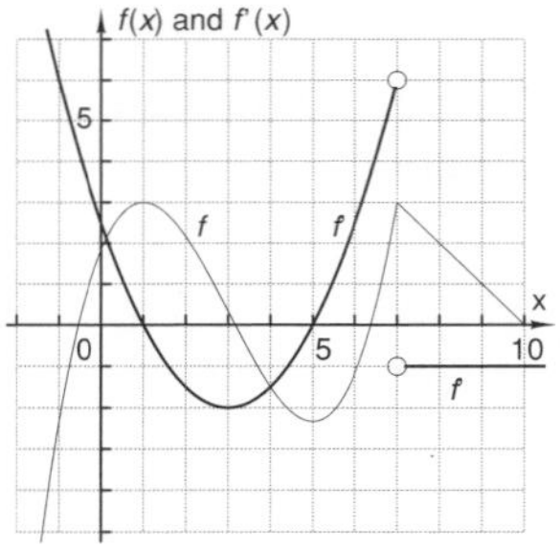


28. Graph. Step discontinuity at $x = 1$

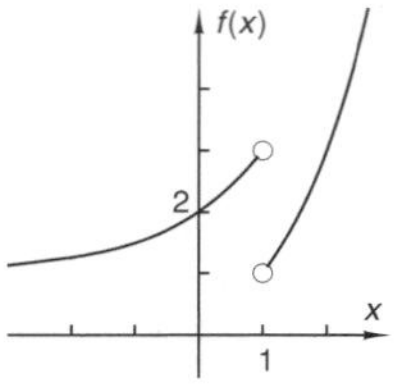


29. $g'(x) = \dfrac{1}{3}x^{-2/3}(4x - 1)$
$g'(0)$ is undefined because $0^{-2/3}$ takes on the form $1/0^{2/3}$ or $1/0$. Graph.

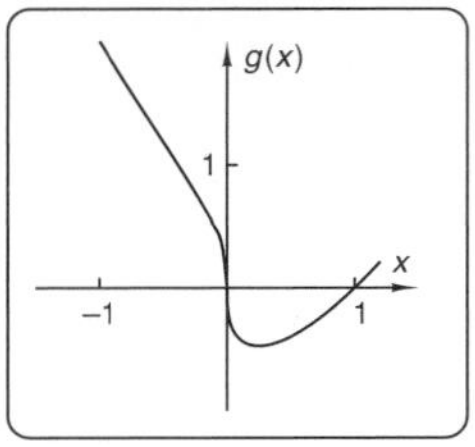


*Differential Equation Problems*

30. Graph, initial conditions: $(0, 3)$ and $(10, 4)$.

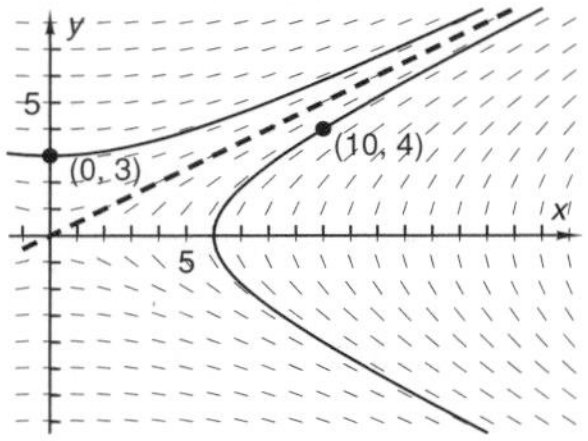


31. Graph, Problem 30. Any initial condition such as $(2, 1)$ for which $y = 0.5x$ gives the asymptote.

32. $x^2 - 4y^2 = 36$ or $y = \pm 0.5\sqrt{x^2 - 36}$

33. $x = 10.5$: $y = 4.30842\ldots$

34. At $(10, 4)$, $\dfrac{dy}{dx} = 0.25 \cdot \dfrac{10}{4} = 0.625$.
Using $\Delta x = 0.5$, $y(10.5) \approx 4 + (0.625)(0.5)$ $= 4.3125$, which is close to the exact value of $4.30842\ldots$.

*Algebraic Techniques Problems*

35. $\dfrac{d}{dx}(\sin^{-1} x^3) = \dfrac{3x^2}{\sqrt{1 - x^6}}$

36. $dy/dx = -\sec t = -y$

37. Integral $= -\dfrac{1}{3}\ln|4 - 3x| + C$

38. $h'(x) = 5^x \ln 5$

39. Limit $= -4.5$

40. Graph, removable discontinuity at $(0, -4.5)$.

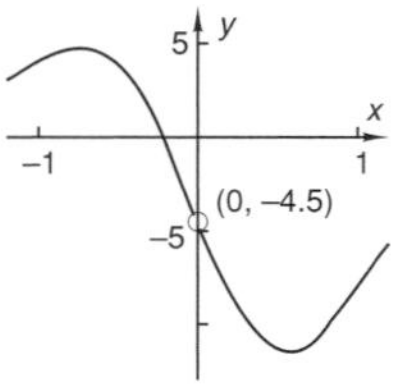


41. Journal entries will vary.

42. Journal entries will vary.

## CHAPTER 8

### Exploratory Problem Set 8-1

*Cubic Functions and Their Derivatives*

1. $f(x) = x^3 - 6x^2 + 9x + 3$
   $f'(x) = 3x^2 - 12x + 9$ Graph.

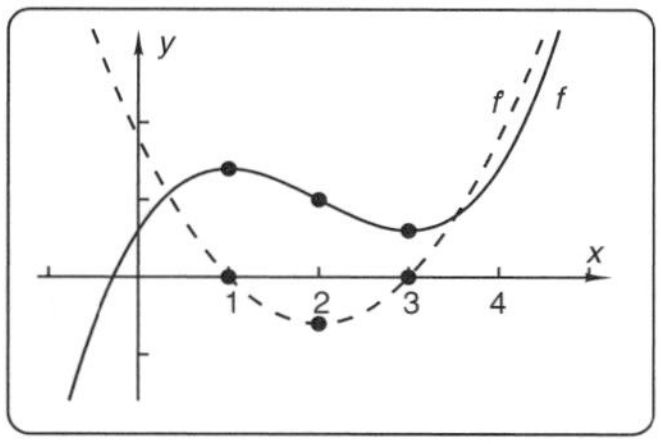


$g(x) = x^3 - 6x^2 + 15x - 9$
$g'(x) = 3x^2 - 12x + 15$ Graph.

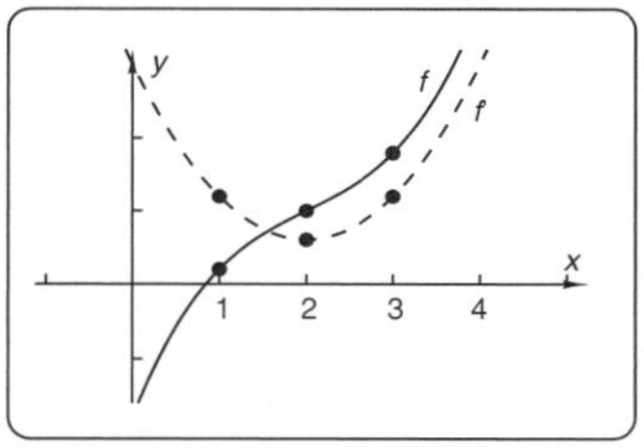


$h(x) = x^3 - 6x^2 + 12x - 3$
$h'(x) = 3x^2 - 12x + 12$ Graph.

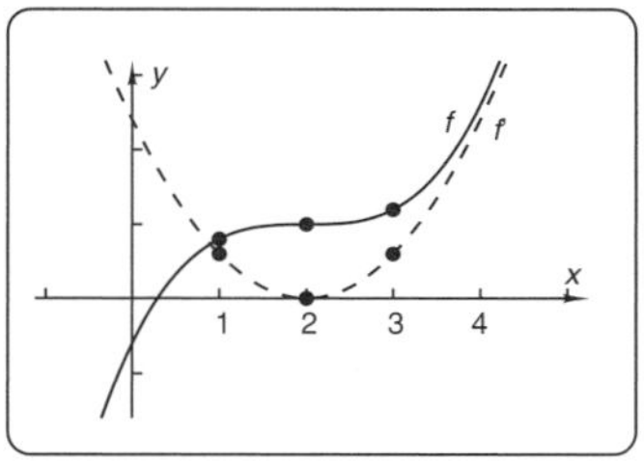


Positive derivative ⇒ increasing function.
Negative derivative ⇒ decreasing function.
Zero derivative ⇒ function could be at a high point or a low point, but not always.

3. $g''(x) = \dfrac{d}{dx}(3x^2 - 12x + 15) = 6x - 12$
   $h''(x) = \dfrac{d}{dx}(3x^2 - 12x + 12) = 6x - 12$
   All the second derivatives are the same!

5. Inflection points occur where the first derivative graph reaches a minimum.
   Inflection points occur where the second derivative graph crosses $x$-axis.

### Problem Set 8-2

*Critical Points and Points of Inflection*

1.

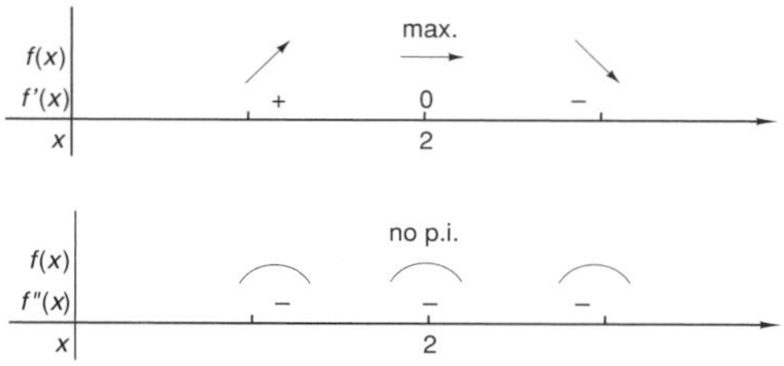


3.

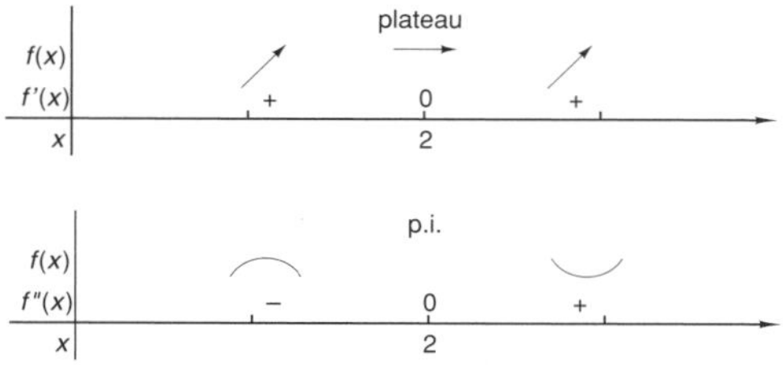


5.

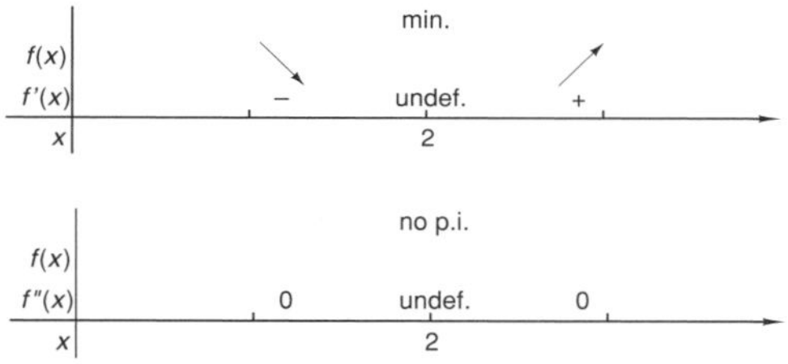


7.

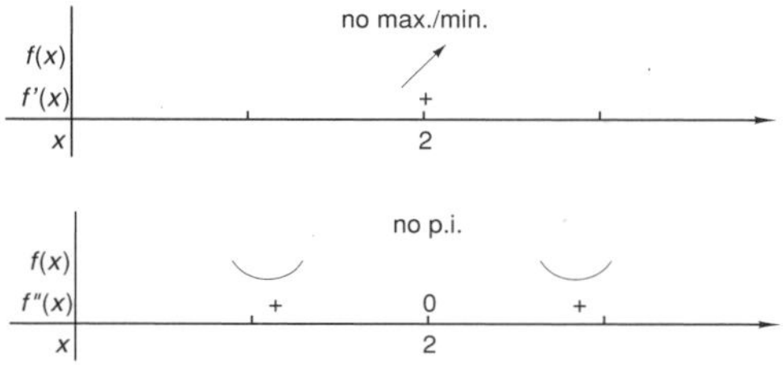


9.

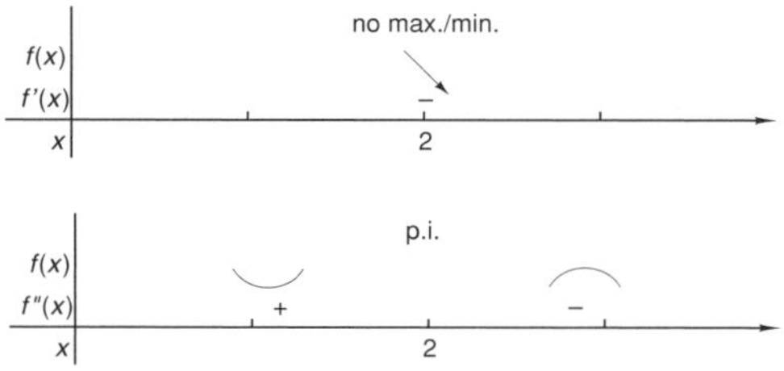


11.

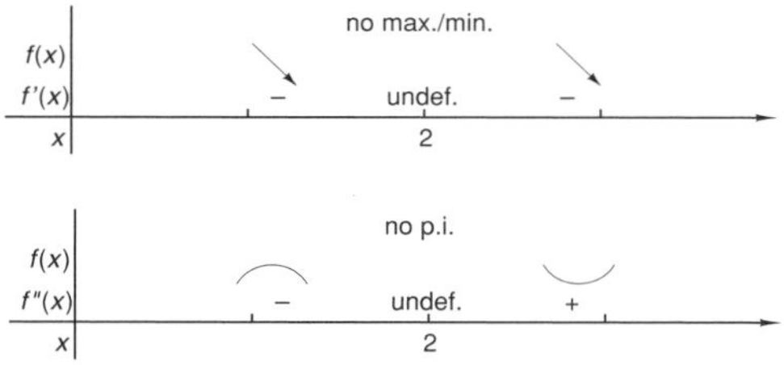

13. Number lines and sample graph.

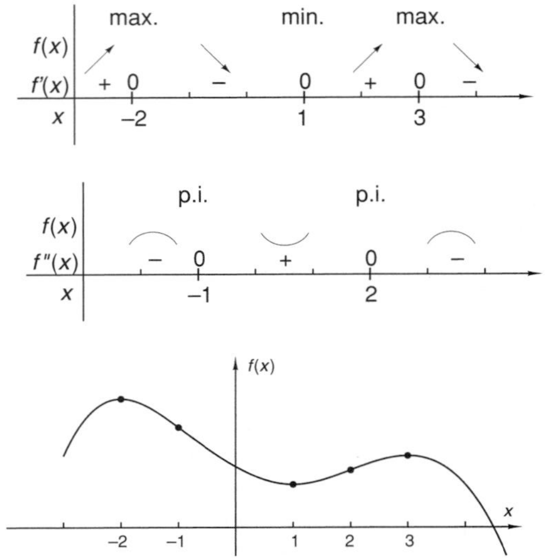


15. Number lines and sample graph.

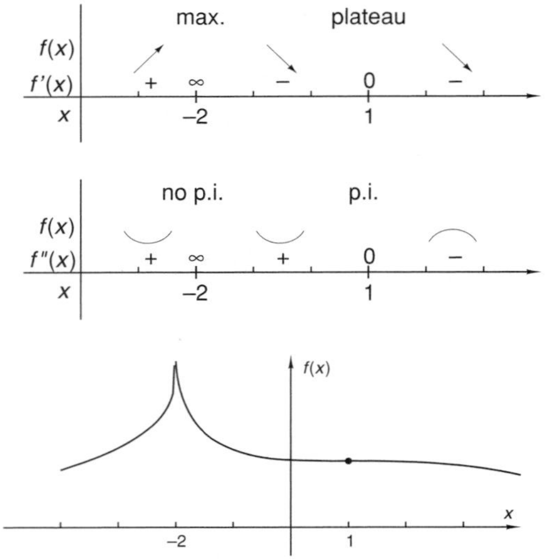


17. Number lines and sample graph.

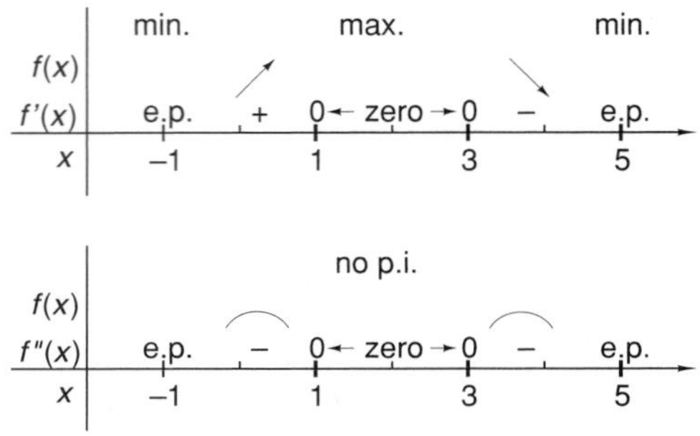


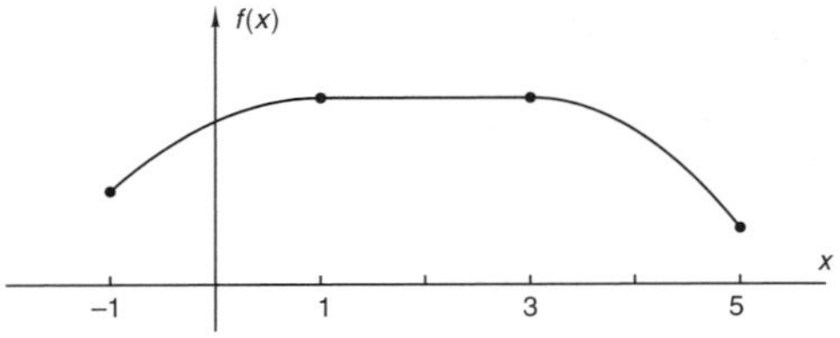


19. a. $x = -1, 0,$ or $1$ (critical points for $f(x)$)
$x = 0, \pm\sqrt{1/2}$ (critical points for $f'(x)$)

b. The graph begins after the $f$-critical point at $x = -1$; the $f'$-critical point at $x = -\sqrt{1/2}$ is shown, but hard to see.

c. $f'(x)$ is negative for both $x < 0$ and $x > 0$.

21. a. $x = 1$ (critical point for $f(x)$)
$x = 2$ (critical point for $f'(x)$)

b. Since $f(x)$ approaches its horizontal asymptote ($y = 0$) from above, the graph must be concave up for large $x$; but the graph is concave down near $x = 1$, and the graph is smooth; somewhere the concavity must change from down to up.

c. No. $e^{-x} \neq 0$ for all $x$, so $xe^{-x} = 0 \iff x = 0$.

23. a. $x = -2$, and $x = 0$ (critical points for $f(x)$)
$x = 1$ (critical point for $f'(x)$; $f'(0)$ is undefined, so $f'$ has no critical point at $x = 0$)

b. The $y$-axis ($x = 0$) is a tangent line since the slope approaches infinity from both sides.

c. No inflection point at $x = 0$ since concavity is down for both sides, but there is an inflection point at $x = 1$.

25. a. $x = 0$ (critical point for $f(x)$), ($f(\pm 1)$ are undefined so $f$ has no critical point at $x = \pm 1$.)
No critical points for $f'(x)$.

b. $\lim_{x\to -1} f(x)$ and $\lim_{x\to 1} f(x)$ are undefined.

c. Levels off to $y = 1$ for large $x$.

27. a. Max. $(2.5, 7.6)$ Min. $(0.8, 4.9)$ p.i. $(1.7, 6.3)$
No global max. or min.

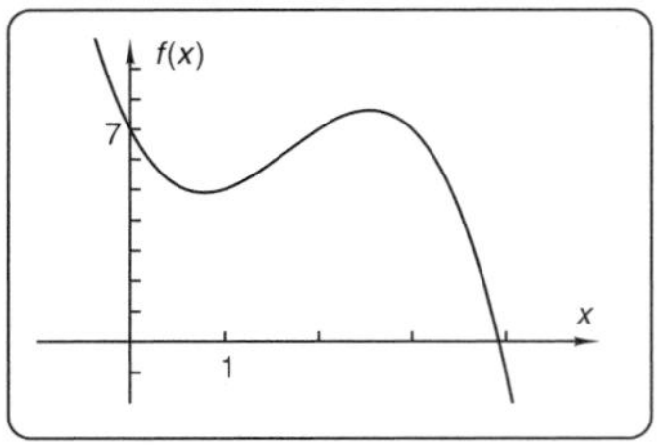


b. $f'(x) = -3x^2 + 10x - 6$
$f'(x) = 0 \iff x = \frac{1}{3}(5 \pm \sqrt{7}) = 2.548\ldots$ or $0.784\ldots$
$f''(x) = -6x + 10$; $f''(x) = 0 \iff x = \frac{5}{3} = 1.666\ldots$

c. Critical and inflection points only occur where $f$, $f'$, or $f''$ are undefined (no such points exist) or are zero (all such points are found above).

29. a. No local max. or min. (Plateau at $(-5, -16)$?)
p.i. $(-5, -16)$. No global max. or min.

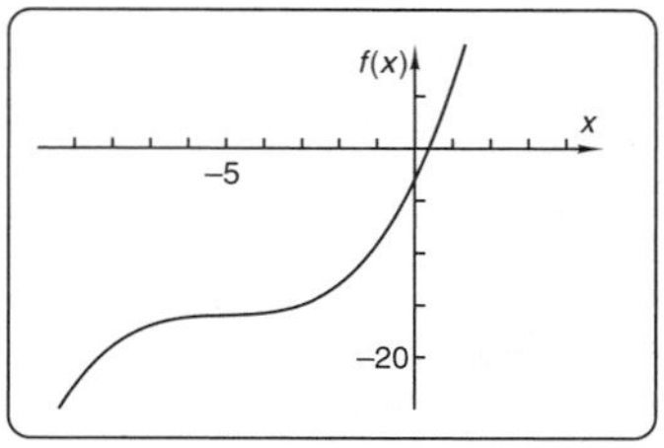


b. $f'(x) = 0.3x^2 + 3x + 7.6$; $f'(x) \neq 0$ for all $x$, confirming that there are no local max. or min., and refuting the apparent plateau at $x = -5$.
$f''(x) = 0.6x + 3$; $f''(x) = 0 \iff x = -5$

c. Critical and inflection points only occur where $f$, $f'$, or $f''$ are undefined (no such points exist) or are zero (all such points are found above).

31. a. Max. $(-3, 82)$, $(-1, 50)$, $(2, 77)$
Min. $(-2, 45)$, $(1, 18)$
p.i. $(-1.5, 45.7)$, $(0.2, 32.0)$

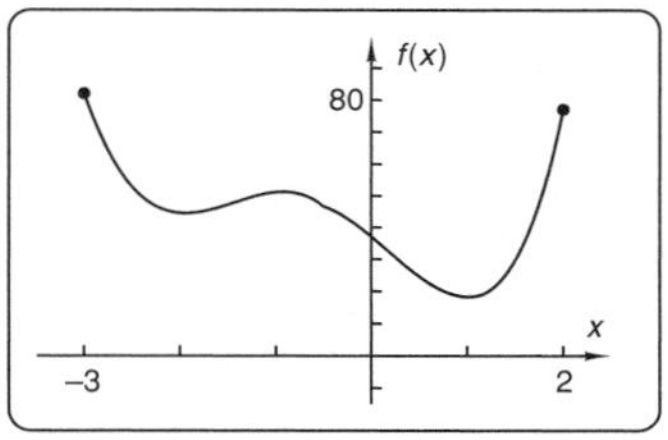


b. $f'(x) = 12x^3 + 24x^2 - 12x - 24$
$= 12(x+2)(x-1)(x+1)$
$f'(x) = 0 \iff x = -2, -1, 1$
$f'(x)$ is undefined $\iff x = -3, 2$
$f''(x) = 36x^2 + 48x - 12 = 12(3x^2 + 4x - 1)$;
$f''(x) = 0 \iff x = -\dfrac{1}{3}(2 \pm \sqrt{7}) = 0.21\ldots$ or $-1.54\ldots$
$f''(x)$ is undefined $\iff x = -3, 2$

c. Critical and inflection points only occur where $f$, $f'$, or $f''$ are undefined (only at endpoints) or are zero (all such points are found above).

33. *Point of Inflection of a Cubic Function*
$f(x) = ax^3 + bx^2 + cx + d$; $f'(x) = 3ax^2 + 2bx + c$;
$f''(x) = 6ax + 2b \Rightarrow f''(x) = 0$ at $x = -b/(3a)$.
Since the equation for $f''(x)$ is a line with nonzero slope, $f''(x)$ must change sign at $x = -b/(3a)$, so the concavity changes and $-b/(3a)$ is indeed a point of inflection.

35. *Equation from Critical Points*
$f(x) = -\dfrac{1}{2}x^3 + \dfrac{9}{2}x^2 - \dfrac{15}{2}x - \dfrac{5}{2}$
Graph, with max. $(5, 10)$ and p.i. $(3, 2)$

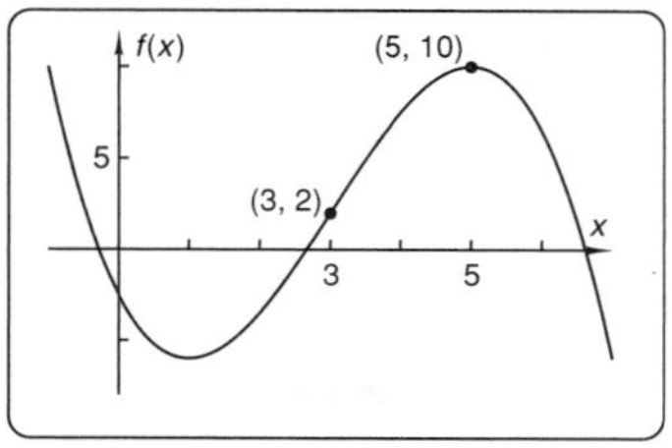


37. *Concavity Concept Problem*

a. $f'(-0.8) = 1.92$
$f'(-0.5) = 0.75$
$f'(0.5) = 0.75$
$f'(0.8) = 1.92$

b. The slope seems to be decreasing from $-0.8$ to $-0.5$; $f''(x) = 6x < 0$ on $-0.8 \le x \le -0.5$, which confirms that the slope decreases.
The slope seems to be increasing from 0.5 to 0.8; $f''(x) = 6x > 0$ on $0.5 \le x \le 0.8$, which confirms that the slope increases.

c. The curve lies above the tangent line.

39. *Connections Between a Zero First Derivative and the Graph*

a. The graph may have a minimum or plateau there.
b. Example: $f(x) = -(x-1)^2 + 4 = -x^2 + 2x + 3$
c. Example: $f(x) = (x-1)^2 + 2 = x^2 - 2x + 3$
d. Example: $f(x) = (x-1)^3 + 3 = x^3 - 3x^2 + 3x + 2$
e. Example: $f(x) = 2$ for $1 \le x \le 4$

41. *Historical Problem—The Second Derivative Test*

a. $f'(x) = x^4 - 4x^3 + 2x^2 + 4x - 3$
$= (x+1)(x-1)^2(x-3)$

b. $f''(x) = 4x^3 - 12x^2 + 4x + 4$
$f'(x) = 0$ at $x = -1, 1, 3$
$f''(-1) = -16$; $f''(1) = 0$; $f''(3) = 16$

c. $x = -1$: concave down, local maximum
$x = 1$: not concave, can't tell max./min.
$x = 3$: concave up, local minimum
Graph, confirming these results.

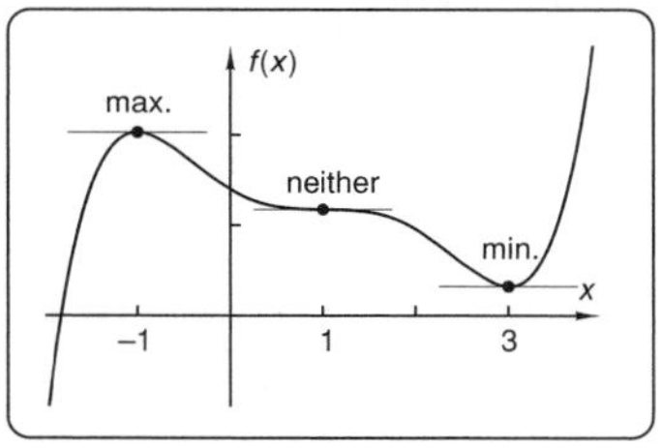


d. Graphs. The third graph shows that if both $f'(x)$ and $f''(c)$ are 0, there could be either a maximum, a minimum, or a plateau.

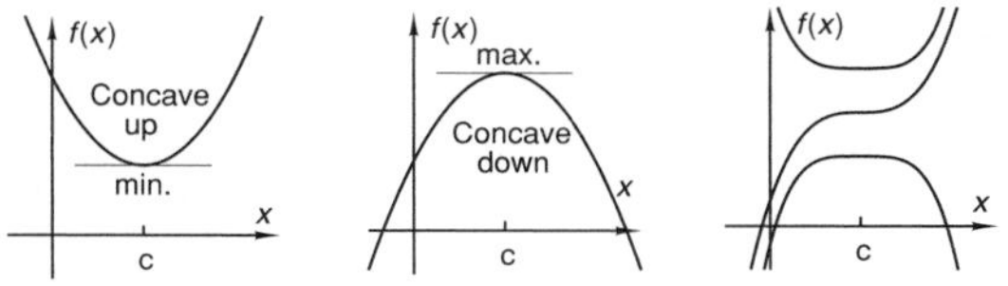

43. *A Pathological Function*
Not selected.

**Problem Set 8-3**

*Maxima and Minima in Plane and Solid Figures*

1. *Divided Stock Pen Problem:*
Make the total width 150 ft and length 100 ft. (Note: The maximum area was not asked for.)

3. *Two Field Problem*
   a. Domain: $20 \le x \le 93.333\ldots$
   b. $A(x) = 22500 - 450x + 4.25x^2$ Graph.

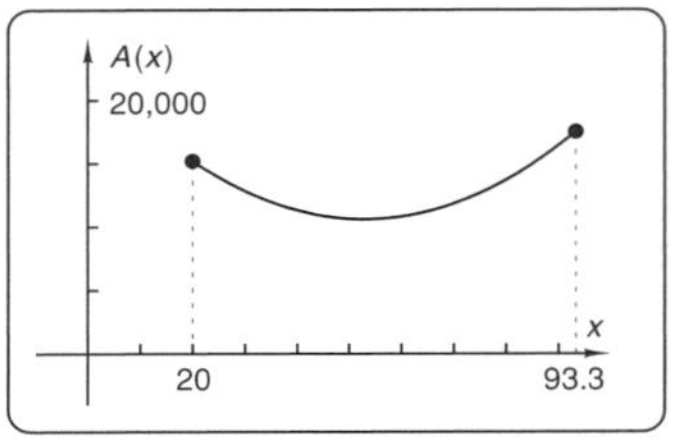


   c. Greatest area = $17522.222\ldots \approx 17{,}522$ ft$^2$

5. *Open Box No. 1*
   a. Max. at $x = \sqrt{40} = 6.324\ldots$, $z = \sqrt{40}/2 = 3.162\ldots$ Make the box 6.32 cm square by 3.16 cm deep.
   b. Conjecture: An open box with square base and fixed surface area $A$ will have maximal volume when the base length is twice the height, which occurs when $x = \sqrt{A/3}$.

7. *Open Box No. 3*
Minimum cost is \$523.47.

9. *Shortest Distance Problem*
Closest point to the origin is $(x, y) \approx (-0.4263, 0.6529)$.

11. *Ladder Problem*
Shortest ladder has length $5\sqrt{5} \approx 11.18$ ft.

13. *Rotated Rectangle Problem*
Max. volume with rectangle 400 mm wide (radius), 200 mm high.

15. *Tin Can Problem*
   a. Let $r =$ radius; $h =$ height.
   $V = 141.2185\pi = 443.65\ldots$ cm$^3$
   b. $A = 2\pi(141.2185r^{-1} + r^2)$
   c. Min. at $r = \sqrt[3]{70.60925} = 4.1332\ldots$,
   $h = 2\sqrt[3]{70.60925} = 8.266\ldots$
   Radius $\approx 4.1$ cm, altitude $\approx 8.3$ cm
   Since altitude = 2 × radius, altitude = diameter. So minimal can is neither tall and skinny nor short and fat.
   d. Normally-proportioned can is taller and thinner than minimal can.
   $1.465\ldots \approx 1.5\%$ of metal would be saved.
   e. Saving is about \$6.4 million!

17. *Cup Problem*
   a. $r = \sqrt[3]{43.75} = 3.5236\ldots$, $h = \sqrt[3]{43.75} = r$
   Minimal cup has $r \approx 3.52$ cm, $h \approx 3.52$cm
   b. Ratio is $d : h = 2r : h = 2 : 1$
   c. Saving $\approx$ \$754,000 per year. Proposals vary.

19. *Rectangle in Sinusoid Problem*
Maximum area $\approx 1.12219\ldots$ at $x \approx 0.86033\ldots$.

21. *Triangle Under Cotangent Problem*
   a. Limit = 1/2
   b. Maximal area does not exist, but the area approaches 1/2 as a limit as $x$ approaches 0.

23. *Rectangle in Parabola Problem*
   a. Max. rectangle has width = $2\sqrt{3}$, length = 6.
   b. Max. rectangle has width = 2, length = 8.
   c. No. The maximum area rectangle is $2\sqrt{3}$ by 6. The maximum perimeter rectangle is 2 by 8.

25. *Cylinder in Sphere Problem*
   a. $V(x) = 2\pi x^2\sqrt{100 - x^2}$
   b. Max. cylinder has radius $= \dfrac{10\sqrt{6}}{3} = 8.1649\ldots$,
   altitude $= \dfrac{20\sqrt{3}}{3} = 11.5470\ldots$,
   and volume $= \dfrac{4000\pi\sqrt{3}}{9} = 2418.39\ldots$
   c. Altitude = Radius $\cdot \sqrt{2}$, $V_c = V_s/\sqrt{3}$.

27. *Cylinder in Cone Problem*
   a. Max. lateral area at radius $x = 2.5$ cm.
   b. Max. total area is with the degenerate cylinder consisting only of the top and bottom, radius 5 and altitude 0.

29. *Elliptical Nose Cone Problem*
Max. volume is $32\pi\sqrt{3} = 174.1\ldots m^3$ at $x = \sqrt{27} = 5.196\ldots m$, and $y = \sqrt{32/3} = 3.265\ldots m$.

31. Not selected.

33. Not selected.

**Problem Set 8-4**

*Area of a Plane Region*

Plan of attack for area problems:

- Do geometry to get $dA$ in terms of sample point $(x, y)$.
- Do algebra to get $dA$ in terms of one variable.
- Do calculus to add up the $dA$'s and take the limit (i.e., integrate).

1. Graph. $A = \int_1^5 (-x^2 + 6x - 5)\, dx = 10\frac{2}{3}$

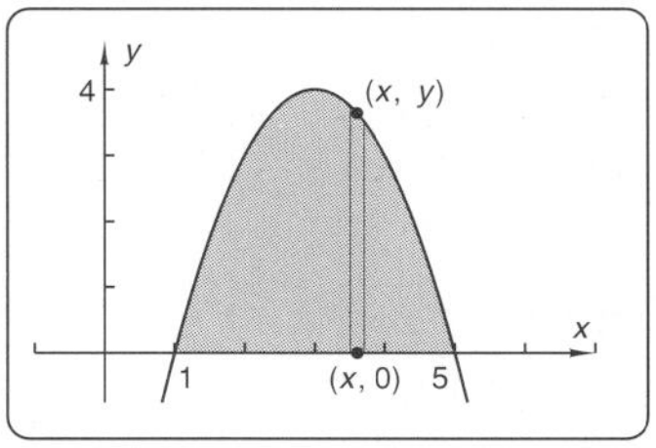


3. Graph. $A = \int_1^4 (-y^2 + 5y - 4)\, dy = 4\frac{1}{2}$

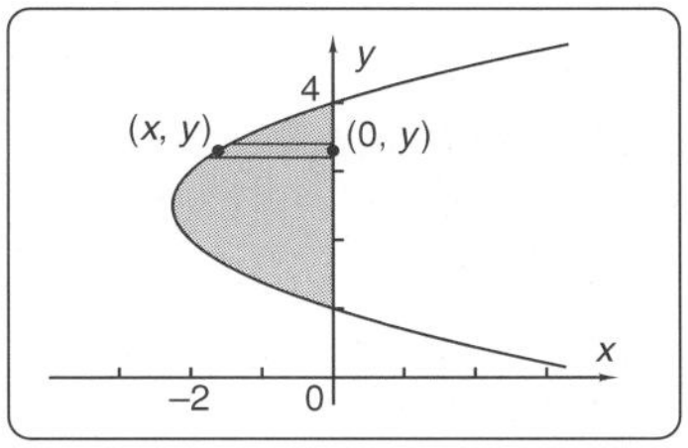


5. Graph. $A = \int_{-1}^4 (-x^2 + 3x + 4)\, dx = 20\frac{5}{6}$

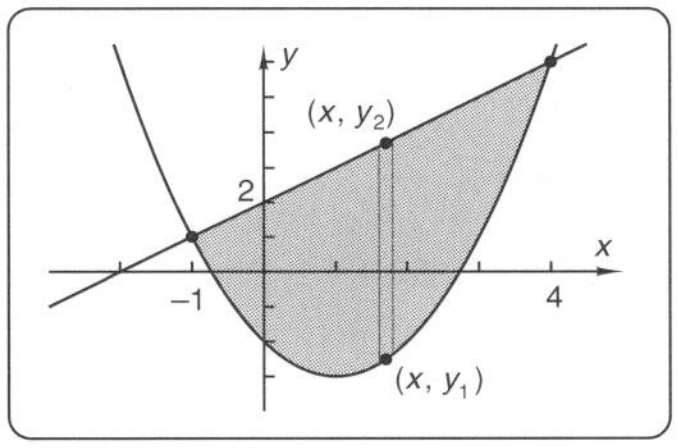


7. Graph. $A = \int_{-2}^2 (-1.5x^2 + 6)\, dx = 16$

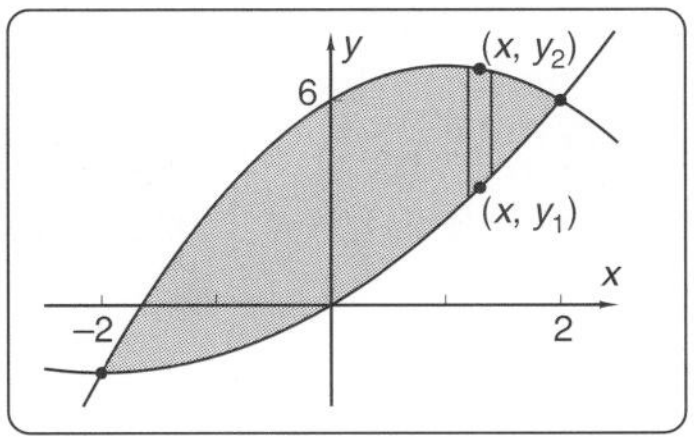


9. Graph. $A = \int_0^5 (2e^{0.2x} - \cos x)\, dx = 18.1417\ldots$

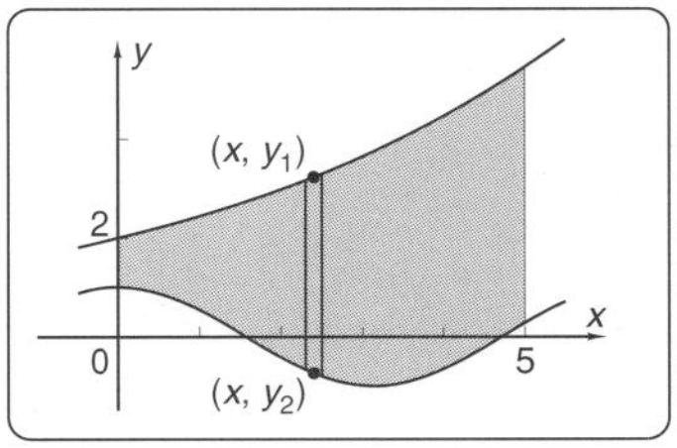


11. Graph. $A = \int_1^4 (-y^2 + 5y - 4)\, dy = 4\frac{1}{2}$

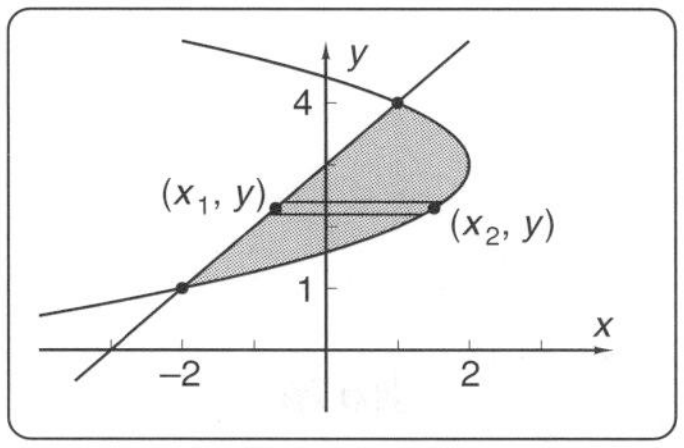


13. Graph. $A = \int_{-1}^2 (x^3 - 3x^2 + 4)\, dx = 6\frac{3}{4}$

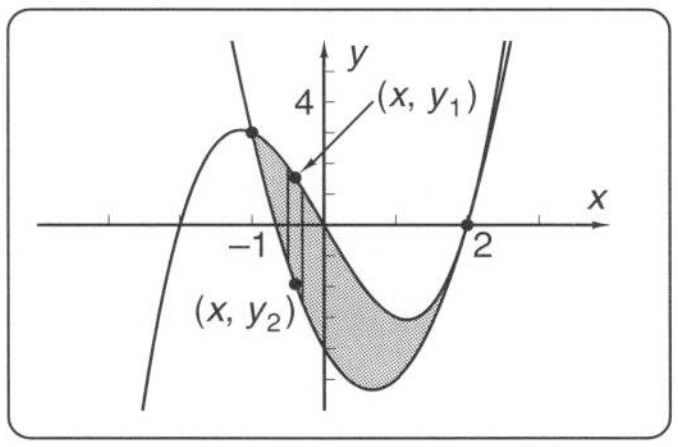


15. Wanda: You can always tell the right way because the altitude of the strip should be *positive*. This will happen if you take (larger value) − (smaller value). In this case, if you slice vertically it's *line minus curve* (see graph).

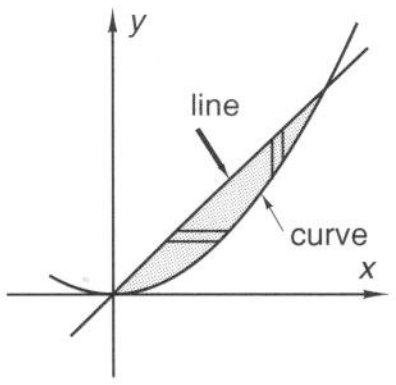


For curve minus line, you'd get the opposite of the right answer. Note that if you slice horizontally it would be curve minus line.

17. *Parabolic Region Problem*
(Proof not selected.)
Area of region $= \frac{2}{3}(20)(60) = 800$

19. *Ellipse Area Problem*
$A = \int_{-5}^{5} \frac{2}{5}\sqrt{225 - 9x^2}\, dx \approx 47.123889\ldots$
Conjecture: $A = \pi ab$, where $a =$ semimajor axis and $b =$ semiminor axis.
This is consistent with the area of a circle with radius $r$, in which $a = b = r$ and the area $= \pi r^2$.

21. *Golf Course Problem*
Approximately 37.1 yd$^2$, counting squares.

23. *Curve Sketching Review Problem*
Graph.

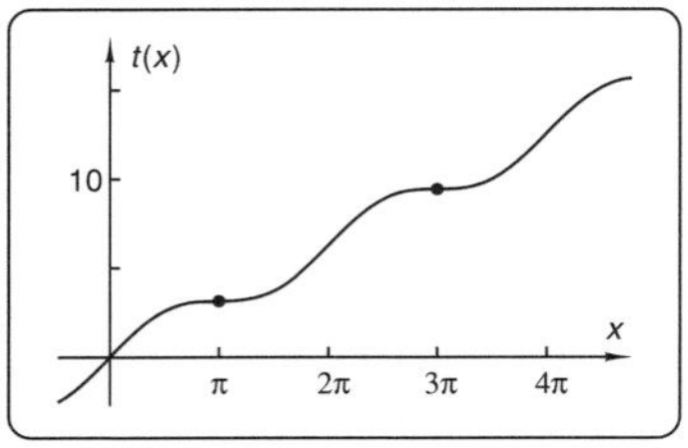


$t'(x) = 0 \Longleftrightarrow x = \pi + 2\pi n = \ldots, \pi, 3\pi, 5\pi, \ldots$
$t'(x)$ does not change signs. (plateau points)

**Problem Set 8-5**

*Volume of a Solid by Plane Slicing*

Plan of attack for volume problems:

- Do geometry to get $dV$ in terms of sample point $(x, y)$.
- Do algebra to get $dV$ in terms of one variable.
- Do calculus to add up the $dV$'s and take the limit (i.e., integrate).

1. *Paraboloid Problem*
   a. $V = 40.5\pi = 127.2345\ldots$
   b. $V \approx 127.2345\ldots$, which checks.
   c. Inscribed cone has volume $27\pi$. Circumscribed cylinder has volume $81\pi$.

3. $V = 30.6\pi = 96.132\ldots$

5. $V = \dfrac{\pi}{2}(e^2 - 1) = 10.0359\ldots$

7. *Washer Slices Problem*
   $V = \dfrac{64}{3}\pi = 67.0206\ldots$
   Circumscribed cylinder minus the cone has volume $= \pi r^2 h - \pi r^2 h/3 = 128\pi/3$
   $= 134.0412\ldots > V$.
   Numerical integration gives $V \approx 67.0206\ldots$.

9. $V = \pi(-500e^{-1.6} + 480.8) = 1193.3394\ldots$

11. Not selected.

13. *Different Axis Problem No. 1*
    Inner radius is $3 - x$, outer radius is 3.
    $V = 24\pi = 75.3982\ldots$

15. *New Integral Problem No. 1*
    a., b. $V = \int_0^{1.2} \pi \sin^2 x\, dx \approx 1.354448\ldots$
    c. $V = \dfrac{\pi}{2}\int_0^{1.2}(1 - \cos 2x)\, dx = 0.6\pi - \dfrac{\pi}{4}\sin 2.4 = 1.354448\ldots$, which agrees.

17. *Pyramid Problem*
    $V = 320$ cm$^2$, which is 1/3 of 960.

19. *Triangular Cross-Section Problem*
    a. $V = \dfrac{1}{4.4} \cdot 4^{2.2} = 4.79821\ldots$
    b. Volume would double, to $= 9.5964\ldots$

21. *Generalized Wedge Problem*
    $V = \dfrac{2h}{r}\int_0^r x\sqrt{r^2 - x^2}\, dx = \dfrac{2}{3}r^2 h$

23. *Sphere Problem*
    a. $V = \dfrac{4}{3}\pi(1000)$ cm$^3$
    b. Formula: $V = \dfrac{4}{3}\pi r^3 = \dfrac{4}{3}\pi 10^3 = \dfrac{4}{3}\pi(1000)$ cm$^3$, Q.E.D.

25. *Volume of an Ellipsoid Problem*
    $V = \dfrac{4}{3}\pi abc$
    Note that the volume formula for a sphere is a special case of the volume formula for an ellipsoid in which $a = b = c = r$, the radius of the sphere.

27. *Submarine Problem*
    a. Graph.

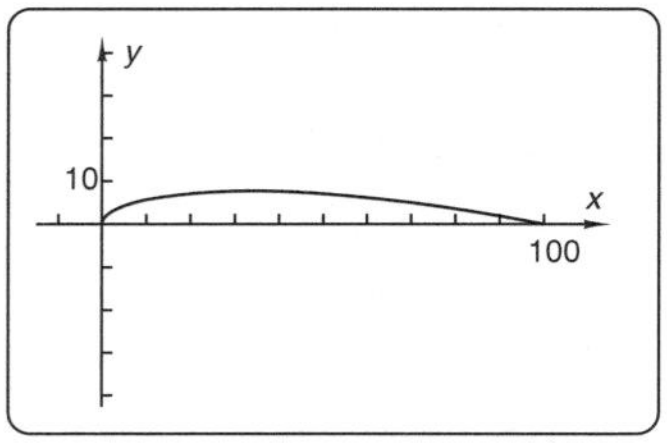


   b. 100m long, or about as long as a football field.
   c. Maximize $D(x) = 2(2x^{0.5} - 0.02x^{1.5})$
   $D'(x) = 2(x^{-0.5} - 0.03x^{0.5}) = 2x^{-0.5}(1 - 0.03x)$
   $D'(x) = 0 \Longleftrightarrow x = \dfrac{1}{0.03}$
   $D(0) = D(100) = 0$,
   $D(100/3) = \dfrac{80\sqrt{3}}{9} = 15.3960\ldots$
   $\therefore D(100/3)$ is a maximum, which is confirmed by the graph in part (a).
   Maximum diameter is $(80\sqrt{3})/9 \approx 15.40$m, $33\frac{1}{3}$m from bow.
   d. Sub will be fairly slow.
   e. $V = 3333\frac{1}{3}\pi \approx 10472$ m$^3$
   f. Displacement $\approx$ 10,912 metric tons

**Problem Set 8-6**

*Volume of a Solid of Revolution by Cylindrical Shells*

1. a. $dV = 2\pi x \cdot y \cdot dx = 2\pi(4x - x^3)\, dx$
   b. $0 = 4 - x^2 = (2 - x)(2 + x)$ at $x = \pm 2$.
   $V = 8\pi = 25.1327\ldots$
   c. $V = 8\pi = 25.1327\ldots$, which is the same answer.

3. $V \approx 268.6061\ldots$ (exactly $85.5\pi$)
   Circumscribed hollow cylinder has volume $329.8\ldots$, a reasonable upper bound for calculated volume.

5. $V \approx 201.0619\ldots$ (exactly $64\pi$)
Circumscribed hollow cylinder has volume $301.5\ldots$, a reasonable upper bound.

7. $V \approx 36.4424\ldots$ (exactly $11.6\pi$)
Circumscribed hollow cylinder has volume $65.9\ldots$, a reasonable upper bound for calculated volume.

9. $V \approx 217.8254\ldots$ (exactly $69.336\pi$)
Circumscribed cylinder has volume $226.1\ldots$, which is a reasonable upper bound for calculated volume.

11. $V \approx 458.1489\ldots$ (exactly $145\frac{5}{6}\pi$)
Circumscribed hollow cylinder has volume $769.6\ldots$, a reasonable upper bound for calculated volume.

13. $V \approx 161.5676\ldots$ (exactly $51\frac{3}{7}\pi$)
Circumscribed hollow cylinder has volume $376.9\ldots$, a reasonable upper bound for calculated volume.

15. $V \approx 390.1858\ldots$ (exactly $124.2\pi$)
Circumscribed hollow cylinder has volume $1055.5\ldots$, a reasonable upper bound.

17. $V \approx 163.8592\ldots$
Circumscribed hollow cylinder has volume $316.1\ldots$, a reasonable upper bound for calculated volume.

19. $V = 36.4424\ldots$ (exactly $11.6\pi$), which agrees.

21. $V = 19.2\pi = 60.3185789\ldots$
$R_8 = 19.3662109\ldots\pi = 60.8407460\ldots$
$R_{100} = 19.2010666\ldots\pi = 60.3219299\ldots$
$R_{1000} = 19.2000106\ldots\pi = 60.3186124\ldots$
$R_n$ is approaching $19.2\pi$ as $n$ increases.

23. *Parametric Curve Problem*
a. $dV = 180\pi \cos^2 t \sin t\, dt$
$V = 60\pi = 188.4955\ldots$
b. $V \approx 188.4955\ldots$ (exactly $60\pi$), which agrees with the volume found in part (a).
c. $V \approx 2072.6169\ldots$ (exactly $210\pi^2$)

## Problem Set 8-7

*Length of a Plane Curve—Arc Length*

1. a. Graph.

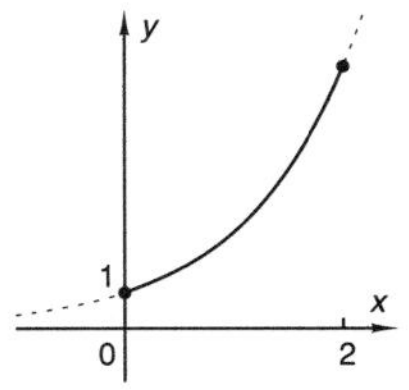


b. $L \approx 6.7848\ldots$
c. $L \approx 6.7886\ldots$ numerically

3. a. Graph.

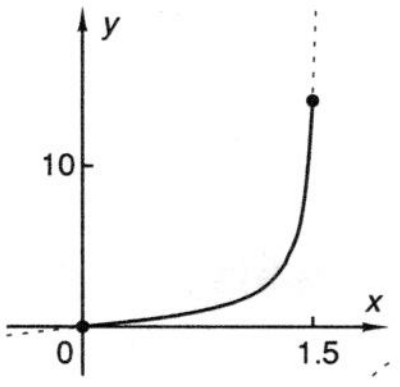


b. $L \approx 14.4394\ldots$
c. $L \approx 14.4488\ldots$ numerically.

5. a. Graph.

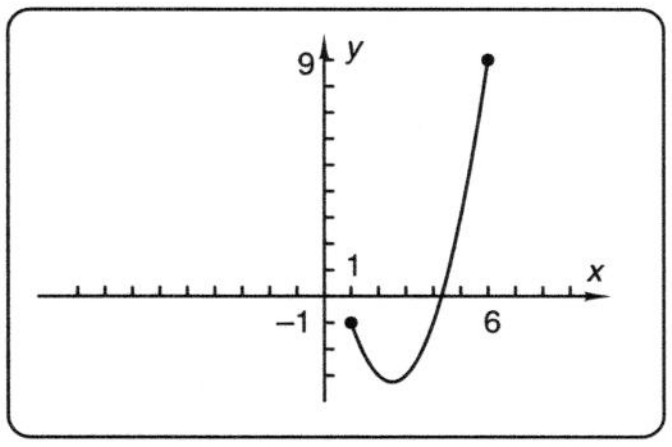


b. $L \approx 15.8617\ldots$
c. Low point is $(2.5, -3.25)$. Chords from $(1, -1)$ to $(2.5, -3.25)$ and from $(2.5, -3.25)$ to $(6, 9)$ have length $15.4\ldots$, a reasonable lower bound for $L$.

7. a. Graph, $y = 16 - x^4$, $x$ in $[-1, 2]$

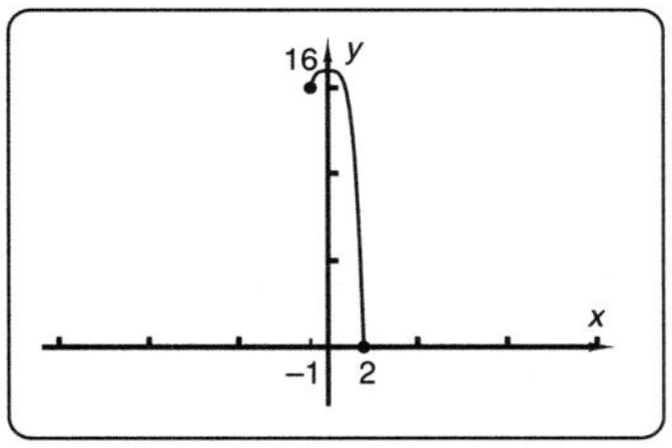


b. $L \approx 18.2470\ldots$ ($L \approx 256.6585\ldots$ for $[0, 4]$.)
c. Chords from $(-1, 15)$ to $(0, 16)$ and $(0, 16)$ to $(2, 0)$ have length $17.5\ldots$, a reasonable lower bound.

9. a. Graph.

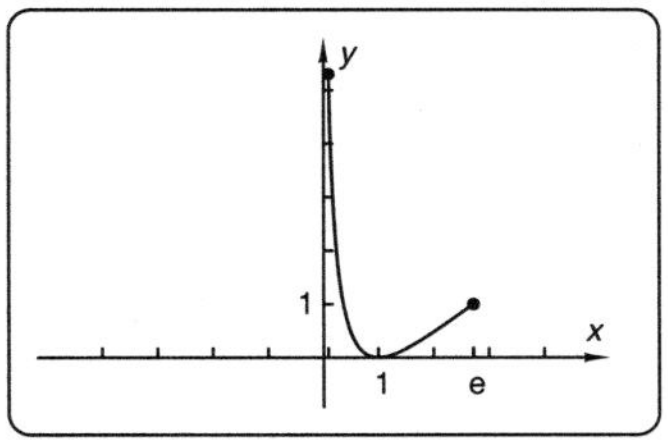


b. $L \approx 7.6043\ldots$
c. Chords from $x = 0.1$ to $x = 1$, and $x = 1$ to $x = e$, have length $7.3658\ldots$, a reasonable lower bound.

11. a. Graph.

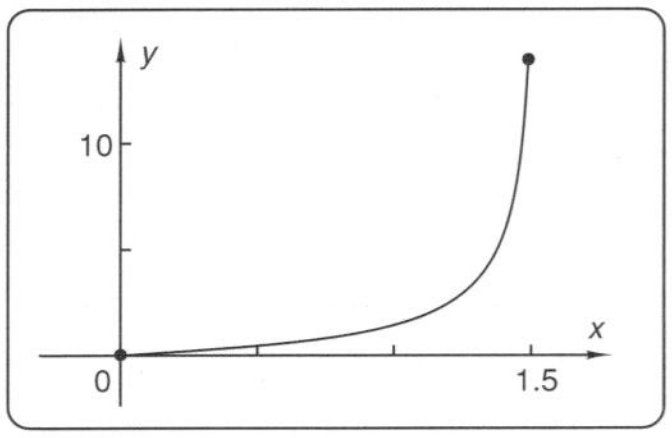


b. $L \approx 14.4488\ldots$

c. Distance between the endpoints is $14.1809\ldots$, which is a reasonable lower bound for $L$.

13. a. Graph, $x = 5\cos^3 t$, $y = 5\sin^3 t$, $t$ in $[0, 2\pi]$.

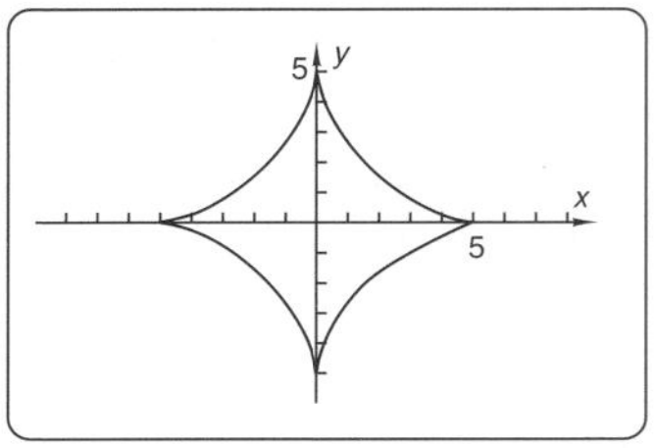


b. $L = 30$ (exactly!)

c. Circle of radius 5 has circumference $31.4152\ldots$, which is close to the calculated value of $L$.

15. a. Graph.

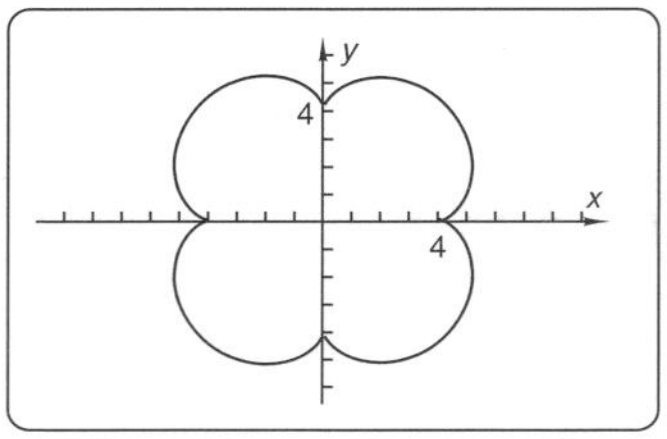


b. $L = 40$ (exactly!)

c. Max./min. values of $x$, $y$ are $\pm 3\sqrt{3}$. Circle of radius $3\sqrt{3}$ has circumference $32.6483\ldots$, which is close.

17. a. Graph.

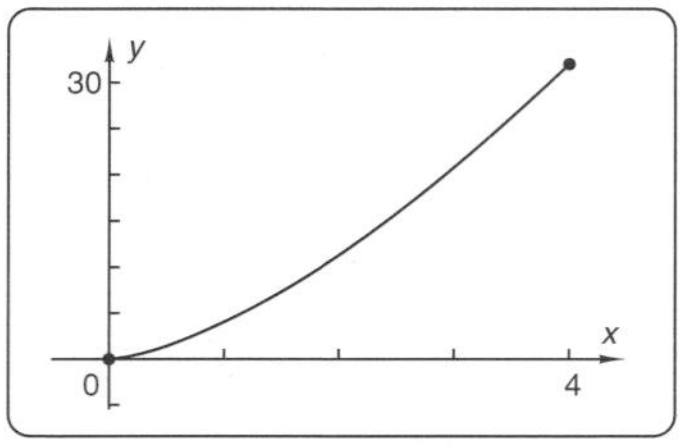


b. $L = \dfrac{1}{54}(145^{3/2} - 1) = 32.3153\ldots$

c. The chord connecting the endpoints has length $32.2490\ldots$, a reasonable lower bound for $L$.

19. a. Graph.

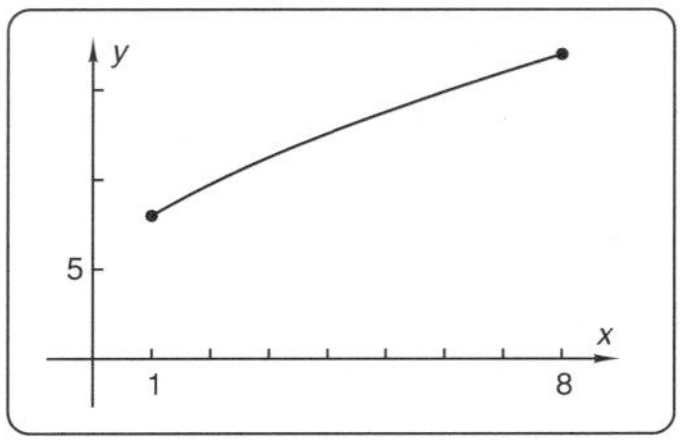


b. $L = 8\sqrt{8} - 5\sqrt{5} = 11.4470\ldots$

c. Distance between endpoints is $\sqrt{130} = 11.4017\ldots$, which is a reasonable lower bound.

21. *Golden Gate Bridge Problem*
Construct an $x$-axis at water level and $y$-axis through the vertex of the parabola.
Equation of parabola is $y = \dfrac{53}{441000}x^2 + 220$.
$L \approx 4372.0861\ldots \approx 4372$ feet
The answer is reasonable since the 4,200 feet between supports is a lower bound for $L$.

23. *Stadium Problem*
Outer ellipse: $L \approx 692.5791\ldots \approx 692.6$ m
Inner ellipse: $L \approx 484.4224\ldots \approx 484.4$ m

25. *Implicit Relation Problem No. 1*
$L = 4\frac{2}{3} = 4.6666\ldots$

27. *Spiral Problem*
Spiral is generated as $t$ goes from 0 to $7\pi$.
$L = \dfrac{1}{\pi}\displaystyle\int_0^{7\pi} \sqrt{1 + t^2}\, dt = 77.6508\ldots$

29. *Sinusoid Length Investigation Problem*

| $A$ | $L$ |
|---|---|
| 0 | $6.283185\ldots (= 2\pi)$ |
| 1 | $7.640395\ldots$ |
| 2 | $10.540734\ldots$ |
| 3 | $13.974417\ldots$ |

Doubling $A$ doubles the amplitude of the sinusoid. However, it less than doubles the length of the sinusoid, for much the same reason that doubling one leg of a right triangle does not double the hypotenuse. In the limit as $A$ approaches infinity, doubling $A$ approaches doubling the length.

31. *Fatal Error Problem*
The function $y = (x - 2)^{-1}$ has a vertical asymptote at $x = 2$, which is in the interval $[1, 3]$. So the length is *infinite*. Mae's partition of the interval skips over the discontinuity. Graph.

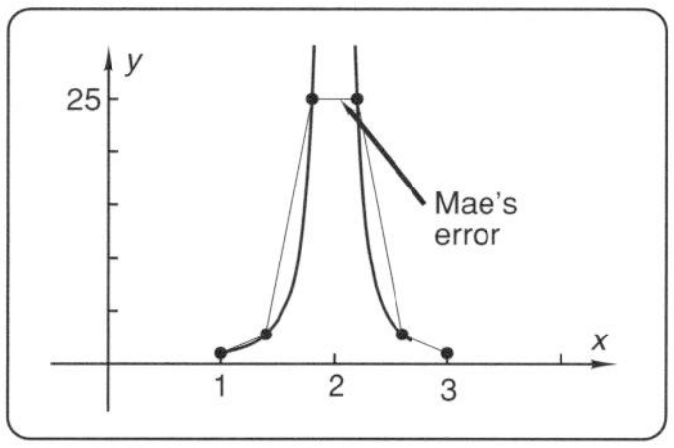

33. Not selected.

## Problem Set 8-8

*Area of a Surface of Revolution*

1. *Paraboloid Problem*
   a. $S = \int_0^3 2\pi x\sqrt{1+x^2}\,dx \approx 64.1361\ldots$
   b. The inscribed cone has lateral surface area 50.9722..., a reasonable lower bound for $S$.
   c. $S = \frac{2}{3}\pi(10\sqrt{10}-1) = 64.1361\ldots$, which agrees.

3. *Ln-Curved Surface, Problem I*
   $S \approx 9.0242\ldots$

5. *Reciprocal Curved Surface Problem I*
   $S \approx 15.5181\ldots$

7. *Cubic Paraboloid Problem I*
   $S \approx 77.3245\ldots$

9. $S = \frac{4\pi}{3}(1.25^{3/2} - 0.125) = 5.3304\ldots$

11. $S = 4\frac{155}{256}\pi = 14.4685\ldots$

13. $S = 49.5\pi = 155.5088\ldots$

15. $S = 101\frac{5}{18}\pi = 318.1735\ldots$

17. *Sphere Zone Problem*
    Not selected.

19. *Spherical Volume and Surface Problem*
    Pick a sample point in the spherical shell at radius $r$ from the center. Surface area at the sample point is $4\pi r^2$. Volume of shell is approximately (surface area)(thickness).
    $dV = 4\pi r^2 \cdot dr$
    $V = \int_0^R 4\pi r^2 dr = \frac{4}{3}\pi r^3 \Big|_0^R = \frac{4}{3}\pi R^3$, Q.E.D.

21. *Paraboloid Surface Area Problem*
    $S = \frac{\pi}{6a^2}[(1+4a^2r^2)^{3/2} - 1]$

23. *Ellipsoid Problem*
    $S = \int_0^\pi 6\pi \sin t\sqrt{(-5\sin t)^2 + (3\cos t)^2}\,dt$
    $\approx 165.7930\ldots$

25. *Lateral Area of a Cone Problem*
    From the figure in the text, a circle of radius $L$ has area $\pi L^2$ and circumference $2\pi L$. The circumference of the cone's base is $2\pi R$, which is equal to the arc length of the sector of the circle of radius $L$. Thus the sector is $(2\pi R)/(2\pi L) = R/L$ of the circle, and has surface area
    $S = \pi L^2(R/L) = \pi RL$, Q.E.D.

## Problem Set 8-9

*Lengths and Areas for Polar Coordinates*

1. a. $A \approx 157.0796\ldots$ (exactly $50\pi$)
   b. The area of the circle is $\pi \cdot 5^2 = 25\pi$.
   The calculated area is twice this because the circle is traced out twice as $\theta$ increases from 0 to $2\pi$. Although $r$ is negative for $\pi < \theta < 2\pi$, $dA$ is positive because $r$ is squared.

3. a. Calculator graph confirms that the text figure is traced out once as $\theta$ increases from 0 to $2\pi$.
   b. $A \approx 64.4026\ldots$ (exactly $20.5\pi$)
   c. $L \approx 28.8141\ldots$

5. a. Calculator graph confirms that the text figure is traced out once as $\theta$ increases from 0 to $2\pi$.
   b. $A \approx 168.0752\ldots$ (exactly $53.5\pi$)
   c. $L \approx 51.4511\ldots.$

7. a. Calculator graph confirms that the text figure is traced out once as $\theta$ increases from 0 to $2\pi$.
   b. $A \approx 117.8097\ldots$ (exactly $37.5\pi$)
   c. $L = 40$ (exactly)

9. a. Graph makes one complete cycle as $\theta$ increases from 0 to $\pi$.

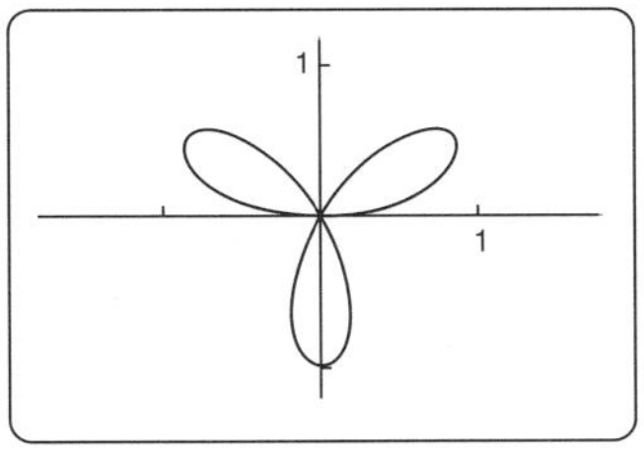


   b. $A \approx 0.7853\ldots$ (exactly $0.25\pi$)
   c. $L \approx 6.6824\ldots$

11. Right-hand loop: $-\pi/4 \le \theta \le \pi/4$.
    Area of both loops is $49\sqrt{2} = 69.2964\ldots$

13. Intersections: $\theta = \cos^{-1}(2/3) = \pm 0.8410\ldots + 2\pi n$
    Region outside the cardioid and inside the circle is generated as $\theta$ goes from $-0.841\ldots$ to $0.841\ldots$
    $A \approx 18.8863\ldots$ (exactly $26\cos^{-1}(2/3) - (4/3)\sqrt{5}$)

15. a. $L \approx 89.8589\ldots$
    b. $A = \frac{13}{16}\pi^3 = 25.1925\ldots$

17. *Column Scroll Problem*
    a. Graph, $r = 5\theta^{-1/2}$, from $\theta = 0$ to $\theta = 6\pi$.

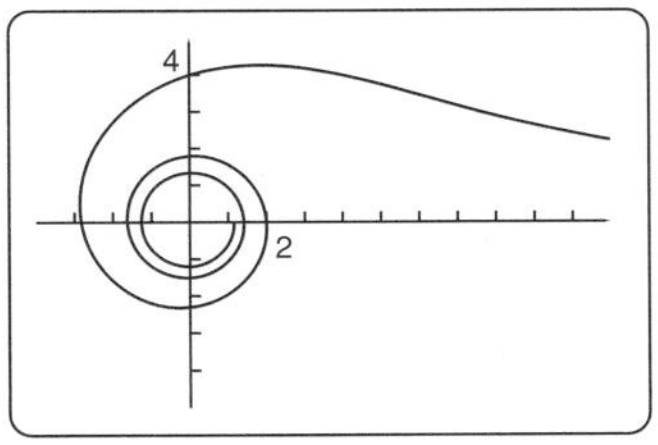


$L \approx 31.0872\ldots$ from $\theta = \pi/2$ to $6\pi$

b. Graph, showing sectors of central angles 1, 2, and 3 radians.

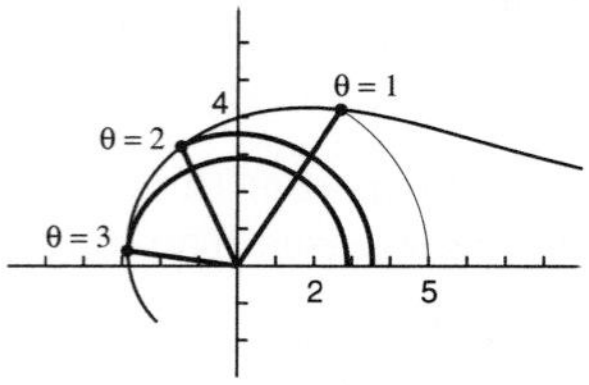


$A(1) = A(2) = A(3) = 12.5$
$A(\theta) = 12.5$, which is independent of the value of $\theta$.

19. *LP Record Project*
Not selected.

21. *The Derivative $dy/dx$ for Polar Graphs*

a. Count 5 spaces to the right and about 7.5 spaces down from the given point. Slope $\approx -1.5$.

b. $r = \theta$
$x = \theta\cos\theta \Rightarrow dx = d\theta \cdot \cos\theta - \theta\sin\theta d\theta$
$y = \theta\sin\theta \Rightarrow dy = d\theta \cdot \sin\theta + \theta\cos\theta d\theta$
$\dfrac{dy}{dx} = \dfrac{dy/d\theta}{dx/d\theta} = \dfrac{sin\theta + \theta\cos\theta}{\cos\theta - \theta\sin\theta}$
At $\theta = 7$, $dy/dx = -1.54338\ldots$, thus confirming the answer found graphically.

## Problem Set 8-10

*Chapter Review and Test*

### Review Problems

R0. Journal entries will vary.

R1. a. Graphs.

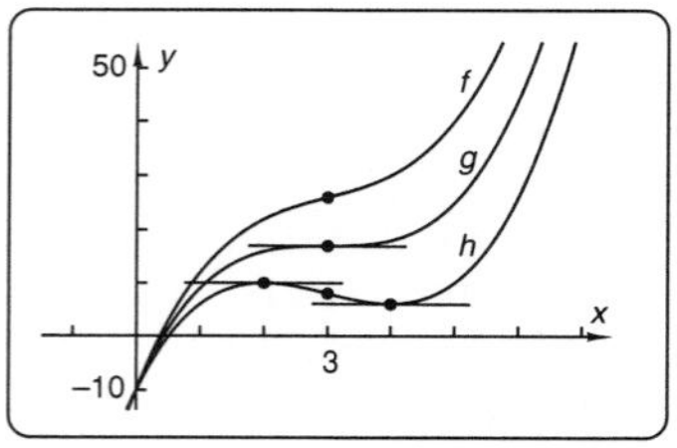


b. $f'(x) = 3x^2 - 18x + 30$; $f''(x) = 6x - 18$
$g'(x) = 3x^2 - 18x + 27$; $g''(x) = 6x - 18$
$h'(x) = 3x^2 - 18x + 24$; $h''(x) = 6x - 18$

c. $h$ has $h'(x) = 0$ at $x = 2$ and $x = 4$.
Local max. at $x = 2$, local min. at $x = 4$.

d. $g$ has a horiz. tan. at $x = 3$, but no max. or min.

e. Each point of inflection appears at $x = 3$, where second derivative $6x - 18$ equals zero.

R2. a. Number-line graphs.

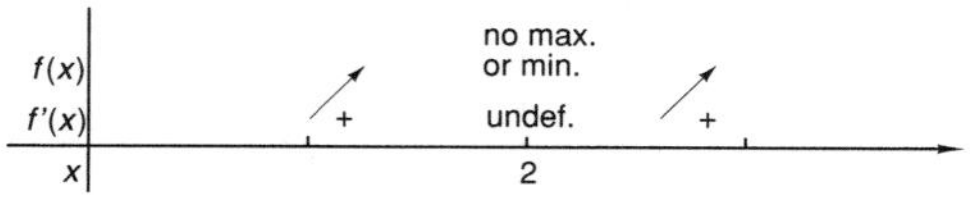


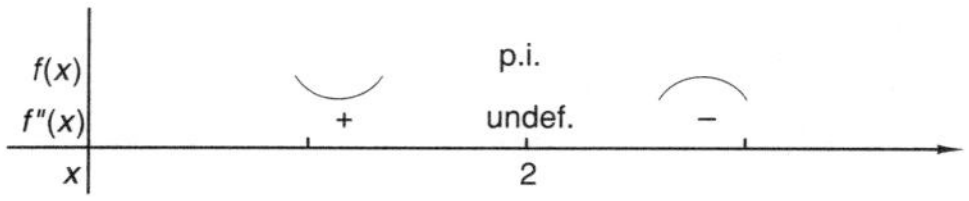


b. Graph, example.

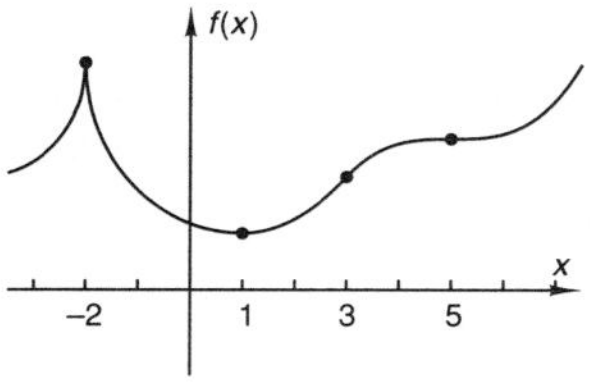


c. $f(x) = x^{2/3} - x$

i. $f'(x) = \dfrac{2}{3}x^{-1/3} - 1$, $f''(x) = \dfrac{-2}{9}x^{-4/3}$

ii. Zooming in shows that there is a local minimum cusp at $(0, 0)$ and a local maximum with zero derivative at $x \approx 0.3$. Graph.

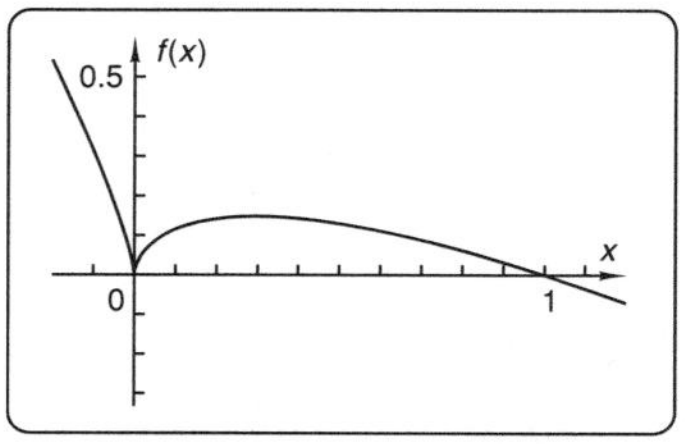


$f'(x) = 0$ at $x = (2/3)^3 = 8/27$, and $f'(x)$ is undefined at $x = 0$, thus locating precisely the min. and max. found by graph. Since there are no other critical values of $x$, there are no other max. or min. points.

iii. $f''(x)$ is undefined at $x = 0$, and $f''(x) < 0$ everywhere else; $f''$ never changes sign, so there are no inflection points.

iv. $f(0) = 0$, $f(8/27) = 4/27$,
$f(5) = -2.0759\ldots.$
Global max. at $(8/27, 4/27)$.
Global min. at $(5, -2.0759\ldots)$.

d. Graph. Local min. at $x = 0$, local max. at $x = 2$. Points of inflection at $x = 2 \pm \sqrt{2} \approx 3.4$ and 0.6.

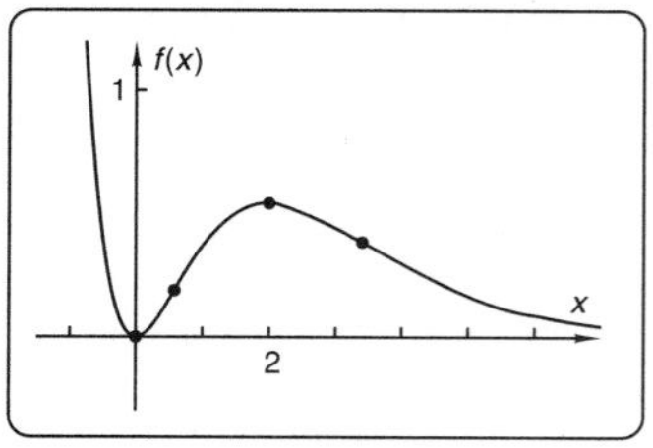


R3. a. *Storage Battery Problem*
Optimal battery has cells $\sqrt{70/12} = 2.4152\ldots$ cm wide and $10\sqrt{12/70} = 4.1403\ldots$ cm long, giving a battery of overall dimensions about 14.5" by 4.1", which is longer and narrower than the typical battery, 9" by 6.7". Minimal wall length does *not* seem to be a major consideration.

b. *Cylinder In Cubic Paraboloid Problem*
Max. rectangle has $x = \sqrt[3]{16/5} = 1.4736\ldots$,
$y = 8 - 16/5 = 4.8$.

R4. a. $A = e^2 - e = 4.6707\ldots$

b. $A = 6.75$

c. The graphs cross at $x = 0$; for $-1 < x < 0$, $x^3 > x$, but $x^3 < x$ for $0 < x < 1$, so the region to the right cancels the one to the left! Mr. Rhee should use:
$A = \int_{-1}^{0}(x^3 - x)\,dx + \int_0^1 (x - x^3)\,dx$

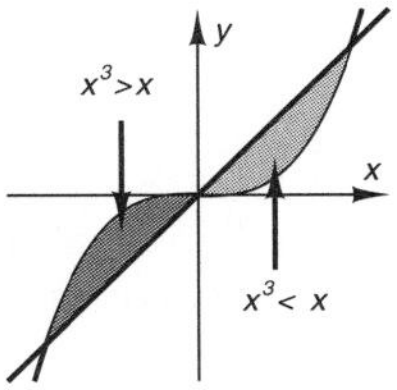


R5. a. $V = 2.5\pi(e^{1.6} - 1) = 31.0470\ldots$

b. $V = \dfrac{2}{9}\pi = 0.6981\ldots$

c. *Oblique Cone Problem*
$V \approx 25.1327\ldots$ (exactly $8\pi$)
The right circular cone also has volume $8\pi$.

R6. a. $V \approx 1.2566\ldots$ (exactly $0.4\pi$)

b. $V = 0.4\pi$, which is the same.

c. *Various Axes Problem*

i. $V \approx 25.1327\ldots$ (exactly $8\pi$)

ii. $V \approx 160.8495\ldots$ (exactly $51.2\pi$)

iii. $V \approx 174.2536\ldots$ (exactly $55\frac{7}{15}\pi$)

iv. $V \approx 201.0619\ldots$ (exactly $64\pi$)

R7. a. $L = \int_{-1}^{2}\sqrt{1 + (2x)^2}\,dx \approx 6.1257\ldots$

b. $L = \dfrac{2}{6.75}(21.25^{3/2} - 1) = 28.7281\ldots$ Distance between the endpoints is $\sqrt{9^2 + 27^2} = 28.4604\ldots$, so the answer is reasonable.

c. $L \approx 25.7255\ldots$

R8. a. $S = \dfrac{\pi}{27}(145^{3/2} - 1) = 203.0436\ldots$
The disk of radius 8 has area $64\pi = 201.0619\ldots$, which is close.

b. $dL = \sqrt{dx^2 + dy^2} = \sqrt{1 + \sec^4 x}\,dx$
$S = \int_0^1 2\pi(\tan x + 1)\sqrt{1 + \sec^4 x}\,dx \approx 20.4199\ldots$

c. $S \approx 272.0945\ldots$

R9. a. $L \approx 32.4706\ldots$

b. $A = \dfrac{7.75}{6}\pi^3 = 38.7578\ldots$

## CHAPTER 9

### Exploratory Problem Set 9-1

*Introduction to the Integral of a Product of Two Functions*

1. $V \approx 3.5864\ldots$
3. $\int f'(x)\,dx = \int x\cos x\,dx + \int \sin x\,dx$
5. $V = \pi^2 - 2\pi$
7. The method involves working separately with the different "parts" of the integrand. The function $x\sin x$ was chosen because one of the terms in its derivative is $x\cos x$, which is the original integrand. See Section 9-2.

### Problem Set 9-2

*Integration by Parts—A Way to Integrate Products*

1. $-x\cos x + \sin x + C$
3. $\dfrac{1}{4}xe^{4x} - \dfrac{1}{16}e^{4x} + C$
5. $-\dfrac{21}{25}e^{-5x} - \dfrac{1}{5}xe^{-5x} + C$
7. $\dfrac{1}{4}x^4\ln x - \dfrac{1}{16}x^4 + C$
9. $x^2e^x - 2xe^x + 2e^x + C$
11. $x\ln x - x + C$

### Problem Set 9-3

*Rapid Repeated Integration by Parts*

1. $\dfrac{1}{2}x^3e^{2x} - \dfrac{3}{4}x^2e^{2x} + \dfrac{3}{4}xe^{2x} - \dfrac{3}{8}e^{2x} + C$
3. $-x^4\cos x + 4x^3\sin x + 12x^2\cos x - 24x\sin x$
$- 24\cos x + C$
5. $\dfrac{1}{2}x^5\sin 2x + \dfrac{5}{4}x^4\cos 2x - \dfrac{5}{2}x^3\sin 2x - \dfrac{15}{4}x^2\cos 2x$
$+ \dfrac{15}{4}x\sin 2x + \dfrac{15}{8}\cos 2x + C$
7. $-\dfrac{1}{2}e^x\cos x + \dfrac{1}{2}e^x\sin x + C$
9. $\dfrac{5}{34}e^{3x}\sin 5x + \dfrac{3}{34}e^{3x}\cos 5x + C$
11. $\dfrac{1}{8}x^8\ln 3x - \dfrac{1}{64}x^8 + C$
13. $\dfrac{\ln 7}{5}x^5 + C$ ($\ln 7$ is a constant!)
15. $\dfrac{1}{6}\sin^6 x + C$
17. $\dfrac{2}{3}x^3(x+5)^{3/2} - \dfrac{4}{5}x^2(x+5)^{5/2} + \dfrac{16}{35}x(x+5)^{7/2}$
$- \dfrac{32}{315}(x+5)^{9/2} + C$
19. $5x\ln x - 5x + C$

21. $\frac{1}{2}x^4e^{x^2} - x^2e^{x^2} + e^{x^2} + C$

23. $\frac{1}{2}x^2(\ln x)^3 - \frac{3}{4}x^2(\ln x)^2 + \frac{3}{4}x^2 \ln x - \frac{3}{8}x^2 + C$

25. $\frac{1}{10}x^2(x^2+1)^5 - \frac{1}{60}(x^2+1)^6 + C$

27. $\frac{1}{2}\cos x \sin x + \frac{1}{2}x + C$

29. $\frac{1}{2}\sec x \tan x + \frac{1}{2}\ln|\sec x + \tan x| + C$

31. $x \log_3 x - \frac{1}{\ln 3}x + C$

33. $-\cos x + C$

35. $-\ln|\csc x + \cot x| + C$

37. $-\ln|\cos x| + C$

39. For the first integral, Wanda integrated $\cos x$ and differentiated $x^2$, but in the second integral she plans to differentiate $\int \cos x\, dx$ and integrate $2x$, effectively canceling out what she did in the first part. She will get $\int x^2 \cos x\, dx = x^2 \sin x - x^2 \sin x + \int x^2 \cos x\, dx$, which is true, but not very useful!

41. After two integrations by parts,
$\int e^x \sin x\, dx = -e^x \cos x + e^x \sin x - \int e^x \sin x\, dx$,
but after two more integrations,
$\int e^x \sin x\, dx = -e^x \cos x + e^x \sin x + e^x \cos x$
$-e^x \sin x + \int e^x \sin x\, dx$.
Two integrations produced the original integral with the opposite sign (which is useful), and two more integrations reversed the sign again to give the original integral with the same sign (which is not useful).

43. *Area Problem*
$A = -4e^{-3} + 1 = 0.8008\ldots$

45. *Volume Problem*
$V = 5\pi(\ln 5)^2 - 10\pi \ln 5 + 8\pi = 15.2589\ldots$

47. *Areas and Integration by Parts*
For integration by parts, $\int u\, dv = uv - \int v\, du$.
Applying limits of integration gives
$\int_c^d u\, dv = uv|_{u=a}^{u=b} - \int_a^b v\, du$
$\int_c^d u\, dv = (bd - ac) - \int_a^b v\, du$
The quantity $(bd - ac)$ is the area of the "L-shaped" region, which is the area of the larger rectangle minus the area of the smaller one. Thus, the integral of $u\, dv$ equals the area of the L-shaped region minus the area represented by the integral of $v\, du$.

49. *Introduction to Reduction Formulas Problem*
$\int \sin^7 x\, dx = -\sin^6 x \cos x + 6\int \sin^5 x \cos^2 x\, dx$
$= -\sin^6 x \cos x + 6\int \sin^5 x\, dx - 6\int \sin^7 x\, dx$
$\int \sin^7 x\, dx = -\frac{1}{7}\sin^6 x \cos x + \frac{6}{7}\int \sin^5 x\, dx$
$\int \sin^7 x\, dx = -\frac{1}{7}\sin^6 x \cos x - \frac{6}{35}\sin^4 x \cos x$
$-\frac{24}{105}\sin^2 x \cos x - \frac{48}{105}\cos x + C$

## Problem Set 9-4

*Reduction Formulas and Computer Software*

1. $\int \sin^9 x\, dx = -\frac{1}{9}\sin^8 x \cos x + \frac{8}{9}\int \sin^7 x\, dx$

3. $\int \cot^{12} x\, dx = -\frac{1}{11}\cot^{11} x - \int \cot^{10} x\, dx$

5. $\int \sec^{13} x\, dx = \frac{1}{12}\sec^{11} x \tan x + \frac{11}{12}\int \sec^{11} x\, dx$

7. Not selected.

9. Not selected.

11. Not selected.

13. $-\frac{1}{5}\sin^4 x \cos x - \frac{4}{15}\sin^2 x \cos x - \frac{8}{15}\cos x + C$

15. $-\frac{1}{5}\cot^5 x + \frac{1}{3}\cot^3 x - \cot x - x + C$

17. $\frac{1}{3}\sec^2 x \tan x + \frac{2}{3}\tan x + C$

19. *Cosine Area Problem*
 a. $y = \cos x$ is on top; $y = \cos^3 x$ is in the middle; $y = \cos^5 x$ is on the bottom.
 b. For $y = \cos x$, area $\approx 2.0000\ldots$
 For $y = \cos^3 x$, area $\approx 1.3333\ldots$
 For $y = \cos^5 x$, area $\approx 1.06666\ldots$
 c. $A_1 = 2$, $A_3 = 4/3$, $A_5 = 16/15$
 d. Based on the graphs, the area under $\cos x$ should be greater than that under $\cos^3 x$, which in turn is greater than the area under $\cos^5 x$. This is exactly what happens with the calculated answers: $A_1 > A_3 > A_5$
 e. Graph.

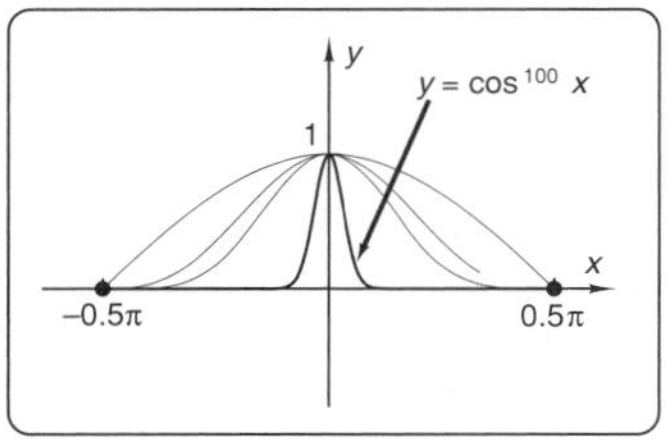


 f. Yes, $\lim_{n\to\infty} \int_{-\pi/2}^{\pi/2} \cos^n x\, dx = 0$.

21. *Integral of Secant Cubed Problem*
$\int \sec^3 x\, dx = \frac{1}{2}\sec x \tan x + \frac{1}{2}\ln|\sec x + \tan x| + C$
Note that the answer is half the derivative of secant plus half the integral of secant.

23. $\int \sin^3 ax\, dx = -\frac{1}{3a}\sin^2 ax \cos ax$
$+\frac{2}{3}\int \sin ax\, dx$

(From Problem 22)

$= -\frac{1}{3a}\sin^2 ax \cos ax - \frac{2}{3a}\cos ax + C$

$= -\frac{1}{3a}\cos ax(\sin^2 ax + 2) + C$, Q.E.D.

Or: $\frac{d}{dx}\left(-\frac{1}{3a}(\cos ax)(\sin^2 ax + 2)\right)$

$= -\frac{1}{3a}(-a\sin ax)(\sin^2 ax + 2)$

$- \frac{1}{3a}(\cos ax)(2a\sin ax\cos ax)$

$= \frac{1}{3}(\sin^3 ax + 2\sin ax - 2\sin ax\cos^2 ax)$

$= \frac{1}{3}(\sin^3 ax + 2\sin ax(1 - \cos^2 ax))$

$= \frac{1}{3}(\sin^3 ax + 2\sin ax(\sin^2 ax)) = \sin^3 ax.$

$\therefore \int \sin^3 ax\,dx = -\frac{1}{3a}(\cos ax)(\sin^2 ax + 2) + C,$

QED.

## Problem Set 9-5

*Integrating Special Powers of Trig Functions*

1. $-\cos x + \frac{2}{3}\cos^3 x - \frac{1}{5}\cos^5 x + C$

3. $\frac{1}{9}\sin 9x - \frac{1}{9}\sin^3 9x + \frac{1}{15}\sin^5 9x - \frac{1}{63}\sin^7 9x + C$

5. $\frac{1}{15}\sin^5 3x + C$

7. $-\frac{1}{56}\cos^7 8x + \frac{1}{72}\cos^9 8x + C$

9. $-\frac{1}{3}\cos^3 x + \frac{2}{5}\cos^5 x - \frac{1}{7}\cos^7 x + C$

11. $\frac{1}{2}x + \frac{1}{4}\sin 2x + C$

13. $\frac{1}{2}x - \frac{1}{20}\sin 10x + C$

15. $\frac{1}{3}\tan^3 x + \tan x + C$

17. $-\frac{1}{42}\cot^7 6x - \frac{1}{10}\cot^5 6x - \frac{1}{6}\cot^3 6x - \frac{1}{6}\cot 6x + C$

19. $\frac{1}{11}\tan^{11} x + C$

21. $\frac{1}{10}\sec^{10} x + C$

23. $(\sec^{10} 20)x + C$

25. $\frac{1}{2}\sin 2x + C$

27. $-\cot x + C$

29. $\frac{1}{2}\sec x\tan x + \frac{1}{2}\ln|\sec x + \tan x| + C$

31. *Area Problem No. 1*

 a. $\frac{5}{16}\sin 5x\sin 3x + \frac{3}{16}\cos 5x\cos 3x + C$

 b. $\int_0^{2\pi}\cos 5x\sin 3x\,dx = 0.$
 Since the integral finds the area above minus area below, this calculation shows the two areas are equal.

33. *Volume Problem No. 1* $V = \pi^2/2$

35. *Limaçon Area Problem*

 $A = \pi + 2 + 10\sqrt{2} + \frac{25}{8}\pi = 29.1012\ldots$, which agrees with the numerical answer.

37. Not selected.

## Problem Set 9-6

*Integration by Trigonometric Substitution*

1. $\frac{49}{2}\sin^{-1}\frac{x}{7} + \frac{1}{2}x\sqrt{49 - x^2} + C$

3. $\frac{1}{2}x\sqrt{x^2 + 16} + 8\ln\left|\sqrt{x^2 + 16} + x\right| + C$

5. $\frac{1}{2}x\sqrt{9x^2 - 1} - \frac{1}{6}\ln\left|3x + \sqrt{9x^2 - 1}\right| + C$

7. $\sin^{-1}\frac{x}{\sqrt{17}} + C$

9. $\ln\left|\sqrt{x^2 + 1} + x\right| + C$

11. $\frac{1}{4}x^3\sqrt{x^2 - 9} - \frac{9}{8}x\sqrt{x^2 - 9}$
 $- \frac{81}{8}\ln\left|x + \sqrt{x^2 - 9}\right| + C$

13. $\frac{1}{4}x(1 - x^2)^{3/2} + \frac{3}{8}\sin^{-1} x + \frac{3}{8}x\sqrt{1 - x^2} + C$

15. $\frac{1}{9}\tan^{-1}\frac{x}{9} + C$

17. a. $\sqrt{x^2 + 25} + C$

 b. $\int \frac{x\,dx}{\sqrt{x^2 + 25}} = \frac{1}{2}\int (x^2 + 25)^{-1/2}(2x\,dx)$
 $= \sqrt{x^2 + 25} + C$, which agrees with part (a).
 Moral: Always check for an *easy* way to integrate before trying a more powerful technique!

19. $\sin^{-1}\frac{x - 5}{3} + C$

21. $\ln\left|x + 4 + \sqrt{x^2 + 8x - 20}\right| + C$

23. $50\sin^{-1} 0.8 + 25\sin(2\sin^{-1} 0.8)$
 $- 50\sin^{-1}(-0.3) - 25\sin(2\sin^{-1}(-0.3))$
 $= 99.9084\ldots$
 Numerical integration: $99.9084\ldots$, which checks.

25. *Arc Length of a Parabola Problem*
 $L = \frac{5}{2}\sqrt{901} + \frac{1}{12}\ln\left|\sqrt{901} + 30\right| = 75.3828\ldots$
 Numerical integration: $L = 75.3828\ldots$ (check.)

27. *Circle Area Formula Problem*
Not selected.

29. *Ellipsoid Problem*
Rotating about the $y$-axis, $V = \frac{4}{3}\pi a^2 b$.
Rotating about the $x$-axis, $V = \frac{4}{3}\pi a b^2$.

31. *Hyperboloid Problem*
$V = \frac{256}{3}\pi = 268.0825\ldots$

33. *Area of an Ellipse, Parametrically*
$A = \pi ab$, as in Problem 28.
With this method, you get $\int \sin^2 t\,dt$, just like with trig substitution, but here you get the integral directly, not indirectly.

35. *Trig Substitution for Negative Values of x*
For the sine and tangent substitution, the range of the inverse sine and inverse tangent make the corresponding radical positive. For the secant substitution the situation is more complicated but still gives an answer of the same algebraic form as if $x$ had been only positive.

## Problem Set 9-7

*Integration of Rational Functions by Partial Fractions*

1. $4\ln|x-1| + 7\ln|x-2| + C$

3. $\frac{7}{2}\ln|x+2| + \frac{3}{2}\ln|x-4| + C$

5. $-7\ln|x+5| + 7\ln|x+2| + C$

7. $2\ln|x+1| + 3\ln|x-7| + 4\ln|x+2| + C$

9. $-\ln|x+3| + 2\ln|x+1| + 3\ln|x-2| + C$

11. $x^3 + \frac{5}{2}x^2 - 7x + 2\ln|x-1| + C$

13. $\frac{1}{2}\ln|x^2+1| + 2\tan^{-1}x + 3\ln|x+4| + C$

15. $\ln|x+5| + 3\ln|x+1| + 2(x+1)^{-1} + C$

17. $-\frac{1}{2}(x-2)^{-2} + C$

19. *Rumor Problem*
a. $y = \dfrac{1000}{1+99e^{-2t}}$
b. $y(1) = 69.4531\ldots \approx 69$ students.
$y(4) = 967.8567\ldots \approx 968$ students.
$y(8) = 999.9888\ldots \approx 1000$ students—everyone knows by the end of the day!
c. $y'' = \frac{1}{500}(1000y' - 2yy')$ is a max. when $y = 500$.
This occurs when $t = \frac{1}{2}\ln 99 = 2.2975\ldots$ hours.
d. Graph, which follows the slope field pattern.

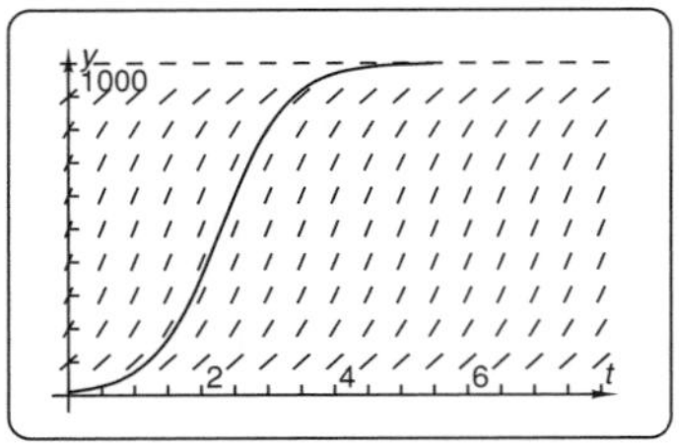


21. *Area Problem*
$A = 5\ln\frac{b-1}{b+4} + 5\ln 6$
$A(7) = 5\ln\frac{6}{11} + 5\ln 6 = 5.9281\ldots$
$\lim_{b\to\infty} A(b) = \lim_{b\to\infty} 5\ln\frac{1}{1} + 5\ln 6$
(l'Hospital's rule)
$= 5\ln 6 = 8.9587\ldots,$
so the area does approach a finite limit.

23. *Equivalent Answers Problem*
a. $\frac{1}{2}\ln|x-2| + \frac{1}{2}\ln|x-4| + C$
b. $\ln\sqrt{x^2-6x+8} + C$
c. $\frac{1}{2}\ln|x^2-6x+8| + C$
d. Each can be transformed to $\ln\sqrt{x^2-6x+8} + C$.

## Problem Set 9-8

*Integrals of the Inverse Trig Functions*

1. Not selected.

3. Not selected.

5. Not selected.

7. *Answer Verification Problem*
$4\tan^{-1}4 - \frac{\pi}{4} - \frac{1}{2}\ln\frac{17}{2} = 3.4478\ldots$ (checks)

9. *Area Problem*
Both methods give $A = 1$.

## Problem Set 9-9

*Calculus of the Hyperbolic and Inverse Hyperbolic Functions*

1. *Hyperbolic Function Graphing Problem*

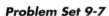

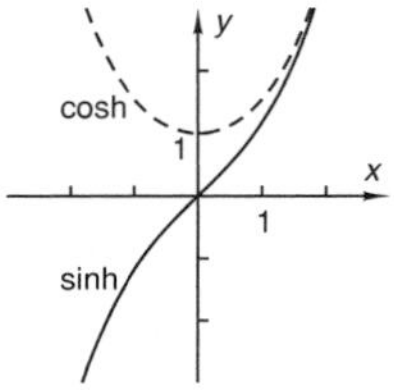


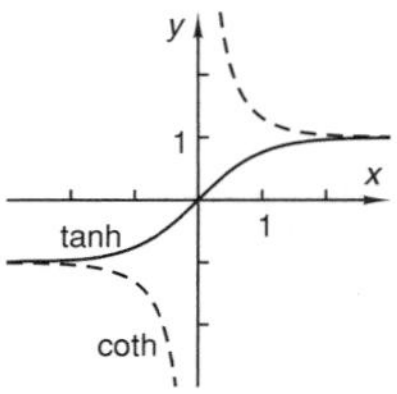

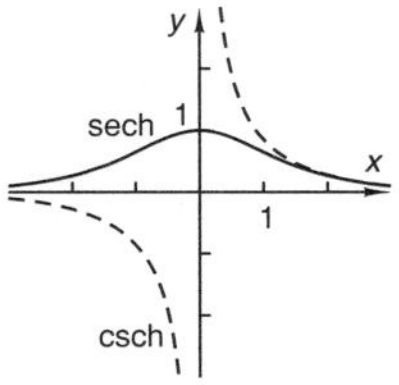


3. $3\tanh^2 x\,\text{sech}^2 x$

5. $\dfrac{1}{6}\cosh^6 x + C$

7. $-\text{csch}\,x\coth x\sin x + \text{csch}\,x\cos x$

9. $\dfrac{1}{4}\tanh 4x + C$

11. $2x\coth x - x^2\,\text{csch}^2 x$

13. $\ln(\cosh 3) - \ln(\cosh 1) = 1.875547\ldots$

15. $\dfrac{5\cosh 5x\ln 3x - x^{-1}\sinh 5x}{(\ln 3x)^2}$

17. $\cosh 1 - \sinh 1 = e^{-1} = 0.36787\ldots$

19. $\dfrac{12}{\sqrt{16x^2+1}}$

21. $x\tanh^{-1} 5x + \dfrac{1}{10}\ln|1-(5x)^2| + C$

23. $0.5x\sqrt{x^2+9} + 4.5\sinh^{-1}\dfrac{x}{3} + C$

25. *Hanging Chain or Cable Problem*
Not selected.

27. *Power Line Problem*
a. $y = 500\cosh\dfrac{1}{500}x + 110 - 500\cosh 0.3$
$y(0) = 87.3307\ldots \approx 87.3$ ft
b. $L = 1000\sinh 0.3 = 304.5202\ldots \approx 304.5$ ft
weight $= 243.6162\ldots \approx 243.6$ lb.
c. $T(150) = 400\cosh 0.3 = 418.1354\ldots \approx 418.1$ lb.
d. $h = 901.3301\ldots \approx 901.3$lb

29. *Bowl Problem*
a. $S \approx 5.07327\ldots \approx 5.07$ ft$^2$
b. Cost $\approx$ \$289.18
c. $V \approx 1.25317\ldots \approx 1.253$ ft$^3$

31. *Derivative Verification Problem*
a. $H'(1) = -\text{csch}\,1\coth 1 = -1.1172855\ldots$
b. $H'(1) \approx -1.11738505\ldots$
The answers differ by $0.0000995\ldots$, which is about 0.0089% of the actual answer.

33. *Integration by Parts Problem*
By parts: $\dfrac{2}{3}e^x\cosh 2x - \dfrac{1}{3}e^x\sinh 2x + C$
By transf. to exponential form: $\dfrac{1}{6}e^{3x} + \dfrac{1}{2}e^{-x} + C$
Transforming to exponential form is easier!

35. *Derivations of the Pythagorean Properties of Hyperbolic Functions*
Not selected.

37. *Hyperbolic Radian Problem*
a. On the circle,
$$L = \int_{\cos 2}^{1}\frac{du}{\sqrt{1-u^2}} = -\cos^{-1} 1 + 2 = 2$$
On the hyperbola, $L = \cosh 2 - 1 = 2.762\ldots$. So the length of the curve is greater than 2, Q.E.D.
b. The area of the triangle that circumscribes the sector is $0.5(2\sinh 2\cosh 2) = \sinh 2\cosh 2$. The area of the region between the upper and lower branches of the hyperbola from $u = 1$ to $\cosh 2$ is
$A = 2\int_0^2 \sinh^2 t\,dt \approx 11.644958\ldots$
Thus the area of the sector is $\cosh 2\sinh 2 - 11.644958\ldots = 2$, Q.E.D.
c. By definition of the circular functions $x$ is the length of the arc from $(1, 0)$ to $(\cos x\sin x)$. So the total arc has length $2x$. The circumference of a unit circle is $2\pi$, and its area is $\pi$. Thus
$$A_{\text{sector}} = \frac{2x}{2\pi}\pi = x, \text{ Q.E.D.}$$
d. Area of circumscribing triangle $= \cosh x\sinh x$.
Area between branches $= \cosh x\sinh x - x$.
Area of sector $=$
$\cosh x\sinh x - (\cosh x\sinh x - x)$
Area of sector $= x$, Q.E.D.

## Problem Set 9-10

*Improper Integrals*

1. a. Graph, $y = 1/x^2$. Might converge. Integrand approaches zero as $x$ approaches infinity.

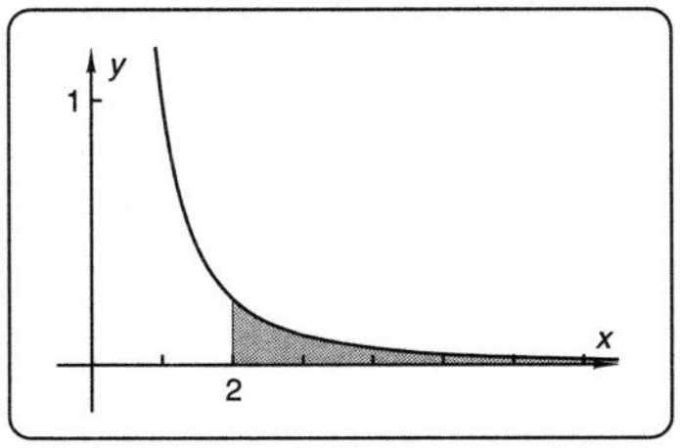


b. Integral converges to $\dfrac{1}{2}$.

3. a. Graph, $y = 1/x$. Might converge. Integrand approaches zero as $x$ approaches infinity.

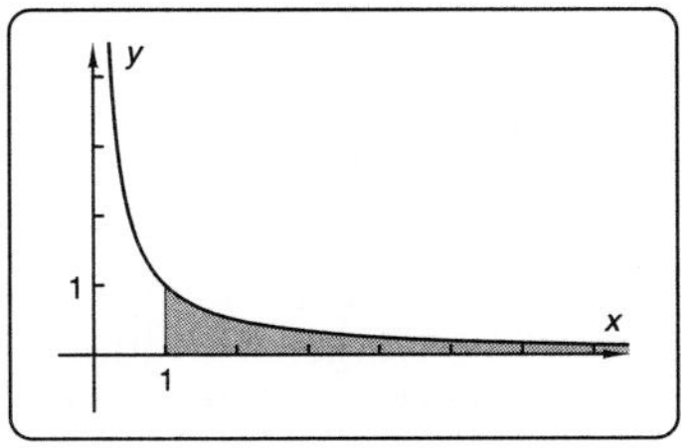

b. Integral diverges.

5. a. Graph, $y = 1/x^{0.2}$. Might converge. Integrand approaches zero as $x$ approaches infinity.

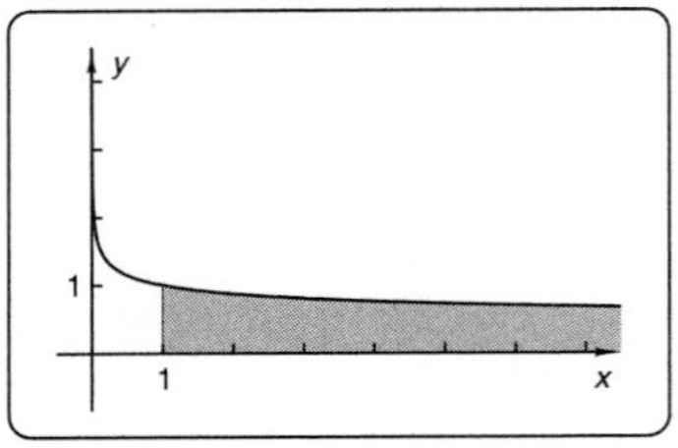


b. Integral diverges.

7. a. Graph, $y = 1/x^{0.2}$. Might converge. Integrand becomes infinite only as $x$ approaches zero.

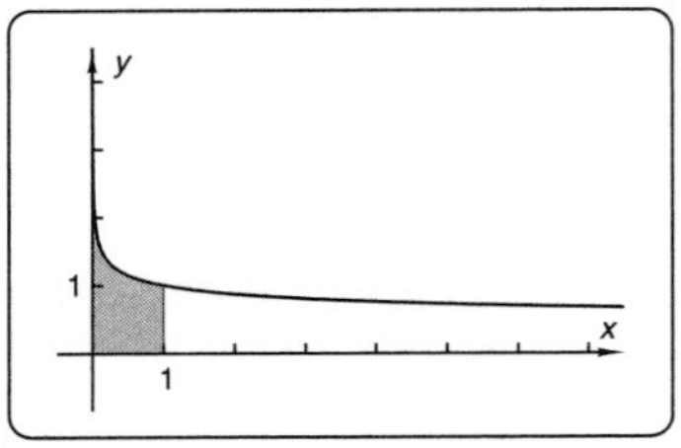


b. Integral converges to 1.25.

9. a. Graph, $y = 1/(1+x^2)$. Might converge. Integrand approaches zero as $x$ approaches infinity.

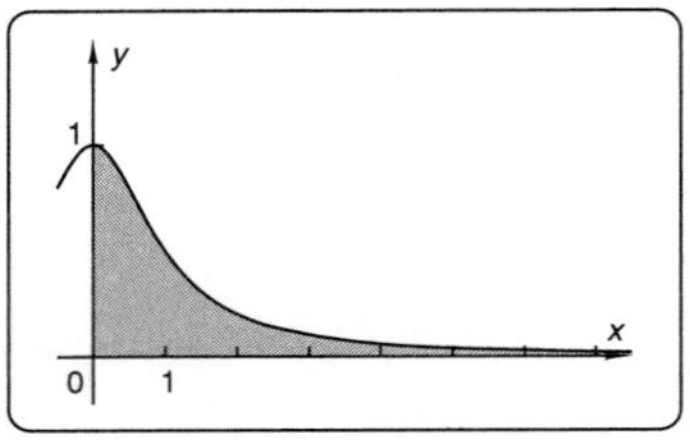


b. Integral converges to $\pi/2$.

11. a. Graph, $y = 1/(x \ln x)$. Might converge. Integrand becomes infinite only as $x$ approaches 0 or 1.

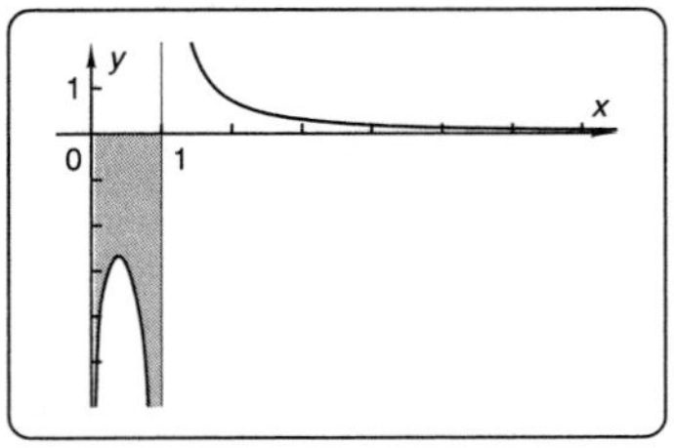


b. Split the integral into two pieces.

$\int_0^1 1/(x \ln x)\, dx =$

$\int_0^c 1/(x \ln x)\, dx + \int_c^1 1/(x \ln x)\, dx$

$= \lim_{a \to 0^+} \int_a^c 1/(x \ln x)\, dx$

$+ \lim_{b \to 1^-} \int_c^b 1/(x \ln x)\, dx$

$= \infty + \infty$

For the integral to converge, *both* limits must exist. Since neither exists, the integral diverges.

13. a. Graph, $y = e^{-0.4x}$. Might converge. Integrand approaches zero as $x$ approaches infinity.

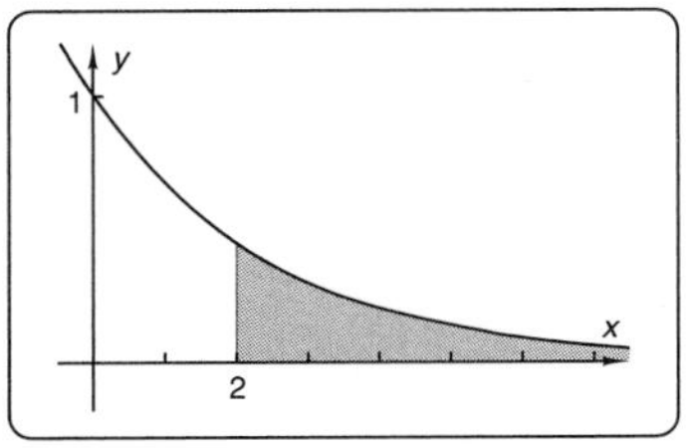


b. Integral converges to $2.5e^{-0.8} = 1.1233\ldots$

15. a. Graph, $y = \sqrt{x}$. Does not converge. Integrand is undefined for $x < 0$.

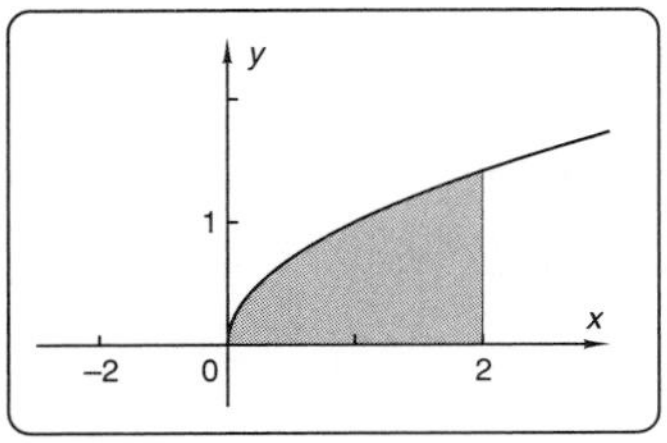


b. (Not applicable)

17. a. Graph, $y = xe^{-x}$. Might converge. Integrand seems to approach zero as $x$ approaches infinity.

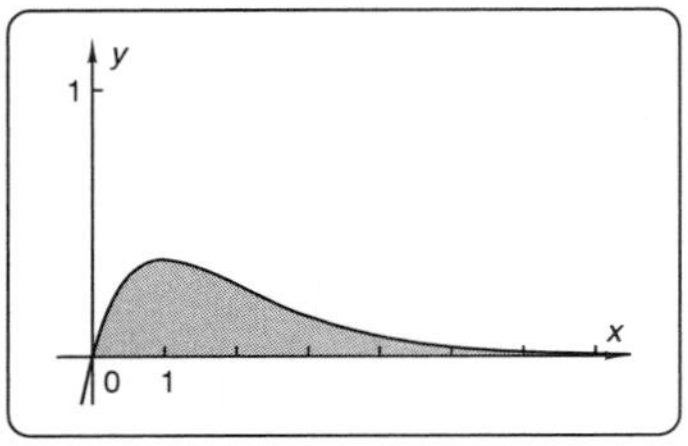


b. Integral converges to 1.

19. a. Graph, $y = \cos x$. Diverges. Integrand does not approach zero as $x$ approaches infinity.

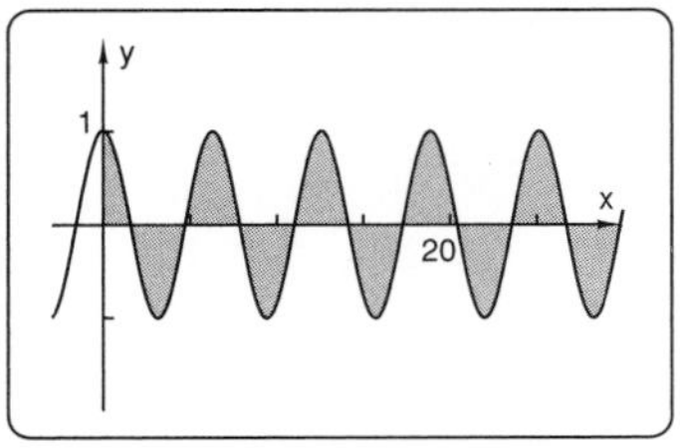


b. (Not applicable.)

21. *Divergence By Oscillation Problem*

As $b \to \infty$, $\int_0^b \cos x\, dx$ oscillates between $-1$ and 1 and never approaches a limit. Similarly $\int_0^b \sin x\, dx$ oscillates between 0 and 2.

23. *Volume of an Unbounded Solid Problem*

a. $A \to \infty$. The improper integral diverges.

b. $V \to \pi$

c. $V \to \infty$

d. False. The volume could approach a constant as in part (b) or become infinite as in part (c).

25. *Gamma Function and Factorial Function*

a. $f(1) = 1$, $f(2) = 2$, $f(3) = 6$

b. Conjecture:
$f(4) = 4f(3) = 24 = 4!$
$f(5) = 5f(4) = 120 = 5!$
$f(6) = 6f(5) = 720 = 6!$

c. $f(x) = xf(x-1)$, Q.E.D.

d. Part (a) shows that $f(1) = 1 = 1!$.
Part (c) shows that $f(n) = nf(n-1)$
$= n(n-1)f(n-2)$
$= n(n-1)(n-2)\ldots(2)(1) = n!$, Q.E.D.

e. $\int_0^b t^3 e^{-t}\,dt < 0.000,001$ for $b \geq 24$.

f. $0.5! \approx 0.886227311\ldots$ using $b = 24$.
From the graphs, $t^{0.5}e^{-t} < t^3 e^{-t}$ for $x \geq 24$.
The error in 0.5! by stopping at $b = 24$ is the area under the "tail" of the graph from $b = 24$.
Error $= \int_{24}^{\infty} t^{0.5}e^{-t}\,dt < \int_{24}^{\infty} t^3 e^{-t}\,dt < 0.000,001$.
The difference between the tabulated value of 0.5! and the value calculated here is
0.8862269255
−0.886227311...
= −0.000000386,
which is less in absolute value that 0.000,001. Note, however, that the difference is *negative*, because the calculated value is larger than the tabulated value. This observation means that either the tabulated value is incorrect or there is more inaccuracy in the numerical integration algorithm than there is in the error caused by dropping the tail of the integral.

g. $1.5! = 1.3293\ldots$
$2.5! = 3.3233\ldots$
$3.5! = 11.6317\ldots$

h. $0! = \int_0^{\infty} t^0 e^{-t}\,dt = 1$, Q.E.D.

i. $(-1)! = 0!/0$, which is infinite. So $(-2)!$ and $(-3)!$, which equal $(-1)!/(-1)$ and $(-2)!/(-2)$, are also infinite. However,
$(-0.5)! = 0.5!/(0.5) = 1.77245\ldots$
$(-1.5)! = (-0.5)!/(-0.5) = -3.54490\ldots$
$(-2.5)! = (-1.5)!/(-1.5) = 2.36327\ldots$,
all of which are finite.

j. $0.5! = \dfrac{\sqrt{\pi}}{2} = 0.886226925\ldots$ (checks)

27. *Piecewise Continuity Problem*

a. $\int_1^3 y\,dx = \int_1^2 (2^x + 1)\,dx + \int_2^3 (2^x - 1)\,dx$

b. $= \lim_{b \to 2^-} \int_1^b (2^x + 1)\,dx + \lim_{a \to 2^+} \int_a^3 (2^x - 1)\,dx$

c. Integral converges to $6/\ln 2 = 8.6561\ldots$.

d. The integral is defined by dividing the interval into Riemann partitions and adding up the subintervals. But the Riemann partitions may be chosen so that the discontinuities are at endpoints of subintervals. Then the subintervals corresponding to each continuous piece may be added up separately.

e. False. Some discontinuous functions (notably, piecewise continuous functions) are integrable.

## Problem Set 9-11

*Miscellaneous Integrals and Derivatives*

1. $y' = 3\sec 3x \tan^2 3x + 3\sec^3 3x$

3. $\dfrac{1}{4}x\sinh 4x - \dfrac{1}{16}\cosh 4x + C$

5. $f'(x) = -3(3x+5)^{-2}$

7. $\dfrac{1}{3}\ln|(3x+5)| + C$

9. $t'(x) = 20\tan^4 4x \sec^2 4x$

11. $\dfrac{1}{2}x - \dfrac{1}{2}\sin x\cos x + C$

13. $y' = 23/(x+2)^2$

15. $6x - 23\ln|x+2| + C$

17. $f'(t) = \dfrac{t}{\sqrt{1+t^2}}$

19. $\dfrac{1}{2}t\sqrt{1+t^2} + \dfrac{1}{2}\ln\left|\sqrt{1+t^2} + t\right| + C$

21. $y' = 3x^2e^x + x^3e^x = x^2e^x(3+x)$

23. $x^3e^x - 3x^2e^x + 6xe^x - 6e^x + C$

25. $f'(x) = (1-x^2)^{-1/2}$

27. $x\sin^{-1}x + \sqrt{1-x^2} + C$

29. $-\dfrac{1}{6}\ln|x+5| + \dfrac{1}{6}\ln|x-1| + C$

31. $\ln\left|x + 2 + \sqrt{x^2+4x-5}\right| + C$

33. $f'(x) = \operatorname{sech}^2 x$

35. $\ln|\cosh x| + C$

37. $y' = e^{2x}(2\cos 3x - 3\sin 3x)$

39. $\dfrac{3}{13}e^{2x}\sin 3x + \dfrac{2}{13}e^{2x}\cos 3x + C$

41. $g'(x) = (3x^2)\ln 5x + x^3(5/5x) = x^2(3\ln 5x + 1)$

43. $\dfrac{1}{4}x^4\ln 5x - \dfrac{1}{16}x^4 + C$

45. $y' = y(x^{-1} - (x+2)^{-1} - (x+3)^{-1} - (x+4)^{-1})$

47. $-\ln|x+2| + 3\ln|x+3| - 2\ln|x+4| + C$

49. $y' = -3\cos^2 x\sin^2 x + \cos^4 x$

51. $-\dfrac{1}{4}\cos^4 x + C$

53. $\sin x - \dfrac{1}{3}\sin^3 x + C$ or $\dfrac{1}{3}\cos^2 x\sin x + \dfrac{2}{3}\sin x + C$

55. $\frac{1}{4}\cos^3 x \sin x + \frac{3}{8}\cos x \sin x + \frac{3}{8}x + C$

57. $g'(x) = 12x^3(x^4+3)^2$

59. $\frac{1}{13}x^{13} + x^9 + \frac{27}{5}x^5 + 27x + C$

61. $\frac{1}{16}(x^4+3)^4 + C$

63. $\frac{1}{5}x^5 + 3x + C$

65. $f'(x) = (x^4+3)^3$

67. $e^2 = 7.3890\ldots$

69. $r'(x) = xe^x + e^x$

71. $q'(x) = \frac{-1-\ln x}{x^2}$

73. $\frac{1}{2}(\ln x + 2)^2 + C$

75. $f'(x) = 2xe^{x^2}$

77. $\frac{1}{2}e^{x^2} + C$

79. $\frac{1}{2}x^2e^{x^2} - \frac{1}{2}e^{x^2} + C$

81. $\frac{b}{a^2+b^2}e^{ax}\sin bx + \frac{a}{a^2+b^2}e^{ax}\cos bx + C$,
(for $a$, $b$ not both 0)
$x + C$, (for $a = b = 0$)

83. $\frac{1}{2}x - \frac{1}{4c}\sin 2cx + C$, (for $c \neq 0$); $C$, (for $c = 0$)

85. $f'(x) = \frac{ad-bc}{(cx+d)^2}$, (for $c$, $d$ not both 0)
(undefined for $c = d = 0$)

87. $\frac{ax}{c} + \frac{bc-ad}{c^2}\ln|cx+d| + C$, (for $c \neq 0$)
$\frac{a}{2d}x^2 + \frac{b}{d}x + C$, (for $c = 0$, $d \neq 0$, undef., $c = d = 0$)

89. $\sqrt{x^2+a^2} + C$

91. $\ln|\sqrt{x^2+a^2} + x| + C$

93. $f'(x) = 2x\sin ax + ax^2\cos ax$

95. $-\frac{1}{a}x^2\cos ax + \frac{2}{a^2}x\sin ax + \frac{2}{a^3}\cos ax + C$,
(for $a \neq 0$)
$C$, (for $a = 0$)

97. $\frac{1}{a}\cosh ax + C$, (for $a \neq 0$)
$\int \sinh ax\,dx = C$, (for $a = 0$)

99. $x\cos^{-1} ax - \frac{1}{a}\sqrt{1-(ax)^2} + C$, (for $a \neq 0$)
$\frac{\pi}{2}x + C$, (for $a = 0$)

101. $2(1+\sqrt{x}) - 2\ln|1+\sqrt{x}| + C$
or $2\sqrt{x} - 2\ln|1+\sqrt{x}| + C_1$

103. $\frac{4}{3}(1+\sqrt[4]{x})^3 - 6(1+\sqrt[4]{x})^2 + 12(1+\sqrt[4]{x})$
$-4\ln(1+\sqrt[4]{x}) + C$ or
$\frac{4}{3}(\sqrt[4]{x})^3 - 2(\sqrt[4]{x})^2 + 4\sqrt[4]{x} - 4\ln|1+\sqrt[4]{x}| + C_1$

105. $\ln\left(\sqrt{e^x+1}-1\right) - \ln\left(\sqrt{e^x+1}+1\right) + C$

107. *Rational Function of* $\sin x$ *and* $\cos x$ *by* $u = \tan(x/2)$
a. $\cos x = 2\cos^2(x/2) - 1$ and
$\sin x = 2\sin(x/2)\cos(x/2)$.
b. $\cos x = \frac{1-\tan^2(x/2)}{1+\tan^2(x/2)}$, Q.E.D.
$\sin x = \frac{2\tan(x/2)}{1+\tan^2(x/2)}$, Q.E.D.
c. $dx = \frac{2\,du}{1+u^2}$, $\cos x = \frac{1-u^2}{1+u^2}$ and $\sin x = \frac{2u}{1+u^2}$
d. $\int \frac{1}{1+\cos x}\,dx$
$= \int \frac{1}{1+\frac{1-u^2}{1+u^2}} \cdot \frac{2\,du}{1+u^2}$
$= \int \frac{2\,du}{(1+u^2)+(1-u^2)} = \int du$, Q.E.D.
e. $\tan(x/2) + C$

109. $-\cot(x/2) + C$

111. $-\cot(x/2) - x + C$

### Problem Set 9-12

*Integrals in Journal*

1. Not selected.

### Problem Set 9-13

*Chapter Review and Test*

### Review Problems

R0. Journal entries will vary.

R1. $f'(x) = \cos x - x\sin x$
$\int x\sin x\,dx = \sin x - x\cos x + C$
$\int_1^4 x\sin x\,dx = \sin 4 - 4\cos 4 - \sin 1 + \cos 1$
$= 1.5566\ldots$, which checks.

R2. $-\frac{5}{2}x\cos 2x + \frac{5}{4}\sin 2x + C$

R3. a. $\frac{1}{2}x^3\sin 2x + \frac{3}{4}x^2\cos 2x - \frac{3}{4}x\sin 2x$
$-\frac{3}{8}\cos 2x + C$
b. $\frac{4}{25}e^{4x}\sin 3x - \frac{3}{25}e^{4x}\cos 3x + C$
c. $\frac{1}{2}x^2(\ln x)^2 - \frac{1}{2}x^2\ln x + \frac{1}{4}x^2 + C$

d. $V = \frac{16}{3}\pi \ln 2 - \frac{14}{9}\pi = 6.7268\ldots$

R4. a. $\int \cos^{30} dx = \frac{1}{30}\cos^{29} x \sin x + \frac{29}{30}\int \cos^{28} x\, dx$

b. $\frac{1}{5}\sec^4 x \tan x + \frac{4}{15}\sec^2 x \tan x + \frac{8}{15}\tan x + C$

c. $\int \tan^n x\, dx = \frac{1}{n-1}\tan^{n-1} x - \int \tan^{n-2} x\, dx$, Q.E.D.

R5. a. $\sin x - \frac{2}{3}\sin^3 x + \frac{1}{5}\sin^5 x + C$

b. $\frac{1}{5}\tan^5 x + \frac{2}{3}\tan^3 x + \tan x + C$

c. $\frac{1}{2}x - \frac{1}{28}\sin 14x + C$

d. $\frac{1}{2}\sec x \tan x + \frac{1}{2}\ln|\sec x + \tan x| + C$

e. $(\tan^9 32)x + C$

f. $A = \frac{113}{8}\pi + 64 - 36\sqrt{2} = 57.4633\ldots$

R6. a. $\frac{1}{2}x\sqrt{x^2-49} - \frac{49}{2}\ln\left|x + \sqrt{x^2-49}\right| + C$

b. $\frac{1}{2}(x-5)\sqrt{x^2-10x+34}$

$+\frac{9}{2}\ln\left|\sqrt{x^2-10x+34} + x - 5\right| + C$

c. $\sin^{-1}\frac{x}{2} + \frac{1}{2}x\sqrt{1-0.25x^2} + C$

d. $A = 25(\sin^{-1} 0.8 - \sin^{-1} 0.6) = 7.0948\ldots$

R7. a. $\ln|x+1| + 5\ln|x-4| + C$

b. $3\ln|x-1| + 4\ln|x+2| - 2\ln|x-3| + C$

c. $5\ln|x| + \tan^{-1}\frac{x}{3} + C$

d. $\ln|x^2(x+4)^3| + \frac{1}{x+4} + C$

e. $y = 3 + \frac{5}{1 + 0.25e^{0.5x}}$

Graph, showing that solution fits slope field.

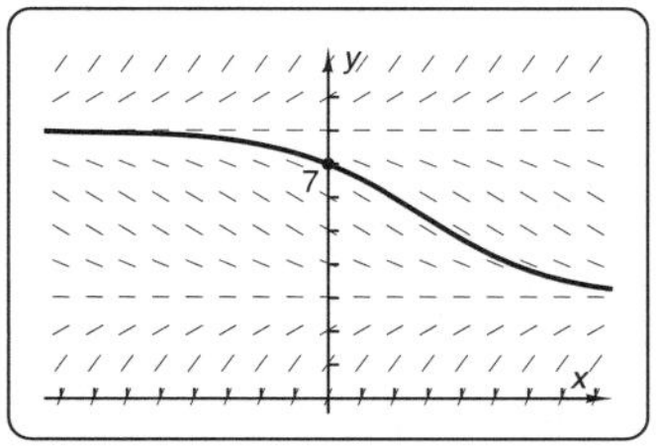


R8. a. Graph, $y = \cos^{-1} x$

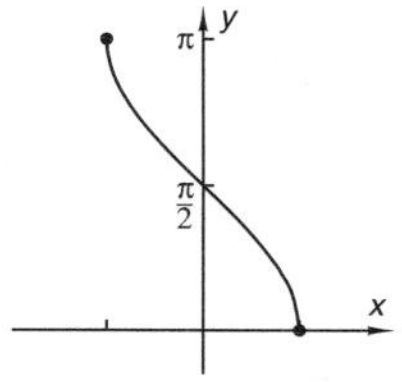


b. $f'(x) = \frac{1}{|x|\sqrt{9x^9 - 1}}$

c. $x\tan^{-1} 5x - \frac{1}{10}\ln|1 + 25x^2| + C$

d. $A = 1$

R9. a. Graph, $f(x) = \sinh x$

b. Graph, $g(x) = \cosh^{-1} x$

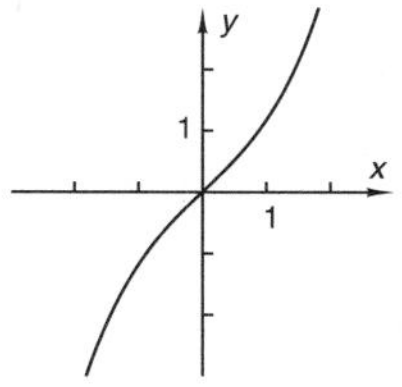


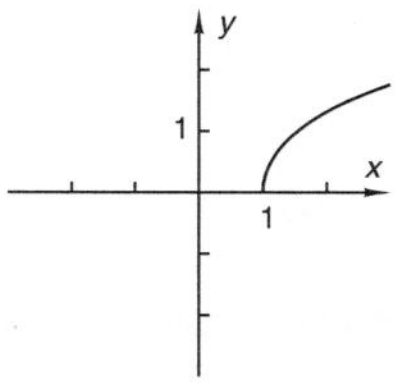


c. $h'(x) = -x^2 \operatorname{sech} x \tanh x + 2x \operatorname{sech} x$

d. $f'(x) = \frac{5}{\sqrt{25x^2+1}}$

e. $\frac{1}{3}\ln|\cosh 3x| + C$

f. $x\cosh^{-1} 7x - \frac{1}{7}\sqrt{49x^2-1} + C$

g. $\cosh^2 x - \sinh^2 x = 1$, Q.E.D.

h. $y = 2.5269\ldots \cosh\frac{t}{2.5269\ldots} + 5$

$-2.5269\ldots$

$y(10) = 68.5961\ldots$

$y = 20 \Rightarrow x = \pm 6.6324\ldots$

R10. a. Converges to 5.

b. Integral diverges.

c. Converges to 6.

d. Converges to $\frac{10}{3} = 3.333\ldots$

e. $\int_1^\infty x^{-p}\, dx$ converges if $p > 1$, diverges if $p \le 1$.

R11. a. $f'(x) = \sin^{-1} x + \frac{x}{\sqrt{1-x^2}}$

b. $\frac{1}{2}x^2\sin^{-1} x - \frac{1}{4}\sin^{-1} x + \frac{1}{4}x\sqrt{1-x^2} + C$

c. $e^x \cdot \operatorname{sech}^2 e^x$

d. $-\ln|x| + \frac{1}{2}\ln|x-1| + \frac{1}{2}\ln|x+1| + C$

e. $f'(x) = -x(1-x^2)^{-1/2}$

f. $\frac{1}{2}\sin^{-1} x + \frac{1}{2}x\sqrt{1-x^2} + C$

g. $g'(x) = \ln x \cdot \frac{1}{x}$

h. $\frac{1}{2}x^2 \ln x - \frac{1}{4}x^2 + C$

R12. For $\int (9-x^2)^{-1/2} x\,dx$, the $x\,dx$ can be transformed to the differential of the inside function by multiplying by a *constant.*

$-\frac{1}{2}\int (9-x^2)^{-1/2}(-2x\,dx) = -(9-x^2)^{1/2} + C,$

and thus has no inverse sine. For $\int (9-x^2)^{-1/2}\,dx$, transforming the $dx$ to the differential of the inside function, $-2x\,dx$, requires multiplying by a *variable.* Since the integral of a product does not equal the product of the two integrals, you can't divide on the outside of the integral by $-2x$. So a more sophisticated technique must be used, in this case, trig substitution. As a result, an inverse sine appears in the answer.

$\int (9-x^2)^{1/s}\,dx = \sin^{-1}\frac{x}{3} + C$

## CHAPTER 10

### Exploratory Problem Set 10-1

*Introduction to Distance and Displacement for Motion Along a Line*

1. $5.3955\ldots \approx 5.40$ minutes.

3. $100.0231\ldots \approx 100.0$ ft upstream

5. $\int_0^{10} |100e^{t \ln 0.8} - 30|\,dt = 203.6452\ldots \approx 203.6$ ft

### Problem Set 10-2

*Distance, Displacement, and Acceleration*

1. a. Positive on $[0,2)$; negative on $(2,6]$.

   b. $[0,2)$: $14\frac{2}{3}$ ft; $(2,6]$: $26\frac{2}{3}$ ft

   c. Displ. $= -12$ ft; Dist. $= 41\frac{1}{3}$ ft

   d. Displ. $= 14\frac{2}{3} + \left(-26\frac{2}{3}\right) = -12$ ft

   Dist. $= 14\frac{2}{3} + 26\frac{2}{3} = 41\frac{1}{3}$ ft

   e. $-4$ (ft/sec)/sec

3. a. Positive on $(8,11]$; negative on $[1,8)$.

   b. $[1,8)$: $4.9420\ldots \approx 4.94$ km; $(8,11]$: $4.7569\ldots \approx 4.76$ km

   c. Displ. $= -0.1850\ldots \approx -0.19$ km; Dist. $= 9.6990\ldots \approx 9.70$ km

   d. Displ. $= -4.9420\ldots + 4.7569\ldots = -0.1850\ldots \approx -0.19$ km

   Dist. $= -(-4.9420\ldots) + 4.7569\ldots = 9.6990\ldots \approx 9.70$ km

   e. $0.1851\ldots \approx 0.19$ (km/h)/h (exactly $\frac{\pi}{24}\sqrt{2}$)

5. $v(t) = \frac{2}{3}t^{3/2} - 18$; Displ. $= -14\frac{14}{15}$ ft;

   Dist. $= 179\frac{7}{15}$ ft.

7. $v(t) = -6\cos t - 3$

   Displ. $= -9.4247\ldots \approx -9.42$ km (Exact: $-3\pi$ km)

   Dist. $= 13.5338\ldots \approx 13.53$ km (Exact: $6\sqrt{3} + \pi$)

9. *Meg's Velocity Problem*

   a. 4 sec

   b. Displ. $= 1\frac{1}{3}$ ft

   c. Dist. $= 4$ ft

11. *Car on the Hill Problem*

   a. Displ. $= 300$ ft

   b. Dist. $= 500$ ft

13. *Subway Problem*

   a.

| $t_{\text{end}}$ sec | $a_{\text{avg}}$ mph/sec | $v_{\text{end}}$ mph | $v_{\text{avg}}$ mph | $s_{\text{end}}$ mi |
|---|---|---|---|---|
| 0 | — | 0 | — | 0 |
| 5 | 2.95 | 14.75 | 7.375 | 0.0102... |
| 10 | 3.8 | 33.75 | 24.25 | 0.0439... |
| 15 | 1.75 | 42.5 | 38.125 | 0.0968... |
| 20 | 0.3 | 44 | 43.25 | 0.1569... |
| 25 | 0 | 44 | 44 | 0.2180... |
| 30 | 0 | 44 | 44 | 0.2791... |
| 35 | 0 | 44 | 44 | 0.3402... |
| 40 | −0.2 | 43 | 43.5 | 0.4006... |
| 45 | −0.9 | 38.5 | 40.75 | 0.4572... |
| 50 | −2.6 | 25.5 | 32 | 0.5017... |
| 55 | −3.5 | 8 | 16.75 | 0.525 |
| 60 | −1.6 | 0 | 4 | 0.5305... |

   b. $v_{\text{end}} = 0$ at $t = 60 \Rightarrow$ the train is at rest.

   c. The train is just starting at $t = 0$; its acceleration must be greater than zero to get it moving, even though it is stopped at $t = 0$. Acceleration and velocity are different quantities; the velocity can be zero, but changing, which means the acceleration is non-zero.

   d. Zero acceleration means the velocity is constant, but not necessarily zero.

   e. $0.5305\ldots \approx 0.53$ mi

15. *Physics Formula Problem*

   a. $a = \frac{dv}{dt} \Rightarrow v = \int a\,dt = at + C$;

   $v = v_0$ when $t = 0 \Rightarrow C = 0 \Rightarrow v = v_0 + at$

   b. $v = \frac{ds}{dt} \Rightarrow s = \int v\,dt = \int (v_0 + at)dt$

   $= v_0 t + \frac{1}{2}at^2 + C$

   $s = s_0$ when $t = 0 \Rightarrow C = s_0 \Rightarrow s = v_0 t + \frac{1}{2}at^2 + s_0$

### Problem Set 10-3

*Average Value Problems in Motion and Elsewhere*

1. a. $y_{av} = 41$

b. Graph. The rectangle has the same area as the shaded region.

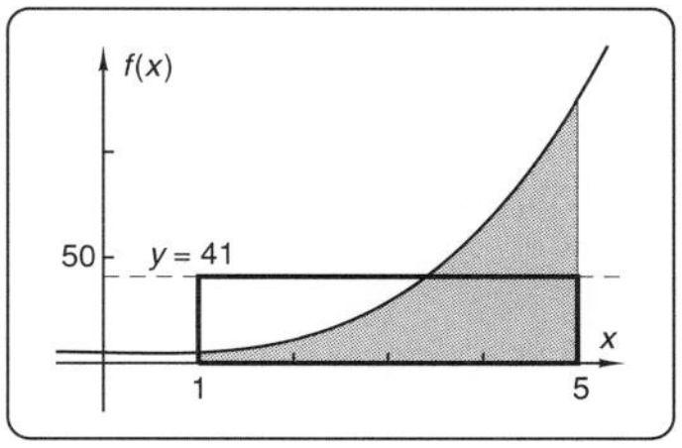


3. a. $y_{av} = 2.0252\ldots$

b. Graph. The rectangle has the same area as the shaded region.

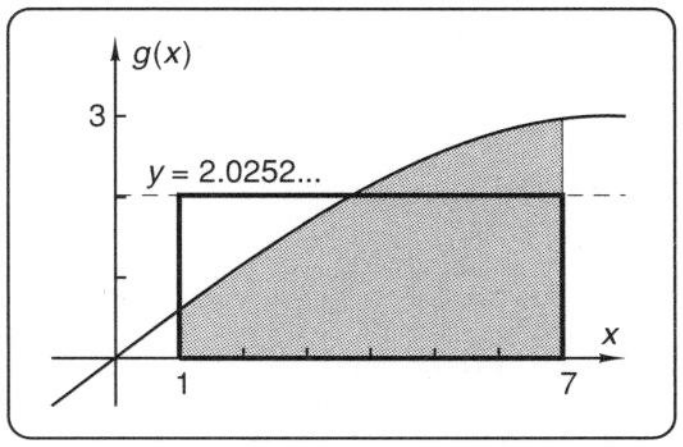


5. a. $y_{av} = 2\frac{1}{6}$

b. Graph. The rectangle has the same area as the shaded region.

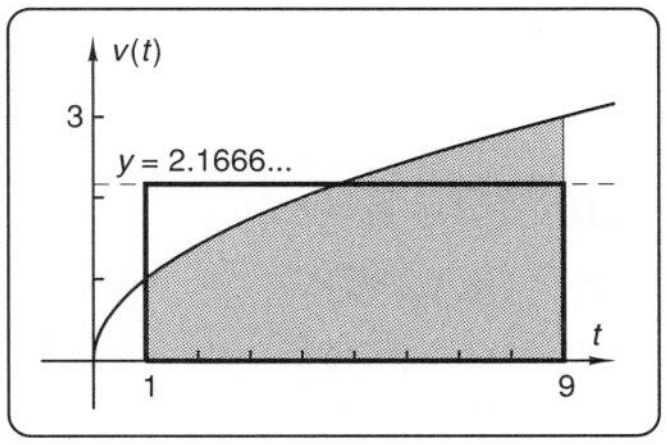


7. $y_{av} = \frac{1}{3}ak^2$

9. $y_{av} = \frac{1}{k}a(e^k - 1)$

11. *Average Velocity from Acceleration Problem*
$v(25) = 120$ ft/sec; Displ. = 2500 ft;
$v_{\text{av}} = 100$ ft/sec

13. *Average Velocity for Constant Acceleration Problem*
Consider an object with constant acceleration $a$, for a time interval $[t_0, t_1]$.
$v(t) = \int a\,dt = at + C$
At $t = t_0$, $v(t) = v_0 \Rightarrow v_0 = at_0 + C \Rightarrow C = v_0 - at_0$
$\therefore v(t) = at + v_0 - at_0 = v_0 + a(t - t_0)$

$$v_{av} = \frac{\int_{t_0}^{t_1}(v_0 + a(t - t_0))\,dt}{t_1 - t_0}$$

$$= \frac{1}{t_1 - t_0}\left(v_0 t_1 + \frac{1}{2}a(t_1 - t_0)^2 - v_0 t_0 - \frac{1}{2}a(t_0 - t_0)^2\right)$$

$$= v_0 + \frac{1}{2}a(t_1 - t_0)$$

The average of $v_0$ and $v_1$ is

$$\frac{1}{2}(v_0 + v_1) = \frac{1}{2}(v_0 + v_0 + a(t_1 - t_0)) = v_0 + \frac{1}{2}a(t_1 - t_0)$$

$\therefore v_{av} =$ the average of $v_0$ and $v_1$, Q.E.D.

15. *Average Voltage Problem*
Average $= \frac{2A}{\pi}$; $A = 55\pi = 172.78\ldots$ V.

## Problem Set 10-4

*Related Rates*

1. *Bacteria Spreading Problem*
$\frac{dr}{dt} = \frac{6}{\pi r} = \frac{2}{\pi} = 0.6366\ldots$ mm/hr
when $r = 3$ mm.

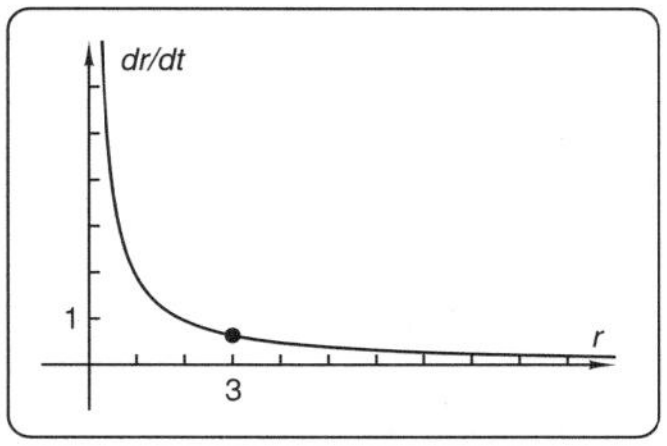


$\frac{dr}{dt}$ varies inversely with the radius.

3. *Ellipse Problem*
Major axis is decreasing at $12/\pi$ cm/sec.

5. *Base Runner Problem*
Let $y =$ Milt's distance from home plate.
Let $x =$ Milt's displacement from third base.

$$\frac{dy}{dt} = \frac{-20x}{\sqrt{x^2 + 90^2}}$$

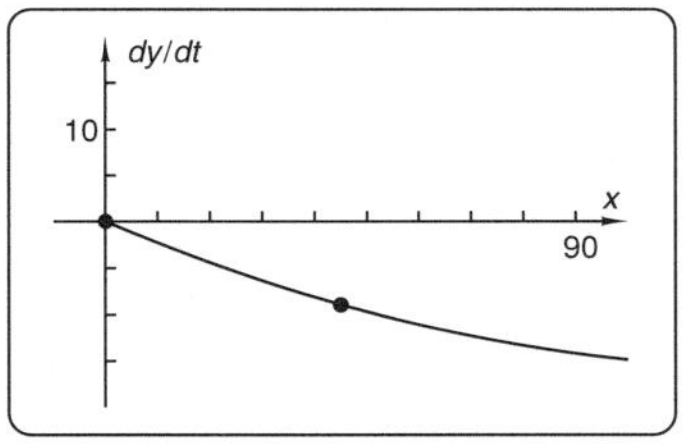


At $x = 45$, $\frac{dy}{dt} \approx -8.9$ ft/sec (exact: $-4\sqrt{5}$)
At $x = 0$, $\frac{dy}{dt} = 0$ ft/sec, which is reasonable since Milt is moving perpendicular to his line from home plate.

7. *Rectangle Problem I*
Area is decreasing at 40 $\text{ft}^2$/min.

9. *Luke and Leia's Trash Compactor Problem*
a. Let $L =$ length, $W =$ width, $H =$ depth (meters)
$\frac{dH}{dt} = -\frac{20}{LW^2}(0.1) - \frac{20}{L^2W}(-0.3)$
b. Depth is increasing at 0.02 m/sec

11. *Point on a Parabola Problem*
   a. $\dfrac{dy}{dt} = 2kx^2$
   b. $k = 2$
   c. 196

13. *Barn Ladder Problem*
   a. Let $x$ = distance from bottom of ladder to wall.
   Let $y$ = distance from top of ladder to floor.
   Let $v$ = velocity of the weight.
   $v = \dfrac{x}{\sqrt{400 - x^2}} \dfrac{dx}{dt}$
   b. $v = -0.6123\ldots$ ft/sec (exact: $-\sqrt{6}/4$)
   c. $v$ is infinite.

15. *Conical Water Tank Problem*
   a. $16.2\pi = 50.8938\ldots \approx 50.9$ m$^3$/hr
   b. i. $\dfrac{-50}{144\pi} = -0.1105\ldots \approx -0.11$ m/hr
   ii. $-\infty$
   c. i. $\dfrac{dV}{dt} = -0.25\sqrt{h}$
   ii. $-0.2$ m$^3$/hr
   iii. $-0.4317\ldots \approx -0.43$ m/hr

17. *Cone of Light Problem*
   Decreasing at $16\pi \approx 50.3$ ft$^3$/min.

19. *Cone in Hemisphere Problem*
   Increasing at 12 in$^3$/sec.

21. *Speeding Piston Project* [Not selected]

## Problem Set 10-5

*Minimal Path Problems*

1. *Swim and Run Problem*
   Swim toward a point about 21.8 m downstream.

3. *Pipeline Problem*
   Go 600 m along road, then start crossing field 400 m up the road from the well.

5. *Minimal Path Discovery Problem*
   a. For minimal path, $x = 100/\sqrt{21}$.
   $\therefore \sin\theta = \dfrac{x}{\sqrt{50^2 + x^2}} = 0.4 = 2/5$, Q.E.D.
   b. For minimal path, $x = 400$.
   $\sin\theta = \dfrac{x}{\sqrt{300^2 + x^2}} = 0.8 = 40/50$, Q.E.D.

7. *Scuba Diver Problem Revisited*
   $\sin\theta = \dfrac{12}{13}$
   $x = 30 \tan\left(\sin^{-1}\dfrac{12}{13}\right) = 72$
   Swim $100 - 72 = 28$ m, then dive.
   The algebraic solution is easier than before because no algebraic calculus needs to be done.
   Mathematicians find general solutions to gain insight, and to find patterns and methods to allow easier solution of similar problems.

9. *Pipeline Problem, Near Miss*
   A graph or a table of times for paths close to the optimum shows that a near miss will have virtually no effect on the minimal cost.

11. *Robinson Crusoe Problem*
   $47.8809\ldots \approx 47.9$ yd. from the line perpendicular to the ship.

13. Not selected.

15. Journal entries will vary.

## Problem Set 10-6

*Maximum and Minimum Problems in Motion and Elsewhere*

1. *Rocket Problem*
   Minimum is $D(1) = 2$, or 2,000 mi.
   Maximum is $D(3) = 3\frac{1}{3}$, or about 3333 mi.

3. *Number Problem I*
   $x = 0.5$.

5. *Fran's Optimal Study Time Problem*
   a. Graph, showing maximum of $G$ at $t = 3$ hours.

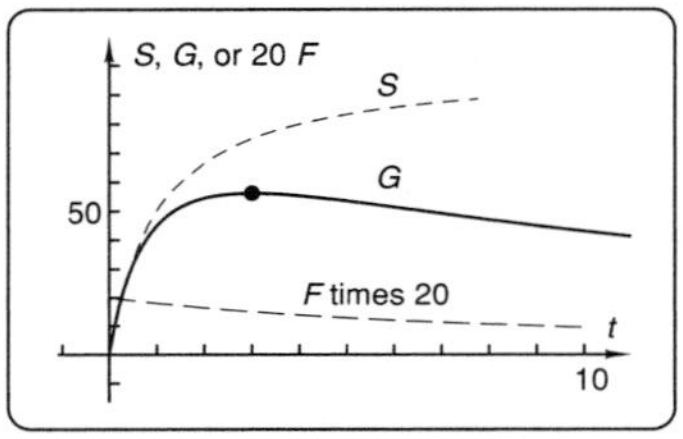


   b. Fran should study for 3 hours.
   c. i. $G(4)$ is about 1 point less.
   ii. $G(2)$ is about 1 or 2 points less.

7. *Cylinder-in-the-Cone Problem I*
   a. Graphs of $V$ and $A$.

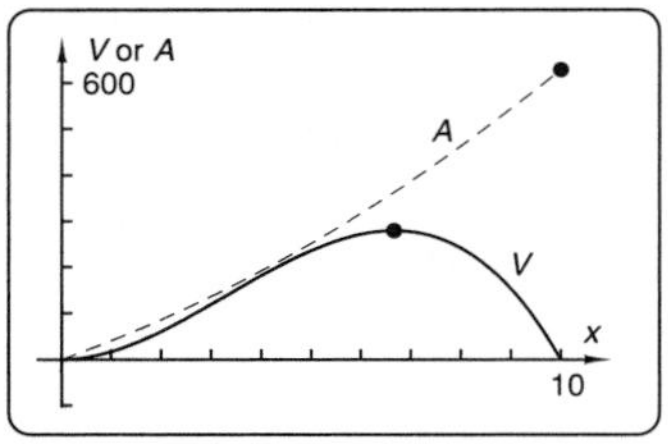


   b. Maximum $V$: $r = 6\frac{2}{3}$ in., $h = 2$ in.
   Maximum $A$: $r = 10$ in., $h = 0$ in. (degenerate)
   The maximum volume and maximum area do not occur at the same radius.

9. *Quartic Parabola Tank Problem*
   $-0.1286\ldots \approx -0.129$ m/min.

11. *Pig Sale Problem*
   a. $w = 1000 + 15t$ (lbs); $p = 0.90 - 0.01t$ (\$/lb)
   $A = 900 + 3.5t - 0.15t^2$ (\$)

b. Maximum $A$ at $t = 11\frac{2}{3}$, not a minimum, since $\frac{dA}{dt}$ goes from positive to negative there.

c. About \$920.42

## Problem Set 10-7

*Vector Functions of Motion in a Plane*

1. *Parabolic Path Problem I*

a. $\vec{v}(t) = (6\cos 0.6t)\vec{i} + (-4.8\sin 1.2t)\vec{j}$
$\vec{a}(t) = (-3.6\sin 0.6t)\vec{i} + (-5.76\cos 1.2t)\vec{j}$

b. $\vec{r}(0.5) = 2.9552\ldots\vec{i} + 3.3013\ldots\vec{j}$
$\vec{v}(0.5) = 5.7320\ldots\vec{i} - 2.7102\ldots\vec{j}$
$\vec{a}(0.5) = -1.0638\ldots\vec{i} - 4.7539\ldots\vec{j}$

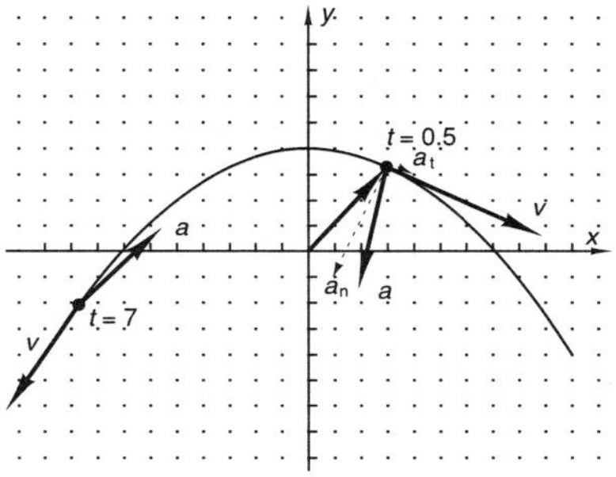


These vectors make sense because the head of $\vec{r}$ is on the graph, $\vec{v}$ is tangent to the graph, and $\vec{a}$ points to the concave side of the graph.

c. The object is speeding up. The angle between $\vec{a}$ and $\vec{v}$ is acute.

d. $\vec{a}(0.5)\cdot\vec{v}(0.5) = 6.7863\ldots$, so the angle is acute.
$\vec{a}_t(0.5) = 0.9676\ldots\vec{i} - 0.4575\ldots\vec{j}$
$\vec{a}_n(0.5) = -2.0314\ldots\vec{i} - 4.2964\ldots\vec{j}$
Graph, part (b).

e. Object is speeding up at $1.0703\ldots \approx 1.07$ (ft/sec)/sec.

f. $\vec{r}(7) = -8.7157\ldots\vec{i} - 2.0771\ldots\vec{j}$
$\vec{v}(7) = -2.9415\ldots\vec{i} - 4.1020\ldots\vec{j}$
$\vec{a}(7) = 3.1376\ldots\vec{i} + 2.9911\ldots\vec{j}$
Graph, part (b).
Object is slowing down. The angle between $\vec{a}$ and $\vec{v}$ is obtuse.

g. $\vec{a}(0)\cdot\vec{v}(0) = 0$, so $\vec{a}(0)$ and $\vec{v}(0)$ are perpendicular. This means the object is neither slowing down nor speeding up at $t = 0$.

3. *Elliptical Path Problem*

a. Graph, showing path of $\vec{r} + \vec{v}$.

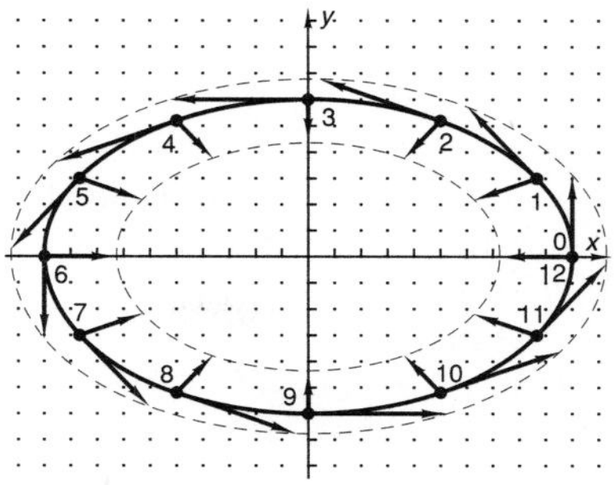


b. Graph, part (a), showing vectors $\vec{v}$.

c. For $\vec{r} + \vec{v}$, show that $\left(\frac{x}{10}\right)^2 + \left(\frac{y}{6}\right)^2 = 1 + \left(\frac{\pi}{6}\right)^2$, which is the equation of an ellipse.

d. Graph, part (a).

e. The direction of each acceleration vector is the opposite of the corresponding position vector, and thus directed toward the origin.

5. *Parabolic Path Problem III*

a. $\vec{r}(x) = x\vec{i} + x^2\vec{j}$; $\vec{v}(x) = \frac{dx}{dt}\vec{i} + 2x\frac{dx}{dt}\vec{j}$

b. $\vec{v}(2) = -3\vec{i} - 12\vec{j}$
Speed $= |\vec{v}(2)| = \sqrt{153} \approx 12.4$ cm/sec.

c. Graph, showing $\vec{r}(2)$ and $\vec{v}(2)$.
This is reasonable because $\vec{v}(2)$ points along the curve to the left, indicating that $x$ is decreasing.

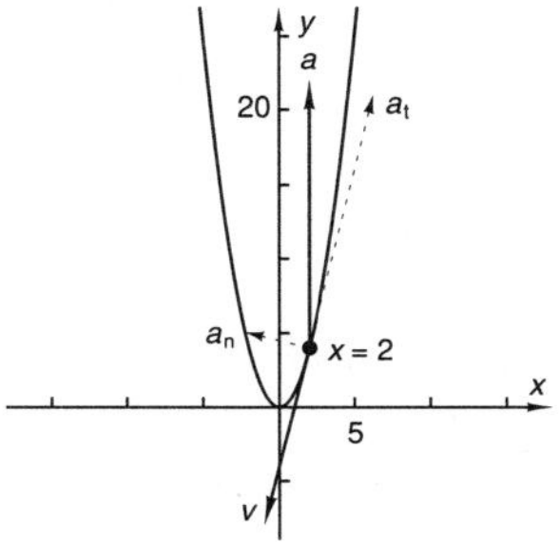


d. $\vec{a}(x) = 18\vec{j}$. $\vec{a}(2) = 18\vec{j}$. Graph, part (c).

e. $\vec{a}_t(2) = 4.2352\ldots\vec{i} + 16.9411\ldots\vec{j}$
$\vec{a}_n(2) = -4.2352\ldots\vec{i} + 1.0588\ldots\vec{j}$
$\vec{a}_t(2)$ is parallel to the curve. $\vec{a}_n(2)$ is normal to the curve and points inward to the concave side.

f. When $x = 2$ the object is slowing down. This is true because the angle between $\vec{a}(2)$ and $\vec{v}(2)$ is obtuse, as shown by the graph and by the fact that the dot product is negative. Also, $\vec{a}_t(2)$ points in the opposite direction of $\vec{v}(2)$.

g. $dL = \sqrt{1 + 4x^2}\,dx$
$\frac{dx}{dt} = \frac{5}{\sqrt{17}} = 1.2126\ldots \approx 1.21$ cm/sec.

7. 12.0858... ft.

9. *Baseball Problem*
   a. $\vec{v}(t) = -130\vec{i} - 32t\vec{j}$
   b. $\vec{r}(t) = (-130t + 60.5)\vec{i} + (-16t^2 + 8)\vec{j}$
   c. The ball passes 4.5346... ft over the plate, which is slightly above the strike zone.
   d. At $t = 0$, $dx/dt = 200\cos 15°$, $dy/dt = 200\sin 15°$.
   As in part (a), $\vec{v}(t) = C_1\vec{i} + (-32t + C_2)\vec{j}$
   $= (200\cos 15°)\vec{i} + (-32t + 200\sin 15°)\vec{j}$
   $\vec{r}(t) = (200t\cos 15°)\vec{i} + (-16t^2 + 200t\sin 15° + 3)\vec{j}$
   e. Phyllis makes the home run since the ball is about 41.6 ft. above the wall when $x = 400$.

11. *Figure Skating Problem*
   a. $d = 90 + 150\cos t$
   b. $\vec{v}(1) = -212.1270\ldots\vec{i} - 13.7948\ldots\vec{j}$
   Speed $= 212.5750\ldots \approx 212.6$ cm/sec
   c. $\vec{a}(1) = 76.2168\ldots\vec{i} - 348.5216\ldots\vec{j}$
   $\vec{a}_t(1) = 53.3266\ldots\vec{i} + 3.4678\ldots\vec{j}$
   $\vec{a}_n(1) = 22.8902\ldots\vec{i} - 351.9894\ldots\vec{j}$
   Annie is slowing down at $53.4392\ldots \approx 53.4$ cm/sec. The angle between the acceleration and the velocity vectors is obtuse, as revealed by the negative dot product.

13. *Roller Coaster Problem*
   a. $\vec{v}(t) = (5 - 12\cos t)\vec{i} + (-12\sin t)\vec{j}$
   $\vec{a}(t) = (12\sin t)\vec{i} + (-12\cos t)\vec{j}$
   b. $\vec{v}(2.5) = 14.6137\ldots\vec{i} - 7.1816\ldots\vec{j}$
   $\vec{a}(2.5) = 7.1816\ldots\vec{i} + 9.6137\ldots\vec{j}$
   Graph, showing $\vec{v}(2.5)$ and $\vec{a}(2.5)$.

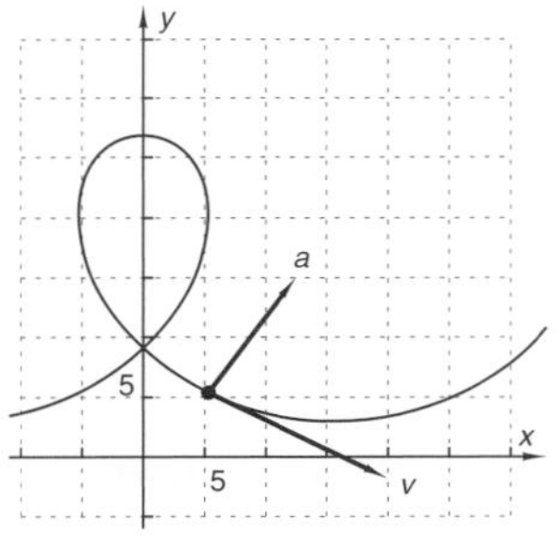


   c. $\vec{a}_t(2.5) = 1.9791\ldots\vec{i} - 0.9726\ldots\vec{j}$
   $\vec{a}_n(2.5) = 5.2024\ldots\vec{i} + 10.5863\ldots\vec{j}$
   d. $\vec{v}(2.5)$ is reasonable since its graph points along the path in the direction of motion. $\vec{a}(2.5)$ is reasonable since it points toward the concave side of the path. The roller coaster is traveling at $|\vec{v}(2.5)| = 16.2803\ldots$ ft/sec. Its speed is increasing at $2.2052\ldots$ ft/sec$^2$, since the scalar projection of $\vec{a}(2.5)$ on $\vec{v}(2.5) = 2.2052\ldots$.
   e. $\vec{a}(0 + 2\pi n) = 0\vec{i} - 12\vec{j}$, pointing straight down.
   $\vec{a}(\pi + 2\pi n) = 0\vec{i} + 12\vec{j}$, pointing straight up.
   f. $78.7078\ldots \approx 78.7$ ft.

15. *Three-Dimensional Vector Problem*
   $\vec{v}(1) = (8\cos 0.8)\vec{i} + (-6\sin 0.6)\vec{j} + 3\vec{k}$
   $\vec{a}(1) = (-6.4\sin 0.8)\vec{i} + (-3.6\cos 0.6)\vec{j} - 1.5\vec{k}$
   $\vec{a}(1) \cdot \vec{v}(1) = -20.0230\ldots$, so the object is slowing.

## Problem Set 10-8

*Chapter Review and Test*

### Review Problems

R0. *Journal*

R1. *Popeye and Olive Problem*
Velocity becomes positive at $t = 9$ seconds. They have moved 9 ft closer to the sawmill.
From $t = 0$ to $t = 25$, displ. $= 8\frac{1}{3}$ ft, dist. $= 26\frac{1}{3}$ ft.

R2. a. i. Graph.

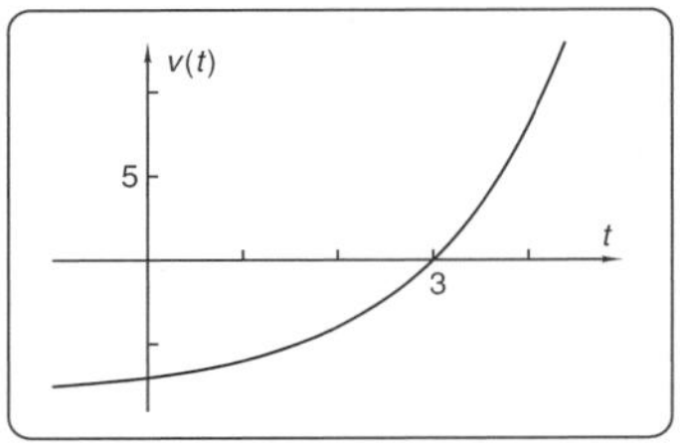


ii. Displ. $\approx -3.8$ cm (Exactly $14/\ln 2 - 24$)
iii. Dist. $\approx 10.9$ cm (Exactly $2/\ln 2 + 8$)

b. *Acceleration Data Problem*

| $t_{\text{end}}$ | $a$ | $a_{\text{avg}}$ | $v_{\text{end}}$ | |
|---|---|---|---|---|
| 0 | 2 | — | 30 | speeding up |
| 5 | 8 | 5 | 55 | speeding up |
| 10 | 1 | 4.5 | 77.5 | speeding up |
| 15 | 0 | 0.5 | 80 | neither |
| 20 | −10 | −5 | 55 | slowing down |
| 25 | −20 | −15 | −20 | slowing down |

Note that the object is speeding up, slowing down or neither, exactly when $a_{\text{end}} > 0$, $a_{\text{end}} < 0$, or $a_{\text{end}} = 0$, respectively, in the original table.

R3. a. *Average Velocity Problem*
i. $v_{\text{avg}} = 2/\pi = 0.6366\ldots$
ii. $v_{\text{avg}} = 0$
iii. $v_{\text{avg}} = 0$

b. *Average Value Problem*
i. Average on $[0, 6]$ is 18.
ii. Graph. The rectangle has the same area as the shaded region.

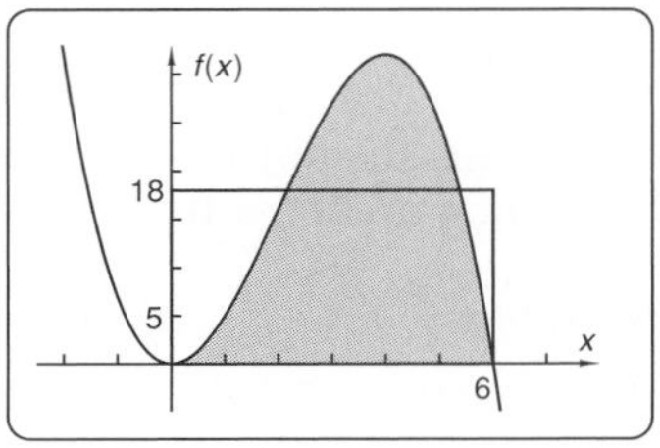

iii. The average of the two values of $f(x)$ at the endpoints is zero, not 18.

R4. *Rover's Tablecloth Problem*
The glass moves at the same speed as the tablecloth, or about 18.7 cm/sec, which is about 1.3 cm/sec slower than Rover.

R5. a. *Campus Cut-Across Problem*
$T(0) = 145.1612\ldots$
$T(467.3544\ldots) = 126.7077\ldots$
$T(700) = 127.7212\ldots$
Heading for a point about 467 ft from the intersection gives the minimum time, although it takes only a second longer to head straight for the English building.

b. *Resort Island Causeway Problem*
The minimum cost is \$122,000 by going 7.5 km along the beach, then cutting across to the island. This path saves about \$29,600 over the path straight to the island.

R6. a. i. Max. acceleration = 9 at $t = 3$.
Min. acceleration = $-40$ at $t = 10$.

ii. Max. velocity = 36 at $t = 6$.
Min. velocity = $-33\frac{1}{3}$ at $t = 10$.

iii. Max. displacement = $182\frac{1}{4}$ at $t = 9$.
Min. displacement = 0 at $t = 0$.

b. *Inflation Problem*

i. Let $t$ = number of days Saul has been saving.
Let $V(t)$ = real value (in constant day zero pillars) of money in account after t days.
$V(t) = 50t(0.5^{0.005t})$

ii. Saul's greatest purchasing power will be after about 289 days because $V'(t)$ goes from positive to negative at $t = 288.5390\ldots$.

R7. a. i. and ii. Graphs.

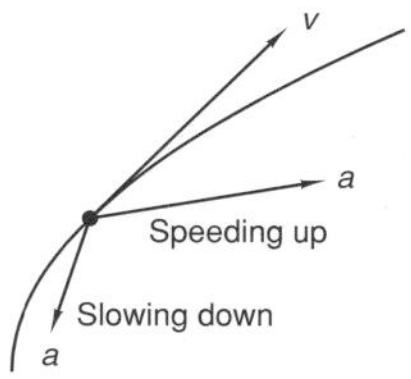


b. i. $\vec{r}(1) = 7.7154\ldots\vec{i} + 3.5256\ldots\vec{j}$
$\vec{v}(1) = 5.8760\ldots\vec{i} + 4.6292\ldots\vec{j}$
$\vec{a}(1) = 7.7154\ldots\vec{i} + 3.5256\ldots\vec{j}$

ii. Graph, showing $\vec{r}(1)$, $\vec{v}(1)$, and $\vec{a}(1)$.

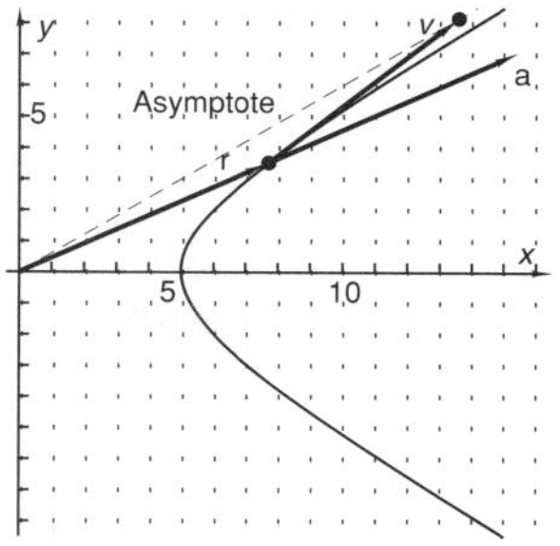


iii. Speed = $7.4804\ldots \approx 7.48$ units/min.
$\vec{a}(1)\cdot\vec{v}(1) = 34\sinh 1\cosh 1 = 61.6566\ldots$
The object is speeding up at $8.2423\ldots \approx 8.24$ units/min$^2$.

iv. $4.5841\ldots \approx 4.58$ units

v. $\vec{r}(t) + \vec{v}(t) = (5\cosh t + 5\sinh t)\vec{i} + (3\sinh t + 3\cosh t)\vec{j}$
Note that the $y$-coordinate is 0.6 times the $x$-coordinate, so the head lies on $y = 0.6x$, one asymptote of the hyperbola.

## CHAPTER 11

### Exploratory Problem Set 11-1

*Review of Work—Force Times Displacement*

1. Graph, showing strip and sample point $(x, F)$.

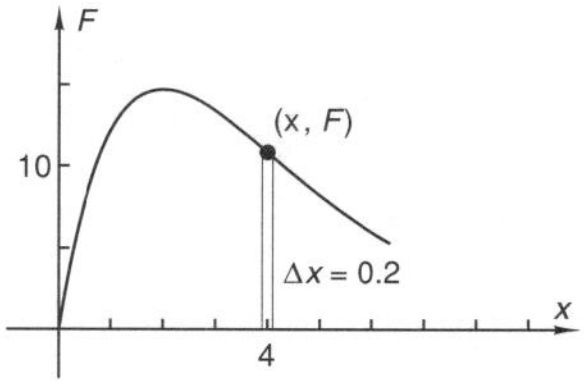


$F = 10.8268\ldots \approx 10.83$ lb in the strip.
$W = 2.1653\ldots \approx 2.17$ ft-lb

3. Integral = $69.1298\ldots$

5. $W = 80$ ft-lb

### Problem Set 11-2

*Work Done by a Variable Force*

1. *Leaking Bucket Problem:* 800 ft-lb

3. *Spring Problem:* 50k

5. *Conical Reservoir Problem*
$1396752.0937\ldots \approx 1.4$ million ft-lb

7. *Spherical Water Tower Problem*
a. $117621229.\ldots \approx 117.6$ million ft-lb
b. $250925288.4\ldots \approx 250.9$ million ft-lb

9. *Carnot Cycle Problem*
a. $1504.7320\ldots \approx 1504.7$ in-lb

b. $-566.9574\ldots$ So about 567 in-lb of work is done in compressing the gases.

c. $937.7746\ldots \approx 937.8$ in-lb.

d. Not selected.

**Problem Set 11-3**

*Mass of a Variable Density Object*

1. a. $8.1419\ldots k$

 b. $108.1103\ldots$

3. a. $40.5\pi k$

 b. $546.75\pi k$

 c. $105.3\pi k$

 d. The solid in part (b) has the largest mass.

5. *Two Cone Problem*

 a. Prediction: Cone on the left with higher density at base has greater mass, because higher density is in the larger part of the cone.

 b. For the left-hand cone, $m = 1305\pi$ oz. For the right-hand cone, $m = 1035\pi$ oz.
 $\therefore$ the cone on the left has the higher mass, as predicted in part (a).

7. $y_1 = 4 - 2x^2$ and $y_2 = 3 - x^2$, rotated about the $x$-axis
 Graphs intersect at $(1, 2)$ in Quadrant I.
 Slice perpendicular to the axis of rotation, generating plane washers.
 Pick sample points $(x, y_1)$ and $(x, y_2)$.
 $\rho = kx^2$, $dV = \pi(y_1^2 - y_2^2)\,dx$
 $dm = \rho\,dV = \pi kx^2(7 - 10x^2 + 3x^4)\,dx$
 $m = \int_0^1 dm = \dfrac{16}{21}\pi k = 2.3935\ldots k$

9. *Uranium Fuel Pellet Problem:* $m \approx 15.14$ g

11. a. $m = \dfrac{1}{2}\pi r^4 k$

 b. $m = \dfrac{1}{4}\pi^2 r^4 k$

 c. $\mathrm{m} = \pi k r^4$

13. $m = 8.6261\ldots$

**Problem Set 11-4**

*Moments, Centroids, Center of Mass, and the Theorem of Pappus*

1. *Paraboloid Problem*

 a. $V = 40.5\pi$

 b. $M_{xz} = 121.5\pi$

 c. Centroid is at $(0, 3, 0)$.

3. *Paraboloid Mass Problem*

 a. $m = 170.1375\ldots k$

 b. $M_{xz} = 612.4952\ldots k$

 c. Center of mass is at $(0, 3.6, 0)$.

 d. False. The centroid is at $(0, 3, 0)$ but the center of mass is at $(0, 3.6, 0)$.

5. *Exponential Region and Solid Problem*

 a. $\bar{x} = 1.3130\ldots$

 b. $\bar{x} = 1.5373\ldots$

 c. False. For the solid, $\bar{x}$ is farther from the $yz$-plane.

7. *Centroid of a Triangle Experiment*
 Construct axes with the origin at a vertex and the $x$-axis along the base, $b$.
 Slice the triangle parallel to the $x$-axis.
 Width of a strip is $b - \dfrac{b}{h}y$

 $dA = \left(b - \dfrac{b}{h}y\right)dy$

 $dM_x = y\,dA = \left(by - \dfrac{b}{h}y^2\right)dy$

 $M_x = \int_0^h \left(by - \dfrac{b}{h}y^2\right)dy = \dfrac{1}{2}by^2 - \dfrac{b}{3h}y^3\Big|_0^h$

 $= \dfrac{1}{6}bh^2$

 $\bar{y} \cdot A = M_x \Rightarrow \bar{y} = \dfrac{\frac{1}{6}bh^2}{\frac{1}{2}bh} = \dfrac{1}{3}h$, Q.E.D.

9. *Second Moment of Area Problem*

 a. Slice the region parallel to the $y$-axis so that each point in a strip will be about $x$ units from the $y$-axis, where $x$ is at the sample point $(x, y)$.
 $dA = y\,dx = \sin x\,dx$
 $A = \int_0^\pi \sin x\,dx = 2$ (exactly)
 (This may be "well known" by now.)
 $dM_y = x\,dA = x\sin x\,dx$
 $M_y = \int_0^\pi x\sin x\,dx = 3.1415\ldots = \pi$ (exactly)
 $\bar{x} \cdot A = M_y \Rightarrow \bar{x} = \dfrac{\pi}{2}$, Q.E.D.
 (or just note the symmetry)

 b. $M_{2y} = 5.8696\ldots$

 c. $\bar{x} = 1.7131\ldots$

11. *Second Moments for Solid Figures*

 a. $M = \dfrac{1}{2}\pi HR^4$, $\bar{r} = \dfrac{1}{\sqrt{2}}R$

 b. $M_h = \dfrac{1}{10}\pi HR^4$, $\bar{r} = \sqrt{0.3}R$

 c. $M = \dfrac{8}{15}\pi R^5$, $\bar{r} = \sqrt{0.4}R$

13. *Beam Moment Problem*

 a. Set up axes with $x$-axis through the centroid.
 $dM_2 = y\,dA = y^2 \cdot B\,dy$
 $M_2 = B\int_{-0.5H}^{0.5h} y^2\,dy = \dfrac{1}{3}y^3\Big|_{-0.5H}^{0.5H} = \dfrac{1}{12}BH^3$,
 Q.E.D.

 b. i. Stiffness $= 288k$

ii. Stiffness = $8k$
Board up on edge is 36 times stiffer.

c. i. Stiffness = $160k$

ii. Stiffness = $448k$ (2.8 times stiffer!)

d. Increasing the depth does seem to increase stiffness greatly, but making the beam *very* tall would also make the web *very* thin, perhaps too thin to withstand much force.

15. *Theorem of Pappus Problem*

a. *Toroid Problem:* $V = 2\pi^2 r^2 R$

b. *Centroid of a Semicircle:* $\bar{r} = \dfrac{4}{3\pi} r$

### Problem Set 11-5

*Force Exerted by a Variable Pressure—Center of Pressure*

1. *Trough Problem*

a. $F = 2.8444\ldots k$

b. $M_x = 2.1880\ldots k$

c. Center of pressure is at $\left(0, \dfrac{10}{13}\right)$.

3. *Ship's Bulkhead Problem*

a. $A \approx 1186.6077\ldots \approx 1186.6 \text{ ft}^2$

b. $F \approx 1199294.1645\ldots \approx 1.199$ million lb

c. $dM_x = y\,dF = y \cdot 67(32 - y)$
$\cdot 40 \left(1 - \left(\dfrac{1}{32}y - 1\right)^4\right)^{1/4} dy$
$M_x = \int_0^{32} dM_x \approx 13992028.2564\ldots$
$\approx 13.992$ million lb-ft

d. $\bar{y} \approx 11.6668\ldots$ ft. $\bar{x} = 0$ by symmetry.
Center of pressure is at about $(0, 11.67)$ ft.

e. $\bar{y} \approx 16.9150\ldots$ ft. $\bar{x} = 0$ by symmetry.
Centroid is at about $(0, 16.92)$ ft.
Centroid is different from center of pressure.

f. $\bar{y} \approx 8.6566\ldots$ ft. $\bar{x} = 0$ by symmetry.
Center of buoyancy is at about $(0, 8.66)$ ft

5. *Airplane Wing Problem I*

a. $A = 763.9437\ldots \approx 763.9 \text{ ft}^2$

b. $F = 4863.4168\ldots k$

c. Make $k \geq 0.0197\ldots \text{tons/ft}^2$

7. *Double Integration Airplane Wing Problem*

a. $dM_{2x} = \dfrac{1}{3}\left(0.25(x-4) - (x-4)^{1/3}\right)^3 dx$

b. $M_{2x} = 0.5333\ldots \left(\text{exactly } \dfrac{8}{15}\right)$

9. The integrals in Problems 7 and 8 can be written in the form $\int_{x=a}^{x=b} \int_{t=c}^{t=d} f(x,t)\,dt\,dx$
Since two integrals appear, the result is called a double integral. (Hiding inside each integral is a second integral!)

### Problem Set 11-6

*Other Variable-Factor Products*

1. *Heat Capacity Problem:* $H = 13{,}200$ calories

3. *Tunnel Problem*

a. $P(x) = 0.002x^2 + 3x + 500$

b. $P(700) = \$3580/\text{ft}$.

c. Cost is about \$2,666,667.

d. Cost is about \$1,416,667
Saving is about \$1,250,000!

5. *Wire-Pulling Problem*

a. Graph, connected scatter plot.

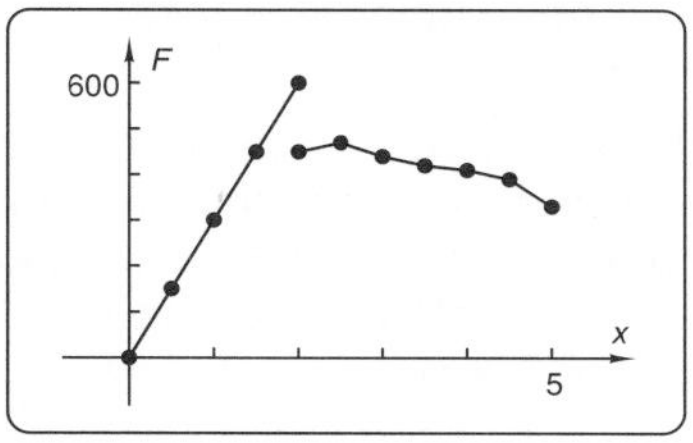


b. $F$ has a step discontinuity at $x = 2$.

c. $W = 600$ in-lb

d. $W \approx 1266\frac{2}{3}$ in-lb

e. Total work $\approx 1866\frac{2}{3}$ in-lb

f. Yes, a piecewise-continuous function such as this one can be integrable. See Problem 27 in Problem Set 9-10 (Improper Integrals).

7. *Moment of Inertia Problem*
$M_{2y} = 33.5103\ldots k$ g-cm$^2$

9. *Rocket Car Problem*

a. $m = 2000 - 5t$

b. $a = 1400(400 - t) - 1$

c. $v(t) = 1400 \ln \dfrac{400}{|400 - t|}$

d. $v(20) = 71.8106\ldots \approx 71.81$ m/sec
$s = 711.9673\ldots \approx 712.0$ m

11. *Sinusoidal Land Tract Problem*

a. $W = 0.5707\ldots k$

b. $W = 0.3926\ldots k$

13. *City Land Value Problem:*

a. $W = 113.0973\ldots \approx 113.1$ million dollars.

b. $W = 71.4328\ldots \approx 71.4$ million dollars.

c. $W = 163.9911\ldots \approx 164.0$ million dollars.

d. This problem is equivalent to volume by cylindrical shells, where the value of the land per square unit takes the place of the altitude of the cylinder. It is also equivalent to the water flow in Problem 4 of this problem set.

15. *Skewness Problem*

a. $f(x) = 9 - x^2 = (3 - x)(3 + x) = 0$ only at $x = \pm 3$.

$$g(x) = -\frac{1}{3}x^3 - x^2 + 3x + 9$$
$$= -\frac{1}{3}(x-3)(x+3)^2 = 0 \text{ only at } x = \pm 3$$

b. $A_f = \int_{-3}^{3}(9 - x^2)\,dx = 36$

$A_g = \int_{-3}^{3}\left(-\frac{1}{3}x^3 - x^2 + 3x + 9\right)dx = 36$

To simplify algebraic integration you could use
$A_f = 2\int_0^3 (9 - x^2)\,dx$
$A_g = 2\int_0^3 (9 - x^2)\,dx$, where the odd terms integrate to zero between symmetrical limits. Thus the two integrals are identical.

c. The high point of $f$ comes at $x = 0$. The high point of $g$ comes at $x = 1$.

d. $\overline{x} = 0.6$

e. False. For the symmetrical region under the $f$ graph, the centroid is on the line through the high point. But for the asymmetrical region under the $g$ graph the high point is at $x = 1$ and the centroid is at $x = 0.6$.

f. False.
Area to left = 17.1072
Area to right = 18.8928

g. $S = -17.7737\ldots$

h. By symmetry, the centroid of the area under $f$ is on the $y$-axis, so $\overline{x} = 0$. Then
$dS = x^3 dA = x^3(9 - x^2)\,dx$
$S = \int_{-3}^{3} x^3(9 - x^2)\,dx = 0$ (odd function integrated between symmetrical limits)
The "skewness" being zero reflects the symmetry of this region. It is not skewed at all.

i. For example, graph $g(-x) = \frac{1}{3}x^3 - x^2 - 3x + 9$.

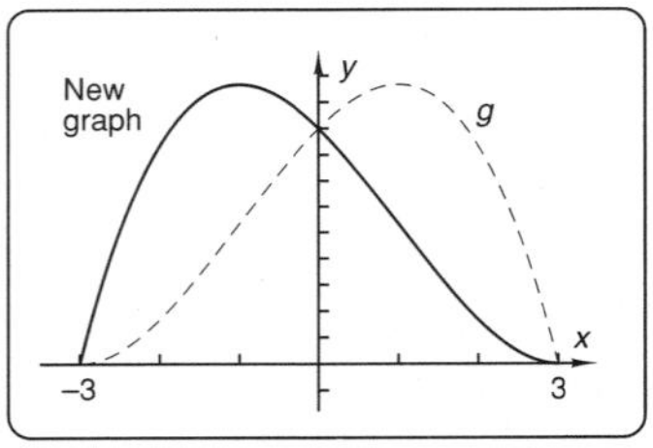


17. *Another Theorem of Pappus Problem:* Not selected.

## Problem Set 11-7

*Chapter Review and Test*

### Review Problems

R0. Journal entries will vary.

R1. *Work Problem*
$W = 129.6997\ldots \approx 129.7$ ft-lb

R2. a. *Magnet Problem:* $W = -\frac{2}{3}k$ ft-lb

b. *Conical Cup Problem*
$W = 11.2814\ldots \approx 11.28$ in-lb

R3. *Variable Density Problem*

a. $m = 57.6\pi k$

b. $m = 64\pi$

R4. a. *Triangle Centroid Problem*
$M_x = \frac{1}{6}bh^2$, $A = \frac{1}{2}bh \Rightarrow \overline{y} = \frac{1}{3}h$, Q.E.D.

b. *Second Moment of Volume Problem*
$M_{2y} = 3.5401\ldots$

R5. *Wind Force Problem*
$F = 3736263.2708\ldots \approx 3.736$ million lb

R6. *Oil Well Problem*

a. $r(x) = 30\left(\frac{5}{3}\right)^{x/10000}$
(or $r(x) = 30e^{-\ln 0.6 \cdot x/10000} = 30e^{0.00005108256\ldots x}$)

b. $C = 6965243.17\ldots \approx 6.965$ million dollars

# CHAPTER 12

## Exploratory Problem Set 12-1

*Introduction to Power Series*

1. Graphs, $f(x)$ and $P_5(x)$.

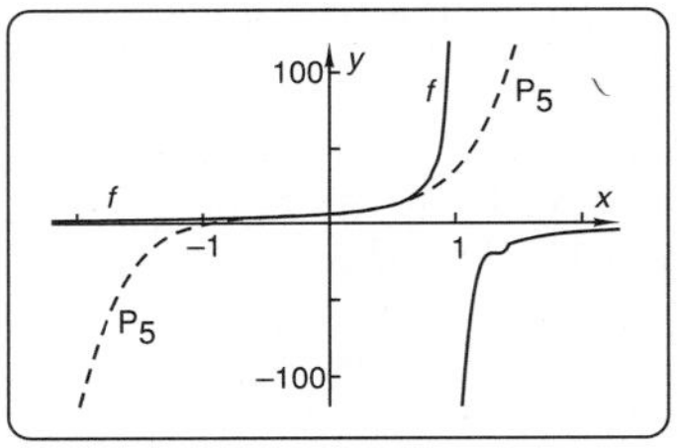


3. $P_5(0.5) = 11.8125$, $P_6(0.5) = 11.90625$, $f(0.5) = 12$.
$\therefore P_6(0.5)$ is closer to $f(0.5)$ than $P_5(0.5)$ is.
$P_5(2) = 378$, $P_6(2) = 762$, $f(2) = -6$.
$\therefore P_6(2)$ is *not* closer to $f(2)$ than $P_5(2)$ is.

5. $P_0(1) = 6$ $\quad P_0(-1) = 6$
$P_1(1) = 12$ $\quad P_1(-1) = 0$
$P_2(1) = 18$ $\quad P_2(-1) = 6$
$P_3(1) = 24$ $\quad P_3(-1) = 0$
$P_4(1) = 30$ $\quad P_4(-1) = 6$

For $x = 1$, the sums just keep getting bigger and bigger as more terms are added. For $x = -1$, the sums oscillate between 0 and 6. In neither case does the series converge. If the answer to Problem 4 had included $x = 1$ or $x = -1$, the conjecture would have to be modified.

7. Geometric series. $x$ is the common ratio.

## Problem Set 12-2

*Geometric Sequences and Series as Mathematical Models*

1. Series: $200 - 120 + 72 - 43.2 + 25.92 - 15.552 + \cdots$
Sums: $200, 80, 152, 108.8, 134.72, 119.168, \ldots$

Graph, showing convergence to 125.

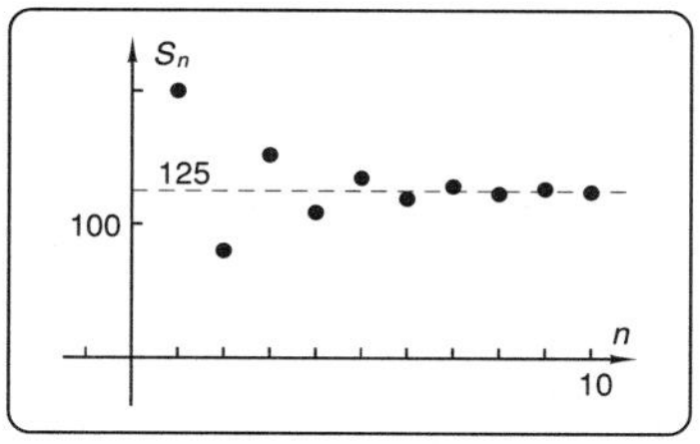


$S_n$ will be within 0.0001 unit of 125 for all values of $n \geq 28$.

3. *Drug Dosage Problem*
   a. Series: $\sum_{n=1}^{\infty} 7(0.8^{n-1}) = 7 + 5.6 + 4.48 + 3.584 + \cdots$
   Sums: $7, 12.6, 17.08, 20.664, 23.5312, \ldots$
   $S = 7 \cdot \dfrac{1}{1 - 0.8} = 35$
   The amount approaches $35\mu$g as a limit, and thus never reaches 50 or $80\mu$g.
   b. *2 puffs*: The amount will first exceed $50\mu$g after the 6th dose, and stay above $50\mu$g after the 11th dose. It will never reach $80\mu$g.
   *3 puffs:* The amount will first exceed $50\mu$g after the 3rd dose and stay above $50\mu$g after the 5th dose.
   The amount will first exceed $80\mu$g after the 7th dose and stay above $80\mu$g after the 14th dose.
   *4 puffs:* The amount will first exceed $50\mu$g after the 2nd dose and stay above $50\mu$g after the 3rd dose.
   The amount will first exceed $80\mu$g after the 4th dose and stay above $80\mu$g after the 6th dose.
   c. *Twice a day*: $r = 0.8^2 = 0.64$, $p =$ no. of puffs
   Amount just after the $n$th dose:
   For $p = 4$ puffs, $S = 77.7777\ldots$.
   For $p = 5$ puffs, $S > 80$, which is unsafe.
   Amount just before the $n$th dose:
   For $p = 4$, $S = 49.7777\ldots$, which is just barely below the minimum effective amount.
   Graph for $p = 4$.

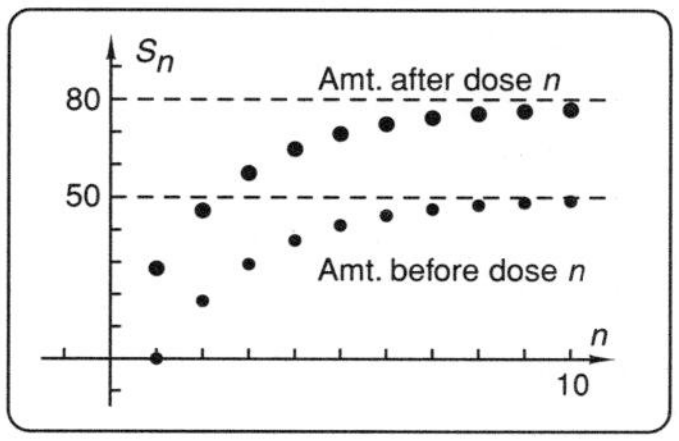


From the graph you can see that if the maximum amounts after dose $n$ are kept below the allowable $80\mu$g, then the minimum amounts before dose $n$ are significantly below the minimum effective amount of $50\mu$g for 3 or 4 days. The situation would be worse for daily doses.

5. *Compound Interest Problem*
   a.

| months | dollars |
|---|---|
| 0 | 1,000,000.00 |
| 1 | 1,007,500.00 |
| 2 | 1,015,056.25 |
| 3 | 1,022,669.17 |

   b. Worth is \$1,093,806.90; Interest is \$93,806.90
   c. The first deposit is made at time $t = 0$, the second at time $t = 1$, and so forth, so that at time $t = 12$, the term index is 13.
   d. 9.3806...% APR
   e. After 93 months.

7. *Bouncing Ball Problem*
   a. Sequence: $20, 18, 16.2, 14.58, 13.122, \ldots$
   b. $S_4 = 20 + 18 + 16.2 + 14.58 = 68.78$ ft
   c. $S = 200$. Ball travels 200 ft before stopping.
   d. 20-foot cycle, $t = 2.2291\ldots$ sec.
   18-foot second cycle, $t = 2.1147\ldots$ sec.
   e. The model predicts that the ball comes to rest after about 43.4 sec.

9. *Derivatives of a Geometric Series*
   $P'(0) = 6$ and $f'(0) = 6$,
   $P''(0) = 12$ and $f''(0) = 12$,
   $P'''(0) = 36$ and $f'''(0) = 36$
   Conjecture: $P^{(n)}(0) = f^{(n)}(0)$ for all values of $n$.

## Problem Set 12-3

*Power Series for an Exponential Function*

1. $f(x) = 5e^{2x}$
   $f'(x) = 10e^{2x}$
   $f''(x) = 20e^{2x}$
   $f'''(x) = 40e^{2x}$
   $f^{(4)}(x) = 80e^{2x}$

3. $c_0 = 5$, $c_1 = 10$, $c_2 = 10$.

5. Graphs of $f$, $P_3$, and $P_4$.

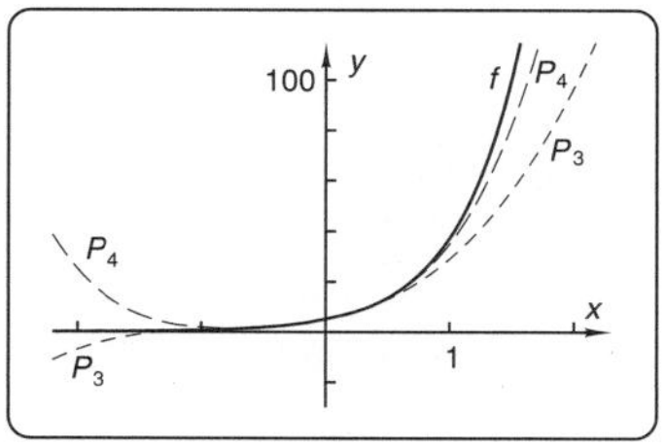


7. $P_3(1) = 31.6666666\ldots$
   $P_4(1) = 35.0000000\ldots$
   $f(1) = 5e^2 = 36.9452804\ldots$
   $\therefore P_4(1)$ is closer to $f(1)$ than $P_3(1)$, Q.E.D.

9. $c_3 = \dfrac{20}{6} = \dfrac{5 \cdot 2^3}{3!}$, $c_2 = \dfrac{20}{2} = \dfrac{5 \cdot 2^2}{2!}$,
   $c_1 = \dfrac{10}{1} = \dfrac{5 \cdot 2^1}{1!}$, $c_0 = 5 = \dfrac{5 \cdot 2^0}{0!}$ $(0! = 1)$

11. $P(x) = \sum_{n=0}^{\infty} \dfrac{5 \cdot 2^n}{n!} x^n$

## Problem Set 12-4

*Power Series for Other Elementary Functions*

1. *Exponential Function Series Problem*

   a. $f(x) = e^x \quad f(0) = P(0) = 1 \quad c_0 = 1$
   $f'(x) = e^x \quad f'(0) = P'(0) = 1 \quad c_1 = 1$
   $f''(x) = e^x \quad f''(0) = P''(0) = 1 \quad 2!c_2 = 1, c_2 = \dfrac{1}{2!}$
   $f'''(x) = e^x \quad f'''(0) = P'''(0) = 1 \quad 3!c_3 = 1, c_3 = \dfrac{1}{3!}$
   $\ldots$
   $\therefore P(x) = 1 + x + \dfrac{1}{2!}x^2 + \dfrac{1}{3!}x^3 + \cdots$, Q.E.D.

   b. Next two terms: $\ldots + \dfrac{1}{4!}x^4 + \dfrac{1}{5!}x^5 + \ldots$

   c. $\displaystyle\sum_{n=0}^{\infty} \frac{1}{n!}x^n$

   d. Graph, $y = S_3(x)$ (fourth partial sum) and $y = e^x$.

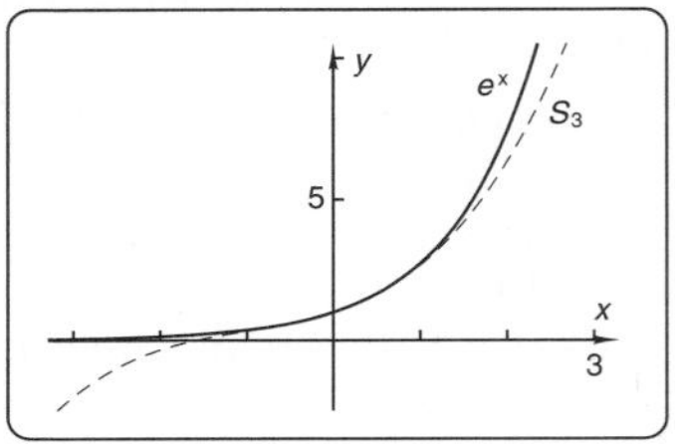


   e. Interval is about $-1 < x < 1$.

   f. Interval is $-0.2237\ldots < x < 0.2188\ldots$

   g. Interval is $-1.5142\ldots < x < 1.4648\ldots$

3. *Sine Series Problem*

   a. $S_3(0.6) = 0.564642445\ldots$
   $\sin 0.6 = 0.564642473\ldots$
   $\therefore S_3(0.6) \approx \sin 0.6$, Q.E.D.

   b. $\sin 0.6 - S_1(0.6) = 0.0006424733\ldots$
   $t_2 = 0.000648$
   $\sin 0.6 - S_2(0.6) = -0.00000552660\ldots$
   $t_3 = -0.00000555428\ldots$
   $\sin 0.6 - S_3(0.6) = 0.0000000276807\ldots$
   $t_4 = 0.0000000277714\ldots$

   In each case the tail is less in magnitude than the absolute value of the first term of the tail, Q.E.D.

   Use at least 9 terms.

5. *Natural Logarithm Series Problem*

   a. $P(1) = 0 = f(1)$
   $P'(1) = 1 = f'(1)$
   $P''(1) = -1 = f''(1)$
   $P'''(1) = 2 = f'''(2)$, Q.E.D.

   b. $\ldots \dfrac{1}{5}(x-1)^5 - \dfrac{1}{6}(x-1)^6 + \cdots$

   c. $P(x) = \displaystyle\sum_{n=1}^{\infty} (-1)^{n+1} \cdot \frac{1}{n}(x-1)^n$

   d. Graph, $S_{10}(x)$ and $\ln x$.

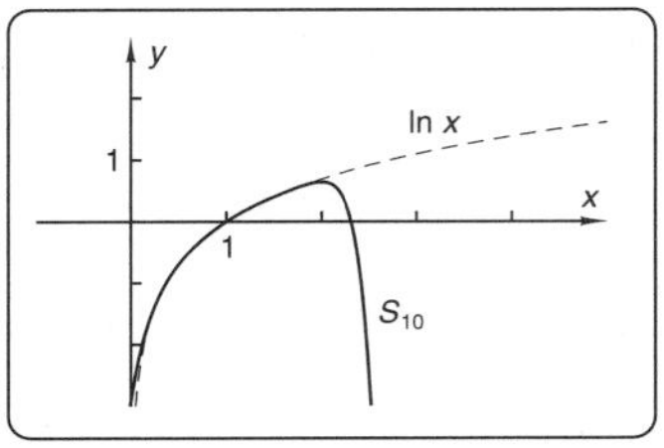


   e. $S_{10}(1.2) = 0.182321555\ldots$
   $\ln 1.2 = 0.182321556\ldots$
   $S_{10}(1.95) = 0.640144911\ldots$
   $\ln 1.95 = 0.667829372\ldots$
   $S_{10}(3) = -64.8253968\ldots$
   $\ln 3 = 1.0986122\ldots$

   $S_{10}(x)$ fits $\ln x$ in about $0.1 < x < 2$.
   $S_{10}(1.2)$ and $\ln 1.2$ agree through the 8th decimal place. The values of $S_{10}(1.95)$ and $\ln 1.95$ agree only to 1 decimal place. The values of $S_{10}(3)$ and $\ln 3$ bear no resemblance to each other.

7. *Inverse Tangent Series Problem*

   a. $P(x) = x - \dfrac{1}{3}x^3 + \dfrac{1}{5}x^5 - \dfrac{1}{7}x^7 + \cdots$

   b. Graph.

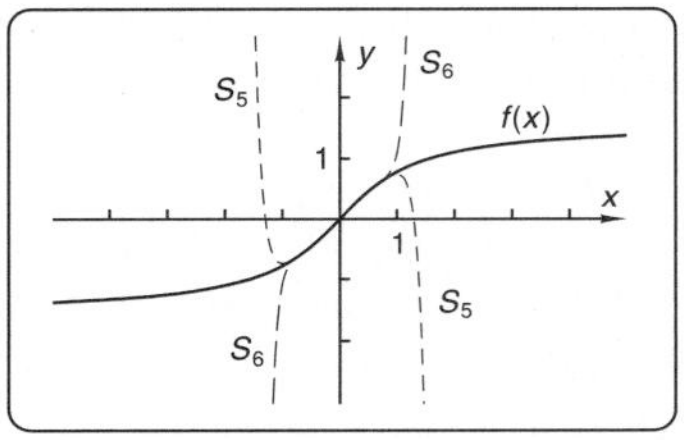


   Both partial sums fit the graph of $f$ very well for about $-0.9 < x < 0.9$. For $x > 1$ and $x < -1$ the partial sums bear no resemblance to the graph of $f$.

## Problem Set 12-5

*Taylor and Maclaurin Series, and Operations on these Series*

1. $1 + u + \dfrac{1}{2!}u^2 + \dfrac{1}{3!}u^3 + \dfrac{1}{4!}u^4 + \dfrac{1}{5!}u^5 + \cdots$

3. $u - \dfrac{1}{3!}u^3 + \dfrac{1}{5!}u^5 - \dfrac{1}{7!}u^7 + \dfrac{1}{9!}u^9 - \dfrac{1}{11!}u^{11} + \cdots$

5. $1 + \dfrac{1}{2!}u^2 + \dfrac{1}{4!}u^4 + \dfrac{1}{6!}u^6 + \dfrac{1}{8!}u^8 + \dfrac{1}{10!}u^{10} + \cdots$

7. $(1-u)^{-1} = 1 + u + u^2 + u^3 + u^4 + u^5 + \cdots$

9. $x^2 - \dfrac{1}{3!}x^4 + \dfrac{1}{5!}x^6 - \dfrac{1}{7!}x^8 + \dfrac{1}{9!}x^{10} - \cdots$

11. $1 + \dfrac{1}{2!}x^6 + \dfrac{1}{4!}x^{12} + \dfrac{1}{6!}x^{18} + \dfrac{1}{8!}x^{24} + \cdots$

13. $(x^2-1) - \dfrac{1}{2}(x^2-1)^2 + \dfrac{1}{3}(x^2-1)^3 - \cdots$
(or $2\ln x = 2(x-1) - (x-1)^2 + \dfrac{2}{3}(x-1)^3 - \cdots$)

15. $x - \frac{1}{3}x^3 + \frac{1}{5}\cdot\frac{1}{2!}x^5 - \frac{1}{7}\cdot\frac{1}{3!}x^7 + \frac{1}{9}\cdot\frac{1}{4!}x^9 - \cdots$

17. $\frac{1}{8}x^8 - \frac{1}{18}\cdot\frac{1}{3!}x^{18} + \frac{1}{28}\cdot\frac{1}{5!}x^{28} - \frac{1}{38}\cdot\frac{1}{7!}x^{38} + \cdots$

19. $\frac{1}{2}x^2 + \frac{1}{6}\cdot\frac{1}{3!}x^6 + \frac{1}{10}\cdot\frac{1}{5!}x^{10} + \frac{1}{14}\cdot\frac{1}{7!}x^{14} + \cdots$

21. $1 - x^4 + x^8 - x^{12} + x^{16} - \cdots$

23. $x - \frac{1}{5}x^5 + \frac{1}{9}x^9 - \frac{1}{13}x^{13} + \frac{1}{17}x^{17} - \cdots$

25. $\frac{\sqrt{2}}{2} + \frac{\sqrt{2}}{2}\left(x - \frac{\pi}{4}\right) - \frac{\sqrt{2}}{2\cdot 2!}\left(x - \frac{\pi}{4}\right)^2$
$- \frac{\sqrt{2}}{2\cdot 3!}\left(x - \frac{\pi}{4}\right)^3 + \frac{\sqrt{2}}{2\cdot 4!}\left(x - \frac{\pi}{4}\right)^4$
$+ \frac{\sqrt{2}}{2\cdot 5!}\left(x - \frac{\pi}{4}\right)^5 - \cdots$

27. $(x-1) - \frac{1}{2}(x-1)^2 + \frac{1}{3}(x-1)^3 - \frac{1}{4}(x-1)^4 + \cdots$

29. $-1 + \frac{7}{3}(x-4) - \frac{7\cdot 4}{3^2 2!}(x-4)^2 + \frac{7\cdot 4\cdot 1}{3^3 3!}(x-4)^3 -$
$\frac{7\cdot 4\cdot 1\cdot(-2)}{3^4 4!}(x-4)^4 +$
$\frac{7\cdot 4\cdot 1\cdot(-2)\cdot(-5)}{3^5 5!}(x-4)^5 - \cdots$

31. Both give $\cos 3x = 1 - \frac{9}{2!}x^2 + \frac{81}{4!}x^4 - \frac{729}{6!}x^6 + \cdots$.
Substitution gives the answer much more easily.

33. *Accuracy for* $\ln x$ *Series Value*
$S_4(1.5) = 0.40104166\ldots$; $\ln 1.5 = 0.40546510\ldots$
error $= 0.00442344\ldots$
fifth term $= \frac{1}{5}(1.5-1)^5 = .00625$
Error is smaller in absolute value than $t_5$.

35. *Inverse Tangent Series and an Approximation for* $\pi$
   a. $4S_9(1) = 3.04183961\ldots$
   $\pi = 3.14159265\ldots$
   The error is about 3%.
   b. $4S_{49}(1) = 3.12159465\ldots$
   $\pi = 3.14159265\ldots$
   The error is about 0.6%.
   c. $4S_9 = \sum_{n=0}^{9}(-1)^n\frac{4}{2n+1}\left(\frac{1}{2}\right)^{2n+1}$
   $+ \sum_{n=0}^{9}(-1)^n\frac{4}{2n+1}\left(\frac{1}{3}\right)^{2n+1}$
   $= 3.14159257\ldots$
   $\pi = 3.14159265\ldots$
   The answer differs from $\pi$ by only 1 in the 7th decimal place. The improvement in accuracy is accounted for by the fact that the inverse tangent series converges much more rapidly for $x = 1/2$ and $x = 1/3$ than it does for $x = 1$. In Problem 17 of Problem Set 12-6 you will see that the interval of convergence for the inverse tangent series is $-1 \le x \le 1$. In general, power series converge slowly at the endpoints of the convergence interval.

37. Not selected.

39. *Ratio of Terms Problem*
   a. $r_n = \frac{n}{n+1}|x-1|$
   b. $r_{10} = \frac{2}{11}$ for $x = 1.2$
   $r_{10} = \frac{9.5}{11}$ for $x = 1.95$
   $r_{10} = \frac{20}{11}$ for $x = 3$
   c. $r = |x-1|$
   d. $r = 0.2$ for $x = 1.2$
   $r = 0.95$ for $x = 1.95$
   $r = 2$ for $x = 3$
   e. The series converges to $\ln x$ whenever the value of $x$ makes $r < 1$, and diverges whenever the value of $x$ makes $r > 1$.
   f. $r = |x-1| < 1 \Rightarrow -1 < (x-1) < 1 \Rightarrow 0 < x < 2$.

## Problem Set 12-6

*Interval of Convergence for a Series—The Ratio Technique*

1. a. $\frac{1}{4}x + \frac{2}{16}x^2 + \frac{3}{64}x^3 + \frac{4}{256}x^4 + \frac{5}{1024}x^5 + \cdots$
   b. Open interval of convergence is $(-4, 4)$.
   c. Radius of convergence = 4.

3. a. $(2x+3) + \frac{(2x+3)^2}{2} + \frac{(2x+3)^3}{3} + \frac{(2x+3)^4}{4} + \cdots$
   b. $(-2, -1)$
   c. $\frac{1}{2}$

5. a. $(x-8) + \frac{8}{2}(x-8)^2 + \frac{27}{6}(x-8)^3 + \frac{64}{24}(x-8)^4 + \cdots$
   b. Series converges for all values of $x$.
   c. Radius of convergence is infinite.

7. $L = x^2 \cdot 0 < 1$ for all $x$. The series converges for all $x$.

9. $L = x^2 \cdot 0 < 1$ for all $x$. The series converges for all $x$.

11. $e^x = \sum_{n=0}^{\infty}\frac{1}{n!}x^n$
$L = \lim_{n\to\infty}\left|\frac{x^{n+1}}{(n+1)!}\cdot\frac{n!}{x^n}\right| = |x|\lim_{n\to\infty}\frac{1}{n+1}$
$= |x|\cdot 0$
$\therefore L < 1$ for all $x$ and the series converges for all $x$.

13. $L = |x|\cdot\infty = \infty$ for all $x \ne 0$; $L = 0$ at $x = 0$.
$\therefore$ the series converges only for $x = 0$.

15. $\cosh 10 = \sum_{n=0}^{\infty}\frac{1}{(2n)!}10^{2n}$
$L = 10^2 \cdot 0 = 0 < 1 \Rightarrow$ series converges.

17. *Inverse Tangent Series Problem*
   a. Open interval of convergence is $(-1, 1)$.
   b. Graphs fit very well for $-1 < x < 1$. Partial sums diverge from $\tan^{-1} x$ for $x$ outside this interval.

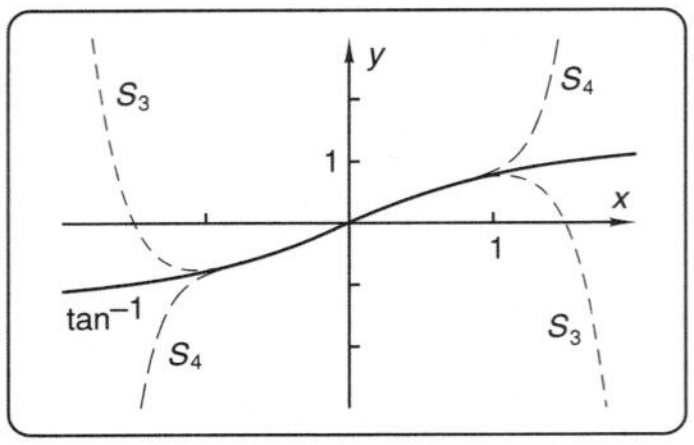


   c. $S_3(0.1) = 0.09966865238095\ldots$
   d. tail $= 0.00000000011020\ldots$
   e. First term of tail $= 0.00000000011111\ldots$, which is larger than the tail.

19. *The Error Function*
   a. $f(x) = x - \frac{1}{3}x^3 + \frac{1}{5 \cdot 2!}x^5 - \frac{1}{7 \cdot 3!}x^7 + \frac{1}{9 \cdot 4!}x^9 - \frac{1}{11 \cdot 5!}x^{11} + \cdots$
   b. Graph. Approximately $-1.5 < x < 1.5$.

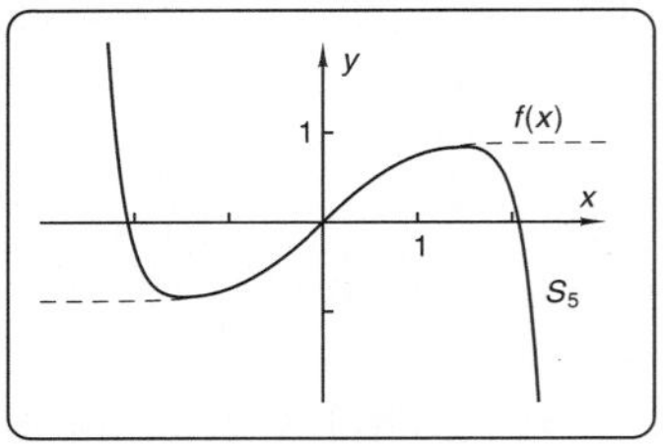


   c. $L = x^2 \cdot 0 < 1$ for all $x$.
   d. Erf $x$ does seem to be approaching 1 as $x$ increases, as shown by the following table generated by numerical integration.

| $x$ | erf $x$ |
|---|---|
| 1 | 0.8427007929... |
| 2 | 0.9953222650... |
| 3 | 0.9999779095... |
| 4 | 0.9999999845... |
| 5 | 0.9999999999... |

21. *The Root Technique*
   Not selected.

23. Open interval of convergence is $(0, 2)$.

25. $L = 0$ if $x = 0$, and is infinite if $x \neq 0$.
   $\therefore$ the series converges only if $x = 0$.

## Problem Set 12-7

*Convergence of Series at the Ends of the Convergence Interval*

1. *Vocabulary Problem I*
   a. $6 + 3 + 1 + \frac{1}{4} + \frac{1}{20} + \cdots$
   b. $6, 9, 10, 10\frac{1}{4}, 10\frac{3}{10}, \ldots$
   c. $\frac{1}{120} + \frac{1}{840} + \frac{1}{6720} + \cdots$
   d. Terms are decreasing.
   e. Partial sums are increasing.

3. *Vocabulary Problem III*
   a. $6 - 3 + 1 - \frac{1}{4} + \frac{1}{20} - \cdots$
   b. $6, 3, 4, 3\frac{3}{4}, 3\frac{4}{5}, \ldots$
   c. $-\frac{1}{120} + \frac{1}{840} - \frac{1}{6720} + \cdots$
   d. $(-1)^{n+1}$ makes the signs of the terms alternate.
   e. $S_2 = 3$, $S_4 = 3.75$, $S_6 = 3.791666\ldots, \ldots$
   The even partial sums are increasing. For the two terms added to get the next even partial sum, the positive term is larger in absolute value than the negative term.
   f. $S_1 = 6$, $S_3 = 4$, $S_5 = 3.8, \ldots$
   The odd partial sums are decreasing. For the two terms added to get the next odd partial sum, the positive term is smaller in absolute value than the negative term. Since the odd partial sums are all greater than the even partial sums, the entire sequence is bounded above by the greatest odd partial sum, $S_1 = 6$.

5. Interval of convergence is $(2, 4)$.

7. Interval of convergence is $[-1, 1)$.

9. Interval of convergence is $[-6, -4]$.

11. Interval of convergence is $[-1, 1)$.

13. Intervals of convergence are $(-\infty, -4)$ and $(4, \infty)$.

15. *Upper Bound by Convergent Improper Integral*
   a. $1 + \frac{1}{4} + \frac{1}{9} + \frac{1}{16} + \frac{1}{25} + \cdots$; $S_5 = \frac{5269}{3600} = 1.46361111\ldots$
   b. The sixth term of the series has a rectangle between $x = 5$ and $x = 6$ (the height of the rectangles being used is the value of the function at the rightmost edge.) So the integral must be from 5 to $\infty$ to include this rectangle.
   c. Tail is bounded above by $\frac{1}{5}$.
   d. The sequence of partial sums is increasing (since the terms of the series are positive) and bounded above. Thus the sequence of partial sums must converge. The series is a finite sum added to the tail, so the series converges.
   e. $S_{1000} = 1.643934\ldots$
   f. Upper bound for tail is 0.001.
   (Lower bound for tail is $1/1001 = 0.0009990\ldots$.)
   g. False.
   h. No more than a 0.0608% error.

i. It would take at least 2 million terms!

17. *Integral Test Problem*
Assume $f(x)$ is positive and decreasing for all $x$ beyond $x = D$.
If $I$ converges, then the tail of the series can be bounded above by the number to which the integral converges. Because the terms are positive the partial sums are increasing. Thus the sequence of partial sums converges because it is increasing and bounded above. Since the tail of the series converges, so does the series.
If $I$ diverges, then the tail of the series can be bounded below by a divergent improper integral. Thus the tail is infinite, which implies that the series diverges.

19. *The Factorial Reciprocal Series Converges*
a. It is difficult to find the appropriate function $f(x)$ to integrate, such that $f(n) = \frac{1}{n!}$ at the integer points. So the integral test is impractical for this series.
b. The geometric series converges to $\frac{1}{8}$.
c. An upper bound for the tail of the series is $\frac{1}{8}$.
d. An upper bound for the entire series is $2\frac{19}{24}$.
e. The sequence of partial sums is increasing (since the terms of the series are positive) and bounded above by 2.7916.... Thus the sequence of partial sums converges, so the series converges.

21. *Alternating Series Remainders Property Problem*
a. $t_3 = -\frac{1}{7!}0.6^7 = -0.00000555428571\ldots$
b. $S_1(0.6) = 0.6 - \frac{1}{3!}0.6^3 = 0.564$
$S_2(0.6) = 0.6 - \frac{1}{3!}0.6^3 + \frac{1}{5!}0.6^5 = 0.564648$
c. $R_1 = \sin 0.6 - S_1(0.6) = 0.0006424\ldots$
$R_2 = \sin 0.6 - S_2(0.6) = -0.0000055266\ldots$
$|t_2| = 0.000648$
$\therefore |R_1| < |t_2|$
$|t_3| = 0.0000055542\ldots$
$\therefore |R_2| < |t_3|$
d. The terms are strictly alternating in sign.
The terms are strictly decreasing in absolute value.
The terms approach zero for a limit as $n \to \infty$.
Thus the series converges by the alternating series test.

23. *Convergence of Sequences Proof*
Not selected.

25. Converges because it is a geometric series with common ratio 1/4, which is less than 1 in absolute value.

27. Converges by comparison with:
Geometric series with $t_0 = 1$ and $r = 1/6$.
Factorial reciprocal series in Problem 19.

29. Diverges. Use the integral test or compare with a harmonic series.

31. Not selected.

### Problem Set 12-8

*Error Analysis for Series*

1. a. $S_5(4) = 27.2699118\ldots$
b. $S_5(4)$ is within 2 of $\cosh 4$ in the units digit.
c. $\cosh 4 - S_5(4) = 0.0383\ldots$, which is well within the upper bound found by Lagrange's form.

3. a. $S_{14}(3) = 20.0855234\ldots$
b. $S_{14}(3)$ is within 3 units of $e^3$ in the 4th decimal place.
c. $e^3 - S_{14}(3) = 0.00001346\ldots$, which is within the upper bound found by Lagrange's form.

5. Use at least 7 terms ($n = 6$).

7. Use at least 32 terms.

9. $c = \cosh^{-1} 1.0309\ldots = 0.2482\ldots$, which is between 0 and 2.

11. $\cos 2.4 = 1 - 2.88 + 1.3824 - 0.2654208 + 0.0273004\ldots - \cdots$
The terms are strictly alternating. They are decreasing in absolute value after $t_1$, and they approach zero for a limit as $n \to \infty$.
Therefore the hypotheses of the alternating series test apply. Use 8 terms ($n = 7$).

13. *p-Series Problem I*
Use 317 terms.

15. *p-Series Problem III*
$R_{99}$ is bounded above by 15.8945....
$R_{99}$ is also bounded below by 15.8865....
So, Amos, the 4.69030101... you calculated for $S_{99}$ is not close to the actual limit to which the series converges.

17. *Geometric Series as an Upper Bound Problem*
By Lagrange form, $|R_{10}| < 0.0004617\ldots$.
By geometric series $|R_{10}| < 0.00006156\ldots$.
The geometric series gives a better estimate of the remainder than does the Lagrange form.

19. Sin $x$ *for Any Argument Using a Value of* $x$ *in* $[0, \pi/4]$
a. $b = 4.9557730\ldots$ radians.
b. $c = -1.32741228\ldots$ radians.
c. $d = 0.243384039\ldots$ radians.
d. $|R_5(x)| < |t_6(\pi/4)| = 3.8980\ldots \times 10^{-13}$, which is small enough to guarantee that $\sin x$ will be correct to 10 decimal places.
Direct calculation would take about 349 terms

e. Not selected.

21. *Derivation of the Lagrange Form of the Remainder*
Not selected.

23. *The Maclaurin Series for $e^x$ Converges to $e^x$*
Not selected.

## Problem Set 12-9

*Chapter Review and Test*

### Review Problems

R0. *Journal*

R1. $f(x) = \dfrac{9}{1-x}$ and $P(x) = 9 + 9x + 9x^2 + 9x^3 + \cdots$
Graph, $f(x)$, $P_5(x)$, and $P_6(x)$, showing that $P(x)$ is close to $f(x)$ for $x$ between about $-0.7$ and $0.6$, and bears little resemblance to $f(x)$ beyond $\pm 1$.

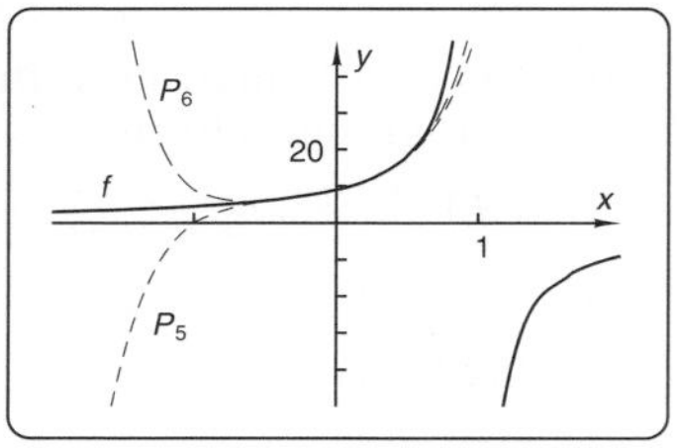


$P_5(0.4) = 14.93856$
$P_6(0.4) = 14.975424$
$f(0.4) = 15$
$\therefore P_6(0.4)$ is closer to $f(0.4)$ than $P_5(0.4)$ is, Q.E.D.
$P_5(0) = 9 = f(0)$
$P_5'(0) = 9 = f'(0)$
$P_5''(0) = 18 = f''(0)$
$P_5'''(0) = 54 = f'''(0)$
$P_n(x)$ is a subset of a geometric series.

R2. a. *Biceps Problem*
About 19.5 mm increase in 10 days.
About 30 mm increase eventually.

b. *Present Value Problem*
They must invest \$81,754.00 now in order to make the last payment.
They must invest \$4,182,460.05 now to make all 19 payments.

R3. $c_0 = 7$, $c_1 = 21$, $c_2 = 31.5$, $c_3 = 31.5$

R4. a. $e^{0.12} = 1.127496851\ldots$
$S_3(0.12) = 1.127488$, which is close to $e^{0.12}$.

b. $\cos 0.12 = 0.9928086358538\ldots$
$S_3(0.12) = 0.9928086358528$, which is close.

c. $\sinh(0.12) = 0.1202882074311\ldots$
$S_3(0.12) = 0.1202882074310\ldots$, which is close.

d. $\ln 1.7 = 0.530628251\ldots$
$S_{20}(1.7) = 0.530612301\ldots$, which is close.
$\ln 2.3 = 0.83290912\ldots$
$S_{20}(2.3) = -4.42067878\ldots$, which is not close.

R5. a. A Maclaurin series is a Taylor series expanded about $x = 0$.

b. $\ln(x+1) = x - \frac{1}{2}x^2 + \frac{1}{3}x^3 - \frac{1}{4}x^4 + \cdots$

c. $\int \ln(x+1)\,dx = \frac{1}{2}x^2 - \frac{1}{3\cdot 2}x^3 + \frac{1}{4\cdot 3}x^4 - \cdots + C$

d. $\int \ln(x+1)\,dx = (x+1)\ln(x+1) - (x+1) + C_1$
$= x\ln(x+1) + \ln(x+1) - x + C \qquad (C = C_1 - 1)$
$= \frac{1}{2}x^2 - \frac{1}{3\cdot 2}x^3 + \frac{1}{4\cdot 3}x^4 - \cdots + C,$
which is the same as the series in part (c).

e. $\int_0^x t\cos t^2\,dt = \frac{1}{2}x^2 - \frac{1}{6\cdot 2!}x^6 + \frac{1}{10\cdot 4!}x^{10} - \frac{1}{14\cdot 6!}x^{14} + \cdots$

f. $\tan^{-1} x = \int_0^x \frac{1}{1+t^2}\,dt = \int_0^x (1 - t^2 + (t^2)^2 - (t^2)^3 + (t^2)^4 - \cdots)\,dt \ (|t| \le 1)$
$= x - \frac{1}{3}x^3 + \frac{1}{5}x^5 - \frac{1}{7}x^7 + \frac{1}{9}x^9 - \cdots$

g. $f(x) = 5 + 7(x-3) - 3(x-3)^2 + 0.15(x-3)^3 + \cdots$

R6. a. $\sum_{n=1}^{\infty} = (-3)^{-n}(x-5)^n$
$= -\frac{1}{3}(x-5) + \frac{1}{9}(x-5)^2 - \frac{1}{27}(x-5)^3 + \cdots$

b. Open interval of convergence is $(2, 8)$.
Radius of convergence $= 3$.

c. $L = x^2 \cdot 0 < 1$ for all $x$.
Series converges for all $x$, Q.E.D.

d. $e^{1.2} = 1 + 1.2 + \frac{1}{2!}(1.2)^2 + \frac{1}{3!}(1.2)^3 + \frac{1}{4!}(1.2)^4 + \cdots$
Error $= e^{1.2} - S_4(1.2) = 0.02571692\ldots$
First term of the tail is $t_5 = 0.020736$
The error is greater than $t_5$, but not much greater.

e. Graphs.

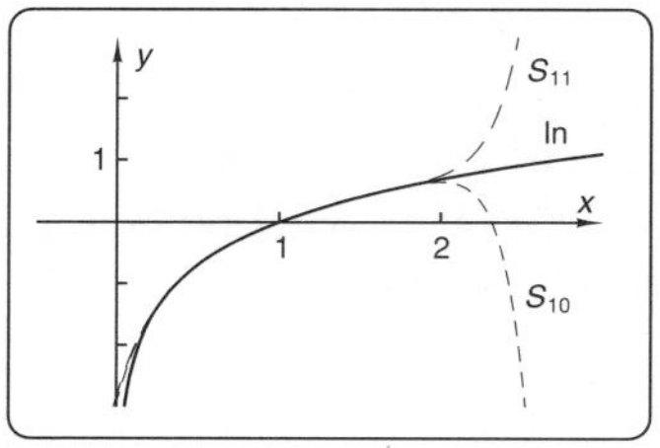


The open interval of convergence is $(0, 2)$. Both partial sums fit ln well within this interval. Above $x = 2$ the partial sums diverge rapidly to $\pm\infty$. Below $x = 0$ the partial sums give answers, but there are no real values for $\ln x$.

R7. a. $S_{10} = 4463.129099$ (exactly)

b. $S - S_{10} = 536.870912$, which differs from the limit by about 10.7%.

c. "Tail"

d. "Remainder"

e. The remainder is bounded above by 0.005.

f. The series converges because the sequence of partial sums is increasing and bounded above.

g. $2/1! + 4/2! + 8/3! + 16/4! + 32/5! + \cdots$
$= 2 + 2 + 1.3333\ldots + 0.6666\ldots + 0.2666\ldots + \cdots$
$= \sum_{n=1}^{\infty} 2^n/n!$
The terms are decreasing starting at $t_2$.
$R_1$ is bounded by the geometric series with first term 2 and common ratio $1.3333\ldots/2 = 2/3$.
Since |common ratio| is less than 1, the geometric series converges (to $2/(1 - 2/3) = 6$).
Thus the tail after the first partial sum is bounded above by a convergent geometric series, Q.E.D.

h. *Use the Alternating Series test.*
The terms alternate in sign, decrease in absolute value, and approach zero for a limit as $n \to \infty$.

i. Upper bound is 1/10001.

j. i. Interval of convergence is $[2.9, 3.1]$.
ii. Interval of convergence is $(-3, 1]$.

k. i. The tail after $S_0$ is bounded above by the convergent geometric series with first term 10 and common ratio 0.5. Thus the series converges.
(Other justifications are possible.)
ii. Diverges because $t_n$ approaches 0.2, not 0, as $n \to \infty$.

R8. a. Error is less than 0.03.

b. Use at least 34 terms ($n = 33$).

c. Using the Lagrange form of the remainder, the value of cosh 4 is given *exactly* by

$$\cosh 4 = \sum_{n=0}^{k} \frac{1}{(2n)!} \cdot 4^{2n} + R_k(4), \text{ where}$$

$$R_k(4) = \frac{f^{(2k+2)}(c)}{(2k+2)!} \cdot 4^{2k+2}$$

and $c$ is between 0 and 4.

$$|R_k(4)| \le \frac{M}{(2k+2)!}|4|^{2k+2}$$

$\lim_{k\to\infty} |R_k(4)| = 0$

Since the remainder approaches zero as $n$ approaches infinity, cosh 4 is given exactly by

$$\cosh 4 = \sum_{n=0}^{\infty} \frac{1}{(2n)!} \cdot 4^{2n}, \text{ Q.E.D.}$$

d. $c = \cosh^{-1} 1.00328\ldots = 0.0809\ldots$, which is in the interval $(0, 0.6)$.

e. Use at least 35 terms.

f. An upper bound is $2.6666\ldots \times 10^6$.

## *Problem Set 12-10: Cumulative Reviews*

*Cumulative Review Number 1—The Dam Problem*

1. Limit: See Sections 1-5, 2-2, 2-5, and 2-7.
Derivative: See Sections 3-2 and 3-4.
Indefinite integral: See Section 3-9.
Definite integral: See Section 5-4.

2. a. Continuity at a point: See Section 2-4.
b. Continuity on an interval: See Section 2-4.
c. Convergence of a sequence: A sequence converges if and only if $\lim_{n\to\infty} t_n$ exists.
d. Convergence of a series: A series converges if and only if the sequence of partial sums converges.
e. Natural logarithm: See Section 6-3.
f. Exponential: $a^x = e^{x \ln a}$.

3. a. Mean value theorem: See Section 5-6.
b. Intermediate value theorem: See Section 2-6.
c. Squeeze theorem: See Section 3-8.
d. Uniqueness theorem for derivatives: See Section 6-4.
e. Limit of a product property: See Section 2-3.
f. Integration by parts formula: See Section 9-2.
g. Fundamental theorem of calculus: See Section 5-8.
h. Lagrange form of the remainder: See Section 12-8.
i. Parametric chain rule: See Section 4-7.
j. Polar differential of arc length: See Section 8-9.

4. a. $f'(x) = \sqrt{1 + \operatorname{sech} x}$
b. $f'(x) = a^x \ln a$
c. $f'(x) = ax^{a-1}$
d. $f'(x) = x^x \ln x + x^x$
e. $\int e^{6x} \cos 3x\, dx = \frac{1}{15}e^{6x} \sin 3x + \frac{2}{15}e^{6x} \cos 3x + C$
f. $\int \cosh^5 x \sinh x\, dx = \frac{1}{6}\cosh^6 x + C$
g. $\int \sec^3 x\, dx = \frac{1}{2}\sec x \tan x + \frac{1}{2}\ln|\sec x + \tan x| + C$
h. $\int (\sin 5x)^{-1} \cos 5x\, dx = \frac{1}{5}\ln|\sin 5x| + C$
i. limit $= -\frac{49}{26}$
j. limit $= e^{-3} = 0.04978\ldots$

5. a. Graph.

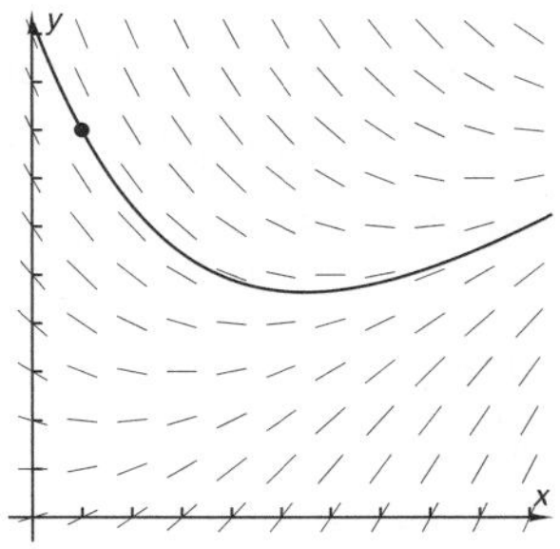


b. If $x = 9$, $y \approx 5.413\ldots$, which agrees with the graph.

6. a. $p = k(40 - y)$
   b. $A = 1066.6\ldots \text{yd}^2$
   c. $F = 17066.6\ldots k$ lb
   d. $M = 292{,}571.4\ldots k$ lb-yd
   e. Center of pressure is at $\left(0, 17\frac{1}{7}\right)$.
7. a. $z = 30 - 0.5y$
   b. Max. at $y = 20$; min. at $y = 0$.
   c. 3840 truckloads.
   d. $L = 92.9356\ldots \approx 92.9$ yd
8. Speed $= 2.9943\ldots \approx 2.99$ ft/sec
9. $\text{Si}\, t = t - \frac{1}{3 \cdot 3!}t^3 + \frac{1}{5 \cdot 5!}t^5 - \frac{1}{7 \cdot 7!}t^7 + \ldots$
   $L = t^2 \cdot 0 < 1$ for all values of $t$, and the series converges for all values of $t$.
   Third partial sum is $S_2(0.6) = 0.5881296$
   Answer is correct to $\pm 1$ in the sixth decimal place.
   $\text{Si}\, 0.6 \approx 0.588128809\ldots$
10. $A = 103.6725\ldots \approx 103.7$ ft$^2$ (Exactly $33\pi$)
11. At $t = 10$, $V = 253.9445\ldots \approx 253.9$ million gal.

*Cumulative Review Number 2—The Ship Problem*

1. Derivative: See Sections 3-2 and 3-4
2. Definite integral: See Section 5-4.
3. Mean value theorem: See Section 5-6.
4. $f'(x) = g(x)$
5. $\frac{1}{6}\tanh^6 x + C$
6. $\frac{1}{2}x \cosh 2x - \frac{1}{4}\sinh 2x + C$
7. $-\ln|x + 3| + 4\ln|x - 2| + C$
8. $x + \frac{1}{3 \cdot 3!}x^3 + \frac{1}{5 \cdot 5!}x^5 + \frac{1}{7 \cdot 7!}x^7 + \cdots + C$
9. Open interval of convergence is $2 < x < 8$.
10. 500
11. $\bar{y} = 39$
12. $f(4) = 16$
    $f(3.99) = 15.9201$, which is within 0.08 unit of 16.
    $f(4.01) = 16.0801$, which is not within 0.08 unit of 16.
    Thus, $\delta = 0.01$ is not small enough to keep $f(x)$ within 0.08 unit of 4.
13. $V = \int_2^{10} A\, dx \approx 2140$ ft$^3$
14. $A = 6.2831 \approx 6.28$ ft$^2$ (Exactly $2\pi$)
15. $A = 17.6021\ldots \approx 17.6$ square units
16. $A = 256$ ft$^2$
17. $L = 42.5483\ldots \approx 42.55$ ft.
18. $F = 113595.73\ldots \approx 113{,}600$ lb
19. limit $= 0$
20. There is a maximum at $x = e$ since $y'$ goes from positive to negative there.
21. There is a point of inflection at $x \approx 4.48$ ft since $y''$ changes sign there.
22. Graph.

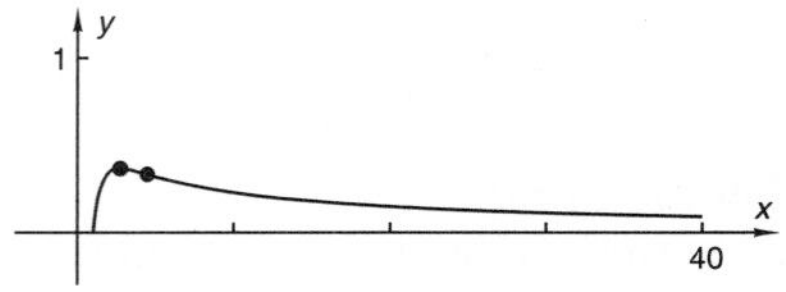


23. $\ln x = (x - 1) - \frac{1}{2}(x - 1)^2 + \frac{1}{3}(x - 1)^3 - \cdots$
    $L = |x - 1|$
    $L < 1 \Longleftrightarrow 0 < x < 2$
    At $x = 0$ the series is $-1 - \frac{1}{2} - \frac{1}{3} - \frac{1}{4} - \cdots$, which is a divergent harmonic series.
    At $x = 2$, the series is $1 - \frac{1}{2} + \frac{1}{3} - \frac{1}{4} + \cdots$, which converges since it meets the three hypotheses of the alternating series test.
    $\therefore$ interval of convergence is $0 < x \le 2$, Q.E.D.
24. Use 46 terms.
25. If the velocity is 0 ft/sec at time $t = 0$, the ship speeds up, approaching approximately 34 ft/sec asymptotically as $t$ increases.
    If the velocity is 50 ft/sec at time $t = 0$, the ship slows down, again approaching 34 ft/sec asymptotically as $t$ increases.
26. $\vec{a} = (-1/t^2)\vec{i} + (-4 \sin 2t)\vec{j}$

*Cumulative Review Number 3—Routine Problems*

1. Graph. $\delta$ is clearly smaller than necessary.

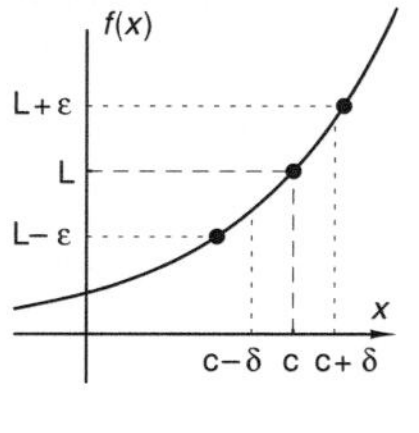


2. See Sections 3-2 and 3-4 for definitions of derivative.
   Graphical meaning: Slope of tangent line.
   Physical meaning: Instantaneous rate of change.
3. $g(x) = \int f(x)\, dx$ if and only if $g'(x) = f(x)$.
4. $\int_r^s f(t)\, dt = \lim_{\Delta t \to 0} L_n = \lim_{\Delta t \to 0} U_n$, where $L_n$ and $U_n$ are lower and upper Riemann sums, respectively, provided the two limits are equal.
5. l'Hospital's rule. Limit $= -0.2$

6. $y = \tan(\sin 5x)$
$y' = \sec^2(\sin 5x) \cdot 5\cos 5x$. Chain rule.

7. $y' = y\left(\dfrac{5}{5x-3} + \dfrac{8}{2x+7} + \dfrac{1}{x-9}\right)$

8. $y' = \dfrac{1}{1+x^2}$

9. $\dfrac{1}{8}\sin^8 x + C$

10. $\dfrac{1}{2}x\sqrt{x^2+9} + \dfrac{9}{2}\ln|\sqrt{x^2+9}+x| + C$

11. $5\ln|x+3| - 2\ln|x-1| + C$

12. $x\sin^{-1}x + \sqrt{1-x^2} + C$

13. Fundamental theorem of calculus.
See Section 5-8 for statement.

14. See Figure 5-6a.

15. $f'(x) = h(x)$

16. Only point of inflection is at $x = 2$.

17. $L \approx 2.3516\ldots$

18. a. Integral converges to 8.
b. Average value = 0.5.

19. $A \approx 13.3478\ldots$

20. $\vec{v}(1) = 2\vec{i} - 3\vec{j}$
Speed = $\sqrt{13} = 3.6055\ldots$
Distance from origin is decreasing at 2.2135....

21. $V \approx 3.5864\ldots$ (Exactly $2\pi(\pi/2 - 1)$)

22. a. $A' = 0 \Longleftrightarrow x = 2$.
$A(0) = 0$, $A(4) = 0$, $A(2) > 0$.
Thus maximum area is at $x = 2$, Q.E.D.
b. Maximum volume is at $x = 2\frac{2}{3}$.

23. $V \approx 394\frac{2}{3}$ ft$^3$

24. a. $f(x) = \int_0^x e^{-t^2}\,dt$
$= x - \dfrac{1}{3}x^3 + \dfrac{1}{5\cdot 2!}x^5 - \dfrac{1}{7\cdot 3!}x^7 + \dfrac{1}{9\cdot 4!}x^9 - \cdots$
b. $L = x^2 \cdot 0 < 1$ for all values of $x$, and thus the series converges for all values of $x$, Q.E.D.

# Glossary

The following are descriptions of the major terms used in calculus, along with references to page numbers where formal definitions and statements of the terms can be found. For references to the many other significant terms used in this text, please see the index.

**Acceleration** (pp. 99, 305): The instantaneous rate of change of velocity.

**Antiderivative** (pp. 119, 182, 189): $g(x)$ is an antiderivative of $f(x)$ if and only if $g'(x) = f(x)$. An antiderivative is the same as an indefinite integral.

**Average value of a function** (p. 514): The integral of $f(x)$ from $x = a$ to $x = b$, divided by the quantity $(b - a)$.

**Calculus** (p. 215): A word meaning "calculation," coming from the same root word as "calcium," chosen because calculations centuries ago were done using pebbles (calcium carbonate). The word is part of the title of an appendix to Isaac Newton's *Principia,* entitled *The Calculus of Infinitesimals,* which means calculating with quantities that approach zero as $x$ approaches a particular value.

**Centroid** (p. 570): The centroid of an object is its geometric center, found by dividing the first moment of area or volume with respect to an axis by the area or volume. If the object has uniform density, the centroid and center of mass are at the same point, and the object will balance at that point.

**Chain rule** (pp. 107, 161): The method for finding the derivative of a composite function, namely, the derivative of the outside function with respect to the inside function, multiplied by the derivative of the inside function with respect to $x$.

**Concave** (p. 356): Literally, "hollowed out," but used to refer to the side of the graph of a function or relation that looks hollowed out (contrasted to the other side, which is convex).

**Concepts of calculus** (p. xiii, 33): There are four major concepts of calculus: limit, derivative, definite integral, and indefinite integral (antiderivative).

**Constant of integration** (p. 182): Two antiderivatives of the same function differ by at most a constant. The constant term of an antiderivative equation is called the constant of integration.

**Continuity** (p. 54): A function is continuous at $x = c$ if and only if $f(c)$ is the limit of $f(x)$ as $x$ approaches $c$.

**Convergence of a series** (pp. 631, 635): A series converges to a particular value if the limit of the partial sums of the series equals that value as the number of terms approaches infinity.

**Critical point** (p. 354): A point on a graph where the derivative is either zero or undefined. Maximum and minimum values of functions may occur at critical points.

**Cusp** (p. 54): A point on the graph at which the function is continuous, but the derivative is discontinuous.

**Cylindrical shells** (p. 396): A technique for slicing a solid of revolution into thin shells so that each point in the shell is virtually the same distance from the axis of rotation as the sample point is. Cylindrical shells are used for setting up integrals for calculating the volume, mass, moment, etc., of a solid object.

**Definite integral** (pp. 16, 197): *Physical meaning:* The product (dependent variable)(change in independent variable) for a function where the dependent variable may take on different values as the independent variable changes throughout an interval. *Geometrical meaning:* The area of the region under the graph of $f(x)$ from the $x$-value at the beginning of an interval to the $x$-value at the end of that interval.

**Derivative** (pp. 10, 80, 81, 91): *Physical meaning:* The derivative of a function $f$ at $x = c$ is the instantaneous rate of change of $f(x)$ with respect to $x$ at $x = c$. *Geometrical meaning:* The slope of the line tangent to the graph at $x = c$. (p. 81)

**Difference quotient** (p. 80): The ratio (change in $f(x)$)/(change in $x$). The limit of a difference quotient as the change in $x$ approaches zero is the derivative.

**Differentiability** (p. 153): The property possessed by a function at $x = c$ if $f'(c)$ exists. Function $f$ is differentiable on an interval if and only if $f'(x)$ exists for all values of $x$ in that interval.

**Differential** (p 186): If $y = f(x)$, then the differential $dx$ is the same quantity as $\Delta x$, a change in $x$; and the differential $dy$ is equal to $f'(x)dx$. Thus, the quotient $dy \div dx$ is equal to the derivative, $f'(x)$. The differential $dy$ is also the change in $y$ along a tangent to the graph, rather than along the graph itself.

**Differential calculus:** An obsolete term for calculus of derivatives only.

**Differential equation** (pp. 119, 310): A differential equation is an equation that contains the derivative of a function. A **solution** of a differential equation is a function whose derivative appears in the differential equation.

**Differentiation** (p. 92): The process of finding the derivative of a function.

**Displacement** (p. 99): The directed distance an object is from a given reference point at a given time.

***e*** (p. 272): A naturally occurring constant equal to 2.71828... used as the base for the natural logarithm and natural exponential function to make the calculus of these functions simpler.

**Euler's method** (p. 333): A numerical method for solving a given differential equation by assuming the graph follows tangent segments for short distances from point to point.

**Explicit relation** (p. 168): A function for which $f(x)$ is given in terms of $x$ and constants only. For instance, $f(x) = 5x^2$ gives $f(x)$ explicitly in terms of $x$.

**Function** (p. 4) A relationship between two variable quantities for which there is exactly one value of the dependent variable for each value of the independent variable in the domain.

**Fundamental theorem of calculus** (pp. 215, 304): The theorem that tells how to calculate exact values of definite integrals by using indefinite integrals. In its alternate form, the theorem tells how to find the derivative of a definite integral between a fixed lower limit of integration and a variable upper limit of integration. (Sometimes called the fundamental theorem of *integral* calculus.)

**Grapher:** A graphing calculator or computer used to generate graphs of given functions.

**Hyperbolic functions** (p. 473): Functions with properties similar to the trigonometric (circular) functions, but defined by points on a unit equilateral hyperbola rather than by points on a unit circle.

**Implicit differentiation** (p. 149): The process of differentiating without first getting the dependent variable explicitly in terms of the independent variable.

**Implicit relation** (p. 168): A relationship between two variables where operations may be performed on the dependent variable as well as the independent one. For $x^2 + y^2 = 25$, there is an *implied* relationship between $x$ and $y$.

**Improper integral** (p. 486): A definite integral in which either one or both limits of integration is infinite, or the integrand is undefined for some value of $x$ between the limits of integration, inclusive.

**Indefinite integral** (pp. 119, 190): $g(x) = \int f(x)\,dx$ if and only if $g'(x) = f(x)$. An indefinite integral is the same as an antiderivative.

**Indeterminate form** (pp. 26, 290): A form such as $0/0$, $0^0$, $\infty/\infty$, etc., that an expression may take as $x$ approaches a certain value, and for which there may be a finite limit.

**Infinitesimal** (p. 595): A quantity that approaches zero as $\Delta x$ approaches zero, such as $dy$, $dA$, $dV$, etc.

**Initial condition** (pp. 120, 310): A given value of $x$ and $f(x)$ used to find the constant of integration.

**Integrability** (p. 197): The property possessed by a function if the definite integral exists on a given interval.

**Integral calculus:** An obsolete term for the calculus of integrals only.

**Integration:** The process of finding either the definite integral or the indefinite integral of a function.

**Integration by parts** (p. 437): An algebraic method for finding the antiderivative of a product of two functions.

**Intermediate value theorem** (p. 67): A property of continuous functions which states that for any given number $y$ between $f(a)$ and $f(b)$, there is a number $x = c$ between $a$ and $b$ for which $f(c) = y$.

**Interval of convergence** (p. 621): The interval of values of $x$ for which a given power series converges.

**Lagrange form of the remainder of a Taylor series** (p. 643): A way to find an upper bound on the error introduced by using only a finite number of terms of a Taylor series to approximate the value of a function. The remainder is bounded by a multiple of the first term of the tail of the series after a given partial sum.

**l'Hospital's rule** (p. 285): A property for finding limits of the form $0/0$ or $\infty/\infty$ by taking the derivative of the numerator and the denominator. (Sometimes spelled *l'Hôpital's* rule.)

**Limit** (pp. 4, 10, 27, 40, 61, 74): The limit of $f(x)$ as $x$ approaches $c$ is the one number you can keep $f(x)$ as close as you like to, just by keeping $x$ close enough to $c$, but not equal to $c$. (pp. 27, 40, 74)

The limit of $f(x)$ as $x$ approaches infinity is the number you can keep $f(x)$ as close as you like to, just by keeping $x$ far enough away from zero. (p. 61)

The limit of $f(x)$ as $x$ approaches $c$ is infinite if and only if $f(x)$ can be kept as far as you like from zero just by keeping $x$ close enough to $c$, but not equal to $c$. (p. 61)

The limit of $f(x)$ as $x$ approaches infinity is infinite if and only if you can keep $f(x)$ as far as you like from zero just by keeping $x$ far enough away from zero. (p. 62)

Limits are used in the formal definitions of derivative and definite integral.

**Linearization of a function** (p. 185): The linear function that best fits function $f$ for values of $x$ close to $x = c$ is $y = f(c) + f'(c)(x - c)$, or, equivalently, $y = f(c) + f'(c)dx$.

**Local linearity** (p. 82): A function is locally linear at $x = c$ if the graph of the function looks more and more like the tangent line to the graph as one zooms in on the point $(c, f(c))$.

**Logarithmic differentiation** (p. 268): An implicit differentiation process where the natural log of a function is taken first, usually so that variables can be gotten out of exponents.

**Logistic equation** (p. 331): A differential equation (or its solution) for population growth that takes into account the assumption that a population will eventually level off at a maximum sustainable value.

**Maclaurin series** (p. 615): A Taylor series expanded about $x = 0$. Sine, cosine, exponential, and hyperbolic functions can be calculated using only the operations of arithmetic by first expanding the function as a Maclaurin series.

**Mean value theorem** (p. 202): The property that expresses sufficient conditions for a function graph to have a tangent line parallel to a given secant line at a value of $x = c$ between the endpoints of the secant line.

**Moment** (p. 568): The product of a quantity such as force or mass and the power of a distance from a point, line, or plane at which that quantity is located.

**Natural exponential function** (p. 279): Exponential function with base $e$.

**Natural logarithm function** (p. 254): The classic example of a function defined as a definite integral between a fixed lower limit and a variable upper limit.

**Objectives of calculus** (p. 71): There are four major things you should be able to do with each of the four major concepts of calculus: define it, understand it, do it, and apply it.

**Parameter** (p. 160): The independent variable in a parametric function.

**Parametric function** (p. 160): A parametric function is a function where two variables each depend on a third variable. For example, the $x$- and $y$-coordinates of a moving object might both depend on time.

**Partial sum of a series** (p. 602): The $n$th partial sum of a series is the sum of the first $n$ terms of the series.

**Point of inflection** (pp. 354–361): A point where a graph changes from concave up to concave down, or vice versa. Points of inflection occur where the second derivative of a function has a critical point (i.e., is either zero or undefined).

**Power series** (p. 609): A series (with an infinite number of terms) in which each term contains a power of the independent variable.

**Radius of convergence** (p. 625): The distance from the midpoint of the interval of convergence to one of its ends.

**Ratio technique** (p. 622): A technique for determining the interval of convergence for a power series by finding the values of $x$ for which the absolute value of the ratio of adjacent terms can be kept less than 1. (Sometimes called the ratio test.)

**Reduction formula** (p. 447): A formula whereby a complicated antiderivative can be expressed in terms of a simpler antiderivative of the same form.

**Removable discontinuity** (p. 26): If a function is discontinuous at $x = c$, but may be made continuous there by a suitable definition of $f(c)$, then the discontinuity is removable. For instance, $f(x) = (x^2 - 25)/(x - 5)$ is discontinuous at $x = 5$ because of division by zero, but the discontinuity can be removed by defining $f(5) = 10$.

**Riemann sum** (pp. 196, 198): A sum of the form $\Sigma f(x)dx$ where each term of the sum represents the area of a rectangle of altitude $f(x)$ and base $dx$. A Riemann sum gives an approximate value for a definite integral. The limit of a Riemann sum as $dx$ approaches zero is the basis for the formal definition of definite integral.

**Rolle's theorem** (p. 204): The property that expresses sufficient conditions for a function graph to have a horizontal tangent for some value of $x = c$ between two zeros of the function.

**Sample point** (p. 196): A point $x$ in a subinterval for which a term of a Riemann sum, $f(x)dx$, is found; or the corresponding point $(x, f(x))$ on the graph of $f$ itself.

**Separating the variables** (pp. 251, 310): The most elementary technique for transforming a differential equation so that it can be solved.

**Simpson's rule** (pp. 233, 305): A numerical way of approximating a definite integral by replacing the graph of the integrand with segments of parabolas, then summing the areas of the regions under the parabolic segments. The technique is similar to the trapezoidal rule, except that the graph is replaced by segments of quadratic functions instead of by segments of linear functions.

**Slope field** (pp. 309, 326): A graphical representation of the slope specified by a differential equation at each grid point in a coordinate system. A slope field, which can be generated by grapher, allows graphical solutions of differential equations.

**Speed** (p. 99): The absolute value of velocity.

**Squeeze theorem** (p. 112): If $f(x)$ is always between the values of two other functions, and the two other functions approach a common limit as $x$ approaches $c$, then $f(x)$ also approaches that limit.

**Step discontinuity** (p. 53): If $f(x)$ approaches different numbers from the right and from the left as $x$ approaches $c$, then there is a step discontinuity at $x = c$.

**Taylor series** (p. 615): A power series representing a function as non-negative integer powers of $(x - a)$. The coefficients of the terms are such that each order derivative of the series equals the corresponding order derivative of the function at the point where $x = a$.

**Techniques of calculus:** There are four major kinds of technique used in calculus: algebraic, numeric, graphical, and verbal.

**Theorems of Pappus** (pp. 577, 591): For volume, Volume = (area of rotated region)(distance traveled by centroid). For surfaces, Area = (length of rotated arc)(distance traveled by centroid).

**Trapezoidal rule** (p. 19): A numerical way of approximating a definite integral by slicing the region under a graph into trapezoids and adding the areas of the trapezoids. The technique is similar to Simpson's rule, but the graph is replaced by parts of linear functions rather than by parts of quadratic functions.

**Trigonometric substitution** (p. 456): An algebraic method for finding antiderivatives where the integrand involves quadratics or square roots of quadratics.

**Uniqueness theorem for derivatives** (p. 264): The property that states that if two functions have identical derivatives everywhere in an interval, and have at least one point in common, then they are the same ("unique") function.

**Vector** (p. 533): A quantity that has both magnitude and direction. Position, velocity, and acceleration vectors are used to analyze motion in two or three dimensions.

**Velocity** (p. 98): The instantaneous rate of change of displacement.

**Vertical asymptote** (p. 53): A vertical line $x = c$ that the graph of a function does not cross because the limit of $f(x)$ as $x$ approaches $c$ is infinite.

**Washers** (p. 387): A technique for slicing a solid of revolution into thin slices so that each point in the washer is virtually the same distance from a plane perpendicular to the axis of rotation as is the sample point. Washers are used to set up integrals for calculating the volume, mass, moment, etc., of a solid object.

# Index of Problem Titles

# General Index

# Photo Credits

*Chapter 1*

**1:** Peter Yates/Saba. **17:** Peter Yates/Saba. **22:** courtesy Paul Foerster.

*Chapter 2*

**37:** Mary E. Messenger/Photo Network. **51:** Mary E. Messenger/Photo Network. **76:** Biological Photo Service/Terraphotographics.

*Chapter 3*

**77:** Chip Maury/AP/Wide World Photos. **103:** Chip Maury/AP/Wide World Photos. **116:** courtesy Paul Foerster. **125:** Eric Sander/Gamma Liaison.

*Chapter 4*

**129:** Griffith Observatory/Anthony Cook. **136:** Dance Collection, NY Public Library for the Performing Arts, Astor, Lenox and Tilden Foundations. **166:** Griffith Observatory/Anthony Cook.

*Chapter 5*

**179:** Paul Fusco/Magnum Photos. **188:** Paul Fusco/Magnum Photos.
**229:** Brophy Collection, courtesy the Bisbee Mining and Historical Museum
**236:** courtesy James R. Stewart, M.D.

*Chapter 6*

**249:** UPI/Bettmann. **277:** Brad Lewis/Gamma Liaison. **283:** UPI/Bettmann. **299:** Geoff Tompkinson/Science Photo Library/Photo Researchers.

*Chapter 7*

**307:** John Gerlach/Tony Stone Images. **314:** Chester Higgins Jr./Photo Researchers. **315:** John Gerlach/Tony Stone Images. **332:** NASA.

*Chapter 8*

**351:** Lou Jacobs, Jr./Gamma Liaison. **407:** Lou Jacobs, Jr./Gamma Liaison. **415:** David Woodfall/Tony Stone Images. **423:** Kathleen Campbell/Gamma Liaison. **426:** Comstock.

*Chapter 9*

**433:** Comstock/Adam Tanner. **446:** courtesy Soft Warehouse. **468:** UPI/Bettmann. **481:** Mike Valeri/AP/Wide World Photos.

*Chapter 10*

**503:** NASA. **511:** Jean-Marc Giboux/Gamma Liaison. **512:** NASA. **522:** Graham Finlayson/Tony Stone Images. **526:** Comstock. **545:** courtesy USAC/RS.

*Chapter 11*

**555:** Garry Conner/PhotoEdit. **572:** *both,* courtesy Paul Foerster. **576:** Garry Conner/PhotoEdit. **577:** David Lissy/The Picture Cube.

*Chapter 12*

**597:** Will & Deni McIntyre/Tony Stone Images. **604:** Will & Deni McIntyre/Tony Stone Images. **650:** Bob Daemmrich/The Image Works. **655:** U.S. Department of the Interior/Bureau of Reclamation.